QUALITY MATTERS

The DECADE of QUALITY
1989 - 2000

Dedication

This book is dedicated to :

John Logan and Albert Prior

Without their creative initiative *Quality Matters*
would not have been established.

QUALITY MATTERS

The DECADE of QUALITY
1989 – 2000

by

G. J. CLARK

SPIRE CITY
PUBLISHING

QUALITY MATTERS
THE DECADE OF QUALITY
1989 – 2000

First impression 2002

Copyright © 2002 ISBN 1-904208-02-9

Published by Spire City Publishing

Northern Office
P.O. Box 84
Clitheroe
Lancs
BB7 2WA
Tel/Fax 01200 428823

Printed by

Information Press

Southfield Road
Eynsham
Oxford
OX29 1JJ

Cover by

Blenheim Colour

Southfield Road
Eynsham
Oxford
OX29 4JB

CONTENTS

List of Illustrations

Section One

Section Two

Section Three

33. Quality Methods Association Chairman Phillippe Rousseliere leads the facilitated discussion on ISO9000 at SmithKline Beecham in Slough in October 2000.

34. David Hutchins, explains the eight management principles underpinning ISO9000:2000, at the same event.

35. John Seddon, in his case against ISO9000' maintains that "there is a better way".

36. Myron Tribus, speaks at the British Deming Association.

37. Peter Scholtes, gives the 1999 Deming Memorial Lecture entitled 'The New Competencies of Leadership' at Sheffield .

38. Hazel Cannon, launches the Deming Forum in June 2000.

39. The National Measurement Partnership Programme launched November 1998.

40. Action at the Learning Company Conference in March 2000.

41. Leaders in IT quality meet in Bournemouth in June 1999.

42. IMS FINSEC Chairman Graham Briscoe.

43. World Productivity Congress hosted by the IMS in Edinburgh in October 1999.

44. Chairman of the Federation of Small Businesses Ian Handford delivers the Millennium John Loxham Lecture November 2000.

45. Masaaki Imai, gave the 1996 Engineering Quality Forum Annual Lecture on 'Gemba' or 'shop floor' Kaizen at the I EE in London November 1996.

46. David Ball, Chairman and 'anchor man' at the London end of the Inaugural CEO Global Best Practices Summit January 1998.

47. Edward de Bono, pioneer of the concept of 'Lateral Thinking', gives the Keynote Address on 'New Thinking for the New Millennium' at the EFQM's Learning Edge Conference in Belfast in April 2000.

48. Portuguese Prime Minister Antonio Guterres opens the First Quality Conference for Public Administration in the E.U. in May 2000 at the Lisbon Congress Centre.

Acknowledgments

The publishers would like to thank all of the people and organisations, past and present, that have assisted *Quality Matters* over the years. In particular we are grateful to the following for their ongoing assistance, without which neither the Newsletter nor publication of this book would have been possible.

ASI Quality Systems

British Deming Association

British Quality Association

British Quality Foundation

Elmia Qualitec, Sweden

European Benchmarking Forum

European Foundation for Quality Management

European Organisation for Quality

European Safety and Reliability Association

Excellence Ireland

Gower Publishing

Institute of Management Services

Institute of Marketing

Institute of Occupational Safety and Health

Institute of Quality Assurance

International Communications for Management

Leicester de Montfort University

McGraw Hill Publishing

National Physical Laboratory

National Society for Quality through Teamwork

Nexus Media

Northern Ireland Quality Centre

Paramount Publishing

Quality Forum

Quality Methods Association

Quality Scotland

SGS Yarsley International Certification Limited

Sheffield Hallam University

The Benchmarking Centre

The Learning Company Project

The Royal Statistical Society

University of Newcastle

Vanguard Consulting

Vision in Business

Vodafone

FOREWORD

The period covered by this book provides, in the publisher's own words, "a snapshot of industrial history" during which time industrial 'procedures and quality controls gave way to management disciplines which are today used in every sector of society, including the Public Sector, and services, and indeed, internationally.

The book provides a unique compendium of events, good and bad, which shaped the embryo quality enthusiasm of the 70's and 80's and turned it into the significant business that we know as the "quality industry" of today, with all it's commercial overtones, its competitive elements, and regulations etc.

A new profession, the "quality profession", has grown up from the early days of the National Quality Campaign and like events, taking on board the growth in quality certification, accreditation, a Register of certified auditors (IRCA) the emergence of Business Excellence and the setting up of the British Quality Foundation, not to mention the many regional and sector Quality Awards that now exist.

The quality "infrastructure" effectively covered in this book has grown from the original 6 certification bodies to the 75 accredited by UKAS today, to include several thousand auditors or assessors, a multitude of trainers and training bodies, a plethora of consultants, advisory bodies, societies and software houses. Then there are standards makers, the regulatory bodies, departments of the government targeted at getting it " right first time" - such a simple objective!

The impact of the EU Directives in 1994, which references ISO9000 alongside traditional inspection for product safety acceptance, was a factor in this growth. Also crucial, rightly or wrongly, was the persistance of public procurement officers, notably in local Government, in forcing quality assurance onto all its suppliers, from coffee bars to local arts performers!

A "gold rush" for quality experts, later to become quality system consultants, was generated in the mid eighties via government funding for them, certification bodies and small businesses, and the book covers well the growth in conferences, books and academic interest.

The 1994 revision of ISO9000 cleared out some of the old manufacturing bias of BS5750 and the 1987 version, but it was year 2000 before significant modifications .and new clauses appeared.

Unfortunately, "*Quality Matters*" is no longer around to review the contention that still surrounds this document, and to some, its reducing benefits.

Meanwhile the wider implications of TOTAL quality management has renewed interest in Six Sigma and the Japanese logic of Kaizen etc. which are increasingly referenced in the journals.

The emergence of I.T. and the Web, throughout the life of "*Quality Matters*" has led to a plethora of software programs for quality people, but there are so many other quality related areas covered, in its time by "*Quality Matters*", that it must have been difficult for the publishers to have been selective.

In 2002 one is tempted to ask "where will it all end ?" Will Integrated Management Systems ever be popular, or will they take over from ISO9000?

Can the service sector or the public sector ever emulate the manufacturing sector in its dedication to the quality parameter? Does quality matter? You can be certain it does!

Norman Burgess

London
July 2002

x

QUALITY MATTERS: THE DECADE OF QUALITY 1989 – 2000

INTRODUCTION

Quality Matters Newsletter was launched in January 1989 to provide a unique and up-to-date information service for quality and general managers following feedback from a number of quality practitioners which suggested, at the time, that there was a niche market demand in this area. After that 139 issues of the Newsletter were published on a monthly basis until April 2000, with the last issue being published in December 2000.

Throughout its twelve year history the publication sought to provide comprehensive news coverage of as broad a range of quality related subjects as possible impartially and without prejudice or bias towards any individual membership institution, organisation or group. As a newsletter it became distinguished from established journals through its direct reporting style and lack of advertising which not only proved popular, but also moderately profitable as the only general publication in the quality field to adopt this approach. As subsequent customer feedback showed, rarely does a publication of this kind remain to serve its market for the duration of an entire decade without recourse to the provision of advertising.

It was, of course, thanks to a dedicated core of loyal subscribers, sustained over many years, that the publication survived against considerable odds into the new millennium.

The author therefore offers profound thanks to all of those who continued to support the publication with such unreserved loyalty over such a long period of time.

With various organisations representing different aspects of quality increasingly looking to mainland Europe for their opportunities, coupled with the enormous technological advances that have occurred during the 1990s, questions ultimately had to be raised about the publication's continued viability in 2001. It was regrettably decided that the investment required to upgrade *Quality Matters Newsletter* to 21st century standards could not be justified. That said, however, its unique coverage and the wealth of information remains, just as interest in many of the topics covered will doubtless remain for many years to come.

In the chapters which follow articles and case studies have been compiled from the publication and grouped under various subject headings. The order is chronological in each case, with some overlapping of subjects acknowledged. It is believed that such a compilation covering such a broad spectrum of quality related subjects in a single volume spanning a complete decade has never been published before and is potentially of interest to many both as a reference document for research and as a source of information and ideas for today's and tomorrow's quality and general managers, with much of the material still relevant to modern business.

Chapter One

ISO9000

One of the hottest and most contested subjects of the 1990s has been the pros and cons of the quality management systems standard ISO 9000, which, in the early days of Quality Matters, took the form of BS5750: 1987. In these early days there was an explosion of interest, partly driven by Government, which indeed was partly influential in the establishment of Quality Matters, coupled with a growth in sector schemes such as the Land Mobile Quality Assurance Scheme (LMRQAS). This trend continued through to the mid 1990s when BS5750: 1987 was superseded by ISO9000: 1994 with relatively few changes. Latterly, in 2000, the standard was revised again, this time rather more substantially, reflecting a convergence between it and the EFQM inspired Business Excellence Model.

Whilst ISO9000 has proven itself to be popular among many leading enterprises, such as TNT (UK), who later went on to win the European Quality Award, and the certification bodies along with a growing plethora of consultants, there were others, most notably in the UK protagonist John Seddon, who were markedly opposed to the standard and the manner in which it was and still is applied. On this issue Quality Matters sought to present both sides of the argument as the following collection of articles demonstrate.

QUALITY IN TRANSPORT

Transportation is going to take on a new dimension in the 1990s according to Alan Jones, UK National Chairman of the Chartered Institute of Transport. In his opening address to the Institute of Management Services conference *'Quality Management in the Transport Chain'*, held on board HQS Wellington on 29th November 1990 he spoke of good service as being a reflection of good management and that whilst a few years ago BS5750 was little heard of in the transport industry , in the next five years companies which had not achieved the standard would probably find it difficult to survive.

He also pointed out that quality had to be for all organisations large and small. Particular attention was drawn to simple details, such as transport companies' approach to telephone responses which he said left a lot to be desired. This was highlighted as a source of lost revenue, and he urged companies to make the effort to analyze the times taken to answer calls and the way in which they are handled.

Quality in Road Haulage

The road haulage industry's representative was Mr.Chris Sturman, Development Director for the Distribution Division of Wincanton Distribution Services Limited, one of the first British road haulage companies to achieve the quality management standard BS5750. His paper, entitled 'Wincanton -A Case Study in the development of Service Quality Assurance' outlined how his company is building on BS5750 accreditation to achieve a total commitment to quality.

Mr.Sturman explained that his company, which has 3,000 employees, 50 depots, and 4,500 trucks (of which 1500 operate with drivers approach with the rest contract hired without driver) achieved its current position "more by trial and error than by any superbly executed strategic plan".

There are five divisions within the company:
Contract Hire (trucks without driver), Transport (oil, chemical and food tankers, and fleet management), Milk (company's original business), Distribution, and Bullens (office removals and high tech transportation). Each of these has service – demanding customers and the need for the company to differentiate itself from its competitors, so as to attract new customers as well as retaining existing ones, was recognised.

There were no registered quality approved firms in the distribution industry at the time, but some major chemical manufacturers were seriously making BS5750 a requirement for contractors seeking their business. One depot, Purfleet , which has 187 employees, 154 trucks, and is engaged primarily in bulk tanker operation, dedicated distribution, with workshop repair and maintenance, was chosen for the initial activities.

Pat Lee, as Development Director of Wincanton Distribution Services, was invited to lead the new initiative. He and his Quality Manager introduced the concept of BS 5750 and its 18 quality system requirements to sell BS5750 to the managers and supervisors on the basis of job security and job satisfaction. (With certification they would keep the business they had safe, win more, and by managing the business better, get things right first time and jobs would become more enjoyable as hassle is minimised).

A Quality Manual was prepared translating BS5750 into a document which was tailored to distribution. It set out what had to be done whilst an Operations Manual described how it had to be done and by whom. Managers and supervisors were divided into teams and asked, as an exercise, to write down in one hour how they would handle a call from a customer wishing to move a load. It was found that the result was 80 per cent of the final version of the operating procedure for a traffic manager.

They were then questioned, for example on how they knew the driver that had been allocated the work was trained to handle the product, the emphasis all the time being on taking the simple approach. He explained:

"When you write down what you do and how you do it, imagine you are going on holiday for four weeks and a stand in has to take your place. Your operating procedure should set out step by step what he, or she, must do and you must be confident that if that is done he or she will get it right".

In this context Mr. Sturman emphasized that it is the managers, supervisors and employees in specific jobs that must write their own parts of the Operations Manual. It must not be written for them. Bottom up is vital in order to ensure co-operation and commitment although these are scrutinised for 'grey areas', He points out:

" .... committing procedures to paper certainly shows up areas of uncertain responsibilities".

The quality management standard BS5750 was described as 'a superb enabling vehicle that provides the necessary first quality target to go for' and at present the company is halfway to achieving BS5750 for Wincanton Distribution Services as a whole.
Some further pieces of advice were given:

* that direction and enthusiasm must start from the top(i.e. the Managing Director and Board must be sold on it).

* one director or senior manager must be appointed to see it through, with the full. visible backing of the Board (not just an internal memorandum).

* this person needs external training to be effective and it helps to put two people through so that one can act as 'devil's advocate' to the other and double check the work as it goes along.
* provide a clear briefing so that everyone understands the intent behind BS5750 and the part they have to play.
* make each operating instruction simple to follow step by step set of instructions that can be understood and followed by a temporary stand-in doing the job.
* allow staff to write the first draft of the Operations Manual themselves.

The certification of the Eastern Region at Purfleet was followed by certifications of the Northern and Midlands Regions, but the first internal audit of Purfleet six months after its certification revealed that reaction to the BSI inspection, coupled with changes in staff, had provided stumbling blocks to maintaining the standard required. Work was needed to ensure that quality was more than 'skindeep'. Positive action was also needed to ensure that all employees were continuously involved in the pursuit of quality improvement.

The company also appreciated that it required more human resources to be allocated if other Divisions were to achieve BS5750. To help overcome this shortfall, assessors from the 20 major depots were trained to act as coaches in their own depots and as auditors at other depots. These also had a secondary and in the end much more important) role as missionaries for a total commitment to quality, starting the long process of changing the company's management style by example and by persuasion. The company has accepted that to 'turn every manager and supervisor into a leader will take many years but the prizes to be won make it the most worthwhile initiative imaginable'.

[Issue 27 (March 1991)]

MARKETING QUALITY

In December's issue of *Quality Matters* it was reported that a new quality specification for marketing, Marketing Quality Assurance, had been launched for British industry. On February 21st 1991 the First National Conference of MQA was held at the Edwardian International Hotel, Heathrow, London, marking a unique step forward for quality in Britain, with Britain leading the way in the formulation of a certification scheme for this vital management function.

With the co-operation of MQA Limited *Quality Matters* presents a review of the conference, which was chaired by Walter Goldsmith, chairman of the Governing Board of MQA Ltd. And included some 160 delegates representing a leading core of companies dedicated to the pursuit of quality to attain marketing excellence in the face of recession.

In his opening address Mr.Goldsmith said:

6

"We have the opportunity to set very clear standards for the organisation and management of marketing services "

He pointed out that in the Single Market Britain's strategy ought to be quality led.

This was followed by a very impressive speech from Dr.Ivan Dunstan, Director General of the British Standards Institute (BSI), which focused on International Developments in Quality Assurance and referred to the Single Market and the endeavour to create it as having 'given a very big push' to the dimension of quality assurance. He referred to IS09000 as being 'one way of making a systematic approach to quality assurance and to customers needing an assurance of quality now that much longer chains exist between producers and users than in the past.

The impact of BS5750 had been, he said, 'quite profound' with large numbers of companies achieving benefits in consistency and reduction of scrap and rework, and customers reaping benefits in the marketplace through trading with these companies. There was also 'an impressive number of services to which BS5750 has been applied' with over 12,000 companies having achieved certification and around 30 third party certification bodies accredited by the N.A.C.C.B. He then spoke of the aim to create a global system of mutual recognition of quality and of a good start having been made in the E.C. and EFTA through the formulation of the E.O.T.C. (European Organisation for Testing and Certification).

Finally he congratulated the Chartered Institute of Marketing who, with the support of the I.T. industry, had helped the UK to take the lead in marketing.

His speech gave rise to several questions, the first being why he thought the UK had initiated this type of programme. He responded to this by saying that it was one way of achieving quality that was particularly suited to Britain, as compared with the Japanese methods which focused heavily on customer assurance and the American in-house system which rendered third party certification as largely unwelcome.

The next question asked for his view on the number of certification bodies that were 'springing up', to which he replied by saying that of the 30 bodies referred to in his speech, only about 5 were general in scope, the remaining 25 in fact being much more specialised.

Another question queried whether a company's success could be related to the body performing the certification, for example, with some being more respected abroad than others. His response to this was that in the regulatory sector all bodies were recognised and the BSI had no real advantage. In the voluntary sector one name may be more important than another, but at the end of the day it was the certification itself that would really count.

His conclusion was that as mutual recognition emerges the defect procedure will soon reveal where deficiencies exist.

The framework of quality and marketing was outlined by Mr. Tony McBurnie , former Director General of the Chartered Institute of Marketing and former Managing Director of United Glass who spoke on 'The Changing Face of Marketing'.

Mr. McBurnie spoke of marketing as being 'the child of competition and customer choice' and suggested that British technological development had suffered as a result of a captive empire market, its education system, and a social culture which 'pays people for playing the game'. The environment had changed dramatically, and British companies were 'living in turbulence without a rudder and with broken paddles'.

Customers, he said, 'cannot be controlled, unlike managing factories' and the influence of the Chief Executive was critical. Management had to become focused on markets rather than budgets, and organisations had to be 'stimulated to be flexible and innovative'. Planning had to change from tactical to strategic. [This is the classical Japanese approach-Ed].

In his summary Mr.McBurnie said:

"Traditionally marketing has been seen as the creative flair orientated area of a company's business, and it is important that this continues to be so. However, the professional marketing disciplines and operations in companies have developed with varying degrees of success over the last decade, and would benefit greatly from being assessed objectively against established standards of good international practice, as would the companies employing them".

He adds that :

"Bringing together marketing effectiveness and quality assurance is a logical and timely development, and the fact that it has happened in the UK reflects the innovative approach and initiative taking attitudes which now exist in at least some areas of British marketing".

Marketing Quality Assurance is described as a 'very significant' development coming at a time when 'even enlightened companies need to jack up their marketing performance if they are to be successful, or indeed survive'.

The MQA Specification

Mr.Ian Griffith, Managing Director of Marketing Quality Assurance Limited, explained 'the Role of Marketing Quality Assurance in the quest for Quality', describing the function of MQA as 'the organisation which will maintain objective standards for marketing and sales based on an ongoing assessment of good international practice'.

He explained how the perception of quality by marketing and sales personnel has changed over the past five years, away from being concerned merely with the physical product or service. As quality has become much more of a boardroom consideration and its principles have become more established so there has become a much stronger rationale for placing marketing and quality together in a broader context.

The marketing function, he says, 'defines the needs, preferences and expectations of the customer and then ensures that the organisation has the capabilities of meeting and satisfying customer needs through the right product or service'. But in many companies the marketing function is still not responsible for these activities, particularly as regards ensuring capabilities.

He believes its key responsibilities are :-
* helping to define business objectives and strategy at board level, along with other business functions

* identifying customer needs and preferences

*co-ordinating the activities of internal departments (e.g. production, design, R and D, and distribution).

*obtaining customer inputs, conducting market research, monitoring customer service, liasing with salesforce, and dealing with external agencies such as advertising, public relations and market research.

[Not everyone would agree to give marketing the responsibility for the co-ordinating of customer activities, since this would be a controversial issue in many companies-Ed]

Mr.Griffith emphasised that all the requirements in the specification are measurable and the specification applies to any company in any industry sector.

He described how the specification had developed over the last five years, and how he as a marketing person had had difficulty comprehending BS5750 as it was written in language he was not normally used to [Not an uncommon problem-Ed]. The specification had, he insisted, to cover all the areas of marketing in a detailed way and was not to be a standard purely for the I.T. industry, although this industry sector was particularly influential in the development of the specification (principal companies were Bull, GEC, Gryphon, ICL, Jamerton, David Kohler and Associates, Logica, Sorbus, and Texas Instruments).

The principal areas covered by the specification are:

* Business plans: companies must be able to show that marketing was and is involved in the development of their business plans.

* Marketing and sales planning: clear procedures must exist which demonstrate how marketing and sales objectives, strategies and plans are developed.

*Marketing, sales and operations: the specification calls for good practice in all operational stages, including product development, promotion, pricing, selling and distribution.

* Customer assurance: assessors will examine explicit and implicit customer assurances to determine if they are being satisfied.

* Resources, personnel and training: requirements exist for well trained, experienced staff, whose responsiveness to the needs of the marketplace will be assessed.

* Requirement for documented quality systems : companies must have the capability to measure their own performance in meeting customer needs.

Mr. Griffith then explained how these criteria would be assessed, for example by talking to chief executives to ascertain that customer expectations are incorporated in business plans by questioning marketing and sales on how they measure the effectiveness of advertising, and asking about what rules companies formulate for example to maintain confidentiality of customer information.

Copies of the specification were handed out to all conference delegates, and in order to highlight the importance attached to meeting and satisfying customer needs and expectations .

Mr.Griffith drew attention to three specific requirements:

(3.7.1) Product and market requirements shall be defined as a result of continually identifying and re-assessing customer needs and preferences and competition (said to be one of the toughest requirements).

(3.9.3.) A process of continuous information monitoring and feedback of customer experience and expectations shall be maintained. Such information shall be collated and analysed for review by management resulting in appropriate action being taken.

(3.10.9.) A procedure shall exist for handling and assessing customer complaints which ensures prevention of recurrence.

Also handed to delegates were a set of executive guidelines in which it is explained that the BS5750 standard, by being limited to quality systems covering design, manufacture, installation, quality control and testing processes, does not cover the essential area of assessing the needs and preferences of customers. By contrast, however, a company does not require BS5750 in order to apply for MQA registration since the relevant parts of BS5750 are included in the MQA specification.

Further comparison of the MQA specification with BS5750 was made by the MQA Operations Director, Mr.Tony James. He compared both BS5750 and the MQA specification with the Malcolm Baldrige Quality Award scale applied in the United States which awards up to 1000 points as follows:

Leadership   100
Information and analysis   60
Strategic quality planning   90
Human resource utilisation   150
Quality assurance   150
Quality results   150
Customer satisfaction   300

A quality system conforming to ISO9001 or ISO9002 would be eligible for a maximum number of points totalling approximately 300, predominantly in categories 5 and 6. By contrast, a quality system conforming to the MQA specification could achieve up to 800 points on the scale.

In order to account for the difference, Mr. James pointed out that in ISO9001 the only requirement which refers to a purchaser's requirements is section 4.3. (contract review). This is the only requirement which addresses the process relating the 'totality of features and characteristics that bear on ability to satisfy stated or implied needs to the production of a specification for a product or service'.[BS4778 definition of Quality - Ed].

He points out that whilst the customer may be the purchaser as defined in 1509001, the purchaser may not be the customer, and the MQA specification therefore contains references to 'customer' as distinct from 'purchaser' .With this important distinction he then explained that the format of the 1509001 standard and the MQA specification is the same, both being designed to be in the form of measurable objectives without generally dictating how the objectives will be met.

The MQA specification, however, includes an additional 35 requirements covering:

* Business plans

* Marketing and sales plans (including demonstration of marketing audits)

* Code of conduct (defined and implemented with regular communication with customers and system for ensuring confidentiality and protection of customer information).

*Marketing and sales operations (including the important (3.9.3.) requirement)

* Customer assurance (including procedures to ensure customers are regularly informed of progress relating to their requests, comments, and complaints).

* Purchasing (including requirements for external sales agents to conform to specified codes of practice).

* Resources, personnel, training and organisation structure (including demonstration that an agreed level of qualified and/or experienced resources exist to implement marketing and sales plans).

The ISO9001 standard and the MQA specification are described as 'combinatorial and complementary to each other'.

Case Studies

The afternoon session consisted of three case studies presented by Gary Coster, Quality Manager for Dowty Case Communications; Bruce Brown, Quality Manager , Kodak Health Sciences (in lieu of Peter Blackwell,Divisional Director), and Ken Cusack, Managing Director of Sorbus UK Limited.

Mr.Coster's presentation started by stating that having a quality culture and being a customer driven company were the only way to remain in business, but whilst many companies had a well established quality culture, it tended only to exist in areas which had direct management focus and good measurement:

"Financial measurement and ISO9000 have been predominantly focused on manufacturing, design and customer service. For a company to achieve a Total Quality Culture, that same focus needs to be applied to those areas which have not yet been fully addressed".

Manufacturing, design and development were highlighted as traditional areas that are covered by existing Quality Assurance Schedules and well established measurement practices where the crucial measurements include costs of scrap, machine loading efficiencies, rework, defect analysis, modification and control costs, post design support costs, and poor reliability costs.

What had not been addressed by a Quality Assurance Schedule, or in many cases by financial control systems either, were costs incurred as a result of bad marketing (kit in stock which cannot be sold, loan kit on customer site in lieu of awaited new kit, product written down in value as a result of bad forecasting, marketing and sales promotion costs which do not yield revenue, non-effective advertising, redesign or rescheduling costs arising from changing requirements); bad sales (extra sales visits to re-specify requirements, team costs of people checking orders, credit control costs due to errors in sales information); and bad customer assurance (credit control chasing costs, sales order lifecycle mistakes, costs of placating customers, re-installation of replacement kit). These wastage costs, it is suggested, may easily exceed wastage throughout the rest of the entire company.

Mr.Coster suggested that by placing a focus on processes such as strategic planning, product marketing, sales order lifecycle, sales performance and customer assurance greater accountability will be brought to management, marketing and sales:

"It is much easier to focus when there is some accolade after all the effort, or if there is a very specific goal. It is even more advantageous if the goal has fixed and clearly identifiable posts. If it is something that will also be independently audited is well, it makes the programme itself more worthwhile. The MQA Schedule should achieve this".

In relation to his own company, Mr.Coster explained how one of the major benefits from IS09000 had been the actual review process which made managers examine their current working practices and seek agreement on them throughout their departments. It is accepted that measurements will show some areas such as forecasting markets to be further from the ideal 100 per cent than, say, production yields, but it is clearly felt that it is better to measure and improve a low success rate than not to measure it at all.

Bruce Brown, in his presentation, described how in his company the chairman and senior management would not accept that quality would be purely the responsibility of manufacturing, even though the focus of many of the sessions concerned with the implementation of the Quality Management concept tended always to come back to manufacturing. Quality was to be for everyone and did not just mean production making properly what we (marketing) wanted and delivering when they said they would.

As part of the company's Quality Improvement Process a central Quality Council was formed to drive and review total company efforts whilst each division formed its own Quality Action Groups from a wide cross section of personnel within it or a work group. These tackled small, relatively manageable problems such as why there were so many credits and adjustments with the customer externally and between other departments internally.

The importance of data collection was recognised:

"Too often we make decisions without the correct data and even worse without checking whether the data is or could be made available".

Facilitators were trained throughout the company in order to assist Quality Improvement Groups with statistical and process techniques, to ensure that problems were correctly identified, the extent accurately scoped and the decision making process effective in achieving wide involvement of all the group members.

Consideration by the author that working for sales provided a focus for all of the quality efforts within the Division was prompted by the fact that the audits to which service engineers had been subjected in parts of the company which had already achieved certification had forced them to question the way they worked and why they did things the way they did. Certification had resulted in a much more committed focus to their work, and the quality efforts, whilst still active, had lost some of their initial drive and enthusiasm.

Mr.Brown explained that:

"As we began to understand the accreditation and MQA requirements we became at times very confident, and then days, even hours later very dejected".

He did not, however, believe that this was unusual. The external pressure from customers to incorporate ISO9000 into the business, coupled with internal pressure from other Business Divisions who were on a parallel course to be the first to come through the sales, marketing and customer assurance standard, provided a driving force for the Division. A manual is now being prepared, involving people from all levels to explain how they meet the MQA criteria.

The final presentation, by Mr.Ken Cusack of Sorbus UK, explained the position from the point of view of a company which had achieved BS5750 some four years ago.

He explained that whilst BS5750 formally covers the operations side of the company and, indirectly, through Design Control, the sales and marketing department, MQA will now allow sales and marketing to be covered to the same depth. He believes that it will have no risk or downside, will go 'hand in hand' with the company's existing
quality culture, and will provide 'another link in the formal quality chain' which may overcome some of the continual problems associated with sales and marketing:

* sales departments historically having a poor image.

14

A disciplined approach is seen as important and MQA 'provides a mirror to the organisation, an external framework for quality improvement and an independent external measurement of the changes which had taken place and the quality system which it had introduced'.

The Key to Total Quality

The second presentation was by Exxon Professor of Total Quality Management at the European Centre for Total Quality Management, University of Bradford, Professor John Oakland. He asserted that MQA 'has brought the marketing fraternity into Total Quality Management'. When people ask 'does quality apply to marketing?' his answer is 'it starts there'. He says he never ceases to be amazed to see how many times you see a mismatch between what the customer really requires and what the supplier perceives to be required.

He spoke of companies' 'obsession with outputs' which they check 'as if it is going to build quality in'. Sure, we need a measure of how we're performing, he said, but if we react every quarter we are not living in the Deming philosophy, in which driving out fear is of paramount importance. Many of us live in a fear driven compartmentalised environment and he suggested that breaking barriers here was part of the key to Total Quality, which can't exist where information is closed in.

"Customers don't see departments. They see a process and if they have to hurdle every barrier they will go somewhere else".

He describes as 'unfortunate' the fact that many companies have sought approval to ISO9000 for contractual reasons only and not because they have a commitment to TQM and says 'these organisations have missed an opportunity to lay a firm foundation for TQM'.

The addition of Marketing Quality Assurance to ISO9000 has, however, 'opened up a new area of debate'. As ISO9000 has been applied to such areas as educational establishments and firms of solicitors, why introduce a separate system for marketing? So, whilst the two systems are intended to be complementary 'the forward thinking quality professional will be seeking ways to develop and harmonize ISO9000 and the MQA system into an effective TQM system'. As for TQM it is suggested that an intellectual understanding of quality is 'only the planting of the seed'. The understanding must be translated into commitment, policies, plans and actions for TQM to germinate, and a series of thirteen steps to TQM are explained in the conference literature.

Newcastle Breweries' Quality Assured Marketing.

Alan Ross, Sales and Marketing Director for Newcastle Breweries Limited, gave an interesting insight into how Quality assured marketing could be applied in the brewing industry. The company has 6,000 employees in the North East of England, operating 2,000 pubs and dispensing half a million pints a day. It is the first brewery to be certificated to BS5750 for its Technical Services Division, a process which was said to have taken the company four years to achieve, inspired largely by one manager who 'approached quality with vigour and passion'.

The brewing business is close to the consumer and consequently the opportunity to work on and provide marketing quality 'is wonderful', but companies can be segmentalist and a department that presses on with quality can find itself isolated. In 1989, however, Newcastle Breweries elevated its technical manager to the Board, whilst the author joined from another division of Scottish and Newcastle, resulting in two 'disciples of quality' being present on the Board. This made for the setting up of a quality council, consisting of senior managers from every department, which 'acted as a signal' to employees that the Board was committed to quality.

The new found commitment to quality resulted in a corporate plan, 'The Brewing Blueprint', and the company closed for one day to enable employees to be informed of the company's sales and market share objectives and how they intended to achieve them, in particular through the use of quality initiatives and customer service improvements.

A Quality Customer Service Package was launched in the spring of 1990 in which trade customers were invited, in groups of 15 to 20, to presentations at the brewery, of which about 120 were made in May and June of that year. A customer council was then formed as a means of monitoring customer service, with representatives from pubs and clubs meeting with brewery representatives every two months. It is noted that these 'are anxious to be helpful', especially in areas of operation where they think the brewery 'is sluggish'. This customer council has recently held a meeting without any brewery representatives and is said to have produced 'a most helpful list of recommendations'.

The start of real marketing quality, however, came when a salesman, who said the company's promotions 'were rubbish' was made chairman of a quality improvement team to resolve that. He was thereby empowered to design, improve and change his basic job so that it could be done better. Any manager in the company is now said to be able to set up a quality improvement team to tackle a business problem. When the speaker 'discovered' MQA he concluded that what the brewery was doing was in fact quite close to the MQA specification and so for most of this year effort has been directed towards formalising the system for MQA.

Training has not been neglected and the speaker is pleased to be on the Board of the Quality North Initiative which is currently running remit to gain BS5750 registration for short course provision whilst at the same time assessing the organisation's readiness for Total Quality.

It is explained how, with the help of Hallmark International Consultants, who were noted for their experience in the field of education, a pilot project was commenced following initial interviews in all areas.

Through BS5750 a better understanding now exists between the Language Centre and business clients, with clients feeling more confident about standards and outcomes. The clients now have a voice in the design, input and delivery of the course and confidence that problems will be dealt with to their satisfaction. Clarity of roles and responsibilities exists and tutors have greater involvement in the design process and freedom to interpret course structure.

The Language Centre, the second in the UK to gain registration, achieved it with no non-compliances or observations.

Experiences of ISO9000 in Sweden.

An international perspective of ISO9000 was given by Matts Carlsson and Dan Carlsson of the Chalmers University of Technology, Gothenburg, whose paper reports on an extensive study of the experiences of Swedish companies in their work towards ISO9000 registration, and forecasts a dramatic increase in the number of Swedish companies gaining registration in the years ahead.

Some 121 companies were surveyed and asked a series of open-ended questions, with the respondent typically being the person who was responsible for the certification (quality manager, production manager or general manager). This was followed with two further stages involving a more descriptive approach based on combined interview and questionnaire data.

The time required for certification varied from 0.5 to 4 years whilst the internal resources required varied from 6 man months to 5 man years. Costs varied from 100,000 to 4 million Swedish Kronors, with external resources dominated principally by the cost paid to the certifying body, which was of the order of 50,000 Kronors upwards.

When asked why they wanted to implement ISO9000 only a few apparently regarded it as a step towards achieving the goal of Total Quality.

It was noted in particular that many companies perceived the documentation involved to be 'very cumbersome and in some cases unnecessarily bureaucratic', whilst the standard itself was 'perceived to be difficult to interpret, which at times resulted in an unnecessarily great amount of documentation'. As a result many of the smaller companies 'called in consultants to a great extent', with help being needed particularly in the early stages.

The certifying bodies 'were perceived to give unclear guidelines during audits' and it is suggested that one of the reasons for this could be auditors' lack of knowledge of specific trades. The use of accredited certifying bodies in which at least one auditor commands knowledge of the trade is therefore recommended.

Some companies experienced initial difficulties creating an understanding of quality ideas on the part of employees and of the benefits of having a well functioning quality system. Some attributed this to lack of efficient communications, particularly between different functional departments. Hence it is recommended that a project organisation be established to manage the implementation, which includes personnel from all functions involved, such that personnel become committed by allowing operators the freedom to document their own procedures.

Various positive knock-on effects of certification are highlighted, notably the fact that company procedures, responsibility and authority are made more explicit, which allows rapid and simple changes to be made, whilst training of new recruits and the identification of internal quality deficiencies at an early stage is made easier.

[Issue 56 (August 1993)]

BS5750: A Vehicle for Change

The first internal consultancy to achieve registration to BS5750 Part 1, Girobank Internal Consultancy, were well placed to spread the message as to why internal consultancy departments need BS5750 and the benefits that they might expect to achieve from having it.

Their presentation, by their Internal Consultancy Manager, David Lewis, described BS5750 as 'a vehicle for introducing major change' and explained a few 'myths and truths' associated with it.

It was pointed out that whilst it is possible to have quality without BS5750, it certainly is not possible to have BS5750 without both a quality culture and a quality working environment. [Note this can be independent of Product -Ed].

In December 1991 the internal consultancy department of Girobank became concerned for its future as Girobank had begun to employ outside consultants to undertake work previously conducted by the department. This was because decision makers within the bank were unaware that their own people had the skills they required, or because they did not have sufficient confidence in their abilities. Consequently this called into question the department's image and profile and begged the question as to whether the

There are 11 other members of the EAC who have signed a Memorandum of Understanding to commit to the developing of the Multinational Agreement to reach recognition of equivalence of systems in the longer term. They are: Belgium, Denmark, France, Germany, Italy, Greece, Portugal, Spain, Ireland, Austria and Iceland.

Certification Expansion

The Mobil Oil Corporation has carried out a survey of the expansion of ISO9000 throughout the world involving 76 countries. The total certification in June 1994, when the results were last collated, were just over 70,000 worldwide. The UK, which has just over 50% of the share was expanding at the rate of around 1000 per month. The Rest of Europe has over 25% of the total. Australia/New Zealand has about the same number as the whole of North America of around 7% each. The Far East has about 5%.

The survey records that in the 18 month period from January 1993 the certification totals expanded from around 28,000 to over 70,000 with the UK base starting at two thirds of the total.

[These results support the last prediction of Dr. Juran for the growth of ISO9000 worldwide and the interest of the multinational companies in the impact of Quality competition- Ed].

[Issue 84 (December 1995)]

DOES ISO9000 WORK?

At the end of 1995 it is likely that the number of companies certificated to ISO9000 worldwide will reach 100,000. As the largest certification body worldwide SGS has a clear interest in more than a subjective judgment of ISO9000 (even if it is their own!). Since the majority of companies registered to ISO9000 are in the UK, SGS Yarsley commissioned the Manchester Business School to conduct independent research into views of ISO9000 from the perspective of the 'end users'. These were irrespective of Certificating Body and included views of those not certificated.

Quality Matters is pleased to publish the results of the research which is given in a joint SGS/Manchester Business School Report entitled 'ISO9000 - Does it work?' The report details the findings of three areas of research to ascertain:

(i) Why organisations seek certification and the impact certification has on their business.

(ii) Why some organisations choose not to seek certification

(iii) Whether companies that have achieved certification are more likely to survive under recessionary conditions

Certification and its impact

In the first instance 4,250 questionnaires were despatched to a random sample of organisations in the 1995 DTI QA Register of Certificated Companies. There were 1,190 (28 per cent) returned. Out of these 69 per cent were reportedly satisfied that their expectations of the standard had been met. There were 31% who thought that expectations fell short in some respects, whilst 21% had a dissatisfaction for some reason. Perhaps more importantly 99 per cent said that they had experienced benefits from certification. Only 5 per cent were reported to be 'very dissatisfied' with the impact that the standard has had on their organisations.

The companies that were most satisfied were noted to be those which had sought certification as a means to achieve improved management control and customer service rather than to keep existing customers or as a promotional tool. As for reasons for seeking certification, the most common reason was reported to be 'anticipation of future customer requirements':

'Large organisations emphasised consistency of operations while small companies sought the standard principally in order to gain new customers'.

Whilst 'Market pressure' was a driving force in the smaller companies relatively few companies with less than 10 employees were required to seek certification.

There was a clear link between management commitment to improve and satisfaction. The majority (57%) said they would recommend ISO9000 to others. There were 16% who stated they would strongly recommend it, whilst 14% said they would discourage others.

Cost Effectiveness.

Findings relating to the cost-effectiveness of certification are less clear, although more respondents appeared to consider that the standard was cost effective than appeared to say it was not. Responses to this showed that 43% thought that certification was cost effective of which 60 per cent believed the costs would be recouped in 1-3 years. Those believing it was not cost effective were measured to be 37%, whilst 20% were undecided.

Some respondents considered that to seek to measure the impact of one among many complex factors that determined profitability was 'to ignore the long-term character of ISO9000 and its influence on company culture' whilst others considered that certification had enabled them to keep existing customers even though it perhaps had not been cost effective in a purely financial sense.

Above Average Growth

Approximately half of the respondents provided sales revenue figures for the1993-94 and 1994-95 financial years and these showed the average sales growth over a year of 20 per cent (26 per cent in the service sector) which compares favourably with the growth of Gross Domestic Product over the same period which was only 7 per cent.

The growth of UK ISO9000 certification since 1992 has been at the rate of 10,000 per year. In the rest of Europe certification has doubled every nine months since 1993.

Drawbacks to Certification

The second area of research involved the despatch of 1,000 questionnaires to a random sample of organisations drawn from the UK One Source databases (1995), which may or may not have attained certification. This yielded a rather lower response rate of 140 (14 per cent), out of which just under half (49 per cent), i.e. less than 7 per cent of the whole, had decided not to pursue certification for five key reasons:

* excessive paperwork

* high cost of implementation

* time required to complete implementation

* time required to write manuals

* high cost of maintaining the system after certification

[These reasons are the common subjective statements often given by companies and/or individuals who have heard of those (or have been) given poor consultancy advice- Ed]

Certification helps Survival

The third research area, that of ascertaining whether companies with ISO9000 were more likely to survive the recession, involved desk research into 185 companies selected from the 1991 DTI QA Register supported by a review of previous surveys and telephone interviews. It is this research perhaps most of all which suggests compelling evidence in favour of certification.

Findings showed that out of the sample, 130 companies still had their certification, while 53 did not, but were still going concerns. Only two of the companies (1.1 per cent) were no longer in business, which compares very favourably with a national average of 5.2 per cent of companies which have gone out of business since 1991.

The conclusion reached was that companies with ISO9000 were FOUR times as likely to have survived the recession than those without.

Research Observations

Other key observations include the breakdown by region which shows that whilst some 35.5 per cent of UK business is located in the south east, the south east only holds 21.5 per cent of the certificates, suggesting a skew distribution by region, of the certificated companies.

The report also suggests that whilst manufacturing still accounts for the majority (54 per cent) of the certificated companies its dominance is declining, with 43 per cent of organisations certificated in the last twelve months being from the service sector as against 40 per cent from manufacturing. Likewise 43 per cent of the respondents that were certificated over the last twelve months were small businesses (under 25 employees).

Large and medium sized organisations experienced greater benefits than did those with fewer than 10 employees.

The report contains a number of comments from the companies which speak in favour of the benefits of certification. Most impressive is perhaps the following:

"We've grown from a £30 million to a £100 million company in three years with a framework which has remained consistent as a result of ISO 9000".

"We gained 95% of possible benefits in preparing for certification".

ISO9000 and TQM

Interestingly there were comments from organisations which were looking at their ISO9000 certification in relation to their approach to TQM:

"We intend to use the standard as a basic foundation on which to build TQM"

"It has proved a sound basis on which to expand our TQM philosophy".

The research showed that nearly 60% of the 1190 respondents which achieved certification over the last year are adapting ISO9000 as part of a larger TQM programme.

[*Quality Matters* comments: This point may suggest further research. Recent evidence has revealed that many TQM programmes have not been

42

The Future of Quality

It is now generally accepted that the concept of "quality" as promoted in the UK over the past decade is no longer sufficient to ensure companies can compete nationally or internationally. Models of business excellence show that quality is dependent upon a far wider range of drivers than has been promoted.

With the maturity of the systematic approach to quality management, companies now look for further ways to add value and create competitive advantage. This often means looking at the softer issues which affect business excellence and where the newer initiatives are generally focused. Changes in organisational structures and business processes may well stimulate further development along these lines.

The Government's recent White Papers on the competitive performance of UK business have highlighted the need for companies to meet world class standards of performance. As general understanding of the role of quality management system standards grows and is placed in perspective, particularly in the context of conformity with product and service standards, there will be an increasing need for a forum in which to exchange views and develop policy.

The chairman of the Task Force (Tony Atkins of QUASCO) emphasises that we should also look at the infrastructure after considering first the more strategic issues and what the objectives really are.

It is fundamentally about the prosperity of British industry and its ability to grow and to generate an increasing contribution to the UK economy.

'The UK Quality Infrastructure needs to contribute and add value. Any component which does this should be nurtured whilst any which have a negative effect should be rooted out. No goal should be pursued for its own sake but only where it contributes to these fundamental principles. Let them be a yardstick by which all those working in the infrastructure judge their actions'.

[Issue 89 (May 1996)

FIRST LEICESTER QUALITY CONGRESS

Leicester De Montfort University opened the conference season with the First International Conference on ISO9000 and TQM. Its objectives were "to provide a forum for identifying the contemporary development in the theories and practices of TQM, and establishing the impact of ISO9000 implementation on TQM". A total of 54 papers were presented.

47

ISO9000 as a Route to Total Quality.

Jeff Bulled, Business Development Director for BSI, described some of the similarities and differences between ISO9000 and TQM, suggesting that 'the most likely strategy is to combine the two'. He argued that whilst ISO9000 is focused predominantly on the needs of the client or external customer and TQM is focused predominantly on the needs of the organisation and internal customers, the needs of the client in practice cannot be separated from the objectives of the organisation. Consequently, 'a more professional organisation' will apply ISO9000 to the totality of its core activities, to all its products and services, and to all the management functions having an apparent direct effect on product quality, including training, purchasing, management review and preventive action'. He warns against the approach of applying ISO9000 solely to particular product or service lines and the management functions such as training and management review which relate to them.

The application of ISO9000 principles to the design function is recommended on the grounds that the benefits of quality assurance as part of the design process 'is orders of magnitude greater than the benefits of applying it as part of the production or service delivery'. Similarly beneficial is the extension of ISO9000 to non core activities such as finance and personnel:

'Many organisations, seeing that the application of the standard was not as difficult as they expected and that it delivered the results they wanted, apply ISO 9000 to non core activities'.

The paper explains how, when a company is applying ISO9000 to internal functions, mechanisms are required to identify, correct and prevent problems; ensure that processes and systems are reviewed to guarantee that they continue to meet business objectives; and ensure that resources are sufficient to meet the business commitment; This is reviewed as being much akin to the fundamentals of a TQM programme, and in some cases, notably where Company Wide Registration has been sought and attained, the author says 'it is almost impossible to spot the difference'.

Where TQM programmes fail it is argued that this is often due to the fact that the reasoning behind the implementation of change designed to deliver improvement becomes 'forgotten' or 're-interpreted':

'Because there were no records of performance before the change it is difficult to demonstrate whether things are actually better or not. A number of similar functions may implement the "improvement" in slightly different ways, resulting in different practices causing frustration from the users of those functions. The result is that the whole process falls into disrepute and disuse'.

It is suggested that the existence of an effective formal quality system in such cases will serve to define the process before the change and identify and record the reasons for the design change and its associated success criteria. This would mean that the business would be able to determine if benefit really had arisen from the so called 'improvement', and identify which if any of the interpretations was consistent with the original vision, and indeed which was the most successful.

In extending the concept the author adds that there would also be a process in place to enable the most successful interpretation to be considered for universal adoption across the whole business. Hence used in this way ISO9000 becomes a means 'to lock in advantages identified from other activities or initiatives'.

The role of the BSI assessor is discussed and described as 'an enabler rather than a policeman', a vision more consistent with TQM, whilst various aspects of the standard such as management review and internal auditing are addressed in a TQM context. The case for process assessment replacing the compliance audit is presented with advantages highlighted. This applied particularly where processes are multi-functional. In conclusion the author argues that 'few quality initiatives of any flavour are incompatible with ISO9000'.

[Issue 92 (August 1996), from IMS Summer School, Cambridge, 21 – 23 July]

London Beat: caught in the ISO9000 Act.

The presentation by Bob King, Quality Manager for the Department of Technology of the Metropolitan Police, focuses on the implementation of ISO 9000 within the Department which was created in August 1992 from the former Department of Computer Services and the Chief Engineer's Department. It serves perhaps to illustrate that whilst ISO9000 may not be viewed as the most appropriate course for all organisations, seeking to invest in quality, there remain some organisations to which it is still clearly well suited.

The Department of Technology has around 1,600 staff and a turnover of around £180 million. It has 33 business units in 18 locations, of which 30 have now been registered to BS EN ISO9000.

The inspiration to pursue ISO9000 certification came originally from Nick Boothman, Director of Technology who had first viewed it as Def Stan 0521 and was reputedly 'sold on it' as an instrument for effecting change. It was some time, however, before the Metropolitan Police became convinced of its benefits, and even in 1993, when Bob King joined the team, there were those who were yet to be convinced, in particular how the standard could support their work rather than compounding it.

After some deliberation it was decided to adopt a business unit approach rather than the top down approach which some organisations had elected to follow, even though the Police was historically a disciplined and necessarily compliant organisation.

The buy-in through personal involvement was all-important, as was the correct perception of auditing i.e. a tool to tease out the business process and provide a 'shopping list' of areas to address, rather than an instrument with which to catch out the unwary. Conscious of the need for a non-bureaucratic approach, business managers were given early ownership of the system whilst working parties were established to agree corporate approaches to common issues.

The whole programme, in turn, was driven by the need for consistent performance, the removal of double standards, and a phased approach which comprised of pilot schemes and pre-assessment.

During 1994 BSI were selected as the certifying body and a quality manual with corporate procedures in place was written. Pre-assessments began in May of that year with the first registrations taking place in the autumn of that year. This led to a number of early benefits being realised, such as: better understanding of the roles of certain branches like Lambeth Transport Services that had previously been perceived as 'a black art that no-one seemed to know about ', and savings through the elimination of much duplication and repetition which were estimated as being of the order of £1 million a year.

Also there was improved credibility of the Operational Technical Support Unit which had previously been notoriously weak in reporting completed work as they rarely determined its scope or audited it. Similarly there was a general improvement in the promulgation of best practice.

The slides from Mr.King's presentation are supported by a description of the path to registration by Sian Rebbitt in *BSI News* (August1995).

AUSTRALIA RELAXES ISO9000 REQUIREMENTS FOR CONTRACTS

The Australian Federal Government has recently announced that it is to relax its requirements for companies to be certificated to ISO 9000 when tendering for government contracts. This action has been taken following widespread criticism of the standard by several leading Australian organisations, particularly in relation to the standard's failure to add value to a product or service or to offer any kind of quality guarantee.

The UK's leading critic of ISO9000 John Seddon has particularly welcomed the news, saying that "it is good news for quality to have a government that has been willing to say enough is enough". He maintains that "ISO9000 has been paraded as a quality standard and nothing could be further from the truth".

[Issue 94 (October 1996), from 7th ICM Conference on TQM, Dublin, 25 – 26 September]

Implementing ISO9000 in the Jurys Hotel Group

The Jurys Hotel Group is well known as a market leader in the Irish hotel industry and visitors to the country have some 13 luxury hotels from which to choose, shortly to be expanded to 14 with a new hotel due to open in Belfast early next year. They have a reputation for innovation and in 1993 launched a sub-brand, Jurys Inns, to enhance their reputation for excellence in the more moderate price range. With this reputation for excellence well established it is logical to support it with a visible formal quality system and the story of how this was achieved was described by the Group Operations Director of Jurys Hotel Group plc., Pat McCann, who also has the distinction of being the President of the Irish Hotels Federation which represents the interests of some 700 Irish hotels and guesthouses.

The presentation described some of the reasons for opting for ISO9000, namely that it was an internationally recognised standard which is important for companies which operate in international markets. It was also a standard which many companies in manufacturing, who were potential customers of Jurys for conferences etc., had already attained, and it provided a baseline from which to set further standards as the company continued to expand.

Mr. McCann then described the actions which followed from the decision to seek certification which was taken in August 1991:

"We thought of ourselves very much like a turtle – the journey would be slow, but you have to stick your neck out to get ahead".

It was acknowledged that in the beginning the wording of the standard gave some difficulty, as it had been written originally for manufacturing rather than for service industry, and although the speaker was familiar with "contracts and all matters legal" there was no denying that the ISO9000 document had to be adapted to meet the needs of the industry before it could be effectively applied. Some help was needed here and so experts from EOLAS (now Forbairt) were approached and agreed to work with Jurys Group management to help with the interpretation of the standard:

"With this initial work complete we were in a much stronger position to do the rest of the work in-house ourselves. We found their help very beneficial. We now had the map and knew what we must do to achieve the standard".

A Quality Policy statement was developed which reflected the enormity of the contribution which the company's people made to its profitability:

"Improvements made to the fabric of the business in upgrading bedrooms, function rooms or restaurants can be easily copied and improved on by our competitors, but the single aspect of our business which cannot be easily replicated is the consistent quality service provided by our staff".

The all-important link between consistency [removal of unwanted variation-Ed] and profitability was therefore recognised as an attribute which could be enshrined in a formal quality system rather than being allowed to drift. The standard's requirements for training allowed this link to be formalised. Staff, supervisors and managers were invited to a meeting so that they could become part of the certification process and the ensuing interaction was "surprising":

"It was expected to be a management bashing session. This did not happen though, because once we got over the familiar 'heard it all before, what's new?' question and had given the commitment of senior management to our plan to begin the quality journey, the contribution from all levels at this meeting was superb. The added benefit was that staff accepted that it was a new initiative and spoke openly to their colleagues on the work floor about it".

More meetings followed and areas of strength were identified which led to a number of objectives and strategies by which they would be achieved. The Mission Statement read as follows:

"We at Jurys are a team dedicated to guest satisfaction, providing the highest quality of products and services, where employees develop as individuals and perform all tasks with great pride for the ultimate success of the company and its shareholders ".

This Statement [which acknowledges that the removal of barriers to pride of workmanship, one of Deming's Fourteen Points, along with the need to understand variation, is essential to a profitable business -Ed], was described as "a statement which personifies the ethos of the company, describing the aims and expectations of those who work for the company".

A Group Quality Manager was appointed to oversee management of the quality system and a working committee comprising of interested parties in the tourism sector was set up to adapt the twenty clauses of the standard in line with advice supplied by the National Standards Authority of Ireland (NSAI). In addition each hotel had a manager (usually the Personnel Manager) appointed with a specific responsibility for quality:

[Issue 109 (January 1998)]

ISO9000 AND PROCESS CONTROL INSTRUMENTATION

A recent survey of the process control instrumentation industry has shown that there is 'little improvement in product compliance by a company with an accredited ISO9000 certificate'.

The survey, which was based on 128 instrument evaluation reports from European and North American manufacturers, revealed that only 50 per cent of the instruments supplied by the ISO9000 certificated companies, which represented 40 per cent of the sample, were fully compliant with the manufacturer s specifications. This compares with 51 per cent for all manufacturers (certificated and non-certificated).

The findings have led the Sira Certification Service, who have been evaluating the performance of process control instruments for over thirty years, to question whether purchasers of such instruments should really be demanding evidence of product certification which would ensure the quality of the purchased product.

[Issue 110 (February 1998)]

IN PURSUIT OF QUALITY: THE CASE AGAINST ISO9000.
(Book Review).

Author: John Seddon.

Publisher: Oak Tree Press (ISBN:1-86076-042-2)

Eight thought-provoking chapters and an Epilogue attempt in no uncertain terms to convince the reader, if not already convinced, that ISO9000 is entirely inappropriate to the pursuit of quality in the modern context. If organisations are serious about quality they should strive to avoid it if at all possible and a 'scathing attack' is made on those who 'have wrought havoc in our organisations and have presumed to label it as quality'.

The author opens with ten fundamental arguments against the Standard before discussing the distorted role of ISO Technical Committee 176, Tick IT, and the pros and cons of registration [mostly cons -Ed]. Three chapters then follow arguing the case for what is clearly presented as a vastly superior approach using Deming principles after which the reader is invited to question whether the ISO9000 assessor really is 'an agent of quality'. The author then returns to his original ten arguments to rest his case.

The ten arguments presented against ISO9000 in Chapter One are as follows:

(i).ISO 9000 encourages organisations to act in ways which make things worse for their customers.

(ii).Quality by inspection is not quality.

(iii). ISO9000 starts from the flawed presumption that work is best controlled by specifying and controlling procedures.

(iv). The typical method of implementation is bound to cause sub-optimisation of performance.

(v). The Standard relies too much on people's, and in particular assessor's, interpretation of quality.

(vi). The Standard promotes, encourages and explicitly demands actions which cause sub-optimisation.

(vii).When people are subjected to external controls they will be inclined to pay attention only to those things which are affected by the controls.

(viii).ISO9000 has discouraged managers from learning about the theory of variation.

(ix).ISO9000 has failed to foster good customer-supplier relations.

(x). As an intervention, ISO9000 has not encouraged managers to think differently.

In Chapter two the author points out that the growth of registrations to ISO9000 has been paralleled by a growth in debate and describes an opinion survey conducted by his organisation in order to gain a clearer picture:

'The 1993 research showed that only 15% of organisations surveyed believed they achieved all of the benefits claimed by the Director General of BSI; that is improved efficiency, better procedures, less waste, lower costs and more satisfied customers.

Some 69% of the respondents believed that ISO9000 improved "procedural efficiency" but the results for improvements in measurable aspects of efficiency (costs, waste etc.) were only half as good, suggesting that the improvements attributed to new procedures were coloured by opinion rather than supported by evidence'.

It is then explained how five companies in the small group which had claimed that ISO 9000 registration had been 'positive in all respects' were visited by the author who found that 'in every case' there was 'activity which was causing sub-optimisation, and which was present specifically because of registration'. On TC 176 the author says the following:

'TC176 spends time on convergence because it is the stuff of the standards movement; it is the flavour of the moment. As new standards are being developed for health and safety and environmental issues, the revisionists want to incorporate them all into general standards for doing business. Where is the evidence to show us this is a sensible thing to do? We fear that convergence will only result in building a larger army of more broadly based assessors. There is little evidence of the likely impact on the matters they would be sent out to address'.

Chapter Three examines some of the points which have been raised in favour of the standard, such as "it's OK if you do it properly", "ISO9000 is a minimum standard or a 'first step' on the quality journey", "There is no choice, it is a requirement for doing business", and "it must be good, 100,000 companies can't be wrong". To each of these counter arguments are given:

'The thinking about control implicit in ISO9000 is diametrically opposed to the thinking about control in World Class operations. What we have learned is that putting control of processes in the hands of people doing the work results in more learning, pride and, in fact, more and better control'.

The excellent Chapter Four explains in simple terms how to view the organisation as a system and introduces some Deming fundamentals in a straightforward and understandable way:

'We believe that "command and control" management thinking must be abandoned. If it is not, our organisations will remain sub-optimised and even more importantly, their "creative anarchy" will never be unleashed; we will not learn, innovate and change. Without optimisation, learning, innovation and change we will cease to compete effectively in the world economy'.

'A systems view leads managers to ask: what is predictable about the process – what will predictably happen in the future if nothing changes? Management by prediction is the hallmark of systems thinking.'

'Variation in parts leads to exponentially increasing variation in the whole system increasing the likelihood of failure'.

'As variation between parts is reduced, in whatever small amounts, the variation in the whole system reduces and thus decreases the likelihood of failure. In simple terms, this is why Japanese cars have become more and more reliable.'

'The anticipation of inspection of one's work by others will encourage anyone to do whatever they have to do to be seen to conform. In this way ISO9000 assessment, just like "management by the numbers", can cause distortion of a system or process, increasing variation – people doing whatever is required to pass inspection (for instance, ensuring that the paperwork is up-to-date, being seen to be applying unnecessary controls, - hiding things) regardless of the impact on the service and efficiency of their business'.

Chapter Five, the longest chapter at 42 pages, presents a series of case studies to support the theory of the earlier chapters whilst the somewhat more positive Chapter Six, entitled 'There is a Better Way', continues the philosophy advanced in Chapter Four, addressing the issues of attitudes to customers, decision making, measurement and supplier relations:

'Managers need to question whether a "contract between two parties" should be the focus of their relationship with customers. Perhaps it had some relevance for the provision of bombs in World War Two, perhaps it was the only way to establish basic contractual controls over the performance of companies building power stations and the like. But a contractual relationship differs from a service, partnering or co-operative relationship.

As seen with 'Metal Co.', the opportunities for partnering with customers (and suppliers) were lost through an obsession with contractual thinking'.

'Measures should be derived from purpose. In 'Tech. Co.' the purpose of the organisation was to sell and deliver products to customers. Knowing how well they did this (capability) and how predictably they worked (variation) would have been a better starting place for improvement than controlling people's behaviour through procedures. Similarly, 'Systems Co.', should have been concerned with measures of their ability to ship and fit what the customers wanted without experiencing failures. Measures derived from purpose help managers to focus their action on the system'.

Chapter Seven, on the role of the ISO assessor, is perhaps the most damning of all. However, it should not be skipped merely because it may make disturbing reading for hardened quality professionals, that is, if they still call themselves that after reaching thus far. For whilst the author is keen not to attribute total blame to the ISO assessor, the reader is left in no doubt that many assessors have a great deal to answer for:

'We have met managers who are prepared to pay as much as £7,000 for a ready-made manual and "automatic" passes of assessments. The fact that this occurs is just one inevitable consequence of coercion. It is also probably true that managers indulging in such nefarious behaviour are seeking to avoid the grief associated with assessment. Having to justify your actions to an outsider is not an attractive use of executive time, especially when one might reasonably doubt the assessor's expertise'.

'We have seen how assessors influence organisations to do things which are themselves causes of sub-optimisation. Beyond that, we have seen how it is in the assessors' interests to keep their clients registered. Assessors have achieved their status because of the marketplace coercion surrounding ISO 9000'.

If by now the reader is not convinced that there is indeed a better approach to quality than ISO9000, then surely by the end of Chapter Eight he or she should be convinced, or at least willing to concede a verdict of 'not proven' in this most compelling case:

'In every sector we have seen obligations being placed on suppliers to become registered to ISO9000; "You comply or we wont buy" being the grossest manifestation. Instead of coercing suppliers to register to ISO9000, organisations could have been working with their suppliers to improve their common lot. That is the way it has been in the Toyota organisation for the last forty years; the results are striking'.

[Issue 118 (October 1998)]

MANAGING QUALITY IN THE FUTURE

The Institute of Quality Assurance (IQA) held its first residential conference for over ten years at Warwick University on 30th September and 1st October under the sponsorship of the Engineering and Marine Training Authority (EMTA) and was a sell-out.

The conference, entitled 'Managing Quality in the Future' featured the long awaited National Debate on the pros and cons of ISO9000 certification. This subject was pointed out by the Chairman of the Organising Panel and former IQA President Norman Burgess to 'continue to dominate the letter columns of *Quality World* each month'.

The UK needs Quality Management Certification?

This was the question posed to delegates and the two protagonists were Jim Spiers, Chairman of the Association of British Certification Bodies, who presented the case in favour, and well known occupational psychologist John Seddon who presented the case against. The presentations and the heated debate which followed, were excellently moderated by Linda Campbell, Chief Executive of UKAS (UK Accreditation Service).

Jim Spiers, who is currently the Managing Director of National Quality Assurance, urged delegates to consider a quality system as a process with an input and an output which could be summarised by means of a one page flowchart i.e. there was no need for it to be represented by many pages of procedures as many people appear to believe. He supported his argument with survey evidence from Japan involving 1400 replies which suggested that the standard was an important instrument in delivering process improvement and enhanced management control, and for the elimination of the process related problems. Further evidence in form of a survey undertaken on behalf of the IQA by Nottingham Trent University, in July, was then presented to support the argument that fewer than 1% of companies which become registered to ISO9000 later deregister, and that improved business efficiency rather than customer pressure was the key driver towards companies seeking registration.

In his attempt to play up the value of certification he pointed out the fact that UKAS currently spend 1000 man-days per year scrutinising the 58 certification bodies which amounts to around 15 times more time than that spent by NQA on a typical client. A certification body is, he said, "constantly looked at to see if it is doing things right and in the right way" and he asserted that as a result of undergoing the certification process NQA's clients "could have the same confidence". He then explained how 64% of NQA's clients "actively promoted ISO9000", whilst nearly 90% considered that it was either "important" or "very important" to have continued certification.

The speech was supported by a short presentation by a delegate from GEC who explained how the bulk of his company's suppliers have both ISO9000 certification and "good systems in the spirit of the standard", although he also pointed to an emerging group of suppliers that "recognise that ISO doesn't go far enough and are now driving way beyond". Thus whilst he accepted that ISO9000 "has lost some of its momentum" he was clear that he did not believe that any of his company's suppliers would want to let go of it. In response Jim Spiers acknowledged that of course "a progressive company will go further", but urged delegates to consider very carefully whether they believed the UK really could manage without certification as he himself clearly believed that it couldn't.

The case against was emotive as ever with John Seddon contesting that compliance does not foster learning, whilst the standard itself teaches nothing at all about the all-important theory of variation, for which he clearly has high regard along with other advocates of the W.Edwards Deming philosophy. In the latter regard he pointed out that the corrective action element of ISO9000 is only invoked where there is common cause variation, not special cause variation.

Mr. Seddon renewed his attack on call centres, for which he has coined the phrase "sweatshops of the nineties", by stating that the waste generated as a result of a preoccupation with the writing of procedures to cement in sub-optimisation "was fantastic". He also did not allow delegates to forget the fact that the drawbacks to certification did not merely apply to ISO9000 itself but also to all the variants thereof, such as QS9000, which he repeatedly described as "ISO9000 on steroids", and TickIT. With regard to QS9000 he contested that the automobiles produced by Ford, Chrysler and General Motors, who insist that their suppliers achieve QS9000 registration, "break down the most" whilst those manufactured by Toyota, Honda and Nissan, who place greater emphasis on the systems approach, "break down the least". With regard to TickIT he challenged delegates to produce any evidence they could which would demonstrate that certification has actually improved software quality. None of them did.

With regard to the utility industries he called on the IQA "to stop them doing things that are undermining their efficiency", warning of "myopia induced by focusing on procedures instead of purpose".

In the debate which followed there was a level of dissatisfaction with the current state of affairs with regard to certification which clearly raised a few eyebrows, suggesting that the pro-Seddon camp is at last beginning to gain some of the centre ground. Most surprising perhaps were the views from one delegate representing the Ministry of Defence, from whom the ISO9000 standard was originally cloned, who said the following:

"It is wrong to push back to the purchaser the quality problems that we have. It worries me that twenty five year agreements are being signed when certification is not delivering. It is not a question of ISO 9000 delivering, it is whether certification is helping and the answer from the MoD is no it isn't".

Another delegate raised serious doubts about the sheer practicalities of educating assessors to the point whether they really were able to evaluate a system to determine whether it would work or not. He backed his claim that the present situation "is farcical" by citing the case of a company which had been audited and found only to have a few minor discrepancies yet when he visited their sites he unearthed no less than 289 serious deficiencies anyone of which "could have crippled the company".

Further discussion raised the issue of self-certification to ISO9000 along the lines currently applied to the Business Excellence Model, a concept which according to Jim Spiers some fifty multinational organisations currently support. The idea, however, appeared to gain little backing from the floor, one delegate commenting:

"We would not be happy with self-certification. For a large number of years we have supported ISO9000 but now we have reached a crossroads. If ISO 9000 is good and has been good, why do we not get quality? Is the system just not delivering? If not, what are you going to do about it?"

Several delegates appeared to agree with the view that perhaps ISO9000 has outlived its usefulness, which led to a call for the IQA "to stimulate interest in taking today's quality systems forward". Others suggested that control thinking was embedded historically in the UK infrastructure and that now was the time to make the move from coercion to trust [a view clearly expressed by John Carlisle at this year's BDA Forum-Ed]

One way of moving from coercion to trust is to build supplier partnerships and one delegate from the electricity industry explained how his organisation was now implementing this approach and in doing so "was moving away from demanding ISO9000 certification". He stated that "some of the biggest names have ISO9000 and give us some real headaches". He called on the IQA "to start developing partnerships instead of setting specifications for everyone".

A few lone voices spoke out in favour of the status quo, but they were few and far between. One delegate, for example asked John Seddon "what's wrong with sub-optimisation?", which met with the simple reply "it will cost you". Another delegate defended certification on the grounds that the revised version of ISO9000 currently being prepared will take account of the need to assure product and service quality to a far greater extent than at present, reflecting public demand for a change of emphasis.

A more impartial view was expressed by Professor John Oakland, who warned of the dangers of being misled by research findings of all kinds since "research can always be designed to show what you want it to show". He defended the principle of certification on the grounds that it "is part of a process that helps you to do things right", whilst ISO9000 itself "could form part of a systems approach". He stressed that he saw no reason why organisations should not implement concepts such as partnering whilst at the same time retaining their ISO9000 certification.

At the conclusion of the debate both protagonists were invited to provide some concluding thoughts on the future of certification. John Seddon used the opportunity to say that "if we taught every manager in the land the theory of variation we would be stupendously better off".

Jim Spiers said:

"Quality is about continuous improvement how we can do things better. Every system should be changing continuously. The new ISO9000 standard does address product and service quality and that's good".

[*Quality Matters* comments: No vote was taken at the end of this debate as might have been expected. Suffice it to say that if this had been done one might have expected the result to have been somewhat more marginal than it would have been say five years ago.]

[Issue 126 (June 1999)]

SWEDISH QUALITY ASSURANCE

Sweden's leading trade fair for quality practitioners, Elmia Qualitec '99, took place in Jonkoping from 18th to 20th May. This fair, which was launched for the first time last year, featured some 114 exhibitors as well as a total of 18 specialised seminars making it the largest event of its kind in Scandinavia dedicated solely to quality assurance. The event was arranged in co-operation with P.E.Schall GmbH Messematernehmen of Germany whose

'Control' fair at Sinsheim has been successful for some years now and from whom the inspiration to launch the Scandinavian event originally came.

The principal seminar, on 'QS9000: the Multitool for Winning Companies', featured Dan Reid, Manager of Supplier Development for General Motors and one of the three originators of the QS9000 standard, who spoke on 'QS9000 Experiences and Future Developments'.

QS9000: Experiences and Future Developments.

In his Keynote speech Dan Reid used the results of two independent surveys in 1997 and 1998 commissioned by the Auto Industry Action Group and the American Society for Quality (ASQ) to highlight the benefits gained from QS9000 to date. In the 1997 survey 1,613 respondents reported a payback of 2.6:1 for all costs of achieving QS9000 certification with benefits listed as follows:

* 76% reported quality improvement.

* 75% reported a better understanding of jobs.

* 54% reported fewer parts returned.

The 1998 survey, which consisted of 207 responses then highlighted an even more impressive 6% of sales cost benefit which derived entirely from investment in QS 9000 certification.

These figures were used as a clear justification not only for having developed the standard in the first place in the late 1980s when quality alignment of a non-competitive nature was seen as being essential for the US auto industry, but also for its continued application and enhancement.

In 1995 Stockholm became the focus for the European launch of QS 9000 and since then there has been a strong desire to find a consensus between QS 9000 and the European car manufacturers and their subcontractors. The efforts undertaken in this area have now culminated in the approval of anew standard, ISO Technical Specification 16949, which will be supported by a common registration scheme which will afford European suppliers the opportunity of using ISO's TS16949 to show that they meet the requirements of the existing QS9000 manual.

A Quality Assessment Workbook with columns for evidence and guidance for use by auditors will accompany the new registration scheme. The current manuals will continue in force until 2001, after which the technical specification will be revised to take into account the new ISO9000 requirements.

In his speech Mr. Reid also spoke of measures currently in place to create a QS9000 Register Quality Performance Metric with the assistance of the US Registrar Accreditation Board, and sought to clear up misunderstandings about the nature and role of continuous improvement:

"QS9000 Continuous Improvement has to begin with a conforming situation not a non- conforming one. Continuous Improvement has to extend to product characteristics not just a few projects. We are striving for processes with consistency and integrity worldwide".

In the panel session which followed Mr.Reid was joined by several speakers from Sweden who also gave presentations. These were Ms.Annette Kind representing the Swedish Institute of Production Engineering Research (IVF); Tor Janson of the Swedish Accreditation Body SWEDAC; Christer Svard, Quality Director of Global Purchasing for 1998 Swedish National Quality Award (USK) winners Volvo Truck; and Thomas Nejmann, Supplier Quality Development Manager for Saab. The session was moderated by leading Swedish consultant Bengt Ake Sorstedt of BAS Horslett AB.

Questioning began with an enquiry about current attitudes to QS9000, which both Volvo and Saab have now embraced, in Sweden and elsewhere and whether it should be "a prerequisite for survival". Thomas Nejmann then suggested that there was a difference, mainly on the part of Swedish suppliers understanding what they could gain from it. "Swedish suppliers still believe Swedish quality is still very shiny", he said.

The next question was directed at Volvo and concerned the preparedness of staff there to questions arising from suppliers. Christer Svard accepted that this was a tough issue as suppliers often have lots of questions. He did, however, stress that it was being addressed in Volvo's internal training policy. In response the questioner replied:

"I hope you can benchmark this with your colleagues because suppliers didn't get answers in some cases and it blocked the certification process for several companies."

The moderator agreed with this and said that he had some sympathy with "the underdog position" of many suppliers. Thomas Nejmann on the other hand did not accept that his company "blocked out" suppliers though he did acknowledge that often skilled answers could not be given in the right way.

Questioning then turned to the subject of second and third tier suppliers and how one could be sure that they conformed to QS9000. Christer Svard of Volvo then said that "we can never be 100% sure but we believe that first tier suppliers will take care of their suppliers". He emphasised that Volvo was not the kind of organisation that intended to perform a large quantity of audits for this purpose.

Thomas Nejmann of Saab then explained how his company had 100% reliance on the second tier on account of the fact that the first tier is always able to judge if the second tier needs certification. Dan Reid explained how the whole issue of subcontractor registration was currently being actively discussed in the US, suggesting that now may be the time to consider its introduction. He did, however, point out that in the US the standard is already reaching the second tier and that the right approach may simply be to make the first tier more accountable.

A question to Annette Kind concerning the investment of SEK 100 million by the Swedish Government into a QS9000 programme for national suppliers, which component suppliers proposed two weeks ago, was met with the answer "we want it processed soon". Discussions then turned to the area of product launches and the problems, such as that concerning tooling, which inevitably arise. This prompted Dan Reid to explain how the US, in contrast to Sweden, was "getting away from sudden launches and starting rolling changes".

On the subject of continuous improvement industry the panel was asked if it could provide some guidance as to when to stop, given that a critical point may be reached where it no longer yields improved customer satisfaction. Dan Reid replied stating that General Motors was now looking for continuous improvement at part characteristic level with Advanced Quality Planning (AQP) being used to reduce variation at this level. Thomas Nejmann said that it was important to have a dialogue with suppliers to work on Key Product Characteristics (KPCs) which "should not be too many or too few".

Finally Christer Svard and Thomas Nejmann were asked about their defect (ppm) targets to suppliers. In answering Thomas Nejmann explained how it was Saab's policy to require all suppliers to commit to zero ppm, although a more realistic target is a six month average of 350ppm. This compares with the current level of around 700 ppm. Christer Svard explained how Volvo's targets were more individually focused, as whilst 60 to 70% of suppliers had a zero ppm, there were other areas where even a 1000 ppm level was a tough target.

[Issue 131 (November 1999)]

INSPEX '99

Around 150 exhibitors were on show at this year's Inspex, the UK's leading biennial show for quality control, testing, and inspection which took place at Birmingham's National Exhibition Centre from 26th to 28th October. A special feature of this year's show, which was co-located with Manufacturing Week, Computers in Manufacturing and Tooling '99, was the seminar and workshop programme organised jointly by Nexus Media (official publishers of *Quality Today*, the UK's leading journal for quality in manufacturing industry) and the IQA.

Countdown to ISO9000: 2000

Steve Dewhirst, Technical Manager for NQA, updated delegates on the current state of progress with the new ISO9000 standard, the draft version of which is expected to be released later this month, replacing Committee Draft 2 following a positive vote in San Francisco. He described the background to the new standard which he said would be "reassuringly familiar yet refreshingly different" and highlighted some of the key changes which are most notably the increased focus on customer satisfaction and continual improvement.

The new standard, he accepted, "will look totally different" with the four principal elements of management responsibility, resource management, process management and measurement analysis and improvement, replacing the current twenty clauses, but he stressed that "no existing requirement will be deleted" and advised that there was absolutely no need for those who were already compliant with the existing standard to remove existing procedures or to attempt to rewrite their present quality systems. "If your quality system currently follows ISO9000:1994 it can easily be adapted to meet ISO 9000:2000" he said, although there were some key areas that clearly were going to warrant some attention.

The first key area which he highlighted was the disappearance of ISO9002 and ISO9003, the consequence of which was going to be that considerably more care was going to be needed with the drafting of the certification scope to comply with the single requirements standard ISO9001. Then, there was the all-important clause 5.2 which requires top management to ensure "that customer needs are determined and converted into requirements with the aim of achieving customer confidence" and that "customer requirements are fully understood and met". Likewise the situation with regard to legal aspects is clearer in the new standard requiring that "the organisation shall establish and maintain a procedure to identify and have access to legal requirements that have applicable quality aspects of its products and/or services".

Clause 5.4 relating to quality policy has what the speaker described as a "changed focus", introducing a requirement for continual improvement "to be reviewed for continuing suitability "whilst clause 5.7 on management review "shall include periodic review of current performance and improvement opportunities related to results of audits, customer feedback, process performance and production conformance analyses, preventive and corrective actions, follow-up actions and changing circumstances". Further requirements of clause 5.7 are outputs in the form of actions related, for example, to improvement of the quality management system.

With regard to 'Resource Management' (divided into five elements: General, Human Resources, Information, Infrastructure, and the Work Environment) the speaker outlined how some of the requirements were new, but they were being highlighted in a different way. Clause 6.3 for example on 'Information' requires procedures for managing information which "ensure access to and protection of information". This clause does not specifically call up BS7799, the standard for Information Security Management, but it is clear that reference to it "might be helpful". The greatest "hot potato", however, is the Work Environment clause 6.5 which requires an assessment of the organisation's work ethics, the auditing methods for which are currently far from clear.

Within the 'Process Management' section the most noteworthy clause is 7.2 on customer related processes which incorporates much of what is presently covered under 'contract review' with the important addition of a requirement for "implementation of arrangements for communication with customers" on issues such as enquiry order handling, responses relating to performance, and product and service information. The 'Measurement, Analysis and Improvement' section meanwhile does not contain any requirements for statistical techniques, although there is clear scope for their application, for example under the measuring and monitoring of customer satisfaction clause and under a similar clause specifying the measuring and monitoring of processes.

In his conclusion the speaker gave a few added tips to those who were already certificated namely, "to think of resources other than human", "to consider customer non-specified requirements", and "to review the methods for communicating with customers". He also advised those who were considering combined quality and environmental certification to familiarise themselves with the new working draft of ISO19000 which is seeking to unite quality and environmental systems auditing under a single "management systems auditing" standard.

[Issue 133 (Jan/Feb 2000)]

THE QUALITY AUDIT FOR ISO9001:2000 (BOOK REVIEW)

Author: David Weallans (275pages)

Publisher: Gower (ISBN 0-556-08245-4)

Details:

The new ISO9001:2000 standard is a complete rewrite of the ISO9000 series of standards reflecting a general trend away from basic documentation and verification and towards business developments and improvements that will benefit the whole company. This complete restructuring has brought with it a need to review auditing methods and adopt a new approach which is different from the impractical and nit-picking methods that have often characterised quality auditing in the past. The 14 chapters in this guidebook take a fresh look at auditing and demonstrate how to gain real benefits from an audit programme as against merely guaranteeing compliance to a documented system.

The first chapter defines auditing and introduces various types of auditing (financial, health and safety, quality and integrated). A vocabulary of terms is provided along with a brief description of the role of auditors. Chapter two then looks at horizontal and vertical audits, management and technical audits, internal audits and variations in technique:

'Audits can cover either the customers, projects and products in an organisation, or an individual project or product. These two approaches are often known as horizontal and vertical audits. Exactly which is which has caused some debate in the past but ISO9001:2000 has now come to our rescue. It defines the horizontal loop as everything satisfying the customer need from identification to completion. A vertical loop is a functional or organisational approach incorporating policy, planning, resourcing, processing and evaluation. Although this represents the converse of the definition that I and many others have traditionally used, at least it defines a reference standard and I have adhered to this new convention'.

In the third chapter, on Quality and quality management, the author compares ISO9000 and TQM pointing out that the new standard has removed the division of styles commonly associated with each by virtue of its 'strong communication and continuous improvement flavour'. Quality documentation is described along with a brief outline of quality costs:

'The approach to the creation of quality manuals may become more practical with the issue of ISO9001 :2000 which specifically states that system documentation does not have to be structured to fit the format of the standard. As, however, most organisations will continue to adapt their old manuals or models borrowed from elsewhere, the current practice is likely to be prevalent for the foreseeable future'.

Chapter four (the longest chapter) provides a detailed description of the new standard, noting its new elements such as the requirement for organisations to have procedures for the identification and tracking of legal requirements and for internal communication and communication with customers, as well as for process measurement and for the handling of information.

The chapter concludes with a short note on ISO10011, the draft standard for quality auditing, which the author hopes 'will address the needs of different audits' despite its current heavy orientation towards third party auditing. He does not advise auditors to make a point of studying this standard unless they have a special reason, for example, to train other auditors.

The fifth chapter deals with quality management system certification starting with the purpose and use of independent certification and then the various pitfalls and problems associated with it, which are dealt with under the following headings:

* choosing an unaccredited certification body

* not allowing enough time to make the system ready for certification

* not giving the certification company enough notice of the certification date

* over-documenting the system

* over-complacency about ways that the standard may be interpreted

'In seminars and conferences everyone will nod their heads wisely when speakers talk about "going back to the words of the standard" when interpreting a particular activity. This is highly commendable but many assessors forget to do it in the heat of an audit. It is an easy reaction when confronted with an unconventional (or for unconventional read "new") approach to a particular requirement. Auditors must remember that organisations can, and should, adopt whatever approach best fits their need and be willing to accept novel approaches on each occasion'.

A step-by-step guide to preparing an organisation for ISO9000 registration is given, along with documentation advice to auditors and those responsible for writing documents. The author is notably critical of sector schemes:

'Sector schemes tend to come and go. Personally, I do not favour them; I believe they tend to create a certain elitism. They can also tend to assessments leading disproportionately toward the sector scheme elements (such as a TickIT assessment in which I participated in a company where about 3% of the people were involved in software activities yet the TickIT auditor insisted that he would spend three days investigating the software related activities. I had to spend three days looking at everything else.) Since auditors are required to have some knowledge of the areas they audit, and have to take account of other documents such as regulations, specifications, contracts and so on during the assessment, the certification body's own procedures should take care of qualifications, making sector schemes an unnecessary bureaucratic complication'.

Where such schemes are optional the author advises companies to consider whether registration to them really is in their best interests.

Chapter six, entitled 'Selection, training and competence of auditors', offers advice on the selection and training of auditors and describes the roles of the International Register of Certificated Auditors (IRCA), the IRCA lead auditor, the IRCA internal auditor, and the International Auditor and Training Association (IATCA):

'When the scheme was first envisioned it was thought that ultimately all certification assessors would register with IATCA, leaving the national schemes such as IRCA for first and second party auditors and consultants. At the time of writing, though, the national schemes are still going strong and IATCA has still to find its niche.'

The chapter continues with a brief description of the American Certified Quality Auditor(CQA) which according to the author is the only 'true qualification 'for auditors other than the basic registration scheme offered by bodies whose focus is primarily on ISO9001 assessment i.e. it indicates suitable status for quality professionals involved in any type of audit.

It then concludes with a short word on the future of auditor registration in which he predicts that it is unlikely that requirements for professional, accredited ISO9001 certification will continue without a parallel requirement for the qualification of auditors and, this being the case, it is probable that in future there could be a requirement for supplier and internal auditors to possess a formal qualification in the form of registration to one scheme or another before their organisation can pass ISO9001 assessment.

The second half of the book is devoted primarily to the business of running the audit and the seven chapters which are grouped under this heading are entitled respectively:

* Planning (dealing with audit planning, scheduling, revision, identifying resources, selecting audit teams, scoping and co-ordinating the audit, the provision of audit collateral, and monitoring progress).

* Preparation (looking at data gathering, making use of background data, avoiding the creation of an 'audit script', team preparation, problem identification, and the use of checklists).

* Conducting the audit (covering the steps in conducting the examination, the opening meeting, commencing the investigation, selecting examples of records, identifying and notifying problems, findings review, the closing meeting, and consultancy audits).

* Reporting and documentation (including choosing the written words, use of the corrective action request sheet and no-action forms, using alternative formats, and report circulation and storage).

*Audit management and follow-up (discussing the role of the audit programme co-ordinator, action tracking, non-compliance arbitration, resource management, audit analysis and reporting and management review).

*Techniques (such as time management, the conduct of meetings, questioning, listening, non-verbal communication, observation, and analysis).

* Product and process audits (where they apply and how to conduct them).

There is nothing to stop you using standard checklists if you like them, Many audit programme co-ordinators feel that it ensures that full coverage is obtained and helps the auditors by giving them direction and reducing the amount of preparation time needed. Whilst I do accept these arguments, the benefits are not as strong as the drawbacks and, although the reduction of preparation time is a strong factor in many cases, I do feel that they have greater disadvantages.'

'Checklists are unlikely to be directly relevant to the individual organisation being audited and are much harder to keep up to date with changes. Audits based on them will be very shallow, taking little account of the specific circumstances of what is being audited. Most second and third party auditors only use standard checklists (often based on ISO9001 requirements) for initial training and development of auditors. This is just the way it should be and no assessor should ever be auditing against a "vanilla" checklist.'

'Senior managers in the audited organisation should never see audit reports, with the exception perhaps of the manager directly in charge of the area audited who may be responsible for taking corrective action. The specific audit findings are there for action to be taken by the process owners and not for comparison between departments or for performance measurement; they are not meant for that and serve that function very badly.

If senior managers in the audited organisation are interested in the results of audits then the quality manager should prepare an analysis of results and what they mean for circulation and discussion, summarising the individual findings and drawing out points more appropriate for top level attention'.

The last chapter considers implications for the future arguing that 'no matter how much some people dislike ISO9001, everybody recognises that a consistent approach, taking care to cure and prevent errors, is important'. The author accepts, however, that 'ISO9001 certification is only popular because of the certificate and logo which come with it', and that 'if the need for an independent certificate, or the apparent business credibility that goes with it, becomes unpopular then ISO9001 will fall from grace'. He foresees an era of convergence with the Business Excellence Model with 'results oriented measures creeping into the ISO9000 family'.

TL9000QUALITY SYSTEMS REQUIREMENTS AND METRICS TWO BOOKS (238 pages)

Publisher: The Quest Excellence for Suppliers of Telecommunications (QuEST) Forum (ISBN-87389-463-4)

Details:

These two books describe a common set of quality system requirements for suppliers of telecommunications products and define a minimum set of performance metrics and cost and quality indicators to measure progress and evaluate results of quality system implementation. This begins with a description of the TL9000 Model which is structured in five layers:

- International standard ISO9001

- Common TL9000 requirements

- Hardware, software and services specific quality system requirements

- Common TL9000 metrics

- Hardware, software and services specific quality system metrics

A short description of TL9000 administration is then followed by a detailed description of the quality systems requirements themselves which uses ISO9000: 1994 clause 4 as its foundation. Each section of this clause is reproduced in italics with interpretations and supplemental quality systems requirements harmonised and added in plain text. Elements for which there are substantial interpretations and supplemental quality system requirements include the following:

- Element 4.2.3 (Quality Planning) with special requirements covering customer involvement , long and short term planning, sub-contractor input, and disaster recovery.

- Element 4.4 (Design Control) with special guidance on project planning, test planning, end of life planning, estimation, computer resources, integration planning, migration planning, customer and subcontractor input, design requirements, content of requirements, identification of software requirements, requirements allocation, design output, services design output, periodic retesting, content of testing, frequency of testing, change management process, informing customers, tracking changes, component changes and tool changes.

- Element 4.8 (Product Identification and Traceability) with requirements for traceability for recall, traceability of design changes, configuration management plans, and product identification.

- Element 4.9 (Process Control) specific requirements here concerning operational changes, operator qualification, an employee skills list, documented procedures for document replication, release management, and software used in service delivery.

- Element 4.10 (Inspection and Testing) which contains guidance notes on inspection and test documentation and records and requirements for the testing of repair and return products and a packaging and labelling audit.

- Element 4.15 (Handling, Storage, Packaging, Preservation and Delivery) with special requirements for anti-static protection, software virus protection, deterioration of materials, and patch documentation.

- Element 4.18 (Training) containing special requirements for quality improvement concepts training for employees whose work has a direct impact on the quality of the product, and advanced quality training and/or electrostatic discharge training (ESD) training where appropriate.

- Element 4.19 (Servicing) containing supplemental requirements for customer support, customer service, notification of problems, assigning of severity levels to customer reported problems, documented escalation procedures to resolve customer reported problems, a supplier recall process, emergency failures of products in the field, problem resolution configuration management, an installation plan, patching procedures, and problem resolution.

In addition to the above and other, more minor additions, a further element 4.21 (Quality Improvement and Customer Satisfaction) is included requiring a quality improvement programme to be in place, employee participation, supplier performance feedback, demonstration of management commitment, customer-supplier communication, monitoring of customer satisfaction, collection and analysis of field performance data including no trouble found (NTF) data, collection and analysis of service performance data, and documented procedures for the introduction of new products.

There are six appendices to the 'Requirements' handbook, namely:

*TL9000 Accreditation Body Implementation Requirements

*Code of Practice for TL9000 Registrars

*Registration Procedures

*Migration Plan and Audit Days

*Alternative Method for maintaining TL9000 Certification/Registration

*Guidance for Customer-Supplier Communications

'The "Alternative Method for Maintaining TL 9000 Certification/Registration" (AM) is a method to determine if a supplier's quality management system meets the ISO9001 criteria to warrant continuation of an accredited certification by a third party. The method is based on utilizing the supplier's (first party) internal audit system as a complement to the certifier's/registrar's (third party) own assessment activities. The objectives are elimination of unnecessary audit duplication and improving the effectiveness of third party TL9000 audits and certification/registration.

Higher value can be achieved by increasing benefits or decreasing costs to "customers". However, the primary goal is not to decrease costs but is to add value when compared to other more traditional methods of third party auditing'.

'One approach to customer-supplier communications is a voluntary shared expectations process. This is a process in which a single supplier works jointly with a customer to create an understanding of each other's expectations and improve quality on a continuing basis. The objective is a closer, long-term relationship between the two participants. '

' A joint team of supplier and customer personnel is formed to review expectations, identify gaps and create the mechanism for reducing the gap. An impartial, telecommunications-experienced facilitator may be added to the team when agreed to by both customer and supplier. The team develops action items and tracks them on an action item register. Often, Action items are worked on by joint customer-supplier task forces. Costs are shared by the customer and supplier. It is recommended that the team will meet at least twice a year'.

The 'Metrics' handbook (separate book) is largely mathematical in content describing the various Common Metrics, Hardware Metrics, Software Metrics, and Services Metrics as required by the standard.

Examples include Number of Problem Reports (NPR}, Problem Report Fix Response Time (FRT), Overdue Problem Report Fix Responsiveness

Measurements, (OFR), System Outage Measurement (SO), Return Rates, Software Update Quality (SWU), Release Application Aborts (RAA), Service Quality (SQ), Corrective Patch Quality (CPQ), and Feature Patch Quality (FPQ), a 'patch' being defined in the Glossary as 'any interim software change between releases (delivered or made available for delivery to the field)'.

The book also describes TL9000 measurement data flow and usage, metrics usage and responsibilities (including levels of usage on three levels, customer and supplier responsibilities, and the responsibilities of the Forum Administrator, Metrics Administrator, QuEST Forum and Registrar), and various General Metrics Requirements. It is noted that TL9000 registration requires the fulfilment of the TL9000 Quality System Requirements and the reporting of the TL9000 Quality System Metrics data specific to that TL9000 registration to the Metrics Administrator:

'Some of the TL9000 metrics may be used as improvement measures by individual suppliers. These metrics undergo careful review to determine that measures are indeed comparable. These metrics are monitored by the Metrics Administrator to assure that aggregation across suppliers into summary statistics are valid and meaningful. The summary statistics definitions will be revised as needed. The definition of these metrics includes the designation "compared data"'.

'Other metrics include the designation "research data". Research data shall not be used for comparison purposes. However, the Metrics Administrator will analyse the data to reveal possible industry trends. These analyses are reported only to the metrics work groups for examination for possible future uses'.

The 'Metrics' handbook contains two appendices. The first, 'Product Category Tables' describes rules for the classification of products along with Product Category Definition, Metric Applicability Tables, and a Metrics Summary Listing:

'Suppliers shall classify their products and report measurements according to the listed product categories. The Metrics Applicability Table (Normalised Units) lists specific metrics that apply to each category as well as the normalised units and other information necessary for compiling measurement reports'.

The second Appendix provides 'TL9000 Customer Satisfaction Metrics Guidelines':

'Feedback is obtained through various mechanisms (such as satisfaction surveys and front line customer technical support input). The surveys should determine the importance of the items surveyed as well as how satisfied customers are. Analysis should include trends and rates of improvement'.

ISO9000 AND THE E.F.Q.M. EXCELLENCE MODEL: COMPLEMENTARY OR DIVISIVE?

This provocative title was the theme for a Construction Industry Seminar on March 8th when the British Quality Foundation and the Construction Productivity Network joined forces.

Most meaningful debates on quality take place at industrial level and this event was no exception. The case for Business Excellence was put by John Carson, Chairman of TQMI, who explained the fundamentals approach - results orientation consistency of purpose people development, beneficial partnerships etc. elements not well covered in ISO9000, although the proposed revisions will cover 2 key elements -customer focus and process management. It was stated that Tony Blair and his Cabinet colleagues had subjected themselves to a 2 day course on the Model, and how the Model was being used in the public sector. The Model had been developed by practitioners rather than consultants and standards makers, and it was holistic in approach.

The case for ISO9000 was made by Tom Harland of BSI who tailored his remarks to the Construction sector emphasising that the revised ISO9000 with its bias towards Process management would allow a ready assimilation with the Business Excellence Model. The special problems of the Construction sector -conformity with specifications, communication with clients and architects-contractual disputes and rework etc., could be eased, he claimed, by working to the systems in ISO9000. He felt that the revised ISO 9001 (due in November 2000) was less prescriptive than before and would allow "site" focus which was very welcome to the industry.

In the discussion the following points were made:

* getting the clients' requirements correct at the outset is a key function for quality

* quality management must be made more relevant to senior managers for there to be any real progress

*for construction there is a need to simplify management systems as far as possible .

* there is still too much subjectivity in assessment against ISO9000 (this problem is common to all sectors)

* clients in the sector, particularly local authorities, are slow in their understanding of quality issues and the Business Excellence Model is presently outside their scope (there were exceptions however)

* initiative overload is a problem (the industry has more than its fair share of them!)

* why wasn't there a construction version of ISO9000 as there was for the automotive, telecoms and aerospace sectors?

During the workshop sessions these and other issues were debated within the theme of "differences between the two approaches – barriers to progress".

Participants felt that the Business Excellence Model was something that companies would want to have "as opposed to ISO9000 which was something that companies ought to have". Whilst the BEM was concerned with internal improvement over time, using self-assessment, ISO9000 was more to do with compliance and meeting external requirements set up by third parties.

Overall there is satisfaction with the Excellence Model but it is still not well enough used or understood. Whilst concern remains about the proper implementation of ISO9000 there is hope that the revisions will better address the industry's needs.

WHEN QUALITY FAILS WHERE IS ISO9000?

All quality practitioners are probably aware of the recent media attention that has been focused on the Sellafield nuclear reprocessing plant concerning the falsification of documents relating to consignments of fuel pellets destined for Japan. A smaller number will be aware that Lloyds Register Quality Assurance (LRQA) has decided not to suspend BNFL's ISO9002 certificate even though the HSE's Nuclear Installations Inspectorate has found that there was 'a systematic management failure' at the plant. Greenpeace argue that quality assurance certification at BNFL is 'a farce' and that the ISO9000 certificate should have been withdrawn forthwith.

So, what do you think? Should an organisation be allowed to retain an ISO9000 certificate when there has been 'a systematic management failure' as the HSE suggest? Should the HSE have the authority to require certification bodies to withdraw ISO9000 certificates? If not, what is the value of such certificates?

The March 2000 edition of the IQA journal *Quality World* contains a more detailed report on the matter, including an explanation of 'What went wrong?'

IS09000:2000- AN INDUSTRY VIEWPOINT

The most radical revision of ISO9000 since its inception is now almost complete. Major changes to the standard, which now has a far more process orientated and customer focused structure than the former 1994 version, include a streamlining of the three components ISO9001, ISO9002 and ISO 9003 into a single standard (ISO9001), inclusion of all of the vocabulary previously defined in ISO8402, and new requirement to measure customer satisfaction. It will also require auditors to have a much greater understanding of management systems, which has been reflected in the upgrading of the IRCA training requirements for external auditors.

The changes have naturally been a subject of debate among managers and quality practitioners alike, and on 24th October members of the Quality Methods Association met with senior quality consultants and managers to discuss some of the implications. The event, was hosted by SmithKline Beecham in Slough.

Management Principles.

The eight management principles underpinning the new standard were outlined by leading consultant David Hutchins and are briefly as follows:

* customer focused organisation

* leadership

* involvement of people

* process approach

* systems approach to management

* continuous improvement

* factual approach to decision making

*working with the supply base

In his presentation he explained how the new standard was going to give new meaning to people involvement by requiring far more evidence of how people are involved in organisations, whilst the process approach would create a major challenge for auditors who will need to be able to ascertain first of all whether it exists and if so to what extent.

This process approach also extends to outsourcing with the new standard likely to accelerate the uptake and development of supply chain management, as well as demanding a much more structured approach to continuous improvement to that which has been found in many registered firms hitherto.

Delegates were urged not to fall into the temptation of believing that the new standard was going to be a mere clone of the 1994 version, despite what may be being voiced by certain certification bodies who clearly have a vested interest in keeping the changes as soft as possible. Likewise the new standard will aim to deter those organisations which have achieved certification by doing the absolute minimum to comply. "If IRCA has its way this will stick out like a sore thumb", Mr. Hutchins said.

Implications of the new Standard

Speaking alongside David Hutchins were consultant David Nurse and former IQA chairman Norman Burgess, who is currently chairman of the Engineering Quality Forum, which meets approximately every two to three months and is presently conducting a project to assess the effectiveness of all quality initiatives that have been introduced in the UK over the last fifteen years.

Output from this study, which is being undertaken in conjunction with UMIST, should include an indication of how the quality of products bought and sold have improved or not, as the case may be, and how the attitudes of purchasers have been influenced by such initiatives. Publication of the findings is expected sometime in the spring of next year.

In his presentation Mr. Burgess expressed his concern about the imposition of pressure on organisations to follow the standard, which is not its intention, but hoped that more organisations will choose to use ISO9001 and ISO9004 (the guidance document which goes much further than ISO 9001) as a pair. He was keen to stress that yes, there were "other ways" of achieving quality objectives than simply following that methodology prescribed by ISO 9000.

As for the standard itself he foresaw some difficulty for organisations with one or two of the new requirements, notably the infrastructure and work environment clauses. Facilities, for example are now part of the quality consideration and some of the smaller companies especially could experience difficulty in this area.

Some of the most profound implications, however, are envisaged to affect auditors with the possible emergence of a two tier auditing system as up to half of today's auditors become relegated to internal auditing roles. David Nurse added to this with a prediction that the new standard "would challenge lead auditors" with clauses that are far more generic in nature than is the case with the current ISO9000 standard. He commented:

"Some of these people are not going to be lead auditors in the next three years because they won't be able to change their thinking, but there will be more added value in the end. "

One key factor which is likely to impact heavily on this is the empowerment of auditors to offer advice under the new standard, as against purely issuing pass/fail type verdicts. The legal implications of these sorts of changes remain to be tested i.e. will it mirror the financial sector where service providers have, for example, been taken to court over advice issued in respect of the provision of mortgages? If so, auditors may be required to take out some kind of indemnity insurance.

Further implications are envisaged for the certification bodies with considerable potential existing for diversity in interpretations, particularly with regard to the new requirements. Most of the new standard's 23 elements are auditable and a parallel was drawn between the possible variation in interpretation between certification bodies and the discipline of case law in which new laws which are passed through parliament are subject to different interpretations, and loopholes.

This is not to say, however, that a vast diversity of opinion between the 60 or so certification bodies was likely to exist, particularly as about a third of them are members of the Association of British Certification Bodies (ABCB) and as such might be expected to adopt a consolidated view.

Mr. Nurse outlined some of the further implications for organisations, in particular for top management, the responsibility of whom is encapsulated in the opening of every clause throughout the first part of the standard. Top management is defined as:

' A person or group of people who direct and control an organisation at the highest level'.

Also, with there now being just one auditable standard, ISO9001, there are implications for design which have hitherto not been incorporated in ISO9002 or ISO9003. With the new standard organisations which do not undertake design will have the option to delete clause 73 in their scope provided that the customer accepts this.

Customer focus, of course, is another major feature of the new standard which, as Mr. Nurse pointed out, has been produced by the ISO Technical Committee as a result of listening to what organisations were asking for to a far greater degree than has been the case in the past. Previously the standard had demanded merely that organisations measure and record customer complaints. Under the new regime measurements will be required of the customer's opinions of the degree to which a particular transaction has failed to meet both their needs and expectations. "Customer complaints are a common indicator of customer dissatisfaction, but an absence does not necessarily signify satisfaction", he emphasised.

In looking to the future Mr. Burgess explained some of the new proposals being put before ISO, which include a proposal for a standard on complaints handling, a standard for quality systems requirements for consultants, and a guidance document on interpretation which is to be closely studied between now and December 2003 when the current ISO9000 standard will be withdrawn.

Other initiatives that are on the cards are a proposal for a document on management systems standards, designed to facilitate the introduction of integrated management standards. A first step in this direction has already been taken by aligning the numbering of the clauses of ISO9001 with those of the environmental standard ISO14001. A management systems standard would allow for further alignment, especially with health and safety.

Additionally, several selection and use brochures will shortly be released to provide help and guidance on quality management principles and the process approach. These will support ISO9004 which includes, amongst other things, an EFQM style self-assessment questionnaire, although it does have a rather different structure from that of the Business Excellence Model. Details of the new brochures are expected to follow shortly in *BSI News*.

Views from Industry

Four speakers from industry gave their opinions of the new standard. These were Herb Hayday, Quality Systems Manager for Kodak and a lead assessor for the UK Quality Award; John Cosier, Quality Manager for Philips Research Laboratories UK at Redhill; David Newey, Site Health and Safety Manager for BP Amoco; and Philippe Rousseliere, Group Quality Manager for Renishaw plc and Chairman of the QualityMethods Association.

Herb Hayday commented that in his organisation top management priority was very much focused on running the business and driving share price than in meeting the specific requirements of ISO9000. He explained how SAP (a software program) had recently been implemented globally to manage the Company's 'order to cash' transactions.

Kodak was structured in global business units for which the Leadership teams had been established on an autonomous basis. These were developing in different ways and at different rates according to their respective markets. The training of quality personnel in the UK has already incorporated most of the changes to the ISO9000 standard, underlining the new areas of focus such as customer focus, human resources, facilities management and customer related processes.

Chuck Goslee joined Kodak as the worldwide Quality Director, bringing Xerox experience with him, and correlated customer satisfaction with market share. Essentially it was concluded that a 4% improvement in customer satisfaction would lead to a 1% improvement in market share, and that a 1% increase in market share would generate around $350 million in revenue.

The Kodak Management System (KMS) has recently been streamlined with eight basic management procedures now reduced to six as follows:

- customers (new heading)

- business planning

- people management

- information and assets (infrastructure)

- processes (formerly operations)

- improvement

Six record tables are used as manager 'checklists' and it takes around two hours for each manager to run through these checklists and identify what they have in place to meet the requirements of these six procedures.

It was explained how KMS2000 is now aligned with ISO9001 : 2000 with shortfall between the detail within ISO9001 and the content of the KMS being addressed through the organisation's training system, essentially by maintaining a network of fully trained quality managers to ensure they are fully conversant with the new standard.

In this description the speaker was keen to emphasise his preference for self-assessment over auditing. These were two terms which he said must not be confused, and managers usually favoured and responded better to the former. The form of assessment he favoured used three to five year trend charts with benchmarks to provide a meaningful context.

John Cosier explained how Philips Research had been implementing ISO9000 since 1995 with nine basic ISO9000 principles, three of which were directly project related. Steering groups meet monthly with typically around 20 projects being implemented per year. Little opinion was voiced about the new standard and its implications.

David Newey, by contrast, urged delegates to "wake themselves up" and ask themselves seriously who the standard was for. He stressed that in a global organisation different teams were likely to be managed according to different national cultures and that the auditing system would have to respect this.

He also alerted delegates as to the dangers associated with auditing processes such as supplier partnerships which may be out of the direct control of those being audited, as well as to the likelihood that many organisations may seek to fudge ways of keeping the 'sticker on the wall', He expressed the opinion that the new standard may be less helpful to internal suppliers than the old one and told the audience forthrightly that if the new standard did not support BP Amoco's objectives and enable them to do business more effectively they would not be continuing with it in some internal support services.

He stressed that these comments did not apply to BP's manufacture and supply of products where BP would continue with ISO9001 as part of the assurance that product specifications were fully met.

Philippe Rousseliere described how Renishaw currently maintained three separate registrations to ISO9000 using procedures that were "very different". He was critical that "the old twenty part shopping list only made sense to the auditor" and therefore welcomed the move away from a focus on inspection and toward the objectives of continuous improvement. He also suggested that in his organisation at least the more generic approach would be beneficial in allowing for an improved alignment of quality with environmental management and health and safety.

In this regard he pointed out the relevance of the COSHH regulations to quality, which impacted on such aspects as the procedures which defined how substances should be stored. He said that we would have to wait and see how some "nebulous areas" of the new standard were going to be interpreted, but was generally positive about the changes, stating that he was very much in favour of seeing auditors playing their role of helping the organisation into improving rather than acting as policemen.

Facilitated discussion.

Phillippe Rousseliere led the facilitated discussion which took place in the afternoon session and provided an opportunity for delegates to raise their concerns and network with the experts.

Questions raised fell broadly into four main subject areas, namely top management, processes, auditing, and interpretations. Some key messages were that efforts needed to be made to talk the language of top management, avoid the quality word because "it had too much baggage", discuss tools, not to launch headlong into process mapping without understanding it, and ensure mature auditors deal with top management issues.

It was generally agreed that there was unlikely to be any common interpretation of the standard, although organisations would have leave to appeal where differences in interpretation were found to exist.

Chapter Two

Health, Safety and Environment

The growth in interest in the principles of third party certification in the late 1980s and early 1990s as applied to the field of quality assurance naturally impacted in two other important areas with which quality practitioners were frequently associated, namely health and safety and the environment. There is strong overlap between both of these subject areas and quality, with good performance in one area usually signifying strength in all three. This naturally led to debate about the benefits of integrating the three subject areas and applying a common auditing framework.

Certification of environmental management systems became a reality in 1992 when BSI launched BS7750, which subsequently became ISO 14001. Progress with health and safety, however, was somewhat slower. Early drafts of what should have been BS8750 were shelved, although a Guidance Document (BS8800) did eventually transpire. Meanwhile the certification bodies developed their own conventions in the form of ISA2000 and OHSAS 18001.

Key events have included Environmental Technology (et), the annual conferences of the Institute of Occupational Safety and Health (IOSH), and the annual Safety and Health at Work Exhibition and Conference traditionally held in London but now amalgamated with the Royal Society for the Prevention of Accidents (RoSPA) Exhibition and Conference as highlighted at the end of this chapter. The compilation below includes a selection from each of these, as well as a few other notable inclusions.

B.S.I.LAUNCHES FIRST STANDARD ON ENVIRONMENTAL MANAGEMENT

The British Standards Institute has now launched its new standard on Environmental Management Systems (BS7750), which is the first standard of its kind in the world.

The standard provides a model management system for all types of organisations wishing to take a systematic and integrated approach to environmental management with the final aim of improving their environmental performance. It adopts a quality systems approach to environmental issues and BS5750 (ISO9000). It does not therefore specify expected levels of organisational performance but rather specifies a standardised management system that is capable of independent assessment and verification.

The standard is currently compatible with the proposed EC regulation on environmental auditing which is due to be adopted by the European Council and Parliament later this year. Any changes in these proposed regulations will be incorporated in a major review of BS7750 due to take place early next year when feedback from a standard pilot programme can also be taken into account. It is anticipated that this pilot programme will be supplemented by the development of various industrial sector codes, which will help to assist specific industries with the application of the standard.

Publication of the standard has been supported by the Department of Trade and Industry, the Department of the Environment and the Advisory Committee on Business and the Environment (a special body set up jointly by the DoE and the DTI) with the aim of creating closer links with business on matters of national environmental policy.

Speaking at the launch of the standard on 6thApril, Sir Anthony Cleaver, Chairman of IBM (UK) and of the Working Group on Environmental Management, set up by the ACBE, said he felt that the standard 'gives business what it wants and needs to meet the environmental challenge' and 'will bring to an end the proliferation of questionnaires that companies are currently using'. Compliance with the standard, he says, 'will carry the same weight as BS5750' without the need to question the company's quality standards. He said that BS5750 had 'paved the way ' for this standard which 'gives the UK a chance to take the lead'.

It is envisaged that the first companies will be achieving registration in the second half of 1993.

QUALITY AND THE ENVIRONMENT

A major conference linking the environment with quality management for the chemical industry was held at the London Metropole Hotel from 18th to 20th October.

Responsible Care and Product Stewardship

Several papers examined the subject of Responsible Care, which was created as a concept by the Canadian Chemical Producers Association in 1984 and essentially involves a commitment to demonstrate continuous improvement in all aspects of health, safety and environmental (HS and E) performance.

Graeme Crombie, Managing Director of Shell Chemicals, describes it as 'the most comprehensive ambitious health, safety and environmental initiative ever put together by manufacturing industry' and explains his role in drafting codes of practice for this scheme. Although based on voluntary principles this has become a prerequisite for membership of the UK Chemical Industries Association. He describes how Shell Canada subsequently reviewed its manufacturing, marketing, distribution and waste management systems over a period of two years and at a cost of £6 million in order to comply with the codes which he had helped to formulate.

Thomas Riggert of Andersen Consulting, by contrast, criticises it as 'not conceived in response to any long term threat to the planet, but to a very short-term and immediate threat to the chemical industry -regulation', He points to the expense involved in complying with it, up to 7 per cent of turnover, and suggests that unless the customer 'is willing eventually to pick up the tab', or the company make money by some other means, the programme 'isn't going to last very long'.

PM Lange is rather more positive, but predicts that CEMAS will have a greater impact. Denying CEMAS would he says, be 'a contradiction to Responsible Care' and he believes that American subsidiaries of chemical industry companies that are applying their Responsible Care programmes in Europe 'will easily adapt Responsible Care to CEMAS'.

Tony Strong points out that whilst Responsible Care was initiated on the American continent ,the UK 'has one of the world's leading Responsible Care programmes. This is largely as a result of its adoption by the Chemical Industries Association, who have published for the first time a quantitative report of their members' safety and environmental performance based on Responsible Care indices. Also published are established guidelines for its adoption in the form of Product Stewardship i.e. 'a management system which promotes through Quality Procedures responsible health, safety and environmental performance throughout the total life cycle of a product .

The Association's paper, by Dr. Andrew Robinson, Senior Executive for the Responsible Care and Sector Groups and Chairman of the CEFIC Task Force on Product Stewardship, describes the concept of Product Stewardship and the guiding principles that the Association has set for its members.

Responsible Care is viewed as 'fundamental to regaining public confidence and maintaining licence to operate'. The guidelines for Product Stewardship are based on Responsible Care together with important principles embodied in the International Chamber of Commerce (ICC) Business Charter for Sustainable Development. The Charter was formally launched in April 1991, and contains 16 essential principles for environmental management, which was itself partly inspired by Responsible Care. Also Product Stewardship is based on the US Chemical Manufacturers' Association Code of Management Practice for the Environment, with best practice, experience, and expertise drawn from member companies themselves.

The guidelines cover all aspects of product concept, research and development, applications and foreseeable misuse, and recycling and disposal, with an emphasis on leadership, risk management, communication and partnership.

The paper outlines key responsibilities for senior management, manufacturing and marketing, drawing attention to the need to review the potential impacts on product risk characteristics of any proposed changes in the manufacturing process or product specifications before implementing them. It recommends Product Stewardship to be regarded, by marketing staff especially, as an integral part of a total product offering and for market distribution strategies to be developed according to product risks. Certification of HS and E systems to ISO9001 is recommended.

[Issue 61 (January 1994)]

BEYOND THE VISION.

The Chemical Week conference was concluded with an enlightening speech from James Whiston, Group Safety, Health and Environmental Manager for ICI plc entitled 'Beyond the Vision'. He spoke of the widespread feeling amongst senior managers throughout the chemical Industry that there were now too many initiatives such as TQM, Responsible Care, Product Stewardship,ISO9000/BS5750, BS7750 etc. all of which appeared to lack coherence. He sought to reassure delegates that in reality all of these initiatives were coherent and needed to take root in organisations if they are to achieve business benefits which must be transparent to all'.

Managers of companies who viewed such initiatives as a 'business cost which does not bring any positive benefits' were urged to reconsider as the 'price of non-conformance' could be very high. The 'costs' of safety, health and the environment should, he argues, be viewed as an investment so as to achieve much larger potential savings, although accepting that these savings 'must be clearly demonstrable rather than acts of faith'. He says:

'I fully believe that we can demonstrate clearly that good Safety, Health and Environmental (SHE) care is good business'.

Six specific cost areas which offered' demonstrable potential savings' were highlighted:

* the cost of accidents, which includes the wage costs of the injured plus the cost of replacing them; investigation costs; and the costs of implementing the recommendations following the investigation.

* the cost of incidents, safety and environmental, and especially those involving loss of containment.

* insurance costs.

* the cost of SHE complaints, including follow up costs and management time.

* the cost of infractions i.e. when a complaint becomes formal, results in prosecution, and the company has to pay fines, legal fees and wages to staff who become diverted away from the running of the business.

*health costs ,including loss of workers' time through chronic symptoms.

These costs can be substantial. The average cost of a reportable accident, for example, is estimated at £25,000 whilst the cost of minor accidents can amount to several thousands of pounds, not to mention the 'opportunity element' of managers' time spent investigating accidents and implementing recommendations instead of developing the business. To gain a measure of incident costs the speaker advised delegates 'just to look at the small incidents and estimate the loss including plant outage', whilst the 'often forgotten area' of insurance premiums was illustrated with the example of the Hickson Welch factory in Castleford where one accident alone last year had resulted in a £500,000 increase in the company's annual insurance premium which already stood at £3 million. He comments:

' I know companies where the annual insurance premium is as high as £100 million. If you take a profit of 10 per cent on sales, as an average, then think of the sales to be made to cover the insurance premium.'

Attention is also drawn to the fact that many insurance companies have become increasingly reluctant to provide full cover and the belief that insurance cover should be seen as a partial alternative to good SHE is simply not valid today.

The cost of SHE is estimated at £2,000 per complaint and whilst no figures are quoted for the cost of infractions (not including the costs of the Public Affairs Department) it is known that in the US particularly it runs into millions of dollars. As for health effects, delegates were advised not to forget them as they were long running.

Most of these costs, according to the speaker, are avoidable, with the cost of non-conformance transferable directly to profit, but the benefits do not stop here. There are also positive benefits to be gained from adopting a systems approach, such as the avoidance of shift to shift variances that cause out of specification product, and there may be 'soft benefits' such as maintaining one's licence to operate. He says:

'We need to ensure that there is an understanding that we operate in the context of a social contract based on mutual benefit with the public and the governments in the countries and communities where we operate. To continue to manufacture, distribute and sell potentially hazardous chemicals requires that we conduct ourselves in a manner that recognises and rewards the public's trust. It is key that we listen to communities and regulators in this very difficult area.'

It was emphasised that in Europe, the Americas and the Asia Pacific region the general public has turned on the chemical industry as a result of its poor safety, health and environmental performance. The speaker left no doubt as to the importance of gaining the public's trust and of responding positively to that trust, with independent third party auditing playing a part in securing that trust and consequently 'a cost of doing business'.

After the speech he was asked how reluctance on the part of management in this area might be overcome. The advice given in such cases was for negative but hard benefits to be taken to the boardroom, scrutiny made of the company's environmental performance, with examination of the costs and demonstration in terms of sales about what is having to be done to cure the problems. Mr. Whiston pointed out that outstanding companies tend to ride recessions well, these are one of the first things usually noticeable about them. This is probably determined by whether TQM is at the root of the organisation or just superficial.

ASSESSING THE MANAGEMENT OF RISK

The fifth Safety and Health at Work exhibition and conference took place at London's Olympia centre with 238 exhibitors attracting around 9,000 visitors. Approximately 800 delegates attended the two day conference devoted to chemicals control and hazardous substances, the management of risk, new perceptions of hazards at work and safety training in four separate sections. Of perhaps most interest to subscribers is the management of risk, which is a quality related subject and one for which many quality professionals have direct responsibility.

Health and Safety Research

The first paper presented on the management of risk was by Jean-Marie Le Guen, Head of the Risk Assessment Policy Unit of the Health and Safety Executive (HSE). This described research which the Accident Prevention Advisory Unit and Economic Advisers Unit (EAU) of the HSE has undertaken in order to provide an estimate of the cost of health and safety management failures both at national level and at individual workplace level. The research involved an analysis of the cost of accidents in five organisations in different areas of employment, in which the number of employees varied from 80 to 700, and the health and safety performance was considered to be average or better than average in their sector.

The companies consisted of a construction company which had been awarded an £8million contract for the construction of a supermarket, a creamery, a transport company belonging to a leading UK dairy products manufacturer, a North Sea oil platform operated by an international oil company, and an NHS hospital which specialised in plastic and oral surgery (the largest employer with 700 employees and an annual budget of around £8million).

The findings ,which are described as 'startling' showed that in the case of the construction company the total loss (due to accidents) was around £245,000 which represented around 8.5% of their tender price for the work, which took 54 weeks. For the creamery the corresponding figure was just below (244,000) which amounted to about 1.4 per cent of their operating costs. The transport company suffered a loss of £49,000 which represented 1.8 per cent of operating costs and a substantial proportion of their profits (37 per cent). For the oil platform the loss was the highest of all (£941,000), which was equated with around 14.2 per cent of potential output. For the hospital the figure was £99,000, which amounted to 15 per cent of their annual running costs. It is noted that the study included only those accidents which the participating organisation agreed could have been prevented by the application of existing procedures or 'other cost effective measures'.

The number of accidents occurring at each site was recorded as follows:

Construction site: 3626

Creamery : 926

Transport company: 296

Oil platform: 262

Hospital: 1232

It can be seen from this that although the oil platform suffered the highest loss in money terms, it had the lowest number of accidents, suggesting perhaps a higher proportion of major accidents [which is perhaps a consequence of the especially hazardous nature of the work -Ed]. Throughout, however, the number of incidents is described as 'considerable' with the average cost of individual incident events said to be small. Furthermore it is noted that the ratio of events resulting in injury or ill-health as distinct from purely damage to property was high in all cases. It is concluded that:

'In all cases the scale of losses are significant and had the losses not been incurred, most of the money saved would have contributed to the profits'.

The paper then explains how the EAU used these findings, along with other information, to present a picture of the scale of accidents and ill-health at national level in terms of compensation costs, costs of maintaining output whilst workers are absent, costs of replacing staff who are forced to quit, and the costs of damage to materials, plant, equipment and finished goods. The estimates show that the costs to employers nationally were of the order of £4,400 million to £9,400 million, whilst for society as a whole the costs were much higher (£11,000 million to £16,300 million). In addition it is noted that most of the costs were not recoverable from insurers, contrary to popular belief.

Problems with Risk Assessment

These studies, according to the author, 'have added considerable weight' to the belief that for many companies failure costs are frequently greater than prevention and appraisal costs, and whilst there is often a wide range of immediate causes of accidents it is suggested that the underlying common causes are usually traceable to poor management of health and safety. It follows that there is a need for improvement in this area, and recent legislation, notably the Control of Substances hazardous to Health (COSHH) and the Management of Health and Safety at Work (MHSW) regulations have sought to stimulate improvement by placing a specific obligation on employers to address the issue of risk assessment. Positive results have been reported:

'Though the Management of Health and Safety at Work Regulations 1992 are slightly more than one year old, some firms (which for the time being want to remain anonymous) have told us that their implementation has saved them considerable amounts of money. They found out, when they did their risk assessment, that a lot of their expenditure on health and safety were directed at risks that were already well under control while the risks that remained uncontrolled were costing them a lot of money'.

Such positive results are not, however, universal, and it has to be accepted that some companies have experienced difficulties with the application. Difficulties have arisen, for example, in deciding when to use a consultant. In some companies a consultant has been engaged when this has not been necessary, and in some cases the assessments produced by consultants 'were not very good'. Some companies have apparently not recognised the benefits of using a preliminary assessment to eliminate those hazards which pose relatively few risks. In other cases assessments have been 'nothing more than a collection of data sheets – like stamp collecting'.

The Risk Assessment Afterplan.

Geoff Simpson, head of ergonomics for British Coal, emphasised the need to have a detailed structured and systematic afterplan if risk assessment is to be effective. Such an afterplan must ensure:

* the identification and implementation of practical control measures for all hazards which are currently insufficiently covered

* the development of a positive and systematic monitoring procedure to enable measures to be assessed as to their effectiveness and the need for new measures to be identified

* the promotion of a proactive approach to safety and the development of line management responsibility for ,and authority over, safety assurance .

In addition the documented plan must be sensitive to the climate and structure of the organisation in which it is to operate and be integrated into the management infrastructure and subject to normal accountability practices, with the responsibility resting with line management.

It is recommended that risk assessments be incorporated within the remit of a regular safety audit as this will ensure that assessments are up to date and fully documented, that identified actions have been taken, that the effectiveness of the controls is being monitored by line management, and that a procedure for review is in place. Particular attention is drawn to the issue of multi-causality i.e. many accidents happen as a result of a chance concentration of a number of contributory factors rather than a single cause, especially in large organisations and where complex technologies are involved.

Other important issues include the effectiveness of safety training, which according to the author is rarely done seriously or systematically. Intervening variables (contributory factors influencing permanent safety improvement) are also relevant and the author advocates the use of questionnaires to aid measurement of risk perception and/or hazard awareness, for example before and after a training course.

Many training courses are said to be geared purely toward the teaching of safety rules without an appreciation of the need for understanding of the rules and the possible consequences of non-compliance. Risk assessment is seen as having a clear role in providing both an outline for training needs analysis and a source of criteria for training assessment. Likewise with human factors in general and human error in particular 'perhaps the major common cause of failure in industrial accident patterns' it follows that both risk assessment and the afterplan need to consider them, particularly where control measures include the application of rules on safe working practices or Personal Protective Equipment (PPE):

''There is no more useless safety device than a rule or an item of PPE which is not used'.

Reference is made in this context to an ongoing study of 'failure -to -isolate' accidents to electricians which has drawn attention to cases where electricians and perhaps worse, their supervisors, have considered procedures like 'Permits to Work' or the use of 'Dead Line Indicators' to be 'unnecessary or irrelevant to safety'. These 'misunderstandings' are said to have 'very clear implications for the effectiveness of what would appear to be sensible risk control provisions'.

Quality Standards for Risk Assessment.

The paper, by John Channing of Kodak Limited, addressed the subject of quality standards for risk assessment. He described risk assessment as 'going as far beyond the essential safety requirements as the balance between the risks, and the cost of reducing them is sensible in the opinion of the competent person making the assessment'. Attention is drawn to the need to assess not just the hardware but also the software and humanware of the systems under consideration.

The author demonstrates clear support for having an integrated approach, such as that adopted by the Chemical Industries Association in their Responsible Care Programme which essentially integrates the environment standard BS7750 with health and safety, pointing out:

'If a company handles methanol, it must carry fire, toxic, airborne and ground water risks. It needs an integrated cross-discipline approach to control all aspects of risk.'

Support is then voiced for international standards, particularly for companies which operate in the third world, and for ISO9000 which is seen as providing 'a framework which will enable us to manage the HS and E challenges'.

No general standard, however, can specifically address the issues which affect any one organisation and whilst international HS and E standards 'set the boundaries and must be followed', it is up to individual companies to 'put flesh on the bones of the system'. In this respect the author asserts that on a day to day basis it is 'unreasonable' to expect line managers to focus at one moment on a law then the next on an environmental standard which is similar but slightly different, then on a present company standard which again is similar but slightly different:

'The goal should be to reduce them to something simple and straightforward that can be used on a day to day basis'.

The emphasis is on simplicity in the internal standards setting process by which simple questions like 'do you have this?' or 'have you done that?' are built into the standards to ensure compliance. As a practical example the author refers to his own company's standards which require an up to date inventory to be maintained for chemicals and materials by each area, and uses questions like 'have you got COSHH assessments?' and 'do you have spill procedures?'

The paper finishes with a reference to the need for behavioural psychology to be interwoven into such a system so as to generate enthusiasm for the standards as well as ensure adherence to them: 'having a great car doesn't make you a good driver', he says.

[Issue 73 (January 1995)]

QUALITY AND SAFETY MANAGEMENT

From a low point of just under 3,000 in 1984, Britain's fastest growing professional institute, The Institute of Occupational Safety and Health (IOSH) has now just under 14,000 members and it is still growing. Further to this their annual conference, held in Harrogate from 5th to 7th December, attracted a record 400 participants, necessitating a slight change of venue to the magnificent Royal Hall to accommodate the increased numbers.

The year of 1995 is a special year for IOSH as it marks their 50th anniversary since they were originally formed in 1945 as an offshoot of RoSPA (Royal Society for the Prevention of Accidents), from whom they became independent in 1953.

The conference featured twelve presentations, plus eight 'Professional Development' sessions, and a lively Debate, at which delegates had the opportunity to vote on the topical motion of 'Will deregulation reduce UK health and safety standards?'. Quality Matters selected two sessions on day one that were felt to be especially relevant to consultants, general management and practitioners in the quality field (Safety Auditing and Total Quality Management in Safety). A report of the Debate on day two is also given.

Safety Auditing

Lawrence Bamber, Senior Consultant for Ajax Health and Safety , addressed this subject, in which IOSH is currently very active with regard to policy formulations.

He emphasised that whilst there is currently no legal requirement of companies to undertake safety audits, as there is for financial audit, it is quite possible that this situation could change in the not too distant future. In this respect he referred to Parliament's flotation of The Corporate Accountability Bill in 1991 which would require companies to appoint independent safety auditors at company AGMs and considered the introduction of disqualification for up to ten years for directors who breached its requirements. He believed that whilst the Bill had become dormant for the time being, it stood every chance of 'being resurrected' and becoming law.

It therefore follows that a more positive approach is needed to the whole matter of safety audits. The all too common approach of retrospective fault finding and blame apportionment simply will not do.

He proposed a seven step checklist for safety auditing:

*identify hazards

*assess risks

*select controls

*implement controls

*monitor effectiveness

*review

*feedback

This, however, was just a guide, the best checklist in practice being one that is developed by the people who are going to implement it:

"You can buy off-the-shelf systems but you will always have gaps".

He suggested that a team of three be appointed initially, consisting of a manager, supervisor and a shopfloor representative. Their remit, he said, should be to 'catch people doing things right' rather than seeking to find fault, with a full audit being undertaken on at least an annual basis. He also drew attention to the importance of conducting such an audit whenever a new company is taken over i.e. a pre-acquisition audit to ensure that liabilities are known and hidden agendas highlighted.

Questions were invited after the speech, which was intended to be brief but sufficient to stimulate debate. Delegates from, amongst others, Railtrack, London Docklands Corporation, Schweppes, Edinburgh Healthcare Trust, the Wellcome Foundation and the London Borough of Harrow, raised several important issues.

London Docklands' Safety Auditor suggested to everyone that it was necessary to have a system that would highlight problems that were not necessarily serious but which were occurring frequently, which her company's Safety Development Unit is pledged to do. It is noticeably separate from the company's Safety Advisory Board, which is itself subject to audit.

Geoff Davies, Safety Manager for Railtrack, sought feedback on the subject of loss control and whether future standards would address it more closely. A representative from Det Norske Veritas then outlined the generic package for loss control which his company was in the process of developing.

Another delegate then asked why it was necessary to have three British Standards i.e. BS5750, BS7750 and BS8750, respectively for quality systems, environmental management and health and safety. In his reply Mr. Bamber cited the historical development of the three standards beginning with the recognition of the commercial potential identified for BS5750, and followed by media attention from HRH the Prince of Wales which later led to action to formulate BS7750, which has since brought commercial connotations in 'being seen to be green'. The third standard, BS8750, by contrast, has until recently received little support, notably from the Health and Safety Executive (HSE) who have apparently viewed it as little more than an extension of the Health Safety at Work Act. This stance now appears to have changed, although one delegate expressed some reservation at the prospect of the emergence of BS8750, on the grounds that it could easily become discredited if it is allowed to become a driver for its own sake i.e. driving for the piece of paper when the objective is to save lives.

There appeared to be general agreement on the view that safety auditing systems must, of necessity, be kept simple if they are to receive managerial support. The Health Service, for example, found it necessary to revise HS(G)65 in order that it might be more digestible for the managers within.

Safety and TQM

The relations between safety and Total Quality Management was explored by Lawrence Waterman, Director of Sypol Environmental Management in a session which became, unexpectedly, highly charged with controversy, not least on the subject of National Vocational Qualifications (NVQs) which the speaker clearly did not favour as a means of securing safety in the workplace.

He was critical of the commonly adopted top down approach to BS5750, arguing that all too often managers seek to develop 'automatons that will follow the rules' and that training tends to be closed with the objective of merely ensuring that people are competent to follow instructions. The supervisor's role is that of a policeman whose job is 'to kick rear ends' rather than to use the quality system as a means to improve safety .

By contrast, Total Quality Management encourages an 'open' style of training in which people are encouraged to develop skills that will help them to identify safety problems not foreseen before procedures are written. This is facilitated through joint ownership of health and safety management by workers and management rather than by having a specific health and safety department which believes that its sole function is to advise management and provide reports exclusively for executives.

The argument put forward for this 'open' style quickly stimulated debate as delegated associated 'closed' versus 'open' with an argument for and against NVQs for safety management. The speaker argued that the whole principle of having a workplace qualification in health and safety was wrong as it omitted an all-important understanding of general principles, and the need to educate people to deal with the unforeseeable, He suggested that the NVQ system applied in this way would amount to little more than a confidence trick as people would believe that they were being trained for life when in fact they were being trained for obsolescence.

In response another delegate then turned to the issue of NVQs for tradespeople i.e. training operatives to operate specific types of machinery, arguing that here they had "a very real role in upskilling the workforce". The speaker then modified his approach, saying that these NVQs were "necessary but not sufficient", but was still adamant that much British training is still reflective of where we were rather than where we are and this had to change.

A delegate from Mercury Communications then explained how Mercury had succeeded in generating and maintaining a high standard of safety through improving the general culture of the company, and intended to continue the approach whereby responsibility was clearly given to those who owned the processes. [Different from the London Docklands approach-Ed]

There followed a discussion of the Investors in People (IIP) standard which was noted for its lack of reference to health and safety. The speaker, when asked to comment, suggested that IOSH should assume the role of a 'lobbying body' in an attempt to integrate health and safety into this standard.

The session concluded with an onslaught on Britain's education system and an IOSH survey of 200 schools in the Milton Keynes area, which apparently highlighted an 'appalling apathy' amongst teachers and a complete lack of understanding of the real world of industry. The high level of injuries amongst children undertaking part time work was highlighted and there appeared to be a general consensus that there was a problem at the interface between school and the workplace which needed to be addressed urgently.

Safety and deregulation

The debate considered the motion 'This house believes deregulation will reduce UK health and safety standards'. There were four speakers: Chris Kaufman, Editor of T and G Record (the Transport and General Workers' Union journal) who proposed the motion; Professor Brian Toft, Risk Analyst for Sedgwick (UK) Limited who opposed it; Alan Dalton, Senior Lecturer in Health and Safety at the South Bank University, who seconded it; and Dr.Alan Waring, Principal of Alan Waring and Associates, who seconded against.

Chris Kaufman opened with an assertion that the argument about safety and deregulation was really fought and won in the last century and that the path of deregulation was the path of anarchy, describing it as "a bumpy killing field with no control and companies pleasing themselves". General duties backed by Approved Codes of Practice would be, he said, "a retrograde step", and even if TQM is as he put it "up to scratch", this would still bear little influence on the "myriad of small suppliers that are operating under sweatshop conditions". Good employers "should not be undercut by cowboys", but whilst trade unions, for their part, arguably, support the removal of ageing legislation, he argued that there "was no case for cuts in existing legislation."

Brian Toft countered this viewpoint with an assertion that legislation often places unnecessary burdens on those who are required to implement it. Although there is merit in having legislation that is clear and logical, the Health and Safety Commission (HSC) points to British legislation that is "voluminous, complicated and fragmented". He added that much of it was .'confusing, clumsy and unhelpful". There was a clear opportunity cost in time spent dealing with outdated legislation at the expense of other health and safety activities ,quite apart from inconsistencies in enforcement.

Deregulation, by contrast, "aims to minimise problems by removing or amending legislation as necessary" and he argued that up to 40 per cent of current legislation could easily be removed without compromising safety standards.

Seconder Alan Dalton drew attention to the extremely large amount of ill-health in Britain, caused for example through asbestos removal, licences for which could be obtained "like a pack of cards". Our health and safety record was, he said, "nothing to be proud of" and he cited HSE reports which he said showed British management to be generally "irresponsible". Even Mrs. Thatcher "dropped many deregulation ideas" because "employers did not want self-regulation". Deregulation had, he said, "no scientific basis", and what was really needed was "more inspectors inspecting workplaces".

Dr. Alan Waring argued that the wording of the motion contains an implicit assumption that increased regulation increases safety , and suggested that this assumption needed to be questioned since there was scant evidence to support it. He contested that whilst in principle regulation implied control, in practice it was merely "reactive to bad situations that already exist" and at best it "results in compliance to a minimum standard". Legislation was, he said, "systematic but incomplete, and doesn't address the prevailing culture of organisations". He suggested that in many major accidents, such as King's Cross and Piper Alpha, many unregulatory factors have been critical and that the masses of safety regulations which exist "are unable to address the uncontrolled variables of human behaviour". Where a weak safety culture exists he said there was "at best a grudging compliance with regulations" and he suggested that the debate should not have been quite so much about whether deregulation reduces safety, quite so much as whether regulation improved it.

After the four speeches delegates were invited to comment and some interesting issues were raised both for and against the motion. Most appeared to agree that there was outdated law which could and should be removed. What was of concern, however, were the Government's 'hidden agendas', such as cuts in the HSE's budget and enforced compulsory competitive tendering (CCT). The current free market ideology was, for example, described as "immoral" by one delegate whilst another suggested that deregulation could pose an unacceptable threat to some clearly essential legislation. Another was clearly concerned that deregulation could allow some local authorities to ignore themselves what they require of others. There was loud applause for the suggestion that it should not be a matter for the present government to decide on others' behalf which laws stay and which do not.

The ensuing vote resulted in a verdict of 76 in favour of the motion and 54 against with 11 abstaining.

HEALTH AND SAFETY AT OLYMPIA

The 1995 Safety and Health at Work Exhibition and Conference at Olympia took place from 7th to 9th February and featured some 240 exhibitors from all over Europe as well as Canada and the USA, who managed to cover two floors of the Olympia 2 Centre. The number of visitors exceeded 9,000 with registrations from some 40 countries whilst conference delegates numbered over 700, serving to reinforce the continued high interest in health and safety and related subjects.

The conference on February 7th and 8th featured twelve presentations divided under four headings:

'The Role of the Safety Practitioner in an Emergency', 'Training: The Key to Safety Success', 'Controlling Risk in a Changing Organisation : Stress and Change at Work', and 'Health Issues of the Future'. Quality Matters selected four for detailed review.

Risk Assessment for Emergency Planning

Ian Neil, Business Development Director for Willis Corrgon Hinton, outlined the statutory duty of employers under the Management of Safety at Work Regulations 1992 to conduct risk assessments and develop procedures for serious and imminent danger, with particular emphasis on emergency planning.

He explains how in many cases emergency or disaster planning has been reactive to a major incident rather than proactive and suggests a Practical Risk Assessment Protocol, for example, to review and quantify emergency staffing arrangements. The degree of preparation of Emergency Plans will, he says, vary according to the type and size of the undertaking as well as its size and activities in neighbouring workplaces, but the basic principles applied will be similar.

Risk Assessment is itself described as 'an imprecise science' which is 'deemed by some to be a very subjective science' but is noted to offer the best defence, if not the only defence, should criminal court proceedings be brought. Its purpose is 'to eliminate risk to the undertaking, its employees and those affected by their operations' or where the risk cannot be eliminated 'to minimize risk by the introduction of effective control measures.' There is no clearly defined methodology laid down, but the law does require 'that assessments should be suitable and sufficient' and that 'where a company employs five or more persons the results must be recorded'. In addition one or more 'competent persons' must be employed to assist in undertaking the measures needed to achieve compliance, and it is noted to be the duty of the employer to ensure that persons so appointed are 'competent':

''The employer must be satisfied that the assessor has sufficient Experience, Knowledge and Training in order to carry out his duties in relation to a suitable and sufficient risk assessment. The assessor should have a knowledge and understanding of the work involved, the principles of risk assessment and prevention and current health and safety applications'.

In his five step methodology for developing a Risk Assessment Protocol the author lists sources of potential hazards and recommends in depth discussion with local managers, particularly, for multi-disciplined organisations with a number of widely dispersed sites. He cautions against underestimating historical data, including accident investigation reports, such as the Cullen Report and statistical evidence presented in the Annual Reports of the Health and Safety Commission.

In his assessment of people and their likely exposure to hazards (the second step of the methodology) he suggests a sub-division of groups into several generic risk assessments whilst in the third step (Identification of existing controls) the reader's attention is directed to HSE Approved Codes of Practice, company documentation, operational procedures, safety policies, method statements and permit to work systems:

'As part of the Practical Risk Assessment it is advisable to review the existing controls to ensure they remain adequate and effective. In the early euphoria of the statutory requirement many companies carried out risk assessments, titled them generic and forgot or chose not to review them. (When considering the control protocol on completion of the risk assessments it is advisable to include a review regime as one of the controls). It is quite common to find this incorporated as part of a company's ISO9000 quality system; however, emergency planning is often overlooked, (as indeed is health and safety in this context).

The fourth step attempts to quantify degrees of risk using a simple matrix system and suggests that when one determines the risk to be identified, it should be those risks which are 'significant' that should be considered. The term 'significant' is noted to be ill-defined in the regulations, codes of practice and the legal profession, but 'can be taken to mean the opposite to that which is trivial':

'The risk of fire occurring in a salmon fish farm on the West Coast of Scotland may not feature very high on the list of emergency priorities whereas a breach in the containment reservoirs/tanks may be extremely critical to the well-being of the business'.

The final step (validation of the Assessment and the Emergency Plans) deals with the preparation of the first draft of the Emergency Plan, and in this connection recommends a revisit of the line managers and supervisors who have been involved in the preliminary hazard identification process in order to gain feedback on the assessment and the proposed plan:

'It is essential for management and employees to take ownership of the Emergency Plan if it is to prove successful in practice'.

Reducing Unsafe Behaviours

Ivan Robertson, Professor of Occupational Psychology at the Manchester School of Management (UMIST) and Dr. Roy Duff, Senior Lecturer in Construction Management at UMIST present an interesting paper which uses results obtained from the application of behaviourally based management techniques in the construction industry to demonstrate that safety behaviour is measurable objectively and reliably, and that with suitable feedback use could enable large improvements in safety performance to be achieved.

The research was in two phases, the first investigating the effectiveness of goal setting and feedback in improving safety at six sites, the second involving the deployment of a practical management tool derived from the research of phase one at twenty three sites.

In the first phase data was collected on three experimental categories of behaviour: scaffolding, housekeeping and access to heights, and a control category, personal protective equipment (PPE), on which there was no attempt to influence behaviour. It was then reasoned that if safety behaviour were seen to improve in scaffolding, housekeeping and access to heights but not in PPE then it could be concluded that the proposed intervention was working.

Development of an objective method of measuring safety focused on contributory factors which caused accidents and involved a detailed review of safety literature and accidents records. Ninety nine items were identified and incorporated into a questionnaire which sought to determine the perceived importance or risk level of each item, and was sent to around 200 construction personnel. The most important items in each category were then selected and used to derive a safety measure which was subsequently used to evaluate the safety performance of each site:

''A scaffold with only 70 per cent of the some of the required toe-boards correctly fixed was assessed as 30 per cent unsafe on that particular measurement item'.

An eleven point rating scale (0-10) was applied for each item and used to record unsafe situations or behaviours as a proportion of total opportunities to be safe.

A standard training package was devised for each experimental category and used at goal setting sessions whilst performance feedback charts showing the goals set were erected at strategic locations and updated weekly.

Twelve weeks of safety performance data charts was collected and not used in the experiment 'to dissipate any effects caused by the presence of observers on site'. Then safety performance was measured for eight weeks to obtain a base-line measure, before the intervention was introduced. In the next eight weeks the change in performance was recorded, whilst in the following four the intervention was withdrawn but with recording continued. The intervention and withdrawal cycle was then repeated, with observer reliability monitored 'by a researcher completing a measure for the same site'. Checks showed over 90 per cent agreement between observers and researchers.

Statistical techniques were used to test for significance changes in safety performance in the three experimental categories (scaffolding, housekeeping, access to heights). These involved calculation of the mean safety performance score for the last four weeks of the base line period (pre-score) and the four weeks of the intervention (post score). This yielded 'a large and positive result for all experimental categories with little change to the control category'.

It was concluded that most measures (14 out of 18) 'showed improvement by the second half of the intervention period ' whilst performance during the withdrawal 'generally continued to rise with 9 of the 18 results showing an improvement' demonstrating ' a momentum in the improved safety behaviour which takes time to dissipate'.

It is noted that whilst no attempt was made in the first phase to evaluate the effect of management commitment, it 'became apparent that this was probably having a significant impact upon some of the results':

'The two best performing sites overall were those where management attended all the meetings with operatives at the commencement of interventions'.

It followed that in the second phase of the research, which began early in 1993, the relationships between management commitment, operative commitment and safety performance were incorporated into the research whilst the cumulative effects of continuous efforts to improve safety through goal setting and feedback was measured. The methodology was as for phase one except that measures were taken, goal sessions run and charts updated by contractors' own personnel, the reasoning being that in companies where management commitment is strong and support and encouragement given to able observers, the intervention would be more successful than when it is applied by outsiders.

Results, as in the first phase, reflected 'a significant improvement in safety behaviour' whilst management commitment 'impacts on all aspects of the intervention'.

Stress at Work: new Liabilities for Employers.

An employer's civil liability for the health and safety of employees has traditionally been confined to liability for physical injuries arising from accidents at work. However, in recent years there has been an increasing recognition of occupational diseases where the cause of the disease or illness is the employment itself. In a paper by Lynn West entitled 'Stress and Depression: Employer's Legal Liabilities and Responsibilities', a number of recent cases where work-induced stress has been held to be an 'occupational disease' are highlighted:

'In America, where stress related claims have tripled since 1980, employers' liability for employees' injuries incurred during the course of their employment is governed by the Workers' Compensation Acts. Claims under the various States' Acts are dealt with on a 'no-fault' basis so that if an employee is injured at work he will be awarded compensation. A fifth of all disability claims under these Acts are based on 'cumulative trauma'.

In the UK the Health and Safety Executive (HSE) has estimated that some 30 to 40 per cent of sickness absence from work is due to some kind of mental or emotional disturbance and has produced guidelines for employers to assist them in making workplaces less stressful. Further to this a High Court ruling in November 1994 has effectively put stress-related disease in the same category as industrial disease cases and workplace accidents'.

In this case (John Edward Walker v Northumberland County Council) a 'landmark court decision' was made which held that 'an employer was liable for an employee's breakdown as a result of an excessive workload'. The judge, Mr. Justice Colman is quoted:

"It is clear law that an employer has a duty to provide his employee with a reasonably safe system of work and take reasonable steps to protect him from risks which are reasonably foreseeable. Whereas the law on the extent of this duty has developed almost exclusively in cases involving physical injury to the employee, as distinct from injury to his mental health , there is no logical reason why risk of psychiatric damage should be excluded from the scope of an employer's duty of care or from the co-extensive implied term in the contract of employment" .

The paper adds that 'once a duty of care has been established the standard of care required for the performance of that duty must be measured against the yardstick of reasonable conduct on the part of a person in the position of that person who owes the duty' and that it is 'a question of reasonableness, taking into account factors such as the nature of the relationship, the size of the risk of injury which was reasonably foreseeable, the seriousness of the consequence for the person to whom the duty is owed of the risk eventuating and the cost and practicability of preventing the risk'.

The paper contends that the above case could potentially 'open the floodgates' for a large number of claims for damages for work-induced stress, but points out that employees 'will have to prove that they have a recognised medical illness brought on by unreasonable work pressures, and that their employers could have reasonably foreseen that they would suffer psychological damage, either as a result of the symptoms the employees displayed or through the nature or volume of their work'. Problems concerning foreseeability and causation are anticipated, particularly in relation to the separation of work induced and domestic stress, whilst the requirements to provide risk assessment and health surveillance 'may now assume greater significance, as insurers begin to take an interest in the preventive and protective steps which employers are taking to reduce health and safety risks especially in highly stressful occupations.

It is noted that breaches of the MHSW regulations 1992 'do not give rise to civil liability', although 'a claim for negligence could be made where no appropriate assessment has been carried out and ill health occurs'.

Strategies for Safety in the 21st Century.

The final paper selected for review, entitled 'Business Strategies for Safety in the 21st Century by Andrew Thomas, Health and Safety Adviser for the Loss Prevention Council, assesses possible developments in health and safety over the next four decades, with reference to the future business environment and consideration of occupational health issues.

He suggests that health and safety in the future 'will be business driven rather than legislative driven' with businesses viewing health and safety as a core management function alongside marketing, production and human resources. Businesses will, he says, have to deal with health and safety issues effectively if they are to prosper and an increasing trend toward a risk management approach is envisaged:

'What may be a 'risk' operation for one person may be common sense to another. It is therefore necessary to quantify the risks in a way which is understandable and credible to all concerned. Risks can be managed using a combination of six approaches: avoid, prevent, control, mitigate, transfer and retain. All sorts of business risk can be approached and treated in the same way -investment risks, trading risks, production risks, operational risks, health and safety risk. In order to succeed at this, business must be pro-active, train their staff, employ professional advisers, and especially, establish an effective management system. '

Health and safety management systems are, he says, 'developing well', but whilst 'verifiable standards which integrate with other issues such as quality and environment are clearly foreseen the threats posed by short termism, balance sheet management, share price management, takeover management, and the cyclic nature of the economy are all too evident, and in this context he points to the important role of the HSE as 'the core repository for the UK's resource of skills, information and research'.

He then points to the development of insurance-based markets as a likely mechanism of providing cover for example for industrial injuries in the event of 'the imminent demise of the Industrial Injuries Scheme' and the costs of healthcare resulting from employers' negligence which are 'currently picked up through the National Health Service system and spread around society'.

A review of current regulations is followed with an analysis of occupational health and various occupational diseases which are causing concern. He points notably to asbestos related diseases where predictions that the death rate would remain static at low levels have proven to be false, and the hazards of working with VDUs where there is similar concern about 'long-tail' liabilities resulting from current working practices.

Some occupational diseases, such as occupational asthma, are seen as 'entirely preventable' although recent research by the Loss Prevention Council 'suggests that we are likely to see a marked increase in the number of employees claiming disablement due to exposure to sensitising agents in their workplace'. This, says the author, 'is an example of where the COSHH regulations have failed to make a difference'.

The paper concludes with some suggestions as to how the current situation might be improved:

- health and safety incorporated into the national curriculum in schools and forming a fundamental component of university degree courses to increase awareness at an earlier age.

- legislation to prohibit companies from failing to set aside a given amount of time and resources for training in health and safety.

- a system of accreditation for health and safety trainers to ensure that time spent on training is of value to the employer concerned.

- cost-benefit analyses conducted for all aspects of health and safety to highlight the advantages of treating health and safety in the same manner as other aspects of the business.

- further research into improving health and safety through better and safer designed machinery, e.g. to reduce noise.

NACCB FORMALLY GIVES ACCREDITATIONS FOR BS7750

The National Accreditation Council for Certification Bodies (NACCB), has given to a group of eight companies accreditation for certification to the environmental management systems standard BS7750. This group includes international certification bodies, SGS Yarsley International Certification Services, British Standards Institution, Lloyds Register, Bureau Veritas, Det Norske Veritas, and national specialists, Aspects Certification Services, Professional Environmental and Caring Services, and Trada Certification.

The RT. Hon. Michael Heseltine MP, President of the Board of Trade, at the presentation ceremony commented:

" I hope that it will not be too long before all UK businesses are considering their attitude to the environment".

He also presented the first accredited BS7750 certificates to 20 companies registered by the newly accredited group. These included Northumbrian Water Limited for their water and sewage services and Personnel Hygiene Services Limited of Caerphilly, currently the UK's market leader in the provision of specialist washroom and clinical waste management services, who were assessed by SGS Yarsley. This follows SGS Yarsley's successful track record for assessing and certificating organisations for the Green Dove Award based on the 1992 version, and subsequently the 1994 version, of BS7750,for which they were the first certification body to issue certificates.

THE ROUTE TO EXCELLENCE

At their 1995 annual conference from 4th to 6th December IOSH was pleased to announce a net increase of some 2,200 members during the year. The total now stands at just under 16,000, and perhaps reinforces the Institute's principal message that good safety is also good business.

This year's conference had much to offer both the quality and safety practitioner alike with the general theme of 'The Route to Excellence' which was aptly introduced with a Keynote Address from Sir Neville Purvis, Chief Executive of BSI. He spoke of "the phenomenal worldwide success of BS5750" which he said "has established a new global management platform". He advised delegates of the continuing work of the International Standards Organisation (ISO) who in the course of their revision of ISO9000 were "inextricably moving in the direction of a single generic management standard".

Also he spoke of the work of the BSI which is currently finalising the Health and Safety Guidance Standard BS8750. He assured delegates that this standard would be published in 1996, as there was "stark evidence that this is an area that urgently needs to be addressed". Health and Safety was, after all "a necessary part of the quality ethos of a company and must be part of the company strategy".

Not surprisingly Sir Neville was asked the perhaps obvious question of why BSI had opted to produce Guidelines rather than a certifiable standard, given the already established existence of the Health and Safety Executive's Guidance document "HS(G)65. The delegate suggested that it was BSI's place to act as a verifier in the field of health and safety. In his answer Sir Neville stressed that BSI had a much wider remit than the mere production of standards and that it served to bring experts together from many different fields, backgrounds, industries and companies. The new Guidelines were, he said, "pointing out best practice and a significant step in the right direction".

Implementing successful Health and Safety Management.

The Keynote Address was well complemented by the presentation 'Implementing successful health and safety management' by Professor Richard Booth of Aston University, who is also Deputy Chairman of Health and Safety Technology and Management Limited based at Aston Science Park, and a former President of IOSH. He described some of the principles underlying the new standard and in particular the Annexes to the standard which he has had a hand in writing.

He began by challenging "the dead hand of traditional archaic legislation" which he said had created "quite good standards, but a poor culture with not much management". The culture to which he referred was one of managing safety reactively which, although relatively easy to accomplish, was in practice totally ineffective. This was because it generally depends unduly on reactive monitoring data whilst the rules and safeguards which result "may be over-zealous, conflict with other controls and fail to keep pace with change". Consequently a pro-active approach is sorely needed, though it is no secret that this is "a jolly sight harder to do even in the larger organisations".

The efforts which have been sustained in order to produce what is hoped is now the final draft of BS8750 is a clear move which has attempted to foster change in a pro-active direction, albeit with its critics. It falls short of perfection, but at least offers a compromise between the already established principles of HS(G)65 and the international environmental standard ISO 14000, which in turn is based on the certifiable British Standard BS5750. The speaker explained how the same wording had been applied to two distinct sections of the standard to convey the same meaning in both the HS(G)65 and the ISO 14000 formats.

The essence of the standard according to the speaker is that business planning and occupational health and safety planning should be defined, prioritized and quantified. Brainstorming should be used to compile five lists of health and safety objectives:

- items to increase or improve

- items to maintain or continue

- items to reduce e.g. trips and falls

- items to introduce e.g. improved information systems and risk assessments

- items to eliminate

Key objectives should be selected, written down and if possible quantified with 'outcome indicators' used to achieve a measure of performance. It was stressed that in some cases several separate measures may be applicable.

A plan is then developed to achieve each objective using specific targets. The plan is implemented and its effectiveness measured and reviewed. Use of pro-active data is required; an example could be the number of individuals trained in occupational health and safety, and measures which reflect the effectiveness of the training. Similarly there needs to be evidence of clear allocations to individuals, with their agreement, of what action is required of them in a health and safety context.

Key requirements of the standard are:

- an initial status review

- a statement of policy

- a health and safety plan

- a description of the implementation and operations methods

- establishment of measures of performance

- establishment of a safety auditing system

- periodic status reviews

In addition the Annexes cover, amongst other things, the links to ISO9000(1) and guidelines for risk assessment.

The presentation attracted a number of questions with particular concern being voiced about the standard becoming potentially driven by customers with preferred suppliers and the possibility that the standard could prove to be "a consultants charter". The speaker did not deny that both of these possibilities were real. As regards the release of the standard he hinted at the early part of the year rather than the autumn, subject to the approval of the BSI management systems standards committee in mid January .

The speaker was asked what he believed the prime target readership of the standard would be. He explained how, when asked to assist in writing of the standard, his brief had been to ensure that the document would be suitable, comprehensible and usable by an organisation with around twenty employees, whilst at the same time being incapable of having a trivial perception by large organisations. Many organisations, he said, wanted to get things right as far as health and safety was concerned, but some were unsure where to start and for them the standard would provide a starting point. He said he hoped that the standard would be seen to be applicable across organisations of all sizes and was confident that in the long term it would prove "more cost effective than reactive health and safety management".

When asked to comment on likely developments over the next five years he suggested that a two tier system could emerge with a proactive culture being adopted in larger organisations whilst smaller companies, as at present, would tend to retain a compliance based culture. He pointed out that, unlike with quality, there were statutory obligations underpinning much of what was in the new standard.

[Could registration to BS8750 ever become law? One or two speakers hinted that with a change of government, and even without, safety audits could become mandatory , as financial audits are. The subject is sure to provoke interest, not least from the certification bodies -Ed].

Risk Assessment at Leyland Trucks.

Risk assessment is a key activity associated as much with quality as with safety and the case study by Leyland Trucks' Health, Safety and Environmental Manager Alan Lark, perhaps serves to emphasise what enormous potential there is for improvement in this area.

In 1989 Leyland Trucks had a none too impressive record of 65 reportable accidents which resulted in 8,000 lost production hours and 21 Employer's Liability Claims for Injury Compensation. The company had aspirations to be a world class manufacturer, but clearly this was not possible with this kind of safety record. Everybody knew that a different culture was required, away from reactive health and safety management and towards a system where all employees would participate in health and safety on a daily basis in an atmosphere of mutual trust.

The speaker described how, using the four cornerstones of teambuilding, empowerment and training the company devised a ten point plan which includes: a CEO open door policy for all health and safety matters; integration of safety throughout the business; monthly bills to Business Unit Managers for hours lost through accidents; adoption of the IOSH safety management course with 27 hour long modules for all Business Unit Managers; investigation of all critical incidents and near misses with one page sets of remedial actions presented to prevent re-occurrences; continuous monthly recording of safety performance; control of reporting systems through a Safety Alert system e.g. to give early warning of repetitive strain injury (RSI); a high priority to housekeeping as this can reduce minor injuries substantially; drafting of safe working procedures by teams who then assume ownership of them; and, critically, a review of maintenance procedures and the vulnerable area of sub-contracting:

'Multi-functional teams are set up to study the requirements of new legislation e.g. a team has recently completed a review of External/Internal Traffic Safety as required by the Workplace Health and Safety and Welfare Regulations 1992. An action plan has been produced for the re-organisation of traffic routes and the further segregation of traffic and pedestrians based on the team risk assessments'.

The speaker emphasised in particular how the company had altered its ethos away from management by direct supervision:

"Now we would not dream of putting in a new process without consulting the shop floor."

He then described how some 730 individuals are now participating actively in risk assessments. No-one has refused to participate and the old style five hour safety committee meetings in which safety representatives would try 'to score hits against management' are long gone. Indeed the speaker cited the case of one individual who in 1987 had been "the most militant shop steward", who currently champions the cause that "safety is a partnership".

The paper supports the presentation with a description of the company's Total Safety Maintenance Programme which is said to be 'a first in British industry'. This essentially involves employees listing hazards, evaluating the risks posed by those hazards that are present in their area of work; Key Operators making a group risk evaluation summary of team members' individual assessments, and use of a risk evaluation database by supervisors to compare team input with formal risk assessment data and determine short and long term priorities for preventative actions. The process has recently been extended to include sub-contractors:

'Contractors, following the completion of a Safety Registration Document and exchange of Health and Safety Policies at the pre-contract stage, are then subject to risk assessment which determines the level of ongoing

113

audit/supervision on the part of the company. Contractors' past safety performance and degree of risk from the work in hand are taken into consideration.'

The improvements brought about by this change in approach need little explanation. Suffice it to say the paper reports no Reportable Accidents and just two Employers' Liability Claims over the last two years. In addition the speaker highlighted at least four other companies in North West England that were seeking to emulate Leyland Trucks' performance by adopting safety systems based on the same concepts.

Other Presentations

In addition to the above papers there are seven other formal papers included in the conference literature. These are 'Competency in the Safety Profession' by David Giachardi of Courtaulds; 'Safety Audits:Making them work' by Lawrence Bamber of Ajax Health and Safety Services; 'Influencing Financial Decisions: A Foot in the Door' by Terry Morgan of Stansted Airport; 'Crisis Management: Proactive Planning' by consultant Michael Bland; 'Information Technology: The Way forward' by consultant Sheila Pantry OBE; 'Insurance' by William Gloyne of Bain Hogg Commercial Property Division; and 'Maintaining a Safety Culture under extreme Pressures' by Wayne Bagnall of the Bagnall Group.

The first of these is a safety management case study from Courtaulds which describes how they learned from the experts (Du Pont) to change their culture away from one of safety specialists attempting to take the lead in safety management and towards one which recognises that safety is an integral part of every manager's job i.e. safety advisors support what general managers need to do rather than seek to persuade or coerce them into doing what they feel is necessary.

The second paper, by Lawrence Bamber, is similar to the one reviewed in Quality Matters issue 73 which describes the what, where and how of safety audits and a look to the future, and of course the link between the EU Social Charter and mandatory safety auditing.

Terry Morgan of Stansted Airport described how a twelve week study at Gatwick Airport into the direct and indirect costs of accidents identified losses of around £750,000 a year attributable to "not identifying satisfactory loss causation measures". The paper describes the approach taken at Stansted, though presents no quantitative results for Stansted. It includes the following quotes:

'A safety advisor is a professional interpreter of safety related legislation, business practice and guidance on safety issues which impinge on the sphere in which the organisation operates'.

'I don't want to hear that we could be 110 per cent certain of a safe solution but the price tag is 30 million pounds and he [the Safety Advisor] hasn't discussed it with anyone'.

'All targets will be set for named Director/Managers so that the issue is completed safely, to an agreed standard , on time and to budget'.

The paper by Michael Bland provides some useful hints for those contemplating the draft of a crisis manual, advising that stand alone instruction books seldom work, and giving an example of a typical set of contents.

The paper by Sheila Pantry is a lengthy affair which cites several sources of information for those interested in research results collected in databases and CD-ROMs, including OSH-CD which the speaker initiated in her past role as Head of Information Services at the HSE, and FOOD SAFETY PLUS (a new database containing legislation and information from the Ministry of Agriculture, Fisheries and Food, which the speaker also initiated).

There is also an informative outline of the World Wide Web which describes how safety is making its debut on the Internet.

[Issue 87 (March 1996)]

HEALTH, SAFETY AND THE ENVIRONMENT

This year's International Safety and Health at Work Conference at Olympia on 27th and 28th February highlighted the important developing role of the safety practitioner in relation to environmental issues by devoting one of its four conference sessions solely to this topic.

Quality Matters selected 'Environmental Auditing- How and Why?' by Dr. Steve Simmons, Director, Environmental Services; and 'Benchmarking for Safety' by Steve Rapson, Health and Safety Manager for Rank Xerox.

Environmental Auditing -How and Why .

This paper describes some of the findings which emerged from the 1993 Advisory Committee on Business and the Environment (ACBE) survey of companies which had invested in the improvement of their environmental management systems pointing particularly to the benefits of improved corporate image, financial savings e.g. through waste minimisation, and improved stake holder relations:

'Banks are more cautious about their relations with companies. Most now require evidence of appropriate management controls as a condition to business finance. They are aware that the costs associated with pollution

may threaten the viability of projects, or even entire companies, and that the value of their security (frequently land and premises), may turn out to be a liability if such assets are adversely affected by contamination'.

The paper then outlines the principal requirements of BS7750: Specification for Environmental Management Systems, the related 'European Eco-Management and Audit Scheme' (EMAS) and the draft international standard 'ISO14001: Environmental Management Systems -Specification and Guidance for Use', and describes some of the similarities and differences between them. It points out for example, that whilst BS7750 and EMAS both require a formal policy statement, an internal environmental protection (management) system and objective periodic evaluation, the EMAS additionally requires a publicly available environmental statement of the effect of the organisation's activities on both the environment and the performance of the management control system to be produced and independently verified:

'It is possible for a multi-site company operating under the same management system to obtain registration under BS7750 which should cover all sites, whereas EMAS would be awarded only to those sites for which a verified environmental statement had been produced'.

By contrast the draft ISO14001 does not require an initial review, detailed reviews of suppliers and their effects, or the same kind of detailed environmental auditing procedures as either BS7750 or EMAS.

The paper then outlines the six principal types of environmental audit and describes a procedure for the design of an audit programme. These cover: the scope of the audit, the development of audit trees for reporting, the development of structured questionnaires, pilot application of the questionnaire, weighing for questions, information requirements, corporate to plant level summaries, company confidentiality, conducting a site-based audit, gaining confidence and credibility, site inspections, de-briefing and initial report production, and recommendations and prioritisation.

The 'scoping' section provides a check list of some 34 questions under 13 sub-headings which range from assessing the validity of the environmental statement and policy document and the handling, use and disposal of new materials, to the adequacy of liason with third parties, existence of documented procedures for accidents and emergencies and insurance requirements. Typical questions include: 'Do you know the source of all wastes produced?','Are you losing recycling opportunities or increasing disposal costs by inadequate segregation of waste materials?',Do you monitor energy and water usage in order to identify leaks in the system?', and 'Is regular environmental monitoring carried out to measure compliance with permits and consents?'.

The need to ensure the free movement of information up and down the audit tree is stressed as is the need to ensure that all who are involved in the audit understand the base-line in-house standards to be used. Regular reviews to identify any changes in legislation or the advent of any new company objectives or procedures are recommended. On the subject of site inspections the author advises the following:

'The site visit should include a review of the questionnaire by whoever has completed the questions. It is appreciated that in practice this may involve interviewing several members of the workforce. Specific issues raised as a result of the response to selected questions should be assessed in more depth and where necessary confirmatory plant visits undertaken to observe working procedures in practice'.

The paper concludes with a brief outline of some of the computer-based audit systems currently available such as S-CHASE and SHARP and a list of further information sources.

The two other papers featured in this session were 'An Environmental Case Law Update' by Professor Malcolm Forster of Freshfield Solicitors Environment Group and 'Your Company and the Environment' by Roger Lyons, General Secretary of MSF (trade union for skilled and professional people).

Benchmarking Health and Safety

This paper by benchmarking experts Rank Xerox emphasises the simplicity with which benchmarking may be achieved and why there are sound reasons for selecting health, safety and the environment for benchmarking activities even if there is some reluctance toward benchmarking in general:

'Benchmarking in the area of health and safety (and environment) is no different to benchmarking any other area of business. Indeed it is often made easier by the fact that health and safety professionals are invariably happier about sharing information with you than in other areas of business, where product sensitivity can get in the way of an effective exchange of information'.

The methodology adopted by Rank Xerox is then explained using the Display Screen Equipment (DSE) Regulations as an example. The requirements of these regulations were effectively categorised with questionnaires developed for individual areas such as eye tests and glasses, provision of equipment and training. The potential benchmarking partners were chosen from a selection of companies which were at the point of seeking to comply with the regulations and as such were 'inventing their own wheel'. It is acknowledged that this is not strictly speaking true benchmarking as the companies involved had not fully implemented their own processes, but it was sufficient to enable the company both to learn from the mistakes of others and to appreciate the concerns experienced by others at the early stage of procedure implementation:

'This ensured for instance that we did not use outside consultants, that we did not buy off the shelf p.c. packages and that we did not opt for a mobile eye screening service (or for an internal screening service). All areas, in my opinion, that led other companies into excessive expense without necessarily ensuring legal compliance'.

The author explains how the exercise helped him to justify the expenditure to senior management describing how, for example, eye screening programmes that appeared to be cheaper in the short term were actually more expensive long term and failed to guarantee compliance.

A second example describes how absence monitoring was benchmarked using around twelve companies. Simple questions were asked such as 'do you monitor absence?' 'how much does it cost? , and 'what, if any thing, do you do about it?'. They sought to determine whether the percentage of blue/white collar staff affected the approach taken to absence monitoring and findings showed that two distinctly different sets of standards were being applied across industry:

'There were companies who had measured absence and as a result of this measurement had introduced absence control strategies. In each case these companies argued that absence had reduced significantly as a result of their strategy. But other companies had considered absence in an entirely different light. Here absence was considered either not to be a problem or to be a necessary evil about which the company did not wish to act. The justification for inaction was that these companies trusted their staff to take no more absence than was absolutely necessary. And if all that was being lost was necessary absence there was little point in trying to control it'.

The author concludes that this type of information 'enables you to consider your own company culture and from this determine the likely stance of the board' and in the absence of compelling absence to the contrary 'there would be little point in attempting to introduce an absence monitoring strategy in a company committed to teamworking and empowerment'.

[Issue 88 (April 1996)]

EU RECOGNITION FOR ENVIRONMENTAL STANDARDS

The European Commission has confirmed that the British Environmental Management Standard BS7750 will now qualify companies for certification under the European Eco-management and Audit Schedule (EMAS). The equivalent Irish and Spanish standards have already been approved. There are currently around 100 sites and 41 verifiers registered to EMAS.

ENVIRONMENTAL MANAGEMENT SYSTEMS: INTEGRATING STANDARDS

Chemical Week's Environmental Management Systems Conference took place at The Inter-Continental Hotel, London, on 13th and 14th March and was sponsored by leading certification body SGS International Certifications Services Inc.

In the first two sessions an overview of the current status of European standards was presented describing some of the requirements in more detail. This includes, for example, a paper by Dick Hortensius, Senior Standardisation Consultant for the Netherlands Standardisation Institute which explains, amongst other things, the position with regard to suppliers and contractors in ISO14000 and the role of the annex to the standard:

'The annex to ISO14001 is explicitly meant to avoid misinterpretation of the specification. That annex therefore includes the world-wide accepted right interpretation of the standard. This is important from the European perspective because via the annex the link between ISO14001 and EMAS is strengthened'.

Oswald A.Dodds MBE, Chairman of ISOTC207/Subcommittee 1 (Environmental Management Systems) follows with a discussion of the role of the standards bodies and the so called Vienna Agreement between CEN and ISO which provides for joint working on and parallel approval of standards:

'A CEN working group has compared the ISO (EN) 14000 documents and EMAS in great detail and produced a 75 page draft document on the issue which CEN has agreed to publish. The group have also identified a number of areas where clarification is needed between the specifics of each approach- EMAS and ISO- to ensure that users of the ISO standards will meet the EMAS requirements'.

Integrating Certification Inspections

With many common threads existing between the three environmental standards as well as between them and the quality systems standard BS EN ISO9000 there is a clear logic in combining the process of third party certification for both sets of standards, and with health and safety certification if and when this concept ever materialises. With this in mind Bruce Prince, Corporate EMS Manager for SGS, explained some of the benefits to be gained from this, notably a requirement for fewer visits to be made by third party auditors, more effective review of the integrated systems, and improved efficiency of site visits by auditors. This is in addition, of course, to the more general benefits, both internal and external, tangible and intangible which third party certification of an EMS can bring, such as reduced operating costs, lower insurance premiums, improved public and community relationships, potentially lower levels of regulatory reporting and/or auditing, and a means of demonstrating environmental due diligence. [The latter has yet to be tested in a court of law, but can only be assumed to be positive-Ed].

The key to making an integrated approach successful, resides, according to the speaker, in the selection of the auditing team. The scope may and can vary for the assessment of each system, systems may be fully or partially integrated, and they may be at different stages of maturity, for example a surveillance visit for a quality management system may be combined with an initial assessment for an EMS.

Integrating EMS and Responsible Care

The case for integration was taken a stage further by Stuart Aaron, Responsible Care Manager for the Chemical Industries Association who advocates the development of a form of one stop certification for ISO9000, ISO14001 and BS8750 (health and safety) coupled with Responsible Care verification covering the areas of Product Stewardship, community liaison and chemsafe (a partnership with the emergency services which predates the now well-established Responsible Care concept).

Some individuals have expressed a belief that Responsible Care (defined as 'a commitment to continuous improvement in all aspects of health, safety and environmental performance'), is, after around twelve years of application, in some danger of losing its momentum. However, the speaker was keen to stress that some 39 countries have now adopted Responsible Care programmes, albeit in different ways.

In comparing Responsible Care with ISO14000 he highlighted three key areas which were addressed by ISO14000 but not by Responsible Care, notably training and competence, documentation and document control and checking and corrective action (monitoring and measurement; non-conformance; records; and management system audit). He then drew attention to the Association's recently released Guidance Document 'Responsible Care Management Systems for Health, Safety and Environment' which addresses these gaps by integrating Responsible Care with the three environmental standards as well as with BS EN ISO9000 and the Health and Safety Executive Guidance Document 'Successful Health and Safety Management, otherwise known as HS(G)65 (1991).

The Association's Guidance Document which is available separately from the conference literature, is based on a Plan-Do-Check-Act cycle and has nine sections and two appendices. This begins with Leadership and Commitment, then outlines principles for initial Review; Health, Safety and Environmental Policy formulation and objectives (with typical extracts from HS and E policies that have been used in practice); Organisational aspects (including structure and responsibility, training, documentation and document control); requirements identification (including risk assessment and definition of screening criteria as specified in HS(G)65 Chapter 4) ; Planning and target setting; Implementation (including purchasing and evaluation of suppliers, process control, management of change, and storage and transportation) ; monitoring (including examples of systems requiring checking and corrective action); and Management Review. Relevant clauses and chapters of ISO9001, ISO14001, BS7750, EMAS and HS(G)65 are displayed throughout.

As regards health and safety, HS(G)65 is referred to throughout, although in his speech the speaker did mention the role of BS8750 which he described as "an important part of the integrated approach". He acknowledged, however, that this document had still to gain universal acceptance, in particular from health and safety professionals. He suggested that some needed to be convinced of the merits of having an integrated approach and stressed that treating safety as an issue separate from quality and the environment "creates problems rather than solutions".

Figures showing the management systems status 200 of the Association's members operating 350 sites in 1994 revealed that as regards quality systems 64 per cent had formal certification to ISO9000 whilst 30 per cent had an alternative formal system with only 6 per cent having no formal system. For safety 9 per cent had formally adopted the International Safety Rating System (ISRS), 68 per cent had an alternative formal system and 23 per cent had no system. Environment had the least inspiring results of all with just 2 per cent having formal certification to BS7750 (which was by then a two year old standard), with 55 per cent having some kind of formalised system and 43 per cent having no system at all. The consequence of this, not surprisingly, is a poor perception of the industry on the part of the public which was confirmed by a recent MORI poll which suggested that less than 20 per cent of the population believed that the UK chemical industry was competent to regulate itself. The speaker described the outlook with such inaction as "serious in terms of its long term licence to operate".

Achieving Success through Integration

The concept of integrating certification inspections is relatively recent, but already some companies are realising benefits. One such company is Akzo Nobel Chemicals Limited at Gillingham, and the conference welcomed their Technical Manager Ken Jordan to describe their approach.

The company, which is sited on 18 acres on the banks of the River Medway, dates back to 1938 when, as Novadel, it began production of white lead and associated paint products for the flour milling industry .It is now one of four European Akzo Nobel sites which produces organic peroxides and other specialised chemicals for the plastics, rubber and glass industries. It employs 140 personnel and exports around 95 per cent of its output. Its many

121

achievements include ISO9002 which it achieved in June 1990, BS7750 in March 1994, EMAS in August 1995 and The 1995 Kent Business Award for the Environment. It is also working toward the Investors in People (IIP) standard on an ongoing project which it commenced in 1993 as a follow through to ISO9000.

The paper focuses principally on the two years from March 1992 to March 1994 and the build up to BS7750 certification with sections describing, amongst other things, the Initial Review, Environmental Policy, Training, Management Responsiblity and the Register of Significant Effects.

It is noted how a Dutch Chemical Industries Environmental Questionnaire was used as the basis for the Initial Review. Also how systems were established to monitor and correlate environmental data on a monthly basis to simplify updating of a Site Environmental Information Manual which two Bradford University Chemical Engineering students compiled in six months:

'The site was split into 25 different areas and different people were assigned these areas to complete the modified questionnaire. The questionnaires were then correlated together and summarised to give a baseline for the site's environmental performance.'

Under 'Training' the author explains how a half day training session incorporating an outline of BS7750 and a group exercise to illustrate how individuals can contribute personally toward the improvement of site environmental performance was given to all employees. Feedback was used as an input to site environmental targets and objectives. This ensured that there was collective ownership of the process of managing environmental performance:

'Carrying out Environmental Awareness performance training at an early stage is essential. To ensure that any Environmental Management System works effectively everybody on site must be made aware of environmental issues, as a paper system will not work without the commitment of people'.

The section on 'Management Responsibility' outlines certain 'prime environmental responsibilities' for which the Health, Safety and Environmental Manager is responsible, as well as the overall responsibility of senior management:

'All senior managers have clearly defined Environmental responsibilities and through our appraisal system all have at least one environmental goal'.

The next section on the 'Register of Significant Effects' describes the steps taken to compile the Effects Register and how COSHH information was used in this regard:

'The COSHH assessments information was modified and put into a form which could be used to assess what the effects of our processes actually are, but not how significant they are. The site was again split into 25 areas and competent people were assigned to fill in the forms. This list was then screened against certain criteria which can define a significant effect.'

The paper then outlines how BS7750 auditing has been combined with ISO9000 auditing:

The site's quality management system and environmental management system structures are very similar and the requirements of BS7750 have been integrated into the site management system. This has many advantages, firstly that we do not carry out internal audits differently for ISO9000 and BS7750. We are also not auditing twice for the different standards'.

It is noted that whilst system auditing is all that is required for BS7750 it is logical to extend this type of auditing to encompass performance auditing which will in turn simplify the preparation of an EMAS statement:

'A certification body will spend less time verifying an EMAS statement if the internal performance audit system is adequate to meet their requirements'.

In his speech Mr. Jordan described how the costs for BS7750 and EMAS certification totalled around £55,000 with some £50,000 of this being in the form of management time whilst £4,000 was spent on certifier costs for a three day BS7750 assessment and £1,000 on the one day EMAS assessment. Weighed against this were an 18 per cent saving in energy costs in the first year, a 28 per cent reduction in waste to landfill and a 0.5 per cent improvement in chemical efficiency.

[Issue 90 (June 1996)]

NEW STANDARD FOR HEALTH AND SAFETY MANAGEMENT

Although Health and Safety management has a high legislative and human profile, formal progress to third party certification has so far been elusive.

A new standard which allows companies to achieve third party certification for their health and safety management systems for the first time has been launched by the International Safety Management Organisation Ltd. Known as 'ISA 2000 (1996) : Requirements for Safety and Health Management Systems and Application Guidance Notes' it contains twenty elements. These have been drafted in a manner similar to those already used in BS EN ISO 9000 in order to facilitate ease of integration with other management standards.

The twenty standards are:

* administration of the system (including a requirement to define the organisation's safety policy, and responsibility and authority of key personnel, and conduct a management review of the system) .

* the safety system (requiring a documented system of procedures to control safety hazards and minimize the risk of accidents, and a Safety Manual).

* process safety capability (requiring that safety is a feature of the design process and that safety assessments are incorporated into intermediate design stages where appropriate)

* control of safety documentation (including requirements for document identification and issue, and a written procedure to describe the method by which changes are made to safety documents).

* purchasing (stipulating a requirement for a list of approved suppliers and contractors and for these suppliers to be reviewed 'at an adequate frequency to ensure continuing receipt of safe goods and services').

*safety in relation to contractor's equipment on site (requiring management to exercise control over, particularly, sub-contractors' equipment).

*identification and traceability (requiring all hazardous materials and safety equipment e.g. master control valves to be identified and an analysis of the need for product traceability to be undertaken).

*safety in action (a lengthy element requiring, amongst other things, identification of safety hazards and associated risks, compilation of an annual safety plan, a written emergency plan, a planned schedule of safety meetings, documentation of all safety rules which must be reviewed for adequacy in accordance with a schedule, incorporation of safety procedures into work instructions, a policy of preventive maintenance, and a policy governing Personal Protective Equipment or PPE).

*safety inspection (requiring a documented scheme for the inspection of certain incoming goods and mobile materials handling equipment, routine safety monitoring of processes and workplaces, a physical conditions audit, and the recording of safety inspections).

*use of measuring equipment (including a requirement to identify equipment used to monitor safety conditions and document the measurement process, and to document a scheme for the calibration of safety measuring equipment with all calibration equipment and standards traceable to national standards and all contractors required to give assurances that their equipment is likewise controlled).

*safety status (requires the identification and labelling of any item found to be unsafe).

*safety failure (stipulates the requirements for the assessment and control of unsafe situations and items, the recording of unsafe practices and incidents, documentation of first aid and medical arrangements, and accident awareness).

*corrective and preventive action (specifying requirements for a written procedure for the assessment of the effectiveness of safety reporting and investigation, and accident analysis).

*materials handling, (considering the manual and mechanical handling of materials, their storage and transport).

* safety records (requiring records to be kept which demonstrate the effective operation of the safety system).

*Internal audit of the operation of the safety system (requiring planned audits of the safety system to be carried out internally by 'competent, trained personnel') .

* personnel (requiring management 'to implement all necessary and appropriate measures to ensure that personnel are adequately trained and supervised', install 'appropriate procedures to facilitate the co-operation of all personnel in assuring safety, prepare an annual documented training plan, and record all formal training).

* off-site activities (requiring personnel working off-site to be 'adequately equipped in terms of accessories and skill') and to report off-site accidents).

* theoretical analytical techniques (an optional element requiring theoretical techniques if used to assess safety, investigate safety failure, or assist in decision making relating to safety, to be based on sound scientific principles and where appropriate, be documented in guide form).

The standard has a Part 2 which gives Application Guidance Notes on each of the elements above covered by the standard.

Certification in the UK for ISA 2000 is available through the certification body SGS Yarsley Limited. At present they are the only certification body accredited to award the bronze, silver and gold certificates. One of these accompany compliance with the standard, after a successful Safety Management System (SMS) audit and interviews with selected personnel.

Sharp's Integrated Quality Standard

Sharp have become the world's second largest manufacturer of photocopiers rivalling the Xerox Corporation. Xerox for their part have gained a world class reputation for excellence that has become well respected, most notably through their benchmarking strategy, about which much has been written and which is featured in the conference literature. Sharp's story by contrast is more recent and has been publicised rather less, but in its own way is no less impressive. Head of Dealer Support for Sharp Electronics UK Limited Doug Henderson, enlightened delegates.

Sharp's strategy is markedly different from that of Xerox, preferring to focus on sales and servicing through dealers rather than directly to the customer. This, however, has brought its own problems as dealers generally have gained a reputation for being unprofessional, recommending unsuitable equipment for certain applications, and introducing unclear terms and conditions to contracts which frequently incorporate hidden costs.

Customers have therefore become apprehensive of dealers, regardless of the reputation of the manufacturer concerned, which has tended to counteract the advantages of improved client contact, flexible response to requests and support to local communities which reputable dealers are able to offer.

It follows that if Sharp's strategy of dealer only retailing was to remain successful a method was needed to ensure that all dealers who retained the Sharp franchise were reputable and did provide the advantages identified over those manufacturers who chose instead to supply direct to the user.

Sharp's answer to this has been to develop an Integrated Quality Standard (IQS) which incorporates all of the elements of ISO 9002, BS7750 (environment), Marketing Quality Assurance (MQA), Investors In People (IIP), and the two draft standards BS 8750 (Health and Safety), and BS7850 (Total Quality Management). This is the first, and understood to be so far, the only publicly declared fully integrated quality specification.

In order to comply with the standard and so retain their franchise each Sharp dealer is required to address each element of each component standard which the IQS incorporates. This, in short, requires that dealers

(i) consistently deliver the high quality of service which they promise their customers (ISO9002)

(ii) work to management principles which demand the continuous improvement of their quality of service (BS 7850)

(iii) ensure that working conditions are safe so that an environment is created in which staff are happier, more efficient and more productive (BS 8750)

(iv) operate an ecologically ethical business (BS7750)

(v) consistently deliver excellent sales and after-sales service (MQA)

(vi) train staff such that all staff are competent and professional (IIP)

Compliance with these requirements, which is assured annually by an audit from third party certification body Bureau Veritas Quality International (BVQi), is acknowledged to be no mean feat, particularly for the smaller dealer. Sharp have therefore supported dealers that have accepted the challenge with a Dealer Development Programme in which Sharp have invested around £1 million. Under this Sharp agree to assist the committed dealer' by helping with various costs, such as consultancy for which Sharp pay up to 100 per cent for ten days, certification costs for which Sharp pay up to 50 per cent, and the pre-assessment audit for which Sharp pay up to 25 per cent.

Benefits identified for dealers include, a business plan with focussed company goals, improved efficiency with cost benefits to the bottom line, improved staff retention, improved customer retention, a much improved image, and substantially improved margins. During the presentation a video was shown in which several dealers voiced their comments, Vic Hughes, Managing Director of Danwood ,for example, commented:

"We'd already gone for BS5750 so we were well on the road. It wasn't a major shock."

Similarly David Esdale of Direct Digital said:

"It has been nothing but a benefit for us. Planning has nothing but helped us."

So far ten dealers have been certificated under the scheme, which Secretary General of the IQA Donald Campbell believes others will soon follow for commercial advantage. A further nineteen dealers are expected to qualify by the end of September with eight more downstream but expected to have qualified by early next year. This is out of a starting list of 52.

[Issue 94 (October 1996)]

BSI PUBLISHES NEW HEALTH AND SAFETY GUIDANCE STANDARD

BSI has announced the publication of BS8800 : Guide to Occupational Health and Safety Management Systems. With reference to the HSE guidance document HS(G)65 'Successful Health and Safety Management' , the environmental standard DIS ISO14001, and BSI's Guide to ISO9001 the new guidance standard describes how the occupational health and safety performance of organisations can be improved through the adoption of an occupational health and safety management system integrated within an overall management system.

ENVIRONMENTAL FIRST FOR BRITISH STEEL TEESSIDE

Redcar Coke Ovens, part of the British Steel Teesside Works, has achieved a unique doubleby achieving both BS 7750 and DIS ISO 14001. This makes Teesside the first cokemaking plant in the world to have its environmental management systems certificated to these standards. Reg Easy, Managing Director of the awarding certification body SGS Yarsley International Certification Services Limited, said in making the award on August 22nd:

"British Steel's scope of registration includes the manufacture of metallurgical coke and associated by-products as well as handling crushed and blended raw materials. This is of particular interest to the market as the possible impact on the environment, if poorly managed, could be quite damaging".

[Issue 97 (January 1997)]

The IOSH conference took place over three days from 2nd to 4th December at The Harrogate International Centre, where it was held for the third successive year, alongside an expanded supporting exhibition featuring around 60 exhibitors. A total of 21 formal presentations were given of which around 14 had accompanying papers in the conference literature. Four of these are reviewed below.

The Role of the Safety Practitioner.

The first paper to be presented was 'The Role of the Safety Practitioner' by David Eves CB, Deputy Director General of The Health and Safety Executive (HSE). This examines how attitudes towards health and safety have changed over time and what space, if any, is available for health and safety advisors in organisations where managers manage everything, with a high degree of competence.

The introduction compares and contrasts the 18,000 members of IOSH with the 1,500 HSE inspectors and asks safety practitioners to consider very carefully the added value that they actually bring to their organisations.

The traditional 'caricature' of the safety officer is described as 'the expert in mechanistic checking of company hardware who also coordinated the issue of safety equipment'. He frequently doubled as fire and security officer and 'would often act as a buffer to shield management from the attentions of the Inspectorate'. It is suggested that there is no longer room for 'this unhelpful mindset' in the world of modern industry.

'We know from experience that organisations which successfully manage health and safety make no artificial distinction between this and any other core element of the business. They set their policy from the top and give their advisors appropriate status within the company to ensure that they have the

128

competence to advise management and workers alike with authority and independence.'

The author proceeds to suggest eleven ways in which the safety practitioners may work to add value to their organisations. For example, by formulating and developing health and safety policies for new acquisitions and processes as well as for existing activities; maintaining adequate information systems for topics such as civil and criminal law, safety management and technical advances; also to become involved in the establishment of current organisational and risk control standards relating to hardware and human performance by advising line management on matters such as legal and technical correctness; and establishing and maintaining procedures, including monitoring and other means. These are, for example, reviews and auditing to ensure that senior managers have a true picture of how well health and safety is being managed. It is hinted that benchmarking may be particularly suitable in this latter context:

'One of the reasons why health and safety is not given the importance it deserves is that many senior managers take a rather narrow view of its relevance to core business processes; more enlightened organisations recognise that it is not just employees who benefit from proper attention to health and safety. It is also shareholders, customers, contractors/suppliers, neighbours, insurance companies and society (including regulators) at large'.

It is emphasised that it is no longer sufficient for the safety practitioner to rely on technical competence alone. Other qualities are needed if his position is to be justified, in particular the ability the way the organisation positions itself to handle health and safety matters, and other skills such as the ability to transfer experiences from one setting to another and the ability to network:

'We should not forget that the most pressing role problem often faced by employers is simply to make sense of the scope of their duties; to know where to begin to assess the risks and equally importantly, to know where to stop'.

The increasing need, for smaller companies especially, to be able to describe what they do to manage health and safety when tendering for a contract is highlighted and in looking forward it is envisaged that 'significant intellectual abilities' on the part of safety practitioners will be increasingly sought after along with awareness of the 'drivers' in organisations which can be used to promote health and safety.

Empowering the Safety Practitioner.

Empowerment' is one of those buzz words that just refuses to go away as more and more companies are opting for so-called flatter management structures. Already a fundamental tool for quality improvement, it is now being viewed in a not too dissimilar way by many safety practitioners and Owen Tudor, Senior Policy Officer for the Trades Union Congress (TUC) discusses some of the implications of this with reference to a recent joint study by the TUC, IOSH, and the Confederation of British Industry (CBI).

In discussing corporate developments the author points to a prevailing picture in British industry in which line managers have responsibility for just about all functions of the teams for which they are responsible, which includes health and safety.

The study itself, which seeks to identify measures which will enable occupational health and safety professionals to become more effective in turning the positive objectives of enterprises committed to better safety standards into practice, (chaired by former HSE Director General John Rimington), is then described, along with progress to date. Essentially a discussion document is being prepared which it is hoped will stimulate responses both from safety practitioners and from line managers and safety representatives (whom safety practitioners particularly need to be able to influence):

'Occupational health and safety professionals from outside IOSH will be asked to play a key role, either by responding to the discussion document formally , or through seminars and conferences as appropriate'.

The CBI for its part is surveying the views of senior managers with the help of the Cranfield Management School:

'We suspect that they (senior managers) are not readily convinced that professionals are delivering what the board of directors wants – either because they are not convinced that "Good Health is Good Business" or because the safety message is being conveyed in ways which either do or do not appear to contribute to the overall objectives of the enterprise. There is a problem with the intra-company status of occupational safety and health professionals because they are too often seen as inhabiting a corporate ghetto – either technical fix-it people, or empire builders without an over-riding commitment to profitability'.

It remains to be seen what the findings will be. Preliminary indications suggest that the role of the safety professional in enabling line managers to build occupational safety and health management into their generic line management capability will feature highly in the discussions. Also will be the need to incorporate risk assessment into the line management approach without it either remaining 'a meaninglessly general' objective or becoming a bureaucratic application. These approaches 'would undermine the whole dynamic of risk assessment as an alternative to "safety by numbers"'.

The patchy existence of health and safety in management training is certain to be addressed with eventual output likely to be in the form of a 'handbook' for occupational safety and health professionals with advice on how to handle members of the board, line managers, contractors and other staff.

The Control of Contractors

One of the areas where quality and safety are particularly closely intertwined is in the field of sub-contracting, which can be decidedly problematic for the quality and safety practitioner alike. Rightly therefore it was addressed by Allan St. John Holt, Chairman of the Hascom Network Limited. Whilst the paper is addressed primarily at the safety practitioner contains little that is not equally relevant to quality and general managers throughout industry .

The paper examines first of all who a contractor is, and then outlines some of the common difficulties experienced with them, such as competitive tendering compromising on health and safety standards, pressure of work, and a desire for speed. These lead to tacit acceptance of a so called 'justifiable' enhanced risk. Serious dangers associated with the practice of 'sub-sub-contracting' below a contractor originally approved as competent are highlighted.

A short description of basic legal requirements is then given, highlighting in particular Regulation 9 of the 1992 Management of Health and Safety at Work Regulations which outlines statutory duties for those who share a physical workplace.

Advice is then given on how to identify suitable contractors, highlighting the fact that where so called 'approved lists' are used such lists need to be kept up to date with the work required being within the competence of those on the list. This is followed by a look at specifications which recommends a preliminary risk assessment to ensure that contractors are given the fullest information for pricing the work. A sample checklist for those with responsibility for the preparation of work specifications is given.

A short section on contractor selection recommends that organisations on 'approved lists' should be able to rely on a tacit general acceptance as to competence so that they may concentrate on specific hazards associated with the proposed work.

Contract negotiation is then discussed with the need for contractors to agree to abide by all of the provisions of the client's safety policy which may affect employees or the work, being emphasised:

'Checking the returned bids should be carried out by staff trained to do so, and not merely by those relying on a checklist which they may not fully understand'.

Benchmarking Health and Safety Performance

Benchmarking is a practice which has risen to the fore in recent years and health and safety is an area where companies are frequently the most willing to share their information, with fewer concerns perhaps than elsewhere about confidentiality. It follows that it can be a very suitable area in which to begin benchmarking, and the paper by Nick Burraston, Head of Occupational Safety and Health for Powergen, describes the approach which has been taken by his company.

The story begins in 1988 when the Central Electricity Generating Board (CEGB) sent a study team to the US to examine, specifically, the differences between the performance of Britain's then nationalised electricity generating stations and their American privatised counterparts. The results, contrary perhaps to the expectations of some, revealed that accident rates at power stations across the US were substantially lower than those in the UK. This prompted a further benchmarking initiative in 1989-90 which involved comparison with the oil production and chemical process industries, which again showed that the British electricity industry was experiencing far higher instances of reported lost time accidents:

'The moment we looked out at the rest of the world, we saw that our accident record was not good enough. For example, our injury rate in 1989 was above the level for UK manufacturing as a whole, more than twice as high as the agricultural sectors, and almost as bad as that most notoriously dangerous of industries, the construction sector'.

In other words as soon as the company began to benchmark, its eyes were opened, and with the need to integrate health and safety into day to day management clearly apparent, a simple internal benchmarking process was established. This was crude, consisting of a monthly league table of accident performance for geographically separate management units, and when disaster struck in 1992 in the form of a pump house fire at a major coal fired power station, it became apparent that the current approach was not adequate.

In June 1992 a programme began to benchmark the safety performance of contractors in relation to that of the company's own employees. This was not easy because a contractor's accident data was scarce, but it has provided some useful results:

'We are at a relatively early stage now in seeking to benchmark in a serious way with companies that build, own, operate and maintain process and power plant in an international context. Clearly, from the information we have acquired, we may be in a position of wanting 'to achieve health and safety standards in overseas operations which represent the high performance end of expectations in some countries. The objective of our current benchmarking activities is to understand how international UK based organisations determine and implement health and safety policy across disparate cultures and legislations'.

The paper highlights an improvement in lost time accidents per 100,000 hours worked from 1.42 in 1989 to 1.12 in 1996, although figures for the intervening years are not quoted. Some interesting benchmarking findings include the following:

*the best companies report a company wide health and safety policy which usually explicitly states a goal of no accidents or harm to people, and often no damage to the environment as well.

*this goal is supported by strong statements that they will comply with local legislation or local best practice, whichever is the more stringent.

*management systems which start with the selection of contractors and end with the feedback loop have been used successfully to change the expectations of contractors and achieve significantly better standards than the contractors had anticipated.

*in some companies safety is one of the performance criteria discussed at managers' annual reviews.

*some companies are not afraid to impose high safety standards on an operation in a part of the world where the norm is different.

In conclusion the author says:

Powergen has used internal and external benchmarking as a lever to facilitate continuous improvement in health and safety performance throughout the period from privatisation until the present time. We are currently trying to achieve wider benchmarking with companies working in international forums and are committed to being recognised as a market leader for health and safety performance within the electricity and gas sector of industry.'

[Issue 99 (March 1997)]

SAFETY AND HEALTH AT WORK

The seventh annual Safety and Health at Work exhibition and conference took place from 4th to 6th March at London's Earls Court No.2 Centre. The move to the centre from Olympia reflects the growing interest in the event which has expanded from a relatively small base of 91 exhibitors and 4130 visitors in 1990 to around 400 companies represented on 270 stands with over 10,000 visitors this year. The physical side of the exhibition was 33 per cent larger than last year and in 1998 a 20% increase in floor space is envisaged following a rebooking of some 65% of the area immediately by existing exhibitors.

The conference, which featured 14 papers divided into four topic areas, likewise proved popular, attracting over 700 delegates from some 20 countries.

The new COMAH Regulations.

Day one of the conference featured four papers on the subject of 'Chemicals: A Factor in every Workplace' of which the paper with the above title, by Gordon MacDonald, Head of the Nuclear and Hazardous Installations Policy Division of the Health and Safety Executive, was one, and three on 'Practical Issues in Environmental Planning for Safety Practitioners'.

Mr.MacDonald's paper is concerned with the Control of Major Accident Hazards involving Dangerous Substances (COMAH) Regulations, a European Directive which was adopted on 9th December 1996 and is set to be enacted in theUK in early 1999. Their basis is the so-called Seveso Directive (named after the disaster in Seveso, Italy, in 1976, in which the accidental production and release of dioxin as an unwanted by-product of a runaway chemical reaction led to widespread environmental damage). This is currently enacted in the UK through the Control of Industrial Major Accident Hazards (CIMAH) Regulations 1984.

The paper highlights some of the weaknesses of the Seveso Directive in its present form, notably its complex nature which has led to difficulty in implementing its requirements; the lengthy and inflexible nature of its various application annexes; and the lack of reference to a key element of the mitigatory package, land use planning. It then describes the review of the Directive, by the European Commission in conjunction with the Committee of Competent Authorities consisting of representatives of all of the governmental bodies of various countries responsible for enforcing its provisions, and the subsequent draft Directive (COMAH or Seveso II) which resulted.

The new Seveso II Directive is noted 'to reflect more clearly the relatively recent emphasis on safety management systems', which are 'seen as the key to high and sustainable levels of safety', and for its greater detail to ensure a more uniform implementation by member states'. Its principal features are as follows:

*application will depend solely on the presence on site of a threshold quantity of dangerous substance with previous distinctions between process and storage activities being removed.

*the scope is to be extended to include chemical hazards at nuclear installations and explosives but exemptions for the extractive industries, transport related establishment pipelines outside of establishments, and military installations will remain.

*greater use of generic categories e.g. 'highly flammable' or 'toxic' which will enable the number of named substance types to be reduced from over 170 to just 37 whilst new substances will be covered as soon as they receive a supply classification.

*introduction of a new 'ecotoxic' category to cover substances dangerous to the environment but not to people.

*a shift in the responsibility for notifying the presence of a dangerous substance from the top to the bottom tier.

*new requirements for operators of 'bottom tier establishments' to have a 'major accident prevention policy' along with the organisation and arrangements to put the policy into effect.

*introduction of new land use planning requirements.

*new requirements to test on and off-site emergency plans every three years and include measures to be taken for remediation and clean up of the environment.

*a new requirement to make safety reports available to the public.

*introduction of new criteria for the reporting of major accidents so as to improve the consistency of reporting from Member States to the European Commission.

*new requirements for competent authorities to communicate the conclusions of the examination of the safety report or prohibit start-up or continued operation where there is evidence that the measures taken for the prevention and mitigation of major accidents are seriously deficient.

*a new requirement for member states to establish a system for the inspection of installations covered by the Directive.

* a new requirement for competent authorities to designate establishments which may potentially create 'domino effects'.

With regard to the provision of safety reports the paper says the following:

'The competent authority will have to assess reports in greater depth in order to ensure that they have fulfilled the purposes set out in the Directive. In particular, that they demonstrate that all necessary measures have been taken to prevent major accidents. Start up or continued operation is conditional on the competent authority being satisfied that there is no evidence that the measures taken by the operator for the prevention and mitigation of major accidents seriously deficient.'

'Safety reports will have to be made available to the public subject to restrictions for reasons of commercial, industrial or personal confidentiality and national security. This is likely to concern industry in terms of the sensitivity of information released and potential costs in making reports available. Clearly reports could not be provided to the public on an individual basis but they could be deposited in places where the public have right of access such as libraries and town halls'.

The paper highlights some of the main issues to be addressed under the safety report regime, such as the nature of the communication from competent authority to operator following assessment of the safety report; how the key test of 'serious deficiency' in measures for prevention and mitigation might be interpreted; and whether for new establishments safety reports will have to be submitted before construction or before operation, or indeed before both. It then elaborates on the concept of the Major Accident Prevention Policy (MAPP) including issues to be addressed by the safety management system, and on certain derogations to the Directive.

Environmental Assessment of Substances and Operations

The paper with the above title, by Mike Richards, Group Safety, Health and Environment Support Manager for Tioxide Group Services Ltd. introduces the concept of Life Cycle Assessment (an emerging scientific technique designed to provide an environmental profile of a product from cradle to grave), and relates it to the more established concepts of Product Stewardship (the responsible and ethical management of health, safety and environmental aspects of a product throughout its life cycle) and Process Stewardship (the responsible and ethical management of the health, safety and environmental aspects of a manufacturing process).

The author presents *Life Cycle Assessment* as a four step methodology consisting of:

Initiation (deciding the terms of reference, scope, and functional units of the activity to be studied).

Inventory assessment (identifying and quantifying the energy and materials input, the products, co-products and releases to the environment involved)

Impact assessment (relating the energy and resource consumption, and releases to the environment to real world environmental issues).

Interpretation (interpretation of the results of the study including an assessment of the need for revision of scope and/or reiteration of all or part of the study to take account of new information).

The author then recommends a life cycle screening approach based on a 'desktop assessment of the potential environmental burdens involved on a case by case basis, with more rigorous studies 'triggered when the screening indicates significant potential or actual issues'. An example of an environmental screening method is then given to illustrate the principles, with tables provided incorporating various questions which an investigating team might wish to address.

The paper explains how Tioxide have used Life Cycle Assessment studies to gain a greater insight into the environmental issues surrounding the manufacture of titanium dioxide, and how they have been used to evaluate the relative environmental merits of two different process routes. This serves to illustrate some of the benefits of Life Cycle Assessment (LCA):

'Manufacturers are faced with choosing between a number of options for each plant. The factors to be considered on a site specific basis include local circumstances such as capital and variable costs, availability of raw materials (e.g. limestone), and suitable landfill sites. Awareness of environmental issues is driving ever tightening standards, and future legislation should be aimed at reducing the environmental burden in a cost effective manner. As investment capital is limited ,it is vital that the environmental impacts of the options available to manufacturers are assessed. This requires consideration of the whole life cycle from extraction of raw materials , manufacture, use, recycling and disposal of products. The findings from LCA studies enable an informed debate on the direction of future developments and will ultimately lead to making better choices'.

Limitations of Risk Assessment in Decision Making

Professor Ellen Silbergeld's paper with the above title suggests that whilst risk assessment 'has become the dominant policy making method for safety and health regulation in many countries' it 'has not improved US policymaking' and 'is substantially limited in both theory and practice'. She argues that the rise of risk assessment has been due largely to a combination of public opinion and government power and that following two decades of its increasing influence on policymaking 'the results of risk assessment based policies are widely distrusted and almost always challenged'. She is notably pessimistic about future efforts to improve methods for validating the predictions of risk assessments on the grounds that 'most regulatory risk assessments describe the likelihood of events in an unreal world' and describes it as 'unlikely' that risk assessment will in the foreseeable future be improved sufficiently both in terms of sensitivity or precision to reduce the uncertainties that are inherent in so called low dose risk estimation.

The paper presents a number of reforms to conventional risk assessment which may be worthy of consideration. First it is suggested that it may be wise 'to lower the stakes for risk assessment as a predicate to action':

'The precautionary principle embodies this concept: "where there are threats of serious or irreversible environmental damage, lack of full scientific certainty shall not be used as a reason for postponing cost effective measures to prevent degradation" (UNCED). This has been adopted by the International Commission on the Great Lakes in North America, and it underlies the proposals to develop a UN Convention on persistent organic pollutants (POPs)'.

A second suggested reform is a shifting of the burden for undertaking a full risk assessment from governments to the regulated parties so as to allow industry the leeway to calculate the relative value of undertaking further research to refine a preliminary risk assessment. This, it is said, 'would change the incentives in risk assessment which currently reward industry by delaying regulation when it is successfully challenged. on the basis of too much uncertainty or too little data'.

The author then advocates the development of 'a calculus that expresses a risk estimate in the context of its uncertainty, and then explicitly sets the range of possible risks for decision makers and the public to select':

'A relatively simple risk assessment may generate an estimate of likely increased risks of cancer with an uncertainty of 200% (that is the "true" risk could be as much as twice or as little as one half of the estimate). In a calculus similar to that done in policy analyses of climate change, a social judgment could be undertaken to determine in a Bayesian mode the relative acceptability of under or over estimating risk by this magnitude'.

Her final recommendation is for a reduction in the reliance placed on risk assessment and for an increase in the value assigned to the value of other elements of the risk characterisation process:

Exposure assessment has been undervalued in recent years as compared to the toxicology of identifying hazard. Although most writers (and manuals of practice) allocate equal value to both elements in characterising risk, it is the case that most focus relates to toxicity rather than exposure assessment. However the determinant of real world risk is greatly determined by exposure'.

The Finn Age Programme

The paper by Professor Juhani Ilmarinen describes how a comprehensive model for promoting the work ability of ageing workers has been created and tested. It is based on three groups of actions which have been found to improve both the work ability and health of such workers over a one to three year period. The three groups of actions identified have related essentially to changes needed in the content and demands of work, work time arrangements and the improvement of the functional capacity of individual workers. By integrating the three groups improvements in both productivity and quality of workmanship were observed with gains for both the employers and the employees :

'The changes in the work ability of women employed in office work is one example of the effects of integrated actions. A figure illustrates how the Work Ability Index (WAI) changed during 11 years among women not involved in any ergonomic, organisational or health promotion activities. A decline in the WAI during ageing is typical with great inter individual variation. Another figure shows first the period from 1981 - 1985 when no actions were taken. The WAI of most office workers declined considerably. During the period 1985-1992 the women participated in activities both at their work place and outside the work. As a result the WAI of most of the women improved slightly- in some individuals remarkably, during ageing. Similar results were obtained in several types of jobs studied both among men and women, indicating that work ability can indeed improve with age.'

The paper describes the methodology underlying the development of the Work Ability Index as devised by the Finnish Institute of Occupational Health, which uses a sum of ratings on seven items (work ability related to life's best; work ability related to work demands ; number of chronic diseases; handicap due to the diseases; sick absence; prognosis for the next two years; and mental resources), and explains how several collaborating projects have been co-ordinated internationally using it. Various trends are identified:

'The prevalence of poor WAI by age gender and type of work showed that among men the highest rates were found in installation (25.6%), auxiliary work (25.3%), transport (25.0%), and teaching work (22.8%) at the age of 58. Technical supervision had the highest rates (6.2%) at the age of 47 and auxiliary work at the age of 51 years (7.2%). Among the women the highest rates of poor WAI were found in kitchen supervision (26.8%), auxiliary work (26.4%), and in home care work (26.3%) at the age of 58 years. Nurses had the highest rate of poor WAI at the age of 47 (5.2%) and kitchen supervisors at the age of 51 years (15.7%)'.

The situation of teachers was good or excellent when they were under 51 years of age; but 11 years later a teacher with an excellent WAI score was a rarity. Male teachers showed a stronger fall in WAI than female teachers during the follow-up. Men doing transport work displayed great intra-individual variation in WAI after the follow-up and a most dramatic decline in WAI was found among women doing kitchen supervision'.

A discussion is also featured on the issue of ageing and professional competence which examines how professional competence might be maintained or improved during ageing:

'Recently a seminar of the Nordic countries was organised to discuss learning, pedagogic and competence development for elderly employees. It was recommended that better training methods should be developed for middle aged and elderly workers'.

[Issue 104 (August 1997)]

ISO PROPOSES ENVIRONMENTAL AUDITING STANDARD

The ISO Technical Committee on Environmental Management (TC207) has laid the foundation for a new draft standard which will serve as a guide for environmental assessment . The new standard (ISO14015) on environmental assessment of sites and entities (EASE) will combine so called Phase 1 site assessments with due diligence auditing. The proposal follows from concerns that due to a lack of international guidance various national standards are being applied in circumstances for which they were never intended, whilst the increasing use of site assessments and the ever present financial risks associated with environmental issues now provide a strong case for standardisation.

[Issue 106 (October 1997)]

SAFETY FIRST FOR PHILIPS

Philips LMS, the Blackburn based manufacturer of high capacity optical storage discs for the recording of computer data has become one of the first companies in their field to become certificated to the new international occupational health and safety standard ISA2000. This standard requires that businesses comply with the published health and safety guides HS(G)65 and BS8800 and address such areas as 'Safety Policy and Leadership',' Task Analysis/Risk Assessment', 'Permit to Work Systems', 'Health and Safety Objectives', 'Emergency Drills', and 'Documented Safety Management System Procedures' as well as basic ISO9000 requirements such as 'Management Audit and Review' and 'Personnel and Training'. Commenting on the achievement Lorraine Whalley of Philips said:

"Compliance with a good safety management system will always ensure optimal use of available resources. Some of the benefits that we have either experienced, or anticipate experiencing, include reduced risk of incidence, which could lead to prosecution, a public demonstration of due diligence, and a reduction in accident costs".

On site assessment and certification was conducted by international certification body SGS Yarsley ICS Limited who are currently the sole provider for third party health and safety certification in the UK.

Growth through Environmental Opportunities

Three papers were presented at this EFQM workshop entitled 'Simplicity without Reduction -Thinking Upstream Towards the Sustainable Society' by Prof. Karl-Henrik Robert of the Swedish international environmental organisation The Natural Step, 'Environmental Strategies with Focus on Shareholder Value' by Per Grunewald, Senior Vice President for Group Environmental Affairs for Electrolux, and 'Environmental Performance Analyses' by Franz Knecht, Head of Environmental Management Services for the Swiss Bank Corporation. The latter is reviewed.

The paper begins as follows:

'By integrating ecological aspects into its management, its products and its production processes, companies can cut costs and give themselves an edge in the marketplace with a positive impact on shareholder value. To gain the benefits of such situations Swiss Bank Corp.is incorporating an Environmental Performance Analysis into the criteria it applies to selected portfolios, to complement its standard analytical techniques. The objective is to identify companies with outstanding performance on both counts, ecology and economics. This sets SBC's products apart from the existing assortment of funds on the market which invest in environmental technologies, as well as green funds that use strictly ethical criteria. The new service is a response to growing customer demand for investment vehicles that include an ecological dimension which was clearly indicated by a market study at one of SBC's main branches in Switzerland'.

It then seeks to explain how environmental performance is related to shareholder value, highlighting the competitive advantages of ecologically optimised products, ecologically optimised production processes, and properly functioning environmental management systems:

'Firms with functioning environmental management systems are likely to have a comprehensive management system in place at the level of the corporate group as a whole: good environmental management is an indicator of competent management in general'.

'Potential financial burdens caused by developments such as stiffer environmental legislation or "green" taxes and ecological levies can be anticipated and appropriate measures can be introduced'.

'The eco-efficiency criteria presented above make it clear that resource-efficient production, and therefore cost efficient production, lead to steady improvements, not only in environmental performance but also in business performance .'

141

The portfolios themselves are then described:

'The portfolios invest exclusively in companies with a record of good environmental as well as economic performance. The new element in this investment approach is a twofold strategy, targeting both "ecological leaders" and "ecological innovators" for investment. With this two pronged strategy SBC's ecological portfolios give investors a chance to profit from the strong growth often experienced by small and medium scale enterprises marketing innovative, environmentally beneficial products, and at the same time to share in the security and performance of blue chip stocks'.

'No particular industry is excluded as a high polluter, because it is precisely the resource intensive industries which can have a significant direct impact on the environment, if they conduct their business in an eco-efficient way'.

A four-step 'stock picking' procedure is outlined consisting of evaluation using "traditional" financial analysis, an environmental evaluation (analysis of company information and outside data using company questionnaires designed for the specific industry), a plausibility check (the quality of the analysis must stand up to external quality examination), and synthesis of financial and environmental evaluations:

'The search for ecological innovators focuses mainly on the decidedly future-oriented sectors, products and services. Having established the target groups, the leading suppliers are identified. Admission to the fund, however, only occurs if the company in question also meets the key criteria for eco-efficiency in production and management.'

'Companies with an unsatisfactory environmental performance and a positive rating from the financial analysis point of view "failed to make the cut", and this applied as well to companies where the situation was reversed. The main thrust is investment in ecological leaders, which are often blue chip companies. This was a way of pursuing a market yield for the portfolio'.

[Issue 111 (March 1998)]

ENVIRONMENTAL REPORTING IMPROVES

The quality of environmental reporting has improved 'dramatically' according to a recent United Nations Environment programme (UNEP) survey.

The survey, undertaken on behalf of the UN by environmental consultants SustainAbility, examined corporate environmental reports from 100 companies in 16 industrial sectors from 18 countries.

They found that the number of environmental reports that are verified by an external organisation has risen from 4 in 1994 to 28 in 1997 whilst the number of reports containing statements by top management has almost doubled from 45% in 1994 to 89% in 1997. The Chairman of SustainAbility John Elkington, commenting on the results said:

"Companies are now publishing [environmental] data in ways which they actively argued would be commercially suicidal as recently as the early 1990s".

[Issue 112 (April 1998)]

HEAL TH AND SAFETY AT EARLS COURT

The annual Health and Safety at Work Exhibition and Conference took place at Earls Court from 10th to 12th March and featured some 300 exhibitors whilst the Conference featured 12 presentations over two days. The theme of this year's event was 'Good Health is Good Business' and on Day three anew feature was introduced in the form of a satellite conference on this subject organised by the Health and Safety Executive. This was pan European and broadcast to influential audiences in 14 countries.

The conference was opened by Angela Eagle MP Environment Minister responsible for health and safety who spoke of the Government's "firm commitment" to reduce the 30 million or so working days which are lost each year as a result of work accidents and work related ill-health. She said that such figures "show in stark and undeniable terms the way in which inadequate attention to health and safety impacts upon the economy and the working population" whilst "this terrible human waste" continues to cost employers anything between £4 billion and £9 billion a year in 5 to 10% of overall company profits and the nation as a whole between £11 billion and £16 billion or 2 to 3% of national output.

She also expressed particular concern about those employers who currently "are trying to evade their health and safety responsibilities by making their employees self-employed." She explained how the Health and Safety Commission has been "asked to look particularly at homeworkers and the apparently self-employed to see if and where changes are necessary to protect vulnerable groups.

Other measures announced include the withdrawal of 'Notice of Intent' administrative procedures on the grounds that they can hinder the use of improvement notices which have been found to be "a particularly effective way of enforcing standards". Also there are proposals for a White Paper entitled 'Fairness at Work' which "will contain a framework for a new era of employment relations based on decent standards and partnership".

The presentations which followed were grouped into three groups of four under the headings of 'Managing Safety and Health', Dealing with difficult issues'; Health, Safety and changing Patterns of Work'; and 'Managing the Working Environment'.

From these the following three papers have been selected for review: 'Can Food Safety Culture apply to Safety and Health?' by Nina Wrightson and Dr. Robert Southgate of Northern Foods plc; 'Benchmarking for Safety, Health and the Environment' by Dr. Janet Anderson, Head of Environment, Health and Safety for the CBI; and 'The Problems of Legislation on Work Equipment' by Dr. Hani Rafaat, Assistant Director of the Health and Safety Unit at Aston University.

Can Food Safety Culture apply to Safety and Health?

This paper under 'Dealing with Difficult Issues', describes how Northern Foods plc built upon the experiences gained from their Food Safety Strategy in order to achieve a sustained culture change which began with health and safety. In particular it covers the strategic and operational tools that were used and how they were refined from the specific to the general.

The principal food safety tool used was the Hazard Analysis Critical Control Point (HACCP) technique which was integrated into a specially designed training programme. It is a tried and tested tool which was developed initially to counter microbiological hazards in the food industry, but which can equally be applied to deal with chemical and physical hazards and indeed any parameter which may constitute a defect in an end product. Thus HACCP may be used to:

* ensure effectiveness of production support systems e.g. cleaning systems.

* enhance equipment design.

* optimise factory design and the layout of production lines.

The technique is viewed very much as a complement to a quality management system which provides 'a means of predicting deviations from an accepted norm and managing them in a logical fashion':

'With HACCP, control is transferred from solely reactive and end product testing (testing for failure) into the design and manufacture of foods and the preventive approach (preventing failure). It has the potential to identify areas of concern where failure has not yet been experienced, and is therefore particularly useful for new operations, products or situations. With HACCP, the emphasis is on raw material and process control, control being taken out of the laboratory and into the manufacturing environment'.

144

'HACCP is not a substitute for generic (horizontal) control systems -e.g. hygiene –which should be in place before beginning the HACCP process. However there are instances where, say, hygiene could have a direct bearing on the hazard in question, and such instances must be considered as part of the HACCP evaluation'.

The HACCP concept was linked with quality assurance to form a complete training module which was devised for production, technical and engineering managers and supervisors in the form of an open learning text:

'A manual is used to guide the individual to carry out most of the work themselves under the guidance of a tutor. The tutors, who are Northern Foods' trained employees, will cope with four or five students at any one time, working as a group'.

A computer based examination leads to a certificate.

With research at four Northern Foods sites in 1994 suggesting that the cost of accidents to the company was beginning to approach £10 million a year despite the fact that the strategy employed in introducing an improved food safety culture had proved to be extremely effective management decided to examine the parallels between the strategic and operational tools in the fields of food hygiene and health and safety. This led to the conclusion that the same framework could be used to achieve much needed improvements in health and safety as a whole.

Benchmarking for Safety, Health and the Environment

This paper from the 'Managing the Working Environment' section Introduces the CBI's latest benchmarking tool known as Contour which is designed to assist businesses to assess their current practice and management of environment, health and safety and identify opportunities for improvement:

'With the growth in environment, health and safety management systems and the increasing emphasis on how to track and evaluate performance, the CBI members felt that there would be significant value in developing an EHS benchmarking service, which provides companies with a comparative analysis of their existing systems as well as a step approach for SMEs to accredited management systems'.

This service was piloted in 1996 with 100 companies and followed by the CBI's already successful PROBE initiative from 1995 which benchmarks key aspects of manufacturing and engineering processes such as total quality, lean production and product development and now has over 1000 participants. It uses a self-assessment questionnaire to analyse the practice and performance attributes of a company in seven key areas including organisation and cultural attitudes, accounting for key stakeholders, pollution control and waste management:

'The Contour diagnosis allows individuals to understand whether their investment in improved practice is giving the results it should compared to their peers, and whether decent performance is firmly based on embedded management systems, rather than luck or one or two undetected heraldic efforts. The key message of Contour is that all companies need to maintain the momentum to achieve continuous improvement towards world class excellence'.

'The service provides participants with an on-site facilitator to ensure consistency of approach, verify the self-assessment answers and give instant feedback. Participants also receive a written report highlighting their strengths and weaknesses and identifying areas for improvement. Improving EHS performance is an integral part of creating a quality business, benchmarking guides management towards achieving this goal'.

Contour is the result of voluntary action which the CBI has been promoting since 1992 through the Environment Business Forum -a cross sectoral initiative providing a network of like-minded businesses to share best practice. A similar benchmarking tool for human resources known as IMPRESS, is currently being piloted.

The Problems with Legislation on Work Equipment.

This paper in the 'Managing safety and health' category examines, in the context of a recent test case, the extent to which machinery and work equipment EC safety legislation is understood with particular reference to the Provision and Use of Work Equipment Regulations (PUWER) which are currently being revised in line with the Amending EC Directive (95/63/EC).

It presents a case history of a machine which was supplied by a UK company which acts as an agent, importer and supplier for an EC based manufacturer, and which later became the subject of investigation following an accident which 'was foreseeable at the design stage if a suitable and sufficient risk assessment was carried out by the machine designers'. The machinery was CE marked and was accompanied by a Certificate of Conformity which showed that it had been designed/manufactured in accordance with the EC Machinery Directive, which suggested to the buyer that it was safe.

A post accident inspection by the HSE, however, found that the machinery breached the requirements of the Supply of Machinery (Safety) Regulations 1992 and that its design failed to comply with two important EC harmonised standards, namely

*BSEN292: 1991(Machinery Safety, General Requirements and Technical Specifications)

*BSEN294 : 1994(Safety distances to prevent danger zones being reached by the upper limbs).

Legal proceedings were instituted by the HSE for breach of Regulation 10 of the 1992 PUWER Regulations:

'Regulation 10(1) places an absolute duty on an employer to ensure that relevant machinery complies with enactments implementing relevant EC Directives. Regulation 10(1) is not qualified by the phrase "as far as is reasonably practicable" and therefore all measures to ensure compliance must be taken. This is regarded as an absolute duty [HSC 1997].'

The paper contests that this regulation is 'unclear and complex' and argues that the Guidance to PUWER: 'Work Equipment' offers little help to companies to assess the measures required in order to comply with the law:

Although HSE's interpretation of the requirements regarding safeguarding of dangerous parts of the machine was justified, such an interpretation could not be applied to other issues such as electrical or control integrity. Therefore there was inconsistency in the application of the provision.'

It also criticises Regulation 11, which requires employers 'to take measures which are effective, to prevent access to any dangerous part of machinery or to stop the movement of any dangerous part of machinery before a person enters a danger zone' and against which the employer was also indicted on the grounds that:

*it focuses only on mechanical hazards

*the text of Regulation 11(2)is not included in the Use of Work Equipment Directive

*the hierarchy of safeguarding options is flawed – a fixed guard is probably the least effective risk control measure if frequent access to the danger zone is required

*it is not clear why stock bars are singled out as a hazard -reference to dangerous parts or rotating stock-bars is not consistent with the terminology used in the essential safety and health requirements (EH and SRs)

*the link between the supplier and users of new work equipment is not clear

The dilemmas faced by employers as a result of these regulations are highlighted:

'It is clear that employers are in a vulnerable position as they must ensure the safety of employees even where new work machinery is supplied with a 'CE mark' and a certificate of conformity. One of the major obstacles in achieving this objective is that the employer has no automatic right to gain access to the supplier's technical file or their risk assessments. This right is only reserved for the enforcement authority (HSE in the case of the UK). The dilemma here is that employers should to ensure that the machine is in fact safe'.

'Although it is a good practice that machinery suppliers would provide a copy of their risk assessments or at the very least, the basis for compliance with relevant harmonised standards some suppliers do not supply any documents to support the "CE" mark. This is usually because they simply do not exist, rather than to protect technical innovation or industrial secrets'.

The author supports his arguments with evidence from Aston University:

'It was noted that almost all Declarations of Conformity/Incorporation provided by 16 out of a sample of 18 major suppliers have failed to make adequate reference to relevant EC Directives. Only one supplier out of 18 did quote a detailed list of the relevant harmonised standards used. Most suppliers have quoted only EN292 Parts 1 and 2 as the only standard used, EN292 is a general "A" type standard which sets out basic concepts and general principles for design applicable to all machines.

This by itself is not sufficient and needs to be broken down into more specific standards which relate to certain aspects of the relevant machine safety features.'

The following advice is also given to employers:

'In order to avoid costly mistakes, it is advisable that employers should be familiar with relevant harmonised standards and legislation, and more specifically with the suppliers' duty for meeting Essential Health and Safety Requirements (EH and SRs). Early involvement at the pre-tender stage for new machinery to ensure that potential suppliers can demonstrate compliance is recommended.'

'The ideal way to ensure that suppliers of new machinery do demonstrate compliance with the "EH and SR" is to invite suppliers' representatives to give a presentation at the different stages of the machine design, construction and commissioning. These presentations should include results of the risk assessment, description of the relevant EC and international standards and how the supplier has demonstrated compliance with them. This requirement can and should be made clear at the tender/procurement stages of the contract'.

'If the machine is not specifically covered by a "C-type" standard, then it is expected that the risk assessment standard BS EN 1050: 1997 be quoted and used. Similarly, if programmable electronic systems are used to safety related functions in the machine, then it would be expected to quote the harmonised standard EN954-1. However, the most relevant standard which covers software and hardware reliability is the International Standard IEC 1508, which is not an EC harmonised standard, but should be identified in the declaration of conformity under "other standards used"'.

'It is not so much that the employer needs to be entirely familiar with the details of all relevant standards applicable to the machine, but by questioning the supplier in this way the employer can demonstrate due diligence in ensuring that new machinery does comply with the EH and SRs'.

The paper concludes that the proposed amendments to PUWER 1992 'are not likely to result in significant improvements in work equipment safety without adequate guidance'. In particular the author notes that 'the wording of the proposed revision to regulation 10 appears to be much more complex than the original text of PUWER 1992' whilst 'the wording of regulation 11 is exactly the same as in PUWER 92'.

[Issue 114 (June 1998)]

I.E.A. BECOMES COMPETENT BODY FOR E.M.A.S.

The Secretary of State for the Environment, Transport and the Regions, has designated the Institute of Environmental Assessment (IEA) as the Competent Body responsible for the administration of the European Eco-management and Audit Scheme (EMAS) in England, Wales and Northern Ireland.

In carrying out the Competent Body function the IEA will build on its success of bringing together the key organisations that have a role to play in managing and improving environmental performance. The Competent Body function also provides a catalyst for enhancing the role of the ISO14001/EMAS Users' Group, for which the IEA is the Secretariat, providing a forum for debating current issues and trends and for contributing to the improvement of the schemes.

NEW QUALITY ASSURANCE SCHEME FOR ENVIRONMENTAL CONSULTANCIES

The Environmental Industries Commission (EIC) has launched a new quality assurance scheme for UK environmental consultancies, through its recently formed Environmental Consultancies Group which has been established to promote high standards amongst environmental consultancies.

The launch, by EC Director Adrian Wilkes, addresses the long standing criticism of variable standards of work in this sector by providing a measure

149

of capability for each consultancy. Malcolm Pratt, Chairman of the EC Environmental Consultancies Group commented:

"Improved standards in the method of working are required if UK industry is to have confidence in environmental consultancies. The Group has been formed largely to review these standards and provide customers with a benchmarking facility that will enable them to select qualified consultancies with experience in a particular field".

The scheme is supported with a Handbook of Environmental Consultancies, which provides an overview of areas of expertise for leading consultancies that form the EC's Environmental Consultancies Group, as well as, a 'Code of Practice for Contaminated Consultancies'. [Unusual, but the correct Title-Ed].

The Environmental Industries Commission was launched in April 1995 to provide an effective voice with Government from the UK's environmental technology and services industry. It currently has around 200 member companies.

[Issue 115 (July 1998)]

CASH-BACK INCENTIVE FOR ENVIRONMENTAL IMPROVEMENT

The Co-operative Bank has launched the first green leasing scheme which gives a cash back incentive for companies that wish to purchase equipment leading to environmental improvement.

Under the scheme, known as Greenlease, the Co-operative Bank has undertaken to pay up to 0.25% of any leasing agreement up to £10M which leads to 'demonstrable environmental benefits'. It will offer all of the usual advantages associated with leasing, such as leaving working capital intact and spreading the cost of equipment over a fixed period with the added benefit of access to The Co-operative Bank's Ecology Unit whose manager, Paul Monaghan, says:

"It is important to stress that our motives for this are not entirely altruistic. We believe that an environmentally sound business is a more creditworthy business and that the supply of such products and services will be amongst the most profitable markets in the future.

However, because many environmental projects have a long term pay back many companies are reluctant to finance investments with a short term loan or by dipping into working capital. Greenlease enables equipment to be financed over a longer period so businesses can enjoy the full financial and environmental benefits of their investment".

Greenlease allows companies to finance projects from £100,000 upwards over up to 15 years.

Amongst the various pieces of environmental equipment on the market the Bank is particularly interested in the combined heat and power sector as it has a proven track record of substantially reducing energy costs as well as reducing carbon dioxide emissions, the major UK contributor to global warming.

[Issue 123 (March 1999)]

NEW CERTIFICATION SCHEME FOR HEALTH AND SAFETY

A new certification scheme for Occupational Health and Safety Management Systems is soon to be published by BSI. Based on the guidance document BS8800 and the environmental management standard ISO14001 it will be modelled on Det Norske Veritas' Occupational Health and Safety Assessment Series 18001 which has been successfully used by many organisations over the last couple of years.

Currently OHSMS 18001 stipulates requirements for example:

- Establishment and maintenance of procedures to identify and evaluate the OHS risks of its activities, products and services, and of a register of identified significant OHS risks.

- Establishment and maintenance of a procedure to identify and have access to legal and other requirements directly applicable to the OHS risks of its activities, products and services, and associated record keeping.

- Identification of operations and activities that are associated with the identified OHS risks in line with its policy, objectives and targets.

IOSH ESTABLISHES NEW REGISTER OF CONSULTANTS

A new Register of Safety and Health Consultants designed to make it easier for organisations to find the right consultant with the right skills for health and safety management has been launched by IOSH.

Use of the Register is free with the Institute also providing detailed guidance on how to go about employing a consultant. All of the consultants on the Register will be Corporate Members of IOSH and active participants in the Institute's Continuing Professional Development programme. They are thus bound by the IOSH Code of Professional Conduct and have to provide proof of appropriate professional indemnity public liability insurance. Commenting on the launch the Head of Technical Affairs for IOSH, Stephen Fulwell, said:

"The service will be particularly useful for the many small and medium-sized enterprises which do not have the need or the resources to employ a full time safety and health practitioner. Likewise in-house health and safety advisors can turn to the register when they need support in more specialist areas".

[Issue 124 (April 1999)]

INTEGRATED MANAGEMENT SYSTEMS

A paper by Stephen Fulwell is based on a document published last year by the Policy Committee of the Institution of Occupational Safety and Health (IOSH) chaired by Richard Booth of Aston University.

This explains the current international position with regard to integrated management systems along with their pros and cons, implications for specialists, and issues relating to the maintenance and development of an integrated programme. It highlights the current work in progress in Germany towards the publication of an Occupational Health and Safety standard which according to the author 'is likely to challenge the UK BS 8800 approach and become the recognised international standard' and various foreign integrated risk management standards which are now gaining international acceptance:

'In 1997 a meeting of ten countries identified six options in respect of the preparation of a Risk Management Standard with only three countries France, Germany and the USA voting against proceeding with the development. This was followed in December 1998 by the circulation of a Working Party document, chaired by Australia, detailing Risk Management Terminology.

The common thread of risk management throughout each of the three disciplines of health and safety, quality, and the environment is envisaged to have the following implications for specialists:

Organisations are increasingly likely to recruit multi-disciplined individuals. These professionals will be competent in all three subjects and operate across the range, but call on technical specialists as and when they are required. The trend towards risk management will result in not only a more general perspective with, knowledge of the overlaps, but also an increasing requirement for business and management skills.

The day of the Health and Safety Advisor with extensive knowledge of legislation, safety engineering and accident performance statistics has passed. All disciplines must begin to interact effectively in order to ensure that the core skills effort and resources across the full range of activities are available.

It is no longer possible to erect clear boundaries between them and seek sanctuary behind a specialism. Positive team and other TQM attributes are essential'.

'Increasingly the concept of integrated risk management will result in the development of organisations and cultures which depend on a multi-disciplined and competence based approach, driven by a positive influence towards the outcome required This will require a new approach to continuous development from the professional bodies and their membership in order to ensure the delivery of the new facilitating role across a wider range of disciplines'.

The author urges recognition, however, of the fact that not all risk profiles will be the same and, consequently, not all requirements will be the same. There will therefore be a wider range of development opportunities both available and required by the professional manager.

The integrated approach is seen to offer advantages in terms of requiring fewer audits with fewer people taking less time, reducing the competition for attention on the part of plant managers which has been a headache for years, and, where systems of work consider jointly the objective required, offering a correctly balanced outcome rather than a conflict of priority:

'A single audit approach, reporting to a central function who is aware of the business priorities across the three disciplines, would enable key objectives to be identified and therefore generate clear strategies and objectives. Today it is not uncommon for the three disciplines to be competing for the same resources of time, money and commitment, often with none succeeding'.

There are, however, also disadvantages identified, in that there is potential for 'evolution of an over-centralised, bureaucratic and complex structure managed by professional specialists who effectively by-pass line management'; 'a previously positive approach to be affected by personalities' resulting in ' a blame culture and a negative influence'; and for 'existing systems, which form the basis of compliance with particular requirements, to fail due to the concentration of effort and resources upon the new approach':

'Audits by enforcement agencies or single topic specialists may prove difficult if it appears their specialism has been either devalued or subsumed by the integration process. This could also affect current specialists unless they are effectively converted to the integrated process and outcome'.

In describing the evaluation and preparation of an integrated programme the author recommends that a detailed review of the risk spectrum of the organisation be made along with the current management controls for each element and external factors such as legislation, insurance, standards and market and customer requirements. He also draws attention to the need to consider the competencies and skills in the organisation and to identify individual requirements for closing the skills gap. This, he says 'will assist with both understanding and communications':

'A strategy must be identified based upon the model of implementation selected, which considers either a gradual or an immediate integration. This will normally be dictated by the business priorities, the existing levels of competence within the team and the climate for change of the persons undertaking the new approach. Experience shows that a gradual and increasingly demanding approach with a flexible timetable is most likely to succeed rather than the dramatic and stressful "big bang" approach which is often favoured'.

Another hazard is the loss of existing practices when new systems possibly governed by other influences are introduced. This, he argues, could create 'a dangerous position where high risk is involved' and consequently it is important that the degree of overlap between the new and old arrangements 'must be understood and carefully integrated if a complete collapse is to be avoided'.

The following advice is then offered with regard to the maintenance and development of the programme:

(i) Ensure that the arrangements allow for changes in specific requirements, customer or legislation driven without significantly affecting the other areas.

(ii) Ensure that major events generate a balanced response across the complete range.

(iii) Ensure that the adequacy and effectiveness of any updating requirement is capable of a specific focus.

SAFETY AND HEALTH AT WORK

The last Safety and Health at Work Exhibition and Conference at Earls Court was held on 9th to 11th March featuring presentations on 'Management for Safety and Health Practitioners', 'Our Healthier Nation', 'Millennial Angst' and 'Practical Environmental Management', along with the launch of the Government's new *'Sign Up'* programme aimed at encouraging employers to register their interest in improving health at work as part of the Healthy Workplace initiative. This latter Initiative involving a partnership between the Department of Health and the Health and Safety Commission (HSC) will lead to a joint programme between the Department of Health and the Health and Safety Executive (HSE).

When launching *'Sign Up'* the Minister for Public Health Tessa Jowell said:

"Through this programme we hope to strengthen the belief that 'improving health is everybody's business'. From today, through the 'Sign Up' campaign, we will be contacting thousands of workplaces of every kind to give them the opportunity to register their interest in the programme. Businesses who reply will be sent regular newsletters updating them on the latest initiatives to help create healthier workplaces and giving them examples of good practice. Other businesses can 'Sign Up' using the website which goes online today".

At the conference a total of 13 papers were presented including 'Contractor-Supplier Relationships' (John Rimington, CB, Former Director General of the HSE), 'Stress -towards a workplace solution' (Dr. Rob Briner, Lecturer in Occupational Psychology, London University), and 'Errors and Error Recovery' (Tierk W.van der,Schaaf, Associate Professor of Human Factors In Risk Control at Eindhoven University of Technology).

Contractor-supplier Relationships

This paper examines current thinking in contractor management (sub-contracting) in a health and safety context with reference to a project undertaken by the author in 1997 which involved discussions with around 30 major organisations on the subject of supply chain management. These organisations collectively employ some half a million workers, have a combined turnover of around £40 billion and are actively engaged in sub-contracting.

The chemical, engineering and energy sectors in particular were heavily represented in the sample, though others were involved such as the British Airports Authority, whose policy of forming 'strategic alliances' with 'preferred suppliers' is used as an illustrative example of what is fast becoming an accepted trend.

The health and safety implications of such an approach is outlined with particular regard for the smaller company which, if desiring to work with larger organisations, 'will need to become both more systematic, and, almost certainly, safer, in their ways':

' There are now a limited number of project teams, each devoted to a specific supply area – let's say washroom facilities – each serviced by a BAA project manager with a prime responsibility for safety both in design and construction, and who monitors progress on each job. Preferred suppliers are chosen after an examination of their management capability, including checks on health and safety management approaches. They are required to engage in a self-improvement programme which BAA call "Strive for Five"'.

'The five aspects of "striving", identical for all the project teams and their included contractors, are respectively safety (put first), cost, time, quality and the environment. Under each of these five heads there is a ladder of deliverables and targets, each of which is tested for progress. The bottom rung of the ladder is easy enough – you have got to have a safety policy. The top rung is harder to attain – zero accidents. On the way you have to put in place training and passport schemes, self-audit systems etc.

Eventually, BAA hope to form their project teams into consortia to secure worldwide business. One aspect of the BAA scheme that is becoming increasingly widespread, is that main contractors are expected to impose on their subcontractors exactly the same conditions as are imposed on themselves, e.g. the same recruitment questionnaire'.

The role of Total Quality Management is described and the fact that many large firms are now working towards standardised procedures is said to be 'good news'.

'With the advent of quality management, quality procedures are extending all the way down the supply chain, not just to subcontractors, but now to employees and hired staff. An outstanding example of this personalisation is the so-called "passport scheme" which began in the petrochemical industry but which is now spreading to many others. The essence of the passport scheme is that individual workers are not allowed on site unless they have a piece of plastic, known as a passport, to show that they have attended a specific course of health and safety awareness training'.

The course is standard and is followed by an assessment to ensure that the individual worker has taken it in. It will not tell him everything he needs to know about health and safety, but the view of pretty well all those who have seen the scheme in operation is that it greatly concentrates a worker's mind to know that he has to take an interest in health and safety and pass an examination to get a job; and that he is much quicker to respond to further training or to learn safe procedure by experience once he has been on the course. It also means that the client firms can -and they do -shorten their induction training at the start of new contracts -a considerable saving to them.

So far, with the scheme only four years old, over 70,000 workers have become passported, mainly in the engineering construction and construction industries, and the number and variety of firms who are demanding passports and assisting in the management of the Scheme is still growing quite quickly'.

The author suggests that as organisations are increasingly putting their own workers through the passport scheme 'the health and safety standards and record of contractors on site are moving towards equality with those of permanently employed staff' whilst between two fifths and half of the total number of workers passported are 'small firm employees being trawled into the Scheme'.

In looking to the future the author points to 'the old highly unionised and fully owned and managed platforms that individual firms were in the last generation' being replaced 'by arrangements that are really quite similar in terms of permanence, but are more flexible, are no longer based on employment contracts, and hence are more savagely performance oriented':

'The aim pf permanence has meant that clients feel a more friendly interest in their contractors. A firm like Shell has an attitude that it is in its interest for its contractors to succeed; if something goes wrong it is not a matter for dismissal, but for both sides to put it right'.

The findings of the study upon which the study is based are explained in more detail in the HSE publication 'Managing Risk-added Value: How Big Firms manage Contractual Relations to reduce Risk'. (ISBN 0-7176-1536-7; 88 pages)

Improving Stress Assessment

Dr. Briner's paper considers the effectiveness of so called Stress Management Interventions (SMIs) in organisations arguing that whilst 'the flourishing stress management industry continues to make extravagant claims for their benefits' there is in practice 'surprisingly little evidence that supports the value of SMIs'. It is asserted that 'few organisations undertake any kind of valid assessment to first establish whether or not an SMI is actually required or to establish the purposes of intervention ' and in the light of this readers are urged to consider ' an evidence based approach to organisational stress interventions in which evidence gathered from valid assessments is used as the basis for choosing and implementing an intervention'.

The three types of SMIs (primary, secondary and tertiary) are described along with their objectives and reasons for their introduction. In particular it is noted that many organisations introduce SMIs for reasons which are not related to their specific goals:

'Some organisations introduce SMIs in the hope that these will safeguard them from litigation and the payment of damages. Although in the UK very few such cases have come to court, those that have and in which employees won substantial damages are used widely within the SMI marketing literature in the attempt to convince organisations to implement some form of SMI'.

'The importance of fashion and fad in determining what an organisation does cannot be overestimated. This seems particularly important in the case of SMIs where it is not uncommon for one organisation to introduce SMIs or

a particular type of SMI simply because another organisation is doing so. Managers from different organisations discuss what they are doing about stress, and those selling SMI products use the names of other organisations with whom they have done business to convince potential customers of the soundness of their products'.

In describing his evidence based approach the author discusses the concept of stress auditing and its various flaws before offering a starting point for the improvement of stress assessment, namely consideration of what the components of "stress" and its presumed effects might be:

'Many of the commercial and research-oriented self-report measures used in organisational stress are simply not based on best measurement practice. For example, it is now widely agreed that affective states have at least two dimensions, often labelled negative affect and positive affect, yet most measures use undimensional measures of mood or feelings. Similarly scores on symptom measures are open to a wide variety of interpretations and in general are unlikely to be good indicators of either well-being or particular medical or clinical conditions.

Although self-report measures are both necessary and desirable, they should be based on what is currently known about the ways in which people respond to self reports'.

'In terms of developing a more sophisticated understanding of the components of stress and, in particular, making sensible interpretations of data from other sources , interviews and other kinds of qualitative data would be invaluable. Exit interviews and absence interviews could be used to examine the extent to which stress is thought to play a role in these behaviours and, more generally, the way in which employees construe their well-being and its relation to their work environment.

Although organisations already have data that could potentially be used in an assessment, such as absence or performance figures, it is often the case that these data have not been gathered or recorded systematically. An evidence based approach would also involve collecting such data and encouraging organisations to take a more systematic approach'.

'An evidence based approach to SMIs must also start with the premise that, following assessment, it may be that stress is found not to be a problem, and that other problems and other solutions may emerge. Although this might be seen (particularly by those keen to sell the stress issue and SMIs) as something of a disappointment, such an approach will ultimately be of greater value to the organisation. For example, it may be that absence is a problem but has nothing to do with "stress" in any sense. In this case interventions should be aimed at managing absence rather than managing stress'.

A valid stress assessment is seen as requiring the following:

- a relatively sophisticated and comprehensive approach to measurement

- designs that permit causal relationships between the phenomena of interest to be established.

- A healthy scepticism toward the claims that are made by organisations about stress.

- A willingness to allow other types of problems and solutions to emerge.

Error Prevention by Human Recovery Promotion.

T.W. van der Schaaf's paper highlights the positive, role that human operators often play in preventing small failures and errors from developing into actual system breakdowns or accidents and proposes a concept known as human recovery promotion and offers this role as an alternative to conventional human error prevention techniques.

Theoretical approaches to modelling error recovery are discussed, and translated into empirical research questions which have been piloted revealing evidence to suggest that the root causes of error recovery are capable of being identified.

Four methods of classifying human recovery in process control are proposed:

(i) Type of preceding failure (technical, organisational or human).

(ii) Reaction after symptom detection (ignore deviating status, repeat sequence of actions, or attempt fault localisation and correction).

(iii) Factors in the man-machine system that triggered or enabled recovery (technical related to process design, interface design, organisation and management, and operator factors).

(iv) Phase in which a recovery factor contributes to the recovery process (detection, localisation or correction).

The author presents a simple incident causation model (shown diagrammatically) to define accidents, near misses and common root causes and makes the following assertion:

'When incident development cannot be stopped by the system's predetermined barriers and lines of defence, the only distinguishing factor between an accident and a near miss effect is the presence or absence of successful "accidental" or unplanned recovery .Although actual accidents also may contain attempts at recovery , it is obvious that near misses as defined above are the optimal source of data to study the phenomenon of recovery as the positive counterpart of failure'.

Pilot studies undertaken in the steelmaking, energy production and surgical sectors investigating safety, reliability and environmental effects of system breakdown yielded the following observations:

* Around 90% or more of all recovery factors are clearly technical, organisational or human in nature and therefore researchable and eventually manageable.

* The same figures show human recovery root causes contributing to 21 to 66% and that the human recovery range varies at lest as much as the human failure range (e.g. 33 to 56 %) suggesting that the human component should be taken seriously in terms of recovery possibilities.

* Rule and skill based factors tend to dominate operator failure whilst recovery also includes knowledge-based insights as very important i.e. the patterns of failure and recovery factors are clearly different.

* Hardly any recovery process goes through the more analytic localisation phase suggesting that if recovery is present only in the very last phase of the accident production chain of events then there may not be time enough for a diagnostic effort, only detection and correction just-in-time.

These observations are seen to have the following implications for designers:

* Consider recovery promotion as an alternative to failure prevention, especially when certain errors or failures are predictably unavoidable.

* Do not simply design out failure factors without considering the possible reduction of recovery factors i.e. raising the level of automation in process control or installing too many decision support tools can leave operators helpless in cases where they need not be.

* Seek to support all recovery phases primarily by means of an optimal man-machine interface.

* Invest in deep process knowledge of operators as reasoning beyond procedures can be essential for many recovery actions.

* Consider the discipline of error management in training i.e. learning to learn from errors.

Further Information

Next year Safety and Health at Work will merge with Health and Safety Expo, and will take place at the National Exhibition Centre in Birmingham. The combined event is expected to become Europe's leading annual safety and health exhibition and conference. This move follows the acquisition of Safety and Health at Work organisers' Paramount Publishing by Miller Freeman (UK) Limited last September.

[Issue 126 (June 1999)]

MOBILE TELECOMMS QUALITY

One of the industries which has made a great impact on businesses large and small over the past decade has been that of cellular mobile networks. Any industry investing heavily in new technology with unknown market potential in a severe competitive position is taking risks. To cope with a subsequent rapid expansion also requires sound management to maintain quality and customer satisfaction.

In order to investigate how this has been achieved *Quality Matters* visited one of the pioneering leaders of this relatively new industry in the UK, Vodafone, to see how the problems of Quality were addressed where no previous experience existed.

Some of the initial constraints still exist. These are for example; planning permission for base stations and antennae, which for technical reasons need to be in prominant locations, and the allocation of frequencies (a finite resource) to suit local demands, However, by providing Technical and Quality solutions many of these problems have been reduced.

For example, base station masts and antennae in sensitive environmental positions have been made to blend into their surroundings (see photograph) and so reduce planning objections, and the introduction of digital networks improves frequency usage.

Coverage

Radio coverage has always been a competitive battleground, and Vodafone pioneered the techniques of the 'Network Quality Survey'. This was initially a manual process in cars and on foot with calls assessed in strategic and troublesome areas; now it is applied on over 450 routes with 36000 calls undertaken by computer between 7am and 7pm in survey vans nationwide. (Now OFTEL use the same technique for assessing all networks). This is practical 'customer oriented' Quality as opposed to 'Prediction Coverage Maps'. It was this approach that revealed to the UK government that performance of the the network was restrained by frequency availability,

161

where commuter bottlenecks overloaded local base stations (e.g. M25 roadworks). Once additional appropriate frequencies had been allocated the mobile telephone industry rapidly expanded.

In 1997/98 Vodafone spent £320M improving coverage and infrastructure and spent £345M in 1998/99, increasing the number of base stations towards 5000.

Establishing Radio Industry Quality

Radio interference has always been a "pollutant" to the radio industry with the Radiocommunications Agency (RA – a division of the DTI) acting as guardian for the purity of the Radio Spectrum. The RA also acts as custodian for allocated licensed frequencies to radio users.

Before cellular radio the industry comprised of Private Mobile Radio (PMR) whose networks are closed to that user group e.g. emergency services, taxis, haulage distributors. The trade association for this group is the Federation of Communication Services (FCS) and the cellular networks joined the established FCS and their professional practices. However, when it was seen that cellular radio was in rapid expansion the RA, Vodafone, FCS, certification bodies and other industry organisations formulated and launched the Radio Quality Assurance Scheme (RQAS) in 1988 to provide a focus to promote good practice, with the RA as the secretariat.

Rapid expansion brings its own problems, particularly in a new industry. The first problems to be addressed by RQAS were for servicing and installation where new and often untrained technicians were employed by emerging support companies. The RQAS produced Codes of Practice which when implemented with BS 5750 (ISO 9000) provided membership certification for the Scheme. The FCS produced guideline documentation and lectures on how to implement the requirements. Vodafone, who had already used ISO 9000 as a management tool, developed the Codes of Practice to train their subcontractor Service Centres on specific relevant techniques and enabled them to attain RQAS membership. [Note they did not just tell them to comply! -Ed]

From this early application of ISO 9000 which Vodafone considered as the first step to a minimum level of quality in a much wider programme of Quality each associated Vodafone company including overseas in countries like Greece, Malta and Fiji is registered to ISO 9000 with a programme of continually improving standards of service.

ENVIRONMENTAL UPDATE

The UK's first ever 'Environment Week' took place from 5th to 11th June, with 5th June being declared 'World Environment Day'. The main event of the week in the UK was et '99, which took place at the NEC from 8th to 11th June and featured around 200 exhibitors, 30 seminar presentations, a half day conference hosted jointly by BSI and the CBI entitled 'Profiting from the Environment' and a talkback session featuring Minister for the Environment the Rt. Hon Michael Meacher MP hosted by former presenter of Radio 4's 'Today' programme, Peter Hobday.

The event was opened by Minister of State for Energy and Industry John Battle who highlighted the Government's desire to support the UK's environment industry and announced two new initiatives designed to help businesses to meet the challenges and seize the opportunities of sustainability. These consist of a joint project with Forum for the Future and BSI to develop a 'next generation' management system for sustainability and the development of a 'one-stop virtual shop' for businesses seeking advice and help with eco-efficiency activities within the UK. He also announced an allocation of additional funds to the DTI's International Technology Service and commented as follows:

"To maintain truly competitive UK companies can learn from examples of business practices, both at home and abroad. This means looking at leading overseas businesses for new ideas, technologies and management best practices and adopting and applying them wherever possible. This is why I am delighted to announce that we are committing £3.7 million this year to our International Technology Service (ITS) to help UK companies gain knowledge from overseas businesses. Supporting group missions, individual secondments, a team forging links with specific countries on behalf of British companies and an information service which highlights technology advances around the world, the ITS provides an invaluable service for UK companies".

Third Party Health and Safety Certification.

Environmental, Health and Safety Business Manager for LRQA, Tim Dowling, described the rationale behind the Occupational Health and Safety Assessment Specification (OHSAS) 18001 which was released in May and now has the backing of all of the UK's certification bodies. He explained how the prime purpose of the standard is to enable organisations to use risk assessment more effectively:

"In many organisations risk assessment has not been translated into management actions. Others have been managing the wrong risks as a result of assigning the wrong priorities".

This new standard, the speaker says, will address this gap, formalising the health and safety management systems which most organisations already have for legal reasons. The act of formalising it will then, he says, identify and prioritise risks in a way which will demand that the correct action will result.

The speaker argued the case for the standard on the grounds that it is systems based, challenging the information flows of organisations as data and decision making processes. In order to comply with the standard an organisation has to demonstrate that it is managing its key risks to rather than merely devising checklists or questions for specific hazards:

"A high proportion of accidents and occupational health problems are attributable to a lack of formal management systems and the standard is trying to address this, making organisations translate risk assessments into action plans to reduce the risk of major accidents".

A further benefit of the standard which was noted was the potential for its integration with quality and environmental management in order to create consistency and best practice. There is, for example, the potential for records, document control, training, auditing and procedures to become the responsibility of a single management systems manager.

The core of the standard consists of the following OH and S management system elements:

* OH and S policy (authorised by top management and incorporating a commitment to improving health and safety performance).

* Planning for hazard identification, risk assessment and risk control.

* Implementation and operation (including structure and responsibility, training, consultation and communication, document and data control, emergency preparedness and response).

* Checking and corrective action (including performance measurement and monitoring; handling and investigation of accidents, incidents and non-conformances; record management and auditing).

* Management review (top management sets own frequency for review of OH and S management system for continuing suitability, adequacy and effectiveness).

There are currently around 50 organisations certificated to the standard with a further 250 under contract. Organisations which are currently leading the way include British Sugar plc, at Wissington, Lucent Technologies Microelectronics (Thai) Limited, Denso Manufacturing (UK) Limited and Odebrecht Oil and Gas Services Limited. An accredited UK standard is expected to be published late next year along with the new ISO9000 standard.

[Issue 137 (June/July 2000)]

SAFETY AND HEALTH AT WORK 2000

This year's Safety and Health at Work Congress brought together two major shows, namely the Safety and Health at Work Exhibition and Conference previously held at Earls Court, and the Royal Society for the Prevention of Accidents (RosPA) Annual Congress which normally took place at the NEC. The National Exhibition Centre in Birmingham offered the capacity to combine the now single show with the other related events of IfSec (the UK's leading security exhibition), and Fire Expo.

Safety and Health at Work 2000 was held from 8th to 11th May and in addition to the approximately 300 exhibitors a full programme of seminars was held under the general subjects of 'Accepting the Leadership Challenge', 'Learning from Prevention Failure', 'Managing Risk on the Road', and 'Enhancing Health and Business Performance'.

A total of 16 papers was presented covering subjects such as 'Trades Unions as Occupational Safety and Health Champions', 'Future Strategy for Occupational Health -from Vision to Reality', 'Healthy, Happy and Here - reducing Stress and Absenteeism', and 'Setting and achieving Corporate Health Improvement Targets'.

The paper by Dr.David Giachardi, Director of Occupational Policy and Strategic Affairs for the Engineering Employers' Federation entitled 'Safety, Health and Competitiveness -Challenges facing the Board' is reviewed, along with the four papers from the 'Learning from Prevention Failure' session.

Challenges facing the Board

Dr. Giarchardi's paper argues that senior managers who rarely see the details of what happens on the shopfloor when things go wrong, sometimes need 'hard and frequently bloody evidence' to convince them, although concedes that 'we are probably past the days when such techniques are necessary' in the case of media sensitive multinationals. Many SMEs, however, remain 'ignorant of what is best practice in such fields as health and safety, and the basics of the law'.

165

He states that 'ensuring that safety is an item on the agenda of every management meeting does send messages to the rest of the organisation, provided those in the organisation know it is happening and explains the case for senior people making site visits 'to make it clear that the Board knows the safety record'. He then examines the relationship between continuous change and risk management, suggesting that change 'brings uncertainty and therefore increases risk, but that the key is to make risks manageable rather than resisting the change'.

No bones are made about the 'considerable effort' that is needed to be proactive rather than reactive.

' I find it difficult to separate good management and leadership from governance. If you have the first the second is irrelevant. If you do not have the first, using the mechanisms of governance to act as long stop is a very poor second best.

The key point is to get those who are actually running the business, whether it is the CEO of a multinational quoted company, or the proprietor of a family business whose idea of a shareholders' meeting is looking in the shaving or make-up mirror first thing in the morning, to realise what safety management and performance is all about'.

The author describes some of his personal experiences at Courtaulds where a major programme of training at shopfloor level was instigated in order to bring 'step function changes in the competence and capability of the workforce' and discusses the issue of motivation at Board level for improved safety performance:

'In a big plc it is essentially image –no company can live for long with a bad public image. A bad image causes you to lose customers, and local public support. It is rarely a direct financial issue, although there are a few exceptions. But unless HSE issues translate into a major financial problem, typically the City will not be interested. The most frequent examples would be financial issues relating to product safety or large scale and chronic occupational health issues, rather than routine occupational safety. But no Board likes adverse public relations, especially if it is a consumer related business or needs local community support for its "licence to operate"'.

'Increasingly big OEM suppliers are checking on whether their own supply chain is accredited to published environmental or quality standards. Rarely yet do these include safety, although as supply chains progressively concentrate, one can see examples of situations where big players are seeking reassurance that a major failure which might be safety related, and want reassurance about the positions of their suppliers and their ability to maintain supplies'.

In his conclusion Dr.Giarchardi is notably scathing of 'the blame culture which our politicians and media encourage'.

Learning from Prevention Failure.

The four papers in this session were entitled 'Review of Policy and Practice in High Performing Companies' by John Kingston of John Kingston Associates, 'A New Duty to Investigate' by Neville Higham, of the HSE's Policy Unit, 'Who's afraid of Woolf?' by Associate Professor of Civil Litigation at the College of Law Nigel Tomkins, and 'The Role of Insurers' by the Loss Prevention Council's Health and Safety Projects Manager Dr. Andrew Auty.

The first paper describes a 'key issue' project on Accident Investigation instigated by RosPA in 1998 and the discussions between experts and various 'key players' in the UK health and safety system which followed. Practical demonstrations of good practice were drawn from seven UK based organisations (CCG, Foster Wheeler Energy, Haden Young, Kelloggs, PowerGen, Scottish Hydro Electric, and Shell Expro UK):

'The majority of the organisations had a common approach to investigating incidents in different domains, that is, health, safety and environmental occurrences. However, whilst the collection and investigation arrangements (people, methods, scaling etc.) were the same, in some cases the information produced would be subject to different channels within the organisation for reporting and remedial measures. As well as the domain of loss, the level of risk was used to scale the investigation. In all but one instance, the companies used consequence to achieve this risk rating rather than consequence and likelihood together'.

'All of the companies put effort into investigating near misses (sometimes called near hits). Here the scaling by consequence was achieved by estimating the "worst credible outcome" of the occurrence. Amongst the companies PowerGen is distinctive in the effort and enthusiasm that has been invested in their near – hit programme at Cottam Power Station. This is subject to considerable discussion in the main report (published by RosPA in December 1999)'.

Only three of the companies used formal analytical methods (Fault-Tree Analysis), though all viewed investigation as 'yielding valuable information that is not obtained by other means', put effort into broadcasting lessons learned from investigations, and invested in tracking systems to ensure that recommendations are tracked through to completion:

'CCG proactively identify themes for health and safety promotion and use incident experiences to illustrate these (and provide additional credibility to the issues). Shell use a similar approach to this; identifying an accident each month to be worked up into a presentation pack (OHPs etc.) for supervisors to deliver and discuss with their teams. What is particularly distinctive – and this is true of other Shell initiatives for lesson learning – is the requirement not just to send a message but also to require the recipients to identify action points for their activities and locations. These action points are then tracked centrally'.

'Foster Wheeler also make imaginative use of investigations in contractor training. For example, the facts of a recent crane accident have been integrated into computer-based training packages for contractors visiting the FW site in Geel, Belgium, This serves as a further demonstration of accident data as a persuasive medium for risk communication. Kelloggs have developed a software system that allows incident information to be exchanged with different modules allowing recommendations to be tracked but also made subject to audit and risk assessment activities'.

The second paper (somewhat shorter) describes a Discussion Document published by the Health and Safety Commission (HSC) in November 1998 which proposed the introduction of an explicit duty to investigate accidents for inclusion in the Management of Health and Safety at Work Regulations 1999. This Discussion Document generated considerable interest and overall support for a change in the law which introduced 'a duty to take reasonable steps to investigate accidents, reportable diseases' and a duty 'to take the investigation findings into account in revising the risk assessment'. A draft Consultative Document has since been released by the HSE, the contents of which are briefly as follows:

* Proposed duty holder to be the person responsible for making a report under RIDDOR.

* Incidents that need to be investigated by the duty holder will be all injury accidents reportable under RIDDOR, all dangerous occurrences reportable under RIDDOR, and all diseases reportable under RIDDOR.

*Investigations to be carried out as soon as possible and in all circumstances within three days of the incident having to be reported.

*Records required proportionate to the scale of the incident and to the need to revise relevant risk assessments.

*Involvement of the workforce in the investigation process

The third paper considers changes to the litigation process along the lines proposed by Lord Woolf with the aim of achieving early liability decisions, early settlement, the avoidance of proceedings where possible and more efficient proceedings. It represents the first serious attempt to set effective and enforceable standards for the efficient conduct of pre-action litigation and has so far led to two protocols, namely the Pre-action Personal Injury Protocol and the Pre-action Clinical negligence Protocol. A third, the Pre-action Occupational Disease Protocol, is on its way. A key feature of these protocols is that they require a pre-action disclosure of documents and provide a means to obtain documents which should have been disclosed but weren't. 'Missing documents and you can expect adverse inference and a case that cannot be defended', the paper warns.

The last paper discusses EL insurance (insurance which indemnifies the employer against the cost of claims made for any personal injury to employees caused by the employer's negligence) and some of the current problems and trends associated with it:

'The idea behind this compulsory insurance is that the employee will have access to compensation no matter how negligent the employer is and no matter whether the employee is solvent or not. What concerns us in today's discussion is that the insurer cannot make any legally binding conditions that would nullify the policy. He cannot impose an excess. He cannot impose a requirement for HSE style risk assessments. He cannot insist on accident investigation. He cannot compel the insured to learn from their mistakes'.

'If a former insurer came to you (a newly appointed manager) and asks you to investigate an accident that happened three years ago, to a member of staff you've never met and whose colleagues have all left because your firm closed the relevant process two years ago, what would you do? With luck you would find a full investigation report filed under the heading "Woolf"'.

'Employers are increasingly recognising the value of mitigation services. However, finding a mechanism for financing them is not yet stabilised. Insurers are involved but the balance of risk retention versus risk transfer, policy clauses and reporting mechanisms are still evolving. Some would prefer a National Health Service role in this but private practice may pre-empt public policy'.

'Post Woolf all EL insurers would advise prompt and thorough investigation of accidents and to seek immediate advice on admission of liability and the potential for mitigation of loss. The practice of mitigation of harm is gaining ground and will continue to do so as more multi-factorial conditions are added to the duty list for employers. Mitigation is by its nature co-operative and consultative and therefore provides an opportunity to learn from mistakes and reduce the toll of ill health in the workforce'.

ISA 2000: THE SYSTEM FOR OCCUPATIONAL HEALTH AND SAFETY

Gower Publishing have announced the publication of two manuals (Mandatory Elements and Supplementary Elements) describing the International Safety Audit 2000 (ISA 2000) system for Occupational Health and Safety Management.

ISA 2000 contains a set of initiatives, comprising over 200 elements, which are categorized as either mandatory or supplementary. Volume One contains those mandatory elements which should be implemented as part of the occupational health and safety management system of any company. The mandatory elements have been selected to provide management controls against the general hazards encountered in all workplaces, large and small. As such they reflect minimum compliance with fundamental safety law.

Volume Two contains a large number of additional elements and for many companies it will be necessary to include several of these either because they already form part of the safety management system or because they are highly desirable additional controls which the companies may feel are essential to achieve broader based safety management systems.

The Introduction points out that the prime thrust of legislation in health and safety in the UK has changed in recent times with the onus now on employers to identify their own hazards and implement the necessary controls. The law no longer defines fully the legal requirements and it is no longer considered adequate to give a manager copies of the legislation and ask them to use it as a starting point for developing a management system. ISA2000, however, 'ensures that a formal management procedure is in place to guarantee full awareness of legal requirements and the implementation of the necessary controls'.

' During its design phase ISA2000 drew heavily from the legislation of the UK and Ireland. However, as the legislation in other countries follows the same general path, and makes broadly similar demands, the ISA2000 approach can be applied in any jurisdiction and is not tied to the legislation of any particular country'.

The 'A-J structure' is followed in recognition of the fact that 'the ISO9001 format is not the most practical structure to use when designing and setting up a management system', although integration with ISO9001 is considered. A cross-reference guide also facilitates compliance with OHSAS 18001, for which ISA2000 is recognised as one of the principal reference documents.

In relation to building a safety management system the text recommends the following:

'When you are considering all the possible options for health and safety controls you should remember the principle of multiple causes – errors are not caused by only one thing going wrong. Too often companies fall into the trap of concentrating their resources in a narrow field. It might seem a good idea to devote most of the resources to engineering solutions, for example. But if sufficient effort is not put into training, corrective action, preventive action, risk assessment and the like, then engineering solutions alone will not achieve the desired result.'

With regard to auditing the following is stated:

'In the audit there are only two possibilities for scoring: full score or zero. If the element is in place and working then the score is awarded. If not, no score is awarded. In that way auditor bias is almost eliminated, that is, there is virtually no qualitative aspect to the auditing.'

With regard to continual improvement, the manual states the following:

'The result of continual improvement should be seen sooner or later in a reduction in the effect of accidents and the resultant cost. Typically, a 40% improvement is achievable within a three year period. However, research by the International Labour Organisation shows that only comprehensive management systems, that is, those with all major issues addressed (as required by ISA 2000) succeed in achieving this improvement. Some safety management systems allow entire sections to be omitted, but the ILO research has shown that these cannot achieve the desired end result'.

The two volumes are (ISBN 0-566-08238-11 and ISBN 0-566 08239-X or ISBN 0-566-08254-3) from Gower Publishing Limited, Gower House, Croft Road, Aldershot, Hampshire GU11 3HR.Telephone: 01252331551.

Chapter Three

Business Excellence

Business Excellence, and the European Quality Award Scheme which accompanies it, has to be one of the greatest success stories of the 1990s. The need for a Model that could be applied across different cultures and boundaries, which businesses of all sizes could use to assess themselves, which could lead ultimately to a major award and which did not depend solely on compliance to a list of clauses was clearly recognised in 1988 when the European Foundation for Quality Management was first established. The European Quality Award was presented for the first time in 1992 by King Juan Carlos of Spain, and the UK Excellence Award followed in 1994, launched by the then Prime Minister John Major. In both cases the Award scheme mirrored that of the already established Malcolm Baldrige Award in the U.S., although differing in the detail.

Milestones which have occurred during the decade include the launch of the Public Sector Award in 1996, which was not won until 2000, and the launch of the Small Business Awards in the same year. In 2000 the Business Excellence Model underwent major revision with an emphasis on the need for continuous improvement, an innovation and learning component and the introduction of the RADAR system of assessment which bears some resemblance to the Plan-Do-Study-Act methodology familiar to most serious quality practitioners.

Whilst the Business Excellence Model has generally received less criticism than the more controversial ISO 9000, it has still had its critics as the following articles demonstrate.

RANK XEROX WIN EUROPEAN QUALITY AWARD

Rank Xerox have become the first recipient of Europe's highest quality accolade, The European Quality Award.

Managing Director Bernard Fournier was presented with the award by His Majesty King Juan Carlos of Spain, at the Palacio de Congress, Madrid on 15th October.

On receiving the award Mr. Fournier praised "the efforts of 28,000 Rank Xerox employees across Europe who, for eight years have increased customer satisfaction and regained market share by employing Quality principles and practices".

The company was selected to receive the Award from a short list of four, which included BOC Limited, Special Gases; Industries del SA-UBISA, and Milliken European Division, by a seven man Jury comprising of:

*Dr.J.F.A. de Soet, former President of KLM Airlines and Chairman of the Jury.

*G.L. Johansson, former Managing Director of AB Volvo, Sweden.

* Prof. Dr .H.G. Seghezzi of the University of St.Gallen, Switzerland.

* J. Negri, Director Human Resources and Quality, Caisse des Depots et Consignations, France.

* A.T.G. Rogers, Executive Director, I.C.I. (UK).

* M. Duffin, Corporate Vice-President Service and Quality, SGS Thomson Microelectronics, Italy.

Other awards presented included The European Quality Award for Media awarded to BBC Radio's 'In Business'; The European Quality Award for Doctoral Thesis awarded to Dr. Tim Schlange of University of St.Gallen; and The European Quality Award for Masters Thesis awarded to Simon Speller of the Middlesex University Business School.

BRITISH QUALITY AWARDS

The Annual British Quality Awards were announced at the Park Lane Hotel, London, on November 11th and this year's winners were aerospace manufacturers Short Brothers plc of Belfast 'for implementing Total Quality in products and processes involving all employees achieving a significant change in culture, resulting in continuous improvement and customer satisfaction' and the Small and Medium Cars Division of the Rover Group Limited 'for the significant and continuous progress made over the last four years in product quality, efficiency and people involvement, particularly against such a severe economic climate'.

The radiotherapy equipment manufacturer Varian Oncology Systems of Crawley, Sussex, received the Highly Commended Award 'for significant achievements towards the Varian Vision of Operational Excellence, particularly in the areas of customer satisfaction and employee participation in quality improvements.

The Awards were presented by President of the Board of Trade, Michael Heseltine MP.

[Issue 51 (March 1993)]

EUROPEAN QUALITY: THE AWARD WINNERS' STORY

This conference took place at The International Convention Centre, Birmingham, on the 11th and 12th February under the title 'Working Towards Excellence'. Delegates had the opportunity to hear at first hand the experiences of the top four companies in Europe in implementing Total Quality Management, and to pose their own questions with the help of the conference Moderator, former newscaster and television celebrity Jan Leeming, who in her introduction explained how she had 'watched and admired the progress made in quality' but expressed concern that 'too few have grasped the principles of Total Quality'.

B.O.C. Special Gases: Change is a Way of Life.

The first of the EQA presentations came from BOC Special Gases for whom two speakers, General Manager Steve Waldron and Personnel Manager Tim Hurdle, spoke on the subjects of leadership and people management.

Steve Waldron introduced BOC Special Gases as a company where change has become a way of life and TQM has provided a structural means of managing change.

The drivers for TQM were identified as being primarily survival, competitive threats, the fact that market leaders generally were now focusing heavily on quality for their survival, rising customer expectations (demand for higher specification products supplied to a higher level of quality), and pressure on prices with value for money being a key parameter.

It followed that the involvement of senior management at an early stage was essential, but whilst TQM is clearly 'fashionable' it was emphasised that those who 'retire early' were likely to be 'serious losers' i.e. they had to be committed and for the right reasons. 'Only embark on it if you are prepared to stay the course' was the message.

The BOC Group Corporate Vision was then displayed, which stated that:

'Success will be built on our absolute dedication to the satisfaction of our customers through constant innovation, operational efficiency, cost effectiveness and the talent of our people. We shall maintain our shareholders' support by outperforming the FT100 index'.

This Corporate Vision was found to be 'compatible in every respect' with the self-assessment model developed by the EFQM and in the remainder of his speech Mr. Waldron spoke of the need to lead by example and for senior managers to become visible practitioners:

'In BOC Special Gases the General Manager attends every trainee course to either open or close it. He also participates in quality improvement teams if he can make a contribution'.

He also spoke of the role of leadership in facilitating culture change by encouraging people to buy into TQM, since TQM can only function if every employee has the opportunity to participate and contribute:

'An upward flow of ideas will be created and with it an expectation that some interest will be shown and some action will be taken'.

Tim Hurdle focused on the company's human resources planning and on the opportunities presented to the company to improve its people management with the establishment of a new £20 million production facility at Immingham on Humberside. The 'people factor' will, he says, 'make or break any TQM initiative', and for the new site a number of significant HR innovations were developed, building on established strengths within the business.

Identification of core behavioural competences was key to this, stimulated by a fundamental belief that behaviours exhibited in an individual's performance can be strong predictors of future success.

External consultants assisted in the work of developing job competencies, whilst competency analysis based on a sample of employee interviews enabled a model of success based on superior performers' behavioural characteristics to be constructed.

Annual appraisal of employees enabled a sample frame of both superior and average performers to be obtained, against which the process of conducting behavioural event interviews could be undertaken. These were typically of two and a half to three hours' duration and undertaken by external consultants.

When the interviews were completed Job Competency Analysis was used to analyse the information to provide a model of all the behaviours, skills and attributes that were used in the jobs selected and to show how frequently they were used in each individual job.

'Distinguishing Competencies' were identified as those that separated the superior performers, whilst 'Threshold Competencies' that were important characteristics for the job, but didn't influence good or superior performance, were used to form generic job titles.'

The competency model generated from the analysis provided the basis for a detailed recruitment model used to select employees for the new site, whilst the behaviours that have been identified as significant are to be used as a benchmark for performance and development across Special Gases as a whole. The process was described as 'non-threatening and stimulating' and there were no objections reported from trades unions. Mr. Hurdle also described how self-managing work teams had been established at the new site, obviating the need to employ supervisors, with the help of the Quality Alert Institute in New York. The concept is said to place considerable emphasis on the need for a rigorous recruitment methodology, 'requires sensitive management control in order not to stifle group and individual initiative', and requires 'precise, visible performance measures' so that teams may effectively manage their own performance. Initial signs are said to be 'very promising'.

Industrias del Ubierna: TQC generates radical change.

The General Manager of Industrias del Ubierna, SA, UBISA, Jose Luis Martinez, told delegates that he had 'no secrets to tell' about the success of his company, just a story of hard work, perseverance, commitment and enjoyment.

Like many companies they faced a period of adversity in the early 1980s with 'low levels of activity with the attendant worsening in earnings' and in 1982 management decided to pursue Total Quality Control with the aim of creating a turnaround. Over the succeeding ten years 'radical change' was generated throughout the company.

In 1983 a 'Colour Lines' programme was introduced in which specific products and small families of similar products were mapped out from receipt of raw material to the completion of the finished product. For each Line a manual sets out, in very specific terms, the aim of the Line, the starting point, the human team involved, the product or products involved, the identification, the separation of qualities where relevant, the working method, the collection and processing of data, the maintenance of equipment, and the procedure for weekly meetings.

Each product-process is designated a different colour (hence the term 'Colour Line') and from a staff point of view the Lines 'amount to an organisation which is informal and flexible, yet integrated, made up of stable groups of employees in a given area, working as a team and with a high degree of autonomy, on the continuous improvement of activities, basing their actions on critical parameters of the process or product, and on the active participation of the staff to foster the integration of all the organisation's levels/departments'.

In 1985 a strategic chart was drawn up to act as 'a clear reference point for all the main fields in which efforts were to be concentrated', which was enhanced in 1988 to encompass 'permanent learning by all, elimination of waste and customer satisfaction'. This chart later became 'The Mission of UBISA' which speaks of 'learning constantly new and better ways to do things', taking an active part in implementing them without delay and, perhaps most importantly, 'detect and completely eliminate any kind of waste in processes and operations'. Policy Deployment translates the mission into concrete objectives for each year or three year period.

Since 1989 there has been an evolution towards an integrated Quality System in accordance with the requirements of ISO9004 with an implementation based on 'developing and turning to good account the Colour Lines manuals ,plus all the practices , procedures and habits connected with quality management that the use of those manuals had generated'. The principles originally applied solely to production have thus been extended to cover processes connected with areas such as equipment maintenance, administrative processes and management processes.

There are currently 17 'Colour Lines' which have involved around 80 per cent of the people since 1983 with 1627 meetings and 17, 032 actions resulting. The meetings, which are voluntary, had a 90 per cent attendance in 1992.

[*Quality Matters comments:* This presentation laid a great emphasis on the need to reduce waste as opposed to purely cutting costs, and the speaker placed great importance on the need to avoid confusion between processes and operations since this 'hinders efforts to concentrate on the former, identifying and eliminating the waste phenomena they contain'. It is concluded that only by focussing on waste elimination within a framework of overall investment can long term success be achieved, as success today is no guarantee of success tomorrow].

Milliken Opportunity for Improvement

The Milliken Opportunity for Improvement story began in 1987 when the 'phenomenal success' of the modular carpet business left 'insufficient time to serve customers as thèy expected'. Firefighting was the norm, there was no control over customer problems or queries, the term 'complaint' was perceived to be negative, and there was no logging or measurement of customer comments. This clearly had to change and Shirley Garstang, Team Leader for Milliken European Division at Wigan (Lancashire) described to delegates how the company dramatically changed its attitudinal approach to customer satisfaction, initially through the training of Admin Associates in the methods of detecting the perceptions of customer dissatisfaction as expressed, for example, through telephone conversations.

This starting point was followed through with action to record every obvious and not-so-obvious registration of customer dissatisfaction and a meeting with the company's major dealers at which a request was made for them to 'dramatically increase' their numbers of ' complaints.' The number received from each dealer was recorded and a reward system for the main Contributors to Improvement was established.

Customer 'complaints' became termed 'Milliken Opportunities for Improvement' (MOFIs) which are dealt with by a specific person:

"Complaints don't mean someone is bad but rather that there is a chance to improve".

The next step was the establishment of a unified system of measurement to facilitate agreement on customer perceptions and on how they are interpreted. Dealer profiles were introduced on a weekly basis so that Chief Executives could examine for themselves how Milliken was performing in terms of criteria set by them. These 'forced the company to be honest with itself ' and ' incredible improvements' in delivery performance were reported as a direct consequence of this honesty.

The company was not, however, purely content with the measurement of actual complaints since the analysis of 'near misses' was also important in order to provide a motivation against firefighting.

By plotting the number of 'complaints' against the number of orders that each individual dealer was placing, the company was able to quickly gain an insight into the number of problems the company was giving them relative to their total contribution to the total business. This enabled the pinpointing of any deterioration in performance with specific customers. Prior to this every month Admin Associates had to break off to examine queries, most notably on invoices, as a consequence of the company's lack of control. Now, the company, 'can resolve any invoice query in minutes' which has had 'a major impact' on the problem of overdue invoices.

[This can be contrasted with other companies- including some BS5750/ISO9000 registered ones- where the Accounts Department s consider themselves to be 'outside the quality system'- Ed]

Other benefits of MOFI include the 'virtual elimination' of non value added time, which has liberated time to develop customer relationships. Staff visit customers to achieve closer contact, and to analyse the plan for further process improvement.

The presentation by Ms. Garstang was then complemented by a presentation on 'people satisfaction' by Ms. Sarah Ashworth, Senior Sales Territory Manager, which reinforced the company's strong commitment towards fostering a positive attitude throughout all education within the company:

We believe that the freedom to achieve is of prime importance, and the working environment is constantly being improved toward that goal. Within this environment people are motivated (self-motivated in most cases) to negotiate and accept Stretch Goals; the achievement of these goals further fuels the self-motivation process: people have self-esteem and do not consider themselves merely payroll numbers'.

Milliken's policy is therefore one of training Associates at all levels to do their jobs; and then making education available to all in order to bring out talent for the future.

Both internal and external courses are offered. As an example of courses which have had an enthusiastic recommendation from Associates the speaker cited The Psychology of Achievement course, whilst The Dale Carnegie Human Relations and Public Speaking course 'proved invaluable'.

Ms. Ashworth spoke of the need of everyone 'to feel wanted, useful and important' and spoke highly of her company in enabling her to find capabilities within herself which she 'never dreamed were possible'. Thus, whilst the company has a distinct commitment to embrace state-of-the-art technology in all operations it is also ready to accept the fact that its people are its greatest asset, as witnessed by the fact that the Associate of the Month (elected by peer review) is the only person to have a reserved parking space i.e. not even the Managing Director has one!

Strong emphasis was placed on the need to drive out fear within the organisation, as advocated by Dr. W. Edwards Deming, and through a policy of making openness the norm an 'entrepreneurial spirit has evolved which has, to a large extent, removed the fear of failure'.

The fear of failure was highlighted particularly for having the effect of stifling innovation and creativity and by eliminating it, the minds of employees have been able to be constantly focused on trying new ideas and exploring new frontiers.

To encourage the development of new ideas an 'Opportunity for Improvement' system has been devised whereby all Associates are encouraged to submit ideas about any factor which is thought to potentially improve any process. There is no great financial reward, but the line manager has to acknowledge submission within 24 hours and team leaders may not reject an OFI without giving factual reasons.

In some of Milliken's locations most of the OFIs have already been actioned by the contributors, highlighting the level of Cross Functional teamwork in the decision making process, and the level of knowledge and empowerment of Associates.

[Issue 52 (April 1993)]

Rank Xerox: Action driven by Leadership through Quality

The presentations by the award winning company Rank Xerox were made by the Managing Director Mr. Bernard Fournier and the Director of Quality and Customer Satisfaction, Mr. Rafael Florez.

Mr. Fournier began by congratulating the EFQM for their achievements to date emphasising how, thanks to their efforts, quality was now becoming an issue for debate in more and more organisations. Then, turning to his own company, he emphasised how effective document creation and management is being increasingly seen as a key to productivity, and how Rank Xerox had recognised its opportunities for diversification, away from the mere production of copiers into such areas as publishing systems and complete document management.

He explained that in his company action had been driven by leadership through quality with an underlying goal of achieving 100 per cent customer satisfaction.

Following the Japanese success in the microwave and automobile industries it became increasingly evident in the 1980s that soon they would be targeting the area of office automation and an issue of survival was fast developing. The company, which had a product trying to find a customer, with nine times as many suppliers and ten times the number of finished product rejects than their Japanese counterparts, had to change and fast.

In 1984 the need for change was recognised and a Leadership Through Quality strategy and process was devised which would 'engage the hearts and minds of all the people, not just a few trouble-shooters'.

Training began at the top and focused primarily on six areas: recognition and reward, process and tools, transition management, training, communications and management behaviour. Implementation followed throughout the whole company irrespective of function or department, with the aim of achieving quality in the whole way that the company worked, i.e. not just product improvement. The concept of 'in the Line by the Line' served to reinforce the fact that all quality processes and tools, whilst facilitated initially by a quality support group, are owned, implemented, used and improved by Line Managers and their staff .This is said to be 'how a quality strategy can remain vibrant and vital to a company instead faltering after an initial implementation'.

By benchmarking with themselves, sharing best practices with the other 22 Rank Xerox companies in Europe, the company has learned how to combat the 'not invented here syndrome' and Mr. Florez described how three surveys were used:

(i)   how the company is performing 90 days after the customer has taken delivery

(ii)   an annual survey inviting six comments on customer satisfaction

(iii)   an anonymous survey asking customers who their top supplier is in a specific target market.

If a customer is unhappy in the first three years of ownership the company undertakes to replace the product free of charge and this was described as a 'call for arms' to all employees to strive towards 100 per cent customer satisfaction. It was noted that in 1992 only 0.5 per cent of the company's 500,000+ customers actually exercised this right.

Two key processes that are said to have emerged as being extremely powerful in moving the company toward Total Quality are the company's Policy Deployment process and the company's self-assessment process, entitled Business Excellence Certification.

Policy Deployment operationalises the company's strategic goals with an annual process of objective setting, identification of Vital Few (Pareto) or breakthrough actions, planning and review. Objective setting is cascaded and incorporates two way feedback for resource planning. Every employee has a 'blue book' which formally communicates the company's goals and objectives for the year along with those for each Unit function. Also communicated is his/her own objectives against the four Rank Xerox business priorities of customer satisfaction, employee motivation and satisfaction, market share and return on assets. These are measured and root cause analysis used, through management review, to initiate action for improvement.

Business Excellence Certification is a self-assessment process whereby each operating unit is able to measure itself against six performance criteria validated by an assessor from another unit. Improvement plans and actions are agreed and certification is annual by means of a Rank Xerox assessor. It is described as 'a coaching exercise by management, not inspection by quality', although each year the bar is raised and certification is purposely made more difficult to achieve. The criteria are based on a combination of the Deming and Baldrige Award programmes and the company's own evolved self-assessment. It is close to the EFQM Model and each key element reduces to around 40 sub-elements.

Bernard Fournier concluded with a summary of what the company had achieved over the past ten years and made particular reference to the company's unified Health and Safety Standard and achievements in exceeding the Dupont industry benchmark of 0.5 incidents per 200 khrs. He also cited the receipt of the coveted German Blue Angel environmental award for six of their machines and copier paper in 1991; which included recycling of around half of the company's spares, that when re-made, are 'as good as new'. These achievements were combined with a 99 per cent reduction in defects, and a supplier base reduced from 5,000 to around 400.

These business results are further supported by vendor relations statistics which show how the company has progressed from being rated as top vendor in 9 out of 75 business sectors in 1989 to being first in 62 last year (1992), whilst customer satisfaction has increased from 71 per cent to 97 per cent in the same period.

At the end it was acknowledged that whilst the company had entered the EQA scheme with the objective of winning, the preparation process had been 'invaluable' in enabling the company to determine ways of making improvement that 'otherwise may never have come to light'.

Questions and Answers

At the conclusion of each speech the presenters were given a short interview by the Moderator (Jan Leeming). This was then followed with a more general question session thrown open to the floor in which other speakers were invited to voice their comments also, along with other representatives of the winning companies.

Steve Waldron and Tim Hurdle (BOC Special Gases) were asked whether people actually enjoyed having no supervisor and Tim Hurdle replied to this by emphasising the fact that it was a different way of working in which line managers had to be seen to be supportive with coaching and counselling.

This required patience. When asked whether he felt it had made people more responsible he replied with a definite yes.

They were asked whether the core competencies covered senior management and Tim Hurdle explained how core competency analysis across board members and Directors is taking place at another site.

Steve Waldron explained how TQM had been applied to the whole business unit simultaneously rather than priorities made in specific areas at the beginning and pointed to the particular benefits of TQM as a means of managing change in an organisation where product life cycles are short.

Jose Martinez (Industrias del Ubierna SA, UBISA) was asked about the effect of Policy Deployment on his organisation and replied by stating its potential to realise goals that were previously considered impossible and to improve ownership through having a global vision. He was then asked whether he could give some recommendations for a small company starting out and advised that, so long as they were committed, they should start, even if some mistakes are made, and learn from these. He warned of the dangers of spending too much time talking about starting, as this was a mistake that he felt his company had made, and suggested those that are hesitating 'could be ducking responsibility'.

He was asked whether he felt that where employees are more involved and treated as individuals they tended to be more dedicated, and to this the answer was a definite yes, with the additional comment that people perceive very clearly if they are trusted. There's no-one, he said, who couldn't change, although some move more quickly than others. On the issue of middle management resistance he said that once they realise that the new culture is much better than the old they tend to follow well.

The speakers from Milliken were asked whether people minded having nothing to aspire to and Sarah Ashworth replied by emphasising that everyone at Milliken had a sense of working to the common good [there is local history of civic pride in this region-Ed]. Jan Leeming then asked whether they felt that the ideas brought out in the speech could be applied in the service industries as well as in manufacturing and the combined view was a unanimous yes with Ms. Ashworth adding that they could be applied anywhere. Particular reference was later made to flowcharting which Shirley Garstang said 'forced people to look at processes to see if they added value'. Clive Jeanes (European Managing Director of Milliken) explained how, by using flowcharting, the company had reduced the length of time taken to process an invoice from 220 hours to 4, and emphasized that the technique was just as applicable to administration as to manufacturing.

The speakers were later asked whether they felt that what they had learned at school had adequately prepared them for industry , and how they felt that the education system could be changed to greater assist people to work in a

Total Quality environment. Sarah Ashworth replied by saying that she did not feel that school education had adequately prepared her. She described how she had been 'timid and shy' at the start, but 'saw great changes in herself' as a result of following the Dale Carnegie course. Shirley Garstang endorsed this, adding that Milliken had been 'amazing', giving her 'heart for creativity'. They don't shoot you for trying and failing, she said. Roger Emms, (Pursuit of Excellence Director Europe for Milliken) then questioned the education authorities' approach to TQM and called on the EFQM to investigate possibilities in this area.

A leading representative of Britain's petrochemical industry asked about the role of ISO9000 in the total quality process and Ms.Garstang explained how working to the standard had helped the company to document its procedures, and had been 'a super training tool for new people':

"Things stopped being in people's heads. New people could see things instead of waiting two to three years to feel part of it."

Roger Emms pointed out that all of Milliken's European plants are currently registered to ISO9000, which he described as a 'meal ticket' to exist in business in Europe today. He saw the standard as 'a platform on which to build', although he clearly felt that the scope for improvement within ISO9000 registration was small, and he appeared to support the Japanese principle, where the TQM process itself is effectively the standard, and ISO 9000 is non-existent.

Bernard Fournier and Rafael Florez were asked what the hardest decisions implementing Total Quality were. Bernard Fournier referred in his answer to the investment decisions, such as the £5billion investment in business certification, and those where there had been a distinct conflict between the short and long term issues. He admitted that sometimes one has to make short term decisions that one doesn't like, whilst 'pushing aside' some staff that do not want to make the quality commitment 'can sometimes be hard'.

A delegate questioned the rumour that Rank Xerox had had to hire some 50 to 60 staff for the Award process. Mr. Fournier confirmed that it had taken six people 8 to 9 months, at around £50,000 per person.

They were later asked what lies beyond benchmarking, now that they had been recognised as the best in Europe, and to this Mr. Fournier warned against the tendency of merely seeking to imitate the benchmark. If you are first in an area then you are into Kaizen, or continuous improvement, and the key is then to have a closed process for solving problems and weaknesses. Rafael Florez then pointed out that 'you're never the best – customer surveys will always highlight areas for improvement'.

EUROPEAN QUALITY AWARDS 1994

Third win for Britain

The European Quality Awards for 1994 were presented in Amsterdam on 20th October and for the third successive year a British based company has been awarded the premier award. The recipient this year was Mr. Alistair Kelly, Managing Director of Design to Distribution (D2D), a wholly owned subsidiary of computer manufacturing giant ICL, based at Kidsgrove, near Stoke on Trent. The company, which produces over a million printed circuit boards (pcbs) a year and serves as the principal manufacturing, supply and logistics arm of ICL, won the Award for ' a very strong performance on all five enablers, satisfaction of customers and people in the organisation' On receiving the award from EC Commission President Jacques Delors, Mr.Kelly urged more companies to consider entering for this prestigious award, praising it as an important milestone on his company's journey" and as "the best bit of free consultancy you'll ever get".

The accolade of winning the European Quality Award represents the culmination of ten years of sustained effort. This began with a focus on conformance quality which has subsequently been enhanced to include advanced benchmarking practices to monitor processes against ICL corporate strategic quality models as well as against customers and suppliers. The system measures quality progress in relation to the EFQM Model and application of Deming principles to the development of lasting and mutually beneficial partnerships. A powerful computerised quality modelling system (QMS) serves as an important tool in the achievement of optimum performance levels.

The company recognised that it could not be successful merely by selling to its parent company and in this highly competitive market the company had no option but to compete. This it has done, as evidenced by the company's current turnover of £290 million in 1993 from 2,000 employees engaged on five sites. This compares with a turnover of £100 million from seven sites in 1980, when they functioned as an operating division of ICL.

Transition from a cost centre to an independent subsidiary resulted in a fundamental culture change, in which change has become away of life. As Mr. Kelly says:

"The moment we stop changing is the minute we start to die"

In common with many other successful organisations D2D has opted to become a 'single status' organisation with open planning which has facilitated re-organisation where this has been required. He emphasized:

"There are no sanctuaries where people can hide themselves away and appear inaccessible."

No-one at D2D receives a guaranteed rise each year as all employees are required to agree objectives for the year with their supervisor, these objectives being designed to complement the objectives of the business. Employees are appraised and rewarded in relation to the objectives which are noted to be self-imposed, and agreed in advance i.e. not set from above in the form of targets. Upward (subordinate) appraisal is also being practised, as is peer appraisal, whereby, for example, an engineer can appraise a finance manager at the same level within the organisation.

In its effort to compete the company has set itself the objective of becoming' Europe's leading electronics manufacturing company in its chosen markets by providing products and services worldwide that exceed customers' expectations'. This is to be achieved by 'providing competitive systems, products and services which fully meet customers' requirements first time , on time, every time '. In this quest it has been greatly aided by a strategic win-win partnership with Sun Microsystems, the company's first non ICL customer, whilst feedback from suppliers and customers is used to assess pricing policies , refine delivery mechanisms and forecast technology directions.

Leadership is demonstrated through the Managing Director talking to all employees face to face in small groups in an informal interactive manner, and everyone is trained in the art of self-assessment.

Self-assessment against the EQA Model in 1992 is noted to have 'produced changes in the critical process list that clearly moved the company's priorities from materials procurement, testing and inspection into product and service delivery, process improvement and people satisfaction, supplier partnerships and cost reduction, self-assessment, recognition and deployment', and is now a major constituent in the company's process reviews.

Process owners agree measures with customers, and utilise scorecards where appropriate to highlight variances between performance and requirements. Where agreement cannot be reached it may be included in the agenda of a monthly management review meeting for discussion at director level. Process owners are then empowered to stop processes at any stage should the agreed control limits be unattained. Where there are changes to a process these are formally communicated by way of a supplier-customer change procedure. This is logged on a database which contains all engineering drawings and specifications. Where new production processes are deployed, ISO9000 trained assessors are commonly deployed to test and validate these as part of a rigorous evaluation and audit to ensure that the new process can support the product concerned.

The company's commitment to environmental issues is evidenced by its total elimination of CFCs and other ozone depleting chemicals from its production processes as well as initiatives to reduce car journeys through video conferencing and to recycle all redundant components. The company emphasises its consideration of product disposal in an environmentally friendly manner as part of its manufacturing service and is currently piloting the British Standard BS7750 for environmental systems.

Previous awards which the company has received include the Management Today Best Factory Award in 1989, the British Quality Award in 1990, the Michelin National Quality Circle Awards in 1991 and 1992, and a European Quality Prize in 1993. In addition the company has also achieved an Outstanding Performance Award from Sun Microsystems, an Investor In People Award and of course ISO9001 and ISO9002.

In the future they hope to expand their electronics manufacturing business to achieve a' $600 million target by 1996.

The D2D story is continued in more detail in the special commemorative issue of 'European Quality'.

[Issue 72 (December 1994)]

THE 1994 UK QUALITY AWARDS

This month the Awards theme is continued with the presentation of the first of the new UK Quality Awards, by the Prime Minister (the Rt.Hon. John Major), at London's prestigious Park Lane Hilton Hotel on 30th November.

The Awards, which unlike the European Awards, are of 'equal status', were presented to two companies: Rover Group plc and TNT Express (UK) Limited after selection from a short list of five which included Avis Rent A Car Limited, BT Northern Ireland and ICL Customer Service Division.

In presenting the Awards the Prime Minister paid tribute to the British Quality Foundation which he said "has raised the flag of excellence" whilst Rover and TNT have "met the tests of profitability , performance, quality and value for money". He said:

"The UK Quality Award has put the spotlight this year on two outstanding companies. I am delighted that next year public sector bodies will be able to compete as well. Britain's success depends on excellence in the public and private sectors alike. I look forward to seeing many more winners of the UK Quality Award".

Hostess Jan Leeming added in her speech that the 1995 Award was also to be open for the first time to the voluntary sectors whilst BQF President and Chairman Sir Denys Henderson paid tribute to the team of voluntary assessors and the jury (Tony Rodgers, Executive Director of ZENECA; Sarah Brown, Head of Companies Division, DTI; Clive Jeanes; John King ,Vice Chairman of Leeds Permanent Building Society; Edwards Roberts, Chairman and M.D. of Heath Springs Ltd.; and Professor John Oakland).

On receiving the Award Rover Group Chairman John Towers said:

"This is a momentous and very satisfactory occasion for us, but the Award really goes to the 35,000 who work for us because without them it wouldn't happen".

Managing Director of TNT Express, Alan Jones, added:

"In a decade where quality is the key to success this is the Award to cherish most. It is an enormous endorsement of the UK transport industry."

Some regret was expressed, however, at the fact that no companies in the Small Enterprise category (under 250 employees) achieved the necessary level of attainment and larger companies were urged "to help and support small companies and colleagues to drive forward the quality message".

[Issue 75 (March 1995)]

UK QUALITY AWARD: THE WINNER'S STORY

In a unique presentation organised by The Quality Forum at the Heathrow Marriott Hotel on March 3rd, one of the winners (TNT Express) described their experiences of preparing for the Award. The presentation was unusual in that it was made jointly by the assessed company, represented by Quality Manager Nigel Turner, and a member of the team which was directly responsible for site visiting them, Quality Consultant for IBM Mr. Lawrence Hanney.

Mr. Hanney began the presentation by comparing some of the attributes of the Award with those of ISO9000, noting that whilst the value added by ISO9000 is limited to preventive action, systems and procedures and some benefits of consultancy, the UK Quality Award offers the potential for much wider 'across the board' improvement with assessment not merely confined to a binary compliance/non-compliance verdict. He then emphasised the separation of enablers from results which differentiates the Award from the US Baldrige Award, and makes it "a cleaner model". He remarked on how a Baldrige examiner on visiting IBM had been particularly impressed by the company's initiative to deploy noise meters in order to address the 'Impact on Society' criterion of the European Quality Award (from which the UK Award is derived), the requirements of which are explicit in contrast to Baldrige.

Mr. Turner followed with a brief description of the path which TNT has followed since 1988 when their Project 2000, which consisted primarily of questionnaires sent to employees and customers, jolted the company into becoming more customer focused. They changed, for example, from measuring the number of failed deliveries to measuring the number if on-time deliveries, a move which the speaker said "sounded trivial but changed the company's whole focus".

The company sought certification to BS5750 in 1989 and achieved it in 1990 for their parcels division. Others, such as Newsfast, followed shortly afterwards and in 1992 the company signed up to the newly created EFQM. Self-assessment to the European Quality Award Model later the same year enabled the company "to gain a measure of its quality maturity" and focus on the objective of continuous improvement. Further improvement was also achieved through alignment and internal benchmarking with TNT in Germany.

The company became a founder member of the BQF last year and with previous self-assessment experiences decided to submit the application document for the new UK Award. The speaker described this as "no mean feat", taking for him the best part of two and a half months (400 man hours) to complete information gathering on nine categories and twenty nine sub-criteria across the whole organisation. It was, he said, 'quite a challenge', and whilst the seventy five pages of the document 'sounded vast' he admitted that towards the end he had been 'desperate for space'. Twenty four copies of the document were eventually produced at a total cost of around £2,500, which he described as 'money well spent', and 'a valuable source of reference' for which there was high demand within the company.

Mr .Hanney described the submission as 'very attractive and packed with information' and explained how the assessors had read the document twice, the second reading being used to highlight significant points prior to scoring each section in accordance with the BQF 'Blue card' . He then explained how, with a score of over 500 points, the assessors concluded that this was 'a pretty good company' which the Award jury duly recommended for a site visit.

With over 60 sites and 7,000 employees the amount of planning which the company could undertake for site visits was clearly limited, and some surprises were certain to be sprung, and they were.

The company was noted for its use of league tables to rank both depot performance and the performance of sales personnel. Mr. Turner argued that these produce 'good healthy rivalry between locations', a fact which the assessors were keen to ascertain. Starting therefore with Wellingborough, the depot which at the time was at the top of the table, the assessors questioned sales personnel on their views towards league tables to examine whether or not a demotivating effect existed. The evidence suggested that this was not the case in this company. "People helped if someone was not successful", said Mr. Hanney. With sponsorship of the local football team adding to positive evidence of involvement in the community and hence impact on society, a key area for which the jury had specifically sought more information, the overall conclusion was that Wellingborough "was friendly and took real pride in their achievements".

The Parcels Distribution Centre at Atherstone, which was noted to be operative only at night, was also site visited. Here there was evidence of technical innovation, demonstrated this time by operators who had devised an original truck lighting system to improve safety in goods handling operations at night. Also there was business innovation in the field of truck maintenance, with the founding of TNT Truckcare which opened the already established TNT truck maintenance department to the free market. Night executives were interviewed, notably on the subject of redundancies, and it was concluded that they "cared for people when business requirements change" whilst "real problems were honestly addressed". Drivers were then questioned randomly in the cafeteria, particularly on attitudes towards sub-contract drivers relative to TNT employees. The replies suggested that there was equal treatment of both, which served to indicate that as well as being a tightly managed company TNT was also people oriented, which was seen as being important to the assessors.

The next stop was Alan Jones, the Chief Executive, who, it was found, answered his own phone, within three rings without filtering, which gave rise to the saying:

"If you want good fast food go to McDonalds. If you want good clothing go to Marks and Spencers. If you want to know about answering the phone ring TNT".

The finance Director of course had to be interviewed as this team of assessors 'didn't want to be the team that blessed a company that went bust', and after examination of the company's internal quality audit records and complaints, which showed that all depots had received an annual audit and all non-compliances had been followed through, the assessment was almost complete. "Universal enthusiasm" had been evident throughout and where there was doubt, for example, in customer complaints, it was invariably interpreted to the customer's advantage. A surprise , however, was sprung : a visit to Cannock.

Cannock was a depot which had not featured well in the company's league tables, although it was not bottom. It was singled out and the depot manager "was taken by surprise" Once there the assessors found the sales team "friendly and enthusiastic", and although the drivers varied and one refused to talk, the assessors remained confident that nothing had been hidden and the establishment was "open and honest throughout".

In his conclusion Mr. Hannay described the experience of assessing TNT as one of the most exhausting but enjoyable weeks that he had had, with the most difficult aspect being "to stay objective". He looks forward to "doing it again in '95".

By coincidence the TNT group also received the Investors In People Award in November 1994 and following the presentation Mr. Turner was asked about how he viewed this award, and whether his company still identified non-conformances with their by now routine BS5750 assessments. He replied that one is 'never perfect' and confirmed that ISO9000 non-conformances still arose but 'in ever decreasing numbers'. The IIP for its part was viewed as 'a subset of the UK Model' which, with a little work, addresses well the people management and people satisfaction criteria.

[Issue 82 (October 1995)]

EUROPEAN QUALITY AWARDS 1995

The 1995 European Quality Awards were presented on 27th September at The International Conference Centre Berlin, under the title of 'Achieving Business Excellence'.

Around 980 participants attended the two day event in which the acting President of the European Council of Ministers, the Spanish Minister for Industry and Energy Sr. Juan M. Eguiagaray Ucelay, presented two Awards, the European Quality Award itself which was awarded to Texas Instruments Europe, and an EQA Prize Award which was awarded to 1994 joint UK Quality Award Winner TNT Express.

The Awards were received respectively by John Scarisbrick, President of TI Europe and Alan Jones, Managing Director of TNT Express. The jury praised TI Europe, for "strong effective process management" and "involvement and commitment to Total Quality throughout the management of the company" which was "quite obvious", whilst TNT Express were complimented for their "powerful ten point strategy, openness, enthusiasm and open culture" and "a visible role from the CEO that made the company come through".

There were five finalists for this year's Awards, each of which is profiled in the special Souvenir Issue of 'European Quality'. The remaining three finalists were printed board assembly manufacturers Alcatel Austria, Turkish telecoms manufacturer Northern Electric Telekommunikasyou AS (formed from a joint venture between the Turkish PTT and Northern Telecom Canada in1967) and British Telecom Operator Services, a comparatively new company formed in 1990 to provide telephone number information and operator assistance on behalf of BT.

Achieving Excellence at TI Europe

The 1995 European Quality Award Winner TI Europe is renowned as a leading manufacturer of semiconductors worldwide. Entering the semiconductor business in 1952 the parent company Texas Instruments has enjoyed an enviable reputation for quality and innovation which has included the invention of the integrated circuit in 1958, the development of the first electronic hand held calculator, invention of the single chip microprocessor and latterly a Digital Micromirror Device (DMD) which forms the basis for a Digital Light Processing (DLP) system which is currently under development for projection displays and hardcopy applications. This last invention only this year earned its inventor, physicist and TI Fellow Dr. Larry Hornbeck, the prestigious Eduard Rhein Foundation Technology Award, an annual Award for outstanding achievement in research and/or development in the field of radio, television and information technology, presented by the Rhein Foundation which is based in Mayen, Germany.

First established in Bedford, England in 1956 TI Europe currently operates in 16 countries with manufacturing operations in five. Some 5,500 employees have helped earn the company $1.6 billion in 1994 and the prestigious 1995 European Semiconductor Vendor of the Year Award from Dataquest, a leading market research and consultancy company which presents the Award annually.

Quality has been a cornerstone of the TI philosophy for over 30 years and TI Europe may thus be regarded as an 'old stager' ranking alongside the world's best. The profile of the company in European Quality highlights the training of TI's management by Dr. W. Edwards Deming and others during the 1980s and the 'Quality Policy to achieve Business Excellence' which was adopted worldwide and disseminated to all employees via a cascade mechanism involving quality steering teams. Significant investment in process technology, new product development and capacity expansion followed in the late 1980s which has included the construction of five new semiconductor fabrication facilities.

The EFQM self assessment model was introduced in 1993 and following the first self-assessment new leadership initiatives were devised in 1994 which included the formation of a high level Quality Team of twelve representing the twelve principal European organisations. In the same year there was major restructuring from national organisations to pan-European business centres:

'The new European management structure is based entirely on the criteria of the European model, with eight Quality Steering teams and the overall Strategic Leadership Team each taking responsibility for one criterion. This ensures maximum synergy and provides a clear, common focus on business excellence across the organisation'.

This restructuring is noted to have been 'very effective very quickly' with overhead costs being substantially reduced and market share being increased significantly.

In order to maintain close links with the customer senior TI Europe executives meet the management of its top 40 customers at least twice a year, whilst the company's European Customer Satisfaction Survey is used to assess external criteria such as product information support, sales support, order scheduling and delivery and quality and reliability, including internal measures such as administrative errors in order processing and fulfilment and the number of partial shipments.

Considerable importance is also attached to the need to achieve balance between harnessing the creative potential of individuals and making the most of teamworking.

John Scarisbrick says:

"Adapting the EFQM Model has not only changed the way we are structured and operate; more importantly, it has helped us turn the company around significantly. Throughout TI Europe we have created a common goal to improve and be the best. Winning the Award is recognition of this ,and is one more milestone on our journey of continuous business improvement".

TNT Express: moving on

With the process of assessment for the UK Quality Award closely resembling that already adopted for the European Quality Award the experience of this assessment without question served the company well in its bid to win the European Award. It follows that pursuit of the European Quality Award would be a logical next step for a company which was, and still is, fully aware that it cannot and must not stand still and must always move on to ever increasing standards of excellence.

The company TNT Express (UK) Limited is recognised as the current market leader in Britain for time sensitive logistics. It was formed in 1978 when TNT Limited purchased the three day parcels delivery company Inter County Express which at the time employed 600 and had revenues of the order of £6 million per annum. This compares with a current workforce of 8,000 and revenues in excess of £7 million a week, which makes for an impressive record in times when job creation has been sorely needed in the UK.

The EFQM company profile of TNT makes reference to a company that 'thrives on internal competition', yet at the same time 'gives all employees clear and regular signals that it is genuinely concerned for their welfare and development'.

'Every part of the order process, from booking to invoicing, is an exercise in collective responsibility. Staff are encouraged to switch roles and responsibilities. Managers are team players; "passing the buck" is not an option.'

The company's ability to use internal competition constructively is without question one of the keys to their success, and stems from the company's never ending commitment to customer service which MD Alan Jones firmly acknowledges "only comes about through people". A careful and perhaps unique balance has therefore been struck between the use of internal competition as a motivator, and the all-important principle of removing fear, enhanced at least in part through their promotion and recruitment strategies. Mr. Jones says:

"People in our organisation know that if they work hard and produce good results they will be promoted. We passionately believe in the principle of promoting from within".

The company is noted for its policy of recruiting staff for their enthusiasm [in contrast to many other UK firms -Ed], and further for its careful application of process mapping techniques that ensure that the correct person is selected for the correct job [again a major problem for many companies - Ed].

This strategy has enabled a company in which 'managers are never too busy to talk about quality' to clearly profit at the expense of 'hierarchical traditionalists' that have not kept pace with change" It has been complemented with innovative customer relationships, for example with co-winner of the 1994 UK Quality Award Rover Group for whom they have designed, built and operated a 200,000 square foot just-in-time component supply facility:

'TNT operates a national collection scheme, picking up parts from Rover Group suppliers, that gives the auto maker significant price, cost and supply chain benefits. By collecting the goods itself, TNT is able to improve delivery frequency to once or twice a day; in the past some suppliers delivered only once or twice a week'.

The philosophy of internal competition which has assisted rather than destroyed the company's success might best be summed up as a philosophy of 'beating personal bests' and the EFQM profile of TNT devotes a complete section to this aspect of TNT's approach. This describes, amongst other things, the 'Seven Star' system which rewards depots financially for achieving seven key targets and the 'five fives' system which initially set a target for finance of 5.5 debtor weeks with overdue debt no more than 5% of the total. After being achieved this was modified to incorporate a 'bull's eye' of five debtor weeks, and no overdue debt. The same section pays tribute to the company's 'air of collective ownership' and many will surely agree that there is a subtle difference between the TNT approach to competition and that which is being followed by a typical company.

Podium Discussion.

A lively podium discussion was chaired by EFQM President Karel Vinck, which raised a number of important points. Perhaps most important of these was the increasing need for management to think in terms of transformation, not just incremental change, and end for good the blame culture that all too often is the norm. Far too much time was, according to the panel, spent on measuring failure.

It was suggested that the tendency of management "to communicate in a formalised and uninspiring way had to change and that smart management will institute change when they are performing well rather than waiting until they have sunk into "the relegation zone'. Leadership was about "restlessness for excellence" and this had to be "communicated with passion".

[Issue 84 (December 1995)]

UK QUALITY AWARDS 1995

The 1995 UK Quality Awards were presented at London's prestigious Grosvenor House Hotel in Park Lane on 21st November. This year it was won outright by ICL High Performance Technology (HPT) of Gorton, Manchester.

The Award was presented by the Rt.Hon. Ian Lang MP, President of the Board of Trade, to the Managing Director Mr. Tom Hinchliffe at the annual BQF gala dinner which was attended by over 1,000 of the country's most senior industrialists.

Hostess Jan Leeming opened the proceedings with a video replay of last year's inaugural UK Quality Award Dinner whilst BQF President Sir Denys Henderson expressed his pleasure at the large turnout which he said "underlines the growing influence of the Foundation".

The winning company, which employs 1,000, is profiled in the November Issue of UK Quality, the Journal of the B.Q.F. As part of the giant ICL group (taken over in 1990 by Fujitstu of Japan) HPT is a mainframe supplier for corporate computer systems. It supplies these to financial services, local & central governments, public utilities and retail markets.

The problems faced by the computer industry over the past decade have been the variability of hardware and software quality, which caused customer dissatisfaction. HPT recognised that solutions to these problems and subsequent consistency of application were critical to survival.

The Award and performance has been made in a declining market and under adverse economic conditions. HPT consider that their planning and involvement of people in self assessment are key to their success. They used the EFQM self-assessment award criteria. Barry Hopewell says:

"The primary aim of the project was improving the business. So the exercise was labelled as a business excellence activity rather than a quality initiative".

HPT was complimented particularly for its "clear and consistent leadership" and on receiving the Award Mr. Hinchliffe said:

"This is the most. significant award we have ever won. Nothing equals the UK's premier award for business excellence. This Award marks the last twelve years' commitment to quality improvement."

There were four short listed companies, the other three being Mortgage Express Holdings Limited, Royal Mail Anglia and The Benefits Agency of Springburn and Cumbernauld.

Mortgage Express, a 300 strong company within the TSB Group, tried a new management approach when on the brink of disaster in 1991. They put their faith in Total Quality and in 1994 was back in profit. TQM co-ordinator Maxine Gabriel explained:

"The strength of our total quality drive lies in the involvement of all our people. The number one priority is to be honest staff have to believe in what you are saying to them".

Mortgage Express Holdings Managing Director Keith Greenough says "Our story is unusual; from threatened extinction to a turnaround through Total Quality. The story shows how Total Quality applies in all circumstances".

Another unusual story in the short list was Springburn and Cumbernauld Benefits Agency. From a low morale and civil service bureaucratic environment, they transformed into an integrated operating unit (by 'shot-gun marriage of two districts') using devolved decision making to provide a customer service rather than an administrative activity.

Royal Mail Anglia graduated from their own 'Customer First' invented approach after reorganisation from the Post Office, to a recognisable Quality method in a 'Business Excellence Model' using Investors in People.

[Issue 82 (October 1995)]

NEW EUROPEAN QUALITY AWARD FOR THE PUBLIC SECTOR

The EFQM have announced that a new European Quality Award for the
Public Sector is to be awarded from next year. Three new self-assessment
Guides have been produced to support the Award Scheme covering the fields
of Education, Healthcare and Local and Central Government . These
describe the key implications for public sector organisations for the nine
criteria of the EFQM Model and explain various alternative approaches
which may be adopted for the self-assessment process. Amongst other things
they say:

*'Self-assessment and improvement should address the management role and
how it interfaces with the political role. The Model does not seek to assess
the "quality" of political policies, but rather the management of excellence
within the organisation'.*

All organisations funded wholly or partly by central or local government
with the aim of delivering public services on a not for profit basis are
eligible, with the exception of political organisations and organisations that
work closely with government and are actively involved in the development
of political policies.

[Issue 95 (November 1996)]

EUROPEAN QUALITY AWARDS 1996

The European Quality Awards were presented this year in Edinburgh on
22nd October at a ceremony which has become an established highlight of
the European business calendar. Around 1500 attended the ceremony at
Edinburgh's Royal Highland Centre, the traditional venue for Scotland's
Royal Highland Show, whilst around 1200 attended the accompanying
conference in Edinburgh's newly built International Conference Centre.

The event was introduced by the well known Scottish investigative journalist
Louise Tait, whilst the Awards themselves were presented by Rank Xerox
Chief Executive Bernard Fournier, who was also the Chairman of the jurors
for 1996.

There were seven companies short-listed for the Awards this year, namely
Brisa (Bridgestone Sabachi Tire Co. SA.) and NETAS from Turkey, Elias
SA (Greek subsidiary of Unilever), and UK based companies, British
Telecom, National Westminster Life Assurance Limited, and TNT Express
(UK) Limited. From these a total of four were selected to receive Awards:
Brisa, NETAS, British Telecom and TNT Express (UK).

Profiles of all seven finalists are given in the special Awards edition of European Quality along with a 'Judges overview' by Bernard Fournier, and details of this year's Doctoral Thesis Award ('Function and use of Quality Management Models for the Introductory Path of Total Quality Management by Dr. Christian Malorny of the Technical University of Berlin, and Masters Thesis Award ('Total Quality Leadership, the Future Leaders in Quality Organisations ,) by Heine Zahill Larsen of Arthur Andersen Business Consulting and Anders Norgard of TERMA Electronik and the Aarhus Business School in Denmark.)

The Quality Scotland Awards were presented alongside the European Quality Awards and featured three winners : Vesuvius (UK) Limited of Newmilns , Ayrshire; TSB Homeloans of Glasgow; and the Inland Revenue Accounts Office at Cumbernauld.

The Road to Excellence at Brisa

Brisa is Turkey's largest tyre manufacturer with an annual turnover of around $275 million. Its headquarters are in Istanbul whilst the manufacturing plant itself is located at Izmet, some 70 miles east of Istanbul on 880,000 square metres of land of which 210,000 square metres are covered. With a production capacity of some 5.3 million tyres per year, which are sold principally to automotive manufacturers and retailers in 40 countries, this makes the Brisa plant one of the largest tyre production facilities in the world located under one roof.

 The company began as Lassa back in 1974 when it was established by the Turkish Sabachi group, but later changed its name in 1988 when it entered into a joint venture with the Japanese Bridgestone Corporation. This year was not an easy one for the company, as the profile article 'On the road to excellence' in European Quality points out, which quotes former Brisa President and now Board Member Hazim Kantarci:

"In 1988 we had a 23 day strike. In 1990 we had a 109 day strike. Two consecutive periods of collective bargaining ended in strikes. During the last period, we decided we needed a complete transformation, from confrontation to co-operation ".

The early part of the Profile conjures up an image of hell in which a Turkish tyre factory 'would run a Siberian salt mine close, second in any list of undesirable places', but as one reads on it becomes clear that 'nothing could be further from the truth' in present day Brisa. It highlights the extensive leisure facilities which would no doubt be the envy of many British companies (pool, gym and games areas open and free to staff, and their families), the 'state-of -the-art machinery , products that are at the leading edge', testing laboratories that 'would not be out of place in advanced pharmaceutical institutions' and safety and environmental standards that 'match Japan'.

Hazim Kantarci escorted seven top union officials to Bridgestone in Japan which 'had not experienced conflict nor strikes for 45 years and the 'attitudinal breakthrough' which later transpired:

'Brisa workers positively revel in the challenge of making better tyres in cleaner surroundings. The benefits of having fewer accidents speak for themselves. Brisa has embraced total productive maintenance practices, which empower line workers to routinely check, report faults and repair machinery in a proactive and holistic way to avoid downtime and boost production standards.'

In his speech to the Edinburgh Forum Mr.Kantarci elaborated further on this describing how the will to change on part of both labour and management led to "a totally different era of industrial relations" which was "based on mutual trust, open communication and co-operation for the benefits of both the company and the by the employees". He explained:

"After establishing this very positive working atmosphere, we cultivated total quality management systems with the full support of the union and the great enthusiasm of our workers. The brains, the hands, and the hearts of 1300 plus employees who were physically doing the job were mobilised with continuous improvement and participation leading to a record high number of quality circle solution teams and total productive maintenance groups".

This "sense of belonging and clear understanding that only successful companies could provide continuous benefits for their employees" was later to prove critical when Turkey's economy took a turn for the worse and the company's survival was once more at stake:

"The solidarity of the company and the employees turned out to be our greatest shield against the serious fiscal crisis which our country faced at the beginning of 1994 during which the Turkish Lira was devalued by 163 per cent in one day and the overnight interest rates sky-rocketed to 1000 per cent, immediately followed by a severe stagnation. Like most companies in Turkey, Brisa had to decrease production sharply. However, we were one of the few companies who did not lay off any employees and used the idle time for intensive training. The motto 'We are the Company' was so strong and well assimilated by the workforce that they themselves asked for a suspension of a part of their income for a certain period of time".

In 1995 Brisa joined the EFQM and gained certification to ISO9001 by BVQi, as well as BS7750 certification. They were also the top scoring supplier for Turkey's leading automotive group.

This year they have enhanced their certification by becoming only the second company in Europe to gain ISO/DIS 14001. At the same time they have won a string of awards including the First Technology Development

Award given by the Istanbul Chamber of Commerce, the Environmental Protection Award (a national award presented by the Istanbul Chamber of Industry), the Green Chimney Award (a local award presented by the heavily industrialised region Kocaelis Chamber of Industry), and of course now the coveted European Quality Award.

Brisa have won the European Quality Award as a first time applicant, demonstrating that this feat is quite achievable, and currently have around one hundred employees, including all managers, trained as internal assessors. The judges praised Brisa for ' persistence, excellence, across all nine criteria of the Model, an outstanding approach with regard to the management of people, and outstanding results in terms of the satisfaction of the people employed'.

The European Quality Prize Winners

As previously mentioned there were three European Quality Prize winners this year in addition to the Award winner. Two of these were British i.e. BT and TNT Express (UK)

The Profile article in the Awards edition of European Quality entitled 'Round the Clock Commitment' pays tribute to TNT's 'absolute commitment to the customer' which is 'instilled in every one of the company's 8,000 employees', its effective leadership which 'helps employees work to a shared vision not a set of rules', and its communication which is 'the company's raison d'etre':

'Employees from across the company are encouraged to interact and overcome problems together. There are no invisible barriers and the organisation has one of the most accessible management teams you could hope to meet'.

The company's business results are highlighted (a 20 per cent rise in turnover in 1995 which compares with an industry average of just 8 per cent, a return on capital of 48.9 per cent before tax, increased market share, and a record which is described as 'outstanding'):

'Seventeen of the top 20 TNT customers have traded for four or more years and TNT Logistics retained every contract which came up for renewal in the past twelve months'.

In looking to the future the article describes how the company's benchmarking is under further development, how experiments with the aerodynamic properties of commercial vehicles could save European industry up to £2 billion a year, and how TNT Express (UK) could realise 'its greatest challenge' to become Britain's second postal carrier.

The judges commended TNT Express for 'strong leadership and sound policy and strategy, tight and effective management of resources and high levels of customer satisfaction'.

The other British European Quality Prize Winner, BT, might well have scooped the Public Sector Award, launched for the first time this year had it been a public sector organisation. In the event, unfortunately this Award was not presented as none of the Public Sector applicants were deemed to have scored a sufficient number of points to become a Finalist, a fact which led Bernard Fournier to express "slight disappointment" on behalf of the judges.

British Telecom entered the private sector in 1984 and the Profile article 'It's good to listen' describes how as 'one of the UK's most important national assets' it is challenging both its customers and its employees 'to make a compelling , and fundamental re-appraisal of what they should expect from a Telecommunications service provider' and is 'redefining the nature of its business in the light of new technological possibilities'.

The Profile describes how self-assessment was first introduced in 1991 and has since become part of the BT strategic planning process, whilst two way communications at every level of the organisation have helped to maintain morale over a traumatic period in which the workforce has declined by 45 per cent from 245,000 in 1990 to its current level of 130,000:

'Sir Peter Bonfield (formerly of ICL and appointed Chief Executive of BT in January 1996) uses his chief executive's roadshows to emphasise his aim to make BT more innovative, flexible and responsive by driving responsibility and accountability down the organisation. The introduction in 1996 of "Trading Units" -BT's internal market of self-contained businesses with profit and loss accountability -signifies perhaps the company's biggest culture change to date'.

Currently BT is challenging its managers to focus company resources on the areas of highest impact in terms of profitability, customer service and performance breakthroughs. BT has introduced 'Matrix Management' an information management infrastructure which includes commercial agreements between customers and suppliers within BT's internal market, to provide commercial performance measurement for the new approach.

The Profile concludes with an outline of how wide BT is seeking to become more interdependent with the help of an employee attitude survey which led to 5,500 local improvement action plans being carried out last year.

The judges commended British Telecom for 'its long term commitment to TQM, well defined human resources strategy, and perceived positive impact on society'.

The third European Quality Prize Winner, NETAS, was established in 1967 as a joint venture between the Turkish PTT (now Turk Telecom) and Northern Telecom Limited of Canada (Nortel). It provides digital central office and rural switching systems, packet data networks, transmission systems, PBXs, and telephone sets (including GSM, power equipment, and multi-layer PCBs) to meet the communication needs of telephone operating companies and private institutions with total solutions. It has a broad customer base in some 20 countries. Its revenues totalled $159 million in 1995 with exports accounting for $34 million. Last year they won the Turkish National Quality Award and were a European Quality Award Finalist.

The article 'Communicating total quality' describes NETAS as 'one of an elite group of organisations dedicated to enlightened management, business and social ethics', whose results 'are a barometer for the business community and visible evidence that quality pays dividends'. It explains the impact which Alcatel and Siemens had when they entered the Turkish market in the late 1980s and how NETAS weathered the storm in 1994:

'While 1994 manufacturing profits plummeted to a 2 per cent operating profit on turnover of $110 million, NETAS generated cash from investments and long term contract income, maintained a positive cash balance and achieved a net profit of $83.5 million'.

The company is noted for its 'extended enterprise ' philosophy which is seen to be 'an important competitive advantage in time to market terms':

'Unlike many manufacturers who have de-skilled in many areas as an inevitable result of outsourcing, NETAS has developed a wide range of in-house skills which are key to flexible manufacturing. It makes state-of-the-art printed circuit boards, for example, and buys in only when expedient from long term suppliers with whom it has strong links'.

Of particular interest is the company's Rand D facility (the largest private Rand D lab in Turkey) which receives around 8 per cent of the company's revenue, employs some 300 engineers and enables 60 per cent of the company's sales to be generated from its own designed products. The Application Specific Integrated Circuit (ASIC) for example, was designed in house, whilst the CAD/CAM capabilities and software design environment are indicative a high potential for technical and scientific innovation:

'We are developing software for Nortel and our software exports reached $11 million in 1995. Today software ownership is very important in telecommunications where 70 to 80 per cent of the value and functionality lies'.

Also noteworthy are the company's environmental achievements (first in the electronics sector to eliminate the CFC-113 solvent from its manufacturing operations in 1991), and the demanding targets which the company has set for itself with regard to its impact on society for the year 2000:

*to reduce total pollutant releases to the environment by 50 per cent, from 57 to 28.5 tons.

*to reduce all solid non hazardous waste for disposal by 50 per cent, from 670.5 to 335 tons.

*to reduce paper purchases by 70 per cent from 10 million to 3 million sheets.

*to improve overall energy efficiency by 20 per cent.

The judges commended NETAS for 'a clear Total Quality culture right through the organisation and very strong linkage from Policy and Strategy through critical processes to Business Results.

The Quality Scotland Awards.

The three Quality Scotland Award winners are not profiled in the special Awards edition of European Quality, although the article 'Missionary Goals' provides an informative account of the Quality Scotland Awards of which there are currently four, presented respectively for Manufacturing, Service, The Public Sector and the Smaller Enterprise(under 250 full-time employees). The latter award, like the EFQM Public Sector award did not attract any applicants with a sufficiently high score to merit the Award, and so was not presented, although B-Mat Limited, manufacturer of roll containers, dairy carts, pallet converters and steel shelving, based in Glenrothes, did receive 'Highly Commended' in this category.

Vesuvius UK Limited, part of the Cookson Group (a British based multi-national which currently dominates the world market in the supply of pouring refractories to the steel industry) collected the Manufacturing Award. They were commended by the assessors, headed by Vice President of Worldwide Manufacturing and Logistics for Digital Equipment Scotland John McClelland, for being 'a well focused company with management and staff united in a common purpose with clear ideas on strategy and methods'.

In the business for over 30 years, Vesuvius currently employ around 300 employees and have a turnover of around $30 million. Recognised as an Investor In People since 1994 they are currently moving toward the provision of a complete service to the steel industry, with the help of British Steel Teesside, with whom they are co-operating in the management and use of refractories at British Steel's Continuous Casting Plant. They have an impressive long-staying record of technological innovation which includes, for example, the pioneering of isostatic pressing to produce refractory tubes and stoppers, which has become the industry accepted method for producing alumina graphite refractories.

TSB Homeloans were the recipient of the Service Sector Award and were commended as 'a company which was established from day one using the principles of TQM and which has a pervasive quality culture at all levels within the organisation'.

Known as 'the mortgage factory' for the TSB Group they have 290 employees responsible for servicing the customers of some 1050 TSB branches. They also have a portfolio of £8.4 billion and administer around 278,000 customer accounts. TSB Homeloans were 'Highly Commended' in the 1995 Quality Scotland Awards and have a well established internal awards scheme which has a monthly budget, although the awards are made when merited. Any member of staff may act as a nominator, with the recipient receiving a written testimony of the recognition coupled with a small prize the value of which is up to £15. In addition the General Manager awards his 'Big a' each year from amongst various winners that have been nominated by the staff .

Finally, the Public Sector Award was presented to the Inland Revenue Accounts Office, Cumbernauld, which was commended for 'vigorous leadership and commitment evident in a consistent quality approach'.

The Office banks and accounts for tax and national insurance contributions from taxpayers in six regions. In the last financial year they handled around one and a half million telephone calls and dealt with over a million letters. It is one of just two such offices in the UK and employs just over 1000 employees who handle money of the order of £75 billion a year. They have no direct competitor for the service they provide, although many non-core aspects of their business are becoming increasingly subject to market testing.

They became the first division of the Treasury to achieve Investors In People in 1994 and joined the Quality Scotland Foundation in March 1995. They have a strong teamworking initiative which has included the establishment of some18 Customer Service Improvement Groups which cover all business areas and include employees from all Pay Banks.

Quality measurement changed from retrospective inspection to 'in-flight' prevention and now 18 Individual Business Units conduct self-assessment with the objective of producing their own Quality Improvement Plans. In addition a High Level Business Unit performs self-assessment at corporate level based on the information supplied by the Individual Business Unit.

UK QUALITY AWARDS 1996

The 1996 UK Quality Awards for Business Excellence were presented on 3rd December at a special Royal Gala Dinner which attracted a record number (over 1,000) attendees. The Awards were presented by HRH The Princess Royal in her capacity as President of the Princess Royal Trust for Carers with the assistance of this year's host, newscaster and journalist Trevor McDonald, and the President of the BQF Sir Denys Henderson.

There were two joint winners this year, Ulster Carpet Mills, who were also short listed for this year's European Quality Award, and Mortgage Express who are based at New Barnet and were short listed for the UK Quality Award last year. These two winners were selected from a shortlist of seven by a jury headed by Clive Jeanes, former European Quality Award Winner with Milliken.

Ulster Carpet Mills' Pattern of Excellence

Ulster Carpet Mills was founded in 1938 as a family business which it remains to this day. It employs around 760 staff at Castleisland in Portadown where it has played a positive role in helping to create a harmonious and successful business climate in one of northern Ireland's most troubled areas. It specialises in the manufacture of high quality Wilton and Axminster carpets , having become the second largest manufacturer of the latter in the world. They have a turnover of approximately £35 million and profits of around £3.1 million.

The company has a reputation for innovation having pioneered the application of the high speed electronic control of looms in the 1970s. It has focused highly on quality since then, introducing quality circles in 1983, achieving BS5750 in 1986,introducing TQM in 1989, preparing for and winning the Northern Ireland Quality Award in 1991, and introducing self-assessment in 1992. There has been a strong emphasis on teamwork with some 300 quality improvement teams being formed since 1989.

There is a flexible working week policy which helps to compensate for the uneven distribution of workloads during the course of the year.

Management commitment is demonstrated by the fact that there are currently seven senior managers who between them share responsibility for all nine elements of the Business Excellence Model, whilst an 'employee of the month' scheme affords employees other than senior managers or directors the opportunity to recognise the efforts of their colleagues. The winner of this receives a ten days all expenses paid visit to the company's South African plant during which five days are spent learning on the factory floor.

Employees also benefit from a 10 per cent annual share of the company's profits.

The judges commended Ulster Carpet Mills for "its open and honest culture, persistent thirst for learning throughout the workforce and a quality strategy which has resulted in impressive bottom line results". In the December issue of UK Quality, Company Chairman Edward Wilson is quoted as follows:

"What we have been doing is similar to the Japanese philosophy of taking the long-term view. That is one of the freedoms of being a privately owned company. The excellence model supports the long-term and we are using it to drive improvement across the business".

Mortgage Express: back from the Brink

Back from the brink for the second year, Mortgage Express has advanced along its journey to excellence over the last twelve months to convert its shortlisted status into winning status at this year's Awards. It employs around 280 at New Barnet and has profits of around £38 million, which compares with a loss of some £70 million three years ago. Its specialism is in the field of assisting those who have special mortgage needs (those with limited or negative equity, self-employed people, those on contract work and those considering investments in property). This stems from an overall strategy which is based on the targeting of niche sectors of the mortgage market which are inadequately or poorly served by the industry as a whole.

During 1993 the company adopted a policy of remaining close to its customers and working closely with them to understand and solve their payment problems. This reaped dividends with fewer customers than forecast removing their custom, including around 5.000 households which would otherwise have very likely have had their homes repossessed. This brought the company much needed time from its parent company, TSB Bank, (who in 1991 planned to wind the business down), in which it was able to demonstrate its capabilities.

There is a strong emphasis on training with each employee having a guaranteed minimum of five days a year for training and development whilst a 'quality time system' provides each employee with a minimum of two hours a month for improvement activities. Around a third of the workforce is engaged in project work in addition to their regular duties whilst some 10 per cent of employees are engaged in formal further education courses funded by the company. This approach has helped Mortgage Express to enact some 4,000 process improvements over the last two years, which works out at around six ideas per person per year.

The judges commended Mortgage Express for "its high level of innovation and creativity", "demonstrable improvements in business efficiency", and " a highly structured approach to process management which was considered to be world class".

In UK Quality Managing Director Keith Greenough is quoted as follows:

"I used to think that we had made total quality and the use of the model central to our mission just to create an energy, to give us a sense of being, of something to strive for. More recently I have come to think that it is deeper than that. You have to focus on business excellence if you are going to survive, whoever you are -I don't think our situation is unique at all. You may be at the cliff edge in some other organisations and you don't know it. The attitude of mind that we have pursued and we will continue to pursue is one of always assuming that you are up against it and we have to keep stretching ourselves because no-one has a God-given right to a customer base".

Other Award Finalists

The five other Award Finalists were BT (Northern Ireland) of Belfast, Griffin Credit Services of Worthing, Lawson Mardon Packaging of Sutton-in-Ashfield, National Westminster Life Assurance of Bristol and Nortel of London. Each of these are profiled in the December 1996 Issue of *UK Quality* along with the two winners and The Princess Royal Trust for Carers. The latter is working to improve the quality of life of the UK's estimated 6.8 million carers for whom HRH The Princess Royal, in her award speech, made a particular plea for the development of a way to provide excellent service.

Self-assessment in Europe: A Report on Current Practice

One 'Breakout Session' which proved to be especially popular with delegates was 'First Steps to implementing the EFQM Model for Business Excellence'. This featured Professor John Oakland, of the University of Bradford Management Centre, who described some of the research which the Centre has undertaken into the status of self-assessment in Europe and the benefits that it has brought.

The research involved the despatch of questionnaires to a targeted sample of EFQM and BQF members which yielded a 70 per cent response rate (151 questionnaire respondents), supported with 36 in-depth case studies in 11 countries and 10 industrial sectors. Within the sample top management had responsibility for self-assessment in 90 per cent of cases, whilst just under three quarters of the sample were considering self-assessment on an annual basis.

Results from the research showed that the highest usage of self-assessment occurred in the financial services industry, which was the second largest industry surveyed, whilst the top four reasons for starting self-assessment were, in order of importance:

*to provide a driver for continuous improvement

*to identify areas for improvement

*to increase awareness of Total Quality

*to increase commitment of line managers to Total Quality

The paper shows the mean and the mode for the reasons for undertaking self-assessment. This enables the reader to compare the popularity of the top four reasons with the less popular reasons of 'competing for a national or international award', 'winning a national or international award', and 'competitors using self-assessment', The mean, for example, of the top reason (to provide a driver for continuous improvement) is 4.48 with a mode of 5, whilst for the least popular reason (competitors using self-assessment) it is 1.06 and the mode is zero.

The objectives which were most effectively met were, in decreasing order of importance to respondents:

*identified areas for improvement

*obtained a base-line measure of the organisation

*identified strengths

*assessed value of self-assessment

*increased line management involvement in continuous improvement

*increased employee involvement in continuous improvement

A total of fifteen benefits of self-assessment are listed, the top six of which, in decreasing order of importance to the respondents were:

*identified areas for improvement

*provided a focus for continuous improvement

*increased customer focus

*increased 'top team' awareness of Continuous Improvement

*increased organisational awareness of continuous improvement *increased visibility of improvement efforts/ initiatives

The third of these benefits (increased customer focus) is noteworthy as it was not one of the original reasons given for starting self-assessment, yet it was identified as a benefit by 82% of the respondents with 66% rating it as 'extremely important'. The follow through case studies supported this finding with enabler results linkages being seen to have a direct positive bearing on customer satisfaction.

The new SME Award

New for 1997 is the Small and Medium Sized Enterprise Award for independent organisations and parts of larger organisations with fewer than 250 employees. The Award criteria cover the same essential business excellence elements as the Model for larger organisations (with the same nine box structure), although some of the definitions and descriptions have been modified and the criteria are basically simpler with fewer component parts. Criterion One (Leadership) has, for example, just two clauses instead of four, whilst Criterion Three (People Management) has two clauses instead of six. On the 'results' side Criterion Eight (Impact on Society) is addressed by a single clause i.e. what results the organisation is achieving in satisfying the needs and expectations of the community in which it is located', in place of the two separate clauses required to be addressed by the larger organisations (evidence of society's perception of the organisation and of additional measurements of the organisation's impact on society).

As regards the application process a 'Cascade System' whereby in order to apply for the Award The SME will first apply for their own National Quality Award (in their own language). This Application will then be scored according to the rules and model of their own National Award and be evaluated by assessors from their own country. The National Quality Organisation will then invite up to four of their best applicants, applying nationally over the last three years, to apply at European level. They will then be required to submit an Application Document of up to 35 A4 pages in English to the EFQM.

It is intended that there will be separate categories of the Award for independently owned organisations and for SMEs that are 25 per cent owned by one or more other organisations. In either case the applying organisation must be run as a complete business or independent business unit. A committee will be established to arbitrate on this in due course if the need arises.

Using Technology for Self-assessment

No quality conference would be complete these days without some mention of self-assessment and the Business Excellence Model. What has been of interest recently, however , has been the deployment of innovative technology in the application. It is perhaps appropriate therefore that at a major event such as the IMS Summer School, a paper should be presented under the 'Technology' heading which looks at a novel approach to self-assessment.

The paper was entitled 'Using Technology to lever the Knowledge and Wisdom of your People through Self-assessment using the Business Excellence Model' by Jeff Earl. He is a Director of Option Technologies (a successful and profitable global company offering meeting support services, sales and training to top corporations, government departments and public utilities) and was supported by a highly interactive presentation with audience participation demonstrating how *OptionFinder* (a tried and tested portable wireless-keypad based group decision support system) may be used to facilitate the self-assessment process:

'In conjunction with EFQM members, Option Technologies Limited has developed an OptionFinder template for the self-assessment process following the guidelines of the EQA Model. This template is included with every OptionFinder system and has been used by a number of EFQM member organisations in Europe. Some have developed their own personalised model, incorporating appropriate questions and language to suit their organisational needs and culture. Some use single axis questions with bar chart feedback to measure current performance and others use a two dimensional graph'.

The paper describes the two dimensional approach and then explains the training that is available for both the use and modification of the template and facilitation of the process:

'Under each of the five "Enabler" criteria are a set of questions on the sub-criteria. For each of these questions the participants are asked to assess their organisation, division, workgroup etc., as defined by the Facilitator, on their approach and deployment'.

Participants may be assigned to sub-groups according to job function, location, areas of responsibility, etc. Participants may be in more than one sub-group, e.g. the Finance Director may be in both Finance Dept. and Senior Management sub-groups. This allows the responses to be reviewed for variations, pin-pointing where improvement activity is best focused. Assessments gathered over a number of sessions can be consolidated to provide a company-wide, or representative sample view, viewable by sub-group classification'.

'The sub-criteria are presented one by one with the results displayed immediately. Discussion follows the display of the results, from which opportunities or improvement are identified and recorded for evaluation. This is done once the self-assessment has been completed when responsibility and time frames for action can be assigned using a more open style of OptionFinder process.'

Any question can be re-taken after discussion if the group wish. Results may be printed immediately or as a separate exercise later. Each question is presented on-screen and the group respond with their opinions through the individual as an x-y graph and the "score" they have awarded for each question is recorded and can be entered into a spreadsheet to calculate the self-assessment score against the section weightings in the EQA model.

There are further OptionFinder modules to help organisations work through Customer Satisfaction, People Satisfaction, Leadership etc. issues at the next level of detail. All are freely available to OptionFinder customers and full training is provided. The models are also used in the Pilot Workshops offered as a service by Option Technologies Limited and its associates'.

The paper concludes with a list of some 36 organisations that have adopted OptionFinder and a case study of one of them:

'Barclays first encountered OptionFinder through networking with the corporate quality team from ICL, the UK based computer maker that has provided winners of the European and the UK Quality Awards. At the time ICL was using the system in improving customer relations. Barclays had identified the need for a decision support tool which would enable it to cascade the self-assessment process through many staff levels in a repeatable way. As well as achieving consistency Barclays aimed to go beyond identifying issues and take workshop participants closer to the action planning process. Of the systems it considered OptionFinder appeared to give the most dynamic capability for displaying evaluation scores in a choice of graphic formats and for inputting potential action points for immediate discussion and evaluation'.

The topics in the agenda are presented on the public screen through the notebook computer but in addition to the sub-items for discussion which the facilitator will have prepared in advance, others can be added during the course of the meeting. For example, since one aim of the self-assessment workshop is to define and agree action plans, ideas can be captured as they arise simply by entering them into the computer.

Such fresh ideas can then be evaluated against appropriate elements using OptionFinder so that the group can prioritise them and establish if there are any perceived barriers to implementation such as cost or competitor activity'.

'Using the OptionFinder system during the decision-making part of the workshops, participants are able to register their opinions in a non-confrontational way. These lead to action plans being adopted which have an above average success rate. Significantly, most of the divisions and business units using the system have recorded improved scores in a subsequent workshop held between six and twelve months after the first.'

'Two of the system's outstanding successes have been recorded by Barclays Home Finance and by the group's UK Systems Development (UKSD) unit. In the case of Home Finance, business performance has been improved notably by shifting decision-making down the management hierarchy, empowering more staff members to react directly to customer needs and freeing managers from routine approval procedures. For UKSD success has taken the form of a radical change in "customer" relationships. At QIS follow-up meetings, the results have been likened to "breaking down brick walls" and "turning long standing issues into positive projects"'.

Optimising Self -assessment.

Of the 77 papers presented at The Second World Congress for Total Quality Management twelve were devoted to the subject of self-assessment and business excellence. These included the keynote paper with the above title by Tito Conti (Italy) which, in introducing self-assessment as a by-product of Quality awards, stressed the need for awareness of the differences between award assessment and self-assessment offering some sound advice:

'Since the aims of the awards and those of self-assessment are quite different the assumption that the means can be the same should not be taken for granted. Many failures in self-assessment stem from simplistic extrapolation to self-assessment of the award approach, often under the pressure of internal awards.'

'The dangers of mechanistic extrapolations from award assessment to self assessment should be evident. The first danger, the most real, is that of retaining the emphasis on scoring. I stress this risk because I have had many opportunities to see it at first hand. It can be useful for a company to perform an award-like assessment when the aim is comparison with other companies and of course when preparing to apply for an award. However, when the aim is improvement, the diagnostic aspects of assessment must take centre stage to focus solely on identifying the organisation's weak points. Scoring and diagnosis may look compatible, but they are not. The former will absorb top management's attention, to the detriment of the latter'.

He suggests reasons why the approach of splitting the self-assessment process into two parts (a unit self assessment followed by an externally managed scoring assessment) can be seriously flawed as the first phase tends to retain too much of the award process to be truly diagnostic:

'Application reports are designed with scoring, not improvement, in mind. Given that the second part of the process, external assessment and scoring, is their ultimate concern, the report writers inevitably tend to present the company in a favourable light. Self-assessment reports take a totally different approach: they are concerned not with appearances but with identifying performance gaps and the underlying weaknesses (in processes and in systematic factors); they dig into weaknesses to identify their root causes and make improvement planning possible'.

He then argues that self-assessment can only be diagnostic if it reverses the traditional assessment sequence i.e. uses a diagnostic sequence which commences with results (or symptoms). The author terms this 'right to left self-assessment ' since it begins with assessment of results (the right hand side of the model):

'The main objective in this phase is to highlight the performance gaps, both in relation to company objectives and competitor performances. A secondary objective can be that of giving a global percentage score to each result category, where scoring should derive – whenever possible – from benchmarking with reference competitors and best in class'.

The second phase identifies the processes that generate the results, particularly the most critical performance gaps, and then analyses them to highlight process weaknesses that are responsible for poor performances. It also incorporates an evaluation of processes that do not generate negative performance gaps but which are key in relation to present or future strategic goals. The third phase then reaches the most critical factors in relation to business excellence i.e. the enablers or systematic factors (leadership, human resources, financial resources, strategy making, organisational issues etc.):

If the right-left approach is followed, assessment of those categories becomes more concrete, since it benefits from previous assessments of results and processes. For example, previous assessment of people satisfaction will certainly provide important information for assessing the way people are managed, developed and empowered. Similarly, previous assessment of business results will shed light on the way resources are managed as well as on strategy making'.

It is noted that the approach advocated follows a course which is opposite to that normally followed in auditing and that the end result is correspondingly different:

'The self-assessment report should be structured in such a way as to provide direct evidence of the weaknesses and strength in the company's (or unit's) processes and systematic factors. Consequent connections between those weaknesses and objectives/results, evidenced by the diagnostic right-left approach, will suggest the priorities of the improvement plan.
Transformation of the self-assessment report into an "application report" -if the company is not applying for an award -is a waste of time, an additional cost and a way to mix up the results'.

The paper concludes with a possible new approach to quality awards which uses self-assessment as the driver, challenging the assumption that future advances will inevitably be linked to developments in present day quality award models:

'Restricting the autonomous development of the business model, and corporate PDCA concepts by coupling them to the speed of development of the award models would be extremely counterproductive, The awards have played an invaluable role to date, but today there is a vital need for the widest possible autonomous research and experimentation, free from all restriction, in the areas of business models, self-assessment and integration of the PDCA cycle with the company planning cycle'.

'Whatever its level of competitive success, to merit an award one of the things a company should demonstrate is a continuous day-by-day commitment -substantiated by appropriate actions -to maintain and possibly improve its success in the future. This should be a key assessment criterion. Since diagnostic self-assessment is a vital tool to help the company continuously to improve and renew its competencies and capabilities, one of the conditions for participation in an excellence award could be proof that the company has successfully conducted the PDCA cycle for an appropriate period of time -say at least three years -and that it continues to do so. This would provide assessors with a "film" of the company's improvement/ renewal activities'.

'With this type of approach to the awards, assessments would be more reliable and the assessor problem would be less critical. Outstanding skills would still be required but above all in the area of methodology, and the search for those elusive beings with the ability to assess every area from strategic planning to finance to personnel management , production and R and D could come to an end. It is certainly much easier to assess the route followed by a company to achieve its results from a documented basis than to make independent judgments on the strengths and weaknesses of a complex organisation in just a couple of days. '

Case Studies in Self-assessment

Five self-assessment case studies were presented, from Royal Mail, BT, Empire Stores, Honeywell and United Utilities.

The paper by P.Maisey and M.J.Pupius, entitled 'Achieving Business Excellence: A Unit based Approach' describes how Royal Mail is currently using the EFQM Model at three distinct levels:

'First, as a whole, Royal Mail prepared a submission for the European Quality Award in 1995. A site visit was undertaken and a feedback report provided. Second, bi-annually, each division or business unit is assessed by an internal team of assessors trained to EFQM standard. Results of the assessment provide inputs to the business plan and good practice processes. A third cycle has just started. Third, a unit is broadly defined as a team with an identifiable leader, outputs and monitoring systems. Typically, this might be a local delivery office or functional team, e.g. customer service team. The process at this level is called unit excellence .

It then describes unit excellence in more detail outlining the nine steps that comprise the unit excellence process: unit register(team leader or member contacts specially trained team of unit excellence supporters); unit briefing (team leader and unit excellence supporter briefs all members of unit); self-assessment (small team of volunteers agree a plan, unit excellence team assesses each element of model, sharing understanding with all unit members, unit excellence teams produce a handbook summarising findings which is then scored to identify an achievement level); action planning (areas for improvement revisited and mapped against an impact matrix detailing positive impact on the unit versus degree of difficulty in implementation); immediate actions (on those areas that will make improvements with only a small amount of effort and/or cost); Unit planning (development of plan capturing all areas for improvement not immediately actionable, prioritised with time-scale of typically 34 to 12 months); communication of plan (via team briefing and display of plan in unit); actioning of plan (nominally the responsibility of the team leader) ; and review and improvement (monitoring of unit plan by team leader and unit excellence supporter every 2,6 and 9 months).

The paper explains how since the introduction of unit excellence Royal Mail North East has assisted over 60 units out of a total of 220 to undergo this process, with a further 50 expected to be on board by the end of the year.

The paper entitled 'Using technology to involve the workforce' by Ms. Jenny Counsell, explains the BT approach which is highly interactive:

'In order to involve greater numbers of employees, BT looked for and experimented with innovative approaches, which utilise various channels of communication, including interactive workshops and the BT Internet. This is a private network using TCP/IP protocols and is known as the Intranet'.

'At interactive workshop sessions and events, employees use hand-held control keypads to answer questions, providing instant perception data as a basis for discussion. The handsets use computer technology to register the vote, opinion or perception of the audience. This can be relayed onto a screen to show the total outcome and spread among the members of the audience. It is also a versatile system, in that it allows participants to ask questions themselves. This method is a very popular way of carrying out workshops. The largest sized technology is the Management Conference or Roadshow led by Sir Peter Bonfield, in which around 1,500 people participated at a single session. In total, it reached 6,000 managers in BT. In their feedback remarks, 90 per cent felt it was a good use of their time.'

'In trialling the use of the Intranet, BT people around the world answered questions, and returned them to a central point where the results were collated, enabling data collection on a global basis. This was ideal for the global division and it was logical that they implemented the trial. The ideal opportunity to put this technology to the test was during World Quality Week (11-15 November 1996). It was very inexpensive to establish, costing approximately £2-3000 for the program and the PC. It received over 300 responses, while eliminating the problem of diverse locations and geographical barriers proved from receiving responses from all over the world'.

'In the World Quality Week trial, it was not solely aimed at those who had prior knowledge of self-assessment. Approximately 60 people in one division knew absolutely nothing about self-assessment, business excellence models, EQA or the EFQM. It still worked successfully, although they did place less emphasis on EQA itself. They tended to mark on average 15 per cent lower than other respondents who had varying degrees of previous knowledge and experience in the use of self-assessment.'

The Empire Stores paper, entitled 'Self-assessment: what's in it for us?'by S.A. Black and H.C. Comuley suggests that self-assessment undertaken within a particular department, section or unit 'has the potential to encourage involvement and increase commitment', but emphasises the need for consistency between local and corporate strategies:

'One danger is for improvement plans generated and implemented at a local level to be rendered futile by a lack of corporate support. Self-assessment should contribute to the development of action plans at all levels but it must be consistently aligned to corporate vision and values if it is to succeed in supporting company objectives. While high-level corporate improvement strategies shared by the business excellence model can be introduced into business plans and fed down throughout the organisation, information at a lower level will also be generated to feed upwards as a result of local self-assessment processes. For real progress to take place, consistency between local and corporate strategies must be established and maintained'.

'The genuine danger for organisations applying self-assessment is making it a missing link: a plan that runs parallel to the main thrust of the business.

*Improvement planning processes should be built into corporate planning
and improvement reviews or assessments should be built into business, unit
or departmental reviews. Remember, if a corporate improvement plan is
parallel, tangential or peripheral to the company's business plans and
cycles, then it is in danger of withering on the vine'.*

M.R. Kruger of Honeywell in the paper 'Benefiting from self-assessment in a
matrix organisation' explains how matrix structures have become
commonplace for multi-nationals with extended geographies and multiple
product lines serving different markets and highlights some of the difficulties
encountered by such organisations with regard to self-assessment:

*'Many such organisations are committed to business excellence, aspiring to
world-class performance, and look to use business excellence models to help
them achieve their goals. They will use self-assessment and subsequent
award application to give effective measurement of progress towards world-
class performance, but the difficulty arises when deciding how to interpret
the feedback at the top level such that it is meaningful for everyone
throughout the organisation'.*

*'In the scenario where self-assessment is restricted to the top level view, it is
unlikely that all leaders will become fully engaged in the improvement
agenda, yet such engagement is one of the necessary conditions to satisfy the
leadership criterion'.*

The author then describes how Honeywell has adopted a strategy of working
from the lowest discrete organisational unit and subsequently moved up
through the layers as the deployment of self-assessment became owned at
various levels:

*'The key benefits of this operating unit level scheme have been strong
ownership of the results of self-assessment and establishment of a managed
improvement style. With some units having begun in 1993 there is evidence
of annual score improvements of greater than 10 per cent over 3 years which
is tangible evidence to management that there is significant added value to
counterbalance the perception of a high overhead in the assessment process
itself'.*

'In 1996 for the first time, all knowledge of the businesses was aggregated at
a pan-European level. The total organisation of nearly 12,000 people in 29
countries was described in a 75 page document , and assessed by a mixture
of company staff and external assessors. This engaged top management in
understanding the effectiveness of the total organisation and, perhaps more
importantly, through feedback showed the areas where further optimisation
would be beneficial'.

*'Benefits of this first top-level assessment were visibility of disconnects in the
organisation and the extent to which processes are optimised for efficiency.*

It also demonstrated that a common business excellence model could be fully developed across a complex organisation'.

The paper from United Utilities (the result of the merger between North West Water Group and NORWEB) is entitled 'The Quality Journey to a World-class Multi-utility' by Jeff Mason of United Utilities plc, Dawson House, Great Sankey, Warrington. This describes how a presentation by Dr. David Lascelles of Paragon to North West Water in 1993 led to a piloting of the Business Excellence Model in the IT department with highly positive effects despite the attainment of just 198 points:

'Employee and customer satisfaction was measured and improved. A help desk was introduced and procedures and measures for processes introduced. Process improvement teams were created and produced immediate benefits. By 1994 a further six departments were being assessed against the Model, including the finance department which achieved an 85 per cent customer satisfaction level and became facilitators rather than controllers. At the beginning of 1995, the average score for the assessed departments had risen to 316 and the benefits of the self-assessment process were clearly recognisable'.

It is then explained how the annual self-assessment was proposed for all areas of the business, facilitated by a small business quality group:

'Three different types of assessment have been used. Initially perception assessments based on questionnaires were used. This was followed by an assessment workbook and finally a full formal assessment of each department was carried out'.

The pros and cons of each of these approaches are outlined along with a list of lessons learned which the author openly presents so that other organisations "can avoid the same errors". In its conclusion the paper says the following:

'There is no claim at the moment that United Utilities is a world-class company. What can be objectively demonstrated is that we have moved the EFQM model measure of our excellence from the 200 mark to around the 400 mark and are increasing it by around 50 points a year. Some of our leading departments are planning entries into regional quality awards. If we continue at our current pace, we should be "world-class" in about five years'.

Conference Proceedings

The proceedings for the Second World Congress for TQM are incorporated in *Total Quality Management Journal* Vol.8 Nos 2 and 3 (ISSN-0954-4127), June 1997, published by **Carfax.**

EUROPEAN QUALITY AWARDS 1997

The European Quality Awards were presented this year in Stockholm by Her Majesty Queen Silvia of Sweden. A distinguished audience witnessed the presentation at the Gala Dinner in the City Hall which represented the centrepiece of this year's EFQM Business Excellence Forum which, under the banner of 'The Global Challenge: Leadership Strategies for Growth' attracted a record 1200 delegates.

There were two Awards presented this year, first the Large Business Award which was won by global independent semiconductor manufacturers SGS THOMSON Microelectronics then the Small and Medium-sized Enterprise (SME) Award, which was presented to BEKSA Steel Cord Manufacturing and Trading. BEKSA was incorporated in 1987 as a 50-50 joint venture between Bekaert of Belgium and Haci Omer Sabanci Holding of Turkey and employs 217 in Istanbul and Izmit in Turkey.

These winners were selected from a total of six finalists (SGS THOMSON, TNT(UK), British Telecom, Netas, Sollac of France and NatWest Life Assurance) in the large Business category and seven (ABB Semiconductors AG of Switzerland, BEKSA, DiEU of Denmark, GASNALSA of Spain, Landhotel Schindlerhof of Germany, Prec-Cast Foundry of Hungary and DD Williamson of Ireland) in the SME Category.

In the Large Business Category three European Quality Prizes [runner-up awards -Ed] were presented as last year to BT, TNT (UK), and Netas, whilst one SME Quality Prize was presented to GASNALSA, a natural gas distribution company which supplies gas to the Basque province of Alava and employs just 43 staff.

SGS THOMSON: Success through Strategic Alliance

SGS THOMSON Microelectronics (Headquarters in St.Genis, France), provides an interesting case study for anyone who is genuinely concerned with the management of quality in the manufacturing sector as it confounds the view that quality in this area is merely about quality systems, tools and standards. For whilst statistical process control, Team Oriented Problem Solving, Design of Experiments and Failure Mode and Effects Analysis are all applied, the emphasis throughout is essentially people centred. This point was stressed on more than one occasion at the Forum by the company's President and Chief Executive Officer Pasquale Pistorio who had the enviable task of receiving the European Quality Award from Her Majesty Queen Silvia.

The company was formed in 1987 from a merger between SGS Microelectronics of Italy and Thomson Semiconductors of France, neither of which was profitable, but with this first strategic alliance a company emerged with the ability to both broaden and upgrade its combined range of products and technologies as well as strengthen its manufacturing and distribution capabilities in Europe, North America and thee Asia Pacific region. It now has around 26,000 employees, 9 advanced research and development units, 31 design and application centres, 17 main manufacturing sites and 60 sales offices in 24 countries. With net revenues of around $4.12 billion in 1996 it has become the tenth largest semiconductor company in the world.

Initial fears of a Franco-Italian culture clash following the merger did not materialise, partly no doubt because the new joint board of directors carefully engineered an equal division of responsibility between French and Italian management. Similarly investment was also initially divided equally between France and Italy. Thus, right from the beginning, neither party in the alliance was caused to suffer a loss of face, a distinctly Japanese principle which was realised in a distinctly European way.

The company's Annual Report for 1996 high lights the continuing role which strategic alliances have had in ensuring continued success in the years which followed:

'Strategic alliances with key customers, suppliers, research institutions and other parties in the semiconductor marketplace play a vital role in SGS THOMSON's continued technological and market leadership. Such alliances allow the company to blend its expertise in semiconductor production with the intimate knowledge of systems and product features contributed by its strategic partners. The alliances may result in joint product development, the definition of a common system architecture, and joint R and D or technology exchanges'.

Examples of specific alliances include those with Seagate Technology and Western Digital in the computer peripheral sector as well as automotive alliances such as that with Fiat/Marelli, and alliances in telecommunications with Alcatel and Northern Telecom. There are also joint development programmes with leading suppliers such as Applied Materials, ASM Lithography, LAM and Air Liquide and with the makers of Computer Aided Design (CAD) tools such as Cadence, Synopsis and Mentor. The company's President Pasquale Pistorio describes some of the more recent initiatives, highlighting the company's determination to remain at the forefront of new product development by harnessing creative talent where it is recognised:

'At the beginning of 1997 we announced an agreement for a joint technology, development and manufacturing programme with Ramtron International, a specialised designer of advanced non-volatile memories. We anticipate that if this venture is successful, our two companies would develop -and SGS THOMSON would manufacture -ferro electric random access memory (FRAM) devices.'

The new FRAM products would combine the high speed of DRAMs, the non-volatility of ROMs, and the flexibility of EEPROMs to create features that are currently not available in any single semiconductor memory device. The resulting products would be targeted for use in communication products, palm-top computers, smart cards and other portable applications. The achievements in terms of business results from this type of approach have been impressive:

'In 1996 SGS THOMSON derived nearly $13 billion in revenues from products that resulted from strategic alliances -a figure that has grown at a compound annual rate of 48% since 1992. Clearly, the company's strategic alliances are a source of exceptional financial stability and growth opportunity'.

Of particular interest is the telecommunications sector where the company's sales to the market increased by 14% in 1996, and contributed 22.1% of net revenues:

'As with the company's other industry applications the telecom segment is migrating to superintegration solutions. For instance the next generation of digital cellular phone can use an SGS THOMSON system on a chip approach using no more than four chips (radio, digital signal processing and protocol, memories, energy management).'

With regard to impact on society the President highlights the notable quality first achieved by the company's facility at Rancho Bernardo in California, which not only became the first plant in the US to achieve ISO 14001 certification as an environmentally friendly manufacturing site, but also achieved compliance with the more exacting standards of the European Eco-Management and Audit Scheme (EMAS). This brings the number of the sites complying with EMAS to twelve:

'At SGS THOMSON we place a high priority on environmental policies, and work to maximise the use of recyclable or reusable materials while reducing consumption of resources and the amount of waste generated. We are confident that we are on target to achieve our goal of having all sites worldwide approved for EMAS before the end of 1997'.

The company's commitment to high standards of training as part of its people management strategy is reflected through the formulation of their very own SGS THOMSON (ST) University in 1994. This works with other training, management and educational institutes to provide a curriculum that offers all employees an opportunity for continuous improvement. Classes are related to current job requirements focusing, for example, on professional selling skills, analytical tools, marketing and management, and technical and technological disciplines.

The tools and techniques required for Total Quality Management and Team Leadership, and for individual and organisational improvement are also part of the ST University curriculum and there is a worldwide recognition scheme promoted throughout the company which ranges from a simple "thank you" to yearly corporate celebrations of achievement.

Teamworking is well established with some 1,200 teams operating throughout the globe. Quality Improvement Teams are formed to tackle specific chronic problems whilst Cross-functional Problem-solving Teams assembled on a temporary basis troubleshoot urgent problems. In addition teams may be drawn from a particular department or set of employees to continually challenge the company's processes and engage in quests for improvement.

The special Awards issue of European Quality, headed 'Aspects of Excellence' highlights the company's Open Door management' policy whereby 'any employees can schedule a meeting with any manager, including the Chief Executive, at any time' and 'most managers spend a significant proportion of their working day on the shop floor'. The article later describes how people satisfaction is measured by means of a "climate survey" which asks questions about people's comfort with their jobs. The company's Corporate Vice President and Director for Total Quality and Environmental Management, Murray Duffin states:

"We don't weight the questions to say 'I like my job', but ask more important questions like 'Are you kept well informed?' and look at the percentage of positive answers. Positive answers tend to run into the 70 to 80 per cent range. There's a very high level of satisfaction, and a lower turnover than industry average in almost every country we work in".

The article also highlights the company's unconventional approach to benchmarking, the rationale for which is again explained by Murray Duffin:

"If somebody's outperforming us in a significant area we don't examine their processes in detail to see how much we can improve. There are three reasons. Firstly, it takes too long and in the same time you can change your own process. Secondly, you learn a lot just by studying company reports, published articles and literature -you don't have to go and visit the guy very often. Thirdly, a lot of what you do learn is not really applicable within your own culture. You have to adapt things anyway. You might as well start from scratch and say 'this company is doing better than we are, they know something we don't so let's figure out how to do it"'.

It is concluded that:

'SGS THOMSON learned that using the EFQM model dynamically means constant self-assessment in situ and in action, not routine activity shut-downs, and examination from a static position'.

The company performs self-assessment to the EFQM Model on an annual basis at both corporate and organisational level and the results are used as a basis for local and company-wide improvement programmes. This is supported by a series of questionnaires and audits which show how far TQM has both spread through the organisation and contributed towards its goals in relation to the company's mission i.e. 'To offer strategic independence to our partners worldwide as a profitable and viable broad range semiconductor supplier'

BEKSA's Business Excellence Triangle

BEKSA, with a turnover last year of around BEF 1 billion, is, despite its size, the largest steel cord producer in its market territory which is defined by a shareholders' agreement as comprising of Turkey, the Middle East, North Africa, the Balkans, and the Turkic Republics of Asia. In addition the yearly production capacity of the BEKSA plant, which covers some 128,000 square metres of land with a covered area of 57.000 square metres, is able to meet the entire steel cord need of Turkey.

Four principal products are manufactured:

*steel cord (the main reinforcing material used in the production of steel radial tyres providing improved safety, mileage, strength and performance).

*bead wire (a major input for tyre producers consisting of bundles of steel wires used to reinforce the bead area of the tyre which is in contact with the rim flange).

*hose wire (a reinforcement material used to increase the flexibility and strength of hoses in high pressure applications).

*spring wire (various wires used in different branches of industry extending from automotive products to the production of mattresses and sofas).

In addition the company also imports and markets Bekaert's steel wires and steel wire based products in particular to the construction sector. These include Dramix (reinforcement steel fibre wires used to enhance the physical properties of concrete surfaces and walls), fencing and netting, and various industrial wires.

When the company was formed in 1987 their market was booming, but recession hit shortly afterwards and a 'life and death' restructuring of the organisation and an accompanying working system was needed to meet the challenges ahead.

Their company was fortunate in that its shareholders were still confident that the market for their product was still there despite the worsening state of affairs. This faith enabled the foundations for a Total Quality recovery to be laid, commencing with Total Quality Control Project-Pilot Team activities, the introduction of Statistical Process Control (SPC) applications and Process Integration (from raw material to finished product) .

By 1991 the initial investment was completed and a week long management workshop was held which reviewed quality and strategy. This resulted in a policy deployment model and a Mission Statement which read as follows:

'We would like to be perceived by our customers as a business partner; one that delivers excellent performing products, one who is reliable and strives for continuous improvement.

We would like to be perceived by our shareholders as a company that keeps its competitive position by effective and efficient use of resources.

We would like to be perceived by our people as an open and well functioning company that provides a good working environment and one that enhances involvement, skills and teamwork'.

This Mission Statement was derived from a 'Business Excellence Triangle' which defined the three main stakeholder groups (customers, shareholders, and people) in a triangular relationship with customers at the apex. This was then supported by the establishment of systems to ensure company-wide excellence.

Three hard years of dedication towards the pursuit of continuous improvement followed, during which time Technology Cells and a Project Approach were initiated. Also a 'Vicinity Perception Survey' was introduced, a Total Environment Care Model based on BS7750 and ISO 14000 was constructed, and various joint projects with suppliers began. Self-assessment to the EFQM Model was introduced in 1994, the same year as the company achieved ISO9002 certification.

In his speech to the EFQM Forum the President of BEKSA Bulent Savas, who received the SME Award from Her Majesty Queen Silvia, explained how he attributed the relative success of BEKSA during the difficult period of 1992 to 1994 (which brought the Gulf War, the Balkan Civil War, and the overnight devaluation of the Turkish Lira by 163%) to his company's commitment to TQM.

He then outlined some of his company's achievements during the period from 1992 to 1996 which included a 40% increase in market share, a 57% decrease in scrap, a 43% decrease in man hours per ton of output, a 67% decrease in work-related accidents, a doubling of capacity, and a realisation of investment goals for new products. There is now "flourishing TQM" at BEKSA, he told delegates.

The article in *'Aspects of Excellence'* elaborates on some of the company's business results and describes the approaches which are taken toward the measurement of customer and people satisfaction:

'The business results trends in its Award submission reflect an improving picture despite a severe economic crisis in the Turkish economy in the mid 1990s. Its share of a shrinking market are up; product costs are down as a percentage sales and well ahead of its main competitors' performance; and in the past five years net profit has increased by 335%'.

'Customer perceptions are measured in an annual customer satisfaction survey (CSS) and through customer vendor audits. The initial CSS carried out in 1992, covered just three customers which between them accounted for 29% of sales by tonnage. Since then the questions have been regularly refined and coverage extended to customers accounting for 96% of tonnage. For the past three years survey questions have also asked customers to rate their other suppliers on the same scale of 1-5.

With five years of data now available BEKSA is able to plot its performance in 20 categories ranging from "accessibility" and "communication" to "willingness to recommend" and "TQ awareness"'.

'People satisfaction, the second element of the excellence triangle, is equally extensively surveyed both formally, through an annual people opinion survey covering the whole company, and more informally through such platforms as face-to-face meetings and performance appraisal'.

'Data from employee surveys and feedback is evaluated by external consultants and presented separately for each department as well as for the company overall. The results of the survey and benchmarking studies feed into the company's yearly action plan'.

In 1997 the company adopted the motto of 'Target : Europe'and began development of a suggestion Evaluation System and established 'Benchsa', an intercompany benchmarking consortium of four companies led by BEKSA.

EUROPEAN LEADERSHIP SURVEY

Leading management and technology consultancy PA Consulting Group have published the results of a pan-European survey on leadership which provides profiles of leadership across a range of European organisations enabling a comparison of individual style and approach with that of the 'perfect leader'. The final report, entitled 'Achieving Business Excellence : Successful Leadership Styles' was compiled with the help of The Aarhus Business School in Denmark and essentially focuses on three key areas:

* defining the profile of the excellent leader.

* measuring leaders based on their own self-assessment and upward appraisal by their staff.

* drawing lessons from the findings, including consideration of national leadership characteristics and the readiness of younger European leaders to take their organisations into the 21st Century.

The survey was conducted between February and April 1997 across Benelux, France, Germany and the UK. It involved an empirical analysis of 202 business leaders from private companies with more than 50 employees and incorporated questionnaire results from over 1000 people in total. Amongst the key findings were that, out of a range of leadership qualities, the attributes which are of significantly greater importance to the achievement of Business Excellence are:

(i) An ability to take a long term views of an organisation's direction and to set clear strategic goals.

(ii) A strong focus on a result-oriented, 'bottom-line' driven, analytical approach to leadership.

(iii) An ability to lead from the front, be creative and maximise the advantages of teamwork.

It was also found that whilst European leaders tend to meet the requirements of Business Excellence on the result-oriented competencies, they deviate significantly from them when it comes to the strategic leadership from the front creativity and teamwork attributes.

Through their answers to an 86-point questionnaire the performance of the 202 European business leaders in relation to the three elements of Total Quality Management, Creativity and Learning was assessed and the 20 highest scoring leaders identified. The same questionnaire enabled a 'leadership profile' for each leader to be constructed. By averaging out the leadership profiles of these 20 highest scoring leaders an 'Excellent Leadership Profile' was created. This represents the leadership profile most closely correlated with the achievement of Business Excellence.

Other findings were that:

* on a country by country comparison German leaders came closest to achieving Business Excellence, meeting the requirements on the key sets of leadership competencies.

* European employees' expectations of an 'ideal leader' vary significantly from the Excellent Leader Profile (ELP). Most importantly they place a

226

relatively low value on the key leadership qualities required for Business Excellence and a greater emphasis on those styles of leadership which are less influential on the ELP. They may, therefore, need to be brought 'on board' by leaders seeking to achieve Business Excellence.

* while the younger generation of European leaders outperform their older colleagues on the result-oriented bottom-line driven competencies, they score significantly below the older group on the strategic side. Achieving Business Excellence in the 21st century may thus require the next generation of leaders to concentrate on developing a significantly stronger strategic focus.

[Issue 108 (December 1997)]

UK QUALITY AWARDS 1997

A record four UK Quality Awards were presented this year at the fourth annual prestigious BQF Gala Dinner at the Grosvenor House hotel in London. President of the Board of Trade Margaret Beckett made the presentations before a distinguished audience of around 1,100 diners on 28th October to BT National Business Communications, BT Northern Ireland, The Dell Primary School (Chepstow), and Hewlett Packard. They were selected from a total of six finalists which also included NatWest Life Assurance and Nortel Monkstown.

BT NBC: Transforming the World of Business

BT NBC was established in Reading in 1991 as a specialised supplier of telecommunications products and services to business customers. It employs around 25,000 and is the leading user of BT's corporate intranet (BT's internal Internet service which provides online information about BT to its people via desktop and laptop pcs). This has proved to be especially effective in promoting and reinforcing a culture of Business Excellence.

Around 1.5 million businesses and government organisations use the division's services which include electronic mail, telephone and video conferencing and ISDN. (Integrated Services Digital Network). In addition key customers can monitor the performance of their networks by means of a specialised Service View facility.

There are a number of obvious benefits to businesses from these services, notably the ability of teleworkers to perform their work from any location so saving time and money on travel, the ability to construct new relationships with employees and customers based on more flexible working practices, and the ability to save on office space and related services.

The division's ability to deliver leading edge business solutions and to work in partnership with its clients was recognised in the 1997 BT Awards for

Quality. This was for the Project Xtra team which consisted of some 130 members and which was commended for its design and development work for an advanced service organisation on behalf of the newly merged Halifax and Leeds Building societies. In addition NBC has its own Achievement Award scheme with winners including Yellow Pages, the first part of NBC to gain the Investors In People as well as the BT Silver Award for scoring over 600 points against the business excellence model, and Managed Network Services who have increased their revenue by 55% over five years.

Customer satisfaction is addressed with approximately 10,000 customer interviews being conducted each month to monitor customer perceptions on specific attributes such as fault repair, service provision, contract handling and invoicing. Customers are divided into two categories: small and medium sized enterprises which account for some 1.4 million sites, and corporate clients and government accounts of which there are about 6,000. The latter are noted for their ability to drive forward the telecommunications industry .

A unique approach to training is demonstrated by the 'Development Fair' training initiatives. This takes the form of a roadshow which takes training events to NBC locations around the country as distinct from transporting employees to specific training centres.

The NBC culture of 'improvement focused enquiry' has earned them the reputation of being 'BT's most highly developed and rigorous user of self-assessment against the Business Excellence Model'. This began in 1994 when, following ISO9000 certifications, facilitated senior management workshops formed the basis for full-scale application style reports for each of its units.

BT Northern Ireland: The Benchmark for Customer Satisfaction

The second BT Award winner, BT Northern Ireland, were, by contrast to BT NBC, no strangers to the Awards stage, having won the Northern Ireland Quality Award twice, in 1994 and 1996, and been shortlisted as a finalist for the UK Quality Awards three times. The Award itself had, however, eluded them until this year.

The company interestingly, operates in the least competitive region of the UK's privatised telecomms market, whish provides them with an excellent opportunity to dedicate their efforts towards providing a high quality service without necessarily having to apply resources merely to outperform their competitors, although there were some competitors, notably CableTel, CWC and various international resellers all keen to gain a foothold.

The company prides itself on being perceived as the province's 'local telephone company' and the assessors made particular mention of the company's outstanding performance in terms of both customer satisfaction and impact on society. It is noted, for example, as being 'best in class' in areas such as the support for charities, education and training, sport and leisure, and the provision of medical and welfare services. It also runs training initiatives to assist the local unemployed to acquire IT and other skills that will help them to find work, and organises events such as 'BT Environment Week', and 'BT Countryside For All'. In addition it has announced that it is to create 750 new jobs in a new telephone based sales office costing around £9million which is envisaged to become operational early next year. In customer satisfaction the company which is still 100% owned by BT and has no shareholders, has, according to BT's strict 'very satisfied' criterion become 'the benchmark division'.

Benchmarking has received a high profile with board members undertaking visits to past winners of the UK Quality Award, and The Malcolm Baldrige Award in the US, as well as to Telia, the Swedish network operator. Also there has been a renewed emphasis on two-way dialogue with employees following feedback from past UK Quality Award assessors.

Business results have been impressive with turnover improving by 22% to £265.7 million against a backdrop of OFTEL regulation which pegged price rises at 7.5%. Turnover per employee has risen from £24, 700 in 1991 to £53,800 in 1996 and the contribution of BT Northern Ireland to BT plc has increased by 27.2% over the same period.

The company currently employs just over 2,500 employees, making it one of Northern Ireland's largest employers, and supplies a network of 683,000 customer lines.

The Dell: Top of the Class.

The Dell Primary School is perhaps the most interesting of the four winners as they are the first organisation to have reached the final via the new category of small businesses (under 50 employees) which was added last year, and the first public sector organisation with an Award. Established in 1989 in Chepstow, South Wales it has a staff of just 34, and its results are impressive with 80% of its 11 year old pupils attaining level 4 in the three core subjects, which compares with a national average of only 45%.

Described as an unlikely pioneer in the advance of new management thinking' the school adopted Total Quality principles in its effort to gain independent assessment of its training and development opportunities. In 1994 they committed themselves to achieving the Investors In People (IIP) standard for staff development and in 1995 they became the first and so far the only Welsh school to be awarded a Charter Mark for 'excellence in the provision of public services'. This brought the school into contact with the Wales Quality Centre in 1996 and, following seminar work there, a decision was taken to enter for the education sector of the Wales Quality Award which they duly won.

With these accolades it was recognised that, although difficult owing to the need to define and measure business results, it was not impossible at least to enter for the 1997 UK Quality Awards and try their chances. Intangible objectives such as the spiritual, cultural and moral development of pupils, for example, did not fit easily into what was essentially a business orientated model although the nine criteria of the Charter Mark did provide a guide at least as to how performance in some of these areas might be measured. It does, for example, include criteria for, 'setting and monitoring standards of service', 'information and openness', 'consultation and choice', 'courtesy and helpfulness', and 'measurable improvements'.

Particular features of the school include an annual survey to pupils allowing them to comment on the running of the school, five minute 'circle times' each week, which allow class concerns to be raised with teachers, termly open evenings for parents which include comment forms should they prefer not to express their views face to face , and consultations with parents six weeks after a child has joined the school, which are designed to monitor the effectiveness of induction procedures. Also there is a 'customer concern process' whereby every issue raised by a parent is logged and addressed with a response guaranteed within seven days, and a comment book which affords parents the opportunity of raising specific questions with teachers.

The process of self-assessment has led to the initiation of a comprehensive survey of teaching and support staff with a view to increasing the empowerment of teachers whilst with teachers acting as 'subject consultants' it has been shown that in practice customer satisfaction and business results have been merged into one.

The Annual Development Plan focuses on curriculum matters, management and personnel, the working environment, and community interaction and has strong parallels with the Business Excellence Model.

The school currently has 390 pupils and has been commended for its 'intuitive grasp on the elusive "soft" issues' to which business managers educated in the supremacy of the bottom-line 'would do well to pay attention'.

Hewlett Packard: Masters of the Undefended Hill.

Hewlett Packard's commitment to Total Quality is, by contrast to the other winners, global and long standing, the company having been a recipient of the prestigious Deming Prize amongst others. Founded in 1939 the company has become a market leader in high technology equipment product, and service provision, with some 24,000 electronic products and systems currently being used for measurement, communications and computing.

In the UK Hewlett Packard Ltd. of Bracknell, Berkshire, was established in 1957 as a sales outpost which now employs 5,480 and undertakes research, development and manufacturing at four major sites. In 1996 it contributed £1.9 billion to the Hewlett Packard group turnover.

Total Quality management was adopted in the UK in 1989 founded on the principles of continuous improvement, innovation, customer focus and people satisfaction which now form the core of 'business excellence'. A proprietary quality maturity system (QMS) was developed in parallel with the American Malcolm Baldrige National Quality Award and considerable emphasis was placed on open management, informal working relationships, teamwork and empowerment.

Continual self-assessment, renewal and improvement have eliminated the need for conventional process re-engineering and a careful balance has been struck between process management and the retention of functional roles.

Strategically Hewlett Packard has achieved substantial competitive advantage through becoming masters of the 'undefended hill' i.e. gaining a niche foothold in an area where there are either no or few competitors or where the competitors identified are notoriously weak. A resultant 'killer product or application which creates its own market' is then introduced which 'defends the high ground by relentless product improvement based on technological advantage, value-enhancement and brand leadership'.

This said, the company is more than aware that technological leadership can be very much a transient phenomenon and to be sustained a tactical approach is also needed involving notably, exemplary levels of service.

Three key principles dominate the business: product leadership (maintaining reliability), operational excellence (driving out waste), and customer intimacy (creating individual value).

Leadership development is rigorous, extending beyond the requirements of the Business Excellence Model to include provision for recommendations as well as assessment criteria, whilst management environment is considered to be central rather than peripheral to job satisfaction. This is enhanced by an 'empowered recruitment policy' whereby managers interview their own teams i.e. there is no central control of the hiring function, so there is a sense of ownership on their part for the success of their personnel. Consequently individuals are helped in their development early on and much undesirable company politics is prevented.

Individuals set many of their own goals at the start of the year, as against having them imposed from above, and there are self-determined improvement targets which greatly enhance people satisfaction. This said, however, it is clear that some areas do need an overhaul periodically, most notably in sales where there has been from time to time denial of the existence of a sales process on the part of sales staff and reliance on superficial factors such as firmness of handshake etc. Similarly Purchasing has developed a well structured buying process based on internal justification financial approval, technical assessment and supplier relationship assessment.

Further information

Profiles of the six finalists for this year's UK Quality Awards are featured in the special Awards issue of *UK Excellence* (formerly *UK Quality*).

[Issue 110 (February 1998)]

ORGANISATION SELF-ASSESSMENT (Book Review)

Author: Tito Conti

Publisher: Chapman and Hall (ISBN 0-412-78880-2)

Details:

Seven chapters by one of Europe's leading quality practitioners:

(i)   To explain the role of self-assessment as a diagnostic tool covering the whole organisation and involving all stakeholders.

(ii)   To explain the self-diagnostic process and how the results should be interpreted.

(iii)   To demonstrate the value of cross-diagnosis as a key element.

(iv)   To develop a methodology of introducing self-assessments in an organisation and integrating it into the company's planning cycle.

(v)   To examine to what extent the European TQM model as it exists today meets the new needs as they have emerged over the years and to suggest appropriate modifications.

The seven chapters are entitled 'From quality audits to self-assessment/self-diagnosis in relation to the company's missions'; 'The Model: an integrated view of the company and its missions'; 'The self-assessment/self-diagnosis process'; 'Assessment of results, processes and systematic factors'; 'Cross-diagnosis'; 'Introducing self-assessment into the company'; and' Preparing for and implementing the self-assessment and improvement planning cycle'.

Chapter One considers the evolution of quality, highlighting the importance of the product life-cycle which is seen as 'a fundamental advance' and of concurrent engineering as an alternative to sequential activities:

'Engineering activities are carried out in parallel, in order to maximize interactivity and thus improve the quality of the result and reduce development time. This is a demonstration of how a simple modification of the interrelations among processes -an organizational, systematic idea - can bring a dramatic change in results'.

'The importance of concurrent engineering lies not in the changes made in the various processes, but in their mutual interaction. An important point is that in corporate organizations process changes are usually governed by those directly involved in the relevant sub-system, while systematic changes are governed by top management. The latter have the greatest impact'.

In introducing the subject of auditing the author is notably critical about the 'over-emphasis' which has been placed on ISO9000:

'Too often ISO9000 certification has been mistakenly regarded as a guarantee of results. "The firearms licence has been confused with the ability to score a bull's eye'".

He thus suggests, with the aid of a diagram, some additions that should be made to the standard in order to progress from 'quality assurance' to 'customer satisfaction'.

In Chapter Two the author explains the case for 'improvement-oriented self-assessment' i.e. that it can achieve levels of effectiveness and reliability far beyond the reach of award assessments, arguing that 'award assessments would be more reliable if they considered the company's self-assessments and consequent improvement plans over a period of at, least three years, together with results achieved .Some characteristics of the Model are discussed:

'A significant indication of the difficulties inherent in the European model due to the absence of an organization category emerged when the model was extended to small/medium enterprises. For these companies, the first positive contact with quality is usually the assimilation of the product life cycle concept and the organization of that cycle to ensure product/service quality at minimum cost. (Quality Management and Assurance and Quality System).

Although the ISO9000 standards are often misinterpreted and poorly applied, they provide the basic ingredients the company needs to organize the product life cycle so as to control variability and attain its product quality goals (although if those goals are extended to competition at the level of customer satisfaction costs and time-to-market, the ISO9000 organizational approach is no longer sufficient) .

Chapter Three considers self-assessment as part of a Plan-Do-Check-Act (PDCA), cycle and discusses the assessment of 'results', 'systematic factors', and 'elements'. In Chapter Four these are broken down further into the assessment of a customer satisfaction, business results, relations with stakeholders, leadership, strategies and plans, human resources, other resources, and organizational architectures:

'Assessment of "organizational architectures" is a step-by-step procedure. The first step is to check whether the company has moved or is moving beyond the bureaucratic-functional stage in which tasks are rigidly allotted to specific functions dedicated to planning, co-ordination and control. If the company is still at this level, it is unlikely to have a global focus on all company missions: each division will tend to concentrate on its own particular goals, which will be related only distantly, and often not entirely legitimately, to the company's goals. In this case, the assessments verdict will necessarily be low'.

Chapter Five introduces the concept of cross-diagnosis i.e. right to left assessment which begins with results, then examines the processes which give rise to those results, and afterwards the systematic factors wherein the underlying causes of the company's main problems are usually to be found. Cross-diagnosis is seen as the main factor that distinguishes between conformity assessment and diagnostic assessment and an excellent description of how to apply both the basic Ishikawa (fish-bone) diagram and cause-effect matrices towards this end is given:

Fish-bone diagrams are satisfactory when dealing with a single, relatively simple problem. In practice, however, circumstances often pose a large number of complex, interrelated problems. The problems that emerge during self-assessment are typical. When a negative result is found or a marked improvement in performance needs to be planned, the company usually has to deal with numerous complex problems'.

'Imagine that the company has to identify the causes that have led to significant dissatisfaction with post-sales service, a state of affairs confirmed by a comparative survey with a reference competitor. A variety of causes may have contributed to this negative result: slow response times; inadequate technical skills; poor resource distribution; service calls that fail to resolve difficulties; poor spare parts logistics; low product reliability; poor communications with customers etc. With such a broad range of possible causes, a whole range of Ishikawa diagrams would be needed, one for each component of customer satisfaction. And since many of these components are the result of several process flows, more than one diagram could be required for a single result'.

'Cross-diagnosis is by nature a highly interactive process. Matrix cascades are built one after another, but the company will frequently have to go back and make adjustments, since the approach proceeds on the basis of hypotheses that must be subsequently verified. In each matrix, the lines represent effects, the columns represent relative causes or remedies. The diagnosis can begin with brainstorming sessions, but the various hypotheses

must be substantiated by quantitative data which means going back to the matrices to add or modify data'.

'The master matrix becomes the improvement planning "chart", the master document, while the sub-matrices provide the back-up details. The managers of all the processes that converge on the result the company wishes to improve should refer to these documents and go back to them, every time changes are made or proposed'.

.

In Chapter Six the author argues that the introduction of self-assessment into a company is too important to delegate and recommends that a ' quality and organization function' becomes 'top management's operating arm':

'Its role is to guarantee that the strategic goals set by top management are properly communicated and ensure that a consistent approach to self-assessment is adopted throughout the company (a self-assessment guide setting out the basic requisites is a useful tool)'.

Other subjects covered in Chapter Six include overcoming internal resistance, the dangers of associating self-assessment with an internal award, developing a communications plan and an activities plan, drawing up the self-assessment guide, establishing assessment teams, training, and post self-assessment activities.

Chapter Seven covers links among strategic planning, self-assessment and improvement planning; the time sequence; gradual integration of self-assessment into the planning cycle; performance gaps and capability gaps; self-assessment review and strategic improvement planning; and deployment of improvement goals.

A very useful book to guide a self assessment team.

EUROPEAN COMPANY LEADERS VIEWS

The Chief Executive Session at the EFQM Forum in Stockholm was chaired by the then EFQM President Karel Vinck. The session posed the question 'How can top executive leaders ensure sustainable growth in Europe?' And in introducing it he described how, in his experience, as a Chief Executive three things were crucial to success, namely:

(i) a mission (including why you are in business and what you want to do with your company);

(ii) a strategy (to realise the mission: how, when and with whom), and;

(iii) a strategic vehicle (to ensure that the strategy is implemented – TQM has been shown to be an ideal vehicle) :

"Without a mission, you run the risk that your message will be neither consistent nor coherent. The mission is becoming more important because it is basic to communication both externally and internally".

He stressed the importance of having good communication in an organisation as the lack of quality of communication is so frequently an organisational weakness. It should, he suggested, always be checked in relation to the content of the mission.

He then suggested how, by using the EFQM Model systematically an organisation gains a better chance of succeeding:

"There are no guarantees, but you have a higher probability".

Dave Richardson, President of TI Europe, who won the 1995 European Quality Award, then explained why TI Europe has taken great pains not to have an HQ, the reason being basically that they do not wish to attract "HQ staff". "The HQ is in my briefcase", he said. He then explained the role of policy deployment, which he takes very seriously:

"Most lack of execution of strategy is a function of communication. People do not see the relationship between their jobs and the strategic plan. Policy deployment bridges the gap between planning and results. We haven't found another vehicle that works".

He explained how he found processes to work best when the priorities are small in number but highly specific, i.e. three concise "must dos", and described some of his organisation's Goals for next year, notably to increase Digital Signal Process System (DSPS) design-ins by 40% and to introduce ten new products which utilise Timeline Technology.

Next, Alan Jones, Chief Executive of TNT (UK), who are in the unique position of receiving the runner-up award for three years in succession, addressed delegates on the subject of innovation and explained why cutting costs is often an inferior option when it is possible to remove time from processes instead, e.g. time saved allowed newspapers to be carried for a third of the price paid in 1985:

"Turning points come when we've innovated to great effect. We have hundreds of profit centres in the UK innovating in local markets. An example was the London to Brighton bicycle race. The last thing people wanted to do was ride back when the local railway operator was on strike. The local person in Brighton therefore arranged for fifty 40 ft trailers to be supplied in an opportunist approach. People are praised when these things happen and are paid well to keep them in the company".

Other principal speakers in this session were Bernard Fournier of Rank Xerox and Jan Stenberg of event sponsors SAS.

EUROPEAN QUALITY AWARDS 1998

This year's European Quality Convention, held jointly by the EFQM and the European Organisation for Quality (EOQ) in Paris from 21st to 23rd October, attracted a record 2100 delegates over the three days. It featured the 1998 European Quality Awards presentation by John Roberts CBE, President of the EFQM, for which there were a record 20 Finalists, 10 Prize Winners and three Award Winners. The Finalists included four Prize winning organisations from the U.K., namely The Inland Revenue Cumbernauld, who were one of just two organisations to receive a Prize in the Public Sector category, BT Northern Ireland, Reading based BT Yellow Pages, and four times Prize Winner TNT (UK) based in Atherstone ,Warwickshire. The latter, who were very close previously, this year were finally victorious in winning the European Quality Award itself in the Large Business category (over 250 employees).

TNT (UK): Bridging the gap

TNT (UK), the global express, logistics and mail service organisation, currently has around 10,000 employees and a turnover of around £500 million. They have been European Prize Winners in 1995,1996,1997 and 1998 as well as UK Quality Award Winners in 1994, but, despite this impressive track record the biggest accolade, that of the European Quality Award itself, has proved elusive to them until now.

The company has rigorously defended its use of league tables which they assert 'now identify not only centres of excellence but also opportunities for improvement throughout the business' and ISO 9000, which they achieved in 1990, and which they claim gave them 'the framework upon which to base improved operating disciplines' as well as much lacking standardisation between locations:

'By our nature as a transport company we are geographically spread and the establishment of. a single standard applicable across all our sites was invaluable in identifying best practice. Our experience of using ISO certification as a well defined objective which is part of a more ambitious total quality journey has worked well for us'.

Ownership of key processes has been extended to named managers at every location whilst the scope of management meetings has been expanded to provide regular forums for exploring new ideas and sharing best practices.

Continued pressure to improve customer satisfaction has resulted in a system whereby hard information on customer query handling, credit notes, client contacts, complaints received and other key outcomes is now gathered and fed back on a weekly basis:

'We realised that customers in our urgent delivery markets are often more impressed by an ability to save time rather than cost. Emphasis on pure cost reduction therefore decreased and we now concentrate on removing time from processes. Our frequent and unrelenting reporting disciplines continue to help us quickly introduce improvements whenever standards are not achieved. A named individual at each depot is responsible for each key performance outcome and our staff are empowered to call on central resources to achieve required results'.

Weekly reports for each location show actual results for all of the following outcomes:

* deliveries on time

* misrouted and missorted consignments

* copy consignment notes raised and not matched with original documents

* late linehaul services arriving at hubs

* failures to deliver on time analysed by reason

A need for improved people management was highlighted from a TNT(UK) people survey which revealed that a strong desire existed within the company for improved cross-divisional knowledge throughout the organisation. Management responded to this call with the launch of Expressionism', a video based training programme that covers for all employees the complete development of the company:

'Our Expressionism training courses have been a huge success and are now regularly delivered via line management facilitators to every person in the company together with a large number of suppliers'.

The company has improved its use of resources through the installation of data terminals in TNT express delivery vehicles which now provide up-to-the-minute information for customers about the status of urgent consignments and enable immediate response to be given to on demand collection requests placed by customers:

Everyone employed in the company now has a computer screen which provides access to reliable real time data thus enabling our people to instantly address external and internal customer requests'.

In applying for the Award the company did not use consultants at any stage of implementation of the EFQM Model and the application document was written by a single manager who had been involved in the preparation of the company's first self-assessment:

'It would have been completely inappropriate to buy in and attempt to impose an off-the-peg solution. All of our Award documents have been written completely in-house. As part of our last application we commissioned external consultants to briefly review our draft document and make some cosmetic suggestions'.

'We work hard to prepare an impressive professionally presented document as this is our shop window. A copy of our EQA application is available at all sites and has come to be regarded as a point of reference setting out the core values of the organisation'.

Assessor feedback reports are reviewed line by line by the whole management team and action points then allocated to individuals.

The review of TNT (UK) in *'Aspects of Excellence'* (the special Awards Edition of *European Quality*) describes the company as 'one of the finest role models which the European Quality Award has produced to date'. It stresses the 'absolute importance of empowerment ' as viewed by the company's Managing Director Alan Jones OBE who is quoted as follows:

"If you're too systematized you might convene a committee, set up working parties, form project groups, appoint a project director, get a new system from head office or bring in a load of consultants. Before long you haven't delivered your parcels, the deadline has been missed and you've lost the plot. We have created an empowered culture where working groups can convene instantly, meeting in the corridor if necessary and allocate responsibilities to make things happen in a twinkling of an eye ".

Also highlighted are the company's 'supreme level of internal co-operation' despite the company's outwardly competitive approach, and the distinct lack of staff turnover problems which bedevil so many of TNT's competitors. On this latter subject Alan Jones states:

"Many companies don't progress because they are engaged in a constant round of reorganisations, restructuring and consequent management changes. We don't have that problem. The people running this company joined in junior positions and have grown through the ranks giving them unrivalled practical experience ".

On winning the Award Mr. Jones commented: -

"Winning the European Quality Award is a tribute to the ten thousand TNT(UK) staff who have helped us achieve leadership in our express delivery and time sensitive logistics markets. The sheer enthusiasm of our

people and the 'must get through attitude' which prevails everywhere in the company keeps us ahead of the opposition".

He described the difference between being a Finalist and winning the Award as "very narrow" and promised that within the week every TNT(UK) depot would have a replica of the European Quality Award as a memento.

B.T. Yellow Pages: up and coming.

BT Yellow Pages have a similar turnover to TNT(UK) though have been in existence rather longer, since 1966. Their publications in the form of 76 printed directories are currently delivered to some 20 million households and around 350,000 advertisers place over 650,000 advertisements in them every year.

Business Pages was launched in the 1980s, as a business-to-business classified directory and their Business Database containing some 1.7 million business locations is now the UK's principal source of business-to-business direct marketing data. They also provide 'Talking Pages', a comprehensive telephone information service providing up-to-date details on businesses, shops and services throughout the UK. Also on the Internet YELL provides access to a comprehensive, reliable and up-to-date guide to UK web sites and businesses as well as electronic shopping through ShopYell.

Self-assessment against the criteria of the Business Excellence Model began in earnest in1994 when it was used primarily as an audit tool, enabling the organisation to identify and focus on a strategic push toward improved customer satisfaction.

The objective was to become closer to their customers and become an essential component in their business enabler framework. It was their particular task of management to convince all sales personnel that building quality into all of their processes was the only way forward for the organisation. This is not always an easy task and it has taken time, but as many would say 'the penny is beginning to drop' and BT Yellow Pages is now shaping up alongside other worthy EQA Prize Winners.

The building of a single sales organisation has undoubtedly helped BT Yellow Pages in its endeavours as they now have direct access to all of their UK customers rather than relying on agents.

A commitment to accuracy and a complete revision of the bonus system have then been at the heart of a campaign for change which is described in 'Aspects of Excellence' as follows:

'Given the cost of failure and the dangers inherent in inaccurate information we focused our sales people on getting it right first time. We needed to change both the way we pay sales people and the systems and processes that

supported them. We changed their remuneration policy to reflect the view that a sale is only a sale when the business collects the money, thus ensuring that our sales people had a clear and vested interest in quality'.

The need to eliminate high levels of staff turnover and therefore to maintain high levels of people satisfaction amongst sales staff is also highlighted:

'We sell every contract every year and we try to ensure the same sales person goes back to the same customers every year. That way they have the opportunity to become part of the customer's business and to work with the customer to design a programme that will work for the customer. If it fails or they do not work with the customer to make sure the paperwork is correct, going back to explain and to win the contract for another year can be difficult'.

The sales team at BT Yellow Pages is equipped with the latest laptop computers which utilise the organisation's own software which was designed in-house. Every field sales representative also has an ISDN link into his own home so that he can up or down load information to or from the organisation's main computers.

In his conclusion Managing Director John Condron states:

"Quality is no accident: we work hard to deliver it and keep on delivering it. Everyone in our company knows that. quality and continuous improvement are vital parts of their everyday job and crucial elements for our continued success".

Further Information.

Other Prize Winners in the Large Business and Public Sector Award categories, in addition to the four UK organisations mentioned above, were third time Prize Winner Netas (Turkey's leading telecomms equipment provider), AYE (a business unit of RENFE, the public sector Spanish rail operator), and French steel manufacturers Sollac.

Profiles of these and the other Finalists are featured in *'Aspects of Excellence'*.

UK QUALITY AWARDS

As with the European Quality Awards there were three UK Quality Awards presented this year at The Grosvenor House Hotel in London's Park Lane on October 29th. Ms Barbera Roche, Under Secretary of State for Small Firms at the DTI presented the Awards, two in the Commercial category and one in the Small Business category, at the Annual Gala Dinner of the BQF which this year attracted just under 1,000 participants.

The two Commercial Award Winners were both from the telecoms sector and were respectively BT Payphones and Nortel Northern Ireland.

BT Payphones: hanging on the telephone

BT Payphones once had an unenviable reputation which severely dented the corporate image of its parent company. It has, however, in the face of mounting competition from the mobile telecoms industry, realised a transformation which a decade ago would have been unthinkable. In addition to their 94,000 street payphones they now operate some 41,000 service payphones on private sites such as motorway service areas and airports.

There can be no doubt that BT Payphones has had to respond to the threat of increasing economic adversity since it became an autonomous unit of BT's personal communications division in 1990.

The growth of the mobile telephone industry in that time has meant that its once guaranteed share of a highly lucrative market began quickly to diminish to an extent where complacency and survival were mutually incompatible. Reliability, quality and customer satisfaction therefore suddenly became priorities for action.

The road to business excellence has been rocky to say the least with an on-style public sector culture needing urgently to be brought in line with that of business units such as Yellow Pages and BT Northern Ireland. The introduction of teamworking proved to be crucial to the success of early efforts which set out to solve problems as they arose. This has now been reinforced with a priority for innovation to find new sources of income which has necessitated building employee confidence and addressing the people satisfaction issue.

The special Awards issue of *UK Excellence* describes in part how this has been achieved through a new ideas programme known as 'Inspirations'. General Manager Malcolm Newing is quoted as follows:

"Rather than an updated suggestion system this programme concentrates on those moments of inspiration that everyone has. Our people are encouraged to come forward with new ideas for growing our business in new ways. The BT intranet site keeps everyone up to date with new initiatives so that we cut the bureaucracy involved to a minimum. We want to make everyone young again, at least in mind, so that they can let their imagination roam free ".

This kind of innovation has led to several new initiatives which have included the leasing of the first advertising space in payphone kiosks to the soft drinks manufacturer Tango, the installation of 'soft buttons' which will take users direct to an advertiser's call centre when a marked button is pressed, and the construction of the UK's first multimedia payphone, in the form of a new information terminal' which combines payphone technology with access to the Internet and e-mail.

Looking ahead BT Payphones is examining its possibilities in Europe where a new deregulated telecomms industry is opening up new opportunities for customer focused operators. Also to changes in the UK voting system which would create a demand for information terminals in supermarkets which would transmit votes directly to returning officers.

These and other developments have of course had a significant impact on Business Results for the organisation, which showed a profit of £78 million for 1997 as against the £73 million loss of ten years previous.

Nortel Northern Ireland: working with the Stakeholders.

Nortel Northern Ireland based in Monkstown, Newtonabbey, currently employ just under 900 employees and are part of the Nortel Group whose pioneering approach to Business Excellence is based on the principle of 'stakeholder symbiosis' i.e. balancing the needs of shareholders, customers and employees. The establishment of partnerships, not least with their suppliers, is critical to the success of this approach which is essentially based on a philosophy of increasing interdependence between the company and its partners.

The term Value Managed Relationship (VMR) has been devised to describe the company's supplier partnership initiative which currently assigns the accolade of 'global VMR suppliers' to ten of the company's key suppliers whose strategies and plans are viewed as complementary to those of Nortel. Six of these supply Nortel Northern Ireland and visit it regularly to exchange information and ideas.

The VMR concept is supported by Portfolio Management Teams which are based on portfolios such as semiconductors or discrete components, involve all relevant internal functions and are central to contract negotiations with key suppliers. They also have a brief to identify new technology solutions for obsolete components.

Goods inwards is handled electronically through electronic data interchange with suppliers and benchmarking of inventory control has led to substantial improvements. Improvement actions are devolved to operational areas such as planning, production, purchasing and stores where teams have been trained in the use of continuous improvement techniques. *'UK Excellence'* highlights some of the improvements which have been made to reduce development timescales and explains how 'Impact on Society' has been addressed:

'Each Monkstown supplier has been surveyed for a database that awards it an environmental rating, and presentations have been made to the top 100 suppliers in on-site seminars. Six suppliers subsequently signed up to Arena, a government and business supported environmental group'.

'An engineer is now responsible for minimising and re-using packaging materials. On all deliveries to BT and Cable and Wireless goods are carried to their point of use, unpacked and the packing materials returned to Nortel. Any damaged materials are consigned to recycling. Further waste production programmes are due to follow the conclusion of a survey this year to establish from which suppliers Nortel can get the most benefit in reducing or re-using packaging'.

Nortel Northern Ireland was the first Nortel site worldwide to eliminate the use of chlorofluorocarbons (CFCs) and in 1995 both the first company in Nortel and in Northern Ireland to achieve certification to the environmental management standard BS7750.

Their environmental management (EMS) was also selected to feature in a CD-ROM published this year as part of a European Commission project to promote the introduction of EMSs to industries within the European Union.

Further Information

The other finalists in the Commercial category were DHL International (UK), NatWest Insurance Services, and Post Office Counters. The sole Public Sector finalist was The Inland Revenue, Cumbernauld. These and the above Award winners are described in more detail in *'UK Excellence'*.

[Issue 120 (December 1998)]

QUALITY AWARDS FOR SMEs

This year both the European and UK Quality Award ceremonies featured Business Excellence awards for SMEs (under 250 employees).

At the European Quality Award ceremony in Paris two SME awards were presented, one for independent SMEs which was won by The Landhotel Schindlerhof of Nuremburg (Germany), and one for SME subsidiaries of larger organisations which was won by Beko Ticeret AS of Istanbul, a subsidiary of Beko Trading Inc. who market consumer durables produced by the Koc Group.

In the UK Awards The Seaview Hotel on the Isle of Wight received the Award.

Landhotel Schindlerhof: realising Joy in Work

The Landhotel Schindlerhof provides one of the more unusual and interesting case studies in recent years. It is a relatively small entrant even by

SME standards, although not the smallest, with just 51 staff who manage the restored 16th century farmhouse which currently has 71 rooms, a restaurant and recently expanded conference facilities.

A Finalist in the 1997 European Quality Awards it is owned by Renate and Klaus Kobjoll and has a turnover of around DM 8.5 million. It was the first hotel in Germany to achieve ISO9001 certification and has since gained a reputation as one of Germany's leading conference hotels with around 90% occupancy in the conference sector and 70% occupancy for the hotel itself .

Self-assessment to the Business Excellence Model began in 1996, but the hotel's unique and uncompromising approach to people management, people satisfaction and customer satisfaction date back much further and, arguably, conform to a much more advanced and obscure set of quality principles which few if any of its rivals would dare to attempt to copy.

Central to all of this is a relentless determination to realise true joy in work for all of the establishment's employees using a unique approach which could best be described as theatrical or even bizarre. The product of over a decade of 'organic growth', the 'game' grows day by day as heads of departments act as directors and set various scenes in which the employees act, whilst proprietors Klaus and Renate assume the role of 'entertainers' to provide 'special effects'. The 'play' is then varied enthusiastically every day by the entire team in interaction with the hotel's guests.

The result has been work that is intentionally fun to the extent that employees or 'fellow entrepreneurs' as they are termed, willingly exchange their valuable free time for the opportunity to realise quality improvements. Consequently the hotel and its management have transformed one of the core problems of the hotel industry as a whole, poor staff morale, into a source of competitive advantage.

In training, considerable use is made of the 'moment of truth' concept which makes use of the fact that many interactions with customers contain elements which cannot be planned or inspected. This as guests continue to demand the unexpected so the hotel's team capitalises on the unpredictability which serves as a driver for continuous improvement.

This is supported with a suggestion scheme which encourages every employee to submit at least one suggestion for improvement per month and much leisure time is spent devising 'efficiency suggestions'.

Staff self-assessment underpins the hotel's annual review with employees required to grade their performance honestly against 18 criteria which notably include openness to innovation and sensitivity. Personal goals for the coming year are then drawn up in harmony with the hotel's annual plan. As for customer satisfaction management consider that customers have complained if they do not indicate the very highest satisfaction category on all appraisal cards which are themselves the subject of continual review in pursuit of ever higher standards. Thus the number of complaints may go up even though quality has improved.

As the finishing touches are now being made to the upgraded conference facility mention may perhaps be made of the philosophy behind its design which, as with the rest of the hotel's management policy, conforms largely to Deming style principles. Essentially the Nuremberg architect Gunther Dechant has adhered to the principle of 'everything from a single source' both in the style of the building and its interior.

The concept of 'holistic architecture', fully in line with 'feng shui', emerges in the new building in which all of the elements are in harmony with shapes and colours which blend together. This harmony, with its surroundings reflected in a modern wooden construction combined with large areas of glass to allow sun to shine through and a roof which has been designed as a garden. area, shows clearly that the Impact on Society criterion of the Business Excellence Model has been taken seriously.

The architect comments as follows:

"I have consciously avoided following any 'fashionable' trends. The building owes nothing to current ideas in architecture. In twenty years' time nobody will be able to say that the building is ' typically 1998'.

As Renate was given the honour of receiving the Award on behalf of the Landhotel Schindlerhof, Klaus Kobjoll commented:

"Even our builders now consider our commitment to TQM. I cannot understand why some SMEs still think it is only for large manufacturing organisations".

Other accolades which the Landhotel Schindlerhof has received include the Entrepreneur of the Year Award 1997 from the Leonberg Management Academy and a special Award from Business Traveller Magazine for the most innovative hotel concept of 1997.

Bako Ticaret: winning with Teamwork

The presence of another Turkish company in this year's list of European Quality Award Winners reinforces the country's determination to be taken seriously when it comes to business excellence. Inspired first by the forward looking and progressive approach of TUSIAD-Kalder (the Turkish Industrialists' and Businessmans' Quality Association) which they joined in 1996, they joined the EFQM in 1997 although they had adopted the self-assessment principles of the Business Excellence Model some three years previously. This followed earlier efforts based on the criteria of the US Malcolm Baldrige Award which they adopted in 1993.

Their approach to quality is based very much on teamwork, both internal with their 237 employees and external with their 4,000 plus dealers with whom they have developed 'an affectionate relationship' as well as a balance of interest. This is reflected in the fact that the company is investing $100,000 in training for its dealers in addition to the $140,000 it is investing to train its own employees. By adopting this approach management have seen their employee satisfaction levels improve from 72% in 1993 to 95% in 1997 whilst turnover has increased from $237 million to $483 million over the same period.

The approach with dealers is to find out about their problems during their biannual and regional dealership meetings and visits and then to develop appropriate solutions. This is supported with special awards to dealers that have been working with Beko for 10, 20 and 30 years. With their own staff job and competency, analyses are conducted for every position and unique Beko methods used to co-ordinate all human resources activities. A quality improvement team established by employees and dealers has, for example, significantly reduced delivery cycle times and the average number of stock days.

Impact on Society has been addressed with support given to the 1997 activities of the Kozalak Dance Theatre featuring Turkish dancers with an international reputation for interpretation and performance and, through the company's cultural and artistic sponsorship programme to a stage production of 'The Little Prince' by French novelist Antoine de Saint Exupery.

Beko gave away tickets to this latter production, which introduced the world of 'The Little Prince' to orphans and disadvantaged children through various charity organisations, foundations and schools, to everyone who visited their dealers.

On receiving the European Quality Award for subsidiary SMEs at the Palais de Congres Aka Gunduz Ozdemir, General Manager of Beko Trading Inc. stated the following:

"The primary and unnegotiable objective of all the Beko employees and the authorised sales force is to ensure that all the goods and services offered to our customers are fully satisfactory and preferred. Our dealers and suppliers first and foremost expect us to display an open, fair and honest attitude. They want us to support them in their happiness and pride, as well as in their worries and bad times; to share their fortune in identifying with and solving their problems as if they were our own. Therefore, we are generous and intimate in our relationships with our employees, dealers and consumers.

Because we know no limit in service, and make use of all our possibilities to solve problems, we have been able to set unbreakable improved bonds between us. The methods that make our objective accessible are placing the necessary emphasis on teamwork and team spirit, trying to do our jobs in a perfect manner, and assuming continuous training and improvement as a lifestyle".

The company currently markets consumer durable goods with the Beko brand to foreign consumers in 45 different countries. The manufacturers, Koc Group, has, by contrast, been the largest trade and industry corporation in Turkey for many years with its 93 companies and 40,000 employees. It has been gaining ground outside Turkey with 24 international companies and 6 international offices.

Meanwhile, in Turkey itself, over 1,000 representatives from Turkish businesses, plus public sector and academic representatives, attended the launch of the Kal Der Turkish National Quality Movement Initiative on 23rd September. It has as one of its primary objectives the achievement of 1,000 self-assessing companies by October 2000 when Istanbul is scheduled to host the European Quality Awards.

The Seaview Hotel: working with Competitors

Commitment, dedication and sheer hard work earned Nick and Nicky Hayward, proprietors of the sixteen bedroomed Seaview Hotel on the Isle of Wight, their UK Quality Award for SMEs. Beginning in 1980, when they jointly abandoned their well established careers in London, the husband and wife team set about the task of restoring what was at the time a somewhat run-down and dilapidated small hotel in a relatively depressed area of Southern England.

For eighteen years thereafter they worked with local suppliers and competitors on a project to generate much needed revenue and create jobs in a place where unemployment has remained persistently at around double the national average.

Involvement with the Business Excellence Model began in1996 following participation in a benchmarking study undertaken by KPMG. They then used it both as a tool to assess relationships with customers and suppliers and as a means of reviewing processes geared toward the customer at every level in order to ascertain if they could be improved.

A 'culture of absolute customer care' has been generated by the hotel's 40 staff which has left them highly respected as an 'engine for growth' on the island. Central to this has been a belief on the part of the owners that co-operation rather than competition would improve prosperity for everyone in their industry and their area i.e. rather than devoting energy toward viewing other hotels as competition they work with them to benefit the whole island by bringing in revenue from a growing number of tourists.

Their first source of steady revenue was the restaurant, a feature of which is the innovative nature of the menu, which is predominantly on home grown island produce. This helped to build up a regular clientele which culminated in 450 bookings in 1997 which came solely from previous guests who had been delighted with their stay. This contributed to business results in the peak week of 1997 of some £50,000 which represented an increase of some 80% on 1995.

A policy of flattening the seasonal income curve by agreeing yearly rates with local businesses has enabled people satisfaction to be enhanced by guaranteeing all the year round employment for all of the hotel's staff .The fact that the hotel's managers (bars, restaurant, kitchen staff etc) have been in residence for an average of eleven years is evidence in itself that employee loyalty is high, not to mention training standards with 90% of staff holding National Vocational Qualifications or higher in an industry
where the average is nearer 20%.

UK Excellence quotes Mrs. Nicola Hayward as follows:

"We are not a country house hotel nor a top London brasserie and never can be. We are just a little, rather peculiar, seaside hotel, but we can strive to be the best in that sector. We understand that there is a wider picture than just the Seaview, this whole island needs help and we are in a position to help it in a small way. Understanding where we stand in relation to the village and the island as a whole is extremely important to our entire business ethos".

At the UK Quality Award ceremony in London the Chief Executive of The British Quality Foundation Malcolm Franks, who retires from this role at the end of the year, commented:

"Many organisations, not just small businesses, could learn a lot from studying how Seaview has achieved its eighteen year track record of growth and success. Winning this national Award is one of the highest accolades any organisation can achieve and it is greatly to their credit that they have been chosen."

Other Awards which the hotel has achieved include the Meridian Television Small Business Excellence Award for the Southern Region.

Further Information

There were seven other European SME Finalists. These were the Prize winner Danish International Continuing Education (team of 50 who provide courses in management development, human resources management, project management , amnagement systems and IT), Bekaert-Stanwick Consultants SA of Belgium, Burton-Apta Refractory Manufacturing Limited (Hungarian kiln furniture manufacturer), Daramic SY (French battery separator manufacturer, part of the US based InterTech Group), Fundera Condals SA (independent Spanish iron casting business),Hermes Softlab (Slovenian software engineering company), and Vallourec Composants Automobiles Vibry (part of Groupe Vallourec of France specialising in the production of automobile suspension systems).

Descriptions of these and the Award Winners may be found in *'Aspects of Excellence'*, the special Awards issue of *European Quality*. In the UK Awards there was one other SME Award finalist, Vista Optics , (contract lens manufacturer based in Stockport). They are described along with the Award Winner in *UK Excellence.*

[Issue 116 (August 1998)]

E.F.Q.M. APPOINTS NEW C.E.O.

The European Foundation for Management (EFQM) has announced the appointment of Alain de Dommartin, formerly CEO of the Renault Quality and Management Institute, as its Chief Executive Officer from 1st July.

He succeeds Secretary General Geert de Raad who is now the Director General of the Dutch Accreditation Office. On assuming this new appointment M. de Dommartin said:

"Within the EFQM we have a lot of knowledge and experience about Business Best Practices. Now, we must make sure that this constitutes an open window to the world. We must emphasise the design of pragmatic and user-friendly EFQM tools as well as encourage research in various management disciplines to make the EFQM the voice of European business corporations".

[Issue 122 (February 1999)]

IRISH QUALITY PROGRESS

The presentation of the first Irish Business Excellence Awards was at the prestigious Conrad International Hotel in Dublin on 11th November along with a re-launch of the Irish Quality Mark to emphasise continuous improvement in place of compliance to fixed standards. Also included is the recently launched joint initiative between Excellence Ireland (formerly the Irish Quality Association) and the Northern Ireland Quality Centre to establish a Business Excellence Recognition Scheme for SMEs in Northern Ireland and the border counties of Eire, (Louth,Monaghan, Cavan, Leitrim, Sligo and Donegal).

In support of the latter, Excellence Ireland's Chief Executive Sean Conlan, who also became Ireland' s first President of the European Organisation for Quality, said:

"The Business Excellence Model has proven very successful in Europe since its development in the early 1990s, but research shows that SMEs have been reluctant to become involved, seeing it as too costly in terms of cash and manpower. This Scheme will introduce such companies to tighter and more efficient management practices and results, which will ultimately improve profitability and result in the better use of manpower".

On the same subject Bob Barbour, Chief Executive of the Northern Ireland Quality Centre commented:

"SMEs are particularly vulnerable in the current competitive climate; thus, continuous improvement and high quality standards of production and service are essential for their survival and growth. The need to improve competitive advantage is particularly acute within Northern Ireland and the six border counties, where SMEs have been disadvantaged through twenty five years of violence and social and political unrest".

Below a review is presented of the first recipient of the Irish Business Excellence Award Lucent Technologies Ireland, based in Bray, County Wicklow.

Lucent Technologies Ireland: achieving Excellence through Policy Deployment.

Lucent Technologies Ireland was established as AT and T Network Systems Ireland in 1983 when the US multinational bought Telectron an Irish-owned manufacturer. They moved to Bray in 1985 and currently manufacture copper cable and components for the SYSTIMAX c range of structured cabling systems. A wireless GSM software development laboratory and Network Services Deployment Team are also based at the site which has around 340 employees.

Quality management is centred around the methodology of policy deployment for which a matrix has been developed based on the familiar principle of Plan-Do-Check-Act. This matrix serves as both a management tool and a communication vehicle and is prominently displayed on notice boards in the main corridor of the Bray plant as well as transmitted electronically to individuals in the company's team based structure. It categorises all company plans according to the so called 'five fixed plans' criteria of:

- engage people

- exceed customer expectations

- increase shareholder value

- enhance quality

- create positive impact on society

The matrix serves to link corporate strategies to individual and team actions and results and incorporates elements of strategy, long term objectives, projects, metrics, goals, and ownership. An external benchmark may also be featured where it is deemed to be appropriate. Each month project owners or 'champions' send monthly updates to Quality Manager Ciaran Burke to advise him of progress, after which the matrix is updated for electronic transfer to team leaders.

Many of the projects originate by cascade from top management, but any employee may request the formation of an improvement team by means of a formal team requisition procedure. Each request is then reviewed by an executive steering team and if it is felt that the formation of a team is merited a cross-functional team may be formed. This will then be provided with the necessary funding, training, leadership and other resources as required. Should specific skills and competencies be required, then specific individuals may be approached to join the team. Should non-specific competencies be needed then team membership may be opened more widely through advertising on company notice boards. The system has appeared to work well with 'full participation' reported. The executive steering team meets weekly to review progress on improvement activities and to receive the twice yearly progress presentations that are required from each team.

Each manufacturing operation is supported by a dedicated quality representative who is responsible for maintaining the quality system to the required standard and for seeking opportunities for continuous improvement, which frequently results in the formation of special teams. A European Quality Team has conducted an annual business excellence assessment of the company since 1995 and prepared an annual report for the steering team which has included scores in specific areas and identification of opportunities for improvement. These reports have led to new projects in the areas of customer feedback and community involvement.

A dedicated quality department manages the company's corrective action system known as the Quality Improvement Request (QIR) System and its associated database which records all opportunities for improvement policy deployment goals and other relevant information. Each QIR has a named owner or team leader who enters key information such as root cause analysis, proposed corrective action, final corrective action and close dates. A quality representative verifies that action taken is appropriate and satisfies all necessary requirements. The QIRs are reviewed weekly between the owner, the quality manager and the general manager to ensure that they are addressing any gaps in activity or performance.

Another key activity for the quality department is testing the results of which are transmitted to a team at Lucent corporate headquarters in the USA who then compile comparative results in the form of a Grade Point Average, which is used as a benchmark between Lucent companies.

Within the Lucent Group, Lucent Technologies Ireland has a score of 4.8 on a scale of 5.0. This compares favourably with a target of 4.5. In addition the plant is audited externally by product certification specialists Underwriters Laboratories on a monthly basis and cable operations have been shown to have achieved defect-free output throughout 1998.

Recent innovations have included the development of a high-tech Customer Solutions Centre which uses multimedia facilities to illustrate how Lucent products may be networked together. Multidisciplinary teams give demonstrations which enable customers and potential customers to visualise how networking applications and products can provide cabling solutions in their buildings.

Impact on Society has been addressed through various community initiatives, links with schools and the Bray Chamber of Commerce, and mentoring programmes for local businesses. A dedicated community relations team has been formed to identify opportunities which could be envisaged to have a positive effect on the environment and open days are frequently held for local residents and school parties.

Plans for the future include the development of a new fibre-optic facility in the Bray area to complement the existing copper-based cable operation and create some 150 new jobs.

At the Awards ceremony Sean Conlan commented:

" As well as an enviable record of achievement of quality standards, Lucent demonstrates an exceptional commitment to internal communications and also to customer satisfaction. There have been regular off-site presentations and workshops which explain the corporate strategy to groups of fifty employees at a time.

There is also an internal TV broadcast to ensure that shift workers do not miss out on receiving the company's information. Their commitment to quality spreads beyond process control into all elements of business, including policy deployment and planning. It is this breadth of thinking that makes Lucent worthy winners of the first Irish Business Excellence Awards".

Managing Director Joseph Lyons said on receiving the Award:

"Quality systems are critical to our business and the Business Excellence approach provides a framework in which we can also measure and improve our internal communications and customer satisfaction activities. As a

global company with a base in Ireland we are eager that our quality systems are internationally focused. The European based Irish Business Excellence Award uses criteria that are appropriate to our location and commercial situation in Ireland".

[*Quality Matters* would particularly like to thank Sean Conlan and the staff of Excellence for their help and assistance with this report -Ed].

[Issue 123 (March 1999)]

QUALITY SCOTLAND

In 1991 Quality Scotland was established by a few highly respected companies keen to develop a quality culture in Scotland. Since then its original base of 14 members has expanded to over 200. It is independent, non-profit making and non-political and works through a Board comprising of senior executives from the governing members, whilst a small central team (with senior management experience totalling over 300 years) manages development and day-to-day administration.

This month *Quality Matters* reports on some of its recent activities and initiatives, which include most notably the 1998 Scottish Forum for Business Excellence (incorporating the fifth annual Quality Scotland Awards) held on 26th November and attended by around 400 delegates. Also we report. where Quality Scotland have introduced various initiatives in the Community. Here Quality Scotland may be seen to be taking the lead in encouraging business excellence where arguably it matters the most, i.e. amongst the young in schools and colleges.

Quality Scotland Awards

There were five finalists for the 1998 Quality Scotland Awards from which two overall Winners were selected, namely Honeywell Newhouse, winners of the manufacturing sector, and Scottish Homes, winners of the public sector category .

The first is a well established facility dating back to 1953 when it succeeded Honeywell's first facility outside the US in Blantyre, Lanarkshire. Since then it has evolved into a site of excellence which excels particularly in processes and supply management. It occupies a 32 acre site and manufactures some 7,000 different kinds of switches and sensors and 500 varieties of timing devices including thermostats, boiler controls and electrostatic air cleaners. Around 70% of its products are exported, with 60% being supplied to Europe and despite the current manufacturing recession in the UK business results have improved over the last four years with a 35% increase in sales.

Quality initiatives include a refinement of the just-in-time principle which has all but eliminated the need for inventory. Operators effectively control the process using a bin system whereby parts are ordered directly from suppliers using a PC. This so called Point Of Use Replenished (POUR) is then integrated with a flexible form of cell manufacturing in which one or two individuals may be responsible for manufacturing a complete product from initial assembly to packaging and labelling. Thus instead of waiting for product to arrive on a conveyor belt prior to undertaking a task, operators progress from task to task within the cell.

This has been proven to be both quicker and more cost effective as well as providing higher levels of people satisfaction and enabling the company to respond more quickly to customer demand. The use of Vendor-Managed Inventories i.e. where suppliers enter cells on a daily basis assists in the achievement of zero working capital, zero inventory and zero lead time.

Impact on Society has been addressed by plans which examined such aspects as the use of fuel oil, the level of carbon dioxide emissions, and the use of water and energy. Over four years the company has managed to reduce water consumption by 60% following a drive to eliminate waste through leakage, implement a project to generate 80% of their own electrical power with heating provided as a by-product, and to reduce carbon dioxide emissions in their entirety.

Their environmental performance has consequently been difficult to rival, with ISO 14000 certification being achieved in 1997 and the Lanarkshire Environmental Business Award being secured early in 1998.

Benchmarking is also well established at Honeywell with partners including OKI and IBM. A group meets every other quarter with these partners to examine such areas as training and documentation. Internally the company monitors performance through a Quality Council comprising of senior managers who meet monthly off-site. At the end of each year the Council meets for two days to set improvement programmes for the year ahead.

In the public sector, which traditionally lags behind the private sector in virtually all European countries as far as quality is concerned, Scotland would appear to have a better record than most and the Scottish case study exemplifies this. Scottish Homes were formed in 1998 as a result of the merger of two so called 'quangos', namely The Scottish Housing Association which had built and managed some 120,000 homes over its fifty year history, and the Housing Corporation of Scotland which provided grants to local housing associations.

In the early days the Edinburgh-based organisation, by its own admission, suffered from "an externally imposed management structure, an unreconciled mix of predecessor's culture, a lack of confidence and direction, low staff morale, plus uncertainty amongst its customers and the wider community". It inherited 78,000 homes under management and a £200 million programme of investment in new housing which, thanks to partnership with the private sector, has now doubled to around £400 million.

There could be little doubt that when Peter McKinley became Chief Executive of Scottish Homes in 1991 (recruited from the prison service) that a fresh approach to leadership was required. In 1992, for example, a staff survey revealed that only 45% of staff believed that they could access the information they required.

Adoption of the EFQM Business Excellence Model in the same year focused attention on leadership and has led subsequently to the formulation of a 20 page blueprint centred around how staff view the Scottish housing market in another twenty years. A culture change programme was set in motion using the driving principles of empowerment and public accountability, and feedback from employees was used to develop a set of corporate values using the mnemonic 'SHARED' (Supportive, Honest, Approachable, Responsive, Empowered, Decisive).

During 1997 there was a deliberate shift in both power and accountability from the centre to managers in the regions and three new networking groups have been established for senior and middle managers under the titles of 'Quality and Leadership', 'Process Improvement', and 'Performance'. There are clear links between these and the criteria of the Business Excellence Model.

Impact on Society has been addressed through the encouragement of greater community participation in housing i.e. encouraging people to take an interest in their homes and look after them better, and through project management centred around the design of houses that are energy efficient and ecologically sound.

The other finalists in the 1998 Quality Scotland Awards were Bekaert of Glenrothes Fifeshire, and The Edinburgh International Conference Centre, (both Highly Commended in the Smaller Enterprise sector category), and Scottish Courage Brands Limited of Edinburgh, suppliers of canned and bottled beer to the UK take home market (formed three years ago from the acquisition of Courage by Scottish and Newcastle, -Highly Commended in the Service sector category).

Junior Quality Scotland.

In addition to the main quality awards Quality Scotland also has an award scheme for 15 to 19 year olds known as Junior Quality Scotland. Under this scheme young people are encouraged to set up Young Enterprise Companies which trade for one complete school year, after which they are wound up. An award is then made to the company which best demonstrates how it has perceived 'quality' and the value it has contributed to their product. This award takes the form of a 'quaich' [A unique form of Scottish drinking vessel -Ed], and a cheque for £150 for their school.

Five finalists were selected for the finals of Junior Quality Scotland which were held at the Scottish Office in Leith in early June. The finalists were: St. George's of Edinburgh, Hutcheson's Grammar School in Glasgow, St. Leonard's of St. Andrews, and two from Dundee High School, one of which, Sunrise Enterprise, was selected as the overall winner . Their project involved the publication of a children's book entitled 'Patsy the Punk Fairy' which evolved from an innovative idea which was market tested in the development phase.

Other Initiatives

Other initiatives in education include the 'Q Project' which encourages sixth year pupils to participate over six months in a business project with a member company, whilst for primary schools 'Quality Quest' has been designed to introduce pupils to basic ideas on quality and the relationship between achieving individual goals and quality service to others. In the latter, participating companies provide a facilitator to go into a school and lead four one hour sessions based on course materials developed by the Centre for Enterprise Education at Strathclyde University, Gorebridge Primary School, Strathclyde Police, Scottish Power, The Benefits Agency, and Royal Mail.

Outside education Quality Scotland have also begun to introduce regional partnerships, the latest of which is 'Business Excellence Ayrshire' which was formally launched on November 4th. A Board is now in place, chaired by Winston Wright, formerly General Manager of Volvo, Irvine, and an office has been established to co-ordinate activities in Kilmarnock. Meanwhile a new Quality Scotland partnership has been set up in Fife where a similar initiative is planned.

[Issue 130 (October 1999)]

EUROPEAN QUALITY AWARDS 1999

A record 27 finalists were selected for this year's European Quality Awards in Brussels. The majority (13) were for the Large Business and Business Units category, three of which were from the UK, with six being selected in the Independent and Subsidiary SME categories and two in a new category, Operational Units, which covers company departments such as sales or marketing which are not strictly business units.

From these Finalists four were selected to receive the prestigious European Quality Award on 6th October in the presence of His Majesty King Albert II of the Belgians at the Heysel Centenary Halls, whilst five further companies were selected to receive European Quality prizes. The four winning companies were Reading based Yellow Pages (UK) in the Large Businesses and Business Units category, Volvo Cars Gent (Belgium) in the Operational Units category, Danish International Continuing Education (DiEU) in the Independent SME category, and Servitique Network Services (France) in the Subsidiary SME category.

The European Quality Prize winners were BT Northern Ireland, ELAL SA (Unilever Greece) and Sollac (France) in the Large Businesses and Business Units category, and Burton Apta (Hungary) and Banc International d' Andorra i Banca Mora in the Subsidiary SME category.

In announcing the Awards the Chairman of the jury for large organisations Mr. Ferdinand de Arriluce de Yoarra of Spain acknowledged the help and support of EC DG 23 who currently provide half of the funding for the SME scheme but echoed the message of disappointment of previous years concerning the lack of applications and standard of entry from the public sector which "had a very poor presence". Once again the Public Sector Award was not awarded and this year there were no Finalists either. On a brighter note Jacques Macmillan, Chairman of the SME jury spoke of the "strong leadership, good process management and concern for customers and other stakeholders" on the part of SME Finalists the standards of which "was even reaching that attained by some large companies".

Below a summary of the winning organisations and their presentations is given.

Yellow Pages: switching the Balance from Process to People

Yellow Pages, a division of BT providing a range of information products to business and residential services and currently the UK's leading supplier of business-to-business direct marketing data. They have a database containing 1.7 million business locations which can be segmented and searched in any way the customer requires, and employ some 3,000 people in eleven main offices.

This year head of External Relations Richard Duggleby addressed the Forum with a presentation entitled "Policy and Strategy: Benchmarking with the best" which perhaps gave delegates an insight into where some of Yellow Pages' hidden strengths lay, quite apart from being strong on all nine criteria of the Business Excellence Model. In his talk he explained how Yellow Pages had adopted a strategy of shifting the balance from process to people in accordance with the belief that quality and strategy "were more about people than processes". He stressed the importance of recognising people "who live the values of the company" and outlined how as part of their approach to policy and strategy the organisation had given all managers a budget to apply recognition rather than having recognition merely featuring in the budget as stationery or similar items. He then described the organisation's policy of upward appraisal (junior managers providing feedback on senior ones), stating that there was "no better way of creating a culture where people can create and make a real change to the business". Thus, whilst many UK organisations were struggling with recognition, Yellow Pages had made strides and, with the help of EFQM guidance, had made the all important breakthrough with empowerment.

Delegates were informed how 85% of staff now agreed that they had training, management support and a wide boundary to deliver customer satisfaction whilst the upward appraisal system began with the top team as there was general feeling that unless people were comfortable with it at this level it was likely to flounder. A questionnaire was deployed which at first was viewed as being somewhat complicated, but after refinement and simplification a format evolved which most people could accommodate.

Other subjects which were seen as critical to policy and strategy included communication and in this connection the speaker explained how his organisation made time (40 minutes} for all staff to complete their annual staff attitude survey, the response rate to which was quoted as 92%. "People know that if they use the survey they will get action", he said. He likewise explained how each employee receives a booklet detailing profits, sales, customer retention and all of the key programmes the company has set itself.

Communication was described a "the key to ensuring that there is some process for staff accessibility" although in the question and answer session which followed the presentation he warned of the potential for e-mail "to devalue communication" if it is over-used and suggested that the Intranet was frequently much more effective. "We'll use anything and every thing to make sure everyone understands the message", he explained.

In the special Awards issue of *European Quality* entitled *'Aspects of Excellence'* Yellow Pages' Chief Executive John Condron, who received the Award is quoted as follows:

'Customer service is misunderstood by many, especially in the UK. It doesn't mean constructing all sorts of processes which act as a barrier between your people and getting the job done. If you introduce process to pin down, regulate and regularise, then you are going to encounter a lot of internal resistance. You don't have to think too hard to work out how this will transmit itself to your external customers. We try to free people, through the sensible use of process, to express themselves as individuals. This builds their self image and reflects immediately on the way they behave to customers. The question is how to stop people doing things that they don't like and how to free them to do things they like. The answer, in part, is better use of technology, tools and processes. Our role as managers is to reduce repetitive, mundane tasks to a minimum'.

The article, entitled *'Yellow Pages: a brand of excellence'* describes the criteria by which senior managers' 'competencies' are measured and how long term partnering with specialist directory printers R.R Donnelley and typesetters PindarSet has helped to reduce cycle times by 15 days over two years and 50 days over five years. It also explains how Yellow Pages has achieved 'best in class performance' in the area of invoicing and debt collection, a critical process in which inaccuracies could have drastic cash flow consequences, and how customer satisfaction is measured 'to a level and depth far beyond its competitors in other media'.

During 1999 Yellow Pages became the first division of BT to achieve full registration to ISO14001 across all offices and as part of their Impact on Society policy they work in association with national charities such as Marie Curie Cancer Care whilst some 4,500 runners take part annually in the Yellow Pages Reading Half Marathon. They have also worked with their printers and paper suppliers to develop processes which have enabled them to produce the first phone book in Europe using 100% recycled paper. In their submission document summary a chart shows how the proportion of general waste put to landfill dropped from 100% in 1993 to just 20% in 1998 whilst the amount recycled has risen from 12% in 1994 to 80% in 1998. Cartridge recycling meanwhile increased from zero in 1995 to 100% in 1998.

 In August 1999 Yellow Pages acquired Yellow Book a leading US independent directory publisher. In 1998 they had a turnover of around £486 million, whilst for the last five years they have achieved a 33% improvement in productivity. They have also published two benchmarking brochures, 'An invitation to benchmark with Yellow Pages' which provides a simple step by step template on how to improve processes both inside and outside the working environment.

Volvo Cars Gent: first in Europe and Japan.

Wednesday October 6th 1999 was an important day in the history of Volvo for on this day not only did they receive the European Quality Award for Operational Units but also the Japanese TPM Award for World Class Achievement, making for a unique double which is unlikely to be equalled for some considerable time. It goes without saying that TPM (Total Productive Maintenance) is central to the organisation's quality strategy and has been so since the early 1980s when it was recognised as one of those key methodologies which would potentially enable them to recover from the economic crisis that bedevilled the whole of the Western automotive industry at that time.

After becoming the first non-Japanese company to achieve the TPM Excellence Award in 1991 and the TPM Special Award in 1996 the company focused attention on using the philosophy in combination with the Business Excellence Model in order to build up and develop a teamwork organisation and to spectacularly improve business results. The company thus evolved a highly original approach to Business Excellence that was soon to pay dividends. Managing Director Hubert Casneuf commented:

"The ultimate aim with the two models is the same; i.e. to ensure continued existence, growth and employment opportunities by being more competitive. This is only possible by focusing oneself on the needs of the four stakeholders -the employees, customers, shareholders and society. EFQM provides us with a theoretical model, a helicopter view of our activities, what we are doing and what we should be doing. It is a very practical instrument for mobilising the workforce and for realising considerable improvements within a short space of time and for directing the company culture towards natural continuous improvement. Thanks to TPM's methodical approach and the results ensuing from this we achieved a high score for EFQM's European Quality Award".

The jury of the commission of the Japan Institute for Plant Maintenance (Professor Yamashima of Kyoto University and the London Business School, Institute vice president Tokutaru Suzuki and Professor Nakamura of Keio University in Yokohama) spoke particularly highly of the company's 'good balance between the technological content and the human factor'. The EFQM jury of six praised 'the culture of total quality and the cultural dynamics whereby respect for the individual is the fundamental upon which teamwork and recognition are built'. All of this points to a strong people management focus which was described in more detail in the 'Benchmarking with the Best: People Management ' workshop which described how people satisfaction was measured and afforded delegates the opportunity to inspect their Policy Deployment forms showing details of five Action Elements, their owners and co-owners, target dates and Level of Realisation.

Teamwork evolution was described in three phases (traditional working structure, self supporting team, self management) along with the company's Competence Management Methodology (ten elements) and Innovative Learning Techniques (simulation and fostering of a learning culture to increase employability). The latter has six principal components:

* Self managing teams (groups of blue collar workers responsible for an assembly part of the welding plant, paint shop, final assembly or material handling with targets based on Policy Deployment, management of resources, responsibility for work organisation, capacity development and competence management).

* Self managing clusters (groups of white collar workers responsible for the total management of an assembly process, engineering process or supporting service with targets based on Policy Deployment, management of resources, responsibility for cluster organisation, capacity flexibility and strategic competence management).

* Networking (network run projects chiefly from engineering department with a matrix type organisation established for each project consisting of salaried staff from the different departments involved).

* Development groups (working groups managing a development pillar with the assignment to develop the tools, to develop the strategy and to locate the various application priorities).

* Study groups (groups of volunteering white collar workers who investigate a particular topic with the main aim of getting a learning experience in any field).

* Thematic work groups (working groups primarily composed of white collar workers applying tools from the development pillars).

In addition modular teams based on platforms (all the models of car which are developed in parallel and which share components, systems, production processes, working methods, structure and architecture) have been conceived by the people involved in developing future products. Each team develops its part (module) of several car models in parallel on the same 'platform' together with the accompanying production process. Each module has development groups which work together at the same place. It is thus possible for modular teams to work on several future car models at the same time:

'The experience which is acquired from a new model under development can be immediately applied to the next model, thereby improving quality and significantly reducing lead times. Each team has a well-specified list of the components it is going to be working on. When the components have to match those from another team the collaboration between the teams is also specified in detail'.

Extensive use is also made of Quality Function Deployment (QFD):

'"Customer clinics", as part of QFD, are an active way of listening to customers. People corresponding to Volvo's customer profile are invited to these clinics. They can be Volvo customers and the owners of rival makes. Without knowing which make is being studied a group of customers are asked to spend a few hours examining a number of cars in terms of component fit and paintwork or to assess the function and comfort of the seats or to give their views on acceleration, for example. The interviewees are filmed and interviewed so that their views can be obtained in a discussion led by a professional moderator. He or she collates all the views and comments on special forms and the results are compared in detail with Volvo's own results. This method is structured and the questions have different levels. The moderator also conducts straight interviews with the respondents. There are many examples of the way QFD has resulted in new technical features and systems in Volvo cars. One is the safe and convenient function in Volvo estates which enables the head restraints to be left in place when the rear backrest is folded down'.

'At Volvo cross-functional groups of experienced people meet regularly and use effective brainstorming to draw up lists of thousands of properties in a future car model. This acts in part as the basis for specifications. The results of QFD surveys and all the other studies are then added'.

'Aspects of Excellence' describes the company's Customer Ordered Production (COP) system and quotes its planning manager Johan Cattoir as follows:

'All the other car makers have their own version of COP but in their case it is customer - oriented production. For customer-oriented production the dealers come to the plant and order cars in a variety of colours and models depending on previous sales and possibly research; ordering is based on allocated quota. COP is different, it places no limitations, no restriction on the customer, if they want a certain car with a certain colour and a certain interior, they will get it, no combination styles is taboo. And they are not restricted by dealers' availability or talk. Dealers can already contact the factory direct, there is no reason why we cannot extend that system to customers via the Internet'.

Volvo Gent is also strong on environmental performance, being the first car manufacturer to begin working to EMAS to which they were duly registered in January 1996, whilst in 1997 they gained the Environmental Charter 1997 from the Gent Chamber of Commerce with the Belgian Auditor's Association nomination for 'Best Environmental Report in Belgium' following in 1998.

Volvo Cars Gent assembles the Volvo S70 and V70 series and around 150,000 cars are assembled per year. They employ approximately 4,000 and have a turnover of around 2.74 euros.

SME Award Winners.

Independent SME Award Winner DiEU is one of the largest providers of courses a year (over 600) on leadership, management development, personal development, project management and quality management and are attended typically by more than 10,000 participants. A recipient of a European Quality Prize in 1998 they were established in 1975 by the Danish Society of Engineers (IDA) and began their formal quality journey in 1994. Since then they have moved from reactive self-assessment through active identification of strengths and areas of improvement to a proactive focus on future opportunities. They achieved ISO9001 certification in 1996 and in 1998 they invested heavily in the company PROGRES Human Resource Development A/S, a consulting company specialising in business psychology which was regarded as a 'perfect partner' on account of their quality focus, size and professional activities.

DiEU is based near Copenhagen, has 72 employees (55 full time) and a turnover of around 14.8 million euros. They produce an Intellectual Capital Report every year, and conduct annual lecturer satisfaction surveys which are used in a dialogue with lecturers to secure the continuous development of co-operation:

'Surveys are carried out with a total satisfaction index, a satisfaction index by departments in DiEU and by the relations we wish to measure. The satisfaction index by department means that individual departments are able to initiate improvement projects on survey results relevant to them. Through our end-of-course evaluations we monitor the quality of our lecturer network on an ongoing basis. Through our customers we measure the quality of our lecturers in the categories of The lecturer's communication and teaching skills, teaching methods and teaching material'.

Their customer database currently covers 98% of all Danish companies with over 100 employees.

Subsidiary SME Award winner Servitique Network Services was established as a subsidiary of Xerox France in 1989with the aim of providing services which were outside the core business of the Xerox Group. Initially hardware maintenance was their main activity but a refocusing of business objectives early in 1996 led to a strategic shift into their current specialism of networking and IT systems. In the same year an empowerment policy was introduced and in 1998 they were awarded the Prix Francais (French Quality Award) by the Mouvement Francais de la Qualite (MFQ). Business results have been reflected in a turnaround from an FF 10 million loss in 1995 to an FF10 million profit in 1998 and the company currently conducts around 4,000 customer satisfaction surveys a year.

They are Paris based, have 205 employees and a turnover in 1998 of FF 133 million.

Further Information

Full profiles of all 27 finalists, including the four remaining UK finalists (BT Northern Ireland, BT Payphones, Govan Initiative Limited and the Edinburgh International Conference Centre) are featured in *'Aspects of Excellence'*.

[Issue 131 (November 1999)]

PRODUCTIVITY MATTERS

As representatives of the Edinburgh International Conference Centre gathered in Brussels to ascertain their fate as Finalists in the European Quality Awards (Subsidiary SME category), the Centre served as hosts to the 11th World Productivity Congress, the biennial event of The World

Confederation of Productivity Science (WCPS) which was last held in Santiago, Chile in October 1997. It attracted around 650 participants and featured, in addition to the ten Plenary sessions, a total of around 117 papers from 21 countries.

State Quality and Productivity Awards: Tools for revitalising the Organisation.

Dr. Gary D. Coleman, Assistant Professor of Industrial Engineering and Senior Associate at The Performance Center of The University of Tennessee Space Institute, and Ms. Joanne Davis, Co-ordinator of the US Senate Productivity Awards and the Maryland Quality Awards at The Maryland Center for Quality and Productivity at the University of Maryland, jointly presented the above paper which presents the case for using award processes as tools for revitalising organisations drawing on recent experiences in Maryland, Tennessee and Virginia.

In their introduction they explain how currently out of USA's 50 states 43 now have formal awards programmes with the number of applications for these programmes increasing from just over 100 in 1991 to just under 1000 in 1997, whilst in 1998 the national and state programmes distributed well in excess of a million copies of the application and award criteria. They then give the following three prime reasons why an organisation should wish to participate in such a programme:

(i) Quality and productivity award processes facilitate business results.

(ii) Feedback received from the award process' external "experts" is a valuable form of consultation.

(iii) The recognition accompanying winning an award is valuable for both the organisation and its employees.

In support of their reasoning the authors state:

'Comparison of publicly traded Baldrige Award winners' stock, to Standard and Poor's 500 stock index, has shown the fictitious "Baldrige Index" to beat the S and P 500 each of the past five years. For the 23 publicly traded Baldrige winners from 1988 to 1993 a weighted index of their stocks produced a total return of 426 % compared to 173% for the S and P 500 during the same period.

A similar comparison of those companies that received site visits from the Baldrige Award process but didn't win the award showed stocks outperformed the S and P 500 ("Baldrige Index 1999"). This doesn't imply that winning the Award causes a company's stock price to increase. Instead, it supports the idea that the strategies and actions that score well against the award criteria also support superior financial performance'.

'Interventions in some areas (e.g. process management) may show results more quickly than others (e.g. human resource focus). The awards' underlying performance models reflect a systems approach that recognises not all areas will improve simultaneously. Feedback from acknowledged authorities (e.g. award examiners) can help organisations get through the lags between interventions and results, as well as help them target specific areas for improvement'.

The paper then proceeds to describe some specific approaches for using awards as revitalising tools along with some of the more novel approaches that have been tried in the US:

'Once an organisation moves beyond the use of a questionnaire, a popular form of assessment is the facilitated assessment. Here the key business leaders gather in a room for a day or two and examine their organisation against the criteria, capturing both strengths and areas for improvement. The discussions are led by an objective, usually external, facilitator. To validate the perceptions, results data may be looked at before or after the meeting'.

'On the more complex end of the spectrum the organisation prepares a written document in narrative format with graphically displayed results data. An external group (drawn from other business units or from outside the company) evaluates the documentation and conducts a site visit to clarify and validate the information provided. A feedback report is developed containing the assessment results. At this point self-assessment has evolved to essentially the process used for award application. Organisations completing a documented review are ready and typically eager to submit an application for their state award'.

'Typically, no feedback is given during a site visit since the purpose is to validate, clarify and further evaluate. The applicants later receive a written report summarising the examiners' findings. One state award has used a novel approach for enhancing these feedback reports. Applicants are given the opportunity to speak with and question their examiners the morning after the annual awards dinner. This "breakfast with the examiners" gives the applicants the opportunity to seek clarification and in some cases ask for guidance based on the feedback they have received. The sessions are conducted on a sector by sector basis, where one team of examiners usually conducted all of the evaluations and site visits for that sector. A good way to start these sessions is to have the examiners share their overall observations generalised across all applicants before allowing applicant specific questions'.

'The Tennessee Quality Award (TQA) has been very successful in implementing a process with levels of recognition. Applicants choose which level of recognition to apply for and they are recognised at that level or lower. Organisations just getting started may participate at Level 1 -Quality

Interest. Level 1 is not actually an award, but recognition for participating. Level 1 applicants complete a five-page business overview and host a half-day education and evaluation visit from TQA examiners. The intent here is to get the applicant to reflect upon their organisation and begin learning about the criteria for performance excellence.

They also receive feedback indicating improvements that may benefit the organisation. Level 2 -Quality Commitment applicants use a short form (5-15 pages) self-assessment. While Blazey (1998) has questioned the usefulness of short form self-assessments, we see these as an excellent learning tool for organisations that are not yet ready for a detailed self-assessment. For Level 2 applicants a one-day site visit is optional. Given the limitations of a short form self-assessment we recommend the site visit to enhance the richness of the feedback provided by the examiners. Level 3 - Quality Achievement requires a complete self-assessment (15-35 pages) against the TQA criteria and a two day site visit. Organisations recognised at this level have demonstrated significant progress and results. Level 4 - Tennessee Quality Excellence Award requires the same application as Level 3, but with a three-day site visit. Organisations recognised at this level exhibit world class processes and superior results (Tennessee Quality,1999).

Experience has shown that recognition of an organisation at the appropriate levels of achievement is very useful for keeping the momentum going'.

Commonalities of Recipients of the Shingo Prize

Dr. Shigeo Shingo, known internationally for his role in the creation of the Toyota Production System, is recognised as one of the all-time greats of quality, in particular for his pioneering of the mistake-proofing concept of poka-yoke and the single minute exchange of die (SMED) technique which was originally designed to remove waste during changeovers in batch production but which is now being applied also in continuous production . In honour of Dr, Shingo, who died in 1990, the Shingo Prize for Excellence in Manufacturing was established in 1988 at Utah State University where Dr. Shingo was presented with an honourary Doctorate in Business in the same year.

The Shingo Prize Systems Model, like the European Quality Award and its American Malcolm Baldrige equivalent, is based on a scoring system with a maximum of 1000 points although the criteria are somewhat different consisting of eleven key elements incorporated into five categories:

(i) Management Culture and Infrastructure (consisting of Leadership Culture and Infrastructure and Empowerment Culture and Infrastructure both worth 75 points each)

(ii) Manufacturing Business Strategy and System Integration (consisting of Manufacturing Vision and Strategy and Market and Product innovation both worth 50 points; Partnering with Suppliers and Customers worth 75 points; and World Class Manufacturing Operations and Processes worth 250 points).

(iii)   Business Functions and Process Integration (125 points)

(iv)   Measured Quality, Productivity and Customer Service (consisting of Quality and Product Costs worth 75 points; Productivity and Resource Utilisation worth 75 points; and Customer Service worth 75 points).

(v)   Measured Outcome Results (based on feedback with the above and awarding up to 75 points for customer satisfaction and business results combined).

Co-authors Ross Robson, Steven Beckstead and Steven Hanks (Executive Director Associate Director and Senior Research Associate respectively for The Shingo Prize for Excellence in Manufacturing at Utah State University) describe some of the characteristics which past winners of the award, which is distinguished by its requirement for organisations to demonstrate a commitment to waste elimination, have in common. They begin with leadership, noting that 'organisational leadership is responsible for the strategy whereas implementation in a Shingo Recipient plant is generally a shared responsibility consistent with the values of empowerment'. Most leaders 'are steeped in the lean paradigm of mentoring and coaching' with facilitative and participative leadership clearly the predominate style':

Each organisation has the overall belief and commitment to an empowered workforce charged with continually improving or doing better tomorrow than was done today based upon the principles and techniques of identifying and eliminating waste. The orientation and level of empowerment is largely set by organisational leaders. In terms of the human resource, the Shingo prize prescribes some level of empowerment. There are unionised and green field Recipient plants that have attained very high levels of empowerment. All recent recipients have demonstrated that they are well into the life cycle of an empowered workforce with some having mature, self directed, all salaried workforces that are without supervisors on the shop floor'.

Empowerment, however, is seen as a means to an end rather than an end in itself and the authors point out that best-in-class Shingo Prize Recipients have training programmes oriented toward individual and team training rather than a set number of hours per year based upon some predetermined plan'.

The element with the largest number of points (25%) is 'World Class Manufacturing and Processes' and in this area the authors point to a predictable pattern of operational methods the Shingo Recipients tend to follow:

'Once the strategy of just-in-time manufacturing has been adopted, most emphasise 5S to instill the necessary discipline for eliminating waste and to ensure a safe and pleasant workplace. Subsequently, all plants that had equipment changeovers achieved tremendous results in reducing cycle time to enhance one piece flow and deliver to customer order. We note that Shingo tended to suggest that changeover was the first key element of just-in-time manufacturing. Other items that are consistently emphasised are productive maintenance, visual control systems, kanban material system, cellular layout where appropriate, standardise work, multi-process handling, and automation, with the ultimate aim of levelling or distributing work intelligently and evenly'.

All recent Recipient companies are noted to have clearly adopted poka-yoke (mistake-proofing) as the foundation for quality improvements. By contrast the application and reliance on statistical process control (SPC) 'has clearly diminished over the last 10-15 years'.

The second half of the paper focuses on Shingo Model outputs beginning with quality and product costs. In this area 'most Recipients report a positive annual reduction in their product costs, as a result of Kaizen or continuous improvement' and some 'have achieved Six Sigma quality'. Equally Shingo Prize Recipients 'excel in measured customer service' and many 'show significant gains in labour productivity, cycle-time and changeover reductions':

'One Prize Recipient more than doubled labour productivity over a five year period. A number of other Recipients have achieved 300 inventory turns per year. As an example of measured customer service, one Recipient had an order cycle-time of 10 days, down from 75 days compared to the industry average of 40 days. The organisation was working on reducing product cycle time to facilitate an even greater reduction in order lead time. On-time delivery for this particular organisation was 99% plus'.

Shingo Prize Recipients are also noted for their close links with their customers:

'To ensure high customer satisfaction one Prize Recipient will visit daily with customers discussing delivery, quality, and any other important issue. In instances where a defect has been passed on to a customer the nature of the defect is discussed, cause and effect analysis conducted and corrective action taken. Then, a new, good part is delivered within hours so as not to disrupt the production flow of the customer. In another example a Shingo Prize Recipient's market share grew from less than 2% to more than 19% over a seven year period. The industry had a 3% growth rate, meaning the company gained market share by taking it away from competitors'.

To date there have been 51 Recipients of the Shingo Prize from the USA, Canada and Mexico, 24 of which have come from the automotive industry. The next (12th) Annual Shingo Prize Conference and Award Ceremony will take place at the Hyatt Regency Milwaukee in Milwaukee, Wisconsin, on 8th to 12th May 2000 and will feature plant tours of Briggs and Stratton, Delphi Automotive, Harley Davidson and Milwaukee Electric Tool. A website is available on www.shingoprize.org.

[Issue 132 (December 1999)]

UK QUALITY AWARDS

Hundreds of organisations apply for the UK's national Business Excellence Awards each year, but only a few get through to the national finals. This year seven organisations reached the finals following a rigorous examination by a team of independent assessors each of whom is an experienced manager from a leading UK organisation.

Four of the finalists were selected from the Large Commercial category (Barclays Direct Loan Services,British Aerospace Military Aircraft and Aerostructures, NatWest Insurance Services, and NatWest Mortgage Services) and three from the Small Business category (Foxdenton School from Oldham, Springfarm Architectural Mouldings from Antrim, and Vista Optics from Stockport). There were, however, no medium sized or public sector finalists.

From the seven finalists three were selected to receive an Award, namely British Aerospace Military Aircraft and Aerostructures, NatWest Insurance Services and Foxdenton School. Her Royal Highness The Princess Royal presented the Awards accompanied by Sir Keith Stuart, Chairman and President of the BQF and Chairman of Associated British Ports at the Annual BQF Gala Dinner in London on November 2nd.

British Aerospace: fostering Creativity.

British Aerospace Military Aircraft and Aerostructures (MA and A} is a business unit of British Aerospace plc, the UK's largest exporter, and employs around 17,000 people in the design, development, manufacturing and support of military aircraft, aircraft structures and associated systems. They have the most comprehensive range of military aircraft of any manufacturer in the world and their product range includes the Hawk, the Harrier vertical take-off jet and the Eurofighter.

BAe (MA & A} have seven primary sites around the UK with headquarters in Warton, Lancashire, and have been using the Business Excellence Model since 1994 when it was adopted as a key component of their 'Benchmark' business transformation programme. Since then the Model has been progressively integrated into their comprehensive supply excellence programme and has formed the foundation for their team-leader workbook which describes the value planning process used by all teams.

The BAe benchmark behavioural change programme pulled together various change programmes whilst the personal leadership of cur rent BAe Chairman Richard Evans played a crucial role in combating the 'endemic cultural arrogance' that had characterised the organisation during the Cold War when the UK Ministry of Defence had been effectively a' captive customer'. Practices such as taking phone calls during meetings, and opening sessions and then leaving after a so-called 'respectable period' were recognised as poor leadership behaviours and addressed at the highest level, whilst the establishment of universities and technical learning centres on behalf of principal customers so as to contribute to general engineering capability worldwide has greatly enhanced the organisation's Impact on Society.

Significant effort has been placed on ending the practice of "store chasing" on the part of people and divisions pursuing business excellence and there have been 'dramatic improvements' In customer relationship management as a result, of becoming 'information hungry' and involving purchasers in final assembly, after-sale training and maintenance skilling. Rework due to misspecification has been substantially reduced and the practice of telling customers who complained to 'go back and read the manual is long gone. Policy and strategy are completely aligned to group aims, objectives and values and business results are reflected in BAe's overall share price. BAe MA and A were Highly Commended in the 1998 UK Quality Awards.

During their assessment for the 1999 Award the assessors 'observed a strong business excellence culture within the company with senior leaders displaying role model behaviour' and 'were very encouraged by the way in which such a large manufacturer had developed an excellence culture which fosters creativity and an innovative approach to creating new intellectual property'. The assessors said that BAe MA and A 'were well on their way to becoming a world class organisation serving a worldwide market'.

Joe Goasdoue, Chief Executive of the BQF, commented:

"BAe is an example of an outstanding organisation which has understood that the best recipe for success is to go for excellence in everything they do".

NatWest Insurance Services: adept at using Feedback.

Natwest Insurance Services (NWIS) is one of 13 key businesses within the NatWest Group. Based in Bristol and employing around 1300 people they serve as an insurance intermediary providing general insurance and independent financial advice. They faced a major challenge in 1993 when the creation of NatWest Life removed half of their income and two thirds of their profit, but since then repositioning of the business and concentration on core businesses helped them to achieve an annual income of £144 million last year. They were one of the first companies within the NatWest Group to adopt the Business Excellence Model in 1995, which has since been tailored to the business in the form of the 'NWIS Excellence Model'.

The company's early submission efforts in 1996 and 1997 led to a review of their customer feedback strategy which was later benchmarked with that of TNT (UK), who had been joint winners of the first UK Quality Award (formerly the British Quality Award) in 1994. In 1998 a consultancy which specialises in the measurement of customer service was engaged to research the needs and expectations of NWIS customers and when findings suggested that telephone surveys were more effective than postal surveys the format was changed accordingly. 'Event surveys' were also introduced as a means of obtaining feedback on process performance, such as claims performance following adverse weather, in all units.

Leaders at NWIS are defined as 'anybody responsible for managing staff' and as such are expected to lead by example using communication meetings, feedback sessions and company hotline as appropriate. There is a strong emphasis on personal development with sponsorship of professional qualifications, the successful completion of which is recognised both with monetary rewards and with further opportunities at work such as multi-skilling.

A learning centre has been established to enable the workforce to learn in their own time and at their own pace. Human resource development advisors selected from within the company help NWIS employees with self-improvement and this year a NatWest New Learning Organisation was set up across all 13 NatWest businesses to share people and experiences. Empowerment has also enabled NWIS staff to develop a website which earlier this year was used to complete the NatWest Group's first Internet transaction (through a travel insurance Internet sales unit conceived and developed by NWIS staff using skills available from within NatWest).

The assessors commented that NWIS 'had been particularly adept in their use of feedback from previous Award submissions ' and 'were impressed by the way in which self-assessment had been integrated throughout the business and was now a way of life'. They noted the pivotal role taken by the Managing Director Steve Wells and the senior management team in the company's commitment to excellence and the fact that empowerment 'is a reality not just a buzzword', which has 'contributed to very high staff retention levels'. The company was described as 'a good example of a company which had embraced the positive principles of business excellence in order to rebuild the company into a major competitive force'.

Foxdenton School: the best Ethos of the Public Services.

Foxdenton School and Integrated Nursery is a state primary school for children aged between two and eleven catering principally for those with special educational needs arising from physical or medical difficulties. It currently has around 100 pupils drawn from the Oldham Local Education Authority by whom it is funded as well as the neighbouring LEA zones of Bury, Salford, Stockport and Tameside, and has 40 employees.

The school was founded in 1973 and adopted the Business Excellence Model in 1995 the same year as it was awarded the North West Quality Award for Education, although its quality policy the longest running quality policy of all of this year's finalists, dates back to 1986. Its annual budget and income for 1998-99 was around £923,650 with results being measured in terms of 'the growing confidence and happiness of pupils and their preparation for life in mainstream society'.

Each year a proportion of pupils move on to mainstream schools and the importance of this as a success measure is reflected in the feedback from parents which shows that 88% of parents agree, 61% strongly, that 'Foxdenton have their processes for mainstream school transfer for pupils more or less right'. Further feedback also showed that in 1998 94% of parents were happy with the quality of communication from the school whilst 98% were reportedly satisfied with school/ parent meetings and an average of 96% were satisfied with the school's academic standards.

Much of the school's success, which has included the achievement of a Charter Mark in 1994 and 1997, Investors in People in 1994 and1998, and a Teacher of the Year Award in 1996, has been attributed to the continuing efforts of its headmaster Mel Farrar since he took charge in 1973.

Trained in the thinking and philosophy of management guru Tom Peters he introduced the Business Excellence Model in order to provide 'a new dimension to the programme'. Each September staff review progress, offer ideas and bid for projects to take things forward and their ideas for improvement integrated into the annual school development plan. Some 70% of this plan runs from year to year whilst the remainder is left open to change according to staff ideas and the 'lightening introduction of government policy'.

The assessors praised Foxdenton for its 'excellent people management and resource management strategies' and were particularly impressed 'by the way in which the school has developed a consistent vision over time and has clearly identified stakeholders' needs and concerns'. They noted especially 'the exemplary attention given to satisfying parents' needs with nothing less than 100% parental approval being acceptable to the staff' and concluded that the school 'embodies the best ethos of the public services allied to an impassioned commitment to continuous improvement'.

Further Information

Both the public and private sector categories are subdivided into organisations of more than 250 people and less than 250 people. The fifth category is designed for small organisations from either the public or private sector which have fewer than 50 employees. The Awards jury is empowered to make one or more equal status awards in any of the five Award categories, but is under no obligation to make an award. Thus, if no role model makes the grade then no award will be made in that category. Full profiles of this year's finalists are featured in the special 1999 UK Business Excellence Awards issue of *UK Excellence*, Official Journal of the BQF.

SCOTTISH BUSINESS EXCELLENCE AWARDS

North of the border Wendy Alexander MSP, Minister for Enterprise and Lifelong Learning, presented the Scottish Business Excellence Awards on 9th November at Quality Scotland's Annual Forum at the Edinburgh International Conference Centre.

Three organisations were 'Highly Commended', namely Brand Rex (copper wire manufacturers, subsidiary of BICC Group, based in Glenrothes), in the Manufacturing sector; Scottish Power Technology Division (East Kilbride), in the Service sector; and Memory Corporation (Dalkeith), who have 100 employees, in the Smaller Enterprise category .There was one 'Winner', St.Ninnian's High School of Giffnock (near Glasgow) in the Public Sector category, who were also the first school to make it to the Awards Finals in Scotland.

In addition to the above awards this year's Forum, which attracted around 470 participants, also saw the first presentation of the new Scotland the Brand Excellence Awards to shortbread manufacturers Paterson Arran. In order to win this Award, which forms part of an initiative run by Scottish Trades International (part of the Scottish Executive) with a mission to market products and services that represent Scotland, applicants have "to demonstrate Scottishness" in their product or service as well as an industry measurement of quality and Business Excellence using the EFQM Model. The Award confers upon the holder a licence to market their product or service under the Scotland the Brand logo.

Further Information

Quality Scotland is cementing its role as a National Partnership Organisation of the EFQM allowing exclusive distribution rights of EFQM material in Scotland.

THE X FACTOR: WINNING PERFORMANCE THROUGH BUSINESS EXCELLENCE

The European Centre for Business Excellence, the research and education division of Oakland Consulting plc, in conjunction with the British Quality Foundation, has published a report on the results of a research project on the linkages between business excellence activities, including self-assessment, and superior business performance and results. Entitled 'The X Factor' it describes 'a wealth of evidence both anecdotal and empirical' which suggests that there are multiple benefits to be gained from adopting the business excellence practices advocated by the BQF and EFQM measured by a range of both financial and non-financial indicators. Examples quoted include:

* Increased sales volume from £4.4 million to £14,3 million for a sheet metal component manufacturer.

* Increase in revenue per employee from £86,000 to £126,000 over five years for an automotive company.

* Increases in sales of 8% during a recession and return on expenditure of 30 to 40% over ten years for a multi-national fast moving consumer goods company.

* Savings of $2.2 billion for a European telecommunications company

* Energy savings of £325,000 per year at Courtaulds Fibres

* An increase in exports from 18% to 40% at FMCG company, part of Unilever.

* Business growth of 7% in a 4% growth market by Elida Faberge.

The research was conducted in four phases with a literature review followed by in-depth analysis of 14 award winning submission documents and feedback reports with performance noted for:

* 3 year trends and sustained good performance.

* 5 year trends and sustained excellent performance.

* Favourable comparisons with targets.

* Favourable comparisons with benchmarks.

Phase Three involved in-depth interviews with four award winning companies selected to provide a balance of market operating conditions, whilst Phase Four involved the development of a 'Route Map' to Business Excellence from the best practice activities identified in phases 1 to 3 using an affinity inter-relationship diagram approach. The Report concludes:

'Winners and applicants are unanimous in agreeing that the real strength of the BEM and self-assessment is that they provide a focus for structured improvement within organisations, creating consistency of direction and consensus about strengths and areas in need of improvement. More than one award/prize winner maintain that as a direct result of the systematic adoption and implementation of the BEM, they measure many more things than they did before. The most important aspect of measurement lies in the fact that the data are used in a positive and encouraging way'.

NEW GUIDE TO EXCELLENCE IN THE PUBLIC SECTOR

A new Procurement Excellence Guide advocating the use of the Business Excellence Model to enhance quality in the public sector has been published by the Treasury. The Guide is in two parts, the first, entitled 'The Procurement Excellence Pilot' explaining simply how to apply the Model to procurement performance measurement and the second, entitled 'The Guide to use for the EFQM Excellence Model in Procurement' offering more in-depth advice specifically related to Government procurement initiatives. It is anticipated that the Guide will be adopted throughout the public sector as part of efforts by the Office of Government Commerce and Departments to realise savings of £1 billion over the next three years.

[Issue 135 (April 2000)]

CHANGE: THE QUALITY CHALLENGE

The Challenge of Change was the theme of this year's EFQM Learning Edge conference for senior and middle managers, which has been a major component of the EFQM calendar of events since1989. This year it was held in the UK, appropriately perhaps in Belfast which has experienced probably more change than any other European city in recent years.

A first rate line up of top speakers and organisations made the event from 5th to 7th April, which followed from the Irish Winners' Conference hosted jointly by the Northern Ireland Quality Centre (NIQC) and Excellence Ireland at Belfast's prestigious Waterfront Hall, one of the most successful to date attracting some 300 participants.

Plenary speakers included world expert and pioneer in the concept of lateral thinking Dr .Edward de Bono (see Chapter 16) whose 57 books have so far been translated into 34 languages, and Brian Bennett of the Ritz-Carlton Hotel Group who last year became the first organisation to win the US

1. The prestigious European Quality Award, first presented by King Juan Carlos of Spain to Bernard Fournier, Managing Director of Rank Xerox at the Palacio de Congress in Madrid on 15 October 1992.

(Photo courtesy EFQM)

2. Hazim Kantarci of Brisa (left) receives the 1996 European Quality Award from Bernard Fournier at the EFQM Forum on 27 October 1996.

(Photo courtesy EFQM)

3. Ed Wilson, Chairman of Ulster Carpet Mills, joint winner of the 1996 UK Quality Award, receives the accolade from HRH The Princess Royal at the Royal Gala dinner of 3 December 1996. *(Photo courtesy BQF)*

4. Mr. Keith Greenhough, Managing Director of second joint winner Mortgage Express, also receives the Award from HRH The Princess Royal.

(Photo courtesy BQF)

5. Pascuale Pistorio, CEO of SGS Thomson Microelectronics receives the 1997 European Quality Award for Large Business from Queen Silvia of Sweden at the EFQM Forum in Stockholm. *(Photo courtesy EFQM)*

6. The SME Award was presented for the first time in 1997 and was received by Bulent Savas, CEO of steel cord producer BEKSA. *(Photo courtesy EFQM)*

7. Alain de Dommartin succeeded Geert de Raad as CEO of the EFQM on 1st July 1998. *(Photo courtesy EFQM)*

8. The European Quality Award for Large Business is presented to M.D. of TNT (UK) Alan Jones (centre) by EFQM President John Roberts (left) and EOQ President Otto Neumayer at the joint EFQM/EOQ Quality Convention in Paris on 23 October 1998. *(Photo courtesy EFQM)*

9. A unique approach to teamwork wins Landhotel Schindlerhof (staff pictured here) the European Quality Award for independent SME's in 1998.

(Photo courtesy EFQM)

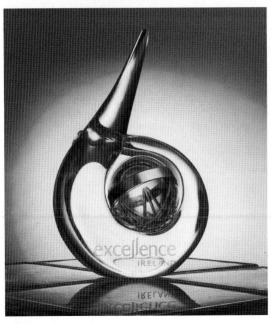

10. Launched in 1998 the Irish Business Excellence Award trophy, sponsored by Tipperary Crystal, was designed by Louise Kennedy of Ireland's National College of Art and Design to capture the qualities associated with Business Excellence.

(Photo courtesy Excellence Ireland)

11. First winners of the Irish Business Excellence Award were Lucent Technologies Ireland whose General Manager John Byrne receives the Award and trophy from Don Flinter, CEO of Enterprise Ireland. Also pictured are Brian Kerr (left) Manager Irish Youth Soccer team, and Sean Conlan (right) CEO Excellence Ireland and President European Organisation for Quality. *(Photo courtesy Excellence Ireland)*

12. Scotland's World Cup '98 soccer coach Craig Brown (far right) presents the 1998 Quality Scotland Awards with (from left) Frank Dick President European Athletics C.A. and Muir Russell Scottish Office, to John Carnell of Bakaert, Peter McKinlay of Scottish Homes, Deborah Lidgett of Edinburgh Conference Centre, John McDougal, Honeywell and Kirsty Henderson, Scottish Courage Brands.

(Photo courtesy Quality Scotland)

13. In 1999 the Scottish Business Excellence Awards were presented by Wendy Alexander MSP (centre), with the help of EICC H. R. Manager Suzanne Burns, to (left to right) Paul Munroe, General Manager of Brand Rex; David Savage, C.E.O. Memory Corporation; James McVittie, Head Teacher St. Ninnians; and Bob McFarlane, Quality Manager for Scottish Power Technology.

(Photo courtesy Quality Scotland)

14. The European Quality Award for Large Businesses was presented in Brussels on 6th October 1999 to John Condron C.E.O. of Yellow Pages, by EFQM President John Roberts. *(Photo courtesy EFQM)*

15. Millennium European Quality Award winners in Istanbul on 27th September 2000 were (from left to right) Marton Varga of Burton-Apta Refractory Manufacturing, Andrew Geddes of the Inland Revenue Accounts Office Cumbernauld, and Anssi Vanjoki of Nokia Mobile Phones with Istemihan Tulay, Turkish Minister of Culture, who presented the Awards (far right).

(Photo courtesy EFQM)

16. Josh Hammond reveals 'The Naked Truth about Business Excellence' at the Fifth Sheffield World Quality Congress in June 2000.

Malcolm Baldrige Award for the second time. Also reported are the special off-site workshop hosted by Northern Ireland Electricity, recipient of the Northern Ireland Millennium Quality Award sponsored jointly by BT Northern Ireland and the NIQC, and the KPMG Alliances workshop entitled 'Dealing in Difference'.

Making Change happen.

Brian Bennett was part of the team that won the Ritz-Carlton Group both of their Baldrige Awards (in 1992 and 1999) and in his speech he explained how their policy and strategy in both cases had been geared toward individual service driven by sound process management. Hotel values were redefined in terms of 'gold standards' and a process put in place to ensure that "warm friendly genuinely caring employees" were capable of anticipating the needs of guests in accordance with the company's 'Credo'.

Alongside the 'Credo' was the 'Motto' which redefined the role of hotel personnel away from the traditional master-servant relationship and towards "ladies and gents serving ladies and gents". This resulted in a different way of thinking which was absolutely vital when it came to changing the culture. Today every employee has the accepted right to be involved in decisions which affect them, in stark contrast to what is still the norm in most hotels which are based entirely on command and control.

The speaker mentioned accolades which Ritz-Carlton has received for their 'gold standards' approach, but he was quick to emphasise that these 'standards' were really only a very small component in a wide and far-reaching system which owed most of its success to its supporting processes and subsystems. "Most organisations write these things but do no more", he stressed, and consequently they failed to make progress.

Another area which has received considerable attention is leadership, as indeed it must if business excellence is to become a reality. The speaker described how in the past the organisation had learnt the hard way by taking key decisions on the basis purely of marketing and financial goals rather than quality goals. "Quality goals were talked about but there was no ongoing reporting mechanism", he said. Now, daily and monthly reports provide a very clear picture of where the Group stands with respect to quality, with key indicators highlighting chronic problems, whilst all leaders align their departments and divisions with clear quality standards expressed in terms of 'twenty basics'.

A serious drive to reduce staff turnover, which was once well in excess of the industry average, has resulted in radical changes to the company's recruitment and selection process which now places great emphasis on finding the right person for the job. Applicants are now given scores corresponding to certain key skills which they possess which in turn routes them toward a specific type of work to which they are personally best suited and best able to align with the 'gold standards'.

The company has since become expert at the process of identifying talents that people possess in relatively short periods of time, and the sceptics, who advocated retaining the old fashioned methods of superficial interviewing and random replacement, have been proven wrong in their prediction that such a change in approach would be unworkable.

The right selection process, however, has to be reinforced with excellence in training, which begins with two and a half days of 'banquet room orientation' in which the trainees experience hotel service from the guest's points of view and hear the 'gold standards' explained. Then, knowing that the Group is serious about quality, they follow a training programme which lasts for about 60 days, but is not rigid in length and may be extended:

"The process that keeps this alive is a daily line up consisting of a discussion of an element of the gold standards for about fifteen minutes. This covers a 'basic of the day' and keeps the gold standards fresh in the mind. In this way the gold standards are brought to life by the employees themselves explaining and demonstrating them".

The Ritz-Carlton currently operates 35 hotels and four private clubs.

Changing from Compliance to Commitment.

The presentation by Northern Ireland Electricity (NIE) focused on the challenges faced by a public utility following privatisation, and in particular how to move from a compliance based culture to one of wholehearted commitment to excellence on the part of employees. They described how ISO9000 provided an impetus for change, having been initially applied for legal reasons, for example in meter test stations, and then in other areas such as plant workshops.

The Business Excellence Model was formally adopted as an instrument of change in 1993 with Investors In People (IIP) put in place to address people management issues alongside the ISO9000 drive in 'processes'. This demanded that 'leadership' be strengthened to create the right atmosphere and culture for the achievement of total excellence and an MSc Corporate Leadership programme was introduced for all managers, coupled with Business Excellence training for all members of the executive team.

Policy and strategy was addressed with the creation of a draft strategy and a series of ongoing three year plans which took a macroeconomic approach. Executive workshops provided the means to outline the initial plans and budgets. Four business units, each led by a director, then developed their own plans and strategies with the aid of Key Performance Indicators. A three year Balanced Scorecard ensured that each business unit objective linked with the overall corporate objectives.

More recently 'change boards' have been established consisting of groups of individuals who are responsible for managing change, and these have proved to be " a very powerful tool" for fostering innovation and process improvement. There has also been a very strong movement away from buying on the basis of a price tag and toward buying on the basis of suitability, resulting in significant cost savings through the removal of duplication and waste. There is widespread use of benchmarking, for example, in substation management and transmission operations, and Reliability Centred Maintenance (RCM) with partners John Woodhouse.

In the electricity industry safety is naturally a prime consideration and in order to achieve excellence here a need for a reform in site management was of paramount importance. Traditional methods of 'policing' sites have thus been replaced by structured auditing by teams and the appointment of 'landlords' for each site each of whom has an appointed 'mentor'. Scorecards are deployed which may reflect whatever the 'landlord' considers to be important, including any trend data which may be relevant.

The management of NIE were keen to point out the fact that they have not raised their prices to customers for four years now, whilst their dividend per share has risen by 153% since 1993. They also paid particular tribute to the trade unions, co-operation with whom has been greatly assisted through a general policy of sharing information at an early stage. This has enabled NIE to largely escape some of the more serious industrial relations difficulties that have bedevilled other public sector organisations.

In the questioning which followed senior executives were questioned on the use of scorecards and at what level in the organisation they should be used, and about the dangers of complacency immediately following their Award success. Their reply to the first point was as follows:

"You have to try it and see what suits you. If you have a target you will start to measure and if you start to measure you should get better. We thought a lot about scorecards and decided to take them down to individual manager level. We found that it was a way of communicating our business plan and we keep working with it because we found that it usually translates down into something. There is a danger that a scorecard can become too generic, and measurement is only beneficial if it is used positively. Achievements have been made at NIE because the entire staff moved together in the same direction".

Concerning complacency they commented:

"If you are going out just to win an award then yes complacency can set in, but we revisit ourselves and this pulls our socks up. With IIP we chose the

rolling assessment option rather than the five year option so complacency would not set in ".

In their submission document for the Northern Ireland Quality Award further information is provided on the organisation's suggestion scheme, appraisal and promotion systems, and a support for TQM outside the organisation:

The Current Ideas Employee Suggestion Scheme provides a mechanism for capturing employees' ideas which can act as a catalyst for setting up improvement groups. Employee involvement in both Current Ideas and project improvement is central to our whole programme. Such ideas and improvements have identified cost reductions, safety improvements and quality improvements. Employees can earn up to £5000 (tax free) for an idea. To date we have paid out £20,000 for the range of ideas shown in the paper'.

Following a review of the company's appraisal mechanisms in 1996 which concluded that appraisals were too narrow in their scope and too subjective, the Performance Planning Review was introduced for staff throughout the organisation. The PPR system combines people's job responsibilities and the company's goals into measurable objectives. Performance towards objectives are reviewed quarterly with the line manager. The training needs analysis completed within the process, directly links the individual's needs with their career progression. The effective use of Performance Planning Review facilitates employee improvement and involvement by linking their personal objectives clearly to the strategic goals of the company. With the commitment of funding to training and development of personnel over the last three years, 98% of promotions into managerial and supervisory positions within NIE have been from internal candidates'.

'We initiated and are presenting a Total Quality Programme entitled "Powerful Insight" involving three managers and a Director at which we explain to business groups, particularly SMEs, our systems of : using the Corporate Scorecard, the European Business Excellence Model, and Problem Solving using our "hexagon method". We have already delivered the programme in Londonderry, Ballymena, Carrickfergus, Bangor and Belfast, and to date have presented to some 240 business people on these key aspects of Business Excellence:

The latest NIE initiative is a programme to introduce Six Sigma techniques in conjunction with Qualitec in the US. This follows from the organisation's recognition that there is still more work to do on process improvement to make it more methodical with stronger linkages if they are to realise their stated vision of becoming ' a premier Northern Ireland company'.

Northern Ireland Electricity is a wholly owned subsidiary of Viridian Group plc and have around 12,000 employees serving 683,000 customers. They operate around 34,000 miles of network and operate 66,500 transformers and substations. Their turnover per employee last year was £337,000 whilst their sales revenue in 1998-99 was £516 million. They are currently developing their own subsidiary organisation called 'Power team' which will offer all of their larger user customers a comprehensive solution service that covers all of their High Voltage power distribution systems needs.

[Issue 137 (July 2000)]

FIFTH SHEFFIELD WORLD QUALITY CONGRESS

'The Naked Truth about Business Excellence' was the theme for the fifth and last World Quality Congress to be hosted by Sheffield Hallam University, at least for the time being. The two day event on 26th and 27th June which attracted some 182 delegates from 23 countries, featured around 70 presentations covering broadly the subjects of benchmarking: excellence in the public sector, excellence in service, customer satisfaction measurement and process improvement.

In the opening plenary the Director of the Best Practices initiative for *FORTUNE* (Time-Warner) magazine Josh Hammond addressed the conference theme by asserting that where the words 'Business Excellence' have merely been used as a substitute for TQM, the opportunities now presented by the modern philosophy of e-commerce are likely to be squandered. Where the 'TQM Business Model' is seen to be formal, structured, hierarchical, and centred around continuous improvement, the corresponding 'Internet Business Model' is spontaneous, flat, self-organising and centred around 'killer applications'. Top management commitment is replaced by top management engagement with the customer considered as a partner and feedback instantized rather than formalised. At the same time the quality journey is viewed as 'a series of short exciting trips where formal design is replaced with spontaneous innovation and call centres give way to instant messaging.

Case studies used to demonstrate the 'lack of flexibility' of the TQM business excellence model included Xerox, who, despite having won numerous quality awards, as well as being a founder of modern day benchmarking techniques, have recently suffered a drop in stock price of some 66%. Other examples included Procter and Gamble and American Express who 'have the same problem' whilst, on the positive side Levi Strauss have largely overcome their difficulties by introducing a formal system for learning from mistakes.

Wine lovers should enjoy reading the paper by Josh Hammond which introduces seven tenets for the natural renewal of business excellence with reference to wine making. The seven tenets are as follows:

* Thoughtful exceptionalism is better than mindless conformity.

* Embrace the distributed workplace values.

* Beware the self-delusion of customer satisfaction ratings

* What you know is as important as what you produce

* Leverage national cultures in the global village

* Aim for a future without limits

* Encompass the total customer experience

'If you go into a great restaurant and order an older bottle of wine -a Chateau Petrus 1962, for example -the sommelier will decant the wine to avoid the sediments in the bottom of the bottle. If you are really lucky and your sommelier is a craftsman, he will hold a candle behind the bottle as he gently pours. There is no precise standard for this practice, nor is it something one would benchmark necessarily. But it does add to the customer's perception of the value of the experience and speaks to the desirability of connecting a product's quality to a heightened outcome for the end user' .

NEW EUROPEAN SOCIETY FOR ORGANISATIONAL EXCELLENCE

A new European Society for Organisational Excellence has been formed to bring together academic and research professionals from a variety of disciplines relevant to quality management , organisational excellence, the management of innovation and change and the development of human resources. The Society is dedicated to the pursuit of organisational excellence in an open architectural approach and has the following values:

* To build effective bridges among different scientific disciplines relevant to organisational excellence

* To facilitate communication and co-operation among members in different disciplines and different cultures that will prepare the way to holistic and well-integrated approaches for organisational performance improvements.

* To maintain an independent spirit of inquiry in all relevant scientific disciplines that will not be constrained by existing mental models for the pursuit of organisational excellence.

* To support all initiatives that will encourage synergy of individual, team and organisational efforts, as free as possible from conflicts and individual scientific differences in well-established perspectives.

* To support the presentation and encourage the understanding of quality-related aspects of historical traditions and cultures worldwide.

* To facilitate various forms of beneficial to all co-operation and exchanges with countries throughout the world.

The stated Mission of the Society is 'to promote, through research and teaching of the highest standards, the focused efforts in the public and private sectors of developing organisations of sustained excellence who will be expected to meet present and evolving future needs of recognisable stakeholders (customer, employees, owners, suppliers and the communities) as well as those of the environment'.

The new Society is based initially at the Faculte de Sciences Economiques et de Gestion, Universite de Toulon et du Var, BP 132, 83957 La Garde cedex, France. Founder members include from the UK Professor Gopal Kanji of Sheffield Hallam University (President) and leading authority on benchmarking Prof. Mohammed Zairi.

[Issue 139 (Winter 2000)]

EUROPEAN QUALITY AWARDS

Three Awards were presented this year at the EFQM Annual Forum in Istanbul on 27th September . These were to Nokia Mobile Phones (Europe and Africa) from Finland, who won in the Large Business category after just their first application, the Inland Revenue Accounts Office Cumbernauld, who won the Public Sector Award for the first time, and Burton-Apta Refractory Manufacturing Limited of Hungary, who were winners in the Operational Units SME category.

Nokia Mobile Phones is the world's largest mobile phone manufacturer and the Europe and Africa Division employs around 7,000. Nokia Mobile Phones won the Finnish National Quality Award in 1991 with self-assessment being introduced in 1995. Customer satisfaction measurement was introduced in 1996 with QS9000 certification following in 1998 and ISO14000 achieved last year.

This year they have introduced Strategy and Action Planning Integration which builds on the application of quality methods which include Current State Analysis (a self-assessment methodology), the Nokia 7 basic method of problem solving, Continuous Process Improvement methodology in Seven Steps, Nokia Benchmarking BM7, Six Sigma and Failure Mode and Effects Analysis (FMEA). The benefits which have derived from self-assessment are reported as follows:

* Discovery of improvement areas

* Effective teamwork

* Role modelling leadership

* Personal development of senior management team members

* Challenging oneself

* Follow-up of strategy

* Date over time to see the improvement trends

* Facilitation of internal sharing and learning

The Inland Revenue Accounts Office Cumbernauld employs around 1000 and maintains approximately half (26 million) of the UK's tax-payer records, banking an average of around 508 million euros per day. They became the first office in the Inland Revenue to be recognised as an Investor In People in 1994 and in 1998 they were awarded a European Quality Prize. They have since also achieved ISO14001 certification. They apply a range of quality methods including empowerment workshops, pareto analysis, cause and effect analysis, brainstorming, process mapping, benchmarking and Kaizen. Benefits deriving from self-assessment are reported as:

* Bringing together previously separate initiatives under one practical framework

* Introducing a structured approach to reviewing all aspects of the business

* Introducing a method of measuring progress in achieving improving activities

* Providing an opportunity to benchmark with best-in-class organisations

Burton-Apta Refractory Manufacturing are located in south-east Hungary and employ 227. They specialise in servicing the ceramics industry, their main markets being the heavy clay industry (brick and roof tile manufacturers) and fine ceramics (tableware, sanitary etc). They won the Hungarian National Quality Award in 1996 and a European Quality Prize last year. Quality methods applied include brainstorming, problem solving in teams, statistical process control, six sigma, benchmarking, Design of Experiments and Quality Function Deployment. Benefits deriving from self-assessment are reported as follows:

* Increased motivation of staff towards quality

* Improved employee involvement

* Diagnosis of the health of the company

* Indicator to initiate improvement actions

* Serves as a good benchmarking tool

* Provides feedback of results and efforts

Prize winners this year were Arcelik AS of Turkey, Eczacibasi Vitra of Turkey, and IRIZAR of Spain in the Large Business and Business Units Category; Arbejds formidlingen Ringkocbing AMT (Danish Public Employment Service) and the Foxdenton School and Integrated Nursery in the Public Sector Category; Avaya Ireland Limited (formerly Lucent Technologies Ireland) in the SME Large Organisation Subsidiary Category; and Water Team srl of Italy and Zahnarztpraxis of Switzerland in the Independent SME Category.

Commenting at the Forum in Istanbul, which had as its theme 'Managing Diversity –A Bridge to Excellence', the EFQM's recently appointed Manager for Model Promotion and Awards Peter Docwra said:

"It is most beneficial for the European Quality Award to have winners from very different countries and in diverse sectors of operation. Moreover, we have noticed that organisations have incorporated and integrated the EFQM Model into their ways of working before their first application, which leads to new and fresh names in our list of winners. This shows our impact has gone far beyond what we have noticed in the past".

UK Business Excellence Awards

The UK Business Excellence Awards were presented in London on 31st October by HRH The Princess Royal and there were four recipients:

* The Inland Revenue Accounts Office, Cumbernauld (Public Sector, over 250 employees)

* St. Mary's College, Londonderry (Public Sector, under 250 employees)

* Springfarm Architectural Mouldings, County Antrim (SME, under 50 employees)

* Vista Optics Limited, Stockport (SME, under 50 employees)

As mentioned above, The Inland Revenue Accounts Office, Cumbernauld, were also recipients of the European Quality Award. The UK assessors, however, voiced the following comments:

285

"The assessors were particularly impressed by the leadership in evidence at all levels within AOC, some of which is at role model standard, aspiring to world class. It is very clear to the assessors that empowerment exists throughout the entire organisation and is truly embedded within AOC's culture".

St. Mary's College, Londonderry, have been reported in previous issues of *Quality Matters*, most recently in Issue 136 (May 2000). The assessors commented as follows:

"The assessors noted that the school benefits from having a truly visionary and charismatic leader, who has brought both educational and business experience to bear on the many challenges faced by the school. St. Mary's has clearly been successful in attracting and retaining a very high calibre of people throughout the organisation, all of whom work extremely well together, providing mutual support and learning.

The assessors believed that St.Mary's is very close to role model standards in many of its approaches and systems. There is a strong leadership culture throughout the entire school, not just at senior management level. The assessors considered St.Mary's to be a role model for UK business and the school as a whole is undoubtedly a role model for the UK school system".

Springform Architectural Mouldings Limited produces a range of architectural mouldings such as skirtings, cornices, architraves, dado and picture rails for the construction and DIY industries. Medium density fibreboard is transformed into attractive range mouldings which are sold through builders merchants. These mouldings are a high quality cost-effective alternative to traditional timber mouldings and the innovation for them comes from Sam McCrea, who, with his wife Julienne, has wholly owned the company since 1994.

The company has 34 employees and a turnover of £3.5 million and was selected as a finalist for the Irish Independent's Growth in Business Awards in 1998. They also won the Northern Ireland Quality Award in the same year. The assessors commented:

"The assessors were particularly struck by the clear leadership and direction from the Managing Director and his top management team. The company has an open and flexible culture which results in a willingness to adopt new initiatives and frameworks to help in the management and improvement of the business. Financial resources appear to be tightly managed, supplier management has led to defined improvements and new technology is readily adopted where it will add value.

The assessors found that the company's production processes were well controlled. The assessors were also impressed by the company's adoption of a range of environmental and community issues. Concern for the environment runs through every aspect of the company's operations".

Vista Optics was founded in 1979 by its current Managing Director, David Walker. They have 17 employees and manufacture a full range of soft, hard and rigid gas permeable contact lens materials as well as intra ocular lenses for cataract implants. They have a worldwide market for their products and currently sell in over 60 countries. In 1991 they became the first contact lens materials manufacturer to gain ISO9001 certification and this was followed in 1994 with IIP and in 1997 with the North West Quality Award for manufacturing companies with up to 25 employees. They have also won the Queen's Award for Export twice and last year were a finalist in the UK Business Excellence Awards. The assessors commented:

"The assessors noted that Vista was clearly a well-managed company that has grown significantly by using business excellence principles. Vista is also a remarkably successful company, especially considering its size relative to its competitors and industry norms. The assessors were impressed by the continuous improvement culture found at all levels within the company, allied to a considerable investment in research and development.

They were struck by the way in which the company had streamlined its customer interface so that staff have more direct contact with customers, enabling them to be more responsive to customer needs. At Vista, mere customer satisfaction is not enough, they strive to 'delight the customer' and more often than not they succeed.

Changing patterns of business, allied to the fact that Vista is a small company in a world-wide marketplace, prompted the company to adopt a partnership relationship with key customers and suppliers. The assessors also noted that Vista's relatively small size means that each member of the staff has to pull their weight. This had prompted them to take extraordinary steps to recruit world class people and support them with appropriate training and motivation. This exemplary attitude to people management has played a key role in Vista's journey towards building a world class team".

The other Finalists for this year's Awards were The City Technology College (Birmingham), Marriott Hotels/Whitbread Hotel Company, Northern Ireland Electricity, NSK Bearings Europe Limited, Turners Optometrics (Bridgwater, Somerset), and Unipart DCM (Cowley, Oxford). At the Awards Ceremony, the Chief Executive of the BQF, Joe Goasdoue commented:

"It is encouraging to see the example of these outstanding organisations who have understood that the best recipe for success is to go for excellence in everything they do".

No Awards were presented in the Private Sector over 250 employees category or the Private Sector 50 to 250 employee award category.

EFQM LAUNCHES RECOGNITION AND ADVICE SCHEMES

The EFQM has launched a new Recognition Scheme to support the revised version of the Business Excellence Model and allow a larger number of organisations to receive formal recognition of their efforts.

Under the new scheme there will be Recognition Commitment to Excellence and Recognition of Achievement in Excellence in addition to the European Quality Award itself. Organisations will be able to apply for whichever of the three strands they believe to be most appropriate to their level of excellence maturity and the policy which limited direct advisory efforts in the past will be amended.

Recognition of Commitment is designed principally for organisations that are at the beginning of their excellence journey and is envisaged to be of particular interest to SMEs. Assessment will take the form of a two stage process involving first an EFQM recognised assessment methodology and second a demonstration that improvement actions have been taken in response to the stage 1 feedback.

A simplified version of the RADAR measurement system will be applied. A pilot project will be conducted during the first half of 2001 with six National Partner Organisations.

The Recognition of Achievement in Excellence will recognise successful efforts to implement excellence and good practice and will apply a simplified submission document for the EFQM Model. All applicants who score 400 or more points will achieve the Recognition.

A pilot will be run by the EFQM in 2001 and with NPOs from 2002. Applications are invited from January 2001.

In the European Quality Award strand confusion which has occasionally existed between European Quality Award Winners and European Quality Prize Winners is to be removed through the discontinuance of European Quality Prizes from next year.

In future the Awards jury will select and recognise Finalists in each Award category and subsequently announce the Winners only in each category. The EFQM also promises enhanced feedback by assessors in their reports.

The Advice Scheme will complement the three above strands and has as its purpose 'to create a body of knowledge and centre of expertise within the EFQM based around the Excellence Model'.

Chapter Four

Benchmarking

Benchmarking has proven itself to be one of the most useful and enduring of all of the tools for quality improvement that have been applied in the 1990s. The principal world authority on this subject throughout this time has been U.S. based practitioner Bob Camp, whilst in the UK The Benchmarking Centre has acted as a focal point for individuals and organisations wishing to apply the methodology.

As with Business Excellence an Award scheme has been established to recognise and reward best practice, which in the later stages of the decade was extended into Europe as distinct from being confined to the UK, under the auspices of The European Benchmarking Forum (EBF) which was founded in 1997. The European Benchmarking Best Practice Awards as they are now known, are currently at a much earlier stage of development than the European Quality Awards which still to an extent overshadow them, although both may be seen as potential growth areas within a common framework.

The articles below trace the development of benchmarking during the 1990s and include notably Bob Camp's presentation at The Benchmarking Centre's Second Annual Forum in 1994 and each of the Award winning and runner-up case studies of The European Benchmarking Best Practice Awards from their launch in 1995 to their re-launch in 2000.

Benchmarking - what is it?

The benchmarking observation began at the, Defence Research Agency at Great Malvern in Worcestershire where, on 18th March, the Quality Methods Association hosted a lively and well attended meeting entitled 'Benchmarking in Research and Development'. This provided an introduction to the subject of benchmarking, well presented by Unilever Research's Dr. Jim Crilly, followed by some tips for practical implementation from Mr. Tim Clark, of Research Machines and a look at where benchmarking relates to strategic planning, from Roger Sugden of Rank Xerox.

In the first of these presentations Dr. Crilly described the key to successful benchmarking as 'recognising what is good, why it is good and how you are going to achieve it'. Product benchmarking, such as that practised by Chrysler in the 1960s when they used to strip down every new Ford model, is just one form of benchmarking. Equally useful can be the benchmarking of strategies and of expenditure in research and development.

The benchmarking definition chosen by Dr. Crilly was that used by Shell, namely 'the continuous process of measuring products, services, and practices against the best competitors or those companies recognized as industry leaders'. This included the search for industry best practices that will lead to superior performance and for industry best performance metrics to ensure that targets are relevant.

It follows that benchmarking fundamentally involves measurement, for example, of the number of design changes involved in taking a product to market.

The benchmarking of world class performance starts with competitive analysis but goes beyond that. He recommended four grades of benchmarking as promoted by a leading management consultancy (Quest):

1. Internal benchmarking: better than we've done before.

2. Competitive benchmarking: better than anyone in the industry.

3. World Class benchmarking: better than anyone anywhere.

4. Customer benchmarking: better than our customer's expectations.

Management has to recognize the level which it is seeking to achieve. If it is World Class then a benchmarking team will be needed, led by the owner of a process who will define and record key metrics.

Identification of the companies that you want to benchmark could be achieved, he suggested, by scanning literature, 'squeezing' information and by attending forum type meetings. By looking at literature you could 'tell a company's market entry strategy by the processes that they strongly emphasise'. 'Innovator' companies can be identified from their relative emphasis on 'people' and 'innovation' processes, whilst 'imitator' companies are identifiable through their emphasis on 'planning' and 'competitor understanding' processes.

Following the presentation Dr. Crilly was asked if he knew any examples of benchmarking where the output was solely innovation. In response he pointed out that innovation, 'means lots of things to lots of people', but one measure could be the number of patentable products produced. He cited the case of AT and T who have attempted to measure creativity, but found this much more difficult than the measurement of productivity.

He was then questioned on the relative merits of British and Japanese research and development and commented that whilst the Japanese have achieved dominance by effectively applying an imitator strategy, they tend not to have had the infrastructure to be creative, and so are now having to change to implement 'discovery' R and D. The UK, by contrast, is 'very discovery driven' but commercial sponsors rarely see where the advantages from inventions are, and he said that this fact was 'very sad'.

Benchmarking – doing it

Tim Clark of Research Machines (microcomputer systems manufacturers) described how benchmarking had started in his company in the manufacturing section early in 1990, and had been extended to engineering later in the year.

Identification of best practices everywhere was central to this, but whilst it was the company's intention to benchmark 'anything and everything' it was seen as important that too much was not tackled all at once. It was recognised that benchmarking can be an expensive exercise and 'should not be done for the fun of it', but rather as part of the normal improvement process. People who owned processes tended to form teams around themselves, look at what is good and bad, and flowchart those processes identifying all inputs and outputs and customers and suppliers. In this way they were able to gain an understanding of their processes, and to think about the questions asked, and information required to aid understanding.

For benchmarking purposes a list of questions were developed with the aim of fully understanding the processes used by another company, but by first answering these questions for their own organisation a 'lot of waffle' was removed.

Deciding who to benchmark depends largely on what the company is seeking to achieve. The most appropriate benchmark could be a competitor or a business which uses similar processes. The recommendation, however, was to 'start slowly' by asking around, examining journals, and approaching associations and benchmark network groups such as the QMA. A world class company may well be inclined to pose the question 'what can we learn from you?' New starters, therefore, may be better advised to examine possibilities on a local level, particularly people and companies with whom they are reasonably familiar and who have similar operations.

The approach recommended was to start initially with a telephone call and to follow this through with letters and a visit. Since visits are expensive, however, it was suggested that these are planned well in advance, involve a group of two or three (often including an engineer), and have a known agenda. Some emphasis was placed on this last point as it is frequently omitted.

Further tips included deployment of a note-taker to write down as much as possible and the training of engineers in the avoidance of jargon and discussion of confidential information. The speaker then outlined how it was his practice to keep a file on all visits, maintain a set of standard questions, and list all changes that the company would like to make to a process.

It was recommended that delegates don't rush to make changes, as it can be a 'waste of time':

"It can take far longer than anything you've done before and you know the company you benchmarked is moving on".

The speaker explained how in his company's field other computer companies were telling them a considerable amount about their personnel practices and engineering processes (although not their business processes), and how Rover had been particularly co-operative in the area of project management. He said that benchmarking had given much greater focus to improvement teams, but the company had learnt from what companies didn't say as well as from what they did:

"If you can see no measures then the company is kidding you about the existence of a quality improvement culture".

The company has now begun to compare itself with the world best and is looking in the future to create an 'amalgam' internally from these benchmarks.

Following the presentation it was asked if anyone is co-ordinating in his company and he explained his role in 'benchmarking the benchmarking process'. He said that there was 'no problem in getting methodology owners out' but it was recognised that unco-ordinated change 'could be a disaster'.

When asked about measures to show how benchmarking techniques relate to profitability he suggested that the number of visits made and the number of ideas generated could be measured, but that it was probably not worth putting a figure to each. Internal benchmarking was recommended.

He was questioned on what he felt the best processes to benchmark were and in reply said that as a software engineer his interest was in knowing how other people are developing software. In this it was of interest to know the languages that were being used and what the approaches were in checking and monitoring lines of code.

Benchmarking was seen as having a role in improving morale in the company, although it could have a demotivating effect when changes are not made quickly. Information from benchmarking visits did not go to everyone, he said, but anyone can inspect the information network, and it is used particularly when there are cases for supplier selection.

Benchmarking and Strategic Planning

Roger Sugden explained how Rank Xerox had developed its 'Leadership through Quality' from benchmarking against Fuji-Xerox, and has benchmarking now as an integral part of its turnaround strategy for survival.

The definition of benchmarking that was presented was that formulated by David T. Kearns, Chairman of the Xerox Corporation and was namely 'the continuous process of measuring our products, services, and practices against our toughest competitors or those companies renowned as leaders'.

The benchmarking approaches adopted have been internal, competitive, functional and generic, but the only justification for benchmarking is seen as the number of improvements made at the end of the day. The 'tough bit' said Mr. Sugden, was not collecting the data, but making the improvement:

"If you haven't made a decision that there is something that you want to improve, then there's not much chance of improving it".

The major international and external benchmarking effort is based on customer satisfaction with a goal of 100 per cent of customers satisfied and 80 per cent very satisfied. Other opportunity areas identified include employee satisfaction and return on assets.

Some 90 per cent of the value of benchmarking is identified as being driven off literature searches, but the way in which it is managed into the business is critical: a benchmark can deliver a 'shock wave' into the system which invokes stress rather than driving improvement. Clearly this has to be avoided.

Amongst the companies that Rank Xerox has benchmarked are Milliken (employee suggestions); Toyota, Komatsu and Fuji Xerox (Total Quality Management); Texas Instruments (policy implementation); AT and T, Hewlett Packard (Research and Development); Proctor and Gamble (product marketing); L.L. Bean and Hershey Foods (logistics), American Hospital Supply (inventory control); American Express (billing and collection); Ford and Cummins (factory layout).

[Issue 42 (June 1992)]

BENCHMARKING FOR COMPETITIVE ADVANTAGE

Benchmarking as a process was the theme at the A.T. Kearney International Conference at the International Convention Centre in Birmingham on April 8th which was entitled 'Benchmarking for Competitive Advantage' and had an attendance of around 540.

This event featured, amongst others, Alan Jones, Managing Director of TNT (Express UK) Limited and Chairman of the Chartered Institute of Transport; Chris Millard, Logistics Director, Rover Body and Pressings (Rover Group); and Roger Davies, Performance Manager, British Airways (assisted by Gavin Halliday).

Service Improvement through Benchmarking.

Alan Jones described a five stage breakdown for benchmarking beginning with planning and investigation of which a key component is identification of the stakeholders (any individuals and/or departments who have a clear interest in or impact on the process being benchmarked). For the process of receiving parcels into a depot this would mean customers, drivers, staff working on the loading bank, traffic office staff and personnel working in the computer department.

Next, one has to measure and analyse, which means ensuring that valid data is gathered:

"You can't benchmark a process until everything known about the process is pooled and analysed by the team who are doing it".

Delegates were encouraged to make use of personal contacts, as well as all existing information to establish how competitors operate and evaluate the same processes, but warned against the danger of misrepresenting oneself when approaching a competitor. TNT has adopted a philosophy of benchmark partnering for specific processes, whereby the partners are not competitors but have similar operations in one part of the business. As an example he cited the case of comparing the company s performance at taking in parcels at a depot with that of a large retailer.

Next the use of a future performance flowchart was advocated followed by the all-important stage of communicating the findings, which he said 'was not as simple as it sounds':

"There's a tendency to rush around when the first results come through. But because of a burst of activity or, equally, lack of co-operation, first findings can be misleading".

A benchmark was, he said, not just the result of one finding, and it was advised that the stakeholders be involved and their reactions to the process obtained.

The next stage is that of planning and implementing action but before the action plan is made operational, the speaker advised to check if a pilot may be needed and assess whether any special training is required. It is implied that it is necessary that those implementing the plan and those affected by it must both accept it:

"When you introduce benchmarking you must be sure that everything and everybody affected by it is fully aware of what is going on".

Delegates were also warned that when the action plan is implemented the company must be able to continue unhindered:

" It's very easy to pay so much attention to a benchmark that something else goes down the tube, when you're not looking".

The last stage, to review and recalibrate, involves evaluating whether the original objectives have been met, ensuring resource and timing plans have been met, evaluating the benchmarking process itself and examining the targets for recalibrating the benchmarks. The ideal recommendation was that from this, benchmarking becomes an integral part of the business.

The speaker concluded by pointing out the most common charts that the company is asked to perform against by its competitors, namely on-time delivery performance, cost per delivery, and cost per case delivered. The advantage for the company is that transport costs become visible, in contrast to an in-house system where 'quite a few costs might get lost in the accountancy system'.

Benchmarking: turning Theory into Practice.

Chris Millard described how in 1990 his company adopted a benchmarking process based on that used by Rank Xerox, with the assistance of Mr. Roger Sugden, whose help was greatly acknowledged. This was stimulated by the company s collaborative relationship with Honda.

The objective was to use benchmarking as part of the 'Total Quality toolkit' with Rover Body and Pressings piloting the benchmarking process within the Rover Group.

It was found that most of the literature on 'Best Practice Benchmarking' or 'world class performance level' identifies the results of the benchmarking programmes, usually in the form of some metric or measure which the organisation has achieved, but if benchmarking is pursued without a clearly defined process then the real opportunity for lasting benefit will be missed:

"The superficial approach without a clearly defined process can foster 'Wow - visits'. That is, to visit a World Class Operation and return in awe of their achievement."

Attention has therefore to be focussed not just on what someone else has achieved but how they have achieved it, and by having a detailed understanding of one's own process it is possible to do this by asking the right questions, and finding quite often that the reasons for their performance are obvious.

As an example it was noted that in one manufacturing operation, changeover times were better by a factor of ten at Honda than at Rover, even though Honda's equipment was older and less automated. By knowing what to look for the benchmarking team were able to return with 2,000 ideas for improvement. As a result Rover can now achieve and in some cases exceed the targets of Honda in this area, having identified that the key was not so much the age or type of equipment as how it is used.

The speaker was questioned on the extent to which Rover benchmark outside the industry and he explained that whilst most of the company's benchmarking for vehicle manufacture is done inside the industry, the company has looked outside their industry for benchmarking distribution, as car manufacturers are not always best in this field. To benchmark the use of rail transport, for example, the preference would be for a company whose transport costs represent a high proportion of total costs, such as a quarry.

He was also asked whether the company had learnt everything from Japan or whether some learning had come from the UK. The reply was that although there had been some learning in Britain especially from the service sector, it tended to be easier to look abroad as there is more published information more readily available, as well as companies that are not competing on one's own doorstep, which leads to greater co-operation.

Managing the Transfer of Knowledge.

The conference on Practical Benchmarking held at the Holiday Inn, Heathrow on 18th and 19th January, which featured 14 very high quality presentations, provided an excellent opportunity for the Benchmarking Centre to introduce itself and describe some of the services which it now provides.

In a presentation entitled 'Managing the Transfer of Knowledge', the General Manager of the Benchmarking Centre Mr. Barry Povey, explained some of the common excuses for the failure of benchmarking projects, namely:

- lack of resources

- lack of process owner commitment

- reluctance to implement improvement

- no perception of the value of benchmarking

- apathy

He warned of dangers ahead for those who attempted to delegate benchmarking since this "gives a compliant activity and those affected will not be committed".

In order to help to prevent these problems from arising he referred to research by IBM Havant and the Strategic Planning Institute Council for Benchmarking in the USA, which currently has about 80 members. He highlighted the need for benchmarking to be firmly positioned as part of the Total Quality strategy and not as a stand-alone event, and to focus on those few processes in which excellence is critical to the success of the business, rather than allow effort to become dissipated in an attempt to improve the unimportant. He also emphasised the need for senior management to be clearly committed to both business process improvement and benchmarking. Also for process owners, process designers and process operators to be integrated together into the benchmarking team.

Those seeking to embark on benchmarking exercises were strongly advised to prepare the groundwork for implementation by having formal reviews with the 'key state holders' before making final recommendations, and to ensure that any impact on peripheral groups is considered.

In order to ensure commitment support was obtained from management for the implementation plan, all participants were advised to seek agreement on how results and recommendations are to be communicated, and in particular not to rely solely on the final report as the means to communicate recommendations.

With regard to the selection of benchmarking partners delegates were warned not to be influenced unnecessarily by the reputation of companies, for example, as a result of winning some much coveted award, as the award in itself provides no guarantee that all of their processes are world class. The case study of IBM, which examined the experiences and results obtained from benchmarking a telecommunications controller assembly process and is presented in the conference literature, explains how the company had initially wrongly selected two companies to benchmark. One of these (another IBM company) was chosen because it also manufactured telecommunications products, but it produced in much higher volumes and many of the build aspects were different. The other, a food product company, was found to be of little practical benefit as their production plans were harvest driven, they built to stock for instant delivery, quality was assessed on the basis of perception (taste, colour, looks etc.) and batches were only tolerant to one defect.

With this background some of the services of the Benchmarking Centre were outlined. These include:

- identification of benchmarking partners for specific processes

- a directory of subscribers

- on-line networking

- advisory services (ethical and practical)

- benchmarking awareness seminars

- an annual benchmarking forum

- a newsletter

- common interest group meetings

Benchmarking: a Tool for a Better Future

Dr. Mohammed Zairi, Unilever Lecturer in TQM at the European Centre for Total Quality at the University of Bradford, and co-author of 'Practical Benchmarking: the Complete Guide' traced some of the origins of benchmarking, in particular to the Japanese principle of Shukko (loaning of one's employees to other firms in the form of secondments or special assignments with the aim of acquiring specific knowledge which the company is lacking). The definition of a benchmark was quoted in the IEE Handbook, i.e. 'a physiological or biological reference value against which a performance is compared'.

This in turn was followed with a discussion about the actual practice of benchmarking and some of the common pitfalls associated with it in the UK. In particular he pointed to the common practice of commissioning consultants and others to compare an organisation's costs with those of competitors using secondary data, and then using the findings as grounds for a cost cutting exercise. He warned:

"You can cut costs anywhere you like, but in the long term this can be very harmful. You eventually come to a point where there is nothing left".

The organisations which are most keen on this approach were noted to be those that are most anxious to see tangible results quickly i.e. those which are most vulnerable to the folly of short term thinking.

Likewise companies were warned to beware of the 'quick dip' approach to benchmarking. Many organisations, according to the speaker, start to benchmark before they are really ready to do so and fall into a trap by taking information as accurate without really being aware of its validity. A false sense of security may then develop with a consequent failure to link the information obtained with the relevant processes:

"Managers just read between numbers and set targets that aren't based on a knowledge of processes or of what they can deliver".

He asserted that companies cannot expect to close wide gaps overnight and need to have a long term focus for their benchmarking, and reinforcement of the link between benchmarking and TQM was strongly advocated.

Four specific types of benchmarking were introduced:

* internal benchmarking (comparison of internal operations).

* competitive benchmarking (specific competitor to competitor comparisons for a product or function of interest).

* functional benchmarking (comparisons with similar functions within the same broad industry or to industry leaders).

* generic benchmarking (comparison of business functions or processes that are the same regardless of industry).

The methodologies associated with each have much in common and to help companies two Plan-Do-Check-Act cycles were presented to provide a framework whereby a successful benchmarking programme might be implemented. This begins with an understanding of internal processes, followed by an evaluation of current performance, identification of process limitations and opportunities for improvement, actual process improvement, measurement and evaluation of improvements made establishment of internal standards and control and management of the processes. In the second cycle processes are selected for benchmarking using information gained from the first, partners are identified and a measurement strategy agreed. Standards are compared and any differences in performance analysed. Relevant practices that are seen to affect performance are then modified and standards again compared. The same principle may then be repeated with the same or new partners on a regular basis, and extended to further processes until all processes are subject to continual review.

It was noted that for some processes there may not be much knowledge currently available and suggested that companies should always be conscious of the existence of new ways to generate knowledge. He also pointed out that benchmarking should not end after the visit. Measuring and monitoring afterwards were essential, and this, he said, should be planned in advance, not added on as an afterthought. He strongly recommended the 'Customer First, Profit Last' philosophy which Rank Xerox currently work to establishing a clear hierarchy of priorities for benchmarking: customer satisfaction first, employee satisfaction second, market share third and return on assets fourth. [The logic is that if the first two are right the others will follow –Ed]

Benchmarking in the Contract Catering Industry.

Carol Rogers, the Commercial Director of Quadrant, described how the company had evolved from Post Office Catering Services, established 25 years ago, into Quadrant, launched in 1988. She then explained how as an in-house company within the Post Office there had been a tendency for the organisation merely to assume that it was performing its function as well as it could, without making any real attempt to measure its performance.

Three years ago, however, it was recognised that both turnover and profit could be greatly improved through the adoption of new management techniques, and with new opportunities arising to tender for other public sector bodies' catering contracts. The company operates around 350 units, employs around 2,500, serves 55,000 meals a day and is the country's largest in-house vending organisation. It sets itself the mission of becoming the best contract catering company in the U.K.

This notion of becoming the best implied a need to benchmark, and so at a relatively early stage in the company's TQM drive, operations directors conducted a critical appraisal of the organisation, which revealed that perceptions of quality and standards within the organisation 'varied enormously' between sites:

'The culture was "we are professional caterers, we know what our customers want", but was this true?'

It soon became apparent that this enormous variation needed attention and so it was decided to develop a uniform set of quality standards for all sites, which could be easily understood by everyone and be measured and maintained. It was recognised that an existing set of standards could not be imported and so the company decided to develop its own Business Operating Standards (BOS), not by management imposing rules or targets on subordinates, but by establishing restaurant teams, which worked together with people from various functions and together created a picture of best practice.

Having ascertained the standards to which the company aspired, six 'restaurants of excellence', which were accepted as operating at or above the BOS levels, were chosen as benchmarks for both internal benchmarking and external benchmarking with other contract caterers. Live training and awareness days take place at these restaurants, the staff using a 'Path of Excellence' in which a customer's route is followed with an invitation to comment on the quality and standards perceived from the customer's angle.

The 'Path of Excellence' is supported with a measurement system used to ascertain the opinions of the company's now 60,000 plus customers on a six monthly basis. This is used to develop customer satisfaction indices that are believed to be unique in the catering industry at the present time as regards the size and scope of the exercise. Replies have typically numbered around 15,000 and results are compiled on a restaurant by restaurant basis as well as providing a national average:

'Where the figures say we are not doing well, we don't try to hide them. We talk through the weak areas with our staff, customers and clients, and set out action plans to rectify our faults'.

The index is tracked by NOP and this third party tracking has clearly given it credibility, with customers and clients able to see it as 'a proof of Quadrant's commitment to improving the service in its restaurants'. It is, however, recognised as only an arms length survey, and so a number of Restaurant Improvement Teams have also been set up to afford customers the opportunity of sitting down with staff to discuss any specific improvement opportunities, take action, and report the results.

External benchmarking has been undertaken with British Home Stores, who were noted for having undergone a transformation both in their high street business and in their company culture:

'Executives shared with us their thoughts on what had gone well with the process of change in the organisation and what could have gone better. We were particularly keen to pick up on their customer facing processes - in fact, on business processes in general - and this has helped us identify improvement opportunities'.

The speaker was critical of her own industry's lack of open relationships and willingness to learn from others' experience, and attributes this largely to the industry's size and complexity, and recent events, such as take-overs and price wars. She used, however, the BHS example to show that as long as there are points of shared experience it is still possible to benchmark. Quadrant is in the process of launching roundtable discussions for personnel directors from various contract catering companies to discuss subjects such as health and safety, recruitment, training and personnel policies. The aim is to establish industry standards for certain criteria such as staff turnover and accidents so that contract caterers will be in a position to benchmark against the average at least in some, relatively non-competitive areas.

The company is also piloting BS5750 in one of its centres of excellence, and in this connection the company has chosen Girobank of Bootle as a partner.

Benchmarking in the Transport Industry.

Another industry that is renowned for its competitiveness is the transport industry which was represented at the conference by David Alvarez, General Manager Business Development for TNT Contract Distribution, who discussed the selection and use of key performance indicators to add value within the supply chain.

In analysing the supply chain the speaker drew attention to the importance of identifying the start and finish of each link and what it is seeking to achieve. Also the need for awareness of any factors which are likely to have an impact on part of the chain and any rippling effects that may result. Similarly there is a need to identify and consider all subsidiary supply chains such as fuel, packaging, waste and other suppliers.

The transport industry is not, according to the speaker, particularly well placed to add value to the supply chain:

'The term juggernaut is frequently heard as a term of abuse, and antagonism will be increased by dirty lorries, aggressive drivers, congestion, exhaust emission, environmental problems and, of course, poor service'.

Consequently transport operators frequently have to 'work hard to stand still' but value can be added nonetheless through such attributes as well liveried clean vehicles, good manners, courtesy, merchandising, emergency response capability, and adherence to a quality management system as would be developed, for example, for BS5750. These attributes are in addition to the basic requirements of on-time delivery, accuracy of delivery, absence of damage, minimal inventory and JIT where appropriate.

Key performance indicators are ascertained by staff asking the question 'what actions can I take as a result?' If the answer is none then it is unlikely that the indicator has any use since the accumulation of facts for their own sake is 'a sterile exercise'. Examples of good indicators include items handled per man hour worked, percentage of on-time deliveries, percentage of order fulfilment, miles per vehicle breakdown, fuel consumption and vehicle downtime. These, however, must have a comparison since piles of computer printouts that are little more than a collection of facts are of little use.

Benchmarking and activity sampling were seen as a means of achieving comparison and the presentation provided an interesting example of how the structured rank of people could be beneficial for a company e.g. by helping to pinpoint defective vehicles rather than the traditional perceived purpose of punishing under achievers.

Benchmarking at European Level.

Early stages in benchmarking at European level were described by Tom Dark, Group Finance Chairman for British Telecom and Chairman of the EFQM Finance Benchmarking Round Table, which was initiated two years ago by the EFQM.

The Round Table, which was initially comprised of 8 companies, but now has over 20, covers a diverse range of industries and is primarily concerned with the benchmarking of mainstream financial functions. Following the first meeting which established the basic objective of improving each financial function, a charter has been produced with the aim of establishing best practices and running active projects with meetings every 4 to 6 months and a policy of information sharing and open membership (not necessarily EFQM members). Described as 'a safe environment where you can expose your mistake', the Round Table has been recognised as offering a number of benefits in terms of shared learning, performance comparison and as a catalyst for change.

It was noted that none of the members claim to be the best in the world for any financial process. There is always someone to learn from and to date a number of important lessons have been learned. British Telecom, for example, found it to be 'a salutory experience' to know their own processes before confirming their benchmarking partner. The speaker explained how they had found, on benchmarking one particular process, a critical part of a process was actually undertaken by another company and was highly confidential. It was thus suggested that an early, structured up front meeting be used to confirm whether a benchmarking partner is the one which is suitable for a particular application.

Another important lesson learned was the need to limit the size of projects so that they do not become so big as to be out of control. As regards measurement, it was recognised that often a basket of measurements may be required to gain a whole picture of the company.

[Issue 73 (January 1995)]

SECOND ANNUAL BENCHMARKING FORUM

The Benchmarking Centre held their Second Annual Benchmarking Forum at The Moat House International Hotel in Stratford on Avon from 20th to 22nd November. The Forum featured some 22 presentations commencing with an address by one of the world's leading authorities on benchmarking Mr. Bob Camp, Manager of Benchmarking Competency for Xerox Inc., USA.

International Perspectives

Bob Camp's presentation was entitled 'How Benchmarking is developing: some International Perspectives', and provided a useful and informative insight into what is happening in the field of benchmarking at a global level.

He described how benchmarking had now become an established practice in over 30 countries whilst many others, particularly in Asia and South America were beginning also to show keen interest, Seven countries now had established benchmarking centres, whilst the process itself, defined operationally as 'finding and implementing best practices', had progressed well from manufacturing into the service sectors. Healthcare, government, education, and even the Inland Revenue service were all active in the USA. Many were now benchmarking outside their own industry. He cited the example of Broken Hill Properties in Australia who were currently benchmarking Disneyworld.

The results of benchmarking have, he said, been "really astonishing" in some areas. He cited the example of healthcare organisations, some of which have "moved with it very smartly" to improve such activities as the treatment of pneumonia and coronary by-pass surgery.

Quality Awards, he said, provided "a good driver" for benchmarking by encouraging companies which felt that they were already excellent to see for themselves whether the belief was true and if so, against what standard. He suggested that even companies which were recognised internationally as being excellent by world standards were fully aware that there was no way that they could claim to being best at everything that they did. They too have to learn but perhaps more importantly they know that they have to.

He pointed to "a good network" of people who were now doing benchmarking very successfully, and described how a series of steps to successful benchmarking was "increasingly unfolding". These steps were summarised in a slide entitled 'The Benchmarking Future' and consisted of essentially:

* software (a method of talking about benchmarking in a common way which delivered a consistent message for process classification).

* hardware (provision of a standalone model, such as the 'ten step process' along with legitimisation of informal benchmarking).

* humanware (incorporating the important activity of networking, with links to benchmarking centres which in turn network between themselves and between countries in what is emerging as "a major capability").

* learningware (achievement of rapid best practice transfer).

The role of benchmarking was also notably now fitting within the broader remit of business process improvement i.e. there was recognition that benchmarking does not exist for its own sake, but as part of a larger initiative to generate improvement. Furthermore organisations are increasingly agreeing on what their critical processes are and how to break them down perhaps to the third or fourth order. This enables a knowledgeable person responsible for the process (owners who can describe how the process works) to be identified and charged with the task of finding and implementing the best practice for performing his particular processes. For this to be effective the management team has clearly to "prioritize the vital few" processes concerned, and be able to highlight the 'lines of sight' from these processes to the company's goals. It was emphasised, however, that 'what' without 'how' is "an empty statement" and that targets without tools are of little use. Care was needed to ensure that measures are not overemphasised or processes overlooked.

Questions to Mr. Camp were numerous and were therefore grouped according to whether they related to strategic, methodological, practical or miscellaneous issues. The first asked whether benchmarking amounted in practice to a mere game of 'catch up', and to this Mr. Camp answered "yes" if in fact it was assumed that benchmarking amounted merely to the practice of another and subsequently implementing it. He suggested, however, that there was actually more to it because the objective is usually to improve on the best practice rather than merely to copy it. He expanded by giving an example of warranties which were benchmarked revealing a 'best practice' that provided a money back guarantee. Later discussions with the customers, however, revealed that the money back guarantee was of little consequence. What they wanted was a product which did what they required.

Next he was asked about the cycle time for benchmarking, which the delegate had found to be typically six to twelve months, and whether it could be improved upon. Mr. Camp's answer to this was "yes" and he then explained how skilled benchmarkers had now taken to benchmarking activities in parallel, and how by having someone in the company responsible for conducting the overall benchmarking activity it was possible to reduce access times into companies to be benchmarked, especially when they too have a benchmarking professional. [This mirrors well the established 'Quality-to Quality' professional approach-Ed]. Contact is thus made easier and quicker, and is frequently facilitated by benchmarking centres.

He was then asked to comment on his statement that measures were often overemphasised, on the grounds that one always needed to have measures, and in particular to state where the line should be drawn between necessity and overemphasis. Mr. Camp accepted that some measurement was necessary if one was to improve, but that it had to be accomplished in moderation and definitely not done for its own sake. Some people, he said, believed that benchmarking meant measurement, for example of the costs of sales and administration, but experience has shown that this view is now significantly outdated.

Another delegate expressed concern about the use of one particular type of measure, namely ratios expressed as a percentage of sales, and asked Mr.Camp to comment on whether such ratios had a tendency to be misread, especially in different industrial sectors. Mr. Camp gave an emphatic "yes" to this and pointed to high levels of variation especially where the measures are financial. He suggested that any measures that are used should be essentially output measures from processes that are devoid of financial connotations, certainly at the crucial stage where the measurement is being made.

This was followed by a request for Mr. Camp to comment on the applicability or otherwise of attributes which were non-financial but were nonetheless difficult to assess for relevance, such as lines of code in a computer program, and then to address the complex issue of how one reaches agreement at board level on which measures should be adopted. In response he explained how in some areas, such as inventory, benchmarking could reveal new measures which can drive a quite different and revolutionary way of working. He referred in particular to the high levels of inventory that used to be common in high tech industries which had driven a move toward larger warehouses to protect demand until benchmarking by several companies revealed that by using inventory turns as the measure it was possible to approach the same problem quite differently, i.e. by moving inventory more rapidly through facilities. He suggested that such observations could be "quite revealing".

Another delegate requested advice on whether an outside facilitator should be engaged for strategic benchmarking and Mr. Camp accepted that in some cases it could be justified, but suggested that in recent years the role of outside facilitators had changed, with more companies commissioning internal teams and using outside help to assist in rather than perform the study in question. This was particularly the case, he said, with major re-engineering projects. [This is the best way to use consultants in almost every case, because the company gains in skills and the consultant's expertise is optimised-Ed]

Mr. Camp was then asked how one might seek to sell benchmarking to a CEO and in his answer suggested that the present bibliography of over 200 articles on the subject made an overwhelming case, demonstrating that it is "an outstanding way to change and change quickly". Many organisations, he said, have "reached the bottom of the idea barrel" and found that it has provided them with a way out. He pointed to "an increasing understanding of benchmarking amongst CEOs".

He was asked about recent developments in competitive benchmarking and whilst accepting that it " had to be done with care", he did point to changes in attitude away from the traditional approach whereby consultants commissioned studies and protected the anonymity of data, and toward agreements being reached on non-sensitive areas such as invoice processing on a one to one basis. He cited several examples from the oil industry, particularly in the field of health and safety, which has been recognised as a matter of common concern.

Another delegate asked how benchmarking might be sustained in an organisation and in answering Mr. Camp stressed the need for benchmarking to be embodied within the planning process of the organisation such that it becomes "part of the fabric". He referred to Xerox's Vision 2000 programme in which benchmarking has become "firmly embedded as a quality tool".

The question session concluded with a discussion of some of the dangers inherent in the use of benchmarking, in particular the dangers of it being used without being understood and of it being either misused or passed off as an excuse for something else. Mr. Camp strongly agreed that there was a need to protect against misunderstandings though the use of consistent terminology, but whilst in the past the term has been misapplied, the risk of this type of abuse is diminishing, not least because of the increasing influence of the current expanding infrastructure of benchmarking professionals and centres.

Benchmarking Absenteeism

One measure that has been well addressed is that of absenteeism and a paper by David Osgerby, Project Manager and Facilitator for GKN Sankey plc at Telford, describes how absenteeism has been successfully benchmarked by this company with a number of important lessons learned.

The project commenced in July 1993 when it was decided that the company's absenteeism rate of 5.5 per cent, which was costing the company of the order of £1 million a year, was no longer acceptable and required action.

The paper describes how a team of seven led by a Personnel manager and consisting of two operations managers, two personnel managers, a health and safety adviser, a systems analyst and a facilitator, bench marked eleven organisations from a list of twenty that were initially contacted. This was in turn supported by parallel research and analysis of published surveys.

The method chosen involved an initial focus on percentage absence rates with low figures used as a prompt for enquiry into company characteristics, including further visits and discussions. Findings showed that the best companies were achieving rates of around 2 per cent, but that GKN's own rate of 5.5 per cent was no worse than average for their industrial sector.

The paper highlights three specific companies, one which had achieved a rate of 2 per cent and was considered to be one of the best performers in the country , one which was not quite so good (3.5 per cent) but which had six months before had a rate of 6 per cent (which was worse than GKN's), and one which had achieved an improvement from 8 per cent to 3.5 per cent but later lost much of what they had gained and were now back to 6 per cent.

In the first company it is noted that absenteeism was treated as a high profile issue with levels measured and displayed and control charts clearly in evidence. Analysis of attendance history was a fundamental part of recruitment whilst performance appraisal at all levels included attendance and the management of attendance. There was a strong team culture that created peer pressure to discourage absenteeism and supervisors were both highly trained and owned the attendance issue. The workforce in this company is noted to be predominantly young, and cultured in a manner which is based on high standards of performance.

The second company had a Total Quality programme which was in its sixth year and had adopted a methodology for continuous improvement which was being applied systematically to targeted departments. These were selected using pareto analysis, the worst areas being tackled first. The participative approach which the methodology introduced was found to enhance peer group pressure and reduced the absenteeism substantially.

The third company adopted a 'hard line' approach which was top down, with responsibility for driving absence down vested firmly in the hands of the Personnel Manager. Evidence suggests that this had a positive short term effect, but control was concentrated through one individual and when he left the system reverted to its former state.

The paper concludes with some 21 'Lessons of Benchmarking', some of which are as follows:

* training done 'on the hoof' can weaken the process installation/role clarity and encourage bad habits.

* investigation skills and effectiveness can be limited without specific training i.e. interviewing may be good but subsequent process analysis is weak.

* development of short-term fixes can deviate the team from its objective of obtaining external knowledge and create delay.

* one meeting per week on average created inputs of two to three hours each which led to a project over a year's duration, which was felt to be excessive and could be improved.

* team leader and facilitator roles can become blurred on the first project, especially if pre-post team meetings are not held habitually.

* major delays occur when business priorities, such as personnel becoming absorbed in annual wage negotiations, impinge and affect the time input.

* visits to benchmarking partners should span three events to allow detailed information to be obtained at the appropriate level.

[Issue 79 (July 1995)]

BENCHMARKING IN THE FINANCE FUNCTION

The third in our current series of reviews of reports from The Conference Board consists of three papers presented at the Board's Second European Finance Forum in Amsterdam.

The Methodology of benchmarking Finance.

The first paper by Theo Klein of A.T. Kearney highlights the common tendency of companies to overlook the finance function when benchmarking is undertaken. i.e. it is a neglected area, with the finance function not being the subject of a redesign for nearly thirty years since the function was computerised in the 1960s, in many multinational enterprises.

Benchmarking is considered as a first step in process re-engineering and the author describes how leaders in the finance function were selected from various industries:

'When benchmarking the finance function it is reasonable to select comparable and best in class companies from a variety of industries because the activities within the finance function are often not industry specific. The major processes in the finance function are similar e.g. the billing activities,

the credit and collection activities, payroll and fixed assets accounting. There is no difference between accounting for a supplier's invoice in a retail, a manufacturing or a service company'.

Two benchmarking studies were undertaken using a common base of data collected from 25 companies known for their excellence in finance such as Ford, Hewlett-Packard and Du Pont. One study examined leadership practices in finance, the other focused on the opportunities and pitfalls stemming from the creation of European shared service centres for the processing of mass accounting transactions. This is noted to be a relatively new concept in Europe. Sixteen major activities were covered, divided into three groups (accounting activities, transactional activities and decision-support activities).

Findings showed that there were significant opportunities for cost savings or improvements in service for the customers of the finance function in all of the participating companies:

'The companies had never realised how big the opportunities were because most, if not all, finance functions are very much focused internally. They hardly ever, if at all, compare their performance with that of other groups. This was the major benefit of the study'.

The first study showed that the leading company, which has a global business, is able to produce an overview of each of its product's worldwide profitability using an integrated system. Here the reconciliation between global reporting and the local accounting data is automated such that information can be presented by product, customer, legal entity or by region. This system is paperless.

The second study revealed that structure and management philosophy affected finance costs with the centralised companies having lower figures. It was found that the more legal entities a company had, the higher its finance cost tended to be. It is concluded that whilst it is not yet possible to have one single European entity, there are benefits in consolidating local units to produce fewer legal entities.

Benefits of benchmarking Finance.

The second paper, by Kaj Thornen, Finance Director of SKF (Sweden) describes how the leading roller bearing manufacturer used the A.T. Kearney study in which they participated as a basis for improvement. Project leaders conducted detailed studies and concluded that considerable savings could be made:

'Studies showed that people had taken a fresh look at procedures and considered how to spread the work load more evenly across the year, rather than having peaks at month end and year end. The project leaders also

agreed unanimously on standard procedures across countries for handling internal finance functions. When dealing with customers and suppliers, however, some country customisation is required'.

The paper describes how savings of up to 85 per cent were achieved, in inter-company transaction costs. Also, in some areas such as cost management and valuation of inventories common systems and procedures were found to be more practical than had initially been believed.

The integration of the finance function into the company's Total Quality programme is described:

'In some areas we found that 90 per cent of our people are just correcting errors, and not errors that are created in the finance function but errors that are created in the procedure'.

The company is consequently aiming at 50 per cent cost improvement attainable through the improvement of procedures, disciplines and standards, which will require little investment or changes in systems. Common systems for general ledger, accounts receivable and accounts payable are also expected to yield savings of around 10 to 15 per cent.

Methods, Uses and Outcomes

The third paper, by Iain Robertson of Whirlpool (Europe) which currently claims to be the world's manufacturer of domestic appliances, describes how a major company which inherited two legal entities marketing two separate brands with separate accounting operations and separate banking in every country in which it operated, also used the A.T. Kearney study. This time the aim was to ascertain what was possible by integrating further at European level or using shared services in European service centres.

Benchmarking had already been used successfully to reduce the number of days for which sales were outstanding and a six step process had been devised. The key to successful benchmarking was seen to lie in the data obtained:

'We found that we needed to spend time to organise the data collection process and make sure that people understood very clearly what was required because the data are fundamental to all the decisions you make afterwards. To collect the data, we formed a dedicated data collection team and identified a single contact with Kearney so that we could make sure we understood what they were asking'.

Qualitative information from the Kearney study was used to create a finance vision and define the role of finance in the organisation. A savings potential of some 20 to 30 per cent was then identified, for example in the company's cost structure. Opportunities for improvement were identified in the company's reporting philosophy, e.g. by consolidating transaction accounting activities and opportunities for process and systems redesign.

The company concluded that it needed to redefine its finance function with the emphasis on the value added activities of operations analysis and decision support. As a result accounting became separated from business planning and operations analysis. This potentially would allow operating managers to make decisions with a centralised accounting system.

A new finance strategy was formulated and the feasibility of moving certain operations from a legal entity to a branch structure examined. This was found to allow for greater flexibility in capital movement and for savings to be realised in audit fees through the absence of requirements for a statutory audit. A new consolidation reporting system has also been developed along with the ledgers and reporting systems:

'Eventually we would like to have a relational database where all the data is in one place and we access it via an executive information system'.

[Issue 84 (December 1995)]

FIRST EUROPEAN BEST PRACTICE BENCHMARKING AWARDS

The first European Best Practice Benchmarking Awards were presented on 27th November at the third annual conference of the Benchmarking Centre held at the Moat House Hotel in Stratford on Avon.

The Award was won by Hewlett Packard Finance Limited for a project called 'Ideas for motivating People and Complaints Training' (IMPACT) which was recently presented as a case study at the annual conference of the Management Centre in Brussels.

The project was initiated following a review of areas for improvement at the company in August 1994 which highlighted customer service as a potential area in which the company could substantially improve its competitive advantage. Also the speaker Ms. Karen Prior-Smith told how HP recognised the banking organisation First Direct were providing exceptional levels of customer service in the form of 24 hours responsive tele-banking.

The company's U.K. Benchmarking co-ordinator approached First Direct and an initial meeting was arranged which "turned into a mini-benchmarking activity with much information being shared from First Direct". A reciprocal visit followed by First Direct who benchmarked Hewlett Packard's self-managed teams and quality systems. This was noted to be "a great success and enabler for them to begin work on an implementation plan for introducing the concept of self-managed teams."

The subsequent gap analysis by Hewlett Packard highlighted three factors which were affecting performance:

(i) At First Direct training was linked to customer service. At Hewlett Packard it was linked to leasing.

(ii) At First Direct service levels were linked to a system of recognition. At Hewlett Packard there was no such system.

(iii) First Direct operated a vigorous process for dealing with customer complaints. Hewlett Packard Finance had no formal complaints system at all.

An implementation plan was thus devised to address these issues which included a First Direct training brochure customised to HP Finance and an introduction of a documented process for customer complaints handling. This incorporated 100 per cent follow up of every complaint and set of visible reminders on how to handle complaints with monitoring via Lotus Notes. A new system of 'on the spot' recognition awards was introduced which managers were empowered to award for "a service level beyond the call of duty".

The presentation prompted some questioning by delegates, notably on the subject of rewards and recognition. The speaker was asked for example how a manager might be expected to know when someone has done something outstanding instantly, and she answered by saying "I listen. People do come and tell me". She suggested that peer groups often are quite effective at doing this.

In another question she was asked if she had ever had a customer telephone her and inform her that one of her staff had done something brilliant. Surprisingly perhaps she was able to recite such a case. This was where a sales representative who had visited BP and whose work had clearly been of sufficiently high calibre to warrant a call by BP to the effect that HP Finance had greatly improved its effectiveness in sending out schedules and dealing with them.

Runner-up Award.

In addition to the winning entry a Runner Up Award was also presented to the IBM National Call Management Centre, (NCMC), in Havant, Hampshire. Business Process Engineer Berit Mortlock described how her company used benchmarking as part of its self-assessment to the Baldrige Quality Award criteria. This aimed "to provide Best of Breed Call Management Service by ensuring value for money through people, facilities and techniques".

A partnership has been formed with Manpower plc where service delivery is provided as part of a managed service and any savings identified in processes, operations or people will be shared between the two partners:

"Working within a global organisation, with international systems and processes, we have adapted the Kaizen approach of incremental improvements in our technology, human resource management and processes through benchmarking, ensuring leading edge and best practices within the NCMC".

A team of five representing the areas of Process Management, Service Management, Operations Management, Business Development and Technical Support Group Management was established, incorporating a mix of IBM and Manpower employees.

Barry Povey, the IBM representative at the Benchmarking Centre, was drafted in to provide a one day workshop on benchmarking to the NCMC management team together with two members of the Havant manufacturing plant who had already a limited experience of benchmarking. World expert Bob Camp's book was used as an aid, along with a teleconference featuring Jerry Balm of IBM's Rochester in the USA. In addition the IBM internal worldwide database yielded useful information on benchmarking from a similar call centre in the USA.

The team visited the benchmarking partner (one of the US Baldrige Award winners) and a number of areas for improvement identified in the use of teams, training needs, the company's incentive scheme, and the service validation process:

"From engineers only being able to be paged they are now able to log onto the Call Management System directly via their laptops and mobile phones".

The Award Criteria

The 1995 European Best Practice Benchmarking Award consisted of 40 elements divided into four sections for which marks were allocated as follows:

* Leadership (20 per cent)

* The benchmarking process (40 per cent)

* Results (30%)

* Presentation and overall impression (10%)

For the purposes of self-assessing benchmarking maturity these are distilled into twelve elements: reasons for adopting, sponsorship provided, use and commitment of resources, innovative selection of process and partners, appropriateness of benchmarking team, understanding of own performance, research methods, probity, making it happen', implementation of change, and win-win relationships.

Judges allocate marks on a score of 0 to 10, from complete absence, through innocence/awareness, understanding, competence and eventually excellence. Thus, for 'innovative selection of process and partners' selection of competitors only would score lowly in the innocence/awareness range.

However, process selection before partner selection with partners still generally within the same industry would amount to 'understanding'. To demonstrate excellence on this count the company is required to engage in 'creative selection outside industry in the search for best-in-class'. Likewise 'research methods' range from 'industrial tourism' (low scoring) to 'creating and building networks in the excellence category.

The 'win-win relationships' criterion (one of the three 'results' criteria) was noted to have caused problems for some companies, with a mutual relationship not established in many cases. To demonstrate excellence here the company is required to have 'a relationship well established and matured beyond benchmarking'.

[Issue 92 (August 1996)]

I.M.S. SUMMER SCHOOL 1996

The I.M.S. held its 23rd annual Summer School at St. John's College Cambridge (one of the oldest colleges in England, dating back to 1511) from 21st to 23rd July. With the theme of 'World Class for the New Millennium' the emphasis was on competencies to support and enhance the role of the 'expert' in a management services context. There were 20 presentations divided into the four subject areas of quality, technology, productivity, and compliance, with a healthy balance between manufacturing and service.

PROBE: The CBI's National Benchmark Initiative

Dr. Fiona Underwood, CBI Project Manager for PROBE (Promoting Business Excellence –the CBI National Manufacturing Council's Benchmark Initiative) provided an outline of the unique benchmarking service launched by the Confederation of British Industry in October 1995 which she project manages.

Developed jointly by the London Business School and IBM over the last three years, PROBE serves as a best practice benchmarking tool for manufacturing industry. This uses self-assessment by a multi-level cross functional team as a vehicle for ascertaining the true positioning of a company. It comprises of a three step process consisting first of a facilitated self-assessment process addressing key areas of manufacturing and engineering practice, then a comparison between one's own sites and others in the sector and abroad (which identifies strengths and opportunities for improvement), and finally provides signposts so that these improvements can be realised:

'The PROBE self-assessment questionnaires take a maximum of 1.5 days to complete and the results are fed back at the end of the facilitated day, during which it is possible to compare a company with other sites in the sector and within European manufacturing'.

The positioning of a company is indicated on a performance/practice graph, an example of which is featured in the conference literature, which also highlights various recognised stages of progress as sites advance toward a process improvement objective. Some figures are also included which compare the performance/practice status of UK manufacturers relative to their German counterparts.

The Initiative is supported by a database of around 800 manufacturing sites whose operations have been assessed using a methodology which is based on a combination of the EFQM Business Excellence Model, the US Baldrige Award criteria, and various Japanese 'lean production concepts'.

The current price for a PROBE assessment is £1,000 plus VAT plus 'reasonable travel costs per site'.

Companies which have applied PROBE include the British Aerospace Military Aircraft division at Dunsfield in Surrey, which serves as the final assembly and flight test facility for the Harrier jet.

[Issue 96 (December 1996)]

EUROPEAN BEST PRACTICE AWARDS 1996

The second European Best Practice Award for Benchmarking has been won this year by Shell UK Exploration and Production based in Aberdeen with the Efficiency and Private Finance Unit of HM Customs and Excise receiving the runner-up award. The Awards were presented at the Fourth Annual Conference of the Benchmarking Centre at Lawress Hall, Lincoln, on 10th October. At the Award presentation Chairman of the international judging panel, SABIC Professor of Best Practice Benchmarking at the European Centre for Total Quality Management at Bradford University, Professor Mohammed Zairi, commented:

"The standard of entry was extremely high, challenging the judging panel. However, Shell UK Expo's submission was exceptional, proving the point, once again, that best practice benchmarking helps organisations to achieve desirable improvement and a competitive advantage".

On receiving the Winner's Award Shell UK's Head of Planning and Production John Russell said:

" We are absolutely delighted to receive this Award as we are striving to improve our business by driving best practice benchmarking down through the organisation. In addition to cost-savings generated, the exercise has opened our eyes to how others approach their business. To use an old cliche –this Award is 'the icing on the cake' ".

Valerie Strachan, Chairman of HM Customs and Excise, whose Award was received by Dennis Battle, Director of Personnel and Finance, said:

"We are delighted by this recognition. Hybrid benchmarking provides a structured approach for delivering efficiency savings, improving the quality of services, and lays the foundations for continuous improvement. It has enabled us to compare ourselves with the best in the public and the private sector in this country and has provided a solid base from which to achieve our aim of being a world class organisation".

The Winner and Runner-up organisations each gave presentations on the final day of the conference (11th October).

Benchmarking at Tern/Brage.

The Shell UK presentation focused on an innovative benchmarking exercise between two North Sea oil platforms, Tern (owned by Shell UK) and Brage (owned by the Norwegian oil company Norsk Hydro), which was undertaken between January and December of 1995. Both platforms are of similar size and complexity, Tern lying 170km east of The Shetland Islands in 167 metres of water with around 24 million tonnes of reserves, whilst Brage lies 120 km west of Bergen in 125 metres of water with around 38 million tonnes of reserves.

Following an initial approach to benchmark by Norsk Hydro via a third party Shell UK cleared the application through its legal department to ensure that it did not breach the EC's Article 85 (anti-competition clause) before using Norsk Hydro's methodology to collect costs and personnel numbers. These were then normalised to take account of legal differences between the UK and Norway. Regular meetings were then held which identified the following principal areas for in-depth study:

* maintenance (Norsk Hydro had maintenance-free oil coolers arising from capitalisation on the low price of titanium, from which they were made, at the end of the Cold War.

* offshore services (Norsk Hydro achieved with four personnel activities which required thirteen Shell personnel).

317

* offshore production operations

* onshore petroleum technology

Site visits confirmed that the two companies did not always speak the same language, for example, in the ways in which service provision was approached, as well as in the ways in which certain jobs such as those of cooks and stewards were defined. In particular Shell UK learned quickly that its personnel policies were working to the detriment of Tern operations and there was much offshore administration that simply not needed. Aircraft services, likewise, was an area where there was seen to be great potential for improvement. The single most important feature identified by the speaker, however, was the potential for cultural change:

"Technicians came back with a willingness to challenge the system".

Action taken since the visits included: changes to the personnel structure, notably the maintenance responsibilities for operations supervisors which was over-specified; and changes to specifications, for example, to coated bolts instead of uncoated bolts which were subject to corrosion and prone to failure. Savings of some 13.5 man years of activity amounting to £100,000 a year were identified as a result of the exercise.

Benchmarking, of course, has of necessity to be a win-win exercise so not surprisingly the speaker was questioned about the benefits which had been brought to Norsk Hydro. These were briefly identified as follows:

• certification of rigging

• operational procedures (Shell could operate some assets of platform management without hardware).

• Potential elimination of their inefficient procedures for the employment of on-shore contractors to certify relief valves.

• Improvements in the efficiency of drill crew operations.

Mr. Russell was also asked if Shell UK was now considering benchmarking outside the oil industry and he confirmed that they were now engaged in process analysis benchmarking with the Royal Navy.

Hybrid Benchmarking at Customs and Excise.

The approach to benchmarking adopted by HM Customs and Excise was also innovative, involving the hitherto largely unknown technique of 'hybrid benchmarking, which is defined as 'an efficiency technique which compares departmental performance in chosen areas with public and private sector performance in similar areas using a structure similar to that of a Market Test'.

The paper by HM Customs and Excise describes how, following the release of the Government White Paper 'Continuity and Change' in 1994, they had sought to use benchmarking as an efficiency tool whilst at the same time preserving the benefits which they had already gained from the more established technique of market testing. These benefits were essentially:

(i) The writing of a specification gave many managers the opportunity to clearly focus on what was required of various systems and the standards that were required.

(ii) Savings of up to 25 per cent had been achieved by allowing certain staff to decide how the work should be done.

(iii) Service Level Agreements/Contracts established a clear relationship between outputs and the resources.

Under their wide ranging Competing for Quality (CfQ) programme HM Customs and Excise managers already had the framework to incorporate benchmarking into their activities:

'The manager will consider whether the work should be abolished or privatised. The scope for use of the Private Finance Initiative will be examined. Consideration will be given to strategic contracting out and market testing. If none of these are appropriate then Hybrid Benchmarking will be used'.

A Business Review (high level review of the needs of the Executive Unit and constraints for a particular service) establishes the needs of the customers of the service, identifies any national systems that must be used, and examines any other factors that might affect service delivery. The information from this review is used to construct Service Level Requirements (SLRs) which are then used to determine benchmark measures. With these measures work to collect the necessary benchmarking information can be commissioned, for example, to consultants.

In parallel, in-house service providers conduct Efficiency Reviews to ascertain how best the service can be delivered to the standards and within the constraints laid down in the SLR. They then produce an in-house proposal consisting of a Quality Proposal and a Costing Proposal. An Evaluation Process compares the benchmarking information with the in-house proposal.

Benefits realised so far from hybrid benchmarking include:

- ability to examine the whole of a unit (not always possible under market testing because often part of a unit's work could not be tested).

- ability to share information with a wider range of companies.

- quality improvement in many departmental services.

- Improved customer/provider relationships in Corporate Service Areas.

The Benchmarking Centre

The Benchmarking Centre was established in 1992 and has this year received a contract as part of a consortium under the European Community ESPRIT programme to develop the World Class Standards Network using the latest technology and communications media.

NEW EUROPEAN BENCHMARKING INITIATIVE

The European Commission has proposed a new programme to develop benchmarking as a tool to improve the competitiveness of European industry. It is envisaged that the programme will be developed in consultation with industry and Member States and will cover the priority areas of quality, innovation, infrastructure, skills, and environmental efficiency. It will operate at the levels of companies, industry sectors and framework conditions (such as productivity of labour and capital and job creation). The EC Industry Council has called for Member States and industry to examine further the scope for benchmarking.

[Issue 106 (October 1997)]

BENCHMARKING THE SUPPLY CHAIN: FIRST CYCLE OF SURVEYS

Partnership Sourcing Limited, on behalf of the DTI have published the first results of a cycle of surveys designed to measure the uptake and extent of benchmarking of the supply chain by British industry.

Four surveys are included, which began with *The Times* UK top 1,000 companies for 1995 which examined a baseline against which further groups of approximately 1200, 1250 and 2800 from lower size ranges were compared. Responding organisations were grouped in four levels according to the number of employees (over 500, 201 to 500, 51 to 200, and under 51) and the largest category of business sector was manufacturing which represented 56% of respondents in level 1 (over 500 employees) and an average of 69% in the other levels.

The surveys consisted of broad based postal questionnaires covering awareness and understanding of benchmarking, details of the areas in which it is practised, difficulties encountered, benefits derived, and the role of benchmarking in supply chain relationships.

Findings showed that almost all Level 1 and Level 2 companies claimed to have some awareness of benchmarking. This declined to 62% for Level 4 (under 51 employees). Only 86% of Level 1 companies, however, agreed that they were practising benchmarking in some form, and at Level 4 the corresponding figure was down to well under a third (27%).

For all companies benchmarking activity was seen to increase from the strategic through the functional to the operational levels of the business with customer service being the most popular area in which benchmarking was conducted. The larger companies tended to benchmark more areas with manufacture being the second most popular area of benchmarking. The smaller companies by contrast tended to benchmark quality after customer service.

Three quarters (75%) of the larger companies claimed to have benefited from benchmarking, although these figures drop to under half (40%) for the smaller companies. The report notes that 'improved margin' was 'outstanding as a secured benefit with Level 1':

'The top three benefits from encouraging suppliers to Benchmark (service, quality, price) always feature strongly in surveys about the benefits from developing long-term customer/supplier relationships (partnership sourcing) and confirm that benchmarking is seen as one of a range of features of these relationships.

The report presents the following conclusion:

'Pro-active promotion of Benchmarking with suppliers is small and declines along the supply chain. Many see the concept as part of a spectrum of facets of their relationships, where benchmarking has a mention but is not driven positively. A minority of companies (mainly in Level 1) do appear to take it more seriously, and have benefited from encouraging their suppliers to benchmark.

The comparisons show that larger companies operate at higher awareness, understanding and practice of benchmarking, have benefited more, exert a higher (though still small) benchmarking influence in customer/supplier relationships, and have a greater experience and maturity'.

'Taken together the results present a compelling indication that benchmarking is weak overall in industry. Large companies are more advanced and have a leading part to play in influencing the supply chain. All channels for raising awareness and practice must be exploited'.

There are five key recommendations for industry, namely that:-

* large companies work with the benchmarking providers to seek ways to improve awareness and promote benchmarking along their supply chains and through their associations - to the benefit of themselves as well as their industries and suppliers.

* the SMEs in particular be targeted by these means.

* companies pro-actively seek information about benchmarking from customers, local, national and industry benchmarking clubs and associations and business links.

* industry leaders support a marketing campaign to raise awareness and practice of benchmarking.

* large companies and providers co-operate in measuring benchmarking trends.

[Issue 108 (December 1997)]

1997 EUROPEAN BEST PRACTICE AWARDS

The 1997 European Best Practice Awards were presented on 7th October at The Benchmarking Centre Annual Forum which, as last year, was held at the Lawress Hall in Lincoln. This year's winning entry was by The Employment Service for their benchmarking study of internal vacancy filling entitled 'Radically reducing the Elapsed Time for filling Vacancies' whilst the runner-up award went to British Telecom World-class Customer Access Network (WCAN) for their 'Strategic Benchmarking Study'. These two presentations are reviewed below.

The Employment Service: reducing the Elapsed Time for filling Vacancies.

The Employment Service is a large government agency within the Department for Education and Employment which employs around 35,000 in approximately 1,200 Jobcentres, 9 regional offices and one Head Office. Its main responsibilities are to assist jobseekers to find work or to gain a placement on an employment or training programme and to ensure that those who are in receipt of the Jobseekers' Allowance are entitled to receive it.

In 1994 they introduced a competency based vacancy filling system for people in their Management Pay Bands which affected around a third of employees and subsequently became the subject of some criticism and debate as it was perceived as being time consuming and resource intensive. An external review was therefore made which found that whilst there were some weaknesses there were also a number of strengths which were deemed sufficient for the Director of Human Resources to wish to retain elements of the system. A meeting of key stakeholders followed which concluded that benchmarking would be appropriate since it would enable a better understanding of the vacancy filling process (including times and costs) to be gained as well as potentially identifying 'break-through improvements'.

The report (18 pages) describes how the benchmarking study was first of all sponsored within the Employment Service and then the six member team selected and trained:

'To encourage the use of benchmarking in ES a Benchmarking Management Group consisting of Senior Managers from Head Office and the regions was set up to oversee benchmarking projects. This was supported at a working level by management consultants in an ES Head Office Division -Process and Systems Division -who were responsible for disseminating information on benchmarking to the rest of the organisation and acting as "Gateway" for benchmarking i.e. they help people set up benchmarking projects and support those projects if needed'.

'The vacancy Filling Study was sponsored by the Director of Human Resources (HR). He took an active interest in the study and the use of benchmarking throughout the project keeping himself abreast of developments through interim reports and Keep In Touch meetings' [An essential ingredient -Ed.].

'Members of the Division who are responsible for supporting the ES benchmarking effort and members of the team responsible for undertaking the benchmarking study into vacancy filling have received comprehensive training in the use of benchmarking and analytical techniques. The training for the latter group was provided by Coopers and Lybrand. In addition senior managers and key stakeholders have received either awareness training or in-depth briefing on benchmarking'.

'The Core Team received comprehensive training in the theory and use of benchmarking provided by the external consultant. They also received a tool kit consisting of good practice tips and techniques to help them undertake the study'.

It is then explained how process mapping helped the team to design a questionnaire which was used to identify potential benchmarking partners:

'The first stage of our study involved the mapping of the vacancy filling process from end to end using IDEF/O. This gave us a better understanding of the process we were examining as we were able to identify the key processes, mechanisms and resources used to fill vacancies and the controls that influence the operation of the vacancy filling system'.

'We then developed a detailed questionnaire based on our process map, internal analysis and research which consisted of a good mix of both qualitative and quantitative questions. It covered areas such as the elapsed time for the process and its component parts; numbers of vacancies filled; costs; performance measures and quality indicators; and the effort put into the process by HR, line managers and applicants'.

'Prior to sending out the questionnaires to our potential benchmarking partners we piloted it on people in ES and on a small number of external organisations. We then revised the questionnaire to take account of their comments e.g. rewording some ambiguous questions and reducing the number of questions'.

'Three members of the project team independently analysed the questionnaires to identify organisations that would be suitable to benchmark against. Interestingly there was a high degree of match between the three lists that were produced'.

'The team were surprised to find that the questionnaires did not reveal an organisation with significantly better elapsed times for the process overall. We therefore focused our attentions on those companies that had better process times for the individual stages e.g. apply, sift etc. and that appeared to use less resources than ES to fill vacancies'.

A total of five partners was identified, one each from the Civil Service, ex-public sector, private financial sector, private multi-national and private retail, although it was also decided to think creatively about processes that were similar to vacancy filling rather than identical to it. This led to some surprise on the part of a leading supermarket when the team expressed an interest in shelf filling (getting the right thing to the right place at the right time) rather than their vacancy filling system.

Two to three members of the team visited each organisation using a structured interview brief:

' We captured the key points from the visits on an interview record form. After each visit a debriefing session was held and the information from this and the record form was summarised for the rest of the team in writing and at meetings'.

Areas for improvement which were identified included:

*the use of IT to speed up the process for filling vacancies and reduce the time spent on administration (the application stage had typically taken 7.4 hours per applicant and the job specification stage 6.4 hours per specification).

*devolution of more responsibility to the line so as to streamline the process and secure ownership of the system.

*provision of additional support to assist managers to undertake their responsibilities and reduce administration.

*improvements in planning.

*improving flexibility in the way in which candidate information is presented.

Regular communications and the involvement of key stakeholders have since enabled 'gradual improvements' to be achieved in the way in which vacancies are filled based on the best practices identified through benchmarking:

'Regions have introduced better planning mechanisms e.g. the use of a vacancy plan is now widespread; have tightened up their procedures e.g. release policy; and started to make more use of IT e.g. in administrative procedures. As a result we know from our monitoring arrangements that the average elapsed time has dropped to just over 9 weeks [it was 12 weeks at the start of the study]'.

'Looking at unrelated, but comparable, processes can help break mind blocks. For example the comparison with supermarket shelf-filling highlighted three approaches that could be applied to vacancy filling: different processes for different goods; daily orders for some goods; and optimising stock levels e.g. waiting lists'.

The paper concludes with some examples of how the learning has been taken forward:

'We have been sharing the learning from our benchmarking study with the wider HR community and the organisation as a whole to encourage its use in other applications. We have done this through a series of presentations to HR divisional managers; Team Leaders in Personnel and practitioners; and an article in the ES Newsletter. In these we have used our experience of benchmarking to outline the approach and to share our learning and good practices. As a result benchmarking is going to be used in a review of one of our other major HR areas- recruitment'.

'We are also promoting the learning in the wider community by co-running workshops with the Cabinet Office for Civil Servants on the use of benchmarking in HR and planned presentations to the Cabinet Office Conference and articles for the Benchmarking Centre'.

BT: A Strategy driven Benchmarking Study

The report by BT (25 pages) describes the role of BT's Benchmarking Forum which comprises of representatives from across the whole business who facilitate benchmarking throughout the company, disseminate results from best practice studies and handle incoming requests for benchmarking from external companies. It then outlines the WCAN study which is described as 'one of the benchmarking studies instigated to help BT learn and improve in support of its vision "to become the most successful Worldwide Telecommunications Group".

'A programme work breakdown structure was established with Tom Johnson, the BT Director leading the Service Delivery Senior Executive Team as client; Ian Thorn, a General Manager in BT's Network Division as overall programme manager; and three strategic studies (work packages) each headed by a senior operational manager. John Enoch was appointed to lead the benchmarking study and Paul Cherret, BT's Internal Benchmarking Consultant was seconded into the team as a facilitator and champion of the benchmarking process'.

'With the overall brief of completing an industry based study on World Class Customer Access Network management with recommendations for change the team membership content necessarily varied throughout the lifecycle of the project. Considerable resource in the early stages helped to dimension the theoretical limits for service standards based on network constituents and environmental factors. BT people from operations, service, finance, strategy, planning, research and development and, of course, the client's representative were matrix managed by the Project Manager. Benchmarking education and training was arranged as a prerequisite to becoming a team member'.

'The initial performance "gap analysis" based on a variety of information sources e.g. in-house performance reports, external consultancy, public domain information, experimental work and earlier benchmarking studies. As a result of this work a clear picture emerged of problem issues, appropriate measures and likely benchmarking partners.

A questionnaire was developed to provide further input from 17 identified partners to help in establishing more robust benchmarks, but more importantly, to indicate leads for "best practice" learning opportunities. From Questionnaire analysis targeted visits were then made to six companies based in Europe and North America to share BT's metrics and best practice on a bi-lateral basis'.

The benchmarking process applied a Deming style cycle of Plan-Act-Do-Review and a checklist that was used in the study is reproduced in the report. Questions included:

*Is the topic something of significant importance to the project?

*What measurable effect(s) are we looking to improve?

*Is there executive commitment to act on subsequent results/ findings?

*Have we defined an appropriate, costed and timely benchmarking process?

*Have we completed comprehensive desk based research?

*Have we suitable test bed facilities for trialling/adapting best practices?

A formal Client Requirement Definition provided the focus for the project and enabled the Project Manager to position the benchmarking work package whilst a Project Requirement Definition document incorporated the deliverables of the study, a work breakdown structure and a project plan. Key milestones of the plan were to be the delivery of a series of three reports with supporting presentations:

'It was agreed by the Executive Team that the "best practice" discovery phase of the study would need to be broad-based as, in the timescales permitted, the number of operational and enabler processes involved in the management of the Customer Access Network were too numerous for individual in-depth investigation and analysis. Furthermore this telecommunications company based benchmarking study was to build on best practice knowledge gained through earlier non-telco benchmarking work'.

In the early stages of the project three major areas were identified for consideration within the benchmarking study, namely resilience of the network, speed of provision of service, and speed of repair. Brainstorming then led to a further decomposition of resilience information as follows:

(i)   Establish the theoretical limits for service standards given the 'Mean Time Between Failure' (MTBF) of the various network constituent parts taking into account variations caused by climate.

(ii)   Establish the degrees to which the policy, practices and equipment used by engineering teams in the normal course of their duties contributed to network interventions and fault rates.

'When the work was concluded it was interesting to note that the very best were operating within a 20 per cent proximity of the theoretical optimum;

327

this gave credence to both the theory and to the metrics of the world leader. Thus we were able to establish a benchmark for world class based on performance of BT and other operators. (Much of this was completed using public domain information)'.

'Public domain information on the US (baby) Bell Operating Companies was the primary source for cost and quality analysis. This material is freely available from the US Federal Communications Commissions. Because of the specialised network related nature of the study this initial stage of the WCAN benchmarking exercise would only consider Telecomms Operating companies as potential partners. However, now that the initial work is complete companies outside the telecomms field are once again being considered under the WCAN banner, and one study looking at "Solution Design" is already underway with a car manufacturer'.

The results of the study led to six key recommendations:

(i) To establish a project to assess costs and benefits of reducing the number of Networks Operations Centres and at the same time combining with Access Operating Centres in line with the best practice identified.

(ii) To establish a project to decide whether the best practice "fast track approaches" could be incorporated into BT s current ANOM strategy.

(iii) That the expert system used at the best practice 'Trouble Reporting Centre' be examined and compared with BT's current plans.

(iv) That best practice Primary Cross Connection Point change-out process be incorporated into BT's network rehabilitation programme.

(v) That the best practice 'record integrity' process identified for 2mBit data lines be implemented in BT.

(vi) That the non-intrusive customer circuit industry changeover techniques identified be introduced into BT to further improve customer satisfaction measures.

The report concludes with a Financial Summary (showing benefits of around £22.33 million cumulative over 5 years directly attributable to the benchmarking contribution in terms of the overall WCAN project), and a Review of Lessons Learned and Next Steps:

'As a direct result of both EQA assessment feedback and the experience gained through the WCAN methodology, BT's MD for Network and Systems is now leading a fundamental review of the way BT strategically addresses learning and transfer with respect to topic selection, information storing and the sharing of benchmark data and best practice discovery'.

[Issue 119 (November 1998)]

EUROPEAN BEST PRACTICE AWARDS

Two awards were presented at this year's Annual Benchmarking Forum hosted by The Benchmarking Centre in Cardiff on 14th and 15th October.

The European Best Practice Benchmarking Award ™ Business Category was won by Johnson and Johnson Medical Limited Business Services whose team of seven undertook to benchmark the process of establishing key performance measures. Also for the first time an Academic Award was presented to Peter Hines, Nick Rich and Ann Esain of the Lean Enterprise Research Centre, Cardiff Business School for their paper entitled 'Value Stream Mapping: A distribution industry application.'

The runner up in the Business Category was Shell UK Exploration and Production who addressed the benchmarking of onshore engineering resources. On day two of the conference representatives of each of the above gave presentations of approximately twenty minutes duration to support their submitted papers.

Johnson and Johnson Medical: establishing Key Performance Measures.

In this presentation Team Leader Janice Kite described the twelve stages which her team used in order to arrive at an approved new format of key performance measures (KPMs) that are shown in an appendix to her paper. Essentially self-assessment to the Johnson and Johnson 'Signature of Quality' (SOQ) Model, which was adopted in 1992 as part of J and J's continuous improvement initiative, last year highlighted benchmarking as one of the company's key Areas For Improvement and this led to the formation of the Benchmarking Process Group which was established to:

(i) undertake key process benchmarking activities.

(ii) spread the knowledge and expertise of benchmarking.

(iii) act as consultants to other business units undertaking SOQ assessment.

Members of the Benchmarking Process Group, along with a number of sales and marketing staff, were then trained by the Benchmarking Centre from whom the twelve step process is derived. They then applied The Benchmarking Centre's Benchmarking Tools and Techniques training in order to select a process to benchmark. This resulted in a list of six processes which were prioritised according to the criteria:

(a) Will benchmarking the process reduce cost, turnaround time and error rate and improve quality?

(b) Does the process cover or involve different Business Services departments and/or Franchises at points throughout the process flow?

A presentation to the Business Services Management Board confirmed 'Benchmarking the process of establishing key performance measures' as the chosen project. Various members of the Benchmarking Process Group were then provided with a detailed set of instructions [detailed in the text-Ed] which they were to apply in particular departments whilst others mapped the process flow to show where they felt the KPMs fitted into the organisation. These are also shown in an Appendix:

'It became apparent that very little consultation had taken place with the Franchises we supported and consequently they were not widely used or understood by them or indeed our own Business Services personnel. To summarise our findings we made a list of "common issues" and "suggestions". We used these to establish our measures for success. We also reviewed and agreed the map showing the location of the process to be benchmarked'.

Identification of benchmarking partners was achieved through a combination of the team's own knowledge of who may be good in the area selected and advice from The Benchmarking Centre which initially yielded a total of 13 potential partners. [Listed in the text-Ed].

These were later reduced to 11 following telephone conversations which revealed that two of the potential partners had no KPMs in place and therefore, were deemed to be less advanced than Johnson and Johnson Medical. [One of these was ISO9000 certificated -Ed].

For the remaining 11 an 'Exchange Pack' was compiled which incorporated a questionnaire and a summary of J and J Medical's key success criteria. This generated five responses from which three organisations (Hewlett Packard, The Automobile Association and Ethicon Limited, manufacturers of Sutures) were selected for site visits:

'These site visits proved very productive and helpful. With Hewlett Packard we achieved a real win-win partnership. We learnt a great deal about their quality and measurement system. They, in turn, undertook a benchmarking partnership with our corporate Management Training Institute, based in Brussels, to understand what initiatives J and J world-wide were implementing to facilitate leadership development'.

A 'Balanced Scorecard' approach was adopted for gap analysis in which four different sets of perspectives formed the basis for the formulation of five 'Critical Success Factors':

'The Benchmarking Process Group was invited to make a presentation to the Business Services Management Board in March 1998. At this meeting we gave an overview of the project to date and then presented our draft new format which encompassed, we felt, all that we had learnt. The Business Services Management Board congratulated the team on their efforts to date and commented that the new format was a significant improvement to the original format. They therefore asked the Benchmarking Process Group to implement the new format'.

'One to one meetings were held with each of the department heads, business plans were reviewed and key measures agreed upon. The measures were entered into the new format and the goal/Low/Medium/High parameters completed for each. These basic departmental KPM sheets were then developed by the Financial members of the team to automatically calculate the colours of the boxes (based on the "traffic light" system) and the bottom line KPM Performance figure. From each of the departmental KPM sheets a top level Business Service KPM sheet was created which showed each of the departmental KPM Performance figures and rolled them up into an overall Business Services KPM Performance figure'.

Line managers now review their departmental KPMs in team meetings, relate the goals to individuals and explain how each person can influence them. The KPMs are distributed monthly and at the end of the calendar year they form part of the review when the Business Services Management Board meets with each of the franchise management teams.

At the end of her presentation Ms. Kite named the team's next project, "product and service complaints" which she admitted "would be longer and more difficult". In respect of benchmarking she said "it is not a panacea but one of those tools you need to be using".

Value Stream Mapping: A Distribution Industry Application

This presentation given by Peter Hines described the application of a new variant of process benchmarking called 'Value Stream Mapping' to the development of a supplier network around a prominent distributor of electronic, electrical and mechanical components. It involved mapping the activities of the firm, identifying opportunities for improvement and then undertaking an improvement programme with the firm. The resulting Supplier Association programme then involved around fifty key suppliers across eight product category areas.

It was argued that whilst results benchmarking is very useful in raising awareness of performance gaps it presents little guidance on how to close these gaps, whilst process benchmarking presents difficulties when it comes to standardising between processes in different organisations. Consequently a new approach has been devised based on the teachings of US benchmarking expert Robert Camp in which the initial performance of a particular process is compared internally with how good that process could be rather than being compared externally, i.e. 'it compares the value adding and wasteful activities now with what the process might look like if a realistic percentage of the waste was removed'.

Unstructured and semi-structured interviews with representatives from the chosen company enabled identification of their strategy in terms of market definition, expansion path, warehousing location and growth path, service requirements of the customer base, and internationalisation. They also provided an understanding of the company's key customer facing and non-customer facing processes, and highlighted the following key business processes:

(i) Order fulfilment (covering all activities required from receipt of order to ultimate delivery).

(ii) New product introduction (covering all activities required to bring a new product to market).

(iii) Sales acquisition (all activities required to market the existing product range and obtain the order from the customer).

(iv) Supplier integration (all activities required to co-ordinate the various suppliers' activities with those of the company including the reduction of inter-company and intra-company waste).

This latter process area was found to be 'underdeveloped' yet with the potential 'to yield significant benefits if addressed:

'In order to identify the opportunities for improvement of the supplier integration process was decided by the authors and the 'Partsco' management team to map the activities between the buyer and suppliers. In doing so it was necessary to decide where the handover lay between the supplier integration process and the customer order fulfilment process.'

A decision was taken to divide the processes at the picking area where the goods were available for despatch to Partsco's customers. In choosing which products to map it was decided not only to look at one product category but also to look at products with different demand and revenue profiles.

The company already defined all of its products according to a Pareto split (A,B,C for both volume of sales and a separate A,B,C for value of sales). As a result there were nine category areas ranging from AA (high volume, high total value) to CC (low volume, low total value).

'In order to simplify data capture one product was chosen from each of the Pareto categories from one product range area. This was particularly effective as the company had already organised its order fulfilment process along value stream lines, that is with mixed streams of buyers, inventory controllers and marketers co-located and controlling all activities for one of the seventeen product areas.

These cross-functional teams were supported by a number of small competency centres focusing on purchasing, inventory control and marketing who provided training and access to knowledge and new developments that could be used by team members. The product range chosen was lighting products as the earlier discussion with the senior managers had identified this as a "difficult" range due to its seasonal variability and fragility.'

Structured interviews were then conducted with the senior management team to identify value adding and wasteful activities. This highlighted unnecessary inventory as 'by far the largest waste':

'The company was achieving stock turns of only around 3 per cent a year at the start of the work in late 1995. In addition, due to the rapid increase in sales such a situation would lead to a requirement for a new warehouse in the UK every 5 years'.

A weighted average of the wastes was used to indicate which mapping tool would be most appropriate using a waste tool correlation chart. Five tools were then selected:

- Process activity map

- Supply chain response matrix

- Demand amplification map

- Quality filter map

- Decision point analysis map

Application of these tools revealed a range of deficiencies which were then discussed with senior management with a "chocolate box" of possible options correlated with the so called seven wastes' then presented. A decision was then taken to trial the use of a Supplier Association i.e. 'a group of companies linked together on a regular basis to share knowledge and experience in an open and co-operative manner' as a structural mechanism to facilitate a supplier integration process.

A three tier cascading system [illustrated in the text -Ed] was then applied to implement a pilot scheme in preparation for later roll-out. The broad guidelines of an optimal supplier integration process were formulated by a process development team whilst ties were formed between product teams so that knowledge of what did and did not work well would be shared:

'The measures chosen were not designed to be a simple audit of supplier performance but were more designed to be a gauge of the degree of supplier integration or what later became termed a Balanced Benefit Benchmark. This was because some of the measures such as forecast variability were designed to be more a measure of Partsco's performance. Others, like delivery on time were more aimed at suppliers' performance with a third group including average stock turns at Partsco a reflection of how effectively the total supplier integration process was working'.

'After only a few months and a continued monitoring of the Balanced Benefit Benchmarking results some rapid improvements began to emerge. The first area to feel change was the on-time delivery performance from suppliers which quickly rose from around 74% to over 90%. In addition lead time also fell from over 8 weeks to around 7 and stock turns rose by 25% for the products from the participating companies. It soon became obvious that the pilot was starting to produce the desired results'.

In its conclusion the paper states the following:

'The views of the suppliers towards the work have been very positive and in many cases the initiatives and drive is coming from suppliers rather than Partsco.'

'The programme has greatly improved communications between Partsco and their suppliers and has raised Partsco's presence within suppliers' thinking as well as the importance of supplier integration with Partsco's senior staff. As an unexpected side benefit, the performance of suppliers not in the Supplier Association Programme also appears to be improving. This may be explained in two ways. First, a spread effect is occurring as members of the product teams start informally to implement similar improvement, if at a slower rate with non-member firms. Second, as some firms may have been initially disappointed not to have been included in the activity they may be putting in extra effort into their relationship with Partsco in order to try and become a member at a later date'.

The paper highlights the fact that as a result of the early successes described the Value Stream Mapping approach has now been adopted by over a hundred UK based companies whilst the speaker explained how the company codenamed 'Partsco' is now looking to fast-track one supplier from each group from whom the others can learn. Bottom line benefits to 'Partsco' are expected to be of the order of £30 million in the next three years.

Shell UK: Benchmarking Onshore Engineering Resources

The presentation by Shell UK described a benchmarking exercise between Shell UK and BP which stemmed from an earlier exercise in 1995-96 which revealed a significant gap in total onshore engineering overheads between Shell UK Exploration and Production (Shell Expro) and BP but did not assist Shell Expro's engineering process owners to develop a clear strategy for reducing engineering costs.

Five strategic areas for improvement were identified and, following analysis of the 1997 Shell Expro business plan, a target saving of £7.5 million was broken down into targets for the five identified areas.

An initial meeting between Shell Expro and BP was held at which each party presented their process for engineering (modifications). The processes were found to comprise of similar steps at a high level. A breakdown structure was then produced along with benchmarking measures for comparison. Also comparison of the organisations and responsibilities highlighted a number of key differences between Shell Expro and BP. For example Shell Expro applied strict control of deviations to standards requiring named technical authorities (often Shell personnel only) to approve deviations whereas BP 'had very few mandatory codes and standards'.

A list of opportunities for improvement was accompanied by the following recommendation:

'This benchmarking work should be extended to include other assets and operators. In particular assets and operators which are understood to have post effective onshore resource structures should be approached. Both parties of this study are committed to this follow on work'.

[Issue 135 (April 2000)]

BENCHMARKING 2000

The European Best Practice Benchmarking Awards ™ were last presented in Cardiff on 14th October 1998. Since then there has been a year of consolidation during which time the European Benchmarking Forum (EBF) has been active holding a number of meetings throughout Europe with the aim of making both the Awards scheme and the promotion of the best practice techniques which have been developed and promoted by the Benchmarking Centre in the UK for some years now, more generally reflecting the needs of European business and more accessible to organisations Europe wide.

The international format which has since been adopted consists of a programme which incorporates a Forum to be held every six months, in the country which holds the Presidency of the EU, and an Awards scheme in which Awards will be presented annually in the autumn, the first of these being scheduled to take place in Paris on October 10th.

This has received considerable support, most notably from the European Commission who have recently given their support to two pilot projects. These are 'Benchmarking for Success', co-ordinated by Enterprise Ireland to develop a common implementation framework for benchmarking across Europe, and the 'Quality and Benchmarking for SMEs' project which has been managed by the European Association of Chambers of Commerce. This essentially promotes benchmarking among SMEs as a tool for continuous improvement.

With Portugal currently holding the Presidency of the EU, Lisbon hosted the first European Benchmarking Forum of the new millennium on March 30th with presentations being made by various members of the Portuguese Government, the European Commission, the Institute for the Support of SMEs and Investment (IAPMEI), the Portuguese Institute for Quality, Enterprise Ireland and Portuguese industry. The event attracted around 260 participants and two of the papers are reviewed below, together with the latest meeting of the European Benchmarking Forum, held immediately after the Forum, on March 31st.

The ABC of European Benchmarking.

Richard Keegan of Enterprise Ireland and the European Benchmarking Forum explained the ABC of European Benchmarking. ABC has been devised as an acronym for Applied Benchmarking for Competitiveness. The presumption behind this is that benchmarking is of little use unless it is actually applied effectively, for benchmarking by itself is merely diagnosis.

The 'medicine' comes in the form of best practice and the ABC consists of simple ideas, appropriate to the needs of SMEs as well as large organisations, that will enable best practice to be put into effect.

The two principal tools which comprise the ABC were introduced. The first is a benchmarking index created in the UK which is now being rolled out across Europe in nine states, providing hard numbers by which to track progress. The second is a complementary qualitative system (known as 'Microscope'), which has been rolled out progressively across ten states since 1998 and now has around 1500 benchmarked companies.

The benchmarking skills programme for SMEs which has resulted was described as "world beating", and distinctly different from the US approach which has been to develop very good actions on one part of benchmarking (process benchmarking). Consequently the European Excellence framework which now exists has "created a new niche" which "addresses 95% plus of the needs of companies in Europe".

Indeed the Index developed in Europe for Europe was now actually being applied in the US as an introduction to the Baldrige Award scheme.

The model for European benchmarking agreed by the EBF is based on the EFQM Business Excellence Model, but it is to be benchmarking based rather than merely following the Business Excellence Model criteria.

Benchmarking and Enterprise Policy.

Mr. David White, Acting Director for the recently established Enterprise Policy Directorate General for Enterprise at the European Commission, did not speak as planned, though he did submit a paper outlining the role that benchmarking will plays as part of the EC's "Enterprise Europe" initiative over the next five years.

He explains how "Enterprise Europe" will be founded on three mutually reinforcing pillars, namely a flourishing enterprise culture, a favourable environment for innovation and creativity, and unfettered access for all enterprises to their target markets:

'To boost Europe's innovation capacity, enterprise policy will focus on three aspects in particular. Firstly, lack of finance. Under enterprise policy, priority will be given to facilitating private sector finance for innovative small companies. Development of financial instruments and the search for best practice will be actively encouraged. Secondly, new ideas will be encouraged. Enterprise policy will support the adoption of a European patent. This will offer reliable protection of ideas across Europe at an affordable price. Thirdly, new areas of business opportunity in services will be promoted. Development of the service sector involves enormous investment in intangibles. The new enterprise policy will address this challenge by promoting awareness of the opportunities offered by the knowledge driven economy'.

The paper then turns to the EC's initiatives to promote benchmarking as a means to monitor improvement in the framework conditions for enterprise, which included a series of pilot projects in the areas of innovation finance, skills, logistics and the impact of new technologies on the organisational effectiveness of enterprises:

'The pilot projects demonstrated the potential of benchmarking as an improvement tool. A number of follow-up projects are currently being implemented which focus on issues which emerged from the pilot exercises. These include the skills needs of enterprises for the information society, the industry-research interface, and licensing procedures for businesses'.

The remainder of the paper describes how the EC intends to take benchmarking forward with a new initiative to benchmark policy performance in relation to entrepreneurial activity, innovation and access to market:

'A novel element of this new initiative is that it will involve use of a scoreboard to monitor the performance of Member States in relation to indicators in key policy areas. The objective is to provide a focus for ongoing debate on progress by updating the indicators regularly. This will be achieved by highlighting the performance of Member States in improving entrepreneurship, innovation and access to markets. The first steps in implementing this initiative are already being taken with the launch of an innovation trend chart. This provides a common reference framework for analysing innovation performance and policies. The output of this exercise will be a European Innovation Scoreboard to assist Member States in assessing their relative strengths and weaknesses. The Innovation Scoreboard will in turn feed into the broader Enterprise Europe Scoreboard. This will highlight Member States with good performance'.

'This new initiative is intended to raise the profile of benchmarking and provide an objective basis for identifying enterprise-related issues. These would then be examined in greater detail through targeted exercises to understand how best practice is achieved in key areas of weakness. In this way benchmarking will be put on a firm medium-term footing with a rolling programme of performance measurement, best practice diagnosis, and improvement monitoring'.

The Future of the E.B.F.

The EBF meeting looked critically at priorities for the future, with particular reference to addressing the needs of SMEs in Europe, many of whom were notably seen as averse to long distance travel, especially if linguistic barriers were also liable to be present. The production of the first multilingual brochure describing benchmarking in clear terms was seen as providing a key role in addressing the latter problem, but this was viewed very much as only a partial solution.

Strong parallels were drawn between the present series of EBF meetings and those held during the early days of the EFQM and there was some support for the concept of structuring events along the lines adopted by the EFQM in order to attract the all-important 'intermediaries' who are well placed to influence change. A key question, however, was whether the EBF should seek to capture companies from all over Europe who may wish to be involved or whether to focus more on the policy makers who are well positioned to take the message back locally.

The Slovenian delegation highlighted research from their country which suggested that many companies are keen to implement bench marking programmes, but are largely unaware of how to do it, and for this reason they advocated a drive to promote the benchmarking process combined with an appropriate methodology. They warned, however, that unless the focus was directed at the companies themselves there was a very real danger that benchmarking could begin to become "a political concept". They advised:

"The concepts have to be introduced properly to groups that know how to use them. Benchmarking must not become a nebulous word which ultimately means both everything and nothing".

Other views favoured an emphasis on attracting top management with the aim of promoting networking in and between organisations which would clearly impact upon the supply chain and draw SMEs in. With this approach, however, there was a clearly identified danger that captains of industry could dominate and "talk over the heads of many SMEs", as well as perpetuation of the perception that benchmarking is only for the large organisations.

Representatives from the UK's Customs and Excise, who have been undertaking benchmarking for some years now, contributed to the highly valid point that the aims and objectives of the E.B.F. should not be geared overwhelmingly to the cause of SMEs, stressing the fact that as the public sector becomes more efficient the burden on the private sector will be reduced. Meanwhile Terry Pilcher, representing the DTI, spoke of the "massive job" which still needed to be done in order to engage the vast number of intermediaries who still knew little or nothing about benchmarking.

Richard Keegan, representing Ireland, expressed his desire to see more directed toward the objective of pushing out the boundaries which exist between the intermediaries and large organisations, but was optimistic for a future in which enthusiasm based on delivery was constantly growing. He also drew attention to the new benchmarking CD-ROM which the E.B.F. had produced which offered " an excellent central core", and spoke of some of the unexpected uses which had arisen from their first CD-ROM, for example, by SIPTU, one of Ireland's principal trade unions. In another example he described how a "nearly dead" company in Ireland used benchmarking as a key enabler of transformation which led to business results of around IR£ 7 million turnover with just 67 employees.

On the subject of the Awards scheme there was clear support from members of the E.B.F. for a pan-European Award which was somewhat less limited than the present scheme which all accepted was only in its early days.

Other discussions concerned the development of closer links between the E.B.F. and the Global Benchmarking Network (GBU), which many believed would lead to a substantially increased knowledge base in Europe, and the expansion of the EBF's website, which was also envisaged to be of significant benefit to Member States and SMEs.

Further Information

The European Benchmarking Forum was established in 1997 in conjunction with the European Commission and Enterprise Ireland, the state development agency for Ireland, and was chartered with three objectives:

(i) To identify the main players in European Benchmarking.

(ii) To identify initiatives underway.

(iii) To suggest ways of building a synergy between them.

A highly representative Expert Group was formed which moved to identify the main problems with implementing benchmarking in Europe.

[Issue 137 (July 2000) – 5th Sheffield World Quality Congress]

Benchmarking and Business Paradigm Shifts.

Kostas N. Dervitsiotis from the University of Piraeus in Greece continued the benchmarking theme by addressing the current need for senior management in large organisations to be able to expand their present scope if they are to successfully endure the transition to a turbulent future environment:

'A tradition of an established organisation from the present to the future competitive environment is often described in terms of a "paradigm shift". This concept is similar to the dramatic changes experienced in physics, when physics as a science moved from a Newtonian mindset to one shaped by the theory of relativity and quantum physics'.

He suggests that under such conditions, which are now present in a number of industries, there is a need to develop a better understanding of benchmarking based not only on its potential advantages but also on the serious limitations which it can have as a performance improvement option. This would ensure that those who decide to apply it are aware of its proper use and effective range.

The critical choices are seen to relate to the choice of level at which benchmarking is liable to be most beneficial (strategic, process or other) and to the' reference entities ' (competitors or best-in-class organisations) with which comparisons are made in order to identify areas for improvement. In this regard process benchmarking is identified as often the most appropriate option, offering the potential advantages of:

* Flexibility in the use of human and other resources.

* Rapid new product introduction.

*Reduced defective output.

*Faster delivery time.

*Lower production and distribution costs as a result of better inventory management and scheduling.

Strategic benchmarking, however, requires more care as the organisation needs to be able to change strategic posture at different times according to its level of maturity, market circumstances and available technology.

Benchmarking teams are alerted to the danger of omitting from their studies the systematic interactions of a process in which a gap is prominent in relation to other interrelated processes in the same organisation:

'When looking at a company as an organic whole, that is a complete system which is a web of interacting parts, one comes to realize that its management throughout the organisation's development history has made a series of trade-offs in the performance of individual business processes, for the purpose of achieving a better overall performance for the entire company. This means that as part of better strategy implementation, management accepted enabling one business process to perform at a higher level by making some other(s) interconnected to it operate at less than their maximum possible level.

For example, to the extent competitive advantage was thought to depend on reducing order delivery times, management might have decided to maintain higher than previously held inventories at selected points of the supply chain. In another instance, the need to implement a strategy with a high priority on quality might have required considerable investments in other functions (in purchasing for better parts or raw materials, in manufacturing for the purchase of state-of-the-art equipment, in personnel for extensive employee training etc.), thus increasing costs at least in the short term'.

Benchmarking is not viewed as the appropriate tool for conducting a reliable exploration of the future competitive landscape:

'For business excellence to become sustained excellence it will require social and technological innovations that will address human, social and environmental needs in ways that are not as yet well understood or proven with sufficient data. Only by "jumping the curve" on time from the current paradigm to a new one, based primarily on intuition and faith and by taking risks on what will prevail in meeting these needs, can long term success be possible'.

Benchmarking a Public Service Management System.

Case studies presented included The Defence Evaluation and Research Agency (DERA) at Farnborough where a benchmarking study has been undertaken to evaluate the contribution of business management systems toward the achievement of organisational objectives.

DERA is a government owned research and technology organisation funded wholly through contracts with its customers. It is geographically dispersed throughout the UK and organised into 14 business sectors and 50 plus sites employing a total of 11,500 staff. Turnover is around £1 billion a year.

The benchmarking study, undertaken with the help of Oakland Consulting plc, aimed to improve the architecture, management, control, communication and deployment of the DERA business management system (BMS) by reviewing current best practice. The primary objective was to benchmark the infrastructure and in so doing to identify improvement opportunities. The study was conducted in accordance with 'The European Benchmarking Code of Conduct' and a questionnaire was developed with the help of a functional expert in questionnaire design recruited from within DERA:

'The purpose of the questionnaire was to provide an initial screen of potential partners to ensure that the site visits were to be of value. Although the questionnaire served this purpose, the real challenge came when it was time to conduct the site visits. Unlike process benchmarking where there are clear process metrics, this study involved looking at the total system. A novel approach to evaluating the effectiveness of the organisations visited therefore had to be developed'.

At site visits various topics were studied and observations recorded on site visit reports which captured the process elements for the topic using the methodology of ICOR (inputs, controls, outputs, resources). A methodology based on EFQM self-assessment was then applied to verify the excellence of this approach. This consisted of six steps:

- Team members to individually asses site visit reports

- Team member to record the strengths and weaknesses for each area

- Team member to score each area

- Team member to repeat assessment for each partner

- Team to meet to reach consensus

- Final report based on consensus view

Personal contact with the proposed partners following despatch of the initial screening questionnaire contributed to higher return rates and a higher degree of willingness to participate in the study, and remaining a single team during the benchmarking site visits was seen to work better than splitting into smaller groups:

"Perceptions about benchmarking were changed and the inexperienced members of the team appreciated that benchmarking was more than just visiting others. It was clear that it was important to study yourself first. In our case, this led to defining the infrastructure design and purpose of BMS more clearly so that it could be communicated better to the user community".

A total of 107 questionnaires was despatched and 47 were returned. The most surprising finding was the response to the question "Do you currently measure your contribution of your system to your business goals?" which showed that 72.3% of organisations surveyed did not do so. This followed from the finding that 95.8% of respondents did actually believe that their systems did actually contribute toward their business goals. Another finding was that the great challenge for almost all of the partner companies was to integrate several systems into one, something which DERA had already done.

In several instances the benchmarking team observed the use of standardised reporting systems which went beyond mere number reporting i.e. they addressed the causes, issues and improvement activities, but little evidence of review of the efficiency and effectiveness of the management systems was found. Some of the partner organisations focused on measuring the systems' capability, but in others the history of the system was a barrier, especially in the larger organisations where the sheer size of the BMS had led to a system that was complex and unintegrated. A number of actions have resulted from the benchmarking study. These have included:

(i) Development of a revision to the DERA BMS

(ii) Initiation of an improvement project with the aim of making the BMS more process based and of making the "look and feel" better suited to users' needs.

(iii) Construction of a top level process model in parallel with development of the future strategy for DERA by senior management.

(iv) Further application of web based technology to enable the elements of the system to be presented to users in away that enables them to find the information they need to do their work quickly and easily.

Five partners were invited back to DERA to share the learning gained.

Benchmarking in three Service Industries.

Case studies in three further organisations (1999 Joint European Quality Award Winner Yellow Pages, The Employment Service in Sheffield and North West Water in Warrington) were presented by Dr. Mike Simpson of the Sheffield University Management School [part of Sheffield's other university -Ed].

Yellow Pages currently have 42 benchmarking projects underway and have ten years of experience of benchmarking. The study, however, focuses on one project which involved the call centre of Talking Pages, the telephone information service based in Bristol which provides up-to-date information on such details as opening hours, payment methods, product details, and special promotions on businesses, shops and services throughout the UK. The Strategic Development Unit conducted the project which sought to ascertain whether the call centre was best in class. The Benchmarking Centre helped the Strategic Development Unit to find 17 companies, most in the UK, but also a few from America, which could be used for comparison.

A questionnaire was despatched to the managements of the call centres of the partner companies and site visits followed. Performance gaps were identified for every aspect of the questionnaire and a ranking was compiled showing the areas which Talking Pages needed to change, improve or keep the same.

Principal findings were that Talking Pages were lacking in strategy and purpose and that the method by which call centre staff were recruited (often on a temporary basis) was inadequate and led to negative impacts on the level of customer service delivered. Action has since been taken to produce a development plan to address these issues, whilst a two day course on benchmarking is introduced for senior managers company wide.

The Employment Service (ES) is the largest division of the Department for Education and Employment (DfEE) employing over 30,000 staff in around 1050 Jobcentres in nine geographical regions throughout the UK. The ES has three years' experience of benchmarking and the first projects were exercises based on the statistical information which the organisation collects. The selection of benchmarking projects is not systematic, but based on individual sponsorship.

In 1997 the Personnel Director of the ES won the European Best Practice Award for their project entitled 'Radically reducing the elapsed time for filling vacancies'. Since then training effectiveness has also been benchmarked by the ES Training and Development Division. This began as an internal benchmarking exercise, but it was soon realised that an external examination of best practices was both relevant and needed.

The test hypothesis was "that the investment the ES made in the training and development of its people is offset by a corresponding improvement in output and/or efficiency, and has a positive effect on the running costs of the agency".

A project team was formed comprising of the representatives from all parts of the organisation whose role was to ascertain whether line managers were identifying training needs and consolidating training needs satisfactorily. Initial findings internally revealed that one region of the ES (South west) outperformed others on operational improvements.

An observation was that it was the only region that had adopted the use of 'learning contracts' i.e. contracts signed between line managers and employees to agree on annual targets and the training needed to achieve these targets.

External benchmarking followed with partners selected according to whether they were

(i) Accredited training organisations with Investors In People that took training seriously.

(ii) Familiar with benchmarking and spent at least 2% of their total payroll costs on training and development of staff.

Eleven companies were found which were later reduced to four (Yellow Pages, GKN West land Aerospace, The Post Office and Rover Group). The project is ongoing.

North West Water have been using benchmarking of a sort for many years, but efforts have intensified over the last two years following a number of successful projects in the areas of customer service reception call handling and laboratory services. The methodology deployed follows the teachings of world benchmarking expert Bob Camp and the organisation is distinguished by its ability to recalibrate its benchmarks.

The case study focuses on a maintenance project which stemmed from an earlier survey that led management to believe that North West Water was underperforming in this area. Both internal and external benchmarking was used. Internal benchmarking utilised the organisation's Management Information System to obtain statistical information on the performance of all geographical areas. External benchmarking involved the selection of partners using the database of the Benchmarking Network of the Royal Group with the criteria of large geographical spread, all day operations and in-depth knowledge of processes.

Four companies were eventually selected, which included Rover and Pirelli. Simple graphical displays were used to communicate performance indicators of processes being benchmarked. Indicators included the ratio of planned to reactive maintenance, amount of planned and reactive work, and response time to breakdowns. Qualitative criteria were estimated via satisfaction and other surveys.

Benefits deriving from the project were:

- lower costs

- easier design of improvements

- reduced costs of the actual benchmarking exercise compared with previous projects

- a recognition that benchmarking should be part of the company strategy

- improvements in internal communications

The three case studies have led to the following conclusion:

'Benchmarking is confirmed as highly effective and very applicable to service industries. Benchmarking can assist in strategy formulation, organisational development and increasing efficiency (e.g. Yellow Pages), improving training (e.g. ES), lowering costs, making easier design improvements, allowing people to learn about new ways of working and improving internal communications (North West Water).'

'All three organisations have considerable experience with benchmarking and have learnt a lot. There is a continuing commitment to the use of benchmarking for improving performance in these organisations'.

BENCHMARKING FACILITIES MANAGEMENT

The short history of facilities management (FM) in Europe has produced several benchmarking initiatives at both national and international levels. Unfortunately none of these systems have ever been integrated with each other and at present a number of European systems function at the national level with at least two at the international level. Consequently the concepts, terms, definitions and performance indicators are markedly different between the existing systems.

In October 1997 the EuroFM board met in Munich and in an attempt to better understand these differences established a steering committee and a project group to address them. The project group made a presentation of the initial work at the joint EuroFM/IFMA conference in Maastricht in 1998 and at the 1999 conference in

Gothenburg a vision document for the EuroFM Benchmarking Project was produced and presented by Per Anker Jensen of DFM Denmark.

Since then various project meetings have taken place between Markens Aschauer (ATGA, Austria), Keith Alexander (CFM, UK), Arend Jan Kornet (CFM, Netherlands) and Per Anker Jensen, with the assistance of Jan Brochner (Chalmers University, Sweden), Heikki Vaarama (KTI, Finland), Alexander Redlein, (TUV, Austria), and Anne Larssen (Multiconsult, Norway).

Meetings were chaired by Andreas van Wagenberg of the EuroFM network in Sint Maarken in the Netherlands and at a meeting in Glasgow in November 1999 Bernard Williams, FM specialist benchmarking consultant, was appointed to oversee the project in an advisory capacity.

The purpose of the project as defined in the vision document is 'to develop a common set of FM indicators and a framework for the cross-cultural comparison of FM indicators within Europe' and at the World Workplace 2000 Conference, held at the Scottish Exhibition Conference Centre (SECC) in Glasgow from 11th to 13th June the current, status of the project was described by Bernard Williams along with the new Norwegian web-based system for the collection, processing and distribution of key figures.

An Independent Critique.

In his independent critique of the project Bernard Williams FRICS explained his role of external advisor which had arisen from a recognition on the part of the group that there was a need to avoid the 'reinvention of the wheel' syndrome which can often beset those who are new to benchmarking for the first time. He then described how he had evaluated the value and practicality of the project in which small groups are organised as benchmarking clubs, stressing the importance of comparing cost and performance data from those undertaking the work, rather than seeking to ascertain best practice from a book as many may be tempted to do.

Early observations included the following:

- All groups understood the need to examine the processes behind the data.

- External publication of results was generally not an objective as it can.

- All groups experienced difficulty in reaching a common classification of protocols for measurement.

- Current stated project objectives may not be achievable in the short term.

- Inter-group exchange of best practice ideas is still at an early stage.

These findings have given rise to the following recommendations:

(i)   Individual groups should continue to use their own protocols.

(ii)   Attempts at common classification in the short term should be restricted to second level service operations and performance levels.

(iii)   The project should develop guidelines for the best practice operation of benchmarking.

(iv)   Sophisticated new tools for data analysis and interpretation should be explored.

(v)   The project team should harness and exploit the experience and enthusiasms of its groups.

Web-based FM Benchmarking.

One of the most recent FM benchmarking initiatives is the establishment of the Norwegian KPI for benchmarking FM (nfb) whose purpose is 'to collect, analyse and distribute KPI indicators in relation to FM'. This organisation is non-profit making and is the result of an ongoing research and development project which began in 1997 and led to a guideline for establishing KPI indicators and revised costs account which is now part of the official Norwegian Standard 3454 "Life Cycle Costs".

The first data collection will be part of a pilot project due to commence in September with 10 to 12 real estate owners. This will involve the feeding of data into an electronic questionnaire on the nfb website or, alternatively, data delivery using a pre-defined export file. The questionnaires consist of three levels:

Level 1: General information about the organisation or company.

Level 2: Information about each building/group of buildings, such as location, areas, age, and technical data.

Level 3: Annual data on costs and consumption (energy, water and renovation) classified according to the standard NS3454 "Life Cycle Costs".

It is anticipated that nfb members will have different needs for KPI indicators and that their possibilities to provide detailed data and resources to perform registration may also differ. The questionnaires are therefore designed to be flexible with a minimum set of obligatory data that needs to be registered, and a set of more detailed information that may be registered voluntarily. The questionnaires calculate some of the key figures (costs and suppliers) directly on-screen to improve the overview during the process of registering data. Inputs are based on official Norwegian standards where these exist, for example with regard to building categories, cost accounts and definition of areas.

The two members of the project team, The Directorate of Construction and Property (Statsbygg), and Building Services for the Ministry of Defence (Forvarets bygningstjeneste) have a total portfolio of 10 million square metres and are anticipated to register between 20 and 40% of their buildings during the first two years. In addition around 50 members of the association, mainly from the public sector, are expected to register during the first year with 50 to 75% of them subsequently contributing with data.

As a start the figures will be presented as average and statistical (mean value, minimum and maximum, standard deviation etc.) analysis with the first version of the system providing cost, consumption and area figures. The ultimate aim, however, is to further develop the system with enhanced KPI Indicators such as post occupancy evaluation (POE).

The annual data collection and analysis will result in a booklet for all members with reports on the total data collection. Each member that supplies data will thus receive a booklet with analysis reports based on their individual data. It will also be possible for each member to buy more detailed or specialised analyses.

Responsibility for the validation of data will rest primarily with the data providers. The web-based questionnaires will, however, have automatic validation functions and on-line help information as well as a users' guide. The cost figures and some of the suppliers' figures are also calculated immediately on-screen. It will not be possible to register data in the database for a building/group of buildings unless a minimum set of data is given (the obligatory data).

Validation of the output will be achieved by advisers from MultiConsult and the secretariat who will check it against available key figures and figures from previous years' analyses. Feedback from members and the external market e.g. by way of evaluation of customer satisfaction, will also be used.

Members of the nfb-association can be any organisation or person involved in FM, such as real estate owners (both public and private sector), consultants, architects and professional FM organisations or companies. Members will pay an annual fee which will give access to provide data and receive the main results of data collection.

The project is financed as a Research and Development project in addition to receiving financial assistance from The Directorate of Public Construction and Property, Building Services for the Ministry of Defence, MultiConsult, and the Norwegian Association for Maintenance. When the KPI-association is in operation members will pay a fee that will cover the operational costs in the longer term. The system and association are envisaged to be in ordinary operation from January 2001.

Further Information

The results and analysis of the EuroFM Benchmarking Project are shortly to be published in the EuroFM publication *'European Benchmarking'* which will have the following chapters:

- Chapter 1: Introduction (including description of criteria for evaluating FM benchmarking systems)

- Chapters 2-6: Descriptions (of each of the profiled benchmarking systems)

- Chapter 7: Cross analysis and evaluation of the benchmarking systems

- Chapter 8: Conclusions and perspectives (including developments in IT that can improve benchmarking processes)

- Chapter 9: Recommendations for improvement of the European systems

Later in the year a further report is expected to be published on the Internet under EuroFM whilst on October 13th a meeting is planned at Schipol, Amsterdam, to review recommendations and discuss the commencement of benchmarking activities with European multinationals.

In addition IFMA Italy are due to publish their research findings under the title of 'Benchmarking 2000' at the First Italian Facilities Management meeting in Milan on 24th and 25th October. This event will involve important representatives from public administration as well as entrepreneurs, members of academic institutions and Italian and European firms specialising in facilities management.

Contacts.

Contact addresses for the above items are as follows:

Bernard Williams FRICS Senior Partner, Bernard Williams Associates, Kings House, 32-34 Widmore Road, Bromley, Kent BR1 1 RY Telephone:02084601111.

Anne Kathrine Larssen, MultiConsult AS, Hoffsveien 1, Boks 265 Skoyen, N-O213 Oslo, Norway. Telephone: +472251 51 51.

Andreas van Wagenberg, Boardmember, EuroFM Network, Sluiswegje 1, 1744 GG Sint Maarten (NH), The Netherlands. Telephone: +31 224551505.

[Issue 139 (Winter 2000)]

European Best Practice Awards.

The European Best Practice Awards™ have been presented again this year, this time outside the UK for the first time, in Paris, on 10th October. The winners were Reading based Yellow Pages who won the accolade for their print management benchmarking project which examined the most cost effective ways of purchasing and managing print throughout the business and prevailed over stiff competition from former Award winners Shell and Johnson and Johnson, the latter receiving the Runner-up prize this year.

Yellow Pages won the 1999 European Quality Award for Large Businesses and Business Units and were a Prize Winner in 1998. An internal assessment of business processes prior to the Prize winning entry of 1998, however, highlighted benchmarking as an area for improvement throughout Yellow Pages and consequently a new strategy for benchmarking was formulated in order to strengthen their benchmarking approach and management.

This meant that in 1999 benchmarking became much more high profile and with the same internal assessment revealing a lack of clarity in Yellow Pages' print buying procedure a project was commissioned and led by the Marketing Communications Department to research how print was purchased and managed and to identify opportunities to improve performance in this area.

Many of the processes undertaken by the Marketing Communications Department are, by their very nature, competitively benchmarked against leading organisations on the basis of, for example, media cost, media impact and advertising effectiveness. Consequently this project concentrated on Functional Benchmarking in which organisations operating similar processes in different industries are compared.

A member of the Marketing Team, Tony Old, who has considerable knowledge and experience of the business of commissioning print, print brokering, agency commissioning and direct printer buying, was chosen to facilitate the project with the assistance of Bob Guy of the Yellow Pages Benchmarking Team which owns a data base of all benchmarking projects within the organisation and is part of the Organisational Excellence Unit in the Strategic Development Division.

In the beginning several benchmarking partners were selected with the selection criteria being that they were well-established businesses who were strong brands within their sector, each with a different approach to print management. Contact was initially made by telephone to introduce the project and this was then followed through with specially produced benchmarking literature which constituted 'An invitation to benchmark'. Meetings were then agreed to discuss questions raised and obtain information as a basis for further recommendations.

Three companies were eventually selected as partners namely Midland Bank, John Lewis and Unisys (Xerox), each of whom already had an established internal print buying resource, and three print management processes were examined i.e. Yellow Pages internal print management, print broker print management and design agency print management all of which are used by Yellow Pages:

'The total print spend comprises communication literature, stationery, reprinted material, promotional material, direct marketing, both externally and internally throughout the eight divisions and amounts to £3.3 M. All the individual figures reflect a configuration of direct creative agency, printer and print broker commissioning processes.

Where commissioning is not direct to the printer i.e. via print brokers or design agency, a mark-up or management fee will always be applied to the final cost. This can vary between 15% and 40% but averages 28%. The mark-up covers the management, quality control and supervision of the print process; using this average figure the total commission cost to Yellow Pages is £930K. Determining the exact amount of mark-up has been achieved through interviewing existing suppliers to ascertain their charging policy, and benchmarking their costs direct with printers and print brokers'.

A list of questions was submitted to the three partners to determine the fundamental issues associated with a print management department, for example, 'What is the staffing to print management spend as a ratio and number of people required?' , 'Are print brokers used or is the resource PAYE?' 'Do you use a grading system for printers and if so what criteria are used?' and 'By what method are printers briefed or asked to quote?'

Findings showed that all of the benchmarking partners operated a PAYE system with full support given to the principle of buying print internally as

352

the process is believed to be intrinsic to producing effective communications and realising savings. They also identified the skill set required to effectively manage print internally.

As a result of these findings three options were considered:

(i) Do nothing (not recommended because although it would not disturb the internal organisational structure it would leave a continuous negative cost burden).

(ii) Introduce a phased approach (further research into logistics of setting up a print management department with assessment of a print management company to yield savings of 15to 25% against agency commissioning with further savings realised on keener print buying).

(iii) Further research prior to installing a print department (establishing a dedicated print management resource internally either by recruiting the skill set from outside or by developing an individual or department internally).

Following careful consideration of these options a recommendation was made to employ a print manager with print technology experience positioned within the Marketing Department so that the high volume of work and tight deadlines could be managed effectively within the Marketing Department. With this approach a potential saving of £904K was identified:

'The process of employing an experienced print buyer was relatively straightforward once the processes, savings and skill set were identified. Consideration was given to where the position should be with the company e.g. Marketing, Communications, Estates Administration or Procurement. The Procurement Department was chosen because of its direct line with the buying processes and the administration resources that existed to support the new position were already in place'.

'Philip Jarret, previously from Boots' Print Buying Department, was appointed as the Yellow Pages Print Buyer in September 1999. He immediately took over all commissioning of print and print management totalling in excess of £3 million. To date Philip has saved the company £42,412 (31%) on straight reprints alone. This accurate figure is possible to determine because a previous reprint quotation already existed for comparison. Keener pricing is also possible by building relationships with printers as opposed to offering continual "one-off" projects.

By guaranteeing a certain level of work the printer can plan his machine time more effectively. He can be more efficient and pass such benefits on'. [This approach to Procurement is very common in Japan-Ed].

Lessons learnt from the project included:

* Making requests for help informal and conversational was the best approach for gaining benchmarking contacts.

* There was merit in preparing a presentation format to aid digestion of the benefits and gain support from senior management.

* Following all of the processes can sometimes be a "means to an end" and developing solid benchmarking relationships is a key solution.

The format of the Print Management Case Study will be the first entry on the business-wide benchmarking database and will be used as the template for how other projects should be conducted and communicated. A recognition programme is also envisaged as communication of successful projects is enhanced and this will be communicated through the new Yellow Pages Intranet. In addition a Benchmarking Communications Plan is to be produced and implemented to encourage the transfer of knowledge and learning about benchmarking itself, as well as, perhaps more importantly, benchmarking findings.

Results of benchmarking studies should become readily available via a database accessible across the entire business and reported on the "good news" area of the business-wide Intranet. Review of the effectiveness of benchmarking will be carried out annually as part of self-assessment against the EFQM Excellence Model.

Following receipt of the Award, from Erkii Likanen, European Commissioner in charge of Enterprises and Information Society, Tony Old commented:

" Winning this Award is testimony to Yellow Pages' commitment to continually refining and improving the ways we work. This Award is a real boost to the team".

Chairman of the judging panel and Chair in Best Practice Management at the University of Bradford Mohammed Zairi added:

" Yellow Pages clearly demonstrates that benchmarking is driven by top management and therefore generates commitment at all levels".

Chapter Five

Teamwork

Teamwork, like benchmarking, has proved to be a popular tool for quality improvement throughout the 1990s enjoying something of a revival during the decade. Interest in the UK has been inspired by The National Society for Quality through Teamwork (originally established in 1982 as The National Society of Quality Circles). In the latter part of the decade it has followed a similar trend to benchmarking with an Award scheme which has proved popular in the UK now being introduced at European level with an accompanying name change for the Society which is now known as The European Forum for Teamwork.

During the 1990s the Award scheme for teamwork had two components, the Michelin Award which recognised the twin achievements of single project/management directed teams and continuous improvement/self-directed teams, and the Varity Perkins Award which recognised which recognised total programme achievement through teamwork. The latter was discontinued in 1998.

The compilation of articles below covers most of the above Award presentation case studies from 1993, but is not confined exclusively to it. Other articles address the philosophy of teamwork as expounded by world expert Dr. Meredith Belbin and coverage of the annual Irish Teamworking Congress hosted by International Communications for Management (ICM).

BUILDING THE PERFECT TEAM

Graeme Garden (of Goodie fame) reported at the HRD 92 Conference on the team role theory developed by Dr. Meredith Belbin who for some twenty years now, has been studying the role of teams in business. The presentation was supported with a showing of Video Art's training video 'Building the Perfect Team', which used a fictional boardroom situation to illustrate the theory.

The essence of the theory is that whilst the 'Perfect Team' is in theory achievable, the perfect individual is not.

Findings have shown that every person within an organisation has two distinct roles: a 'functional' role (related to the type of job that the individual performs, such as accounts, sales and marketing), and a 'team' role (related to the behavioural attributes that the individual can bring to a team).

Further to this, people usually fall into one of nine team role types, each of which has strengths in the form of benefits which the individual can bring to the team, and weaknesses which can be thought of as the price which must be paid for the strengths, and have to be allowed for. A person's team role profile is ascertained from a 'personal inventory' obtained by methods such as Self Perception and Observer Assessments, which produce scores which can be measured against the various types. Highest scores reveal the one or more natural Primary and Secondary team roles which characterizes the individual.

The nine types identified are:

1. The Co-ordinator

Strength: ability to motivate

Weakness: inclined to be manipulative

2.The Completer-finisher

Strength: meticulous

Weakness: can be a worrier

3. The Implementer

Strength: organised and disciplined

Weakness: inclined to be inflexible

4. The Monitor Evaluator

Strength: often careful and objective

Weakness: can be uninspiring

5. The Plant

Strength: can be clever and creative

Weakness: often non-conformative

6. The Resource Investigator

Strength: often flexible and outgoing

Weakness: easily bored

7. The Shaper

Strength: tends to be dynamic and positive

Weakness: can be perceived as blunt and sometimes rude

8. The Specialist

Strength: often dedicated and knowledgeable

Weakness: has a restricted contribution

9. The Team Worker

Strength: usually diplomatic

Weakness: prone to be indecisive

It may not be possible to have all nine team role types in a team, but it is always possible to have the right balance. Belbin confronted a number of teams consisting of different combinations of role types with a series of business problems and in every case he and his associates accurately predicted the team that would find and implement the most effective solution.

Further research showed that when managers are considering an individual for a position in a team, eligibility (qualifications, experience etc) tends to be considered rather than suitability (ability to fit into and contribute to the team). Analysis of eligibility/suitability in relation to performance showed that ineligible and unsuitable candidates performed badly (no surprise), as did eligible but unsuitable candidates. More surprising, however, was the fact that eligible, suitable candidates 'turned out to be the most disappointing of all':

'Unstretched and unchallenged they rapidly became bored and failed to achieve their potential. Very often they tended to move on after a short time, in search of more interesting and demanding work'.

By contrast, the ineligible but suitable candidates 'fitted comfortably and confidently into the team and worked conscientiously to overcome their lack of qualifications and experience'. They 'performed enthusiastically, learning and contributing, and making a strong commitment to both the team and the organisation'.

Quality Matters identifies the following as a key quotation:

' Team role theory helps us to understand why a team will sometimes succeed, yet sometimes will fail; why it will sometimes reach the right decision, sometimes the wrong one; why it may not perform as well as expected, with tensions and misunderstandings developing between the members. Very often the root of these problems can be found at the personal level – how the team members feel about themselves and about each other'.

[Issue 52 (April 1993)]

QUALITY CIRCLES

Pira International held a seminar at their Leatherhead HQ devoted to the subject of Quality Circles.

Total Quality: Reasons for Failure.

According to John Wright, Teamwork Advisor for the NSQT, around 80 per cent of Total Quality initiatives failed in the UK during the1980s, the reason, in most cases being that the senior management team was not fully committed and often did not realise that it had to change the way it managed, and, in particular, its style of management.

Most companies, he said, think they know the answer to basic questions like management style, but in practice they don't. Team building, for example, is not just about getting half a dozen people around a table and calling it a team. Lots of organizations tried to go 'too far too soon' and the result invariably was failure. Too many teams too soon could not be supported and a policy of creating 15 to 20 teams without a supporting infrastructure was clearly 'no good'.

Quality Circles: the Comeback.

Delegates were not, however, to infer despair because a high proportion of companies have learned by their mistakes and are in fact succeeding second time around. Only a minority of companies, he said, 'had made a mess of it and not had a second chance', and although a time period of between one and four years may be needed for 'the dust to settle', coupled perhaps with some personnel changes, there was every reason to suppose that a second go was worth trying.

It was pointed out that many organizations had chosen not to call their teams 'quality circles', perhaps as a result of negative associations with failure in the past, and had adopted instead terms such as 'Quality Action Teams' and 'Quality Improvement Teams', but in practice it was what these teams did rather than what they were called that was important.

He described how, whilst most textbooks recommend 4 to 12 people as the optimum size for a team, he preferred the range 3 to 10 with 6 to 8 being the 'ideal size' and the average now in the UK. Often they comprise of people who do the same kind of work, but there is an increasing tendency to find 'hybrids'.

Most, unfortunately, tend to start off in a 'reactive mode' even though they are generally voluntary, and he pointed to the need for teams to be action orientated rather than being allowed to become 'bitching sessions' or 'talking shops'.

Most successful teams are free to select their problems, with the exception of matters relating to pay and conditions and have a role in prioritising problems, but not in identifying individuals as problems. Also they reinforce management rather than seeking to by-pass it. Everyone in the team is equal regardless of rank i.e. there is no status control and individuals are free to enter or leave as they wish. Leaders are elected, usually by peer nomination, but the recommendation was for teams not be reliant on one person for their leadership. The practice of appointing a first line supervisor as leader was not recommended.

Leaders are characteristically trained to be trainers. This training involves techniques in brainstorming, presentation skills and Pareto Analysis as well as leadership skills. Also to co-ordinate problem solving in a structured manner (not just analysing problems and making assumptions about them), with experimentation and testing of solutions where possible, with particular attention to evaluation of the impact of the solution, which is often omitted.

There then followed an outline of a nine point plan as recommended by the NSQT, designed to assist companies in the development and harnessing of quality circle/teamworking skills:

1. Obtain management commitment.

A two day off-site workshop with the top team, examining the need for change and potential to develop the TQ strategy, followed by a 1 day middle management implementation workshop. The NSQT can act as a catalyst.

2. Survey employee attitudes.

The NSQT has specifically developed a unique audit system in five parts which allows change and improvement to be measured over five years.

3. Appoint a facilitator.

Programme facilitators and team facilitators promote the concept and act as trainers and educators. They are the first to receive the formal training that the teamleaders experience.

4. Appoint a steering committee.

A steering committee of up to ten members is needed with cross-sectional membership not constituted wholly from management. It is important that the committees are not too big as otherwise they can become 'just committees'. Also, they need to be action orientated, not just 'talking shops'.

5. Institute employee awareness.

The steering committee liase with facilitators to plan employee awareness presentations, often conducted by external specialists.

6. Identify items for phase 1 teams.

The steering committee will usually have responsibility for the establishment of teams in perhaps 4 to 6 work areas. Care is needed to avoid elitism, and there must be more than just one team because if that one were to fail there would be 100 per cent failure.

7. Identify leaders for phase 1 teams.

Existing leaders or peer group nomination may be used for this task, with a reserve leader also appointed and trained.

8. Train the leaders.

Skills such as team dynamics, interactive skills, quality circle methodology and problem solving are required. In Japan and Korea this is done at age 7, so that when the pupils enter the world of work they 'wouldn't dream of working any other way'. Here, by contrast, 'it has taken a long time to get it into the seats of learning' and is highly necessary.

9. Start phase 1 teams.

Allow teams to try ideas on actual projects. Some organisations place teams in a classroom environment for 8 to 10 weeks and then they leave. Remember they are volunteers and they left school years ago.

Following the presentation Mr .Wright was asked whether, since the teams are voluntary, this could result in the wrong people to solve the problem. The reply was that there were several teamworking types of which quality circles were just one. Mandatory teams were a 'different beast'.

He was later asked where the people could come from in a company with just 17 employees. He suggested that two or three teams could be formed in a company of that size.

Another delegate asked how unions typically react to the introduction of quality circles and the reply was that nowadays the majority provide no opposition, and indeed are largely supportive. Mr. Wright said that it had been 'a long time' since he had seen any opposition at executive or branch level, and he said that he no longer perceived it as a problem.

Another delegate questioned how one could take personnel off the production line for training when the company needed their productivity. It was explained that, what was required was just one meeting for one hour per week, with the training incorporated in a real life project. The only person that has to be 'dragged' away from the production process initially is the team leader and often the shift changeover period can be utilised for team meetings.

[Issue 58 (October 1993)]

TEAMWORK '93

The National Society for Quality through Teamwork (NSQT), formerly the National Society for Quality Circles, held their 11th annual conference, Teamwork '93, at the Moat House Hotel, Stoke on Trent, on 30th September and 1st October, and featured the presentation of this year's Michelin Awards for quality circle excellence in problem solving, and Perkins Awards for Continuous Improvement, which the NSQT co-sponsored.

1993 Michelin Awards

The Michelin Awards final took place on 30th September and was the fourth such final, the first being in 1990 when Michelin, following recognition through the Perkins Award of the previous year decided to visibly support the quality circle movement by establishing their own set of Awards. Up to three Awards are made each year to individual quality circles who are able to illustrate excellence in problem solving through involvement and use of appropriate techniques with points allocated as follows:

* 55 for 'vitality and commitment' covering involvement of team members, evidence of thinking and working outside of meeting time, regularity and effectiveness of meetings, programme completion and learning from previous projects.

* 55 for choice of project with reference to people impact, complexity and benefits to the company, brainstorming, consensus on final choice and establishment of viability.

* 45 for approach, including use of specialists and resources, planning and use of tools.

* 65 for solution development, including evidence of originality, explanation of options available, consideration of the overall impact, ease of implementation and verification that the solution is effective and permanent (i.e. monitoring the implementation).

* 20 for structure and presentation of the project log and other outward communications.

* 55 for actual presentation, including how well the team emphasised the key points, notified their solution, and demonstrated an effective action plan for implementing the solution.

* 30 for overall effect (whether the solution was implemented and if so whether everyone affected appreciated it).

There were six finalists this year from Land Rover, Solihull; Hill Samuel Life Assurance, Croydon; Carello Lighting of Canada (2 teams); European Components Company Limited, Belfast; and Whiston Hospital Trust of Prescot, Merseyside.

Three awards were made to the teams from Land Rover, Carello Lighting No.1 team and Whiston Hospital Trust, by a jury chaired by John Steele, Head of Personnel and Training for Michelin.

The presentations by Hill Samuel, the European Components Company and Carello (No.2) focused on improvement of group communications, reduction of scrap in the processing of Latch Plates, and the maintenance of jigs used for the processing of a high volume head lamp reflector.

The Carello No.1 team 'All for 1' focused on the problem of material waste in the company's Thermostat Moulding section which until thoroughly addressed by the team accounted for a loss of around £57,000 per year. Analysis of the moulding machines and maintenance of those creating the most waste enabled a dramatic reduction to be achieved and an ongoing monitoring and control system now ensures that there will be no re-emergence of this specific problem.

The Land Rover team, known as 'SEEDS' (Service, Electrical, Engineers, Departments), likewise addressed a specific problem, namely the high levels of traffic congestion around their Solihull delivery site. The potential danger of lost production was evident when suppliers arrived late or not at all at the receiving decks, whilst maintenance vehicles were unable to address breakdown jobs owing to the presence of on-site delivery vehicles at critical exit points. A study of the problem showed that a prime cause was incorrect use of the site traffic flow system by the drivers which resulted in them blocking a narrow road which should not have been used for that purpose. A survey of drivers showed that non-regular drivers frequently lost their way with a consequent loss of production. Examination of the site signs revealed the existence of numerous redundant signs, and a lack of clear Block and Deck numbers. Following an idea gained from visiting a doctor's surgery a colour zoning system was devised, which the judges praised for its elegance.

The third winning presentation, by the Whiston Hospital Trust, was made by a six member team of nurses, who adopted the title of 'Quality Pursuits' and considered the problem of over-demand for electrical resources in their intensive care unit, which was by no means unique to their hospital. The project was highly original and the team's presentation also won the 1993 NHS Team of the Year Award.

Quality Pursuits.

'Quality Pursuits' was formed in 1990 following Sister Elaine Povey's attendance at a quality circle study day organised by the Quality Development Unit. She then communicated the quality circle concept to staff at the intensive care unit, who quickly recognised its significance as a tool to improve and solve long standing problems, such as the evacuation of critically ill patients in the event of fire.

Early successes soon motivated the team to tackle the more substantial problem of the serious over-stretching of the department's electrical resources, which was identified as the single most important issue warranting their attention in July 1991 following brainstorming from a short list of problems displayed in the staff lounge.

A cause and effect analysis revealed a variety of electrical hazards posed as a consequence of the numerous banks of plugs that were currently being used. This prompted an assessment by an electrical engineer and a survey of five other intensive care units in the area to examine how they had approached the problem.

363

Technical advisors explained that whilst each piece of electrical equipment in Intensive Care was tested to ensure that it met British Safety standards, such standards were no longer met once the equipment became plugged into a plug bank of the type used at Whiston Hospital. The hospital consequently was advised not to use the plug banks in question.

The team then considered three possible solutions, which resulted in the development of a prototype bed in January 1992 and a two month trial followed in which a number of potential improvements were identified.

In December 1992 Clinitron SSI Medical Services Limited evaluated the modified prototype at their Nottingham Development Unit and subsequently agreed to sponsor the conversion of five more beds.

In February of this year the prototype was returned to Whiston with all of its electrical system complying with British standards and, following a second trial, it was displayed at the St. George's Hall Exhibition of Innovation and Excellence in Nursing Practice, Management and Education. Interest is now being shown, from amongst others, the Great Ormond Street Hospital for Sick Children in London.

1993 Perkins Awards.

Day two was devoted to the presentation of the 1993 Perkins Awards presented to the organisations which can demonstrate the highest level of progress in their continuous improvement over the past year. There were again six entries for this award, which is now in its sixth year, and, since last year, has had two trophies available for the winning entries in the large company (over 250 employees) category , and small company (under 250 employees) category.

There were five judges, led by Chairman Myles Coleman of Perkins Engines; and the points were awarded as follows:

* 150 for clarity of company mission, strategy for continuous improvement, and evidence of an improvement strategy and supporting plan which portrays a vision of how the company will evolve into a Total Involvement Operation. Study of the NSQT 'Mix of Six Ingredients for Change' is recommended.

*250 for teamworking and people involvement including a review and recognition system which is part of the normal management system, and evidence of innovation and flexibility in the types of teams. Study of the NSQT's 'Total Teamwork Way' is recommended.

*150 for quality education and training, the company's commitment to it and evidence of programmes of improvement for all individuals, including job skills training, teambuilding training, techniques training, general education and company awareness.

* 150 for the use of measurement systems throughout the company, including well communicated customer satisfaction measures, employee satisfaction measures, key business process measures, measures of key process criteria at departmental level, and measurements identified so that everyone has an idea of how they are performing and an improvement goal.

* 150 for visible management commitment in the form of practical action such as changes to terms and conditions, removal of us/them barriers, improvement in information flow and team recognition actions and events.

The six finalists, selected from an initial short list of 35, were Prudential Assurance, Amersham International of Cardiff, Campbell Lee Computer Services Limited of Scotland, Barbour Campbell Threads Limited of Northern Ireland, BBC News and Current Affairs Engineering and Ford Motors of Dagenham. From these Barbour Campbell Threads were selected to receive the Large Company Award and Campbell Lee Computer Services the Small Company Award.

Barbour Campbell Threads: highly commended.

Barbour Campbell Threads Limited provide the largest range of natural and synthetic threads in the world and were highly commended in the Northern Ireland Quality Awards.

Their Production Director Mr. Jeremy Lee, gave an overview of their Quality Journey which was founded on the achievement of AQAP certification in the early 1970s, and, more recently, BS5750 Part1 certification which the company achieved in 1987, becoming the first thread manufacturer in the UK to become so registered.

The journey incorporated visits to various companies in the United States who had achieved recognition by gaining the prestigious Malcolm Baldrige Award and a TQS initiative that led to 'true ownership, leadership and commitment'.

Three steering groups covering the fields of waste management, customer first, and training and domestic issues have been formed, whilst 35 teams tackling specific project areas have been set up over the past three years. This expansion in the number of teams has prompted recognition of the need for in-house courses to be devised to enhance leadership skills. Barriers to communication have been overcome by means of an internal Newsletter, inter-departmental teams, recognition of innovation and a more open style of management. A notable milestone was achieved in 1991 when the company became the first and only thread manufacturer to gain the Ford Q1 Award.

Tom MacWhinney, Synthetic Production Manager and a self-confessed sceptic for over 20 years, delighted the audience with his original brand of Irish humour which both retained attention and delivered a serious message. He explained how he thought he knew how to do it all after 30 years of working with a 'completely autocratic' system of management. However, in the first day of a training session, in which he became rapidly educated in an alternative way of thinking, he came to appreciate that there might just perhaps be a better way of managing. He recognised that autocracy led to arguments, frustration, and people being hurt and he accepted 'this was not a successful state of affairs'. He then explained how, after the second day, he had returned to his post and taken action to involve others in this alternative way of thinking. The job now 'took on a new shape and form' as he began to realise far more fully the importance of ascertaining the root causes, rather than the perceived causes, of problems.

The success of the company's training policy was exemplified by the display of a letter from the company's senior shop steward, which referred to the new style of training as 'a major step forward between shop floor workers and senior management'.

Other success measures included a graphical illustration of falling waste costs in proportion to the number of teams, with such costs being reduced from around £18,000 per year in January 1992 to around £9000, with some 15 teams now functioning under the umbrella of the waste steering committee. The achievements of the Customer First steering group were likewise impressive with delivery performance improving from 25 per cent to 72 per cent, telephone responses averaging 3.5 seconds instead of the previous 7.5 and an order backlog of 33 tons being whittled down to 9.

The company was praised by the Chairman of the judging panel, Mr. Myles Coleman, for their 'tremendous progress in 1992'.

Campbell Lee: Teamwork and Total Quality most significant.

Campbell Lee Computer Services, based in Paisley, Falkirk and Aberdeen, described teamwork and Total Quality as 'the most significant factor in the development of the company over the last four years', having set out with the aim of involving all people in every process.

The company made a significant step in 1992 when it departed from its tradition of keeping all Quality Improvement Teams (QITs) management led. It was recognised that communication difficulties were resulting from the hierarchical management structure and Quality Manager, Mr. Alistair Arthur, explained how he and his colleagues began a complete reappraisal of the company's approach to teamwork.

Quality circle representatives were brought together and a 'team from teams' was formed, together with a policy of solving problems through the involvement of multi-functional, multi-disciplinary teams. In particular the company integrated teamwork with pursuit of ISO9001 registration, identifying the 'vital few' problems which were then allocated to QITs.

In 1992 the company achieved registration to ISO9001 and TickIT, retained their highest technical rating from IBM, and have gained new business in local government, substantially increasing their turnover. They have integrated their quality programme with the Investors in People scheme.

The judges, who were reported to have been 'very impressed' with how the company began its programme and listened to advice from its customers, were clearly interested in how the company had managed to reconcile BS5750 with TQM. They asked in particularfor an elaboration of problems encountered in doing this and in reply it was explained how, whilst BS5750 was about conformance and Total Quality was about attitudinal and cultural change the company had recognised a clear need for both to co-exist. Informal processes had to move a bit more formally together, and BS5750 can help to enable this to happen, but following registration there can be a 'post natal depression' when everyone realises that nothing startling has really happened.

Other Presentations.

It was remarked that the task of the judges to select the two eventual winners had this year been exceptionally difficult and the other presentations contained much of interest and were all of an exceptionally high standard.

Prudential Assurance described their strategy for quality as 'one of great simplicity' and explained how employee feedback had been used to effect change in their reward and recognition scheme. Quality forums indicated a clear desire for no bureaucracy, instant recognition ,some adventure and an end to league tables which had clearly been unpopular. The achievement of BS5750 in no less than seven areas in 1992 broke new ground in the field of insurance administration.

Amersham International, whose principal markets are in healthcare, life science research and quality and safety assurance, were praised by the judges for their innovation, involvement and business aligned to improvement activity. The Cardiff site, which specialises in life science research and has 400 employees, used a quality council to focus attention on those vital few problems [Pareto analysis- Ed.] that were causing most concern. Chaired by the site director this council meets monthly. With failure rates down by over a third the company has now begun to tackle the 'trivial many' problems with voluntary improvement teams. Now over 70 per cent of employees have become involved in at least one project. There has been a strong emphasis on statistical process control (SPC) training and in Taguchi Methods, to which the company is clearly very heavily committed. The company achieved

BS5750 Part 2 registration in March and amongst its successes are a reduction in the cost of poor quality of around £3 million.

The BBC News and Current Affairs Engineering presentation described how the department, which employs 200, have pioneered the introduction of a quality philosophy in an organisation which now enjoys a significant degree of producer choice. A particular problem was the shift work associated with the provision of 24 hour news services, with difficulties of maintaining communication between team members because many employee paths never crossed. An innovative system that overcame this, using electronic mail, was described whilst major improvement to video repair and calibration enabled a time reduction from half an hour to just a few minutes, and an equipment downtime reduction of up to 80% [very significant in the news business-Ed]

Ford Motors' presentation focused on two years of work which has been done at Dagenham to achieve their company's Q1 Award. This was acknowledged to be both more exacting and more widespread in scope than BS5750. A team was set up to facilitate communication between management and workers and in April 1991 a Q1 Steering team was established to develop and publish a statement on quality and productivity. Some 120 teams now exist, 68 of which have management members. Successes to date include improvement of packing methods and specifications to minimise damage to sheet metal, development of a new stock-keeping system which reduced "warehouse denials" by 30 per cent, and improved dealer relations. The company achieved the Ford Q1 on 29th September.

Finally, as in previous years, the conference featured a poster competition sponsored by Josiah Wedgwood and Sons, which consisted of two awards for the best professional and non-professional poster designs on a quality/teamwork theme. This year's winning entries were from National Westminster and Ford Motors.

[Issue 81 (September 1995)]

TEAMWORK MATTERS

The NSQT annual conference Teamwork '95 was held at the University of Warwick on 22nd and 23rd August and featured the finals of the annual Michelin and Perkins Awards. It was a well attended event attracting over 750 delegates despite the heatwave.

There were a number of new features to the conference this year, including a new format for the Michelin Awards, which are now in their sixth year, and a new Perkins Schools Award which was supported this year by Cambridgeshire County Council, and English Nature. In addition the Perkins Awards themselves featured for the first time an entry from the Republic of Ireland.

368

1995 Michelin Awards

When the Michelin Awards were last reported in 1993 up to three Awards were granted to quality circles which demonstrated excellence in problem solving through the involvement and use of appropriate techniques. At that time there were up to 55 marks awarded for 'vitality and commitment'; 55 for 'choice of project'; 45 for 'approach' (use of specialists, and resources, planning and use of tools); 65 for 'solution development' (including originality, explanation of options, implementation and verification of solution effectiveness);20 for 'structure and presentation of the project log and other outward communications'; 55 for 'actual presentation'; and 30 for 'overall effect'.

Since then the award format has been modified so that it now consists of two award categories, the single problem/management promotion award for teams established by management to analyse and solve a specific problem or improve a selected part of the business, and the continuous improvement/self-directed team award for the best voluntary team which has selected its own problems.

There are seven award criteria for both categories: 'Team Vitality', 'Project', 'Plan', 'Solution', 'Log Book', 'Communication', and 'Implementation and Monitoring'. The weighting of marks between the categories are, however, different for the two categories and there are one or two slight differences in the way the categories are defined. An example of this occurs in the 'Project' section where the single project/management promotion award examines how clearly the project objectives were specified. what resources were provided and whether the team verified the problem definition and its basis and identified appropriate problem measurement criteria. The continuous improvement/self direction award, however, considers how the project was selected, whether there was a large range of possible ideas or a series of projects against a common theme, and whether the team considered the people, complexity and company benefits and identify them in measurable forms. The distribution of marks for the seven criteria in each award category were as follows:

Criterion	Mgt.promotion	Self Direction
Team Vitality	55	55
Project	20	55
Plan	55	45
Solution	75	65
Log Book	20	20
Communication	65	55
Implementation	35	30

Six finalists, three in each category, gave presentations from which a single winner was selected for each category.

Bug busting at Severn Trent.

The winning team in the single problem/ management promotion category was The Goscote team from Severn Trent Water whose members were charged with the unenviable task of resolving a scum problem at a recently refurbished sewage treatment works.

The problem centred around a biological scum which formed regularly on separator tanks which necessitated a costly and time consuming, not to mention unpleasant, cleaning task for operatives, which if not completed properly threatened to render the Walsall based Goscote Works liable to legal action from the National Rivers Authority.

The annual cost of disposing of the scum was valued at £97,900 and it was the team's task to try and reduce this whilst at the same time maintaining compliance and throughput. They met for half a day each fortnight sharing tasks to investigate possible effects of changing operating practice. Cause and effect and fishbone diagrams were used and a series of trials involving the measurement of flow rates and the sampling of effluent were instigated.

Statistical irregularities highlighted a major deficiency in tank feed which was later traced to a blockage caused by a 16 inch steel plate lodged in the main feed pipe. This was extracted and was on show at the conference.

As a result of their work savings of around £95,400 were realised, the biggest component of which were analytical savings of around £33,000.

Following the presentation the judges asked, amongst other things, how they measured the morale of the workforce. In their answer they highlighted the unpleasant nature of the work involved, the fact staff no longer have to devote as much time to this work, and availability of monetary rewards for improvements in effluent quality. They were also asked how much effort was given outside works time and in reply the team confirmed that a considerable amount of work had been taken away from meetings although the meetings themselves had taken place in works time.

The judges praised The Goscote Team for "Good use of problem solving techniques, a very good plan and jolly good solutions"

Project Dyane at Perkins.

The Continuous Improvement/Self Direction Award was won by a team of five engineers from Perkins Engines of Peterborough, who are already renowned for excellence in the manufacture of diesel engines.

This team's chosen problem concerns the honing process which finishes the bores in cylinder blocks in which the pistons operate. The process is critical to the working lives of engines particularly with regard to power, performance and emission control.

The hones in question occur in groups of four and operate simultaneously. They have a value of £10,000 each and have a life expectancy of around 500 hours which equates to continuous production over about four weeks. After that time they require replacement or refurbishment.

At Peterborough some 54 hones are required which equates to a value of £540,000. Should a hone not be available serious delays to production may result and on many occasions have happened. This is because a lead time of some 4 to 6 weeks is the norm for hone replacement in the UK coupled with an absence of control and accountability in supply.

The team agreed that this state of affairs was unacceptable and when it was found that none of the UK's handful of suppliers could improve on this the team began to brainstorm for solutions. This led to consideration of improving the utilisation of their own tool-house in the development of an in-house process for having head replacement.

Subsequent evaluation showed that the external refurbishment cost of £1,000 per hone could be brought down to £326 if the work was undertaken in-house, which would mean that the cost of refurbishing 27 hone heads (the number required during 1993), would be reduced from £27,000 to £8,802 resulting in a saving of £18,198.

In May 1994 the new process was introduced which incorporated a new colour coded storage system for total control and an improvement to the containers used for the transportation of hones. The result was a reduction in lead time for hone refurbishment to just 3 days and the total elimination of downtime of machines waiting for hones.

The team was questioned on the frequency of their meetings and in reply they explained how the shift system had made the meetings irregular in terms of timing, although one meeting per two to three weeks had been typical. They were also asked whether they had witnessed an improvement or otherwise in the life expectancy of the in-house refurbished hones and confirmed that there had been a slight improvement there in addition to the cost savings. In addition they were questioned about the involvement of the toolroom personnel, in particular whether the toolroom personnel had been co-opted into the group and whether there had been any staff increase there. It was confirmed that there had been no staff increases there, they were happy to take the work on and provided much help to the team, although they were not specifically a sub-group of it.

The judges commended the Perkins team for "good planning, implementation and monitoring and good minutes of the log".

Other Presentations.

The two remaining presentations in the single problem/management promotion category came from chemical manufacturers Albright and Wilson UK Limited of Warley and high value automotive component suppliers UEF Garsington of Bromsgrove. Those in the continuous category were from Britannia Airways Limited of Luton and Land Rover of Solihull.

Albright and Wilson's presentation concerned the improvement of a critical process related to the production of potassium phosphate in response to changes in demand. There were two targets; one to alter the split between solid and liquor output from 40:60 to 85:15, and the other to increase total production from 6,500 tonnes to 10,000 tonnes. Improvements were centred around the key activities of solids handling and kiln operation. A Taguchi study identified important parameters for improvement which ultimately enabled output to be increased to 10,600 tonnes per year with a solid:liquor ratio of 90:10. The team was commended for being "strong on planning and the use of trials".

The team of three from UEF Garringtons investigated the phenomenon of hub run-out in the machining and assembly of front wheel hubs supplied to a leading UK automotive manufacturer. It was suspected that the phenomenon was a principal cause of brake judder. High process variability was diagnosed and a system of weekly process checks was introduced. Key points for action were identified, such as cleanliness of work holders, wrong setting of gauge probes, and inadequate coolant strengths and supplies. A three page improvement summary was produced and following presentations at their customer's design centre process change approval was given for two design changes. The total saving arising from this is estimated at £34,631. The judges commended the team for being "very good at keeping colleagues up to date with a clear plan of progress and customer involvement".

Britannia Airways' presentation, although representing Britannia Airways Limited of Luton, was actually undertaken by a team called 'Quality Street' based at Manchester Airport. Their problem concerned their deployment of ash trays in the non-smoking areas of charter aircraft, and in particular whether such ash trays were necessary. Consensus voting selected this project after it was ascertained that the cleaning of these ash trays, which in non-smoking areas are commonly filled with paper and the like, was taking a disproportionate amount of turn-round time (up to three times more than in the smoking areas). Furthermore the airline was spending some £13,385 per year on the replacement of missing, broken and damaged ash trays. Following contact with the Civil Aviation Authority for technical and legal advice the team devised a solution and used a solution effect diagram to investigate possible impacts. An aircraft is to be modified and tested late next year and savings are estimated at £133,850 over10 years. The judges praised the team for a 'Very good structure of how to solve problems", but pointed out that the predictions of the consequences of the modification had yet to be seen.

The presentation from Land Rover was perhaps the most original, taking the form of a stage presentation to illustrate practically and comically how paint damage can commonly occur to the rear floor panels of Land Rovers during assembly. The Big Cover Up' was thus presented by a team of seven 'New Star Trekkers' to illustrate how Land Rover employees successfully damaged 16 per cent of their vehicles and then spent £45,000 a year to put it right. Liaison with support engineers led to the replacement of primitive protector boards, with a set of 96 rubber mats at a cost of £4,000. The team claim that the new mats will save around £6,000 per annum and confine paint damage to just one or two vehicles per week. The judges commended the team's log book as "most vibrant" and praised their "sense of fun and good implementation".

The Quality Dot.

In addition to the above presentations, Cyril Atkinson, Director of the National Society for Quality through Teamwork, highlighted one further entry which was clearly considered to be worthy of inclusion, though it had been rendered ineligible by virtue of the fact that it had been submitted by an individual rather than by a team.

The entry was entitled 'Things that go bump in the night' and was submitted by auxiliary nurse Mrs. Pat Bickerton, who works a permanent night shift at Southend Hospital, which is part of the Southend NHS Trust.

After reading an extract from the submission which "did very well in the judges' eyes", Mr. Atkinson introduced the concept of the 'Quality Dot' i.e. an individual who possesses all the characteristics of a quality team and without whom many quality teams may never in fact come into being.

Mr. Atkinson subsequently challenged every business to act as a 'Quality Dot' within the overall quality framework, and to act on their initiative as demonstrated by Mrs. Bickerton.

[Issue 82 (October 1995)]

TEAMWORK '95 (Part 2):PERKINS AWARDS

As with the Michelin Awards there were finalists from which an overall winner was selected by a panel of five independent judges.

R.H.P. Bearings: Total Manufacturing.

The winning entry as selected by the judges was submitted by R.H.P. Bearings Limited of Ferrybridge, West Yorkshire, which is one of seven

European sites of R.H.P. This has been a wholly owned subsidiary of the Japanese bearing manufacturer N.S.K. since 1990.

The Ferrybridge factory has 620 employees and specialises in the manufacture of self lubricating and water pump bearings. Their Total Quality programme was launched in 1992 under the banner of the Total Manufacturing Concept and has given teams a new role in the annual policy deployment process in which relevant local initiatives are determined to achieve set company objectives.

The new culture has made Kaizen (continuous incremental improvement) the language of the company whilst a system of 'catch ball' promotes the sharing of information in both directions throughout the business.

Considerable emphasis has also been placed on training with a training plan drawn up every year. In 1994 eight days of training were provided for each employee which equated to 1.5 per cent of wages costs. A 'radar chart' is used to show the competence level attained by each employee and investment has included provision of a self development room with interactive video.

A display board incorporating the 'Plan- Do-Check-Act' cycle has "assisted task teams in tackling problems in a systematic way", and facilitated the development of standard operating procedures by task teams. Some 200 of these standard operating procedures have now been written and benefits to date have included a 30% reduction in the number of etching rejects, a 50% reduction in the number of face grind rejects, and a 54% improvement in scrap reduction since 1993.

In 1994 the company began to undertake self-assessment using the EFQM Award Model, which has greatly assisted management in measuring the progress of the Total Quality programme. Results from the self-assessment are fed back into the annual policy deployment process.

Future plans include the objectives of achieving the Investors In People (IIP) standard which the company believes will help them to continuously improve on the standards which they have set for themselves as well as making work more enjoyable.

The presentation attracted a number of questions from the judges, not least from one EFQM Assessor who was keen to ascertain from the team the company's current self-assessment score. The team confirmed that their present score was around 300 following a self-assessment earlier in the year, and that the company's 32 trained self-assessors would be performing another self-assessment around October.

Another judge questioned how the company measured its impact on society and in reply the team described how a monthly environmental audit had been established, and how they had developed close links with the National Rivers Authority and other agencies, as well as assisting with a local children's football team.

The team was asked how training effectiveness was evaluated and what measures were used particularly to evaluate the effectiveness of the new interactive video facility. It was explained how the company kept a log of all of the usage of the facility, scrutinised end of course questionnaires and checked the effectiveness of the completion of SPC charts on the shop floor.

The judges were also keen to establish the extent of management involvement in teamworking and it was explained how managers had purposefully worked for a while on the assembly line and other areas of the shop floor. Managers also frequently assumed a facilitating role in the teams themselves.

A question about employee attitudes gave rise to a description of the company's three year old employee attitude survey system which has revealed "incredibly pleasing changes". It was accepted that early indicators had been poor with only around 40 per cent of employees expressing a desire to be involved in teamwork. This has since risen to around 60 per cent.

Finally the team was asked what the term 'world class' meant to them and in reply they said that they would look to achievements of a minimum of 80 per cent in each area of the of European Quality Award model as one possible measure. They also made reference to their Japanese sister companies which they had benchmarked internally, saying that they believed one or two of them to be world class.

The company was commended by the judges for "a very comprehensive submission that shows an organisation with total improvement planning in place".

Other Presentations.

There were five other Perkins finalists: The Slag Reduction Company of Redcar, the Benefit Enquiry line of Preston, Royal Insurance Life and Pensions of Liverpool, the Britannia Topsides Project (London), and Wellman International Limited of Kells (Irish Republic).

The Slag Reduction Company, the Industrial Service Division of Faber Prest plc and a specialist in the provision of steelworks services, were invited by British Steel to operate the Redcar One Terminal and retrain its personnel in partnership with British Steel following the abolition of the National Dock Labour Board in 1989. The terminal supplies iron ore and coke to the Teeside Steelworks. There are currently 44 employees working in multi-functional teams. The presentation described the specialist work of three Action Teams formed in 1994 to address respectively Wharf Raw Materials

Handling, Slab Loading and Grab Damage, and Ship Finishing. All three of these teams realised substantial technical and financial improvements and these were described. In the first case a 40 per cent improvement in throughput was realised since 1989 whilst the cost of demurrage (compensation payments to shipowners for delays in loading and discharging of vessels) has been reduced from over £3 million to under £250,000 in the same period. In the second the time taken for slab loading was reduced from 97 hours to 69 hours as a result of using a safer and faster method with estimated financial gains of £450,000 a year. The third team reviewed working practices and reduced grab damage repair costs from£3,227 in 1992 to £630 in 1994. Other benefits include a 30% reduction in injuries at work, elimination of lost time accidents over 17 months and commencement of export shipments from what has been an import only berth, through reduced berth occupancy. The judges praised the company for "addressing the real problems that have threatened their business".

The Benefit Enquiry Line of Preston by contrast cited few financial benefits from their TQM programme which they began in 1992, but have achieved not inconsiderable intangible benefits. Their services are free so cost savings from improvements in areas such as customer arrears are not visible. They were launched as a national service as an executive department of the Benefits Agency in 1991 and in the absence of any role model to follow, investigated the requirements of numerous quality award criteria [possibly too many judging from some of the questions posed by the adjudicators-Ed].

They then set themselves the mission of becoming "the best benefit advice and information service for the disabled, their carers and representatives". Their efforts have been rewarded with the Benefit Agency Quality Award and Charter Mark in 1994 and the IIP standard earlier this year. They are also working for ISO9002 in their distribution centre as it has "an almost mechanical process that lends itself to it", and a self-assessment process based on the EFQM Model has been introduced. Some cost savings have been achieved, (around £50,000 last year) from tangible items such as investment in a telephone answering machine. Their recognition system involves few cash awards and those that there are small (up to £50 maximum). The now 200 strong team is now working towards attaining the UK Quality Award in 1996. The judges commended the organisation for their "real commitment to the service they provided".

Royal Insurance Life and Pensions were quite different, celebrating 150 years of survival in a business which they described as "hard" with a heavy emphasis on audit and control. Their presentation centred around a quality programme which was introduced in 1993 and has led to the formation of no less than 174 continuous improvement teams as part of a Business Improvement Programme. During 1994 all directors attended Total Quality workshops led by line managers, whilst managers attended training sessions on EFQM self-assessment. Company initiatives are launched every three months and Quality Function Deployment is used in product development.

A reduction in the number of levels in the organisation from 19 to 6 has been accompanied by the introduction of Activity Based Costing which has reportedly saved £500,000 in six departments. External recognition has come through the achievement of winning the Micropal Unit Trust Manager of the Year Award in 1994 along with five other awards. Annual cost savings were quoted at £30 million, with £1.5 million arising from cost of quality savings. The judges praised Royal Life for "Clearly making a big effort to move its, culture and handle the new regulatory framework", which they agreed was "a huge task".

Britannia Topsides, part of the Britannia Development Project, a major collaboration between the oil giants AMEC, Conoco and Chevron, described how a twelve storey refinery, drilling rig and hotel is currently being planned occupying an area no greater than a football field. The aims of the project are to create a 99 per cent operable safe facility for a cost of £381 million that will ultimately allow the Britannia gas field, which is located some 130 miles NE of Aberdeen, to supply enough energy to heat and light 1 in 12 British homes. During 1994 various teams shaped how the project's objectives would be achieved and produced an Execution Plan that identified and explained various initiatives.

An important aligning of goals and teamworking practices with around 170 suppliers took place through a system of review meetings. On the soft side there was thrust to tackle behaviours based on the premise that behaviours and attitudes were a function of circumstances and environment. Personnel were invited to select the training which they felt they needed. An IT competence programme consisting of self-training modules supported by experts ensured that everyone had a pc and could use it. The introduction of process mapping enabled certain processes to be updated and a greater understanding of who the customer was. Two of the judges complemented the team on a "very impressive engineering project" and it was hinted by the judging panel that should they achieve all of their objectives as planned by 1997 they would be in a position to "make a clean sweep of both the Michelin and Perkins Awards".

Wellman International, the Irish entry, are specialists in the production of synthetic fibres for the automotive, domestic furnishing, clothing and manufacturing industries and were the last to present. It is a subsidiary of the American company Wellman Inc.. having been family owned up to 1989. Following the attainment of ISO9000 in 1990 the company's level of employee involvement "reached new heights" and in 1992 a Total Customer Satisfaction (TCS) initiative was launched with the help of PA Consulting which involved 62 employees, 19 customers and 7 suppliers. A custom built training facility has since been provided to allow teams to meet in comfort away from the workplace and in 1994 some 23 teamworking projects were undertaken so as to reduce noise in the sorting and preparation department, to improve order to delivery time, and to improve the reliability of photocopiers which has been a headache for administration. A Family Plant

Visit Project was described and a project to reduce the failure of packs (specialised metal blocks used in production), which applied Pareto techniques to realise a cost saving of £81,000 by reducing the failure rate from 12 to 3 per cent. Achievements in 1994 have included a 17 per cent improvement in productivity, a 27 per cent reduction in sub-standard products, a 26 per cent reduction in the cost of non-conformance, and a 13 per cent reduction in lost-time accidents. The judges complimented Wellman on " a very professionally developed plan, very well presented and with real commitment".

Perkins Schools Award.

The Perkins Teamwork Awards for Schools attracted 13 entries, all from Cambridgeshire from which six finalists were selected, five from Peterborough, one from Soliam in Ely. Each of the entrants undertook projects to develop and enhance specific areas within their school grounds for various purposes.

The winning entry, from Highlees County Primary School, Westwood, Peterborough, involved the development of a 'wildlife haven' designed 'to charm and educate' which 'will fulfil a desperate need for more opportunities for children to study natural habitats and living creatures'. Also it would serve as focus for learning with uses in many topics of the national curriculum. The surrounding area is not relatively well endowed with wildlife and although a wildlife area had been planned, nothing had happened until the school was inspired by the Perkins Awards. Teacher Mrs. Shirley Stapleton and her team of pupils began the initiative which they hope to continue.

The winning team received a £500 cash prize at the Perkins world headquarters in Peterborough, in addition to the £250 award which was presented to each finalist. These teams were also present at Teamwork '95.

Wedgwood Poster Competition.

The Wedgwood Poster Competition is a popular feature every year at the NSQT Annual Conference and this year was no exception as 40 entries were carefully considered for both the 'professional' and 'non professional' award categories.

There were three finalists from each section from which an overall winner was selected. In the non-professional category the winning entry came from Ford whose poster entitled 'Teamwork Bridges the Gap' was praised for conveying "a simple but effective message that instantly catches the eye". The second prize went to UEF Garringtons and the third to Perkins. In the professional category the winner was Nationwide whose poster 'Quality Counts' was praised for being "very memorable for everyone". The second prize in this category went to Sun Alliance and the third to the BSS Group.

The Teamwork Revolution

NSQT Executive Director Cyril Atkinson presented a keynote speech and paper to describe how teamwork concepts are being adopted in an evolutionary way with revolutionary results.

The paper begins with a historical perspective back to the last century when the French engineer Max Ringelmann conducted experiments to show that when a group of individuals pull together on a rope the average pull is around 75% less than would be the case if each individual were pulling alone [probably due to a synchronisation error which is invariably introduced whenever a team is required to co-ordinate itself in this way-Ed]. This is followed by a further example concerning the Kennedy Administration in America whose 'group think' activity during the Cuban 'Bay of Pigs' affair led to insulation from the key information which they needed to effect good decision making i.e. they opted for a first option under a consensus dominated by an apparently strong individual. Not a very good start for teams, but, as the speaker soon showed, with a different kind of approach the results can be very different and highly positive:

'In mining the introduction of group goals led to a greater quantity of rocks being mined. In timber harvesting the introduction of team goals led to a higher output rate. In restaurant services the introduction of group working was associated with higher customer service ratings. In tyre manufacturing teamworking has led to almost a 30 per cent improvement in productivity, 15 per cent process/material cost reduction and absenteeism reduced significantly. In garden centres using teamworking has doubled the size of the business over three years and increased profitability'.

In the remainder of the paper Mr. Atkinson seeks to demonstrate some of the expertise required in order to ensure that teamworking efforts succeed in their objectives and are not fruitless. He explains the NSQT Teamworking Experience and gives some recent examples of teams which have been successful. One was the NHS team from a geriatric ward that achieved a 90 per cent turnaround of patients' clothes with traceability to the owners [Not an easy problem – Ed]. Others were; the team of a hotel kitchen that used a 'white board technique' to overcome shift problems, and the car harness manufacturing teams (20 to 40 in all) which were too numerous to work as a single 'sit round the table' team, but who have overcome this problem by using a 'post it' system with a core team which everyone has the opportunity to join for a period.

A key message is that teamworking needs to be voluntary, since typically 60 to 80 per cent of the workforce will desire to become involved if they are invited, although each manager and supervisor needs also to understand their role, be familiar with the methodology, and feel responsible for the support and sustenance of the teamworking programme:

'With good support those volunteer teams grow in number and membership to thecritical mass point where it is considered a normal part of the culture to be in a team. This stage of growth is typified by team titles such as Workplace Teams. The focus is still very much on problem identification and solving '.

The paper concludes with a discussion of the NSQT's Total Teamwork Model which distinguishes between team solvable problems and non team solvable problems and proposes a methodology for the solution of 'non team solvable problems' using teamworking techniques. It is argued that such problems need to be addressed so that workplace teams feel supported and listened to. Provision is also made for teamworking principles to be applied to 'overhauling' designated parts of the business without necessarily addressing specific problems or even looking for problems:

'In National Westminster Bank they call them Core Process Redesign Teams and they have devised for example new regular payment processes and account opening processes. In Castrol a Process Improvement Team reduced changeovers from 140 minutes to 16 minutes wastage per changeover down from 5000 litres to 18 litres, and stockholding down some £120,000 permanently'.

Questions from the floor included an enquiry about clashes of values in teams and how to prevent or minimise them. In response Mr. Atkinson highlighted the essential role of the team leader in monitoring team dynamics. He asserted strongly that leaderless teams were "absolute nonsense".

[Issue 93 (September 1996)]

TEAMWORK MATTERS

At Warwick University on 20th and 21st August the 1996 Michelin and Varity Perkins Awards were presented at Teamwork '96 which attracted an impressive 800 delegates.

The conference was opened by NSQT President Peter Mutter who welcomed in particular a delegation from Hungary where it is hoped a National Society for Teamwork will be established in the near future. This was followed by an enlightening presentation from Roger Pratt, Managing Director of NRS Limited who described 'The British Steel Challenge', an east to west round the world boat race undertaken by ten essentially amateur crews in identical 67ft long boats and the eight Michelin Award presentations. The six Varity Perkins presentations took place on day two.

The 1996 Michelin Excellence Awards.

The Michelin Awards, now in their seventh year, are divided into two categories; the single problem/management promotion category for teams set up by management to solve a specific problem or improve a specific part of the business, and the continuous improvement/self directed category for teams consisting of essential voluntary members which select their own problems. There were four finalists in each category with marks being awarded as follows:

* Team vitality (55 points)

* Project (45 points)

* Plan (45 points)

* Causes and solutions (75 points)

* Communication (55 points)

* Implementation and monitoring (50 points)

The first category was won by 'The Pit Stop Team' from Castrol (UK) Limited of Ellesmere Port, which overcame three particular obstacles to process improvement in order to reduce production line changeover times.

The second category was won by 'The Drill Squad' of NSK Bearings Europe Limited of Peterlee County Durham which determined to reduce the amount of drilling tool waste generated by their multi-auto lathes.

A third additional award was also presented to the Legal and General Litigation Team' of Kingswood, a multi- functional team formed to restructure a newly formed litigation department into a cohesive, process driven, cost effective unit. Also they investigated the efficiencies achieved from the introduction of a 'fee earner system' designed to compare in-house with external litigation processes. The presentations from these three teams are described below.

Castrol UK: The Pitstop Team.

This shopfloor team was established in 1995 following a recognition by marketing that a more flexible manufacturing operation was required. At the beginning of the year large buffer stocks and high inventories characterised the company's operations whilst production line changeover times exceeded two hours. A changeover process flowchart highlighted the lack of set procedures, high levels of waste and rework, and an absence of teamwork in production areas.

With the aid of a Gantt Chart an overall plan was produced with Pareto Analysis used to identify those areas where the application of quick changeover techniques would be most likely to have a positive impact. Training was then instituted in new process flow methods and statistical process control which highlighted an oil flushing system as a substantial source of waste.

This led to the design of a new flushing matrix which enabled the quantities of oil used for flushing to be reduced from 500 to 90 litres per flush, whilst at the same time maintaining a 100 per cent quality pass rate for the operation. This amounted to an annual saving of round £12,000.

A five month programme to improve supply flexibility subsequently achieved an 85 per cent reduction in production line changeover times with overall savings amounting to £126,256. This confirmed the belief that increasing the number of changeovers in an operation need not have an adverse effect either on safety or the cost of quality, and with the extension of these principles to other areas of the Stanlow site, further savings of the order of £240,000 are envisaged.

In their questioning the judges asked notably if the team had undertaken any external benchmarking in just-in-time techniques and in reply they described their company's Project Gold Scheme which monitors European units for best in class, though they accepted that they had experienced some difficulty in finding benchmarking partners specifically for just-in-time techniques. The judges commended the team for their strong communication, good results, and demonstration of ongoing improvement.

N.S.K. Bearings: The Drill Squad.

This team undertook a three phase project which had as its primary objective the reduction of drill waste in tool grinding. Some 38 machines each use two drills which were clearly not being utilised to their full potential. In particular the collapse of screws inside drill holders after a certain period of time inhibited further use of the drill.

A fishbone diagram was used to examine the causes of drill waste and resulted in the identification of 16 items of which the material related elements were seen to be most important. In particular it was found that drills were being insufficiently tightened whilst drill pre-setting was taking up over half an operator's day. These were clear areas for improvement.

A system was devised to spread the presetting workload, which resulted in a reduction in drill pre-setting times of some 12.5 per cent and consequently freed up more of the operator's time for checking. There was as a result an immediate improvement in waste control, the flow of tools and queueing for drills, and drill waste was reduced by 20 per cent. In financial terms this reduced the drill budget by 30 per cent and created an annual saving of £26,595 with a payback period of just eight days.

A fourth stage of the project, aiming to remove pre-setting altogether so as to end for good the bottleneck in drill supply has since been commenced and the savings from this are estimated to be potentially to be around £50,000 a year.

The judges commended the team for their good use of team strength and a good plan.

Legal and General : The Litigation Team.

This team from the first Award category was charged with the task of reviewing the process and practices associated with debt collection which, following the property slump in the early 1990s, was resulting in huge payments to solicitors with little or no return. There were, for example, six firms of solicitors being employed with no formal review system in place for any of them, whilst commission debts from agents soared.

The team undertook process mapping with the aid of brainstorming which resulted in considerable simplification of otherwise complicated processes which suddenly made them more understandable. These highlighted deficiencies such as the absence of procedures for the control of invoices or the grouping of expenses between solicitors.

Solicitors were later approached and it was confirmed that many of them had received little or no management information:

"We were working in the dark and paying for it".

These investigations convinced the team that many of the tasks involved could be conducted in-house at a fraction of the cost being incurred by the deployment of these solicitors and a phased move towards the implementation of in-house litigation was initiated. This resulted in the redirection of hundreds of cases, particularly where the sums involved were small in relation to solicitors' expenses.

The final savings resulting from this move amounted to around £660,000 prompting a group wide review of all solicitors' services, the establishment of an internal Centre of Excellence, and numerous external presentations on debt collector recovery.

In their questioning the judges asked notably if the team had considered involving solicitors in their teamwork, and in reply the team said that they had, with three "very motivated teams of solicitors" now helping the company with its benchmarking initiatives.

The judges commended the team for its motivation, its ability to successfully break down a difficult problem and for its ability to establish itself as a centre of excellence.

The 1996 Varity Perkins Award.

The Varity Perkins Award (formerly the Perkins Award) is currently in its ninth year and is due to be re-launched as a European Award from next year. This Award is made to the company which demonstrates the highest degree of excellence in managing a programme of change leading to the total involvement of staff in continuous improvement. The marks were awarded as follows:

* The Quality Journey (150 points)

* Deployment of quality improvement throughout the organisation (200 points)

* Quality education and training (150 points)

* The system of measurement applied (150 points)

* Achievements as recorded by the measurement system (100 points)

* Management commitment and the recognition process (100 points)

* Future continuous improvement plans (150 points)

The Award was won by Glaxo Wellcome Operations of Barnard Castle, County Durham, the UK production arm of Glaxo Wellcome plc who are currently the world's largest manufacturer of pharmaceuticals.

Their programme was initiated in 1991 following a benchmarking survey which revealed that far from leading the industry they had longer lead times, more waste and lower levels of employee involvement than even the average performers in the industry.

Quality circles were formed by throwing people from different parts of the organisation together but it was later found that 'natural work teams' supported by an independent facilitator functioned far more effectively. These led to the development of a Waste Elimination Process which was piloted in two sites and later rolled out across the whole as dramatic improvements were realised. These included a 60 per cent reduction in rejects, a 50 per cent reduction in changeover times, and, perhaps most importantly, considerably improved staff morale.

Training, in half day sessions over a three month period, was given to 960 people and some 120 improvement teams were formed in which the willingness of the people to participate was described as "incredible". Most of this training was not new, only the approach adopted, which focused on real and relevant problems rather than on hypothetical situations.

Developments have included a change in the role of production operators, a clock for changeover systems which has resulted in a more even sharing of workloads, and a handbook of tools and techniques which serves as a reference document after training. The company has also attained the Investor In People (IIP) Award.

The judges questioned the team about the role of facilitators in the organisation and how they were chosen. In reply one speaker described how she had worked with a small number of teams which had become successful as a result of her facilitation. This highlighted potential benefits from the facilitation process and led to self-facilitation on a departmental basis. The team was also asked about changes in the company's organisational structure, which has essentially changed from one of functional management to one of product streaming.

The team was commended for being "a large learning organisation with an adaptive structure where managers have real trust in the ability of the team".

Other Awards.

The above awards were complemented by the Varity Perkins Schools Awards which are supported by Cambridgeshire County Council and English Nature and is now in its second year. Following its popularity, the original Award has been extended this year to incorporate schools in Staffordshire and Shropshire where Varity Perkins also has manufacturing sites.

Five Awards were presented, to Thriplow Primary School in Royston, Biddulph High School in Stoke on Trent, Seabridge Junior School in Newcastle under Lyme, Coleham County Primary School in Shrewsbury, and St.Lawrence Primary School in Church Stretton.

Teams from each school have projects judged on the use of teamwork, sustainable environmental benefits, and educational value. The winning school(s) in each county receives a cash prize of up to £600 with which to put their ideas into practice. In addition each finalist receives a cash award of £250.

In addition the conference featured the annual presentation of the ever popular Wedgwood Poster Awards in two categories (professional using design equipment and non-professional produced freehand). There was a total of 40 entries with the 'professional' category being won by Graham Briscoe of Sun Alliance Life and Pensions and the 'non-professional' category being won by Jerry Thompson of Ford Motors.

TEAMWORK '96 (PART 2)

1996 Michelin Award Finalists

There were eight Michelin Excellence Award finalists which (excluding the three Award winners) were the QIP 44 Team from Edwards High Vacuum International of Shoreham, The Packaging Team from the Royal Brewery in Manchester, the Tech 19 Team from Britannia Airways in Luton, the Guesswork Team from Varity Perkins in Peterborough, and the High Speed Milling Team from Scottish Stampings (British Steel Forgings) in Ayr.

The first of these, the QIP 44 Team, had as their task the reduction of multiple failures on new vacuum pumps of a rotary type which were introduced in 1993. They described how a reject rate of 16 per cent of motors supplied to the manufacturing cell had prompted many to believe that the motor design was at fault, but thanks to an unbiased problem statement the team did not assume this and a 'voyage of discovery' led to quite different findings. Pareto analysis showed that whilst most of the returned motors failed noise tests, when they were connected to new pumps most of them passed the tests.

Tests showed that the main reasons for failure were a combination of 'out of balance' and 'hunting'. A controlled batch of motors incorporating a new gasket type was produced and tested, which eliminated the 'out of balance' problem, but aggravated 'hunting', a problem that was fundamentally associated with underloading or running at too high a voltage. Underloading was suspected and rubber coupling elements found to be at fault, with a low carbon black content affecting damping properties.

A new specification was agreed and the number of rejected motors fell to 2 per cent with a consequent saving of £35,000 p.a. The judges asked if zero defects was now on the cards and the team hinted that with further work with suppliers this could be possible. They now claim to produce "the quietest vacuum pump in the world".

The Packaging Team from Royal Brewery (Scottish Courage Brewing. Limited) was a cross-functional team charged with the task of investigating a problem on a can pasteuriser which was causing a dramatic decrease in line efficiency and output when running on one particular product. The pasteuriser, although one of the most modern in Europe, did not have the process capability to operate to the extremely tight specification demanded by this product and consequently it suffered from a high reject rate (10 per cent destruction). Investigations showed that under certain conditions water from one deck of the pasteuriser interfered with the temperature profiles of another.

The solution was to introduce a process control mechanism with a cold water feed which virtually eliminated product destruction and saved £188,000 as a result. With further savings in packaging time, brewing processing tome and sampling costs an overall bottom line benefit of £485,000 per year was realised. Other benefits have also included an ability to handle other tight specification products the conditions for which competitors have difficulty in meeting.

The Tech 19 Team from Britannia Airways was concerned with the problem of document control for service and serviceability labels for aircraft components. These labels form an essential part of the airline's statutory responsibilities for the safe operation of aircraft in service and the tracking and filing of delayed labels potentially had serious implications if it remained unchecked:

"In May 1994 only 53 per cent of the labels created were being received and obtaining the technical information required many hours".

The team explained how they set the goal of achieving 100 per cent receipt of labels in their Technical Records Department during the 1995 to 1996 Winter Maintenance Programme, visited the departments that controlled the supply of labels, and developed a process flowchart to ascertain what was happening. Cause and Effect diagrams were then used to identify three root causes of the problem:

- complacency on the part of engineers responsible for completing and returning the labels.

- an absence of procedures governing the control of labels.

- A deficiency in the training of personnel responsible for the completion of labels.

Brainstorming for solutions revealed that reminders and phone calls only had a limited effect in remedying the situation, and that what was really needed was an awareness course. Such a course was then devised and presentations made by the team. Benefits have since included improved speed of updating the engineering computer system, savings of around 750 man-hours previously required to progress chase unreturned labels, and improved compliance with legal requirements. The 100 per cent return of labels which the team sought has now been achieved with 89 per cent being in perfect condition. The remaining 11 per cent had to be sent back for clarification. The judges expressed concern at the level of paperwork in such a high tech industry and questioned the team on whether they had benchmarked to ascertain how their competitors approached the same legal obligations, which appeared to represent a distinct opportunity for improvement on the part of the team.

The Guesswork Team from Varity Perkins described how their operators in the rectification area selected engines which had failed in testing for rework. This was essentially achieved by operators selecting engines with defects which were supposedly within their capabilities to correct. It amounted to pure guesswork and the failure rates for rectified engines was around 25 per cent.

Cause and effect charts showed that in many cases operators had insufficient relevant information to perform their tasks effectively, limited ability to interpret the information which they did they receive, inadequate diagnostic skills, and ineffective training. It was explained how the option chosen took the form of a package to reduce the number of engines being stood down in the first place.

A section training facility accommodating up to ten employees was developed along with a user friendly work signature card to accompany each engine through the assembly process. Also focused training videos and relevant and effective visual aids were introduced. Savings of £138,412 p.a. were obtained of which £65,570was in the form of customer quality improvement, £45,322 was in the form of rectification costs on defective engines, and £27,520 was in the form of savings from in-line quality improvement.

The final presentation, by the Scottish Stampings High Speed Milling Team, concerned the process of die machining for axle beams for the bus and truck industry. This used the technique of high speed milling which is potentially innovative in this area as it is normally associated with the machining of much smaller dies. Following problems with both a UK and a Japanese supplier the team were instrumental in designing a new type of cutter in-house which eventually made for a 33% reduction in the time taken to cut a set of dies, as well as eliminating a £77,000 a year expense incurred from sub-contracting operations. Further benefits include vibration reduction, elimination of tool re-setting and grinding, improved accuracy and finish quality, and healthier working conditions as a result of a removal of the need to use cutting fluid. The experts said that it couldn't be done, but the team proved that it could. The judges asked if they had visited other factories, and in reply the team explained how as pioneers there was little point, but as a result of their success others were now seeking to visit them.

The judges commended QIP 44 for their "stickability and good end result" as well as their ability "to deal very well with the technical aspects". The Packaging Team of Royal Brewery were commended for "good motivation, an informality that seemed to pay off and good focus on the customer". The Tech 19 Team were commended for their "systematic approach and good communication". The Guesswork Team were commended for being "highly motivated" although they "could have looked outside". The High Speed

Milling Team were commended for having devised "an innovative solution which others would like to get involved with".

1996 Varity Perkins Award Finalists

The remaining five presentations came from British Steel Strip Products of Shotton, Dutton Engineering (Woodside) Limited of Sandy (Bedfordshire), The John Hampden Unit from Aylesbury, Legal and General of Kinswood (Surrey), and Denso Marston Limited of Shipley (West Yorkshire).

British Steel Strip Products' Shotton Works is operational headquarters for five coated products sites in the UK and specialises in the application of metallic and paint products to provide a permanent protective and decorative coating for strip steel. It employs 1,600 of the company's 2,000 employees, which represents around 10 per cent of the workforce of the 1970s:

'From the days of a buoyant steel market when everything made had a ready customer, the present scene is fiercely competitive and customer focused. Nothing but the best will do'.

The company had little option but to involve all its remaining people in teamworking and quality improvement. Awareness workshops were designed by consultants and in late 1993 the company began to benchmark companies such as Cadbury's and Chevron Oil which had implemented quality programmes. With the help of consultants they sought to identify the attributes which had yielded success for these companies:

'It was recognised that management thinking had only just begun to change, and people were only just beginning to get used to being involved. Old habits die hard'.

The team described how process mapping had been used to simplify processes leading to savings of the order of £1.5 million and achieved the Investors In People (IIP) standard in January 1996. A trade union representative and mechanical craftsman then outlined how teamworking as part of an overall Ongoing Programme for Ultimate Safety (OPUS 2000) had substantially decreased accident rates with zero accidents by the year 2000 being seen not as a distant dream, but a very possible goal. The judges asked if the trade unions had been allies or opponents in all of this, and "definitely allies" was the response, although it was accepted that a promise of "no compulsory redundancies " had been needed to secure the agreement of teamworking to proceed.

Dutton Engineering were by far the smallest company to present, having just 26 employees. They are specialists in the precision fabrication of stainless steel, mild steel and aluminium and were founded originally in Luton in 1972 as suppliers to the electronics industry. They achieved BS 5750 registration in 1984, becoming one of the first companies in their sector to do so. After developing specialist skills for the fabrication of stainless steel housings for electronic components, notably for the ink jet printing and electronic weighing equipment market, they embraced TQM in 1989.

The team described how teamworking was introduced in 1994 in order to improve flexibility and help the firm become more customer orientated. Clocking was abolished and replaced by a 1770 hour working year and a 'Kaizen Scheme' replaced the traditional suggestion scheme which was anonymous and to which few bought in. Process mapping was introduced greatly reducing paperwork and this year has seen the introduction of cell manufacturing which has replaced batch production with a system of one piece flow:

"At Dutton it is the team that talks to the customer because they do the job. The days of stopping one urgent job to start another are over".

The company has recently begun to implement self-assessment to the EFQM Business Excellence Model and is working for IIP in a programme which at first sight would appear to be somewhat ambitious. Indeed the judges suggested that it could be "overkill" in a sequence of questions which appeared to play more on the company's size than on its achievements. The team insisted, however, that they were quite capable of being world class and that there could be some advantages to be gained from being a small business, for example, in training the whole company in one room.

The John Hampden Unit is part of the Aylesbury Vale Healthcare Trust and is based on the Stoke Mandeville Hospital site in Aylesbury. It specialises in mental health services for older people and has a staff of 85 organised into multi-disciplined teams which take various medical and nursing skills out into the community catering for the needs of some 500 patients. Its quality programme began in 1992 as part of an overall TQM initiative throughout the Aylesbury Vale Community Healthcare Trust, with teamwork a prime component in the development of a quality improvement culture. This was facilitated by the Trustwide Management Consultant in Healthcare.

The team described how the number of projects undertaken since 1992 had steadily risen with much improved conditions for patients and staff. A visit to Gothenburg in November 1995 provided an international perspective of a country which was renowned for its high standards of healthcare. The advances made in carer training has become recognised throughout the Trust. Environmental projects have also been undertaken, most notably the design of a 'reminiscence room' for sufferers of dementia who frequently had good memories of the past e.g. 40 years ago, but poor recent memory. The room had a distinctly 'old fashioned' character to which such patients could readily relate.

The judges' questions soon exposed the barriers to quality improvement which had been encountered. Examples were the reluctance or fear of healthcare assistants to come forward and express their views, and the difficulties associated with building trust in an environment which historically has not been well suited to teamworking. The quality improvement team was seen to have the role of "a think tank or nucleus for ideas". A spokesperson for the team said:

"We have entered to demonstrate that Quality Improvement has a clear and positive role to play in the NHS, and to express our commitment to ever-higher standards of healthcare for the elderly people we serve in our community".

The Legal and General Varity Perkins presentation was by the sales and marketing department specialising in the provision of life, pensions, savings and protection policies in the UK. This department has 1 ,581 employees following re-structuring in 1994 and in 1995 all staff attended a one day quality awareness event:

'The progress tracking systems for two quality schemes, Opportunity For Improvement and Quality Improvement Project, were more finely tuned'.

The team described how the new regulatory regime of disclosure (of commission earned by sales staff at the point of sale) jolted the whole financial services industry in 1995. Also a much needed interface between the company's already established quality forums and the salesforce was introduced in the form of a quality forum of twelve specifically for the sales channels which meets every other month. This was enhanced by a pool of 45 part-time facilitators in nine business units which have since identified 400 potential improvement areas.

Management development centres have been created specifically for sales managers and training provided in quality improvement tools such as Buzan Mind-mapping and Belbin Team Profiling. Salesmen that once "thought they knew how to run the organisation" now know otherwise following a general reduction in the size of the salesforce from 4,000 to 1,500 in just over two years:

"Many salesmen think that quality problems are not theirs. This is not so. Many delays in writing new business is down to them. We got a cross departmental team to process map and discovered that 30 to 40 per cent of business submitted could not be processed. We are now looking to make the quality of business submitted much higher".

Since taking this approach Legal and General's market share of the life industry has risen from 3.5 per cent to 4.5 per cent, with repricing being achieved in weeks rather than months, whilst their share price has accelerated from £4.50 to £7.00 in three years.

The last Finalist to present, Denso Marston Limited, design and manufacture radiators, intercoolers and oil coolers for automotive applications. They employ 900 at their factories at Shipley and Leeds and were acquired by the Denso Corporation (the world's largest automotive components group) in 1989.

The company was certificated to ISO9001 in 1993 and in 1994 they introduced quality circles and a New Product Introduction System which adopts a preventative approach to eliminate any problems prior to a new product going into mass production. Together these two initiatives were said to have provided 'the greatest stimulus to improvement and change':

'The quality improvement programme was designed, implemented and managed totally in-house, with the benefit of advice from colleagues in other Denso subsidiaries'.

The team described the philosophy behind their quality circle activity i.e. selection of an easy theme to which members can relate, and regular display of results. This was supported by a description of a tube manufacturing operation where a few simple changes inspired by teamwork had produced some dramatic improvements such as a 90 per cent reduction in inventory, an 80 per cent reduction in changeover time, and a five fold increase in the number of changeovers achieved. Other benefits have included the ease with which they have been able to assist suppliers when they experience problems, thanks to a highly structured approach to quality circle activity and an effective nine step method. The judges expressed some interest in this and asked how readily suppliers had bought in to the concept. The answer was "very easily" since "when you offer help to people, especially free help, they usually accept".

The judges commended British Steel Strip Products for their ability " to gain unions as allies" and for their "good communication links with their customers". Dutton Engineering were commended for having provided " a refreshing ,clear and energising look at a small business" and for being "a company that can expect a lot of requests for visits".

The John Hampden Unit received the accolade for being "the most challenging and difficult to measure finalist" whilst Legal and General were described as "a very worthy finalist" with " a lot of success" and " a clear commitment to change". Denso Marston were commended for "simple strong measures and clear achievements".

TEAMWORK '97

THE 1997 VARITY PERKINS AND MICHELIN AWARDS

The Annual Conference of the NSQT featuring the Varity Perkins and Michelin Awards for outstanding achievements in teamworking, were presented at the University of Warwick on 19th and 20th August. The Varity Perkins Awards for organisations that can demonstrate the best progress in continuous improvement through the application of teamwork were presented on day one. On day two the Michelin Awards for Single Problem/Management Promoted Teams and Continuous Improvement/Self Directed Teams were presented to three teams which demonstrated excellence in identifying a problem, solving it and implementing a solution.

The 1997 Varity Perkins Awards.

There were six finalists selected for this Award: The Savoy Group plc of London, Legal and General Sales and Marketing of Kingswood, Magnox Electric plc, Dungeness A Power Station, Land Rover Vehicles of Solihull, Case UK of Doncaster, and Legal and General Customer Services of Hove. From these the five judges (Myles Coleman of Varity Perkins, Lynne Dickerson of Nat West, Giles Eldred of Perkins Motoren, Tony Patey of joint sponsors The European newspaper, and David Selby of Glaxo Wellcome Operations selected Case UK to receive the Award.

The Case Corporation is a multi-national manufacturing organisation producing a full range of agricultural and construction equipment. It is well-established (150 years) and currently has some fifteen manufacturing sites around the world, eight of which are in Europe, including Case UK which manufactures around 12,000 tractors per year and, following a world-wide restructuring programme and a $15 million investment, has become the 'European Centre of Excellence' for assembly operations.

The transformation of the tractor assembly involved a complete redesign job consisting of extensive rebuilding with simplification of the production line sequence which was completely re-routed. In order to achieve this some 70 volunteers were recruited from all levels to form five multi-disciplinary teams each of which had a sponsor manager responsible for resources, equipment and training.

The teamwork concept was then extended to suppliers, including the contractors who were responsible for building the new line. This was said to have enabled "many illustrations of triumph against very difficult odds", with, for example, a substantial reduction in rework being realised through the design of a revolutionary cab electrics testing facility. Good supplier partnerships with built-in flexibility agreements have led to a halving of the time taken from order to delivery, from fourteen weeks in 1995 to just seven weeks in 1997. Also the introduction of just-in-time sequenced delivery has removed the need for costly on-site materials storage facilities.

Electronic data interchange has also allowed for the virtual elimination of human error in paper-based transactions. In all a total of 600 suppliers has been reduced to 276 and there is a goal now to reduce this further to under 100.

The company is now delegating minor sub-assemblies such as radiators, with main suppliers now fitting subsidiary items and long-term contracts have been introduced subject to review. This is said to have resulted in "more open and interactive relationships". Tangible improvements have included a 30% reduction in repair frequency over the last two and a half years, a 75% reduction in defects per unit and a first pass yield without repair that is approaching 90%. The company, which last year became the first tractor manufacturer to achieve the Investors In People (IIP) certification, has identified six areas in which it is striving to become world class:

* Customer focus (a thorough understanding of customers and a total commitment to delighting them).

* Superior products (products and services that are reliable, durable and easy to use).

* Outstanding dealers (a network of dealers and distributors who share the same commitment to customers).

* Cost leadership (an ongoing systematic effort to reduce operating costs).

*Speed (a sense of urgency evident in everything that the company does).

* Real partnerships (enduring relationships with dealers distributors customers and suppliers to foster mutual success).

Following the presentation the team was asked by the judges if there were any measures of improvement in staff attitudes. In response they explained how "considerable improvement" had been evident from employee attitude surveys conducted by the human resources department. On training they were asked about whether assessments of competency were conducted following the training to ensure its effectiveness. In reply they described how team training matrices were used linked to a series of quality measures. They were then asked about important milestones and explained how an "intermediate measure of progress" was made on a quarterly basis. Finally they were asked if any partners were being assisted with continuous improvement and it was explained how lots of meetings were arranged for this purpose. "If there is a problem we all get together", they said.

The Varity Perkins Award, the tenth to be presented since their launch in 1988, was made on the basis of a 30 minute presentation followed by questioning, and an accompanying written log-book submission.

The 1997 Michelin Awards.

There were eight finalists in all for the Michelin Awards, consisting of four in each category .These were 'The Double Sided Designers' from NSK Bearings Europe of Peterlee (County Durham), The Mission Impossible Team from RHP Precision Bearings of Newark, 'Project 60' from Denso Manufacturing UK of Telford, and the 'The value Added team' from Kennelmetal Hertel UK of Kingswinsford (West Midlands) in the Single Problem/Management Promoted category. In the Continuous Improvement/Self Directed category the finalists were 'The Topicals team' from Glaxo Wellcome Operations of Barnard Castle (County Durham), 'The Wombats' from Britannia Airways of Luton, 'The No Sweat Again Team' from NSK Bearings Europe of Peterlee, and 'The Pioneers' from Denso. From these the judges (Bob Bell of Michelin Tyres, Susan Cottrell of Milliken Industrial, John Edwards of Barnsley MBC, Alan Ferryhough of JCB and Richard Lee of Castrol UK), selected 'The Mission Impossible Team' as outright winners in the Single Problem/Management Promoted category, whilst 'The Topicals Team' and 'The Pioneers' shared the Continouous improvement/Self Directed category Award.

Wedgwood Poster Competition.

A popular feature of the NSQT Conference is the annual Poster Awards sponsored by Josiah Wedgwood and Sons whereby a company may enter up to ten posters to be judged in two categories:

(i)   Professional (produced using specialised design equipment)

(ii)   Non-professional (produced freehand)

The Professional category was won by Legal and General for a poster which was described as "eye-catching with a quick and punchy line". The Non-professional category was won by the Clay Breakages Group of Claridge's Bathrooms of Kent.

Team Write Competition.

Looking ahead to next year's NSQT conference a new feature is to be introduced called Team Write. This is intended to recognise the best short article on the subject of Quality Improvement through Teamwork and is open to all. Articles, with illustrations as appropriate, should be of between 500 and 1000 words and based on the general theme of 'Quality Improvement through Teamwork'. Possible sample topics include special teams, individual likes and dislikes, things that worked (and things that didn't), problem solving methods and any of the myriad of items that are associated with teams. The main criterion is 'interest' with secondary criteria of style.The winner will receive £200 and a certificate and a further £200 will be available for other deserving entries.

Attendance figures at this year's event were 578 on day one and 675 on day two.

[Issue 111 (March 1998)]

ICM FIFTH ANNUAL TEAMS CONGRESS

At the ICM Fifth Annual Teams Congress of 16th and 17th February in Dublin an opportunity was provided to learn about how teamworking principles are currently being applied in Irish industry. Examples are taken from Bord Gais (the Irish Gas Board), NEC Semiconductors Ireland and Waterford Crystal.

Work Teams versus Project Teams.

Kevin Battams, Strategic Development Co-ordinator for Bord Gais, described how, in relation to improving its customer service, Bord Gais has benefited from a Project Team rather than a Work Team approach. He described how the Customer Service Project took its Terms of Reference from the company's recently adopted Customer Needs and Satisfaction Strategy and how four teams were formed to address it, covering the subjects of:

* adding new customers

* servicing existing customers

* managing large industrial and commercial customers

* managing the gas supply

Unlike Work Teams, which are essentially structured along unwritten lines and confined to a particular function or location, these Project Related Teams were cross-functional and multi-skilled. In particular the teams were grade-free (non-hierarachical e.g. with managers working alongside clerks) and formed according to Belbin Roles rather than Job Roles.

Delegates at the conference were afforded the option of learning their Belbin Roles (so named after the well-known research work conducted by Dr.Meredith Belbin at Henley Management College) at a workshop hosted by Kathryn Heslin of Intel Ireland. The Roles are clearly described in the conference literature as are the means by which they are ascertained (using seven questions with eight answers to each). For the benefit of readers who may be unfamiliar with them, however, they are listed below:

(i) Chairperson (directs the group and prevents discussions from becoming uncontrolled).

(ii) Shaper (inspires action, dispels complacency and beneficial when political complications are apt to hinder progress).

(iii) Innovator (creative, providing new ideas and novel strategies often to age-old problems).

(iv) Evaluator (rationalises ideas to enable critical decisions to be taken sensibly).

(v) Networker (contributes information, often by probing, which allows decisions about feasibility and strategy to be made).

(vi) Finisher (ensures that detailed aspects of a project are planned into schedules).

(vii) Team Player (facilitates co-operation between team members).

(viii) Implementer (manages aspects of work on a process basis which may be difficult or undesirable).

At Bord Gais team members were made aware of their primary and secondary Belbin Roles and of any role which was found to be missing within the team. Also they were given an insight as to what type of person they and their team colleagues were based on a Matrix where the axes were Direct or Indirect and Deliberate or Spontaneous. This helped to alleviate any potential interpersonal clashes which otherwise could have arisen.

Staff were allocated to teams according to their skills, for example, The Service Existing Customer Team consisted of members from accountancy, quality control, information technology, sales, customer service, operations and billing. Further skills were then developed by exposure to strategy, re-engineering, process mapping, problem solving, communicating, presenting and reporting, planning, teambuilding, leadership and championing. There were also site visits and case studies such as that to Brooklyn Union Gas in the United States, the British Telecom Contact Centre at Enniskillen, and Texas Instruments.

An Executive Steering Group and Team Champions were established for the project and Arthur Andersen were appointed as support specialists. The Team Champions were nominated executives but were carefully selected so as to be independent and working outside of their normal field of Operation. For example, the Head of Finance was the 'Champion' of the large Industrial and Commercial Customers Team. The Executive Steering Group met bi-weekly.

Several benefits arising from this approach were cited:

(i)   The project delivered many recommendations for short, medium and long term implementation. Examples included, in the short term the establishment of a quality council, in the medium term establishment of Key Accounts and Key Account managers, and in the long term direct computer links with business partners.

(ii)   The project challenged the organisation/functions of the company and led to restructuring on a process basis.

(iii)   Friendships between team members were built and barriers between Cork, Dublin and HQ were lowered as was the case between the company's executive and other levels in the organisation.

(iv)   Many of the recommendations formed the basis for major work practice changes being negotiated with the unions.

' There is no doubt that projects assist greatly in staff development, taking them out of their normal role, giving them new skills, exposing them to new ideas and horizons, and new ways of working. It gives members exposure to senior managers and their thoughts so they understand the direction of the company and the problems to be overcome. It also gives people an arena where their talents and potential can be seen by those of influence within the organisation'.

' Friendships, Teamwork and future contacts are benefits that derive from a project team approach. With also the breaking down of the "functional silo" which leads people to seeing the full picture and the breaking down of barriers between areas, both geographical and departmental'.

In addition the project approach was seen to be particularly suitable where issues or tasks are special but definable e.g. on-off tasks which require concentrated effort to deliver, or complex e.g. where significant change is required or change in a strategic direction.

This was the case with customer service, which was seen to offer considerable opportunities, particularly with entry to the UK gas market in mind.

Teamwork and Total Productive Maintenance.

The presentation by Tom Malone, Operations Manager for NEC Semiconductors Ireland, was one of two which described the application of teamwork to Total Productive Maintenance (TPM), the other being from Bourns Electronics Ireland Limited. It describes how, following the introduction of TPM in 1990, when the company received a National Training Award, it was subsequently refined enabling the organisation to gain the coveted Japanese Institute of Plant and Maintenance Award in 1996, a year in which memory prices fell from IR £29.00 per piece to just IR £2.90 per piece.

The speaker described the company's TPM policy as being "to maximise competitiveness through Total Employee participation in TPM activity" whilst TPM itself was described as "a series of pillars that you build your business on, underpinned by teamwork". Each pillar has a departmental process and team leader, whilst internal benchmarking e.g. of cost per piece with Japan, Scotland and Singapore provides a measure of how well the company is performing at least relative to itself.

In 1996 these measures turned out to be quite enlightening for whilst the company was clearly delighted to receive the Japanese PM Award for its efforts of the previous six years the measures still showed that NEC Semiconductors Ireland was lagging behind its Far Eastern rivals in a number of areas. Productivity, for example, was only 70 Yen per piece as against over 90 Yen in Ireland. This convinced management that there was still much more work to do and so a new phase of TPM was launched which began with an examination of how to improve machine performance.

Three types of team were formed as part of a revitalisation programme for TPM, namely:-

*autonomous maintenance teams

*process improvement teams

*business improvement teams

These in turn were spearheaded by TPM Area Lead Teams and a TPM steering committee. Objectives were set to reduce the cost per piece by 65%, improve output by 100%, reduce turnaround time to under five days and to improve customer satisfaction.

A seven step system was devised for autonomous maintenance such that groups could progress toward an eventual goal of autonomous management, TPM being viewed as a key enabler of Total Productive Management. In order to progress from one area to another groups examine a machine and then form a team headed by an operator. At the first level operators develop an ability to identify problems with machines 'by feel' or otherwise using a methodology known as FUGUAI, whilst at the second level they learn restoration and how to reduce cleaning time. At the third level they learn to set tentative standards whilst at the fourth they have a good command of general inspection.

Level five graduates to autonomous inspection with accompanying standardisation being introduced at level six, overseen by a management audit. In all there are sixty groups, about half of which are currently at level four, progression through which takes approximately one year. A few (about ten) are at level five.

With process improvement the Area Lead Teams decide upon a process which they believe is capable of being improved and then carefully select a team to proceed with a redesign. A ' breakthrough philosophy' is adopted accompanied by step by step (incremental) improvement in five clear stages. Root Cause Analysis is applied as a matter of routine and there are weekly team meetings. Teams consist mainly of engineers and production staff working to a 'Plan-Do-Check-Act' methodology. An example of the resulting Improvement Activity Report is provided in the conference literature.

The Business Improvement Teams follow a similar set of principles but involves a focus on more long term issues and importantly, involves senior management. There is an emphasis on leadership by example, dialogue with staff and bottleneck management.

With the approach adopted the company, which employs 520 at its factory in Ballivor, County Meath, and has annual sales of around IR£153 million, now has a cost per piece which "rivals that of Singapore" and was awarded a PM Continuity Prize from the Japanese Institute of Plant Maintenance this year. [We know of no European company which has done this -Ed].

Making Teams effective.

In days of old Ireland had something of a reputation for being a place where time stood still and certainly Waterford Crystal did its best to live up to the mark with its motto of 'timeless in the age of change'. Unfortunately, however, this is not a recipe for success in the modern commercial world and with a reward structure based on piecework for individual handicrafts coupled with investment starvation the company soared downhill during the 1980s and by 1989 was suffering record losses of the order of IR £21 million. Sales per employee averaged IR £30,000.

The presentation with the above title by Michael J. Wincote, Manufacturing Director, described how, with many organisations in Ireland, the traditional image has been retained whilst at the same time "economic literacy " has been instilled as part of a revolutionary approach to the management of working practices.

Prior to 1993 the company employed 1500 at its four plants in County Waterford, which was identified as being at least 300 more than the company could realistically sustain and the threat of redundancy loomed.

The management of Waterford Crystal, however, really did believe that its people were its greatest asset and was, unlike many others in the UK and elsewhere, keen to explore other avenues in order to effect a turnaround. Thus, as sacking one group of workers in order to preserve the livelihoods of others ran against the grain of Irish culture, management looked toward the long term preservation of all jobs through reformation of the company's reward system along the lines advocated by the late Dr.W. Edwards Deming and the introduction of teamworking.

Right from the start this philosophy began to yield dividends restoring the company to profitability again by the end of 1993 and enhancing it to IR£13 million in 1994.

By 1996 sales per employee had risen to IR£64,000 enabling an IR£30 million investment to be made in new manufacturing technology. Profit share per employee has since risen to IR£1,200 from zero in 1993 and not only does Waterford Crystal still have all four of its plants, it has actually increased its workforce to 1,600 i.e. 1,000 new jobs have been created in County Waterford providing much needed employment.

These impressive bottom-line benefits owe a lot to the introduction of team based techno-craft operations which comprised the core of the presentation which was underpinned by a vision to become "the most advanced technified crystal manufacturer in the world".

These operations involve the formation of teams in which each person contributes to and agrees the team's success criteria and every member commits to critical actions in order to ensure that they are achieved. The team starts with a workshop which clarifies the team's purpose, the success criteria, critical actions and working relationships. This is followed through with review sessions two or three times a quarter which address a running agenda of team issues and critical actions and invited open feedback on performance.

Twice a year the review ensures that the team and every member of it maintains dynamic roles which match corporate progress and change. This involves a two and a half hour 'face-to-face' session in which groups of 100 interact with the Chief Executive, Manufacturing Director and Human Resources Director. In addition there is a weekly 'Task Group Forum' chaired by the Manufacturing Director which involves shop stewards, front line management and technical staff where a vision is detailed and minutes with action points are e-mailed two days later. Detailed investment plans are discussed but there is no reference to collective bargaining i.e. these issues are expressly excluded.

Five years ago, said the speaker, "no-one had heard of Pareto and scatter diagrams" and whilst there was latent creativity ever present, at least half of the ideas which people had never materialised because people were unable to articulate them. Now, looking back, he says "it's amazing how things have changed". Six levels of hierarchy have, for example, been reduced to three, demoralised employees have become motivated by involvement, there is ownership of vision and empowerment to action, and the company magazine which "used to be very stuffy" is now "written by the employees".

The speaker was careful, however, to emphasise the fact that teamworking is "no five day wonder". External facilitators from a small hands-on company were employed for three years before it was able to be self-managed continually as it is today.

Further Information.

This event was supported by Saville and Holdsworth (Ireland) Limited who, through work with leading Irish organisations, have acquired extensive expertise in identifying the gaps which exist between front line roles and team leader positions. They are also in the final stages of developing a competency model for teamwork in World Class Manufacturing organisations.

[Issue 117 (September 1998)]

BUILDING COGNITIVE THINKING

The Institute of Management Services celebrated 25 years of its annual Summer School this year at Christ's College, Cambridge. 'Building cognitive thinking capacity for knowledge utilisation: transfer of know-how and continuous improvement was by Brenda Clur, Director of QUANTUM People Productivity Management PTY Limited, Republic of South Africa.

The principle concerned the transfer of knowledge between teams. She argued that approaches to quality such as ISO9000 and business process re-design fail to include a vital step in the continuous improvement process, namely the development of the cognitive thinking capacity that is required to utilise knowledge and deal with rapidly changing technology:

'Instead of resolving problems on behalf of employees after the event, managers need to learn how to transmit their know-how and high level thinking needed to enable employees to pre-empt mistakes. Predicting tomorrow's trends today -building cognitive capacity for knowledge

creation, will be the key to maintaining business excellence and continuous improvement beyond 2000'.

Drawing on her background of 14 years of consulting experience in major South African and multi-national organisations she explained how a practical approach to improving productivity and cognitive capacity in industry has been pioneered. She gave two specific examples, the Elandsrand Gold Mine, and a well known cosmetic manufacturer in Johannesburg.

Management failed in both cases to comprehend the differences in conceptual thinking which existed between different types of employee. By communicating in broad concepts they reinforced deficiencies in thinking. Managers assumed that workers would think things through in the same manner as they did themselves and in the end some workers took short cuts.

Later, however, when the management of the transfer of tacit knowledge was incorporated as an integral part of the change intervention, sustained improvements in safety and productivity were recorded (the mine doubled its productivity in two years). Central to this was the development of new habits of thinking when situations that involved managers communicating with workers were studied:

"We got managers to direct attention to what workers needed to think about when there was a change in requirements or a new standard or procedure".

Thinking was then practised as a deliberate skill and employees were encouraged to become self starters with regard to thinking. Small pockets of excellence emerged where people put these techniques into practice and of course once these were identified their examples were followed to the extent where "people actually enjoyed coming to work".

A project was initiated in the cosmetics company whereby the Assembly Floor Manager and the Industrial Engineer were trained to perform the role of "Master Trainers" responsible for training line Supervisors and Team Leaders on how to transfer their know-how, skills in visualisation and problem solving skills to employees through on-the-job coaching.

Team members had acquired the tacit knowledge needed to pre-empt making mistakes. An improvement of 36.9% in plant efficiency and an improvement of 19.6% in line efficiency were recorded by the Industrial Engineer, based on the previous year's figures. During the twelve month period after implementation of the project, the company experienced no further losses due to contamination of products as a result of human error.

'Team leaders experienced difficulty in visualising how they could personally apply company commitments and principles on the Assembly Floor. After much debate, they selected to "strive for excellence" and "put

the customer first". However, they could not agree on who the "customer" was.

When they came to the realisation that their "customer" was in fact the distribution department, a group of Team Leaders (with a maximum of ten years of formal education) produced a list of practical, work-related ideas for improvements which the company immediately implemented'.

TEAMWORK '98

The 1998 Perkins and Michelin Awards for excellence in teamwork were presented on 25\26 August at Warwick University at the Annual Conference of the National Society for Quality through Teamwork (NSQT). The Perkins Engines European Quality Award for the company which demonstrates the most outstanding programme of change leading to the total involvement of staff in continuous improvement was presented to H and R Johnson Tiles Limited of Tunstall. The company was established in 1901, now part of the Norcross Group, and is currently the UK's leading manufacturer of ceramic wall tiles. They were selected as outright winners from a shortlist of six finalists. The Michelin Excellence Awards are awarded to up to three teams which demonstrate excellence in the way they have identified a problem, solved it and then implemented effective solutions. These were presented to NSK Bearings Europe of Peterlee County Durham, (outright winners in the Continuous Improvement/Self Directed Team category) ; to agricultural machinery specialists Case UK of Doncaster; and Glaxo Wellcome of Barnard Castle, who were joint winners of the Single Problem/Management Promoted Team category. These winners were selected from a shortlist of four in each category .Below a review is presented of the above four award winning presentations.

1998 Perkins winner: H and R Johnson.

H and R Johnson's presentation was outstanding from the point of view of its bottom line savings arising as a result of teamworking activities. In all the company, which employs just over 800, involves over 500 employees in a total of 105 teams which collectively examine a range of business related issues including cross-functional activities such as product launches as well as the improvement of working practices. The savings generated by these teams are of the order of £600,000 per annum.

The presentation described the Johnson Improvement Programme which followed from a SWOT analysis initiated by the newly appointed Managing Director David Dry early in 1994 and highlighted the savings generated by various teams in the early days. These early efforts were not without their problems, as conflict grew for resources as Total Productive Maintenance (TPM) was rolled out independently of teamworking, something which with the benefit of hindsight the company may have done differently.

The efforts of one particular team, the Ambience Improvement Team which investigated the range of faults on rustic tiles, were explained in some detail. A fishbone diagram was constructed which provided the clues for the later elimination of the major problem of coloursplash, and an achievement of 90 per cent ambience quality. The work of the team led to savings of £10,000 through the reduction of the number of tiles which had to be downgraded to seconds, plus a further £15,000 achieved by reducing the number of waste tiles. The training of teams via three one day workshops at Keele University was also described along with plans for the future which incorporate the introduction of process mapping.

The Perkins Award now augments the company's certification to ISO14001, the environmental management standard, and the Queen's Award for Environmental Achievement which they received last year.

Following the presentation the judges questioned the presenters, and asked a number of quite searching questions, as indeed they did to all of the finalists for both the Perkins and Michelin Awards. In particular they were quizzed on the involvement of senior management and replied by stating that "every other week we have a Keele session". They were then asked about their awareness of customer needs, how they become aware and how improvement activities are related to them.

In their answers they highlighted how benchmarking has been undertaken, for example, with the textile industry, and how teams have been deployed to identify gaps between actual and theoretical performance. They were also asked how they measured the effectiveness of training and explained how they had calculated their return on investment to be of the order of £20,000 a year. This, they said, was "an immediate indicator" in addition to the £870,000 already realised from the various improvement teams to date. They emphasised the fact that all training was linked directly to what the company wanted from its business.

The other finalists for this year's Perkins Awards were Hydro Aluminium Alupres Limited of Caerphilly, The Edinburgh International Conference Centre, DFDS Transport Limited of Coggeshall, retailing construction specialists Styles and Wood of Salford, and Peebles Electric of Edinburgh.

Michelin Excellence Award Winners.

The presentation by the Profactor 97 Team from NSK Bearings Europe Limited concerned the modification of a grinding process which traditionally had consisted of three stages namely surface grind, rough grind and finish grind. Again the bottom line savings have been very considerable i.e. a one-off saving of £409,030 plus a saving of £66,948 per year thereafter.

The team described how, from a shortlist of six problems outlined on a decision making matrix they had selected medium size grinding process improvement as their challenge, with reduction of the three stage grinding process to a two stage one as their specific objective. They explained how ten specific machine improvements necessary for two stage grinding had been identified and implemented and how statistical process control (SPC) was then applied to confirm the feasibility of the process. In particular it was noted that a larger width grinder wheel would be required for the finish grinder, as well as a reduction in grinding speed, although there would be no net loss of time since only two stages would be needed instead of three. The process capability was found to be "substantially increased" and better than expected. Other positive benefits included a floorspace saving of 28 square metres which provided a much needed ring storage area, and a reduction in noise levels. The principal saving arose from the need only to purchase two new grinders instead of three, which was offset against the cost of the new improvements which were around £3,730.

The judges asked whether the team had encountered resistance from other people in the organisation and the team explained how the quality assurance department had initially resisted their attempts to change what was essentially an established process that worked well. One manager, however, helped them by keeping the QA department informed and up to date on the trials and their potential benefits. They were also asked about how work was allocated and they explained how it was "mainly based on the experience of individuals" and what each person could do and wanted to do. They were then asked about their 'list of six matrix and how they chose their project'. This they said had been done quite simply with a whiteboard on the shopfloor which enabled people to mark which project they felt was potentially most important and would yield the greatest benefit to the business as a whole. The judges praised the team for "a very good example of what can be achieved all in the business context".

The CX11 launch Team from Case UK met the challenge of launching a totally new tractor with new engine, transmission and cab within a timescale of two years where previous new product introductions had taken six years. The team devised its own system and monitoring tools to track the progress of the project. This necessitated special training to enable the team members to operate new systems and gain familiarity with new products. Four core members steered a project team of 40.

The team explained how their project had arisen following an announcement by their German engine supplier that they were soon to close, which would mean an end to the supply of engines for their existing models. They thus had a brief to build an entirely new tractor in two years, and to do this they had to completely overhaul traditional ways of working. Simultaneous engineering replaced the traditional workshop approach and it was explained how members "worked twelve hour shifts and weekends and postponed holidays to solve problems". The team spirit and morale "was excellent" inspired by a desire to have the new model ready for the next

Agritecknica Exhibition which was perceived to be the ideal launch opportunity.

The Tractor Assembly Problem Identification and Resolution System (TAPS) which resulted from much of the work "proved to be an excellent planning and tracking tool". The training of assembly operators in the use of computer aided design (CAD) systems enabled operators to rework their own parts and design teams to amend their drawings as appropriate. In all 52 prototypes and 120 pilot builds for training purposes were developed and "new frontiers in working practices and tractor technology were realised". In February 1997 the first CX11 tractor was shipped to Burr Ridge, USA, for testing with a new range of powerful lean burn high torque engines. The result was a new breed of 50 to 100 hp tractor which "redefines customer perceptions of design excellence".

Benefits described by the team included an improvement in bill of material accuracy from 62 to 94% and greater commonality of parts across product ranges. Lessons learnt included a greater appreciation of the length of time required to complete legal paperwork in projects of this type.

Following the presentation the team was asked how the team acquired the skills needed for simultaneous engineering. They explained how it had been an early task of theirs to identify the skills that people would need and how individuals themselves had broadly identified the training that they required. They were then asked to elaborate on the operation of TAPS and did so by describing how any problems that TAPS identified were later directed to the department responsible. "Every problem that TAPS raised had a team working on it". They were also asked about ongoing continuous improvement processes that the project had generated and they explained how the simultaneous engineering concept was now being applied to every new project. "We pilot every change to a vehicle down the line and wait for feedback before releasing it to manufacturing", they said. The judges praised Case UK for "very good project management and a very good example of a task achieved".

The Fillability Group from Glaxo Wellcome addressed filling problems associated most notably with the production of 'Dermovate' cream, the product for which the majority of filling problems were identified. A process of elimination and trials by the team, which was composed of staff from several departments including manufacturing, filling, quality assurance, operations planning and new product introduction/product technology, eventually led to savings of £125,000.

The presenters explained how certain problems, for which no-one initially assumed responsibility, kept repeating across four core filling pack lines. These problems, namely hardness of product, popping products and aerated products, were creating an unacceptably high reject rate as well as down time and frustration to operators.

407

Six weeks of production monitoring showed that one particular production line, line 81, was not performing as well as its neighbour, line 82, which was in many respects a similar line. The differences in performance were found to be related to a gasket installation. A gasket change sheet was devised, along with alteration to the placement of elbows (mechanical components) which were found to be a contributory cause of the popping problems. Further brainstorming to ascertain the root causes of hardness and aeration led to an examination of temperature fluctuations on the line over a two week period. The temperature variation of finished product was measured and a trend emerged which prompted an investigation of the stirring process. The minimum stirring time could not be adjusted, but the speed of stirring could i.e. it could be slowed down to produce a more consistent mixture. Comparison with a product with a different method of mixing later showed that a different technique could be used. This reduced the aeration problems and preserved the improved consistency. A validation exercise followed which "went very smoothly" and has now resulted in a product of a softer consistency which is not only easier to fill but also has the key benefit of easier application on the patient.

The judges in their questioning pointed out that this was the first time that members from the various different departments had worked together as a team and asked about what they had managed to learn as a result of coming together. The team described how the co-operation had led to a breaking down of the barriers which had previously existed between filling and manufacturing staff. They were then asked how motivation had been maintained and they explained how the frustration to which they had referred "had always been at the back of their mind" and "acted as a motivator". They were also asked what they did to plan the duration of the project and in their reply they described how they "set little monitoring goals in brainstorming" even though they were largely unaware of how long their task would take. The judges praised this team for "very good root cause instigation and very good team motivation".

The other Michelin Finalists in the Continuous Improvement Self Directed Team category were 'The Ventures' from Denso Manufacturing of Telford, 'The Weight Watchers' from Perkins Engines (Peterborough) Limited, and 'The United Stations' from Komatsu UK Limited of Birtley, County Durham. In the Single Project/ Management Promoted Team category the other finalists were 'The Gino Ginelli Team' from Birds Eye Walls of Gloucester and 'The Community Dental Team' from the South Warwickshire Combined Care NHS Trust.

Other Awards.

In addition to the above Awards there was, as in previous years, the presentation of the annual Wedgwood Poster Competition, which was slightly different this year in that only one award was presented rather than the previous two for 'Professional' and 'Non-professional' entries. This year's winner was submitted by Caradon Plumbing Solutions of Brighton. There was also the Perkins Environmental Teamwork Awards for Schools, which this year was won by the Wilnecote Junior School from Staffordshire:

'In the centre of the school was an old greenhouse which was a bit run down but once the "Ground Planning Committee" set to work it became a gleaming nursery for the school plants. What an organised committee they are – all areas being improved have a reference letter and minutes are taken at their regular meetings. All news and developments are broadcast to the school via Eco Board and table; it was decided that this should go in the reception area so that visitors could see improvement being made. A rockery was built on one of those wetter days earlier in the year – everyone got filthy dirty, but the job was completed and all those involved had lots of fun. Regular checks are carried out to make sure that the plants are healthy. The committee has also organised the canteen staff into using a composter for any waste food and set up a bin for the other children to recycle paper and cans'.

Wilnecote Junior School was selected from a short list of four finalists; The King Edward Junior School from Cambridgeshire, The Beckbury Church of England Primary School from Shropshire and The Bollin Primary School from Lancashire.

[Issue 118 (October 1998)]

TEAMWORK '98 (PART 2)

1998 Perkins Finalists

This month concludes the event with a review of the presentations of the remaining finalists, beginning with the five Perkins Award finalists.

The first presentation was by Hydro Aluminium Alupres, a specialist aluminium extruder and anodiser established in Bedwas, Newport, in 1970 and part of Norsk Hydro, Norway's largest public company. With a workforce of 200, aluminium extrusions are made for a wide range of markets such as building, access equipment, shower cabinets, electro-technical applications, and the automotive industry, including the prestigious Lotus Elise sports car.

Their continuous improvement programme began in 1993 with the support of the Wales Quality Centre, and was reinforced in 1996 by the appointment of a full time Process Improvement Manager. Teamworking training for senior management followed in 1997 and in April of this year a team coach for manufacturing shifts was introduced as part of the current culture change initiative.

The team explained how training has subsequently been extended to cover visiting customers and suppliers and how all employees have now been trained in the link between environmental benefits and quality processes. Notable achievements included registration to ISO14001, a safety record of 1,000,000 hours with no lost time at July 1998, and energy savings' of 58% since 1995.

In the judge's questioning the team was asked if they felt that poor safety had been one of the reasons for the company's poor profit prior to 1995 and they agreed that this had very much been the case. They admitted that the company had been "underperforming the rest of the industry" and that "people at the top never accepted and understood the issues". On the subject of training they were asked if training was structured and focused on achieving a business plan; they stated that training was based on visiting customers and sub-contractors. When asked how benchmarking was used to set targets and how people were involved in setting their own targets they replied "all target setting is top-down".

The second finalist was the Edinburgh International Conference Centre which readers of *Quality Matters* may recall as the venue for the 1996 European Quality Awards. Their presentation was entitled 'Meeting Promises – The EICC Story' and incorporated an impressive video presentation which arguably occupied a disproportionately large proportion of the time allocated to the presentation. The ideal EICC person was described as "having an eye for detail" and being "wackily creative", and in June 1996 teams were put together to examine issues such as capital expenditure and quality management.

Four times a year the Chief Executive hosts training afternoons focusing on team exercises and mock events and cross functional workshops are held for example to develop roomy layouts. In January 1997 a training award for casual staff was introduced and current developments include work to devise an SVQ (Scottish Vocational Qualification) for banqueting skills. Achievements have included registration to ISO9001 and IIP, a decrease in deficit funding of 41% over three years and a sales increase of 257% over the same period.

The team was asked about the extent to which sub-contractors were involved in the continuous improvement process and in reply they emphasised that sub-contractors were regarded as business partners who are encouraged to adopt a business scorecard approach with the EICC. They were also asked whether employee surveys were undertaken and they confirmed that they were not, although consultants were commissioned to undertake periodic "health checks" on the organisation which have, amongst other things, highlighted a bonus scheme that was "divisive".

The entry from DFDS Transport highlighted the company's enviable track record of profitability which has increased from £0.1 million in 1989 to 2.9

million in 1998 whilst turnover has increased from £59 million to around £234 million this year. The company employs 1,600 today against 470 in 1989, in 28 locations in the UK and Ireland.

The presentation described the company's new Vehicle Electronic Management Information System (VEMIS) which has been piloted at Tamworth and aims to achieve a 5% reduction in fuel costs with the help of teamwork from lorry drivers and a personal shipper project which aims to provide one key contact person for each customer.

In their questioning the judges asked if there were any ways other than by way of the company's suggestion scheme by which new ideas could be generated and it was explained how team briefings were used to carry suggestions up the line whilst the Managing Director "was not instrumental in wanting to know what was going on". They were then asked how they intended to measure the success of their suggestion scheme and the team explained how they were currently in the process of formalising a system.

The next presenters, from Styles and Wood, described how four years of hard work has made them a market leader in retail interior contracting with a reputation for excellence in customer service. Their ambitious business plan called 'The Way Forward' identified head office support and information technology as critical areas for improvement and in 1995 the organisation achieved Investors In People. It was explained how monthly team briefings and key performance indicators acted as a measure for team performance against company goals whilst multi-disciplinary teams tackle key development issues. Each team has a leader and is supported by a main board sponsor and the case for strong teams with mixed strengths and attributes was emphasised.

Achievements have included a £60,000 saving in procurement following a detailed review of subcontractor performance by a team whilst "much about personal development" has been learnt through benchmarking with Unilever and "much about human resource planning" has been learnt from a similar exercise with TNT. Ongoing initiatives include the introduction of client partnering, project improvement appraisals, and a commitment to the EFQM Business Excellence Model. This organisation has also had an enviable improvement in profitability from zero in 1994 to around £215 million this year.

The judges asked how the subject matters for teams were determined and the team explained how 'break-out' projects which were aligned to the Business Excellence Model were rolled out to 15 live teams which meet formally three times to address the task. They were then asked where their organisation stood in relation to the scoring criteria of the EFQM Model and it was explained how two audits in 1996 and 1997 had arrived at scores of 350 and 425 respectively.

The final presentation by Peebles Electric, whose history can be traced back to 1898 when Bruce Peebles supplied gas street lighting and associated equipment throughout Scotland, described how process mapping had been used to accelerate employee involvement with all employees encouraged to recreate business processes as part of their work.

Various projects were described which yielded impressive cost savings along with the multidisciplinary People Controls, Processes, and Technology (PCPT) Team which applies a powerful holistic approach to change and continuous improvement with the most appropriate member taking the lead at the most appropriate time. This team facilitated and supported all of the improvement activities in the company with some projects being led by PCPT members whilst in others PCPT members would be team members or facilitators.

Specific business drivers were selected to measure and improve, such as delivery performance, supply chain management, engineering processes and learning opportunities for all employees. The company currently employs around 650, and manufactures large power transformers, electric motors and generators which are chiefly used in the offshore oil and gas industry. They have also supplied the world's largest quadrature boosters for National Grid.

In their questioning the judges asked what had made people buy into the change process and the team replied with one word- "empowerment", as for the first time people were being asked to contribute. They were also asked how operators had been trained on the shopfloor and it was explained how, starting with a customer specification they were able to apply Quality Function Deployment as a translation tool for their work. [A rare skill for shopfloor operators in the UK- Ed].

Michelin Finalists.

In addition to the three winners there were also five other Finalists in the Michelin Shortlist, two in the Single Problem/Management Promoted Team category and three in the Continuous Improvement/Self Directed Team category.

The first to present were the Gino Ginelli Team from Birds Eye Walls' who took their name from an ice cream product about which there had been a sharp rise in customer complaints in the early part of 1996. The complaints concerned a lack of inclusions in a new one and a half litre tub size which had occurred following a change of supplier. A team was formed to investigate the problem with the aim of reducing the level of customer complaints from the unacceptably high level (280 per 10 million portions) by 50%. A Pareto chart showed that the majority of complaints were specifically about toffee fudge inclusions, or rather the lack of them. Subsequent investigation showed that the traditional Crepaco fruit feeder was unsuitable for the fudge supplied by the new supplier. Plans to replace the feeder were then supported by recommendations to improve the process and packing arrangements and make a few simple recipe changes to prevent problems of fudge dissolving in the ice cream.

The judges asked the team how competitive they felt their target was and in reply they explained how lots of companies measured their complaints per million rather than per ten million, and they described their new level of six per million as "a pretty good result". They were also asked about changes to their measurement systems and they explained how substantial variation leading to inaccurate reporting of results had been traced to the fact that each individual had previously taken so-called wash-out measurements in a different way. The judges commended the team for "strength in working in the process of production and good use of expertise".

The next presenters, joint winners Case UK, were followed by The Community Dental Team from South Warwickshire Combined Care NHS Trust which was formed in April of this year as a result of the merger of South Warwickshire Health Care and South Warwickshire Mental Health NHS Trust. The new organisation provides services such as community nursing, services for people with learning disabilities, rehabilitation hospital services and mental health services for all age groups to a catchment area of 225,000 residents.

The team, which comprised of ten members, described how they had set about devising a training programme for hospital and community nurses to raise knowledge and awareness of oral diseases. The training itself was supplied by dental officers working within the service following a conclusion that nurses could prevent many of the problems stemming from oral diseases simply through improved training. The team highlighted particularly cancer of the mouth and lips from which four people die each day in the UK whilst for each 100 cases currently diagnosed only 50 can expect to still be alive five years hence. Following a preparation period of three months eight training sessions for nurses were held last October with 104 participants which represented 27% of the target audience of nurses, auxiliaries and healthcare assistants.

It was noted that prior to the training most participants believed that the survival rates for the cancers in question were better than they actually were and as a result of the training the increase in knowledge of ten oral conditions improved from 6 to 33%. In addition 99% of attendees said that they felt that their knowledge of oral diseases had improved whilst 96% planned to make changes to their working practices as a result of the training. The effectiveness of the training was further evaluated by two oral hygiene surveys six months apart pre and post training which showed an improvement in denture cleanliness of patients from 59% to 82%. Other unexpected benefits included the detection of one case of oral cancer by a nurse who attributed the early diagnosis directly to the training, and an improvement in oral hygiene at a nursing home which followed from an initiative by one attendee.

The judges in their questioning asked how, having succeeded in attracting just 27% of the target audience they intended to improve their strategy to attract more participants and in their reply the team explained how they intended to repeat their training exercise in anticipation that others will appreciate the benefits. They also pointed out that in many cases nurse managers had "to go out of their way" to free people who wanted to attend. The potential national significance of the project was also raised by one judge who then asked what the team was doing to pass on their findings. They explained how they are currently networking with health authorities in the West Midlands. The judges commended the team for "a very good solution with a very good measured effect".

The first team to present in the Continuous Improvement/Self Directed Team category was 'The Ventures' from Denso Manufacturing whose project concerned a major quality problem which arose during the manufacture of car air conditioning systems. The team, which was originally formed in 1994, decided to scrutinise production line efficiency following examination of daily monitoring sheets of line defects. They conducted time trials for each stage of the line and produced a Pareto chart of line stoppages which highlighted an air leak problem as the largest single source of stoppages. Further analysis showed that insertion of couplings, which did not feature on control charts, was a major contributory cause. Brainstorming for solutions followed and the three most common reasons for failure identified and addressed. A new coupler was then designed to improve the process by providing a hands-free operation for operators which eventually saved an average of 5.9 man-hours a day and "removed a very boring job which nobody liked".

The judges questioned the team's principle of adopting rotating leadership for different projects and asked if this ever caused problems. The team confirmed that no tension had resulted internally from this approach. They were also asked how they communicated the team's progress to their associates on the line and explained how results were pinned on a board on a daily basis. "If we brainstormed and a fishbone diagram resulted it would go up", they said. The team was commended for "very good analytical work".

The 'Weight Watchers' from Perkins Engines followed with their presentation which concerned the problem of con rods of different weights being mixed in the same bins. They were a multi-skilled team which had formed to investigate the reasons why they were continually receiving reject components from their internal customers, the engine assembly lines. Con rod weight identification turned out to be a major problem which team leader Ron Slaw identified, following a whole week's work with the piston-fitting team on the engine assembly line.

A brainstorming session yielded a fishbone chart which revealed that a flawed etching process was a root cause of the problem. Various alternatives were examined which included making improvements to the etching device and restricting the number of etching personnel to one per shift. Eventually it was decided to use a colour coding process which has since been standardised across the con rod range. The improvements led to a dramatic reduction in rework costs. The company lost £24,500 through lost engines in 1995 and in 1996 savings amounted to £27,856. With a new assembly line making 44 engines per hour commencing operation in 1997 it was concluded that without the team's efforts the company "would have had lots of problems".

The judges asked how skills were passed on and the team explained how they were gratified that more people were involved in different teams. They were then asked how they intended to perpetuate the improved relationship between departments that had resulted from their work and they explained how by talking to people working on the process it has become natural "without even trying". The team were commended for "very good project selection and a simple result".

The 'United Stations' Team from Komatsu UK, which was originally formed as a quality circle in 1991, consisted of members from various stations within the paint department who have already successfully completed several teamworking projects. Their latest, entitled 'New for Old' recently won Komatsu's internal teamworking competition which afforded three of its members the opportunity to present at Komatsu's head office in Japan.

The project concerned the recycling of solvents used on site and involved an examination of the amount of solvent used in the paintshop to prevent paint hardening, along with the associated disposal costs. Spent solvent was transported to an oil waste storage area where spillage was a major environmental hazard. A chemist then had to analyse the composition of the waste before the company paid for its disposal. In 1996 the company spent £20,343 on solvent and paid £1,627 in disposal costs.

A cause and effect chart showed that the company was losing money in every area associated with solvent and with new legislation that could shortly impose a solvent tax also more than a possibility, there was every incentive to improve. The feasibility of filter recovery was examined but later rejected on the grounds that it was both time consuming and resulted in recovered solvent of uncertain purity. Alternatively they could have paid a contractor to clean the solvent but this offered little if any cost savings. The team therefore opted for solvent distillation which would be relatively safe, offered a rapid payback, and had the advantage of full technical support from a British manufacturer. Two units, Fercell and Spiritman, were trialled each with 25 litres of spent solvent which yielded 18 litres of pure solvent in the case of Fercell and 16 litres of not so pure solvent in the case of Spiritman.

415

A decision was made to purchase the Fercell unit which resulted in a saving of £25,457 in1997, for a one-off purchase price of £17,822. The seven month payback period was described as "excellent" whilst environmental problems had been reduced "to an insignificant level".

The judges asked about the extent to which other departments had been involved in the project and the team explained how engineers had been present at team meetings and subsequently relayed information to relevant personnel. They also invited supervisors and managers to meetings. They were also asked if they had looked outside their organisation for solutions to their problem and they confirmed that they had, although they had found that most other organisations they had contacted were experiencing the same waste disposal problems. The only exception was a small garage which operated a much smaller machine on a smaller scale. This team was commended for "a good choice of project with tangible benefits".

Further Information.

The judges for the 1998 Perkins Engines European Quality Award were: Mark Williamson (Chairman) of Perkins Engines, Lei Howell of Fermec Holdings Limited, Veronica Husband of Tower Hamlets Healthcare Trust, Steve Joiner of Caterpillar (UK) Limited, and Sheila Knight of the NSQT. The Michelin judges were: Bob Bell (Chairman) of Michelin Tyre plc, Juliet Anderson of Buckinghamshire NHS Trust, Ian Turner of Mason's Ironstone and Peter Davis of Land Rover Vehicles.

[Issue 123 (March 1999)]

DEVELOPING TEAMWORK IN IRELAND

There were many excellent presentations at this year's ICM Teams Congress at the Conrad International Hotel in Dublin on 26th and 27th January which had a strong industrial relations theme indicative of the country's desire to form effective team based partnerships between unions and management. This focus is particularly well illustrated in the case study papers by John Kelly, Manager of Employee Development at Tara Mines (underground zinc mine in County Meath owned by Finnish based metals group Outokumpu) and John Keenan, Manager of Human Resources for Iarnrod Eireann (Irish Rail).

On a more general level the theme was explored further by Pat Savage, Director of Partnerships and National Co-ordinator for the New Work Organisation for Ireland Programme organised by the Irish Productivity Centre, and Liam Doherty, Management Training Executive for the Irish Business and Employers' Confederation. Both of these papers are reviewed below together with that by Senior Training Officer for Dublin Corporation

Michael Sands, which examines how a team based structure may be used to improve communications.

Emerging Best Practice in Teamwork.

Pat Savage's presentation on this subject highlighted Ireland's leading role within Europe in terms of the management of partnership agreements, especially those which tackle non-value adding activities, and used survey evidence to highlight the importance of selecting the right team leader for the task in hand. He spoke of the best teamworking initiatives being those which emphasise the "natural gains approach" and used modern day shift working to demonstrate how more flexible operator cover and higher levels of co-operation frequently make night shift results "at least on a par with performance on day shifts". He explained how he had seen traditional demarcation "vanish at night and reappear the next day" to the detriment of teamworking performance.

Amongst the issues which he said "must be confronted" he cited the deconstruction of old fashioned job grading which "hinders flexible team development" and the need to guard against the temptation of overmanning teams at the outset which "is a grave mistake that can be hard to rectify after six months". He therefore advocated a strategy of under resourcing coupled with empowerment which would later allow the team to request more manpower as and when it needed it.

With regard to the automotive sector he described how latest initiatives at Ford in Detroit and Volvo in Gothenburg have concentrated on developing teamwork with dealers by stopping production lines for one hour per month whilst dealers for example from Ireland are brought in to interact directly with the builders of the cars. This, he said, was "a good exercise in manufacturing accountability" which not only afforded dealers the opportunity of seeing how vehicles were produced but also allowed the car builders to hear at first hand the complaints which were being voiced.

Following the presentation he was asked what background he felt that a team leader should have and in reply he said that there was "no set pattern", but suggested that it "can be useful for credibility if the team leader is at least as knowledgeable as the team members". He suggested that team leaders should be selected from the same grades as team members whilst senior management "needs to have predictability and consistency of response from team leaders" and "keep a close eye on cronyism".

He explained how one automobile manufacturer "lost a lot of cars" by attempting to tone up a team leader with the aid of consultants when in reality he had been totally unsuited to the role. In the panel session he elaborated further on the "high incidence of team failure" which derived from poor team leader selection, stating that the team leader's influence on success was "very big" and "should not be underestimated".

417

Developing Competitive Advantage through Teamworking.

The presentation by Liam Doherty with the above title summarised the findings of a research project undertaken by IBEC late last year and has since been published as a comprehensive report on the incidence and experience of introducing teamwork in Ireland. This has nine chapters which outline the survey results, describe the introduction of project and operating teams, highlight the changing roles of managers and facilitators, explain the three key training phases required to establish successful operating teams, and elaborates on various payment systems for operating teams. Nine tools for teamworking are described along with two teamwork case studies from Aughinish Alumina Limited (aluminium manufacturer located on Aughinish Island in the Shannon Estuary) and SIFA Limited (manufacturer of organic nitrate located on the Shannon Industrial Estate).

In the industrial relations context the report highlights the most recent National Agreement in Ireland, known as Partnership 2000, and the mechanism which it provides for the introduction of new forms of work organisation by employers and trade unions at enterprise level. Attention is drawn particularly to Chapter Nine of this document which provides a Framework Agreement within which management and employees can develop positive initiatives such as teamworking in their mutual interests:

Chapter Nine provides for discussions to develop partnership for Competitive Enterprises. Paragraph 9,16 sets out the focus for such discussions, including the provision that discussions will be conducted in a non-adversarial manner and will be governed by Clause 6 (Stabilisation) of the agreement on pay. International and domestic experience suggests that further development of the partnership approach at enterprise level will enhance the competitiveness of firms, the quality of the work environment, and the access of employees to lifelong learning'.

Recent developments in Ireland's Labour Court are also discussed, namely its scrutiny of proposals to introduce teamworking as part of a re-organisation plan, and cases where disputes have arisen as a result of attempts by management to eliminate the foreman category as part of a move to teamworking, and where 'poor teamwork' formed part of an unfair dismissal claim:

'The Court has investigated a number of disputes arising from the introduction of comprehensive rationalisation programmes where teamworking is one element of an overall package of changes. The Court has supported the adoption of teamworking in these circumstances and in some instances had recommended that joint implementation/monitoring groups be established to oversee the process '.

In presenting the survey results, which consisted of 64 responses from companies employing a total of 26,387 employees, the report shows that marginally more unionised companies (77 %) have adopted teamworking than is the case for non-unionised companies (71 %), but when it comes specifically to semi-autonomous teams there is a higher incidence among non-unionised companies (71 %), as against unionised companies (39%). For self-managed teams unionised companies had an incidence of 28% whilst for the non-unionised companies the incidence of these types of teams was just 14%. Similarly with project teams the incidence stood at 74% for unionised companies as against only 43% for the non-unionised companies. Project teams existed in 70% of the organisations surveyed whilst semi-autonomous teams existed in 42% and self-managing teams in 27%. The report notes particularly that those companies which have more advanced forms of teamworking have earlier introduction dates and that consequently the process has to be measured in years rather than weeks or months.

In assessing the benefits of teamworking the report presents a list of actual savings identified by companies in the survey:

- inventory reduction of 80%

- cycle time improved by 14%

- improved efficiency by 5%

- lead times reduced from 4 weeks to 1 week

- material costs improved by 15%

- absenteeism reduced by 2.5%

- improved productivity by over 20%

- scrap reduced by 80%

These benefits are in addition to the 'numerous references' to less tangible benefits such as the impact on employee satisfaction, morale, commitment, customer focus and, in one case, ' a substantial saving from the removal of a layer of management as part of a move to teams'.

The section on 'Payment Systems for Operating Teams' makes interesting reading presenting evidence from a recent IBEC survey on reward/payment schemes which yielded 316 responses from companies with a total of 101,860 employees. This survey revealed that the incidence of skill based pay and team based pay was just 6% (18 companies and 17 companies respectively). The following advice is issued to those considering their introduction:

' The aim of team-based rewards is to encourage group effort by providing team members with an incentive to work together. The result, it is hoped, is that team-based reward systems will motivate members of a team to achieve and exceed targets. Unfortunately this may not always be the case. A reward system can cause teams to work against the aims of the organisation in the pursuit of their own interests. Team rivalries may occur, resulting in a decrease in communication, and teams can also insist that their members succumb to the team ideology which in turn removes independent thought from the team. To avoid the above problems, it must be kept in mind that teams are concerned with task completion and the building of relationships, therefore team rewards should reflect this fact by recognising not only what the team has achieved but also how the results were obtained'.

The report points out that 'a significant proportion of companies' stated that the results of these schemes had been only "moderately significant" or else had been "unsuccessful".

Similarly useful advice on performance appraisal is also given in the following section (Summary and Conclusions) :

'Appraising teams or appraising individuals in the context of a team requires a significant change on the part of organisations with respect to how they operate their performance appraisal system. Despite all of the literature on teams and the increased adoption of teams, most organisations still have individual performance appraisal systems and individual merit pay schemes. These practices conflict directly with the development of highly effective teams, but fit the values and experiences of most managers. Simply measuring an individual's contribution to the team in a traditional performance appraisal system is not the answer. An entire redesign of the performance management system may be needed -a redesign which recognises the team structures which are in place'.

In his speech Mr. Doherty concluded that whilst there was "ample evidence to suggest that a move to teams helps to improve job satisfaction and can improve the quality of life" it was also true that "case studies delivered from a podium can conceal the demands made on everyone". In order to maintain the momentum he advocated an audit of transferable management activities i.e. activities that are capable of being transferred to teams. He also explained how IBEC had developed a database to assist organisations that were interested in benchmarking teamwork development for competitive advantage.

Using Teamwork to improve Communication.

One of the key barriers to the introduction of teamworking which is highlighted in the IBEC report is that of poor communications i.e. a low level of information sharing to support teams. The case study by Michael

Sands is therefore interesting as it explains how teamworking has actually been applied as an enabler to help overcome this weakness.

Essentially Dublin Corporation employ 6,500 staff who work in 173 separate locations throughout the city of Dublin providing some 500 separate services with a budget of around IR£850 million. The services vary from the supply of 445 million litres of drinking water to the collection of 190,000 tonnes of rubbish per year, the supply of library services and the provision of leisure facilities and the fire service. More specific projects include the redevelopment of Ballymun, the revitalisation of the North East Inner City and environmental improvements to Dublin Bay with the objective of achieving an EU Blue Flag for water quality.

In order to tackle these challenges inter-disciplinary teams i.e. teams consisting of staff with different professional backgrounds working together for the benefit of the citizens of Dublin, have been established. A Strategic Management Plan was formulated in 1996 and one of its core values and objectives was 'to establish open and accessible information and communications channels'.

In October 1997 the City Manager appointed an in-house team consisting of nine people, including the speaker, from different backgrounds and areas which was charged with the task of developing a policy to improve communications within the organisation. This coincided with the appointment of another similar team charged with the task of improving customer care and external communications.

' The team spent several months looking at other organisations both in the private sector and the public sector and also examining what would best suit Dublin Corporation. We developed a Communications Policy for Dublin Corporation. This policy document has been accepted by the City Manager and is now in the process of being implemented'.

The Communications Team recommended that the Communications Policy be rolled out on a departmental basis (there are ten departments in all) over a time period of one year. A key element of this was the launch of the publication called "First Post" in June 1998. This is published fortnightly and includes anything of corporate wide interest and has proved to be both successful and popular:

'It has answered a major criticism of the organisation, namely that it was very difficult to get information and often the people who needed to know what was happening (i.e. the people in the depots, fire stations etc) were the people to get the information last, if at all'.

In November 1998 "First Post" was used to advertise for volunteers to assist a firm of consultants in the roll-out of the Policy which yielded 145 responses. With the help of these volunteers the Communications Project team has devised the concept of "Team Talk" to serve as the medium by which the Communications Policy will be enacted for all of the organisation's 600 teams, which average eight members.

Essentially each of the 600 teams will have a Team Leader who will identify the members of his or her team, which typically will have between eight and twelve members. The consultants and volunteers recruited above will then, working in pairs, facilitate the first meeting of each team which will introduce "Team Talk" and agree a day for the future regular meetings of that team:

'It is our intention that the Team Talk meetings will take place as a minimum once per month. The meetings will be used to communicate with the staff on items of local as well as Corporation wide interest. The Communications Policy contains a formal feedback sheet. This will be used for the team to seek information/clarification on whatever subject. It will be the duty of the Team Leader to forward the feedback sheet to the appropriate person in the organisation, up to and including the City Manager, for reply'.

In his presentation Mr. Sands explained how an independent survey had shown that communications in Dublin Corporation had improved by 75% during 1998. "Different people used to dig up the same part of the same street on the same day because they had not talked to each other", he said.

Following the presentation he was asked what indicators one should look for to prevent team failure and in his answer he highlighted the importance of probing for cynicism. He urged all those associated with the implementation of teamworking to make sure that there are always small incremental gains on a regular basis.

[Issue 125 (May 1999)]

NEW BELBIN TEAMWORK VIDEO

Video Arts have released a new video commissioned by Dr. Meredith Belbin entitled 'Does the Team work?'. It features a cargo freighter called Nostradamus which is lost in space because, although each crew member knows his own job, they are not working effectively as a team. Caroline Quentin arrives as Cristal, Agent of Trans-century Development, to give each team player a colour corresponding to the roles they perform. The crew then use this colour classification system (devised by Meredith Belbin-Ed) to become aware of which are individual and which are team tasks:

* *BLUE* tasks are carried out in a particular way and are assigned to an individual.

* During *YELLOW* work an individual is charged with responsibility for an outcome and will be judged by results.

422

* **GREEN** work looks at tasks based on communications between the team and covers jobs which can be split up between two or more people.

ORANGE jobs involve collective responsibility for whatever decisions are reached.

This system defines what type of work is appropriate to the team to eliminate timewasting tasks and encourage work flexibility and feedback.

The video, written by Graeme Garden (of Goodie fame),complete with course leaders' guide, training resources disk and self-study workbook , is available from: Video Arts Limited, Dumbarton House, 68 Oxford Street, London W1N 0LH.

[Issue 129 (September 1999)]

MICHELIN TEAMWORK AWARDS

South Tees NHS Trust and Perkins Engines of Peterborough were the recipients of this year's Michelin Awards for Teamwork Excellence presented at Warwick University on 24th August. The Awards, as in the past, were presented in two categories, the first for management promoted single project teams, and the second for continuous improvement self-directed teams. In congratulating the winners the chairman of the jury Mr. Bob Bell, Director of Personnel Northern Europe Region for Michelin Tyre plc praised South Tees NHS Trust particularly for their "vitality" and "ability to break down professional demarcations" whilst the Perkins team had "very strong team vitality" and " got communication right very successfully."

Below the winning presentations are reviewed and followed with a brief summary of those of the other six finalists.

South Tees NHS : pioneering Teamwork in Healthcare.

This presentation concerned the combining of a unique set of expertise to tackle the problem of patient care following the diagnosis of Motor Neurone Disease or MVD. The team was multi-disciplinary consisting of a Registered Nurse, a Speech and Language Therapist, a physiotherapist, an Occupational Therapist, a Dietician, and a Regional Care Advisor from the Motor Neurone Disease Association.

Together they run a clinic within the South Tees Acute Hospitals Trust, although the team members were drawn from both the Acute and Community Trust and the voluntary sector. This has existed for three years and during that time it has instigated protocols on patient management and addressed communication between the Hospital and Community staff.

The presentation incorporated, unusually, a role play which helped to acquaint members of the audience with the key symptoms of MVD, namely progressive paralysis accompanied with other disorders notably of speech. It also pointed out that as yet it cannot be cured and is ultimately fatal, but the fact that the disease is not amongst the most common has meant that it has tended to be neglected creating a nightmare for patients suffering from it and requiring to find their way through the maze of information and services associated with dealing with it.

In many cases patients are unaware of how to access help, care management is woefully inadequate, and a catalogue of common failings were revealed to the audience such as:

* lack of knowledge on the part of general practitioners.

* absence of clear lines of communication to contact professionals.

* uncertainties on the part of patients and carers about different professional roles.

* patchy expertise on account of the comparatively rare nature of the disease.

* absence of any formal review system of patients resulting in deterioration being neither predicted nor managed.

The team brainstormed to devise solutions to these deficiencies and used process mapping to verify the causes of problems. The results were used to generate anew model of care provision in which patients and carers jointly met with the team, which intentionally had a flat structure to facilitate inter-disciplinary teamwork. Formal audits were conducted to assess progress and over the last three years there have been. no crisis admissions to neurology wards. A patient review forum had been held and the education deriving from it has been presented outside to other authorities and conferences.

The speakers emphasised the fact that communication has subsequently improved on many levels, such as professionals to patients, professionals to carers, and carers to patients. They also stressed that a low cost solution had resulted in high cost savings as a result of the utilising more effectively of skills which already existed, for example in health, social services and the voluntary sector.

Questions from the judges included the issue of funding, the answer to which revealed that this project had in fact been non-funded and relied entirely on the team members taking time from their own work once a month with help from their managers. Further questioning examined the efficiency of the method devised whereby patients meet the whole team at once rather than serially as in the past.

The team explained how patients frequently became exhausted through having to tell the same story to six different people when once could suffice, and how now, by seeing up to four patients per afternoon it has become much easier to pick up problems.

Perkins Supersavers: improving the Environment through Teamwork.

The members of the multi-disciplinary Supersavers Total Quality Team came together with a shared view that within Perkins Engines a major resource for making environmental improvements was largely untapped due to a lack of awareness by the workforce of the contribution it could make.

Having confirmed this view by survey the team set about raising awareness levels through the use of personal booklets, posters and newsletters. A follow up survey showed clearly that a shift in awareness levels had taken place but, more importantly, it had also triggered many grass roots improvement initiatives. The success of the team has been recognised nationally through an award for best practice and by citation in Government and commercial publications.

It all began when one of the team members attended a five day training course organised by the trade unions which suggested ways in which unions could become active in environmental initiatives. Union representatives were keen for their messages to be taken back to the workplace and with Perkins striving for ISO14001 certification the member decided to use the company's TQ scheme to raise a project with this objective together with the help of a fellow shop steward.

A team was formed which later brainstormed for reasons behind employees' apparent lack of awareness and involvement with environmental matters and devised a questionnaire. This revealed that around 80% of employees believed that the company was wasting energy whilst 90% were concerned about the environment. Half of the employees, however, accepted that they had done nothing about it.

The 'nominal group technique' was applied to determine the top four communication techniques (booklets, posters, newsletters and presentations) and efforts followed culminating in a novel simultaneous use of all four methods. The effectiveness of this was measured by means of a second survey which later indicated a 50% involvement in action (up from 10% pre-launch).

Their project could have ended here but it didn't because the team was committed to making the initiative part of a continuous improvement strategy. This became more detailed with three further posters and the devising of an area metering system and use of the internet to promote environmental awareness. Now every employee undergoes an hour long environmental awareness induction and the team has since enjoyed a high profile in all Perkins UK sites, the Caterpillar Works Council and the Caterpillar Quality Council in the USA.

Quantified savings from the initiative are of the order of US$500,000 from electricity, water and waste initiatives with other key saving areas being air pressure leaks and con rods ($50,000).

The judge's questions asked first how the team developed and it was explained how this team had been hand-picked by management. They were then asked about the extent of management support and stated in reply how "when management see commitment they tend to put money in" as "they can see things being done and this grows with time". A similar answer was given to a question about how the team dealt with apathy and cynicism. This time the response was "when people see things being done they take more interest".

Other Presentations.

Other presentations in the single project management promoted team category were 'Project Abacus' by Perkins Engines of Shrewsbury, 'The Area Three Objective' by NSK Bearings Europe of Peterlee (County Durham), and 'Project Acorn' from Denso plc of Telford (Shropshire). In the continuous improvement self-direc ted category the remaining entries were 'Ever Decreasing Circles' by Komatsu, 'Current Systems Engineering' by Motorola Commercial Enterprise Division, and 'The Blockbusters' from Denso.

'Project Abacus' concerned the accuracy of stocktaking which in 1997 stood at just 30%. A steering committee was formed to oversee each functional area around the business utilising local knowledge specific to individual activities. A potential saving of £40,000 per year was identified as a result of avoiding the need for future stocktakes through the implementation of a perpetual inventory system. Procedures were simplified and owned by the right people and there was an overall inventory reduction valued at £1 million.

'The Area Three Objective' project involved the reorganisation of machining operations at NSK with particular regard to the elimination of inspection activities. The goal was to reduce the base cost for product manufacture and the team looked at factors such as the time taken to complete an inspection round and whether it would be possible for operators to assume responsibility for their own quality. Work Confirmation Sheets were devised and a three month trial of operators initiated. Product quality traceability improved as a result and 164 man hours per month, valued at £14,371, were saved. The annual saving deriving from removal of the inspection role was valued at a total of £110,000. The six inspectors were "re-deployed".

'Project Acorn' was about improving productivity levels on an aluminium production line, the need for which became apparent when rapid production growth occurred in 1998. Productivity needed to rise from 60,000 to 440,000 to cope with demand and the team's task was to identify bottlenecks, improve quality by reducing scrap and defect levels, and increase capacity. Particular attention was paid to managing changeovers which increased with the addition of 20 new product lines in 1997.

The team set a target of 15% productivity improvement and identified the brazing area as the chief bottleneck. A jig set up procedure was devised to counter this which allowed for a saving of 700 man hours per year which translated into 26,544 more pipes brazed per year. Other improvements included machine layout changes, changes to bending procedures which allowed one operator to operate two machines, and introduction of the Associates' Ideas Matter (AIM) scheme which led to several simple but effective changes.

'Ever Decreasing Circles' began in 1993 and since then has successfully completed eleven projects. Their current project, entitled 'I'd rather see nipples than elbows' takes its name from the hose fitting operation which was found to be at the root of a mechanical fouling problem that resulted in assembly quality defects in the wheel excavator range.

The hoses concerned were those that linked the cab controls and the main control valve which tended to foul at the rear of the cab. A problem definition sheet was compiled and subsequent brainstorming suggested that the best solution was to find a way of replacing elbows with connectors so that hoses would be naturally set in the right position. This also resulted in time savings in assembly as the fitting of the nipples down one side could be achieved through the use of an impact gun. Shop floor staff hardly noticed the change, but the effect on performance was substantial with zero defects achieved in this problem resulting in an assembly time reduction of 2 mins 30 seconds and a parts cost reduction of £9.07 per machine. This translates into an annual saving of £15,000.

The 'Current Systems Engineering' team represented the engineering department of Motorola in Basingstoke which deals with customers' technical problems. In order to resolve these issues in a timely manner a strong process is needed and two years ago this did not exist. Issues accumulated and cycle time was high and this was seen as incompatible with the organisation's SEI Level Five status.

The team constructed an 'As is/Should be' chart which showed that there was no tracking of customer complaints, no performance metrics and no long term strategy for defect prevention. Analysis of the customer complaint backlog showed that 60% of complaints were long term issues over 90 days old and a target was set to reduce this by 75% in 1997-98.

New Customer Complaint Information Forms were devised so that technical staff. could understand complaints. A break down of all issues and status was conducted and monthly reports compiled. A customer complaint management system was also developed and now 80% of problems are less than 60 days old and the backlog is down by 50%.

The purchase of Bosch by Motorola early in 1998 provided more scope for the team as they inherited their issues resulting in a big backlog increase, but this was improved with the aid of a Hotline, a multi-site reporting tool and a customer complaint database. Berlin and Switzerland have since been able to close any of their issues which have been identified in the UK. The team was formed according to Belbin principles which helped to speed up the consensus and deal with these new developments effectively.

[Issue 133 (Jan-Feb 2000)]

IRISH TEAMS CONGRESS 2000

The Annual Irish Teams Congress hosted by ICM in Dublin and now in its seventh year was held at the Alexander Hotel on 27th and 28th January.

Stock Options as an Incentive for Teams.

Peter Ryan, Human Resources Manager for Elan Corporation plc. Described how Employee Stock Option Plans (ESOPS) had been used as a motivator for teams and a subsequent survey undertaken to measure their success in changing attitudes. The 'Incentive Stock Option Plan' was introduced in 1996 and all employees across all grades and categories were granted option at the price of $28.50 (pre-split). In July 1998 (one year prior to the first vesting date) recipients completed the attitudinal survey in questionnaire form:

'Consideration was given to the impact of the option grant in terms of changes in respondents' sentiment towards the company in a number of different aspects. Assessments of the impacts in terms of continuity of tenure, interest in company performance, importance of share options, changes in levels of motivation, loyalty and commitment as well as the nature of commitment changes were all examined. The results of this analysis point to significant positive effects arising out of the option grant under the circumstances which prevailed'.

Managerial personnel accounted for 18% of the respondent group whilst supervisory personnel accounted for 25% and more junior personnel for 57%. Supervisory and managerial personnel, however, received a greater allocation of share options in both absolute and relative terms and this was considered to explain some of the noted differences between the sub-populations.

Findings showed that over 60% of respondents believed that share options served to influence their decision to remain with the company, whilst 85% stated that they took a greater interest in the company's activities and performance since receiving their option allocation, and 99% of managerial personnel confirmed that this was the case.

Similar results (100% of managerial personnel) were obtained on the question of taking a greater interest in the company's financial performance. Around 65% of respondents stated that the granting of options had served to make them more interested in the company's goals and objectives whilst 74% said that they felt that their individual performance could serve to positively affect the share price. On the broader question of the 'Elan Team' 81% said that their concerted contributions could positively affect the company's share price.

With this confirmation that respondents did perceive that their actions could potentially influence the company's stock price the survey proceeded to examine perceived changes in motivation arising from the receipt of share options. Findings on this question revealed that 70% of respondents felt that they were motivated to work harder as a direct result of the ESOP, although only 39% said that they actually did work harder for this reason (47% of supervisors, 30% of junior personnel and 26% of managers). Of this 39%, two thirds said that they worked between 10 and 25% harder.

Around 48% of respondents claimed that the granting of share options had made them more attentive to the issues of quality and productivity with 32% disagreeing and 20% indifferent. On the subject of commitment 79% of respondents rated their level of commitment at 8 or more on a scale of 1 to 10 as a consequence of the option grant. This compared with 51% who rated their commitment at this level prior to the ESOP:

'Levels of pre-existing commitment among managers were found to be quite high with a mean of 8.0 noted among this category compared to 7.5 for supervisory personnel and 7.2 for more junior personnel. The granting of options served to increase commitment levels across all categories with the managerial mean score increasing from 8.0 to 8.7, the supervisory score moving from 7.5 to 8.7 and the score for more junior personnel moving from 7.2 to 8.4'.

'When considered by department significant increases in commitment levels were noted across all sub-categories. The mean score increased from 7.8 to 8.8 among those in manufacturing/maintenance, from 7.5 to 8.4 in R and D regulatory affairs and from 7.5 to 8.4 in the admin/finance/engineering group. Likewise mean commitment levels in the quality assurance/quality control group increased from 6.9 to 8.2'.

The paper suggests, however, that the observed changes in commitment levels were not solely due to the financial implications associated with the

ESOP (only 24% of respondents indicated that their commitment had increased solely as a result of the financial benefits). The paper concludes as follows:

'The strong link between the option grant and positive sentiment in terms of respondent levels of commitment, motivation and loyalty, as well as a closer alignment of employee and shareholder objectives, point to the significant benefits associated with the grant. In short, the granting of options under the prevailing circumstances can be said to have had a positive effect upon employees' dispositions and sentiment towards the company'.

Linking Key Performance Indicators with Performance Appraisal.

Brian Duncan, Head of Performance and Reward Practice for Mercer Ireland said that in order to achieve successful performance management it is essential for one to be clear how KPIs and performance appraisal link together . He suggested that in this regard it was preferable to establish perhaps five or six KPIs rather than "a shopping list that most people just ignore" and that once established competencies should be linked in with KPI measures.

He stated that in his experience most organisations at unit level have relatively little difficulty setting their KPIs, but when it comes to linking them with performance appraisal somewhat more difficulty tends to be encountered. "Most organisations have nowhere near the system that they should have", he said, stressing the need for remuneration to be divorced from performance management and highlighting the divisive effect which individual bonuses imposed on top of a performance management system can have.

The difficulty associated with linking reward to performance increases top down, he suggested, raising the question of how far down the organisation one should really attempt to push it. The value of the system, he said, does not depend totally on the linking of performance to reward, but rather on personal development, particularly at the lower levels, consequently the linking of bonuses with KPIs should basically be confined to the more senior levels.

The KPIs, on the other hand, "should not be exclusively financial" as this "can drive the long term value out of the organisation". Many organisations, he said, have learnt this the hard way as their systems have become "hijacked by accountants". He suggested that KPIs "should cascade from corporate objectives" and "must be seen as relevant to what teams see their work as". For example, in a production team such measures as wastage, rejects and numbers of reshipments are both visible and meaningful to their work. Secret measures must be avoided as this was like playing a game of football with the referee refusing to disclose the score at the end of the match:

"KPI measures must be set on a realistic basis and in the short term people must meet a small number of realistic measures. Otherwise nothing will change".

He urged teams to be empowered to set their own objectives and KPIs and stressed the need for managers "to stop setting ridiculous targets" and to appreciate the often critical work undertaken by project teams which is frequently overlooked or neglected. In the performance appraisal process action plans may be related to KPIs, but performance planning must review the previous action plan i.e. review what was agreed including KPIs that were relevant, and assess the performance since the last review against appropriate competencies. Delegates were warned strongly against penalising good people who elect not to undertake performance appraisal.

This short, forthright presentation was designed to be interactive and generated a number of questions from the audience. These included the question of what management should do when there is no means to deviate from a structured pay system, where no culture of appraisal exists and where there may be outright fear on the part of employees at the thought of one being introduced. The speaker replied as follows:

"I do not accept that performance appraisal has to have a short term reward. Employers don't always see this. People look for training opportunities and this can be part of a proper performance appraisal system. We don't provide bonuses on an individual basis for the majority of staff. People see the appraisal as an opportunity to see how they are doing, find out where the organisation is going, and a chance to express their view. A system does not absolutely require a reward at the end of the day. The system often doesn't work simply because people do not put enough time into it. This has nothing to do with pay".

"Performance management is a philosophy, not something you do every six months. It must be seen this way. Most people do not think from one appraisal to another. The good people do and see it as ongoing. Take time to prepare. Lots of complaints from people being appraised are about the lack of preparation on the part of the person doing the appraisal and about following up paperwork quickly. Taking two months to communicate follow-up is not good enough. Even if it is only a meeting in the corridor people will respect the system and not just feel that they want bonuses".

Another key question concerned the consultation process that management should adopt to get buy-in to the appraisal system. In his discussion which followed the speaker spoke of the role of quality:

"Look at what the organisation is expecting and what it can do to deliver. It is amazing what quality can contribute given the opportunity".

431

Eliminating the Silo Mentality.

A joint presentation by Communications Manager Peter Waller and Career Development Manager Nigel Crainey of the Liverpool Victoria Group, the UK's third largest direct insurer and one of the UK's top five richest insurance companies, described how teamworking had been introduced over a two and a half year period in a mature organisation (160 years old). Naturally in such a well established organisation some of the more traditional problems associated with modern management techniques can be that much harder to eliminate and one of these was the so called 'silo mentality' from which Liverpool Victoria have been by no means unique in suffering.

Internal communication strategies provided the vehicle to deal with this problem and the presentation described how 14 months ago a communications audit was undertaken as part of a drive to reform "a culture of fear and mistrust" in which one in three employees perceived the organisation's internal communication system to be "inadequate".

Central to the audit was a call centre which employed 1,200 people, handled 5 million calls a year, and which provided "a tense working environment". According to the speakers there was a real crisis here as three "islands" each talking in what was effectively a different business language, suffered a breakdown in communication.

Something had to be done to rectify this situation and the solution devised involved the development of core competencies to serve as a common language to prevent the call centre from becoming "flooded out with calls". A competency framework was subsequently devised in which teamwork formed one of a number of competencies which collectively made up a language for people to talk together and arrive at quality outcomes.

The need for people to be able to understand each other's values and beliefs proved to be crucial. Psychometrics were used as an enabler to provide people with the ability to understand the impact of their behaviour on others. These dealt with, for example, the relative speeds with which different individuals processed particular types of information:

"We all process information in different ways. People can have strengths but not use them with each other. We have to enable individuals to understand themselves and how they impact. We need to find the right channel to ensure staff feel that their preferences are being listened to".

The audit revealed that 60% of employees wanted less general information through corporate media and that most people valued hearing and seeing from managers, communication champions, discussing rather than telling, and receiving information that was consistent particularly where changes in structures and job roles were concerned. "A real shock" was ascertaining that staff wanted information in strategy, vision and values, which management believed that it was communicating effectively. It was later proved that management was in fact presenting this information in the wrong form for the intended recipients.

The Role of Coaching in Teamwork.

The paper by John Findlater, Training and Development Manager for Guinness Dublin Brewery and Projects Manager for Guinness Adapt Projects, and the accompanying CD ROM which was provided free to delegates, examined how concepts successfully applied in sport may be transposed into the business environment.

The paper poses the question 'Can we learn from sport to improve business practices?' and describes how the author's participation in a range of coaching and tutoring programmes at the National Coaching Training Centre for Sport in Ireland led him to initiate a joint project between this Centre, Guinness Ireland Group and The Dublin City Enterprise Board to examine the transferability of best practice in sports coaching to business and small enterprises with the aid of EU funding.

The project culminated in a coaching programme for entrepreneurs based on sports coaching principles. The premise was that entrepreneurs wanted to grow their business and that this was best achieved by growing and developing those working in the enterprise through coaching:

'Most medium sized businesses rely on external consultants to educate their trainers and managers. The NCTC education system is based on qualified tutors tutoring the coach. This structure offers medium sized businesses a low cost alternative to being dependent on external consultants'.

It is emphasised that teams need to go through a number of team building stages in order to become an effective team and these stages are described in the CD ROM entitled 'Business Development Now' which contains modules and case studies from Guinness Ireland, Aughinish Alumina, SIFA, Golden Vale and Shannon Development. The Guinness Ireland module is concerned with 'How to develop your Team through Coaching'.

The module contains thesis material which asks 'Is there a need for business coaches in Guinness?' and presents three chapters which:

- distinguish the difference between coaching, mentoring and facilitation

- review definitions of coaching highlighting the role of the manager as coach and explaining the barriers and enablers to coaching.

- Identify what it takes to coach top performers to world class performance by outlining the skills and qualities of an effective coach and a number of coaching models.

- Attempt to identify factors that can be developed to ensure consistent and peak performance.

The module suggests that the managers of cross-functional or project teams may need to adopt a coaching approach particularly where their team has specialist skills and knowledge. It then compares talking speed with speed of thought:

'The average person speaks about 125 words per minute whereas thinking speed is in the region of 500 words per minute. The result is that people miss out on what is currently being said because they are composing their response to what they have already heard'. [Very interesting observation-Ed].

Various models are described the application of which 'must remain fluid and flexible because not all coaches go through all of the stages'. It is up to the coach to decide which approach to adopt for a particular situation and to be aware of 'the continuum of coaching styles'.

The Future of Teams.

Ms. Kate Quinlan, Human Resources Director for Aventis Pharma, chaired the panel session which rounded off the conference. This covered essentially what is the best way to set up teams, how to sell the team working concept to managing directors who then have to sell it to their management team, and how to sustain and regenerate teams for the future.

Of course for teams to have a future they have to be set up in the first place and the panel debated some of the best ways of doing this some of the pitfalls to avoid.

Peter Ryan cautioned against the danger of underestimating resistance to change when teams are established. Nigel Crainey suggested that when teams are initially formed individuals should be asked to recognised their own values and discuss them with colleagues in order to ascertain what is blocking teamwork. "We took people from silos and forced them to think on things that were common", he said.

In introducing the subject of selling the teamworking concept Ms. Quinlan accepted that this presented "a hard role for a managing director". She suggested that involving people first and establishing ethics were among the first steps. "We don't hear as much about senior management changes as we do about middle management ones", she said, acknowledging that some reshuffles were inevitable as part of the management restructuring needed to gain a buy-in from the full management team.

Brian Duncan highlighted the need for experienced line managers to be put at ease with regard to the old centralised idea of partnership without responsibility which they may fear or use as an excuse to block teamworking initiatives.

Success in sustaining and regenerating teams was, according to Peter Ryan, dependent on people being able to see that change was in their best interests rather than detrimental to them. He urged delegates not to underestimate the difficulty associated with this and to afford it a high priority.

Peter Waller reinforced this admitting that Liverpool Victoria had experienced this problem themselves following a review which recommended downsizing. " We tried to create a bottom-up approach and there was some resentment in the team leader's role", he acknowledged. Another delegate explained how, having paid a high price for teamworking implementation following negotiation with trade unions, it later fell apart through lack of buy-in from supervisors. Ultimately the only solution was to remove the supervisors' posts in their totality, replacing them with team leaders.

A further problem raised was that of teams wanting to decide upon everything, which of course had to be prevented.

[Issue 138 (Autumn 2000)]

MICHELIN EXCELLENCE AWARDS 2000

The Michelin Excellence Awards for Teamwork are now in their 11th year during which time 26 Awards have been made to 20 organisations. As in previous years the event provided the principal focus for the annual conference of the NSQT, which this year has been re-launched as The European Forum for Teamwork in line with the current quality trend of 'Europeanisation'.

Three Awards were presented at this year's event at Warwick University on 22nd August, to NSK Bearings who were winners in the Single Problem/Management Promoted category, Denso Manufacturing Limited's 'Car in Front' team who won the Continuous Improvement/Self Directed category, and the 'Smash to Cash' team from H and P Johnson Tiles who were given a special Award (discretionary on the part of the judges) in the closely fought Continuous Improvement/Self Directed category.

The presentations of the three Award winners are detailed below along with an overview of the remaining team presentations.

Grinding Right at NSK.

This team, one of two from the NSK Bearings at Peterlee, County Durham, was concerned with a historical raceway grinding problem which produced a high rework rate which was costing the company around £100,000 per month. The grinding shop is at the heart of the manufacturing process and is responsible for the achievement of final dimensional tolerances, accuracy and quality prior to assembly. Roughness, when grinding the ring ball raceway, thus had a serious impact on quality.

A breakthrough improvement in the grinding process was sought by the team, who considered in some detail the complex issues which contributed to raceway roughness. In the course of their work they concluded that it was possible to reduce machine generated faults by half and the overall inspection rate by 20%. Cause and effect charts were used to prioritise action areas with a realisation that 55 % of machine performance was affected by grinding roughness.

A key finding of the project was that traditional Japanese production theory needed to be challenged in order to achieve the breakthrough type of improvement which was desired. Outside assistance was therefore sought from the Institute of Grinding Technology in Bristol which led to the introduction of a British inspired innovation which greatly improved machine stability leading to a substantial decrease in inherent noise factors.

The impact of the improvement was measured using statistical process control, with further improvements being realised through the deployment of Q Prime (an analytical tool which was used to optimise the grinding cycle parameters). With further refinements machine faults were reduced from 28 to zero in two years and the following benefits reported:

* 75% fewer machine stoppages

* a 30% reduction in noise rejects

* a 45% reduction in machine breakdowns

* a 50% reduction in the inspection rate

* a 52% reduction in machine setter workload

The bottom line benefits reported were a one off inventory saving of £27,000 plus an annual saving of £516,000, all for an outlay of around £19,500.

The judges' questioning began with a question about morale and whether it faltered during the 14 month long investigation phase. The team gave the following response:

"We had our ups and downs but we had all worked in the grinding process for a long time. We had lots of experience. The setting operators were demanding changes and we knew it was difficult. Even the Japanese hadn't managed it".

They were asked about communication and about how their small team of three experts involved others:

"We challenged the Japanese philosophy and invited leading experts from outside. We could then see the results. Communication came easy".

This led to further questioning about the so called 'catalyst' for the team's activity:

"Two years ago we took a stance with the Japanese. We asked if we could bring in people because we believed that the problem could not be solved with diagnostics alone. When Japanese engineers saw the results they knew we were tackling the right problem. The Japanese realised they had exhausted their technology".

Further questioning covered the adoption of the techniques by the rest of the NSK group:

"The company has recognised the skills of the team. The technology has been transferred to Japan, there are questions coming forward and they are keen to adopt".

The team, which was praised by the judges for their "clear analysis, shopfloor involvement and thoroughness", is now looking to establish new small group activity in the company's automotive side.

The NSK Company was inaugurated in 1916 and produced the first ball bearings to be made in Japan. Since then they have developed a full range of bearings which have made NSK the top producer in Japan and second in the world. They have recently diversified into automotive products, precision machinery and Mechatronics with the Peterlee Site (consisting of five plants employing 735 providing the first example of Japanese inward investment in North East England. They are now aiming to become The European Centre of Excellence for Automotive Products.

The Car in Front.

Denso's team took their name from Toyota who have the same motto and for whom they manufacture air conditioning units, along with Honda. The team examined line stoppages, which they selected as a principal area by means of a self evaluation table for line performance. A Pareto diagram for line stoppages revealed that a crimping operation was the main cause of stoppages and this was therefore prioritised for further investigation.

The subsequent investigation looked for where and when in the process operations were performed which led to the scrapping of unit cores valued at between £4.59 and £6.58 each. During the three month trial some 233 of these units were scrapped and a target was set to halve this.

More intensive analysis was conducted, involving a 100% check of cores at storage and then at lineside over a five day period with checksheets being used to record incidences of damage. Following from this a countermeasure was introduced involving the packaging of boxes in bubble-wrap which led to a 42% reduction in the scrap rate of cores. In addition engineering design was approached to construct a new set of jigs with equalised pressure points, but this could not be implemented as the design of a pipe sub-assembly prevented it.

Attention now turned to machine capability and a series of trials was designed to see how this could be improved. For this batches of 50 cores were 100% checked before crimping at pressures of 4 bar, 5 bar and 6 bar. The variation in failure rates at the different pressures was then studied. Findings revealed an 18% failure rate at 4 bar, a 6% failure rate at 5 bar and a 25% failure rate at 6 bar. A pressure relief switch was then designed into the process to eliminate unwanted variations in pressure and savings of £276 per month were reported.

This team won last year's Directors' Award for Teamwork within the Denso Group, and presented at both the 1999 Michelin Excellence Award finals and the European Quality Circle finals in Barcelona. The judges praised them most notably for their "structured approach", ability "to follow a problem upstream", and their "simple and effective" solution.

Questioning began with a challenge to the team as to whether crimping was in fact the best way of securing a pipe to a core, and the team answered by emphasising that the crimping schedules operation was "a customer specification". In reply to a question on senior management commitment the team said:

"We have lots of quality circles and they are very important to our company. Senior management will join with a team if they are struggling and are on hand at any time. They are only a phone call away".

Later questioning asked if perhaps the team had underestimated their savings as they had reported only the direct material cost of the scrapped cores. They confirmed that the line stoppages also affected other sections and that if this was taken into consideration then the overall savings "could be much higher".

Denso Manufacturing was formed in 1992 as a joint venture between Magnet Marllee of Italy and the Denso Corporation of Japan. The UK operations are based at Telford where evaporators, condensers, heater cores, pipes and hoses, mouldings and assemblies are produced. Quality circles operate on a voluntary basis and are run by associates aided by advisors and facilitators. The aim of each Quality Circle is to:-

* investigate and analyse quality concerns

* set targets and work to pre-arranged schedules

* trail and eventually implement counter-measures

* continuously monitor and check their own progress

* evaluate and learn from experience

Twice a year each Quality Circle is given an opportunity to present its material to senior management, producing and presenting its own material.

Smash to Cash.

The 'Smash to Cash' team was formed from the amalgamation of two teams, one from main stock warehousing, and the other from the finance department. Both teams had 'hot spotted' the problem of returned stock accumulation which not only accounted for a large amount of money but also impacted heavily on cash flow and customer satisfaction. It transpired, for example, that a number of customers were withholding payments as a consequence of awaiting credit for returned goods.

Ceramic tiles were composed of either a red or white body and the team examined the details associated with credit notes for customers for returned tiles. The returned system was found to be "a mess" having no audit trail and a lack of storage resulting in hauliers keeping a lot of returns in warehouses. The time taken to book stock back into the system was also found to be excessive.

The core team of three (monitor, evaluator and co-ordinator) used an Ishikawa diagram to pinpoint the causes of problems, such as unidentified returns being held at hauliers due to a lack of appropriate documentation, and cases where small items e.g. a £10 Goods Received Note were holding up the processing of major orders of £10,000 plus.

A policy of improving communication with hauliers was immediately implemented, with weekly consultations now being mandatory.

The team set itself the targets of reducing the value of invoices held awaiting credit notes from £850,000 to £250,000, of reducing landfill costs from £230 per week to £75 per week, and of increasing the amount of production returned from landfill from zero to 90%.

These targets were believed to be quite achievable once the team realised that they had overlooked their own group recycling scheme, and benchmarked with a local floor tile manufacturer who offered the prospect of 100% red body tile reclamation.

Further analytical work showed that frequently it was costing more to return tiles than they were actually worth, and that tile resale was often a much better option. The landfill cost targets have thus been achieved, whilst the policy for credit note issue has been overhauled, following the realisation that the only reason for non-issue in the first place was abuse by a small number of tile users.

The team, which became a small team in June 1999 and met on alternate weeks, was asked about its senior management support which they said "was great when realised" i.e. once they realised that a problem existed and they were able to put a figure on it. They stated that the problem was also a health and safety issue which would potentially release money back into the company.

Other questions focused on the duplication aspect i.e. how two teams had ended up working on the same project without the knowledge of the other, and how such duplication of effort may be prevented in future, and on how the targets were set for the amount of returns i.e. whether they were arbitrary or calculated. The team explained how facilitators are now deployed to pick up cases of duality and how the targets were calculated from the invoice totals held for Goods Received Notes. They were praised for "office involvement and practical warehouse involvement, good interfacing and a real sense of team vitality".

H and R Johnson are based in Stoke on Trent and are a member of Norcros, an international group located across five continents providing a specialised range of ceramics, printing and packaging, and construction products and services. H and R are currently the UK's leading tile manufacturer producing wall, floor and fireplace tiles and associated products.

They were also the first company to develop and patent 'the universal edge' (a unique tile which allows for an even spacing of wall tiles) and leases the application process. In April 1997 they won the Queen's Award for Environmental Achievement for their unique waste recycling project which saves over 5,000 tonnes of waste from landfill every year.

Other Presentations.

Whilst there can of necessity only be a maximum of three Michelin Excellence Awards presented, the savings achieved by all of these teams are considerable producing real bottom line improvements. Far from being a cost to the organisation, they justify their existence to the organisation in money terms many times over in many cases. Such is the value of teamwork.

The remaining three teams in the Single Problem/Management Promoted category were 'The Small Parts Paint Line Improvement Team' from Case UK of Doncaster, the 'Smartcard Technology Team' from ID Data Systems of Coventry, and 'The Incident Management Team' from NACCO Materials Handling Limited of Craigavon, Northern Ireland. In the Continuous Improvement/Self Directed Category the two remaining teams were 'PCB Fallout' from Clairemont Electronics Limited of Greenock and 'Let's Get Packing', the second finalist from NSK.

Case UK's team were involved with the improvement of productivity and efficiency of the small parts paint process (the line which paints items which are not painted in the main spray booths) prior to assembly to tractors. Over the years new tractor models had been introduced but the small parts paint line had had little modification.

As a result new and changed parts were, for example, hung on hangers that were not designed to carry them, whilst scheduling relied on inaccurate and incomplete documentation. The threat of outsourcing provided the impetus for the team which virtually eliminated parts shortages, reduced overtime working and saved around £750,000.

Case Corporation has recently merged with New Holland and the Doncaster plant is shortly to be sold as a going concern as part of the divestment conditions for European approval of the merger.

The 'Smartcard Technology Team' were also formed to bring about change in the face of adversity, in this case £400,000 a month losses which threatened the company, formerly a subsidiary of GPT (who merged with Marconi in 1998) with closure. The team was cross-functional and involved all areas and departments of the business in a conversion to cellular manufacturing techniques.

Operational equipment analysis was undertaken which revealed shortages of material despite a huge inventory .The requirement for 27 transactions to be undertaken to process a product was reduced to just four, and 35% improvement in productivity made the organisation viable again once the old functional areas or 'baronies' were removed and inventory reduced from £890,000 to £520,000.

New sales areas have since been found, including 50% of the business for Barclays' smartcards and CIM modules for mobile phones.

The 'Incident Management' Team were impressive not least for the amount of estimated savings (£1.3 million) which they achieved through a company-wide reduction in lost working hours. The team reviewed health and safety across the business and implemented a revised incident management programme. This involved:

- removing the fear associated with reporting incidents and reversing it i.e. disciplinary action is now for failure to report an incident.

- Defining the responsibilities of everyone from plant managers to shop floor staff.

- Introducing a 'close out' principle to ensure that incidents did not recur.

- Training a team of 'originators' to originate documentation around incident investigation.

- Bringing in barristers to train staff in legal awareness.

- Introducing a procedure which required at least two 'originators' for each incident investigation.

- Applying a 'near miss' concept similar to that used in civil aviation.

The improvements have resulted an increase in 'near miss' reporting from 33% in 1998 to 47% whilst the number of new claims pursued against the company dropped by 53% over the same period. Accidents have also fallen by 17%.

'PCB Fallout' concerned a Compaq cable assembly injection moulding problem which led to a high reject rate and threatened to jeopardise a contract worth £5 million. The team of five commenced work in April 1999 to reduce the number of scrapped parts and the number of employee hours spent rebuilding cables. A 'think tank' was created in the centre of the shopfloor which enhanced the team's openness and the quality department was involved to determine whether the cause of the problem was due to an in-house process or from outside material.

Confirmation that the source of the problem was in-house led to the use of fishbone charts which revealed that the actual on-line process did not reflect the process as detailed in work instructions. A capability study was conducted on the machine analysis of scrap and a mould tool investigation showed that a pin height measurement discrepancy was a potential source of excessive vibration.

Mould tooling was then refurbished and a documented moulding process and preventive maintenance system introduced along with attribute charts that were "so effective that they be put forward to senior management for every assembly".

The 'Let's Get Packing' entry from NSK had an ambiguous title reflecting its objective to eliminate the role of packers from their department. (Area Two Small Size Assembly). Packers packed bearings on four lines and the team sought to combine the role of line operator and packer, removing the need for the extra employees.

A manning reduction of three was achieved in July 1999 which saved NSK £54,000 per annum, although the team was keen to point out that whilst the need for these packers had been removed the packers themselves "were still packers in another area" i.e. there were no bad feelings. The company's sister plant in Poland is shortly to adopt the same system.

Further Information.

The Michelin Excellence Awards are made on the basis of equal length presentations combined with log book submissions and peer review. Details may be obtained from The European Forum for Teamwork, 2 Castle Street, Salisbury, Wiltshire SP1 1BB. Telephone: 01722326667.

Chapter Six

Innovation and Creativity

The UK has traditionally enjoyed a good reputation for innovation and creativity, although in recent decades some of this capability has undoubtedly been diminished through the increased pace of life and emphasis on compliance management. Time for free thought has been eroded and the so called 'white heat of technology' has largely passed into history. Intense pressure on organisations to cut costs has created a climate of risk aversion and a desire on the part of many simply to take old ideas and tinker with them, rather than opt for revolution which could prove costly if unsuccessful.

Recognition of these problems has given rise to some new thinking by quality practitioners such as the application of concepts like Attractive Quality Creation as described below, and the emerging discipline of knowledge management in which the EFQM has recently taken a leading role both in addressing the subject and through the incorporation of an Innovation and Learning component in the recently revised Business Excellence Model.

In the compilation below mention is made of some of the leading European and American organisations which have gained a reputation for success in innovation during the 1990s and of the role which the IQA has played in attempting to bring this issue to the fore.

QUALITY AND CREATIVITY

Many practitioners in a creative environment are apprehensive when 'Quality' is introduced into their activities. This occurs particularly in companies where a design function is carried out in proximity to an operating or production environment. It is perceived by staff in a creative role that 'Quality' will inhibit their creativity, by somehow introducing legislative procedures into their creative processes. There is nothing in Quality philosophy to inhibit creativity or the entrepreneur, but the perception introduced (historically through inspection methods) into more mechanistic activities, gives the impression that 'some Quality requirement' will impinge on the thought processes. The interpretation given by some to the Design Control clause of ISO9001 does not dispel this misconception.

In order to address more fully the relationship which exists between quality and creativity the Quality Methods Association R and D Study Group held a one day presentation, hosted by the P.A. Consulting Group, at their Cambridge Laboratory at Melbourn, near Royston, Hertfordshire, on 25th March.

Creativity versus Control

Mark Clargo of P.A. Consulting described creativity as ' a system of opening up from the obvious solution to a range of solutions which can be narrowed down', with the opening up phase being the part which normally creates the greatest degree of difficulty.

This tied in well with the presentation by Gary Lane of The Wellcome Foundation who asserted that people tend to speak about creativity far more than they actually do it. The essence is to learn to play with ideas and build on them. If you kill ideas they can't grow, but by the same token some control is needed. This he likened to pruning fruit bushes so that they can become more fruit bearing in the future.

He described how, in auditing structures for the Australian Design Council, he had observed that in many cases manufacturing processes had not been consistent with creativity such that whilst the designs won accolades the ensuing product failed to meet fundamental quality criteria.

A list of problems that cause quality problems in the Rand D function were then highlighted:

*inability to trace original data

*missing data or slow retrieval

*missing details and obscure logic

*absence of quality planning at the design stage

*poor material selection

*poor piloting of new products

* lack of quality standards and procedures

* no policy on quality in design

It is towards such problems that clauses such as the Design Control clause, in ISO9001 are fundamentally directed, in recognition of the fact that without such attention creativity 'can go off uncontrolled', with the consequence that the driving force becomes the concept not the customer.

Design control was noted to be 'the hub of the problem', although management responsibility was 'the first and most important requirement' and the purchasing clause was clearly important in helping to ensure correctness in specification, which was highlighted as a particularly common problem for Rand D departments. The need for adequate document control and contract review that ensures that customer requirements are adequately defined and documented, was also stressed.

The Importance of Mistakes

An important principle emphasised by Mr. Lane was that of mistake acceptance, learning from which 'is fertile', as distinct from mistake denying which 'is sterile'. This was further expanded in a video in which celebrity John Cleese, a founder member of training company Video Arts, addressed an audience in New York on the subject of mistake acceptance.

This speech focused on the principle whereby by making a substantial number of small mistakes it becomes possible to avoid the overall main mistake of missing the real target, drawing an analogy between organisational systems and the feedback and control iterations of a guided missile. He thus asserted that people are acting 'unrationally, unscientifically and unsuccessfully' if mistakes are not tolerated, and referred to an old English proverb which says 'the man who does not make mistakes is unlikely to make anything'.

This is linked with creativity in that if the fear associated with the risk of doing something wrong is not removed, then creativity 'goes out of the window', since the essence of it lies in the 'supreme indulgence' of doing something for its own sake i.e. being able to play and follow impulses of immediate interest.

Unfortunately, however, most organisations 'are paralysed by the fear of making mistakes, however small' and to make matters worse there is a resultant tendency for individuals to attempt to deny or cover up mistakes. Consequently the unacknowledged mistake remains uncorrected, sometimes with disastrous effects.

The amount of lying required to conceal the original mistake 'breeds exponentially', and it was implied that one of the main reasons for the failure of totalitarianism is the sheer escalation of problems arising from failure to correct early mistakes:

'When failures have to be repackaged as successes, disaster cannot be far away'.

[This links in very closely with Deming's Eighth Point i.e. to drive out fear, and it may perhaps be inferred that unless fear is driven out an organisation's or a country's capacity to innovate can be seriously impaired-Ed].

Stimulating Creativity.

Tudor Rickards and Christian de Cock of the Manchester Business School devised an interactive session designed to stimulate open discussion about some of the barriers which managers were currently facing, which raised issues like how to break 'mindsets' in organisations, the use of customer contact as a route to ideas, how to combine creativity across departments, and the prevention of 'managerial squashing' where creativity is present.

A highly critical appraisal of the 'elitist' philosophy of creativity whereby certain individuals, notably from prestigious universities, somehow possessed the attribute, followed from Mr. Rickards. The elitist view, he said, blames poor selection as the cause of the absence of creativity in an organisation, and it was suggested that this concept was bogus. He asserted that everyone has the capacity to generate new and valuable ideas, and that such creativity was fundamental to the implementation of managerial change.

It followed that the kind of creativity that was most needed in industry was organisational rather than technical, as most companies with a scientific policy tend to have an adequate core of scientific people to realise scientific objectives.

Innovation, likewise, has been 'assumed to have been originated and then developed in the market place'. In practice, however, all organisational change is a kind of innovation that has to be managed.

It was clearly necessary to break organisational mindsets which impeded change and in this respect Mr. Rickards distinguished between single loop learning which develops norms, works to maintain norms, may gradually improve performance but fails to challenge those norms, and double loop learning which seeks to 'break out of old norms and is needed for major innovation'.

Three stages were suggested for the achievement of success through innovation:

(i) unblocking (constructive use of dissatisfaction, shared dissatisfaction, a shared vision).

(ii) acting (one or two clear obvious steps so people can be convinced they are not being sold 'pie in the sky', wide involvement, selection of 'doable bits').

(iii) resetting (rewarding successes and taking stock).

In relation to this third point it was suggested that British management was absolutely lousy' in managing reward schemes for creativity, with most schemes 'aimed to humiliate 98 per cent of the workforce without rewarding them' and having no proper feedback to those who contribute.

Most managers, he says, do not have powerful models to introduce change and need to beware of thinking that they can dream up these models.

Christian de Cock described some of the practical research which has been undertaken into adaptive creativity in continuous improvement; programmes in Pilkington Glass, Pilkington Insulation, British Nuclear Fuels Limited, (BNFL), and British Aerospace. Some of the problems identified included:

1. Lack of a role model:

"People know that a lot of people are only doing it because they have been told to do it. That has been a hurdle to a lot of people. They see their managers trying to get them involved and they do not accept the manager doing it for the right reasons".

2. Conflicting signals:

"A manager will send out the signal 'we have to improve the way our business works' and the same man will demand a few minutes later 'I want the bits for my aeroplane now'. A person fairly low in the organisation sees these two signals coming from the same person. Which one does he respond to? The one that pays his wages is the one that says 'Where are my bits?'"

3. Inappropriate symbolic behaviour:

"We are saying to people 'You can't just use as many pencils as you want' and then you see someone in a more senior position having a grand lunch somewhere or travel first class".

4. Personal qualities:

"The big thing that I found is that individuals who drive the TQ process need to be very genuine people. They need to be extremely honest, extremely open. That might be very hard to do sometimes, especially when you have to explain why things are happening the way they are. The more uncomfortable it is to talk about something, the more response you can get from people because they appreciate the fact you do know it is uncomfortable and you are being honest with them. You probably gain more from that than anything else".

5. Focus on process.

"Some 75 to 80 per cent of our people are graduates' type level. They are educated to think of improving what they are doing but mainly in terms of improving products. If they are designing something they are always looking for a way of doing it better from a design point of view, putting some different facility into the product or in some way make it better. But they have not necessarily found it easy to think also in terms of the way they do things, the way they can improve those activities. That would include their management processes, their personnel processes and all that, and recognising that it is just as important to improve those processes as it is to improve the product. It is getting that message through to the technical community which has been more of a challenge than we thought".

Managing Creativity

Speaking on behalf of conference hosts P.A. Consultants, Technical Director John Fisher described from experience some of the characteristics of innovative companies, introducing the management of creativity as 'turning creation into effective innovation for business advantage'. Innovative companies:

*have visionary leaders and small, flat organisations (typically under 400 personnel and two levels of management).

*have top managers setting broad challenging goals for new programmes.

*accept that innovation is concerned with dealing with chaos.

*encourage and reward entrepreneurial fanatics.

*minimise bureaucratic structures and give easy access to early development funds for good ideas.

*tie their vision strongly to the practical realities of the marketplace, anticipating tomorrow's customers' values.

*ensure close interaction between technical and marketing people at all levels.

*beware of accounting practices that load corporation costs onto development projects, as it is 'totally unfair'.

*pay attention to encouraging both formal and informal communication routes with formal training recognised as important for making friends as well as for learning from the course.

*accept that without failures there will not be successes.

*create heroes for outstanding achievement.

The importance of recognising the need to change from a cost cutting to an opportunity seeking culture in the future was underlined as one of the key factors to delivering success through the management of innovation, as was the need to direct more funds towards the early phases of creativity and innovation.

The views expressed by Tudor Rickards about the elitist view promoted by certain advertising agencies was reiterated:

"If you give people responsibility it's remarkable how they reward it. There's creativity in everyone".

[Issue 88 (April 1996)]

ATTRACTIVE QUALITY CREATION

Innovation – Where does it come from, the supplier or the customer? According to Dr. W. Edwards Deming the answer is the supplier, and in his celebrated seminars, as well as in his best known work 'Out of the Crisis' he quotes examples such as transistors and fuel injectors which represent breakthrough innovation on the part of the supplier. There is probably little possibility of ever disputing this theory as everyone is capable of a moment's inspiration. What may be questioned, however, is the matter of whether all innovation can and should be left to the supplier. Recent evidence suggests that it should not.

On 20th March members of the Quality Forum had the opportunity to gain an insight into a technique which has been developed and tested in Japan within

450

the last three years and, yet more recently has been applied in the United States.

The technique is known as 'Attractive Quality Creation' or 'Innovating the innovation process' and was described by Ron Thorogood of Weissner Consulting. It involves using customer psychology to drive the innovation process in an organisation. The case study presented from the USA concerned a service industry (car parking and related services), but the technique is equally applicable to manufacturing as several Japanese examples showed.

A.Q.C. in Japan

In introducing AOC the speaker made reference to some words of Dr. Deming on the importance of innovation i.e.:

' It is necessary to innovate, to predict the needs of the customer, give them more. Those that innovate and are lucky will take the market'.

He then outlined details of a recent DTI survey of innovations which suggested that 98.9 per cent of innovations conceived in the conventional way, i.e. not by AQC, had no market or even merit. A further 1 per cent had merit but not market leaving just 0.1 per cent having both merit and a market. Some reasons for this were given, namely that many innovations were not original, whilst others were original but not wanted by anyone, or else good but not good enough, or simply too costly to produce. Some such as the quadrophonic sound systems developed in the 1970s, were feasible but so complicated that their market potential was severely limited. This was contrasted with the early results from Japan among AQC which suggest that at worst 30 per cent and at best 60 per cent of ideas developed using the process are both new and feasible and perhaps more importantly, customers are willing to pay for them.

Innovating Service Innovation.

How does it work? Well, the first stage is to identify the lead and heavy users of the product or service as distinct from the regular users, the reason being that it is these users which are commonly the most accurate predictors of future customer needs i.e. they face needs which will be general, but face them months or even years in advance of others. Lead users are identified from their exhaustive use of the product or service which frequently results in their finding unusual, unique or novel uses. Heavy users are identified for their intensive, rather than exhaustive use. In the American study the lead and heavy users were identified as principally commuters, shoppers and office workers.

A project team is usually charged with the task of interviewing lead and heavy users in a process of contextual enquiry, which essentially involves asking them about how they use the product or service with the objective of ascertaining or identifying any unusual patterns of use attributable to specific causes. The result should be a list of expressed and latent needs of a few users who can be considered to be in advance of the general market. These needs in turn may be sub-divided into purely 'product issues' such as whether the service is too expensive or the service point closes too early, and 'circumstantial issues' which are more closely related to the context in which the service is used, such as feeling safe at night, provision of shelters in wet weather, or the provision of a meeting point for a rendezvous.

With this information it should now be possible to interview the regular users, or a representative sample of them, about the circumstantial issues in order to ascertain which, if any, of them are critical. In the case of the parking lot study, for example, it was found that most regular users did not use the service at night, which meant in effect, that at this time the service providers were catering for a minority of lead and heavy users.

Focus points, i.e. the essence of the cause of the issue, are identified for each circumstantial issue. In the case of the parking lot study four focus points were identified:

- Passenger transfer

- Passenger waiting

- Passenger contact

- Transport availability

These focus points are used to develop detailed unambiguous statements about customer needs, which are known as cognitive images. In the American case study three of these arose from the four focus points identified above and were:

(i) A need to develop a system to transport customers safely from the car park to the nearby station which it served.

(ii) A need to install a meeting point type system to facilitate customer meeting and interaction.

(iii) A need to develop a system to minimise the waiting time, hassle, frustration, loneliness and inconvenience associated with a breakdown.

Once these statements are made the innovator is able to predict to a degree the likely expectations of the market place for the future and so design products and services that will address these issues. It is now possible to interview the 'regular users' about possible tolerable cost increases associated with quality improvements based on addressing the issues involved. Typical questions might be: "How much extra would a system to minimise the waiting time, hassle, frustration and loneliness of a breakdown be worth to you?"

Statistical distributions can be plotted for the results obtained, which in turn are used to classify the cognitive images into unitary (to develop ideas for solving problems that exist in existing products or services), attractive (to develop ideas for completely new products or services), and attractive or unitary (a hybrid category suggesting development of ideas for major new features of existing products or services).

The resulting distributions in the American parking lot study showed that for the transport to station issue the cognitive image was attractive with 80 per cent of customers willing to pay 20 per cent or more. For the breakdown issue 60 per cent were found to be willing to pay 10 per cent or more. For the meeting point issue 90 per cent of customers said that they would not wish to pay.

These findings now enabled the team to select a small number, in this case two, cognitive images to translate into strategic themes i.e. issues which can be worked on to provide innovative quality improvement which will have a direct impact on the bottom line. All that remains is to assess the barriers to implementation and conduct the relevant cost-benefit analyses for possible options. In the American case study this last stage revealed that whilst the development of a system to transport customers to the station was perhaps more attractive than the development of a system to minimise hassle in the event of a breakdown, it was in fact the latter which was easier and more profitable to deliver.

A.Q.C. in the Quality Cycle

In concluding his presentation Mr. Thorogood spoke of the role of A.Q.C. within the Plan-Do-Study-Act (PDSA or PDCA) cycle of continuous quality improvement advocated by the late Dr. W. Edwards Deming. He referred particularly to the potential for the technique to serve as an indicator of where to begin the process of design, which very often is far from clear. He then compared the technique to the related more established techniques of Quality Function Deployment (QFD) which is concerned with designing products and services optimally. He explained clearly how, by contrast, AQC is concerned about establishing what is actually being designed rather than merely optimising a known design, and with less reliance on "educated guesses". Few were left in any doubt that the two techniques were indeed different.

With two years' track record of application the credibility of the new tool would appear to be assured, with at least one of its pioneers, Sumitomo Heavy Industries, now able to boast that it can "maintain market share almost at desired levels". What is less clear perhaps is how the technique will be received in the West and indeed whether a similar pattern of success will be repeated. Techniques such as Taguchi Design Methods and SMED have, for example, more than proved their worth in Japan, yet have been largely ignored by Western management. Whether AQC will receive the same low levels of attention remains to be seen, although logic would suggest that it should not, given the potential for a fast return to the bottom line, which most quality practitioners and managers would appear to desire.

Further Information

Information about this technique is not widely available at present. The American case study described would appear to be the only one of its kind undertaken in a Western country and as such is unique. Information on the Japanese case studies would appear at least at present to be confined to the Japanese language, although the British Library is currently undertaking to make reference work on the subject more widely available.

[Issue 103 (July 1997)]

FIRST INTERNATIONAL KNOWLEDGE MANAGEMENT SURVEY

The results of the first recorded international survey of corporate practice in knowledge management have now been published by Business Intelligence. Based on three main strands of research conducted during the second half of 1996 and early 1997 which included a series of case studies and a joint Business Intelligence/Ernst and Young survey of US and European senior executives which generated 430 responses, some key findings have been that

* Most organisations are not managing their knowledge well and achieving the potential benefits of its exploitation. They do not capitalise on ideas and creativity and lose knowledge through downsizing and staff turnover. They have knowledge assets which they do not exploit, and buy in expertise which they already possess because they do not know what they know.

* Measuring the value and the contribution of knowledge is the most difficult aspect of knowledge management faced by most organisations in practice. However, its bottom line benefits (the so-called 'value proposition' of knowledge management) are visible, even though sometimes indirect. They include better quality products, faster time-to-market, better resolution of problems, more efficient operations, improved customer service, identification of new market opportunities, and increased shareholder value.

* Two main thrusts characterise the focus of the knowledge management agenda. The first and most common, is the dissemination and application of knowledge that already exists somewhere in the organisation. The second, and potentially more valuable in the long term, is the creation of new

knowledge and its rapid conversion into new and improved products, services and processes.

* There is an emerging set of practices that have been found to successfully leverage organisational knowledge. These include knowledge mapping, knowledge databases, and improved knowledge refinement and diffusion. Information technology, and in particular collaborative technologies such as Lotus Notes and Intranet, has played a key enabling role in leveraging an organisation's potential.

* A significant barrier to effective knowledge management is lack of knowledge sharing organisational culture which values and rewards ideas, learning and the speed with which new knowledge is exploited. Other inhibitors are the level of top management endorsement, clarification of the scope of knowledge initiatives and the ascribing of value to knowledge.

* There is an emerging 'Community of Knowledge Practice' that is developing a common language and orchestrating these competencies into furthering the knowledge agenda.

Around 96 per cent of respondents apparently regarded customer knowledge as the most important asset for maintaining competitiveness, followed closely by knowledge of best practices, corporate competencies and capabilities, their own products and services and market trends. Around 86 per cent of respondents believed that they were in knowledge based industries, although only around a quarter considered the role of Chief Knowledge Officer to be either very or extremely valuable.

Case studies which have confirmed the clear benefits which can be achieved from increasing one's focus on knowledge management include Steelcase who, by focusing on the knowledge of their customers and users, have created award winning office environments which improve knowledge worker productivity; CIGNA Property and Casualty who, by focusing on the knowledge of their best underwriters, have transformed a loss making situation into a profit; Dow Chemical who, by focusing on the knowledge encapsulated in their patents, have generated over $125 million of additional revenue from a patent portfolio; Thomas Miller, a London based mutual insurance funds manager who, by exploiting the accumulated expertise of their professional staff achieved a strong global market position in certain classes of complex insurance risk; and Hoffman La Roche who, by focusing on the knowledge needed in the drugs approval process achieved much improved time-to-market for new pharmaceuticals.

Other in-depth case studies include Buckman Laboratories, Anglia Water, Monsanto, Price Waterhouse, Glaxo, Scandia, and The Department of Trade and Industry (DTI) with further examples from Rover, The US Army, BP, Hewlett Packard, Standard Life, Teltech, Ernst and Young, Booz Allen and Hamilton, and BNFL.

For those with little understanding of the knowledge management concept, some advice is given on how to begin:

'Mapping of an organisation's existing knowledge is often a good starting point in many knowledge initiatives. This involves identifying what knowledge is important, and where it is held, then collecting, classifying and storing it. The tools and techniques of the well understood but underutilised discipline of information resources management have been found to be of value here '.

Those who have already read the report and found it to be of benefit include Marcus Spell, Advisor Corporate IT of Shell International who has commented:

" I have greatly enjoyed reading your report on knowledge management, one of the hottest issues of our decade. There is a lot of material pulled together in this report from a variety of different sources -especially useful if you need to sell the benefits of knowledge management to the board members of your company. Few other sources will be needed as background reading for knowledge management".

'Creating the Knowledge-based Business' by David Skyrme and Debra Amidon is available from Business Intelligence, Third Floor 22-24 Worple Road, Wimbledon, London SW19 4DD.

[Issue 107 (November 1997)]

EFQM STOCKHOLM WORKSHOPS

Knowledge Management: a Strategy for Growth?

This session, chaired by Geoff Carter, New Knowledge and Service Development Manager for the EFQM, featured two speakers, Rob van der Spek, Senior Manager for Strategy and Development at the 'Kenniscentrum CIBIT' (an independent centre of excellence in the field of knowledge management and innovation of business processes based in the Netherlands) and Leif Edvinsson, Vice President and Corporate Director of Skandia AFS of Stockholm (a leading Swedish financial services organisation specialising in insurance).

Dr. van der Spek outlined the key activities of the Knowledge Management Network which was established in the Netherlands in 1989. This organises a network of some 600 professionals and is currently assisting the EFQM in its ongoing Knowledge Management Benchmarking study. The members of the Business Network for Knowledge Management include the airline KLM, Hoogorens (steel) Dutch Railways, Centraal beheer (insurance), AON Group (insurance) ING holding, the Royal Dutch Navy, the Dutch Ministry of transport, Nedlloyd, Fokker (space)and KPN (telecomms).

The focus is the continuous improvement of knowledge assets and on achieving business excellence through knowledge management. This involves consideration of knowledge as an innovation factor (learning and applying new knowledge faster than competitors) and as a production factor (exploiting existing knowledge assets to their fullest potential). The importance of linking knowledge management to strategy was stressed, along with the need to recognise it as a learning experiment rather than searching for blueprints. Some examples of knowledge management initiatives were listed, notably from BP, ICL, Unilever, Skandia, Monsanto and Texas Instruments. The speaker has recently co-authored a book on knowledge management entitled 'Knowledge Management: dealing intelligently with Knowledge'.

Leif Edvinsson spoke of the growing obsolescence of management and its replacement by Intellectual Capital Navigation. He emphasised the need for organisations to adopt the stretch goal of determining that which is unknown, and of raising questions beyond knowing what we already know and the mere recycling of information. He explained how new systems of accounting (Intellectual Capital Accounting) were being visualised at Skandia, who currently have a number of 'prototyping centres' under development, in Sweden's Archipelago. Reference was made to the company's supplement to its 1996 Annual Report, which was handed to all attendees of the workshop and states the following:

'Skandia began reporting on the group's intellectual capital and its connection to business success and value appreciation in a supplement to the 1994 Annual Report. Since then, increasing numbers of people are recognizing the value of this type of supplementary reporting'.

'Skandia has thus far developed a range of methods of reporting its Intellectual. Capital and its various components, through IC Indicators. The next step is to consolidate the various IC Indicators into one measurement that will dynamically describe the group's Intellectual capital. This will facilitate benchmarking of units within Skandia and with other companies. It will also provide an avenue for comparing changes in intellectual capital with changes in the company's market value, and thereby provide a forecasting value. Skandia is breaking new ground by applying this IC Index, which is a compilation of various IC indicators' relevance, robustness and relative weight'.

' Consolidating a list of various IC indicators into an IC-index is the first step toward visualising the interaction between investment and future earnings potential. Skandia will continue its IC exploration and will present its findings on a forthcoming CD-ROM.'

Leif Edvinsson has also recently co-authored a book on knowledge management entitled 'Realizing your Company's True Value by finding its Hidden Brainpower' (co-author Michael S. Malone).

Further supplementary information for delegates included the recently released publication by EFQM Benchmarking Services entitled 'Knowledge Management in Europe' which presents the results of a questionnaire based survey on knowledge management commissioned by the EFQM earlier this year.

The questionnaire was mailed to a sample of 350 organisations which yielded 141 responses from 20 European countries. The breakdown of respondents by industry was as follows: Manufacturing 43%; Services 25%; Consultancies 16%; Non-profit making organisations 16%. The breakdown by company size was: under 50 employees 19%; 50 to 499 employees 35%; and over 500 employees 46%.

Analysis of the questionnaires showed the following:

*around a third of organisations have no goals for knowledge management; 18% have clear explicit goals; 43% have implicit goals; and 6% don't know if they do or if they don't.

*just over half (51%) of organisations with more than 50 employees are currently measuring the linkage between their most important assets and their organisation's performance.

*the most important knowledge carriers in larger organisations are considered to b 'paper' and 'magnetic media' rather than people.

*63% of organisations never track knowledge sharing.

*two thirds (67%) claim to facilitate knowledge sharing.

*most (79%) say that they either occasionally or most times capture 'lessons learnt' from daily experiences.

* 70% of organisations do not have a function or individual responsible for knowledge management.

* 'organisational culture' is perceived as being the biggest barrier to the implementation of knowledge management in larger companies whilst 'insufficient understanding of the potential benefits' rank highest for the manufacturing and non-profit sectors.

Some key findings include the following:

* The Board may be unwilling to commit to a formalised knowledge management strategy until the perceived benefits can be proven but, paradoxically, the benefits will not be proven (or refuted) until a systematic approach is implemented.

* Most companies are lacking a set of approaches that accord with the EQFM Self-assessment Guidelines and the identification, creation, dissemination and maintenance of intellectual capital is frequently left to chance.

* Most of the surveyed companies see Knowledge Management as a catalyst for product or service quality, but the current commitment within the surveyed organisations to measuring the (potential) impact of KM is 'weak'.

* Once an organisation is willing to invest some time in understanding, on a practical level, KM within its own business context, the methods for tracking and measuring become clearer.

The Report makes the following comment:

'We believe that the survey results provide a fascinating snapshot of current thinking and practices. The results tell us two things. Companies are very interested in KM and recognise its potential rewards but only a small minority has developed and implemented an integrated set of business approaches that enable them to fully exploit their knowledge. In the majority of cases anomalies exist. Managers' and employers' ambitions to utilise knowledge fully and develop a learning culture are often hampered by the very mechanisms and processes they use to manage their businesses'.

[Issue 110 (February 1998)]

INAUGURAL CEO GLOBAL BEST PRACTICES SUMMIT

Sixteen CEOs of Global FORTUNE 500 companies in London, and twelve in New York, debated in a live interactive satellite broadcast on 21st January. The facilities of the BBC were used to co-ordinate the event. Under discussion were three specific fundamental components of leadership, namely innovation, alliances and 'stakeholder symbiosis' (belief in the interdependence between financial performance, customer loyalty, employee motivation and good corporate citizenship).

A special tool was devised to support the event by US Consultants Arthur Andersen known as Global Insights '98, a discovery tool which has three central questions:

(i). Are you innovating faster than your competitors? How do you know?

(ii). Can you grow faster than your competitors through alliances? What makes alliances work or not work?

(iii). Do you have a symbiotic relationship with your stakeholders (employees, customers, shareholders, suppliers and society) that has moved beyond simply achieving a stakeholder balance?

Each central question is supported by a number of detail questions which, together with the central question are designed 'to disturb or challenge' one's present mental model for each topic.

The debate in London was chaired by David Ball, President of Nortel plc and European Chairman of the Initiative, whilst that in New York was chaired by L.D. DeSimone, Chairman and CEO of 3M and North American Chairman of the Initiative. Other participating CEOs included in Europe John Roberts CBE, CEO of the Post Office UK and President Elect of the EFQM; Ahmed Piker, President of Brisa; Manfred Ahle, CEO of J. Vaillant, GmbH. of Germany; Professor Dr. Hans Dieter Seghezzi, Professor of Technology at the University of St.Gallen (Switzerland); Jan Walburg, President/CEO of The Jellinek Centre, (Amsterdam); Wayne Brown, Managing Director of 3M (UK); and Richard Snook, CEO of Bull (UK).

In the USA other participants included Bill Lowrie, President of the Amoco Corporation; Bob Lutz, Vice-Chairman of the Chrysler Corporation; Mitchell Fromstein, CEO of Manpower Inc.; Jeremy Coote, President of SAP America; Ed Harper, President and CEO of Commodore; Robert Hiebler, Managing Director of Knowledge Space, (a new electronic knowledge service of Arthur Andersen); and Carla O'Dell, President of the American Productivity and Quality Center (APQC).

Moderators for the discussions were, in London, Fons Trompenaars, Managing Director of the Amsterdam-based Centre for International Business Studies (now known as United Notions), and in New York, Marshall Loeb, Editor of Columbia Journalism Review and presenter of 'Your Dollars' (popular US radio show).

Leading in Innovation.

Organisations which have earned a reputation for leading in innovation include 3M, Chrysler, Amoco, Vaillant GmbH, Jellinek, and Bull UK.

At 3M creativity is defined as 'the thinking of novel and appropriate ideas' and innovation as 'the successful implementation of those ideas within an organisation' i.e. creativity is the concept and innovation the process. They argue that the application of new ideas 'cannot be compartmentalised within a corporation' i.e. innovation in the laboratory is, by itself, not enough for

460

those wishing to establish themselves as leaders even though laboratories may in practice 'set the tone' for innovation for example in accounting marketing and sales, the factory floor and the boardroom.

It has to be, they say, 'a corporate character trait' that is 'built up over time'. Thus, the person who starts up a company is an innovator and the challenge for those who follow is 'to sustain that willingness to embrace new things and new ways of behaving'.

Unfortunately, 'extraordinary pressures from investors and stock analysts' who 'expect their investments to have consistent and high returns' discourage executives from 'long-term and inherently risky investments in new technologies and products'. This, combined with an emphasis on short-term mission oriented projects, has resulted in even corporations with a long-standing tradition of innovation 'feeling the pressure to hold back on the pursuit of new discoveries'.

Senior executives at 3M clearly believe that to surrender to such a reluctance to embrace innovation compromises not only leadership but survival, as they equate survival with an ability to grow. Only through the development of innovative products and technologies do they believe customer needs can be addressed and loyalty assured.

Delight, they say, 'comes from giving customers something startling, new and valuable'. This may derive from solving a problem which they have complained about over a long period, or possibly from solving a problem which they did not even realise that they had. Alternatively it may derive from unusual attention to their ongoing business processes e.g. serving their needs by delivering 'just-in-time' or by offering superior technical service. Furthermore, the solution to a problem may derive from any part of the organisation.

The organisation sets stretch goals for innovation, namely that they will derive 30% of all sales from products that have been introduced over the past four years, and that 10% of sales will derive from products that have been in the market for just one year. Both of these, however, are subject to a stretch target which prioritises products that will change the basis of competition i.e. redefine what is expected by the customer and leapfrog the competition.

In the debate L.D.(Desi) Desimone added:

"It is people that are creative and they have to be motivated to be so. Across the organisation if a failure comes from good work we treat it as a learning experience. The idea of senior management encouraging thought and not shutting it off is important".

At Chrysler, an 'innovation pipeline' has been created known as CA TIA (Computer-Aided Three dimensional Interactive Application) which, based on technology supplied by Dassault Systems connects virtually every corner of the company to every other. With this comparatively recent form of innovation the need for costly and time consuming physical prototyping is reduced or eliminated whilst, at the same time, computer aided testing can be carried out on thousands of design iterations in order to establish that which " works best i.e. CATIA defines, simulates and tests the entire build process before the first car moves down the assembly line.

Thus, an engineer may think of changing the point of attachment of a hinge on a car hood [bonnet -Ed] with the aim of making it easier to open. The system then effects the required design change, determines how other related components would have to be changed to accommodate this e.g. hinge design and die used to stamp the hood from a metal sheet, and communicate the changes to all appropriate personnel throughout the enterprise. Consequently an innovation in one area of the development process can often be applied in other areas immediately.

In the debate Bob Lutz commented:

"The creativity of engineers is not a problem so long as you get rid of risk aversion and the fear of punishment. You get the behaviours you reward and there has to be daily, even hourly, informal recognition by senior management to encourage surfacing ideas in meetings".

At Amoco, Shared Learning (the capability to capture, store, transfer and use knowledge, learnings and effective practices across the corporation to accelerate improvement) is used to foster innovation via the Amoco Common Process (a five-step stage-gated process which utilizes the principles of knowledge management which was derived from external benchmarking). Project teams review past experiences and effective practices at the beginning of each stage using a project outline and at the end of each stage a 'Gatekeeper' (project leader) and project general manager decide whether to proceed, put the project on hold or kill the project. Lessons learned are then stored for others to learn from whatever the fate of the project in question.

In the debate Bill Lowrie said:

"People watch how leaders lead. If you are intolerant of a contrarian thinker, it will be seen. If you want people to take risks you have to recognise that".

At the European end neither Vaillant GmbH nor the Jellinek Centre (Amsterdam) are in industries that are traditionally associated with innovation. The former manufacture domestic heating boilers and appliances whilst the latter is a healthcare organisation specialising in dependency and addiction. In both cases, however, leadership in innovation has been clearly demonstrated. Manfred Ahle commented:

"Legislation drives us to get innovation right first time. We have to involve stakeholders and service people to do this. We had to clarify what real innovation is. It's not a matter of chance, it's the result of structured management systems, though it can be the result of chance discoveries. Awarding is more important than rewarding".

Jan Walburg commented:

"Healthcare systems are not developed for innovation but preventive innovation is very important. In the next ten years there will be a significant growth in predictive genetics and we are looking to improve the knowledge of where problems are likely to be".

Richard Snook of Bull UK and Ireland added:

"Bull tried to develop innovation by introducing calculated risk taking into values and sponsoring of ideas, freeing people from bureaucracy in order to develop them and measuring the effectiveness of that. We found that most people had an inhibitor, namely the pressure of work and time".

In addition John Roberts spoke of "stealing shamelessly" to "innovate as a follower" and advised that "when you see something innovative you can take it and use it possibly in quite a different way".

In summarising innovation Carla O'Dell said:

"Think of two stages, Invention and Innovation. New ideas don't always lead to success in the market and the two aspects need different kinds of best practices. Companies like 3M, Chrysler and Amoco try to understand unspoken customer ideas. Even in markets fifty years old a new approach can transform that market".

[Issue 111 (March 1998)]

NEW SIMULATION TOOL TO MANAGE INNOVATION

The Building Research Establishment and the Open University Business School have joined forces to develop a new educational tool to simulate the management of innovation based on case studies from the UK construction industry. The simulator replicates the management of change and the function of interactions within an organisation and then illustrates the differences and similarities in organisations specialising in different product markets. It then captures the innovation process and the evolution of risks and their assessment. The tool is envisaged to be of particular use to organisations which are seeking to heighten or improve their managers' awareness of the innovation process. More information may be obtained from The Building Research Establishment, Garston, Watford WD2 7LR.

MANAGING QUALITY AND INNOVATION

In 1998 the Institute of Quality Assurance held its first National Conference for around 15 years when it addressed the subject of Managing Quality In the Future [reported in *Quality Matters* Issue 118 -Ed.]. This year it held another at the Dunchurch Conference Centre near Rugby on October 5th and 6th which this time looked at Managing Quality and Innovation at which the IQA launched its new membership criteria and set out some of its plans for the future.

At the event the IQA's president, Dr. Ivan Dunstan, assured delegates that despite the fact that quality is not a subject that is known for rapid change, the IQA "will be changing". He pointed specifically to the IQA's drive to become recognised as a Chartered Institute in the not too distant future, further details of which were revealed by the secretary general Frank Steer who spoke of the need for the Institute to grow both in stature and status. In setting out the IQA's objectives he explained how the IQA "would become a learned society with a revitalised Centres of Excellence programme" and "would go a long way forward as fast as it can". He emphasised that there would be clear outputs for the IQA, citing participation with the Cabinet Office in the DTI's 'Fit for the Future' campaign and in Project Sigma with the DETR and other bodies as examples of deliverables to date. He also informed delegates of the domain name (CIFQ) for the Chartered Institute, and of the formation of the IQA's new Deming Special Interest Group which promises to be an exciting development.

A key feature of this year's event, as in 1998, was the debate for which the proposed motion was 'Does the quality profession hinder innovations?' Below we review the debate, but first an overview of the four presentations beginning with the Opening Address by Mike Harrison, Team Leader for the Supply Excellence Programme at BAe Systems.

Managing a Complex Supply Chain.

Mr. Harrison explained how change at BAe Systems had been "driven by crisis following the end of the Cold War", the nature of which had allowed the organisation "to become arrogant" about their production. The consequence of this was that "a culture of arrogance" had characterised the organisation's supply chain, which was no longer appropriate for the market which they served.

Had this culture continued, the speaker was in no doubt that the organisation "would have gone to the wall". They did, however, have one stroke fo good fortune in that one of their major customers, McDonnel Douglas, had conceived a preferred supplier certification programme which BAe Systems was invited to join. The processes in this programme left BAe management "so impressed" that they became inspired to use the process themselves to develop their own preferred supplier programme.

The programme itself was based on a combined Deming and Baldrige approach, but with the ascendance of the EFQM in the mid 1990s, the EFQM Business Excellence Model was viewed as being perhaps more appropriate for European applications than the US inspired Baldrige Model. It therefore "made sense" for the EFQM Model to be used as part of the organisation's supply chain management strategy.

In an effort to improve the performance of its supply base BAe Systems developed a phased approach from 1994 which included, most notably, "tough nut" suppliers such as GEC Marconi Avionics and Rolls Royce. Suppliers were invited to participate, most notably according to the amount of spend which they represented combined with the degree of criticality of the components which they supplied. Initial goals for the 'Out of the Crisis' programme included a 50% reduction in elapsed time, 100% schedule adherence to quality, and a 30 % reduction in the cost of operations by 1999, when they hoped to have around 60 preferred suppliers, with much of the duplication associated with the auditing process substantially reduced.

The objectives of the programme were stated as follows:

(i) To deliver a process, to assist optimised supplier performance to receive on time, and at the "point of usage, defect free products and services.

(ii) To create partnerships with a small number of high performance suppliers.

(iii) To embed the concept of continuous improvement as part of the process.

Driving up the learning and progress of suppliers was established as a key priority early on, with the measurement of performance simplified but challenging. With this approach it was hoped that the Eurofighter project would break the mould of the old time arrogance to which the speaker referred at the beginning.

Early experiences with the programme suggested that the original McDonnel Douglas approach needed refinement, most notably so that it could be applied easily beyond the first tier of suppliers, and this has now been done with the help of Kawasaki, whose production system BAe Systems subsequently benchmarked. A toolset has since been incorporated into the programme which begins with the '5S' applied to housekeeping. This has been found to be "very powerful", particularly when applied in conjunction with a continuous improvement plan, which all BAe suppliers are now expected to have.

Later refinements have focused on the management of continuous improvement which the speaker stressed "could not happen on its own". Recognition of suppliers which attain particular levels of performance in this regard are therefore motivated by an awards scheme based on a bronze, silver, gold approach. A total of £3 million has so far been spent on the programme.

The presentation was lively and attracted several questions from the floor. These included an enquiry as to how BAe measured responsiveness and reviewed the so called 'seven wastes' which the toolset requires suppliers to address. In reply the speaker explained how specific headings were used for attributes such as communication and competence with a one to five scale for performance on each. He then outlined a 'responsiveness metric' which was powerful but simplistic.

Consultant David Hewings asked how the organisation dealt with suppliers outside the preferred group and, in particular, enquired as to whether relationships were being enhanced in this area or just left to rest. Mr.Harrison admitted that BAe "was struggling to put together a strategy" as the resources required for the programme were large, but did point to one recent initiative in the form of the North West Aerospace Alliance which was actively encouraging more involvement from SMEs.

Mr. Harrison was asked to define world class and in his reply he said "I wish I could tell you what world class is". He could not, however, but advised that "when you're there you'll know". He was also asked whether certification bodies could be potentially included as key suppliers to the programme and about the extent to which key suppliers were expected to use individual tools as part of the toolset.

In his answers he stated that he saw no reason why certification bodies should not be involved, but the benefits would need to be studied very carefully. As for tool adoption, he pointed to about ten or twelve high level tools the scope of which would normally be drafted for each supplier depending on the application. "We assess tool usage and agree which tools are applicable", he said.

Quality and Working Practices

Dr Elena Antonacopoulu of the Human and Organisational Analysis Department of the Manchester Business School enlightened delegates about the effect on quality of Changing working practices, pointing specifically to the growth of strategic alliances which has placed much higher demands on the ability of organisations to collaborate to raise standards. "That is what world class is all about", she said, suggesting that as a result there were likely to be new measures of quality in people and new competencies emerging quite quickly.

Amongst the new competencies which she highlighted were the ability to develop team based work systems and to apply knowledge management, which was notably deficient in case studies and "elusive". There was a notable lack of ability to manage knowledge rather than just looking to capture it and with organisations becoming ever more complex adaptive systems, the management of knowledge was fast becoming an important influence of quality.

The new workplace was in the process of redefining the psychological contract between employer and employee and there was a strong implication that where this was being ignored there could be a serious negative impact on quality. She warned of the dangers of falls in productivity stemming from the isolation inherent in virtual teamworking, and, in particular, teleworking.

Several questions were raised as food for thought for the future, including the following:

* If quality as a notion continues to be elusive can it afford to continue being so?

* Should we not liberate the term by avoiding rigid definitions surrounding it?

* Do employees possess the skills and knowledge to speak the language of different functions and disciplines.

* What is the longevity of skills and knowledge requirements?

* What is the meaning of quality of life in the new workplace?

In the questioning which followed there was some discussion about the role of counsellors and of psychometric testing and its associated measurements. She stressed the need for care with regard to the setting under which psychometric testing is undertaken, and in assuring that one does not simply measure a set of impressions rather than achieving a true reading of personal capabilities.

Web Technology and Quality Systems.

This paper, by Nigel Girling, Strategic Advisor for The Joined Up Thinking Organisation, considers how web-based technology can be used to overcome many of the problems associated with traditional quality systems, namely a proliferation of paper and records, procedural documents that are rarely read, and large amounts of administration and maintenance:

'Almost every organisation has Microsoft Office and can therefore use the web engine that drives Internet explorer to create 'hypertext' links that enable any two or more documents to be linked together. This gives the user the ability to jump from one document to another, simply by clicking on link-enabling uses, such as the explanation of jargon terms – simply by putting a hypertext link or 'hyperlink' between the word that needs to be explained and another document, such as a glossary, giving the explanation. The user can simply jump into the other document and then jump back to the original one.

The same logic applies in linking to another related procedure; a more detailed explanation of a step in a procedure; a screen form; an e-mail form; another application such as a spreadsheet or slideshow; even an on-line training session showing how to carry out a particular step in a procedure'.

It follows that if a user does not need to see an explanation of jargon terms, he merely does not follow the links. Similarly if he does not need the on-line training he does not see it. With larger quality systems procedural documents can be broken down, possibly starting with just a top-level flowchart or checklist so that those who are familiar with the process receive a 'memory jogger' whilst others who need more detail can 'drill down' by following hypertext links to explanations, more detail of each step, training and guidance notes or other related procedures or documents:

'Document and version control is reduced to a simple one step updating of the master on-line version and an e-mail to users notifying them of the change. Changes and new processes can be introduced into the on-line quality system with -in-built links to initial training and guidance notes to assist the users in implementing the new process. The advantages and savings in time and paper are innumerable'.

'Once you are familiar with the basic concept of creating a link, it is possible to convert existing procedures into flowcharts, with levels of detail underpinning them and accessible through these hyperlink gateways'.

'There is apparently no limit to the number of levels or links through which one can drill down - the maximum I have used is 25 levels - so the only limit is your ability to structure and break down your system into the most advantageous chunks. It is even possible to insert bookmarks into a document and then enter them into the hyperlink screen along with the file and pathname, so that your link takes you not just to the file, but to a specific paragraph or section. This is especially useful in, for example, quality manuals.'

In his speech Mr. Girling spoke of this technology, written instructions for which are included in the conference literature, as being "the unbricking of the door to the granary annexe", which is what many quality systems have become. With the help of such technology quality systems can thus be transformed into databases and sources of information rather than merely sets of rules.

After the presentation he was asked how one might set about persuading old fashioned managers that such an investment is a good idea. In answering he suggested that one could start by singling out processes for which such managers are responsible and encouraging them to seek out best practice, allowing them to think about what they are best at and feeding it in as a contribution. Enabling thereby replaces command and control.

Process Mapping and Quality Improvement.

The fourth presentation by John Quinlivan, Strategic Consultant for Bywater plc, encouraged delegates to think more in terms of processes than procedures and introduced the process mapping concept as a means of improving the management of cross-functional interfaces. He spoke of re-engineering and innovation as being two areas where organisations are beginning to achieve real successes from this application, citing the following examples:

- Harley Davidson cut product delivery times from 360 to 3 days.

- Citibank cut mortgage application processing from 36 days to 15 minutes.

- Ford slashed warranty costs per car from $1,100 to $100.

- Taco Bell eliminated management layers and went from 350 supervisors for 18 restaurants to 100 for 2,300.

- Hallmark Cards re-engineered product development from 2 to 3 years to less than 1 year.

These benefits were described as "real achievables and real success stories" and there were many more, assured the speaker. The opportunities for improvement everywhere in the organisation were, he said, "limitless", with many organisations now mapping processes on intranets to achieve efficiency improvement of 50% or more. Some organisations, such as water companies, are being driven to map their processes as a result of regulation which is setting objectives for around 40 high level measurements. In other cases global human resources programmes are being rolled out with mapping being undertaken by the employees themselves.

In order to help organisations to gain a foothold with this methodology, the speaker provided some tips and a list of lessons learnt by those who had already been down the route of process mapping application. These included the following:

*Develop a process model before you start to map objectives.

*Define the scope of the process being mapped, its start point and its finish point.

*Consider how best to represent the process (paper documents, interface with IT systems, web enabled etc.)

*Map the process and how it works now, not just how it should work, including any error and rework loops.

*Quantify cycle time and throughout if possible to model, for example, 100 units going through the process.

* Map at a common level of detail (nobody can understand a hundred boxes on a piece of paper).

* Clearly define business objectives e.g. reduce process cycle time by x days.

* Use process teams to translate objectives into metrics (cycle time metrics are best worked backwards through the process to ensure that the required output is achieved on time).

The Debate.

The debate was chaired by former IQA President Norman Burgess with the case in favour of the motion being put by Dennis Barlow, Quality Manager for Stanmore and Portsmouth of BAe Systems, whilst the case against was advanced by Trevor Wilmer, Managing Director of EAQA and Director of the Association of British Certification Bodies (ABCB).

Mr. Barlow argued that whilst quality assurance invariably strives for consistency the meaning of the word 'quality' is rarely interpreted consistently, and that often there is a considerable difference between the interpretation of quality as 'compliance to specifications' and the definition of quality in the Oxford English Dictionary which specifies 'technical excellence'. Quality professionals, he said, traditionally discourage change by insisting on conformance to specifications and this leads to a fundamental problem when it comes to managing innovation. He suggested that the future focus had to be on customer satisfaction and risk management and the failure of some quality professionals to recognise this is hindering innovation. He concluded his case as follows:

"Until there is true customer focus and involvement in managing risk, quality professionals will not be a true part of the management team and until they are part of the management team, and relinquish their fixation with compliance, they will hinder innovation".

In his counterargument Mr. Wilmer contested that quality assurance provides a basis for innovation that can be checked by internal audit. This basis, he said, depended on the individuals and culture of the organisation, not just the quality professional. Then he urged the audience to consider the question 'Who is the quality professional?'. If this was the quality manager, then he would not inhibit innovation as he is essential to the process of examining the development of change. If, on the other hand, the quality professional was the consultant, he pointed to a whole range of new tools and techniques which consultants were introducing. If it was the quality systems assessor, then the new standard ISO9000:2000 had to be considered along with its many changes.

When both men had put their case the debate was opened up to the audience. One delegate suggested that many people who may wish to be professional simply cannot because the system impedes them, and that many quality professionals lately simply haven't survived because they have been prevented from being professional. The role of the quality professional was argued to be to enhance people doing things rather than stopping them and this delegate concluded that whilst the quality professional may not hinder innovation, the systems of compliance under which he is required to function most certainly do.

Another viewpoint was that 90% of industry limits what the quality professional can achieve through the imposition of job specifications, whilst another was that the new ISO9000 standard "was in danger of scaring off top management" by virtue of making them responsible for quality in place of the quality professional. Nigel Girling argued that the perception of what the quality profession is and does on the part of chief executives "was a problem" whilst another delegate contested that the most important process for any quality professional was the management of change.

One delegate presented the argument that people who follow procedures are frequently not very good at creating them. He concluded that quality professionals "probably do hinder innovation even though we like it ourselves". This idea was supported by another delegate who claimed that "quality professionals hinder innovation because of the tools used", auditing and management review being seen very much as tools of compliance and regulation. A lady delegate then explained how as a quality professional she had been able to introduce many ideas for people to discuss and that as a result people in her organisation "had been very receptive".

Discussions then returned to the role of auditors and a suggestion that auditing should be against results rather than procedures. It was argued that "quality professionals will support and promote innovation if they do this". In response Mr. Wilmer assured that "a quantum leap of auditing expertise is on its way".

Some delegates expressed the view that most quality managers have neither enabled nor inhibited innovation because they have been traditionally too much at the sharp end, whilst others were of the view that quality professionals could either inhibit or assist innovation depending on which 'hat' they were wearing.

In the vote which followed around 60% of the audience came out against the motion with 40% in favour, i.e. the majority felt that as quality professionals they did not hinder innovation.

SWEDES LEAD INNOVATION INDEX

Sweden leads the first EU Innovation Scoreboard drawn up with guidelines to boost performance and take full advantage of the knowledge society. The scoreboard aims to help benchmark and build on best practice in other Member States using indicators from the four areas of human resources; knowledge creation; transmission and application of knowledge; and innovation finance output and markets.

Sweden has above average figures for 12 of the 16 indicators and is followed by Finland (8), Denmark (7) and Germany (7). Further details may be obtained from The European Commission, 8 Storey's Gate, London SW1 P 3AT.

Chapter Seven

Achieving Transformation

The British Deming Association (BDA) was active throughout the 1990s until sadly, an act of fraud brought about its demise shortly after the Millennium. The late Dr. W. Edwards Deming, to whose teaching this chapter is specifically devoted, regularly addressed the BDA's Annual Forum which, until 1995, was traditionally held in the spring at the National Motorcycle Museum. It later moved to Loughborough University where it continued to be held for the second half of the decade.

In 2000 a noble attempt was made to resurrect the BDA in the form of The Deming Forum which at the time of writing still exists. The IQA meanwhile has established a Deming Special Interest Group to serve as a think tank for former BDA members.

The BDA events of the 1990s featured a regular clientele of high calibre UK and international speakers who brought quality to life with their varied and alternative viewpoints. The death of Dr. Deming in December 1993 was thus one of the sadder highlights of the decade, which undoubtedly altered the fortunes of the BDA which in its time made an outstanding contribution to quality in the UK.

The following compilation of articles begins with Dr. Deming's address to the Fifth Annual BDA Forum in 1992, which proved to be his last. It also includes his final European seminar in Zurich in July 1993 and Quality Matters' obituary. Other articles include most notably the Deming Memorial Lectures which became an annual feature of the Sheffield Hallam conferences from 1995 onwards, and the Deming Forum of 2000.

SURVIVAL IS NOT COMPULSORY: DEMING SPEAKS AT ANNUAL FORUM

The British Deming Association held its Annual Forum at the National Motorcycle Museum in Birmingham from 28th to 30th April with the theme 'Survival is not Compulsory'.

Dr. Deming delivered his presentation on Day Two in two sessions lasting approximately an hour and fifteen minutes each, beginning with a challenge to delegates to 'turn overboard the theories and practices of the present', including the present style of rewarding and dealing with each other, and the all too common practice of ranking people, judging them and introducing competition between people and teams.

It is the simplest thing, he said, to destroy a system by making components strive to achieve individual competitive measures, and he suggested that it should be a function of government to assist business rather than to harass it.

He made reference to a meeting of top business executives in Japan in which some 200 suppliers and customers had met with a common aim of not putting each other out of business, or of creating unemployment, which all acknowledged to be bad in the long term for their mutual survival and for the survival of the country. The goal was optimisation for everybody and they worked for 13 hours a day, five days a week for a month to ensure that this was achieved. With this startling example of management co-operation, delegates were asked to consider whether they feel that it is going to be they or their Japanese competitor that will be ahead in five years. [This could be the beginning of a Japanese cartel!-Ed].

The message was clearly that the formation of win-win relationships was crucial to the survival mode. Win-lose relationships are pointless because in the long term they merely degenerate into lose-lose, because everyone loses ultimately through their proliferation. Unless you optimize the whole system you all lose.

The role of the monopoly in achieving optimization was then discussed, with the assertion that it was monopoly organisations which were in fact best placed to be of service to the world. The contribution of welfare from monopolies has been, he said, very great, and he spoke of the US telephone service as 'once the envy of the world'. Now, however, it has become 'telephones without a telephone system'.

Similarly in the automotive industry three companies in Detroit in 1960 each had a monopoly but they were worried about their share of the market and each wanted to take more by taking from their competitor. Hundreds of thousands of families wanted motor cars, and the huge untapped market for cheaper, more dependable cars was there for the taking, but by being preoccupied with competition between themselves, the opportunity for win-win was lost and it was the Japanese who consequently succeeded. Will they ever learn? Was Deming's message.

We are now in the best position, Deming says, to help everybody in many areas, provided that we are able and prepared to view the whole world as a system and accept that a system must be managed – it won't manage itself. The bigger the system the more difficult it is to manage, but the greater are the potential benefits from optimisation. Destroy the people of a country and you don't have much left.

To obtain the desired win-win situation, components of a system must work for the common good of the whole system and not for individual profit centres. Delegates were asked if the abilities of their companies were equal to the sum of people's abilities in it [which presumably it would be if everyone worked for the good of the system-Ed].

Dr. Deming then turned to education and asked how many students or pupils had failed as a result of the teacher failing to understand the concept of variation. Management, education and government operate under the supposition that all people are alike and they're not:

"People are born with a need for esteem and a yearning for learning, but what do we do with it? Institute bonuses for high rank and a system of humiliation".

Money, says Dr. Deming, is no motivator. Doubling the pay of everyone has no effect. He described how he had been to meetings where people had been in a position to leave for another job for higher pay, but had not done so because they felt they could contribute more where they were.

Finally, Dr. Deming stressed that demoralizing people was not going to create any incentive for improvement. Once demoralized most people stay demoralized. It's no incentive. He described as 'pitiful' the fact that so many should be made demoralized by the systems in which they work.

Questions and Answers.

One feature of the Forum was a substantial allocation of time to afford delegates the opportunity to question the speakers, in particular Dr. Deming and Myron Tribus.

Dr. Deming was asked at the end of his speech if he felt that the Japanese were happy and he said he thought they were because they had a purpose in life. Most know what their job is and why it was important.

He was asked to elaborate on his views on monopoly and to comment on the role of regulatory authorities when one supplier is dominant in the market. His response was that if people understood the concept of a system there would not be a need for regulatory authorities. Regulatory authorities often do not understand that any monopoly has a requirement to undertake research. They feel that they have done their job if they succeed in driving prices down and in this respect he said 'they can go too far'.

In the context of regarding an industry or a country as a system Dr. Deming was asked to comment. on. the reasons for the failure of Communism in Eastern Europe, and he answered briefly by asserting that in these regimes the concept of achieving maximum benefit from the development of win-win situations did not exist. [It was clearly impeded by the command system - Ed].

Another question highlighted the fact that people who often rise to the top are the power seekers rather than the best leaders, and Dr. Deming said that such individuals 'were not leaders at all' and suggested that to resolve this problem a new theory was needed.

He was asked if he could supply an example of a system where change had begun at the bottom rather than at the top and in reply quoted the example of the abolition of merit rating in General Motors where benefits achieved in one part of the organisation resulted in the principle 'catching on' in the rest.

Dr. Deming was asked to comment on the usefulness of BS5750 as an international standard for industry and said that he still felt that it was 'quality by inspection'. Myron Tribus, however, was of the opinion that it could still have benefits in allowing people at lower levels in organisations to obtain some of the attention that they needed from the top and for some organisations it 'can get them started', but he questioned the amount of energy and effort that was being spent on it.

[Issue 55 (July 1993)]

LEADERSHIP MATTERS

The BDA's sixth Annual Conference at Birmingham's National Motorcycle Museum on 12th and 13th May examined Leadership in some detail. Papers focused on how to lead as well as how to manage. The emphasis was on the fostering of win-win relationships, development of the win-win society, and the ability to adopt a systems approach to economics and management.

The Quality Way

In the opening presentation Myron Tribus, a Director of Exergy, whose company specialises in the design of advanced high efficiency power production systems, drew a parallel between computer systems and

476

organisations which compared a Disc Operating System (DOS) to the corporate culture of a company, which is termed a 'Brain Operating System' or BOS.

Most of the BOS is not written, as it exists only in the minds of the management. Just as the improvement of computer programs through changes in application programs is limited by the DOS, so economic problems arise because companies attempt to change their brain application programs without changing the BOS. The company thus gives up with application programs such as QC Circles, Just-In-Time, statistical process control and quality function deployment as a result of failing to realize that the problem is not the application program but the fact that their culture is obsolete.

Dr. Deming has been leading a crusade in the West with the aim of loading a new BOS into our organisation. Unfortunately many have become discouraged after loading the new BOS version, because they have allowed it to cohabit with the old one. Others have loaded the new BOS successfully but failed to update their application programs (QC Circles, SPC etc.) so their performance did not improve. This compares with the attempt to run old application programs with a new DOS giving the effect of slowing down a computer.

Clearly it is necessary to introduce both the BOS update and updated application programs. To do this the company has to overcome its resistance to change, which is not just a psychological problem:

'Any genuine system improvement comes only after a thorough study of the system, by the people who are trying to improve it. Nobody is too old, nobody is too high in rank to learn the new management theory, the theory which is at the root of the new BOS, and to use this theory to study the system'.

It follows that the BOS needs to be able to deal with quality improvements that are cross-functional. The tools and techniques of the 'quality sciences' work within a social system that is embedded in a management system designed by management. These tools and techniques require co-operation to be effective and are thus either helped or hindered by the social system.

The latest versions of the BOS 'must contend with application programs for all aspects of profound knowledge (theory of variation, theory of knowledge, human psychology and systems theory) and must be able to deal with them simultaneously'. The Chief Executive Officer (CEO) needs to be able to manage the managerial system, the social system and where the work gets done.

It is emphasised that everything a CEO undertakes to do involves both management and leadership, with an act of managing badly being also an example of bad leadership.

The BOS 'must be able to deal intelligently with variation', just as the DOS and hardware have to be able to contend with numbers in the handling of statistical computer programs. Also there must be an understanding as to how variation 'can infect a system and produce bad effects far from the location where the variations are caused:

'The managers who do not understand the elementary theory of variation cannot know what will be the results of the actions they decide to take'.

The need for the CEO to understand the concepts behind the design of experiments is emphasised since without it , it will not be known what is reported is reliable.

Likewise making management decisions on the basis of ratios and business status reports is criticised as any sense of the variability in the data which produced them tends to be absent. Also management by walking around 'can be a menace' if the CEO does not understand variation and the theory of sampling.

The old BOS, characterised by 'the relationships of power that lead to a win-lose logic and to the progressive destruction of our world', has to be replaced with one based on win-win logic that establishes between people relationships based on knowledge rather than power. This is described as 'a revolution of thought as important as the birth of scientific thought in Europe that Rene Descartes promoted three hundred years ago'.

Leadership today

John Adair, an international consultant in leadership and management development, continued to expound on the relationship between leadership and management in his speech entitled 'Leadership Today'. This introduced the attributes of motivation and teamwork, drawing attention to the recent Japanese trend towards examining more deeply the motivational side of quality.

He explained that half of our motivation comes from within, whilst the other half comes from outside, most notably from the leadership that we encounter. A key message for senior management was to get their half right before complaining about others. "You hold the cards, or at least 50 per cent of them, in relation to Quality", he asserted.

With this in mind, eight principles of motivation were outlined:

* be motivated yourself

* select people who are highly motivated

* treat each person as an individual (because treating them as a set of numbers will not motivate)

* set targets that are realistic but challenging

* always remember that progress motivates

* provide fair rewards

* give recognition

This was followed with a set of hallmarks of a high performance team, namely:

* setting of clear, realistic objectives

* existence of a shared sense of purpose

* best use of resources

* an atmosphere of openness

* review of progress

*ability to build on experience i.e. learn from mistakes

*ability to ride out storms

It was suggested that the more people are able to share in decision making the more motivated they will be to carry out those decisions. The art of leadership was seen as being akin to conducting an orchestra, with the objective being to develop a high performance team.

The modern trend is towards the leader manager and an 'hourglass' model of career progression was used to show workers moving through the 'narrow neck of specialisation' into broad based disciplines of management.

A culture where people own their own development was said to be very much needed, as was the need for trust:

"If you trust boys, they may let you down, but if you don't trust them they will do you down".

[It follows that trust is an essential prerequisite for the elimination of the fatal syndrome of power struggles that has ruined companies and wrecked economies-Ed].

Leadership, Furniture and Results.

The first of two presentations focusing on the practical aspects of leadership was given by Jim McIngvale, President and owner of Houston based furniture retailers Gallery Furniture. This is recognised as one of America's top furniture retailers with the highest sales volume per square foot in the USA. The company experienced a 20 per cent sales increase over nine months which is attributed to the implementation of Dr. Deming's Quality Improvement Process coupled with 'Mattress Mac's' visionary leadership.

The starting point was top management's frustration at the fact that the store's closing percentage (the ratio between the number of visiting customers and the number of sales) persistently held at around 45 per cent, irrespective of whatever management incentives, competitions or threats were imposed. To improve it was decided to institute a system whereby at the end of the month the best sales people would be rewarded by being allowed to take as many customers as they pleased the next month in a 'batting order', but it didn't work. The few who won became embarrassed by the differential treatment they received, whilst the losers (the majority) felt as if they were failures, and figures started to be fudged:

'At the high point of the madness the first placed salesperson received $500, the second place would get $300, and the third would get $200. The thinking was that people worked harder for a carrot, but the only thing that changed were the faces'.

Not long after, the company experienced a turnover of salespeople of 10 to 15 a month, spending an ever-increasing amount of time and money hiring, training and firing in the search for the super-achiever and was bewildered at why half of the staff were 'below average'.

Something clearly had to be done and in October 1990 the speaker attended an inspirational seminar in Houston where he was enlightened by the Deming philosophy. However, he remained sceptical at the suggestion that merit pay, incentive pay and commissions should be abolished. Discussions with Carl Sewell, founder of Sewell Village Cadillac, a successful Cadillac dealership and later with Ed Baker, Head of Quality at Ford, convinced 'Mattress Mac' that there could well be some merit in doing this and moving toward a salary based salesforce. This was obviously going to test his leadership skills quite considerably.

With the system of commission then in force the salespeople had to achieve a minimum of $7000 a week in sales plus $400 in add-on 'chemical' sales (such fabric, leather and wood-care protection) to receive a 10 per cent commission. Otherwise, whatever the circumstances, the commission was just 5 per cent. Crossing the boundary from a loser to a winner was therefore of paramount importance to the sales staff who were readily motivated, by hook or by crook, to meet the quota:

'On Thursday evenings it wasn't uncommon to see customers leaving with a dumb-founded expression on their face, their arms full with up to 30 bottles of furniture polish at one time'.

In January 1991, an 'act of faith' was taken with the removal of quotas, but still with the retention of commission. Some improvement was reported, but still some fear remained.

In March 1991 Dr. Deming was approached and asked for his opinion as to whether incentive pay or commission could be better for sales people. "Will you ever learn?" was the response.

Eventually, exasperated with the old problem of disputes over commission when more than one salesperson had helped a customer, a salary system was introduced based on incomes received in 1990, with a profit sharing plan whereby if the company profited, everyone would profit equally.

The fear of management that salespeople would become lazy and have no incentive to do their share never materialised. In practice the reverse happened : they worked more and were eager to contribute and prove their worth. They developed a vested interest in what they and their fellow associates do in contributing to the total system:

'Now a furniture buying team meets with representatives and travels to market, making decisions that were once made by overpaid buyers who had little or no contact with the buying public. This change alone has saved our company tens of thousands of dollars'.

In another example a team of associates pooled their talents to build two display galleries, which the speaker described as two of the most beautiful he had ever seen, at a cost of under $7,000. The commercial cost would have been over $70,000. The saving 'went straight to the bottom line' and was shared by all in the company's profit sharing programme. In the past associates would have felt that they were losing out by doing something other than selling, and this saving would have been unlikely to have been realised.

Cross training, which previously could not be justified in terms of the time and assumed revenue loss, has become 'rampant'. The older and more senior are helping the newer salespeople rather than viewing them as competitive or as a threat to their income. The thousands of dollars spent each week advertising for sales staff was now able to be saved and redeployed.

481

Payroll takes an hour a week (where it used to take nine) and the role of management has changed from one of ranking, rating, firing and refereeing commission battles to one of helping, coaching and nurturing.

A system must, however, be managed. It will not manage itself and if left to do so, its components will tend to revert to competitiveness and selfish instincts. Positive interactions and co-operation between people and departments is essential. To achieve this management needs to focus on optimization (the process of orchestrating the efforts of all components toward achievement of the stated Aim). This needs a combination of independence and interdependence.

Thus the balancing of the sense of being an individual with the sense of being a team member are seen as being a clear step forward.

The speaker points to a failure to understand variation as a central problem and warns the business community not to be 'sold down the river on competition'.

Leadership Experiences in a Manufacturing Company.

Jim McIngvale's presentation was well complemented by the second presentation on practical leadership, this time from the UK manufacturing sector. It was given by Mark Canny, Managing Director of South Wales based consumer durables manufacturer Hills Industries, who employ around 130 staff and have a turnover of around £6 million. This is a wholly owned subsidiary of an Australian company.

On his arrival from Australia, Mr. Canny was confronted with a scene which is probably all too common in British manufacturing industry (at least amongst those companies which are still managing to survive), namely performance which at best could be described as 'lacklustre'. It had a hierarchical management structure, with management by control exercised by the Managing Director; a management group that was 'anxious and broken' and not prepared to be critical for fear of being disciplined. There was an inconsistent approach both strategically and culturally, with ground rules that changed with each new managing director. Management would wait to see what the new rules were and adapt their behaviour accordingly in order to survive or keep their job:

'Slow-moving and obsolete stock was not highlighted – to do so would mean assigning blame to someone (followed by retribution). But stock was held "just in case" to hide the problems of "returns" and lack of accounts forecasting'.

Clearly this situation had to change and as Managing Director the speaker saw that it was his responsibility to lead the change. [The system would not manage itself-Ed].

A window of opportunity existed in that traditionally the Managing Director had at least been supported by his team. A 'pretty tough couple of days' thus allowed a set of aims to be developed in the form of a set of statements:

There was 'pretty strong agreement' on what the company believed in, but the speaker was clear about his view on mission statements : "many are glib and the one liners are something of a joke".

The key issue in making these beliefs happen was identified as development of pride of workmanship, for which the ownership of processes on the part of employees was crucial [N.B.: Deming's Twelfth Point –remove barriers to pride of workmanship-Ed]. The speaker accepted that "initially I got in the way far too often", and there was a clear exercise in learning for the leaders in being able to balance the role of coach or counsellor with the need to allow managers to manage.

Experiential learning was introduced to help break down the barriers, allowing managers to explore customer/supplier relationships in a non-threatening way. In particular the need to afford the less forceful managers the opportunity "to show their colours and demonstrate their contribution".

Some 'amazing discoveries' were then reported as people began to understand what their associates were doing up and down the line, and learned how to view their organisation as a system. As a practical example the speaker described the rectification of an intermittent fault in sprayers, for which there were no formal goods returned analyses. The supplier changed his process of manufacturing 10 inch length tubes such that one in seven became 12 inches. The company never complained but the effect was potentially very harmful to the business because the longer tubes jammed against the base of the sprayer preventing it from functioning correctly. Many of these were returned, with unknown liquids inside, which inhibited or prevented testing. Inspection was seen as' a means to assign blame' and therefore not the answer.

It was emphasized that the company did not introduce the belief system in accordance with the Deming approach as an 'instant solution'. It had a gentle introduction via an outside consultant. In common with Jim McIngvale the speaker sees a spreading of the understanding of processes and variation as a key to future prosperity. He pointed out that his company had not 'jumped overnight to be a model company' although there had been clear benefits such as the 'milestone' of ISO9000 certification and substantial savings like the 'appearance of £60,000 of scrap saved'.

Quality Matters Comments: Each of these four presentations have brought out some common features relating to leadership; training for the future; the need for an understanding of the principles of variation by top management, and recognition that an organisation as a system will not manage itself. John

Adair explained well the need for humility to prevail over arrogance as far as leadership is concerned. This was well supported by Myron Tribus' call for an end to relationships based on power and the foolhardy win-lose logic, which was well exemplified in Jim McIngvale's presentation.

[Issue 56 (August 1993)]

DEMING AND SOCIETY

Towards a Deming Economy.

Ian Lambert, co-founder of the Motivation Marketing Board, based in London, described how the principles of the Deming philosophy of win-win logic could be translated into a macroeconomic environment. An organisation can be viewed as a system, and considerable benefits gained as competition gives way to co-operation. So, why not apply the same logic to a country and improve the quality of life for all?

Ian Lambert argues that companies now need a Deming Economy whilst we all need a win-win society in which both companies and individuals can flourish. History has shown that the unjust society ultimately becomes the impoverished society. Consequently it is imperative that all philosophies and policies that seek to benefit some people at the expense of others be abandoned. To do this requires a whole new political economy which goes beyond the conventional ideas of socialism, capitalism and the mixed economy and towards the mating of ideas so that more powerful ideas can be bred. The Motivation Marketing Board's guiding principle is therefore that:

'You can achieve whatever you want if you will only help enough people to achieve what they want'.

The starting point for such a political economy is not easy to establish, but one possibility might be an examination of a country's system of taxation.

One of the worst ways in which government creates uncertainty and inconsistency is, according to the speaker, to have a system of taxation with no coherent framework that is constantly being tinkered with, once or twice a year in Britain's case, more frequently in the case of some other countries:

'The uncertain tax environment makes long term investing a hazardous business, and thus contributes to the much castigated "short-termism" in the investment markets'.

It follows that the distorting effect which taxation has on the markets for goods services and investment needs to be reduced, and to do this the speaker recommends the establishment of a 'Taxpayers' Constitution' in the form of a cross-party framework of principles for all taxation. Government, he says, 'needs to stop its tug-of-war taxation where the tax burden falls heaviest on the most productive and they in turn seek to throw the burden onto others', i.e. taxation must be incentive based rather than disincentive based.

All of the present income, corporation, capital gains and inheritance taxes are win-lose and in consequence it is 'little wonder taxpayers go to such lengths to avoid them'. The resulting redistribution of wealth continues to cripple the economy, reduce the quality of government services and reduce the quality of lifestyles generally. Sooner or later win-lose becomes lose-lose and this system according to Ian Lambert therefore has to change.

The change which is recommended is based on the principle of restitution, already used in law as a remedy for 'unjust enrichment', for example when two parties make a contract which later becomes void by virtue of a common mistake of fact and one party has profited at the expense of another. It is argued that there is a moral basis to apply this principle whenever a benefit is conferred on another without a contract, as in the case of non-market based government services where there is no contract. The government has the right and arguably the duty to fund these by taxation levied on the basis of restitution. This is win-win as payment is made according to the value rather than the cost of what is received.

A primary example of a restitution tax is a tax on land values i.e. on the annual economic rent of every site, valued in its unimproved state:

'This is quite unlike the old rating system, because there would be no taxes on buildings and improvements, and therefore no disincentive to produce and improve'.

The imposition of such a tax is said to be win-win as the government reclaims for the benefit of the community the value of the benefits it bestows on the community through infrastructure spending, whilst at the same time dampening unproductive real estate speculation and the resulting boom and bust cycles that have crippled the economy (the British experience).

In his paper the speaker gives his own views on the subject of privatisation, pointing out in particular that for privatisation to succeed there must be identifiable suppliers and consumers both of whom have the freedom to decide whether or not they wish to contract. It follows that privatisation is inappropriate for the police, courts, national defence and emergency services, but not for activities such as air transport, telecommunications, oil production or road haulage.

Non-privatised government services 'must be improved by government setting quantity and quality targets and informing citizens of what they can expect' as there is no consumer market to provide 'the necessary discipline'. Dr. Deming has stressed the need for care in this area, as the goals 'present significant practical problems for public administrators who are not trained as managers'. The training of such people in how to motivate their staff to achieve collective goals is seen as 'one of the gaps the Motivation Marketing Board seeks to fill'.

The vision of the win-win society presented by Mr. Lambert is described in more detail in the BDA publication *'Out of the Crisis with George, Mises and Deming'*. It is but one of probably several approaches to this subject, and the mating of ideas could no doubt result ultimately in a more powerful theory. What does appear to be clear, however, is that at present economists and politicians, none of whom successfully predicted the depression in the first place, appear to have no solution for it, as Mr. Lambert says. The business environment is characterised by 'chronic uncertainty' and the need for a whole new approach to the economy and to politics in general is clearly evident. Quality Matters can only endorse the conclusion that 'competition is completely antiethical to free trade' and is at best 'win-lose', with more in common with war than free trade. Interested readers are referred to the book *'No Contest: the Case against Competition'* by Alfie Kohn (ISBN 0-395-63125-4)

Following the presentation it was suggested to Mr. Lambert that whilst the philosophy of his presentation may make sound sense to an audience of logical thinking people, such as those at the BDA conference, outside, the actions of evil people are having a very profound effect on communities, and he was invited to comment. In response he pointed out that whilst this may be the case, we needed to have a goal towards which we could all move and that that was the aim of the presentation.

(The *Quality Matters* view is that where evil people exist in a system, they are largely from the extreme end of a statistical distribution that represents the product of that system. The closer one moves to a win-win society the more the distribution will shift away from the range where these extreme cases are found. In short, they will tend to disappear altogether, as mutual trust, respect and the desire to work for the common good take over from a desire to compete for reward at the expense of others.)

The Fladbury Philosophy: A Vision for Team Britain.

Ian Lambert presented a vision for a win-win society. This, it is felt, was well complemented by the presentation by David Train, an engineer by profession, who has subsequently turned to consulting and has coached the British Olympic canoeing squad since 1979, who gave his vision for Team Britain.

In a lively one hour speech he pictured England, currently floundering in the wrong water with 'no coach in sight', having 'scrapped very good industry stupidly' and 'wrecked all our small businesses as a result of stupid economic policies', which have been based on the foolhardy idea that people dont like work or only work for money. This idea, he said, 'is rubbish'.

In practice we don't live in a world where everyone is independent, but in one where everyone is different and interdependent. There is a place for everyone in the crew. Mr. Train explained how following World War II Dr. Deming and other American 'coaches' achieved 'one of the greatest coaching achievements in peace in the history of mankind by getting 90 million people to pull together as a crew. This 'remarkable achievement' is, he says, 'a lesson for any coach or leader, whether it be parent, grandparent, teacher, manager or politician' and he suggests that if the world is to survive it is one that all of our children should know.

Dr. Deming gave the industrial leaders of Japan a vision and showed them how to achieve it in a time of crisis. Now Europe, America and almost all of the world is in a state of crisis and there is consequently ' a magnificent opportunity for a coach to emerge with a new vision and a new way of doing it'.

Mr. Train explained how, inspired by Dr. Deming, he asked himself the question 'what would I do faced with the situation Dr. Deming was in when he went to Japan?' and came up with the following aim for Britain:

'To show the world how to transform a society moving increasingly to cut-throat competition, conflict and increasing criminality to a one based on care, co-operation and creative competition'.

In order to illustrate how this might be achieved the speaker introduces 'The Fladbury Philosophy' in which group psychology can be used to overcome the problems of fear and humiliation in learning:

'If we wish to teach co-operation it is in the doing that it will stick. It is easier teaching co-operation and teamwork in a boat......in a rapidly fragmenting world, our children will need to look at where we are going and for their survival have to co-operate with others'.

The 'raft' of 'The Fladbury Philosophy' is a 'Bell Boat' designed to provide, through fun and fitness, the starting point in doing, making, thinking, and managing for people of all ages and levels of abilities, including those with special needs, and a series of events to promote the philosophy of care, co-operation and creative competition has been created.

Helped by the Deming philosophies which transformed Japan, and which are based on co-operation and the removal of internal conflict, Britain is nervously preparing for its voyage into Europe. It is 'a long term marathon' for which young people in particular need to be prepared, and whilst they 'watch their elders argue on the bank of mainstream Europe' it is hoped that the paddle coaches 'can inspire them to take to the water and find their place in a new world order'. The 'Bell Boat' on which the young of Britain 'can help their nation rediscover its vision' is now on the water, providing 'a new image of fun and creative competition' and 'a new team boat for a new world team'.

[*Quality Matters comments:* One of the key principles upon which this new vision is founded is that of creative competition. Opinions may differ as to what this exactly constitutes, but there would appear to be a general consensus that for competition to be successful it must support continuous improvement of the whole group and not create a culture of winners and losers with the inherent fear of failure that that induces. It could be argued that creative competition in this context is not really competition at all, but more a form of benchmarking in which 'competitors' seek to improve their own performance by working alongside the best in class so that the performance of the whole group is continually improved].

[Issue 57 (September 1993)]

QUALITY, PRODUCTIVITY AND COMPETITIVE POSITION

Recent issues of *Quality Matters* have included reports from this year's Annual Conference of the British Deming Association. Dr. W. Edwards Deming did not speak personally at this event, as in previous years. He, did, however, address an audience at the Swissotel, Zurich, Switzerland, from 6th to 9th July giving what many believe could be his last seminar on the European continent. The title was 'Quality, Productivity and Competitive Position' and there was a good representation from the United Kingdom, aided by the British Deming Association.

Now 92 years of age, Dr. Deming has been acclaimed as the 'Founding Father' of quality management, helping amongst other things to pioneer the quality system that turned around Japanese industry.

His latest book, *The New Economics*, on which much of the seminar was based, builds on the principle that a transformation for improvement is not automatic; it must be learned and led with profound knowledge consisting of:

* appreciation for a system

* knowledge of the principles of variation

* an appreciation of the theory of knowledge

* an understanding of the psychology of individuals, society and change.

All four of these concepts are related and apply the principle that the components of any system should reinforce each other instead of being competitive. They apply to government and education as well as to private industry, providing a new map or theory for the whole country, as well as optimising individual organisations.

As a first step towards achieving transformation, Dr. Deming recommended that one considers the notion of transformation of the individual, i.e. looking to ourselves to change our thought processes, so that we begin to use co-operation and win-win as the basis of negotiation rather than win-lose, which ultimately is lose-lose. In time these individuals too become 'transformed'.

Appreciation for a System.

A system ,according to Dr. Deming, is 'a network of interdependent components that work together to accomplish an aim'. The aim is important because without one there is no system, and the interdependence is important because it is through this that success is gained. The greater the level of interdependence, the greater is the need for communication and co-operation. The interdependence can then lead to greatness(e.g. in an orchestra) everyone supporting each other, i.e. there are no 'prima donnas'.

A system will not, however, either understand itself or manage itself. It has thus to be managed. Left to itself it will merely 'break up into individual profit centres and become destroyed'.

If it is accepted that a system must be managed, the next question must surely be how one could or should set about doing it. One method that seems to have found favour with some managers is that of Management by Objectives (MBO). This 'sounded great', but as practised, the company's objectives become parcelled out to divisions, reducing interdependence such that the system returns to individual profit centres, and consequently the system self-destructs.

In 'The New Economics' Dr. Deming introduces the Management of People as fundamental to the management of a system, suggesting that:

'We are living under the tyranny of the prevailing style of interaction between people, between teams, between divisions. We need to throw overboard our theories and practices of the present and build afresh. We must throw overboard the idea that competition is a necessary way of life'.

Unfortunately most of management and government at present are pressing for localised profitability regardless of the harm that it is doing, with the result that companies, organisations and whole countries are being sub-optimised. Their overall abilities do not equate with the sum of the abilities of their people. Negative interactions occur which hamper the organisation. Dr. Deming comments:

'One of management's main responsibilities is to know about the existence of interactions, to perceive how they originate, then to change negative and zero interactions into positive interactions'.

Current accounting practice unfortunately reinforces the incorrect perception that decisions made during development are independent of future costs, including capital expenditures plus maintenance operations and losses suffered by customers. The phenomenon of divided or shared responsibility results often in nobody being responsible for a particular task:

'If the worker can fill out his [payroll] card correctly, expect him to do it -let him do it. Do not take responsibility away from him by sharing it with his foreman'.

Divided responsibility has to be distinguished, however, from joint responsibility, and Dr. Deming asserts that anyone who works in an organisation works jointly, or should, with their suppliers and customers. Thus, two people who sign a note are jointly responsible for payment, whilst greater interdependence between customers and suppliers makes for joint responsibility in providing a product or service. [This would include internal customers -as with the orchestra example -Ed].

Responsibility implies decision making, individual or joint, which in turn implies that an element of risk is necessarily a part of management, since there is always a risk of being wrong. It follows that management in any form is prediction. The simplest plan requires it. In order to predict, however, meaningful data and a state of statistical control is required.

The Red Beads Experiment.

The concept of statistical control was shown by means of the well known Red Beads Experiment, which has been a classic feature of Dr. Deming's seminars for many years. Six 'willing workers' produced output (50 beads) using a process which showed variation in the amount of defective red beads (as distinct from white) that are produced. Results showed that no 'willing worker' could be predicted to be better than any other in the future and differences between them and between days were attributable to common causes. Action against the workers, such as putting them on probation, made no difference, although one way to reduce defective output is to reduce the proportion of defective incoming material (a managerial responsibility).

Ranking and Reward.

The Red Beads Experiment shows what happens when classic bad management is applied i.e. rewarding and punishing the 'willing workers' (who each gave their best efforts) for the performance of the process, for which they were able to offer no suggestions for improvement.

It shows in a simple way why the ranking of people, teams, salesmen, plants, divisions, departments etc. merely ranks the effect of the process on people. Pay on performance 'sounds great but cannot be done':

"You need to know what someone can do, but it is fatal to set quotas. People think that by meeting them they have done their job".

The ranking and reward of individuals, schools and districts does not improve the system. The scales are arbitrary and achieve nothing. The scores which a school achieves is not a measure of knowledge in the nation. In the UK there is a belief by some politicians that regular testing and ranking of schools will produce improvement. "Could anything be worse?", suggested Dr. Deming.

Most schools teach information, not knowledge, and the high grades are achieved by cramming one's head with information, killing the joy in learning on the part of the pupil.

The notion of rewarding 'outstanding teachers' is also flawed, posing the question as to whether report cards on results really measure education or just information. He suggested that in practice only years later does a student really gain an appreciation for who is a great teacher.

One French representative suggested that until we change our education system out of this mode we will not change industry. Many people mistakenly believe that if it is good for education it must be good for industry, and this of course is not the case. Dr. Deming endorsed the comments, adding later that:

"Our education system would improve immeasurably by the abolition of grading".

Further improvement, he suggested, would come from teaching an understanding of variation at an early age as this would "prepare people for life". Management, for example, needed to stop asking for explanations of ups and downs day by day, year by year, -it was clearly foolish in the "Red Beads" to ask for explanations for random variations:

"If someone has had no chance to learn he will attribute every up and down to a special cause, which will surely lead to more trouble".

Schools of business currently teach how business is conducted at present i.e. they teach the perpetuation of the present style of management, yet a school of business 'has an obligation to prepare students to lead the transformation to halt the decline and turn it upward', e.g. to teach why forced ranking is wrong.

Knowledge of variation contrasts sharply with ranking, and not surprisingly Dr. Deming placed great emphasis on the need for this understanding throughout the conference. He laid particular emphasis on the need to study extreme values, identify cases where special help was required, and to the need and entitlement of the beginner to have a master for a teacher. "Do not try to save money for the beginner", he asserted.

Henry Neave of the BDA then illustrated the danger of using specifications (set by designers) as control limits on a process. The system acts as if all is well if production stays within specifications, and he demonstrated by practical example that this is not necessarily the case.

Innovation comes from Freedom.

Many managers see innovation as one of the keys to future prosperity, yet experience great difficulty in harnessing it. This was exemplified by Jan Gillon of the BDA (formerly of Pilkington Glass) who described how in the late 1950s a new method of making glass was devised at Pilkington's St. Helens plant in Lancashire (the Float Glass Process). This was, as Dr. Deming described it, "an unbelievable contribution to the world", which is now taken for granted. It came from a family owned business where individuals had a very considerable amount of freedom to experiment with new ideas. In the 1970s the company became publicly owned. It attempted, by way of its shareholders, to create innovation, but was unable to do so. No amount of money was going to achieve it. The clear message was that one cannot plan to make a discovery. Innovation comes from freedom. Governments which seek to manage innovation invariably do not succeed.

[*Quality Matters* can confirm this environment at first hand as W.N. Clark participated in and contributed to the Float Glass Project at the time of the innovation-Ed]

One characteristic of innovators, therefore, is that they tend to be responsible only for themselves. There is a common notion that innovation comes from the customer e.g. from feedback, but this, asserts Dr. Deming, is not the case. Almost all innovation comes from the producer, and Henry Neave supported this by asking delegates whether their companies could have, for example, have thought of fuel injectors in the days of carburettors or have thought of a fax machine before having seen one or known that they had existed. He asserted:

"If you wait for the customers to tell you what they need you will invariably be late in providing it".

There are of course, some exceptions to this, as one delegate clearly illustrated with a description of how a certain brand of soap had become strangely popular as a form of fishbait [a use for which the manufacturers would surely never have imagined -Ed], but the advantage of producers to develop new products with teams is clearly there.

It remains true, however, that he that can make a product cheaper can take over from the inventor, as witnessed by the fact that the fax, the video recorder and the Compact Disc player have all become Japanese products, The explanation, according to Dr. Deming, comes from the fact that the so-called Zero Stage of product development (the source of ideas, concepts and imagination, e.g. through brainstorming) should exhibit the highest level of cost and effort, being the first element in a geometric series.

Unfortunately in many Western companies it doesn't, as a result of pressure on people downstream to 'look busy', and a failure to reduce backtracking. Consequently excessive time and money are lost at these later stages. Dr. Deming pointed to the following as being one of the most important paragraphs in 'The New Economics':

'One reason to shorten the development of a method by which to make something is to move into an existing market for a product or service that is already well established, or will be. Speed in development of the process captures profit at the point where profit is easiest to capture. This track may be far more profitable than development of a new product or service' .

Whilst the development of new products might have been the right course for America, [and presumably Britain also -Ed] in 1960, it may not necessarily be the right course now, although it is generally accepted that innovation has to come from somewhere. The answer, according to Dr. Deming, lies in learning. Innovation comes from learning, and different people learn in different ways and at different speeds. Understanding this is an important part of psychology.

There is creativity in everyone, but to harness it people need the freedom to develop ideas and make mistakes, and one delegate pointed out the fact that one company had already begun to reward its employees for doing so, but whilst there may be some merit in this, Dr. Deming warned of one further phenomenon of which management must beware: that of overjustification, i.e. rewarding someone, usually with money, for an act or achievement which was done for sheer pleasure and self satisfaction.

[The message is that by rewarding employees for suggestions in the wrong way, management could stifle the very innovation that they are trying to conceive-Ed].

Questions and Answers.

The seminar afforded delegates the opportunity to raise a number of issues and questions interactively and through discussion in the working groups.

Not surprisingly the subject of ISO9000 was raised with one French delegate asking whether it is a waste of money or whether it would really help to give a message to top management. Dr. Deming did not say that it was a waste of money, but was clearly critical of its principles, which he described as 'exhortations towards conformance'.

A company which merely conforms to requirements will find itself out of business, and he warned that ISO9000 'will not produce quality and will not keep you in business'. Henry Neave's view was that ISO9000 'will do for quality what an audited accounting system will do for your profits' and he urged participants to treat it as they might treat their audited accounts.

Another delegate asked Dr. Deming what one should do when their company has lost its market for its staff, and in particular how to select who must go in such circumstances. Dr. Deming replied by saying that if it must be done the Japanese way is best and supported this with an example from Japan where a steelmaking company (Kawasaki Steel Co.) had, in 1974, reduced pay by 15 per cent throughout, but retained its people. The company later recovered and returned to regular scale, putting US steel out of business in the process. Dr. Deming urged delegates to learn from their example.

Another lesson came from the case of a company which wanted to improve and involve its employees, but was afraid to do so as personnel perceived that by improving their processes they were liable to lose their jobs. Management was prepared to take the risk of guaranteeing to re-educate should this happen, in preference to creating unemployment. The result was a 32 per cent improvement in profits over a three year period.

Dr. Deming was asked about how one might construct salary scales, and described it as 'ridiculous' that anyone's pay should be a hundred times more than anyone else's, pointing out that in Japan the ratio of highest to lowest was around 3.5:1. This ratio, was, he said, not necessarily right, but at least people could work together with this kind of ratio.

Another interesting question concerned Dr. Deming's opinions on the ranking of companies associated with the Deming Prize in Japan, since the winning company receives a considerable amount of recognition. Could this perhaps imply a win-lose logic? Dr. Deming acknowledged that he had been present at the award ceremonies, but made it clear that he neither suggested the Award nor the selection of companies nor the judging criteria. "The Japanese did it", he said.

[This answer could imply that the Deming Prize could be less associated with Dr. Deming personally than many imagine-Ed].

DR. DEMING'S LAST WORDS.

Dr. W. Edwards Deming's prophetic last words in Zurich last July were "c'est fini" as he stood to receive a standing ovation from the many delegates from many different countries who had come to listen and learn from this great man. Sadly, although thankfully peacefully, he passed away at his home in Washington, USA on 20th December 1993. Aged 93, Dr. Deming has been described as 'the founding father of modern Quality' particularly for his work in Japan, yet surprisingly was not recognised by his native America until late in his career.

Dr. Deming was trained as a mathematical physicist. His main early interest was in statistical variation and understanding this subject he believed taught everyone about natural events.

Unlike other 'gurus' he did not seek the 'limelight' but developed the philosophy of Quality and Management, which he spread with missionary zeal. Dr. Deming was at his best revealing flaws in management thinking. He is perhaps best remembered for his famous Fourteen Points and his Red Beads experiment which he used to demonstrate practically the futility of blaming workers for faults which were really inherent in the system under consideration. Throughout his life he has attached great importance to learning and his system of profound knowledge which forms the basis for transformation is an inspiration to us all.

Dr. Deming's work may be over, and at least for the moment 'c'est fini', but his teaching lives on. It is being continually refined as Western management is increasingly receptive to his message. The philosophy can no longer be ignored. As he said in Zurich 'we will go on learning forever from the Red Beads'.

Several full obituaries have been reported in the past few weeks, notably in *The Guardian* (22 Dec.1993) and *Quality World* (Feb. 1994).

Tony Carter, Secretary General of the British Deming Association, says 'life goes on, and we shall redouble our efforts to spread awareness of his teachings'.

COMPETITION MATTERS

It could be argued that in a democracy there should always be an element of competition in order to ensure that democracy continues. Recent developments, however, (and arguments) should perhaps lead us to question just how much competition there really ought to be both at Parliamentary and local level, as well as within companies as a whole.

The quality of life in a company or a country will be determined by the quality of leadership that is present. It has been shown time and again, some types of competition produce sub-optimal results, and in the long term a degeneration of the quality of life. The fall of the Berlin Wall in 1989 demonstrated clearly what ultimately happens to a weak and fatally flawed system (in this case Communist dictatorship) when a superior one (Capitalist Democracy) existed. In the next century, however, it is likely that a new kind of system will emerge, in fact it is already there, in the form of a Co-operative Democracy. This rescued the Japanese economy after World War 2 and has continued to give that once shattered nation very great economic supremacy. It continues to prosper alongside what has become an outdated, and flawed form of Western management (Competitive Democracy).

This year's British Deming Association Annual Conference, at the National Motorcycle Museum in Birmingham (27th and 28th April 1994) focused the mind perhaps more than ever previously on the need to transform and supersede this outdated model giving many sound reasons as to why it is doomed. It did not attempt to suggest that the West should copy Japan's example, far from it, but it did suggest that in our own way we should and must move with the times and end our current obsession with competition.

Competition and Reward.

The physical presence of Dr. Deming was clearly missed at this year's conference but the spirit of Deming was very much alive and exemplified by this year's key speaker, American author and broadcaster Alfie Kohn, who has appeared now on over 125 television and radio programmes and has been described as 'the USA's leading critic of competition'.

In this, his first appearance in England he gave two speeches which mirrored the subjects of his two books: *'No Contest: the Case against Competition'* and *'Punished by Rewards'*. These together convey the message that competitiveness is the opposite of excellence whilst rewards amount to not more than a means of securing temporary compliance in a way that is little better than by the threat of punishment.

In his first paper, entitled 'Why Competition kills Quality and what we should be doing' he explains why competition 'makes no sense from the bottom line'. He cited the factual evidence of Dean Tjosvold, Professor of Business Administration at the Simon Fraser University, British Columbia, whose studies showed that 'serious competition undermines co-ordination' and that 'competitive goals were related to ineffective interaction, negative feeling, little progress and weakened relationships'.

Many in the audience remembered 'Mattress Mac's' moving presentation last year on the subject of competitive sales commissions and the devastating effect that they can have on company performance. This year Alfie supported this with some research of his own which suggested that by changing away from a competitive quota system most companies can dramatically improve both their sales and their revenue, not to mention job satisfaction and morale. Competition, alongside rewards, is thus seen to be 'a destroyer of intrinsic motivation'.

'Even when the desire to push oneself to succeed isn't grounded in intrinsic interest -being in love with the challenge itself -it doesn't have to come from trying to defeat someone else. It can be based on comparing one's performance with some absolute standard or with how one did last year'.

Competition between teams, just as between individuals is, he says, 'both unnecessary and undesirable', and it was asserted that in any competitive workplace the only stake that an individual has in others' performances is a desire to see them fail, to the detriment of all concerned. 'Healthy competition' was seen as a contradiction in terms and competition as part of human nature a myth. He echoed the words of Dr. Deming:

"We compete because we are raised that way, not because we were born that way".

Those who advocate competition were accused of "rarely specifying what they mean and rarely producing data", and even the often quoted pro-competition success story of the Apollo Moon Landings was countered on the grounds that the USSR was still wasting time trying to solve problems which the US had already solved with the implication that competition had done little more than delay the whole project. [In industry this type of duplication is rife -Ed].

Surprisingly, Mr. Kohn did appear to advocate one form of competition, that between corporations, on the grounds that it was 'central to our economic system', but the overwhelming conclusion was that overall competition "comes from a deep sense of insecurity not from strength" and "is to self-esteem what sugar is to teeth".

His first paper leads neatly into his second with the assertion that co-operation need not rule out the use of bonuses and other incentive plans, and indeed accepts that these 'can be effective motivators' as long as they are not applied in excess or structured such that they can only won by one person or group, as this will create artificial scarcity and result in no rational person wanting to help anyone else. The problem is that all too often a reward system is praised for solving a problem which it has in fact caused, and Performance Related Pay was used as the classic example. Most managers, he says, 'too often believe in the redemptive power of rewards' and evidence is again unearthed that suggests that 'the failure of any given incentive

497

programme is due less to a glitch in that programme than to the inadequacy of the psychological assumptions that ground all such plans'.

The fact is, he says, 'incentives do not alter the attitudes that underlie our behaviours' because once the rewards run out there is a natural reversion back to the old ways. Temporary compliance is thus all that is achieved:

'At least two dozen studies over the last the last three decades have conclusively shown that people who expect to receive a reward for completing a task or for doing that task successfully simply do not perform as well as those who expect no reward at all'. Furthermore, 'In general, the more cognitive sophistication and open ended thinking that was required, the worse people performed when working for a reward'.

Further studies, examining whether pay, particularly at executive level, is related to corporate profitability and other measures of organisational performance are reported as revealing 'slight or even negative correlations between pay and performance', and it is suggested that such attempts to reward quality are no more than 'a fool's errand'. He quotes Frederic Herzberg, Distinguished Professor of Management at the University of Utah Graduate School of Management:

'It is plausible to assume that if someone's take home pay was cut in half, his or her morale would suffer enough to undermine performance. But it doesn't necessarily follow that doubling that person's pay would result in better work'.

The use of incentive schemes as a substitute for providing workers with what they need to do a good job was severely criticised but whilst most of the argument centred around the misuse of monetary rewards, it was not exclusively confined to it, as even the giving of praise for a job well done, could have the effect of 'a verbal doggie biscuit'. It follows that the negative implications of all types of rewards, not just monetary, have to be considered. It is concluded that:

'Managers who insist that the job won't get done right without rewards have failed to offer a convincing argument for behavioural manipulation. Promising a reward to someone who appears unmotivated is a bit like offering salt water to someone who is thirsty. Bribes in the workplace simply can't work'.

Competition versus Co-operation

The stark contrast between the failure of the Western ideology of 'competitive democracy' and the Japanese achievements through the concept of 'co-operative democracy' was brought home vividly by Professor Kosaku Yoshida, Professor of Statistics at the School of Management, California

State University, who received his PhD from New York University after studying under Dr. Deming.

'You are going to hear a strange concept in a strange accent', he said, as he introduced his paper, entitled 'And you still believe in Competition?' in which he asserts that the 'unfettered competition and rugged individualism' which has, over the centuries, built up American prosperity now threatens to break it down. He challenged vigorously the claims that Japan's so-called 'closed system' is old and unfair, suggesting instead that it is the Western system of so-called free trade and free competition which is unfair and outdated:

'The US cannot tolerate for long the current level of bankruptcy among many of its airlines, banks, savings and loan association and trucking companies that is saddling American taxpayers with an enormous economic burden in bail-outs, in addition to throwing thousands of American workers into unemployment'.

Using financial services as an example he explained how a policy of deregulation followed by three successive American governments has left the US financial services industry amongst others in deep trouble. The collapse of over 1000 savings and Loan Associations alone in the 1980s created a debt of over $20 a month for each US family for the next 30 years, as $500 billion worth of government guaranteed deposits had to be written off.

By contrast, Japanese banks have come to hold 40 per cent of total assets by the world's 100 largest banks, whilst the proportion held by American banks has declined to a meagre 11 per cent. In the meantime Japanese stock expanded by a factor of six during the period from 1969 to 1985. It is suggested that long before the strongest bank wins and controls all other US banks it is likely that foreign banks will acquire all American banks, for whilst competition between banks in the US is increasing, national competitiveness globally is declining. Deregulation 'has not created the results originally intended'.

A similar tale of woe is told for the American telecommunications industry where the break-up of AT and T in 1984, which was opposed by 64 per cent of the public according to a survey by *'Business Week'* magazine, has led to drawbacks that are 'critical and far reaching'.

'Before the break-up customers had one-stop trouble free service from AT and T. Since the break-up when something goes wrong, the customer must not only know what part is faulty but also determine the right repair person to fix it. Competition in price-cutting neglects good service which in turn negatively impacts long term demand and profits'.

Again the objective of deregulation to encourage competition did not work out as had been intended, and the conclusion is that 'the cost of maintaining competition is enormous, causing the quality of both products and services to be sacrificed'. So what is the alternative?

The Japanese approach has been to make harmony through co-operation the dominant and guiding principle, with 'an exquisite balance between competition and co-operation maintained at all levels'. It is pointed out that never in Japanese history has a ruler encouraged competition as the dominant principle. This has given rise to a set of principles referred to as 'Keiretsu' (business groups), which may be vertical or horizontal.

Vertical Keiretsu, whereby a manufacturer such as Toyota may exercise a decisive influence on suppliers and distribution outlets, may be likened to the relationships which exist between such companies as General Motors or Ford and their suppliers, except that suppliers learn from the parent company all of their methods of quality improvement, inventory control and management expertise, rather than just assuming ownership of suppliers' stock. The result is that suppliers 'progressively develop into being independent speciality parts producers who possess rich know how in technology' whilst parts produced by different companies within the group 'fit together very well so that together they tend to produce better quality products with low costs'.

Horizontal Keiretsu involves a principal bank, insurance company, trust banking company, trading company and a number of large manufacturers with smaller ones under their wing, combining by way of reciprocal stock ownership to become interdependent. The Mitsubishi group, which consists of 28 core companies and has a sales turnover of around $175 billion and 'vast business interests' from mining to food and real estate, is an example.

The principle is highly effective at protecting against take-overs from outside, although no member depends on other members for more than about 15 to 20 per cent of their business. Other benefits include early access to information concerning new business opportunities within their field of technical expertise and access to resources that will allow 'swift, bold and decisive action' to be taken should business opportunities be developed which require large capital investment and relatively high risk.

Another key feature is that should a member company face a crisis, the others will attempt a rescue, for example, by taking on excess labour in a section of industry.

Professor Yoshida then turned to the role of trade unions in the 'co-operative democracy', explaining how when the benefits of the Deming approach were realised, Japanese management had purposefully given them the first cut, in stark contrast with the West. He then asked how many trade union leaders were present at the conference, and with not one response, suggested that there had been 'a big mistake'.

Professor Yoshida does not pretend that the Japanese system is perfect by any means, and in his paper he openly explains some of its failings, notably the absence of a checking system and even suggests that should the US fully adopt co-operative principles it could 'become even more balanced as a society than Japan' by virtue of 'the checks and balances and inherent sense of fairness', the existence of which he could only praise.

[An alternative viewpoint on the functioning of the Keiretsu principle is presented in Chapter 16 – Ed]

Some Questions on Competition

Questions to Alfie Kohn included a query about the provision of recognition when someone has done a good job, the need for which appeared to be universally accepted, given the fact that praise had been termed 'a verbal doggie biscuit'. In his response Mr. Kohn said that most of the literature on the need for recognition is descended from the 'behaviourist tradition' and that care was needed to ensure it did not become "an attempt to manipulate by catching someone doing something right". The emphasis had to be on improving interfaces with others, encouraging learning and enabling people to prove to themselves that they could achieve things which perhaps they had perceived as impossible.

The same delegate then asked for examples of some real organisations which had succeeded without instituting competition and rewards, and was referred to the example of Marshall Industries in California which had reaped "enormous benefits from dispensing with competition and rewards, especially in sales". [The interested reader may wish here to refer here to the speech by Jim McInvale-Ed].

Next he was asked about his views on profit share schemes given that they could be made fair. His answer was that the workers who made a profit should have it and that profit sharing "is a fine thing", but again he emphasised the need for care to ensure that the scheme did not become "manipulative".

Then a delegate questioned his use of the term 'manipulative' and asked Mr. Kohn how he would distinguish between being manipulative and telling people about the real world. Mr. Kohn then accepted that it could be difficult to diagnose exactly when something was manipulative, but suggested that when people were able to become members of a collaborative community they would be less likely to feel manipulated. Suggestion boxes were, by contrast, "a sign of a disenchanted workplace".

On the subject of rewards he was asked about his views on the Baldrige Award and commented that both the Baldrige and Deming Awards were competitive rewards, the worst kind of all, and the fact that they were called awards for quality made no difference to that.

In the last question from the floor he was asked about his views on Communism, which the delegate suggested was non-competitive and did not seem to provide any kind of reward. In response Mr. Kohn urged the questioner to think again about whether rewards really were absent and whether co-operation was even present, never mind encouraged. The system failed, he said, due to the absence of self-determination which was the same ingredient that is missing in our present competitive system. He emphasised that a move from competition to co-operation certainly is not a move to the failed system of Communism.

Questions to Mr. Kohn by A.J. Vogl in the April issue of *Variation* include that of how to motivate those whose jobs are perhaps dirty or boring. Mr. Kohn accepts that these people perhaps should be paid more, but the key issues were finding ways to make the work more compelling by giving them more say over what they are doing and how they are doing it, and more interesting by allowing them to perform their tasks in a collaborative way:

"More creative organisations are able to spread grunt-work around so that you don't have certain people forced to do it all the time".

Elsewhere in the interview he challenges the sales commission principle in much the same way as Dr. Deming has done previously and condemns the rewards often given by supervisors on the grounds that they provide a disincentive to ask for help when this is needed.

Like Mr. Kohn, Professor Kosaku Yoshida was questioned from the floor, and was asked first about the Japanese education system and whether it was at variance with Japanese industrial practice with regard to competition. He explained that the Japanese Ministry of Education was now in the process of eliminating the grading in public schools in Japan, but was maintaining a policy of retaining a cross section of society in every class. He condemned the US system of ranking on the grounds that it is impossible to attempt to identify real winners until often 20 or 30 years have elapsed, whilst the Japanese practice of lifetime employment was defended on the same grounds.

Another delegate from the electricity generating industry explained how he felt that his company owed its existence to competition, owing to previous rejection by existing groups, and how significant advances were later made. When asked for his comments Professor Yoshida accepted that there had to be a mechanism whereby a newcomer could enter the fray, as new creativity had to be encouraged.

Finally he was asked how long it might take for his message about competition to become accepted, and to this he replied that it could take time, given that Dr. Deming's work had received little recognition in the US prior to the early 1980s. He said that "it may take longer than we wish, but we have to keep trying". Earlier he had warned in answer to a question relating to the policies of the present British Government, that "in ten years, if you still believe in competition, you are going to be wiped out".

[Issue 68 (August 1994)]

DEMING IN PRACTICE

The Deming Management Method can be and is being successfully applied in British industry, and this year's BDA conference contained several interesting and informative examples to prove this. They illustrate that it is not by accident that certain companies and societies survive and prosper whilst others do not. Rather it is by embracing a set of principles that have a proven track record of success spanning four decades. Companies can choose whether or not they wish to follow them.

Deming in Britain

Management consultant and founding Chairman of the BDA, Ian Graham, described in his paper 'Deming in Britain' how Deming principles have been incorporated into the management systems of companies engaged in house building, furniture manufacture, information technology and the provision of ferry services.

In the first example, (Wimpey Homes), Mr. Graham explains how to view the process of house building as a system and explains how this approach led to substantial improvements notably in the provision of drawings to the building site:

"Drawings going to site often have errors. The wrong materials turn up, things don't fit, power points are put behind radiators, contractors arrive at the wrong site, safety suffers and patching up problems afterwards becomes the norm".

Likewise he explains how the same company changed the way in which it measured customer satisfaction using a Customer Care Control Chart which revealed common cause variation that proved why forcing managers to explain meaningless above and below average satisfaction ratings was not only futile, but potentially dangerous. The company is, he says, 'at an early stage but already becoming seriously interested in working with systems and variation as a way of taking them forward'.

The furniture manufacture company (not named) has devised an original high level process diagram, which is reproduced in the conference

503

proceedings, which shows one way in which key business measures can be connected to show their relation to the whole system. Described as 'a major step forward' it represents a departure from traditional techniques of merely measuring customer satisfaction or financial performance at the output.

The information technology company (ICL) has applied control charting techniques to 'time to fix' (the time taken for an engineer to fix a computer system from the moment of call out), and realised that attempts to compare one country with another were both unnecessary and potentially dangerous since different countries inherently have different environments and different characteristics. The control chart shown in the paper also revealed an important positive system change which had previously not been identified. Control charts are now being presented at board level in accordance with Dr. Deming's recommendations.

The final example from a ferry company shows how the principle of 'conformance measurement' after the event, as advocated by Philip Crosby, can be flawed since it often only shows data from a small part of the overall information. In this case a Ferry Punctuality Report recording ferries more than five minutes late has been improved on by the creation of a Ferry Performance Chart (a run chart which is later converted into a control chart) which has prompted the company to ask far more searching questions about performance than merely why a particular ferry is late.

He concludes:

'What I see happening is that companies are beginning to work with methods such as system mapping and graphs showing variation because they are realising that the real purpose of using these methods is not results but learning about themselves and what change really means'.

Following the presentation leading American consultant Myron Tribus, a regular guest and speaker at BDA events, commented:

"Most people don't know how little time it takes to build a house. A two bedroomed house can be built in four hours. This is documented and it gives an idea of the levels of waste currently in the building process".

Nine Links in the Chain of Transformation

His paper, entitled 'Nine Links in the Chain of Transformation', featured in the conference documentation, gives an account of what is frequently absent in today's companies and provides a list of nine 'Additional Competences required for Managers in the New Era'. He also makes some interesting comments about rewards:

'The leader of the transformation should be especially sensitive as to whether the existing system of rewards supports the transformation. Anonymous

504

surveys should be used to uncover inconsistencies between what is said and what actually transpires. Do not be upset if, at the start of the transformation, there is great cynicism. Remember, the existing reward system was based on the paradigm which is about to be replaced'.

Deming in a Non-manufacturing Environment

The Deming Management Method has brought dividends to the service sector as well as to manufacturing, and to the public as well as the private sector. In the UK The West Midlands Employment Service provides an example of a public sector service organisation which has realised a number of benefits from the application of techniques advocated by Dr. Deming in particular in chapter 7 of *'Out of the Crisis'*, which is devoted to the service sector and the solving of problems in clerical environments.

Martin Raff, regional Director of the WMES, with the assistance of Jane Crutchley, Clerical Officer at Burton on Trent Jobcentre, Denise Mather, Quality Co-ordinator at Coventry Jobcentre, and Steve King, Manager of Moseley Jobcentre, described how some key problems have been resolved. Problems identified include:

*many mistakes were never discovered

*absence of definite procedures

*procedures not fully defined or followed

*difficulty in describing procedures

*different interpretations of the same procedures by different people

In the 1980s the WMES consistently failed to achieve the contribution to the annual performance which had been agreed for the Employment Service nationally with Ministers. Traditional methods to change this, such as exhortation, setting demanding objectives, agreeing improvement strategies, and moving managers who had supposedly failed to deliver, were tried but they didn't work. The poor performances continued. There appeared to be few options available. Initiative was needed and it came in 1989 in the form of a visit to auto manufacturers Nissan, the purpose of which was to study the company's communication strategies and examine possible new ways for people in WMES to work:

'The methods Nissan were using were not only effective, they had intrinsic attractions. For success they depended on teamwork, cutting out hierarchical privileges, reducing fear between manager and employee and valuing data as the key to performance management'.

It was recognised that although Nissan was a manufacturer, like WMES they too were dependent on people and processes for the delivery of their product. It was soon recognised that the methods which they were applying to produce better cars and increase value for their customers could equally be applied to their own service provision.

A fair bit of action followed this visit, notably improved discretion to front line staff, abolition of league tables, and use of performance information as data for analysis rather than as a means of punishment and/or reward. Local office teams were encouraged to learn from each other instead of competing, and the role of managers redefined in terms of team leadership. Other action included: adoption of open plan working, encouragement of open and honest debate to alleviate internal politics, adoption of universal training in the use of SPC tools and empowerment of staff to make data based changes. The Seven Tools of Management and Planning were used as a means of working on the system and working on barriers to improvement, with a requirement for data to support 'pet theories'. Customer interfacing was improved by removal of counters and screens which separate customers from staff. Customer Panels were established as a means of obtaining advice on how service might be improved and an associated feedback mechanism provided to Head Office.

'Data, and taking a systematic 'Plan-Do-Check-Act' based approach, has brought us to a place where our problem solving and planning of new initiatives is now almost universally data based, involves people and can be tracked and reviewed'.

Whilst the WMES accepts that it 'knew little at the beginning' they started slowly, tackled things in parts and were prepared to experiment even if this meant making some mistakes. The result has been improved morale, a dramatic improvement in the pace of personal development, improved job satisfaction and commitment to the service, and a once poor performing element of Britain's public sector administration becoming a top performer on many indicators.

The Deming philosophy is noted as being 'the cornerstone' of the approach taken and it is concluded that:

'The most satisfying thing about the approach has been achieving a high performance by a process which has developed people and made them feel valued'.

Following the presentation the speakers were asked how the WMES has approached the issue of target setting in the public sector, given that the principle of it is at variance with Dr. Deming's teaching. In reply Mr. Raff confessed that his organisation did have both performance related pay and targets because they had to have them, but stressed that they were working hard to "marginalize their ill-effects" , for example by allowing teams to set and own some targets.

Deming via Investors in People

There are many ways of approaching and applying the Deming Management Method. It is not a prescriptive process. Some may use BS5750 (ISO9000) as a starting point, or even flirt with the methods advocated by Philip Crosby as ICL and others have done. Alternatively they may wish to consider using the comparatively recent 'Investors in People' standard, which was the option chosen by Taylor Valves of Huddersfield, a family owned business which manufactures a unique range of valves for steam applications.

Having concluded that traditional management methods were no longer appropriate for employees, customers or shareholders the company embarked on a series of changes. These involved the abolition of clocking in and piecework, harmonisation of sick pay, holiday entitlements and hours of work, and a revision of the company's pension scheme. Progress, however, remained slow and it was evident that something more was needed to 'weld the whole workforce into a cohesive team, sharing the same vision'.

This led to a study of the Deming Management Method and the Investors in People programme in which it was concluded that 'there is nothing in the programme which is absolutely at variance with our company philosophy, or the teachings of Dr. Deming'.

Discussions with the local Training and Enterprise Council (TEC) enabled the company to obtain much needed grants both for IIP and attendance at Deming seminars. An Action Plan for IIP, which is in two parts, has resulted.

Deming in Steelmaking.

The impact of recession on some industries in the UK has been quite devastating and steelmaking is one such industry. The last decade has left, it would appear, just one steel foundry in Scotland with its ownership and financial structure intact, which interestingly is one which has elected to follow the Deming Management Method.

The company is Dewramet, a long established steel manufacturer based at Hillington, near Glasgow, which provides three service manufacturing products and one end product which includes design, development and market launch. Around 70 employees are engaged in predominantly highly skilled, multi-technology processes. It consists of four units: a sand foundry manufacturing castings; a castings foundry (Castings Universal); a pattern shop which supplies wood, resin patterns, models, jigs and fixtures; and an engineering shop (Kelburn) which manufactures steam, gas and air separators for steam turbine and compressor protection.

The company, like many others, attempted 14 years ago to improve supervision and bolt on a quality programme in order to save itself in the adverse climate of the day, but it didn't work. Labour relations remained strained for many years and even as late as 1988 none of the workforce wanted to be promoted to a supervisory post. A definite fear existed.

The paper, by Phillip J.F. Horton, describes how following a meeting with Management Counsellor Bryan Webster at the Glasgow University Business School, a programme of change was initiated based on the concept of empowerment and a move to self-initiated training.

It describes how ownership and vision and values were achieved by meetings involving employee i.e. not by issuing a vision and value statement from above. A 'Way of Life Team' and a parallel monthly review team were set up to ensure movement towards the vision and values so agreed. Instant decision making, blame and recrimination are prohibited. The review is designed to 'help the enabling process, identify process problems and move away from results orientated reporting'. Likewise appraisal systems and job descriptions have been replaced by a self-assessment system which indicates 'growth through excellent mastery of process':

'The key is that managers, including the Chief Executive, are required to assess themselves and to have a colleague, preferably a subordinate, provide a comparative assessment. During the monthly manager review conducted by the CEO, no opinion is given but the session is geared to ensure that the manager is accepting change, committing to it and can demonstrate evidence of it'.

Managers and supervisors devise Personal Improvement Plans (PIPs) using a Personal Discovery Record which poses a number of pre-set questions. Feedback is provided from the monthly Management Review and Manager Review.

Teams operate 'with a protocol controlling the process of decision making' which defines the limits of decision making whilst at the same time encouraging the team to make informed decisions. The emphasis is on highlighting the system rather than human faults, and a requirement that project aims are compatible with a four year business plan unless a modification or addition to it is requested.

A 'huge release of employee synergy has been achieved as the company has progressed from a low added value, low integrity base to a high added value, high integrity manufacturing company:

' Employees know that Scottish or UK competition is to some extent irrelevant. We supply to multinationals who source on a world basis and measure all suppliers in that way'.

Deming's Bricks.

Another industry which has felt the effects of recession is construction and during the four years from 1988 to 1992 the turnover of the red brick industry declined by almost 60 per cent. One company which has weathered this, however, is Yorkshire Brick of Barnsley, who have also elected to follow the Deming philosophy.

In their paper, entitled 'Quality, Productivity and Environmental Position', Director Alan Winlow describes how, having reached crisis point after a survey by the Brick Development Association showed that the dimensional variation of their products was well below the industry average, the company worked to minimise variation using a Plan-Do-Check-Act cycle:

'Endlessly it seemed we measured bricks from our kiln packages layer by layer, analysed the results and acted upon the information. The bulk of the variation came from the kiln operation and by investing a modest amount in new burners we were able to dramatically reduce the extent of common cause variation'.

He then described how elements such as Deming's 'Production Viewed as a System' has made more and more sense with time, and by applying the Deming philosophy in the works considerable savings have been realised.

The achievement of the company's small Quality Improvement Steering Group, for example, have included a reduction in waste, in the form of waste bricks, which has saved around £390,000 a year, a reduction in energy utilisation of around £35,000 a year, and an 80 per cent saving in the company's water consumption.

A further description and illustration shows how following attendance at a BDA workshop, a supervisor gained an understanding of the effect of tampering with a system which exhibited common cause variation, which led to a 25 per cent improvement in landfill gas production from the company's Landfill Gas recovery system which is used as a source of energy for firing. It is concluded that:

'The application of the Deming Philosophy makes money and lots more besides'.

[Issue 76 (April 1995)]

SHEFFIELD WORLD QUALITY CONGRESS

Sheffield has been at the centre of the quality scene this month with the staging of the First World Quality Congress for TQM hosted by Sheffield

Hallam University in conjunction with the Royal Statistical Society with the support of the EFQM and the BQF.

Held on 10th to 12th April the event featured some 108 papers on a diversity of quality related subjects, each of which has been meticulously edited by the conference Chairman and instigator Professor Gopal K. Kanji who is currently Head of Applied Statistics at Sheffield Hallam University. They are published in an attractive hardback book of 615 pages with the papers grouped conveniently under eleven subject headings: TQM Principles and Practices; Measuring Performance; Leadership and Quality Strategy; Quality in Service; Quality Systems and Learning Culture; Continuous Improvement; TQ and Statistical Applications; Quality in Education; Achieving Excellence and Benchmarking; World Class Enterprises and Quality Culture.

From these papers *Quality Matters* selected eight for review, beginning with the Deming Memorial Lecture as a key feature of the conference which may become an annual event in Sheffield.

Deming: the Man and his Message.

The feature entitled 'W. Edwards Deming: the man and his message' was delivered by the British Deming Association's Director of Education and Research Dr. Henry Neave and focused predominantly on the man, his character and beliefs, in contrast to the paper itself which focuses primarily on key aspects of his teaching. This concentrates on the system of profound knowledge about which much has been said and written.

In his presentation Dr. Neave referred to Dr. Deming as 'a modest man and an unceasing learner', who, although born into a far from affluent family, was known for his generosity. He was sometimes perceived as cantankerous and even rude in executive circles, but this attitude was invariably an expression of his frustration toward those who were arrogant, closed minded or were influential and possessed the power to change things for the better but were failing to exercise it. Where senior executives had to deal with the bureaucracy associated with governments, and stockmarkets in various locations, his approach was decidedly softer.

Intentionally perhaps Dr. Deming never established a commercial organisation of his own as this left him free to do and say what he believed was right. Although the content of his seminars changed over the years, the fundamental message that teaching, learning and working should be enjoyable to all concerned remained and was reinforced.

Above all, according to Dr. Neave, Dr. Deming wanted people to think in a deeper, more positive, way, challenging established beliefs and accomplishing a transformation through improved use of the brain. This is neither fast nor easy and in the UK particularly lack of deep thought is commonplace. Why? Well, Dr. Neave suggested several reasons, most of which were traceable to Britain's education system which has become notorious for rewarding memory and cramming for pass/fail examinations. This, he says, "is a wastage of the huge potential of brain matter".

He then turned to one or two of the myths that have tended to surround Dr. Deming's teaching. This addressed particularly the suggestion that his work revolved primarily around the teaching of tools and techniques such as statistical process control and the use of control charts. He referred delegates to a message that Dr. Deming gave in 1950, i.e. that 'the control chart is no substitute for the brain'. Similarly, the Fourteen Points were not, as some believe, a summary of the Deming philosophy but rather a consequence of it.

He concluded by describing Dr. Deming as "a very special man with a message of unparalleled importance that we will ignore at our peril". Whilst there has clearly been a massive humanitarian impact, it never started that way. He said:

"I do not believe anyone can make serious progress without demonstrating Dr. Deming's humility just as he acknowledged his debt to Walter Shewhart".

Following his speech Dr. Neave was asked how one might attempt to communicate the message to the shareholders who call the tune for many organisations. In response he pointed to the BDA's approach which, as for politicians, was "gently, quietly and on an individual basis".

In his paper Dr. Neave describes further the journey to transformation which he says is much needed in industry, government and education. He highlights the need for components of all systems to reinforce each other for optimisation rather than being competitive, emphasising the role of the transformation leader in establishing the vision of the transformed organisation and of understanding people so as to guide the organisation toward its aim. He proposes the aim of everyone gaining over the long term. At the same time he warns against the use of hierarchy diagrams which 'not only fails to aid optimisation of the system but actually destroys the system (if ever one was intended)'. The teaching of modern day economics also receives some criticism:

'If optimisation needs co-operation then competition must lead to suboptimisation. If economists understood the theory of a system, and the role of co-operation in optimisation, they would no longer teach and preach salvation through adversarial competition. They would, instead, lead us into optimisation in which everybody would come out ahead'.

He points to 'serious losses' from competition, and highlights the lack of knowledge on the part of accountants of losses arising from the confusion of special causes with common causes of variation and vice versa.

DEMING'S QUALITY: PAST, PRESENT AND FUTURE

Tributes continue to be paid to the late Dr. W. Edwards Deming and to the legacy which he has left. This month the BDA staged its eighth Annual Conference (10th/11th May) in Birmingham and on the day which would have been Dr. Deming's 94th birthday a teleconference was held in North America. This was video recorded and replayed at a workshop hosted by 3M Bracknell on behalf of the BDA in April. The telecast took the form of a lively four hour broadcast modelled on a television news programme with journalists and authors Lloyd Dobyns and Clare Crawford-Mason acting as studio anchors and panel moderators. It featured presentations from amongst others, consultants Dr. Myron Tribus and Peter Scholtes, and the President of Process Management International, Lou Schultz, who has attended no fewer than 25 Deming seminars since 1980.

Myron Tribus spoke of Dr. Deming as "the arsonist of the century" explaining that it was now our job "to tend to the fires and ignite people's minds with the joy of learning". The lessons which Dr. Deming taught were, he said, "essential to survival" and in his report on the improvement of Federal Government he highlighted the need for Agency Heads to broaden their concepts and understanding of the Deming approach. He accepted that in many cases this would take time since they reflect a population which itself suffers from a lack of knowledge about such concepts. As a step forward he advocated the establishment of an ombudsman for (USA) government.

Peter Scholtes likewise stressed that it would "depend on us for his legacy to thrive and continue" and that "if his message is going to mean anything it must address the serious issues we face". In this context he highlighted trouble spots such as Moscow, Somalia and Haiti, where the system of Profound Knowledge urgently needs to be applied. As an example of how this might work he outlined an interesting loan system which he helped to introduce in Bangladesh. In this system, access to credit is not denied because of absence of collateral. The success of this could not be denied with 97 per cent of loans paid on time, and 100 per cent eventually. The system is now said to be "embryonic" in the USA.

Lou Schultz explained how he had witnessed "a thirst for methods to improve performance" whilst the Deming philosophy "provides hope for workers around the world". He pointed to the now 32,000 Deming User Groups which currently exist around the world.

In the debate which followed Lloyd Dobyns raised the issue as to whether the Deming philosophy was compatible first with Baldrige, and later with ISO9000. Consultant and former Baldrige Assessor Brian Joiner highlighted the areas where Baldrige may not be compatible, notably the fact that it allows for only two winners per category , with which he clearly disagreed. There were also compatibility problems with the deployment of goals and objectives, though he stressed that it was not so much whether a company had them as how they were used which was important. As regards ISO9000 he said that he believed ISO9000 could be positive if it was used in the context of understanding Deming principles, though unfortunately few companies used it that way. Consultant Gipsie Ranney said:

"I think Deming would not lead to ISO9000, though a company that practised Deming should have no difficulty with Baldrige".

She continued on the subject of process re-engineering which she said "doesn't necessarily touch on the management of people" and although it was "good as far as it goes" it "doesn't accomplish transformation".

Further Tributes.

Further tributes to the late Dr. Deming may be found in the last two issues (January and April) of the BDA Newsletter 'Variation', which include, amongst others, one from Dr. Ernest Kurnow, Professor Emiritus of Statistics at New York University. He is noted to be the co-author of what is apparently the only introductory text on statistics of which Dr. Deming approved.

He praised Dr. Deming's excellence as a morale builder and a 'very thorough researcher' who was 'very careful to acknowledge any ideas that he had received from others':

'During assignments I came upon interesting problems which I would discuss with him. Very often our discussion would find its way into one of his papers or books, and my contribution was acknowledged'.

He then paid tribute to the 'deep interest and affection that Dr. Deming had for his students', pointing out how 'somehow he always found time to consult with students outside of class, no matter how tight his schedule was'.

Dr. Deming's unparalleled sense of fairness is perhaps best exemplified by the following quote from Dr. Kurnow, which relates to an oral examination of a PhD student:

'I did not believe that it was fair for a professor to ask a student to remember a footnote when the professor himself did not know the answer from memory........I informed Ed. Deming of what was happening. He took the management professor to task, and the examination was called off and rescheduled'.

Other tributes are paid by Hazel Cannon and Professor David Kerridge of the British Deming Association. Ms. Cannon explains how she remembered a man 'who looked for something valuable in every thing' and 'who didn't prejudge people, but welcomed everyone'.

David Kerridge paid tribute to Dr. Deming as 'a great patriot, who did not believe in hating his enemies' which in consequence 'made a great difference to the way his message was accepted'. The fact that people need to be treated as special 'showed in everything he did', whilst the notion of placing a numerical value on a human life 'would be contrary to the dignity of human life'.

The Future of Deming's Legacy

A key speaker at this year's conference was US consultant Dr. Michael Tveite who assisted Dr. Deming at over 20 of his seminars and presented two papers which addressed the future of quality. The first of these was entitled 'The Future of Deming's Legacy' and is reviewed below. The second, entitled 'New Ways to Think about the World' presents contrasting viewpoints on organisational structure, variation, knowledge, cause and effect, and relationships.

In 'The Future of Deming's Legacy' Dr. Tveite draws attention to some concerns which he has about the future of Deming's Legacy .These stem from what followers have done to the messages of leaders in the past, as well as from interactions which he has had personally with various individuals in which the subject has been raised.

In particular Dr. Tveite highlights the need to move away from the notion of a need to defend the philosophy i.e. 'how can we stop the charlatans coming out saying they knew Dr. Deming or his teaching?' and toward the much more positive objective of ascertaining what Deming's ideas mean, what their implications are and how they might be better applied. It is more challenging, he argues, 'to keep our minds open and strive to apply our ideas and learnings in the world we live in.'

He then turns to the idea of the 'Deming canon' or complete teaching of Deming and explains his concern that some of the people he has met apparently felt more comfortable with Dr. Deming's ideas in the past than more recently. He says:

'If these people were deciding the complete and true Deming, they might well stop at some version of Deming's Fourteen Points for management. Doing this would result in missing what I believe is very important material and thought'.

He then turns to the belief, which he suggests is erroneous, that Dr. Deming's ideas are now complete. He suggests that Dr. Deming never thought of them in that vain and, had he been alive today, he would be 'revising and updating his ideas and materials to reflect his newest learnings'.

The concern about how we can stay true to Deming's fundamental principles as a result of progressing on from his materials and teachings might, he says, be legitimate and is more of a challenge. If the System of Profound Knowledge is used as a 'guiding lens' he suggests that there will be little difficulty in remaining true at least to Dr. Deming's intentions. Focusing on where Dr. Deming was at some point in time, however, would be likely to lead us astray such that 'over time Rule 4 of the Funnel Experiment is likely to occur'.

He discusses how the System of Profound Knowledge might be used as a framework for learning, arguing that if Dr. Deming had passed away whilst his teaching was focused on the Fourteen Points, there would have been little hope for his philosophy to have a continuing impact on the world:

'If Dr. Deming hadn't articulated a system of profound knowledge we would be left with people arguing about the Fourteen Points, none of whom could speak with Deming's authority'.

He explains how he has sought to place the writings of leading authors such as Russell Ackoff and Peter Senge into the context of Deming ideas. Also to study the previously mentioned work of Lewis and Shewhart to gain 'a new appreciation for Deming's System of Profound Knowledge'.

He asserts that if we are to remain true to Dr. Deming as a model of learning it is essential everyone works to extend his ideas beyond what he taught in his lifetime:

'The kind of thinking that says we can only learn from Deming will, by its very nature, limit what we can learn, know or do'.

In conclusion he says:

'My hope for the future of Deming's Legacy is that we follow his model as a learner. I hope that we begin with the solid foundation formed by his ideas, especially by a system of profound knowledge, and build on that foundation. My personal goal is that the ideas that we'll be talking about and applying in ten or fifteen years will clearly have Deming as a root, but will be far beyond what he taught us'.

QUALITY THROUGH CHANGE

The BDA held its ninth annual conference on 15th and 16th May at the National Motorcycle Museum and was predictably popular with some 235 attendees. The theme this year was 'Extraordinary Change through Ordinary People' and featured some 15 presentations and 13 papers.

Three of these were from UK Chief Executives and were combined under one session heading of 'The Chief Executives: Lessons from leading Transformation'. Another paper is from Ms. Hazel Cannon, who, following six years as a consultant and formerly a personal student of the late Dr. W. Edwards Deming, has recently been appointed as a Director of Penhaligon's, the Royal perfumers and luxury gift company. The guest speaker was Carl Klemm, General Manager, Car Manufacturing for Toyota Motor Manufacturing UK.

Lessons from UK Chief Executives.

The Chief Executives' session was a feature introduced for the first time at this year's BDA conference and was similar in format to the small company presentations at this year's BQF conference in March. The three Chief Executives, Alan Taylor of the AT Group, Anthony Robinson of Flender Power Transmission and Ms. Denise Howard of the White Rose Line each spoke for twenty minutes about how their companies have been transformed as a result of implementing strategic management based on Deming principles. All three are members of the BDA Chief Executives Group which meets regularly to share learning and understanding.

The first to present was Alan Taylor who described his Wigan based engineering company which was formed twelve years ago and currently employs 400 with an annual turnover of £16 million. It has five divisions: Control and Automation Systems, Electrical and Instrumentation Contracting Services, Airfield Ground Lighting, Willand UV Systems and Vehicle Protection Security Posts. Despite the recessionary conditions associated with British manufacturing over the last twelve years they have managed to reverse the trend and achieve 50 per cent expansion or more in each successive year. This has not, however, been without its problems:

'Due to the significant growth of the company and resulting increase in the number of employees, I realised that we now had people in positions, particularly in managerial roles, with either little or no appropriate training. Therefore in 1991 a comprehensive 'in-house' management training programme was initiated in conjunction with the local TEC'.

The paper describes how the ensuing training programme was introduced i.e. with the premise that good teamwork was essential to ultimate success, and some of its benefits, notably the opportunity afforded for the company to rationalise its values and aims:

'We recognised that true success would I only be achieved by working closely together with both our Clients and Employees and that in order to bring about this success in an ever more demanding, competitive market, determination must become our byword. This spirit of determination is epitomised in our Company Logo which shows two salmon swimming upstream, against all obstacles, to reach their spawning ground'.

It is then described how certification to BS5750 'focused attention on the need for co-operation and the importance of teamworking', though this was clearly not in itself going to guarantee the survival of the company. It merely helped 'to lay the foundations of something, whilst TQM, Quality Circles and the like 'seemed to be isolated initiatives' that 'did not appear to fulfil the company's needs adequately'. It was not until the speaker received an invitation from the BDA promoting their 1993 conference that he was finally convinced that there was something available which really would address the problems with which he was faced following certification.

The speaker attended the conference and through its unique networking environment met BDA consultant Jim Murray whose experience and expertise provided the necessary missing link which enabled the company to continue to achieve further success at a time when it was urgently needed. A new interest emerged:

'We began to introduce the [Deming] philosophy to the company by holding a number of one day seminars, firstly for the directors, and then the managers, followed up by two day seminars. The directors of the company formed a leadership group to guide the company through the transformation process and provide a lead by their example'.

Some 30 managers were trained in this way during 1994, with training later enhanced by regular weekly 'twilight' sessions from 4 to 7 pm which examined in depth the Fourteen Points, flowcharting techniques, variation control, and process and systems analysis. The group learned how to question their progress, and, perhaps more importantly, to see how certain traditional practices like the bonus system were inflicting great harm on the company. This was seriously jeopardising success and quite obviously had to be changed.

The paper describes what went well and what did not, and reveals some of the lessons which the speaker had learned personally as a result of his ongoing association with the BDA and application of its teaching:

'As a result of attending Alfie Kohn's presentation two years ago I came to understand the meaning of "Co-operation and not Competition" and have successfully applied this to several business relationships. Unfortunately in

today's economic climate it is not easy to build lasting and meaningful relationships based on honesty, trust and integrity. However, I believe these to be pre-requisites for successful long term co-operation'.

'In the infancy of our Deming days I, along with the vast majority of our employees, would have found it well nigh impossible to believe that we could improve our performance by 20 to 30 per cent as we had been told. However, we can now see the opportunities and envisage the ways in which we can massively reduce our costs and maybe improve profits by six figure sums'.

The second company, Flender Power Transmission, is a subsidiary of Flender AG of Bocholt in Germany and was established in the UK in 1967. They assemble gear units, geared motors and power transmission packages including couplings, have 72 employees of which 28 are shop floor personnel, and have a current annual turnover of £11.75 million. Their story and experiences bear many similarities to those of the AT Group, although they are extended over a somewhat longer time period.

Like the AT Group, Flender achieved BS5750 certification (in 1986) and this 'helped to assure that the company met basic operational standards', but when TQM was explored, as a follow through, they found that they appeared to lack what can only be described as a core element to the activities:

'Many in the company really thought that TQM was nothing more than a "flavour of the month"'.

Again, like Alan Taylor, Tony Robinson received a BDA invitation and "found confirmation that the intuition was right". He attended three BDA seminars during 1992 and 1993, and also became acquainted with Jim Murray who delivered two half day in-house seminars to the management team which 'proved successful and led to a desire to learn more about Process Analysis'. This, however, was only the beginning:

'Our culture change began by the management team undertaking to learn about the methods and tools of Process Analysis through three one day in-house courses conducted by Jan Gillett of Process Management International (PMI). We understood the necessity to use process related criteria as opposed to historical results for the purpose of management and control. We understood the Theory of Knowledge and its components so that we could focus on learning and understanding the key processes of our company and thereafter having achieved process stability seek to improve the process'.

With this grounding in theory the company was well placed to pilot its first process improvement team in January 1995 with the assistance of PMI who provided a two week facilitator training course for one director:

'Initially the team had two days off the job every three weeks on the basis that one day would be for learning and one day for "doing"'.

This team worked very effectively and so two more directors were trained as facilitators, and subsequently a further director and a middle manager were trained. This has brought the number of process improvement teams to five, the latest being a Training Steering Team, with responsibility for planning training and education for all employees.

The speaker described how the curiosity invoked on the part of middle management had been "a good sign of success" and elaborated on some of the lessons learned, in particular the need to cease dependence on current results as an indicator of success and the need to discard appraisals, performance related incentives and the use of arbitrary targets. He described the company's latest initiative of self-assessment to the EFQM Model, which to date has produced a 'Rapidscore' of 381 Points.

The third speaker Denise Howard, provided perhaps the most extraordinary case of all, that of a husband and wife team which since 1989, has created a successful sightseeing river cruise business in York from all but nothing. The company, The White Rose Line, began with two boats and one employee in April 1989 and since then has expanded to five boats, with 16 permanent and up to 12 seasonal employees. Turnover has increased by 450 per cent and profit by 550 per cent, and in 1991 they successfully bought out their main competitor. More recently they have formed a separate company to handle travel and tour arrangements of overseas visitors and established a catering company.

Their involvement with the BDA dates back to the summer of 1992, when at a chamber luncheon, the speaker was persuaded to invest in a half day seminar led by Jim Murray. This convinced both the speaker and her husband that the Deming Management Method would, without doubt, make White Rose Line a superior place of work. At this time the organisation was also working for the Investors In People award, which they duly achieved in 1993, although later decided against working to maintain:

'As part of our work towards Investors In People in 1992 we had introduced an appraisal system. Well, it seemed like a good idea at the time. We quickly realised that we couldn't make this format work and abandoned it completely. Now we have individual planning and review meetings with all staff at least twice a year, and we allow up to half a day for each meeting. The purpose of these meetings is to give everyone an opportunity to discuss with us what the company is going to do and what this has meant or will mean to them. It also contributes to the identification of training meetings but everyone values them'.

The paper describes in some detail why the company has decided to adopt a multi-skilling philosophy based on roles rather than job titles, and outlines how a role matrix has been developed to define purpose rather than job description and identify individuals who are suitable for particular roles and where there are gaps i.e. this is enabling the company to relate business needs to people development. It also explains how a training team has been established which has used Deming principles to 'dramatically improve the training of crew and skippers' and improve the recruitment of seasonal crew:

'For a small company this was a tremendous leap forward and some of my colleagues in tourism in York cannot comprehend why we "allow" members of staff to recruit crew or skippers'.

This year further Deming training has been undertaken such that everyone, in the company now has knowledge of the Deming principles and benefits of their application:

'We shut the office for three days at the end of January and took everyone to a local hotel for a tailor-made workshop led by John Norrie. It was incredibly successful and we have observed some differences in behaviours and an individual motivation to want to learn more in others. People are working together better and are less inclined to mutter and complain about others and how they do their jobs and seem to value the differences in people with greater understanding and tolerance'.

The £5,500 which the company won as Barclays Small Business of the Year has been put to good use allowing all employees the opportunity to benchmark top boat operators on the continent, which has helped to reinforce learning:

'We have learnt that quality means delivering our cruise services consistently well, and not by luck or superhuman effort. To do that we have had to learn about variation and system control, the voice of the process'.

All of this astonishing success so eloquently described would surely lead any rational thinking individual to ask the question: 'if it's so good, why isn't everybody doing it?'. The answer to this perhaps lies in the concluding section of the paper which describes the stance adopted by the company's three direct competitors which now carry a mere 5 to 10 per cent of the business:

'It is difficult to co-operate and grow the market when you are playing by different rules. And it has to be said that they are convinced we are trying to put them out of business because we are so successful and they are not. That is not our aim, but it may well be a consequence of how they and others run their businesses '.

[After reading this paper one might be forgiven for presuming that these competitors are a dying breed-Ed]

Real Help from the Outside.

Another successful British company, although somewhat older than White Rose Line (120 years to be precise), is the Royal perfumers Penhaligon's. It made a name for itself in the late nineteenth century as a supplier of after shave and essences to the aristocracy in a fashionable district of London, but it was clearly born in another age and by the 1970s was clearly in need of revitalisation.

This revitalisation came in the form of Ms. Sheila Pickles who steered it in the direction of the luxury perfume market. It now holds two Royal warrants and designs, manufactures and retails original perfumes and various luxury gifts and accessories. It now realistically looks to becoming a world class retailer of classic scents and fine English gifts with a little help from the BDA. Also, of course, from Hazel Cannon, who enlightened a spellbound audience into a few of its little secrets:

'We try to create the environment where every purchase is either a gift for others or a gift for the purchaser. Our aim is not just to have delighted purchasers and consumers but also to indulge them. In this environment, where many purchasers want instant gratification, people within the organisation often want or need quick fixes. Intensive planning and evaluation is an intention rather than a regular reality. Our strategic plan and its review using the PDSA cycle will become invaluable to the organisation'.

In her paper Ms. Cannon confesses that there is 'no-one else' other than Sheila Pickles for whom she would have sacrificed the freedom and challenges of consultancy in order to become a manager, but this company clearly needed her as a change agent:

'One of the big issues for me at Penhaligon's is the relationship the "ordinary people" have with the system and the leadership in the organisation.........The person who had been in charge of the Operations Department before me had a very controlling style of management and transacted in a parent/child style'.

She clearly saw it to be a necessity 'to bridge the gap from the way people were used to working to an environment where they are able and equipped to take on and extend their responsibility'. Only by working within the company where she had had a consulting role could leadership be instituted in accordance with the Deming philosophy:

'Penhaligon's is an organisation where we have to manage the central costs. Thus, it is inappropriate for the senior managers to gad about town in taxis unnecessarily. I go out of my way to use the tube when I can, and challenge my colleagues to do the same much to their chagrin'.

Likewise the speaker was keen to dispense with status symbols, and made a point of bringing her two year old car from her former employers rather than doing the done thing and buying a new company car:

'If you are to sustain an effective environment then there must be what is called "felt fairness". No favours or pets or special deals done'.

She argues that values must determine group as well as individual behaviour but accepts that agreeing and maintaining values and behaviour ground rules is difficult:

'When I was a consultant I would constantly challenge clients and give them a hard time if they even looked like they were going off the path they had agreed. As a manager I am constantly tempted to just fix one thing for people, to occasionally take something away and perform some magic rather than spend the time helping them understand and coaching them. I had no idea how difficult it would be and eight months later it is causing them and me considerable stress. However, they understand why I am doing it and in the case of the staff who report to me, there is unanimous agreement that it is the right thing to do'.

She voices particular concern about ground rules created by managers for people who work for them arguing that these 'can often turn into petty rules if the organisation operates in a parent/child manner'. Consequently there is a need for 'an intrinsic belief in shared values':

'The task I have is to ensure that useful process control flowcharts are developed and ways of working are clear. The Managing Director and I then have to make clear what is non-negotiable and what is. The negotiable parts of the process are where people can use their creativity and discretion'.

'I did not expect as an incoming senior manager to be told "what colour of ink the MD liked" and thus what I was allowed to use. If people should only use one colour of ink then it must not be a secret. In fact, it is a myth exaggerated from a true story'.

The paper continues to describe at some length the issue of joint and shared leadership introducing the concept of 'a leadership partnership' enhanced by 'deep knowledge of one another'. Strengths and weaknesses are not kept secret but are utilised professionally to optimise each leader's contribution.

Ms. Cannon described it as a 'privilege' to work with a leader who is prepared to 'take a chance' with this style of leadership. She then elaborates in more detail on the ideas associated with the change from a 'parent/child' (i.e. controlling style of management), towards a system based on interdependence in which fear is replaced with passion. Here employees join, rather than work for, their organisation, and where mistakes and successes both lead to expanded thinking and further contribution.

[Issue 92 (August 1996)]

THE APPLICATION OF DEMING'S 14 POINTS AT TOYOTA

Carl Klemm joined Toyota in 1990 following 23 years at Vauxhall Motors. His paper, entitled 'Deming USA to the UK via Japan' describes where the company stands today, with reference to its ongoing Total Quality journey which formally began in 1961 with the adoption of Total Quality Control (TQC).

It was a company which realised long ago that it needed to change if it was to survive, never mind prosper, and its story is well known. What is less well known is how the Deming philosophy is continuing to be applied not just in Japan, but also here in the UK. One could be forgiven for believing that the approaches taken in the UK and Japan are identical, but it is quite clear that there are differences:

'In 1982 Toyota in Japan developed a very clear concept of TQC which all employees could grasp. For us at Toyota UK it was important to use these same principles, which we took and developed into our own Quality Principles'.

The paper describes these Quality Principles and gives examples of how they are applied in practice with particular reference to Deming's well known Fourteen Points which are aptly termed 'Tools of the Trade'. This begins with Point One i.e. 'Create consistency of purpose toward improvement of product or service' which of course implies proper planning:

'For long term or annual plans for the company, for Divisional or project plans, for individual training and development plans, PDCA (Plan-Do-Check-Act) is the basic rule for controlling and ensuring the success of an activity. Planning in Toyota UK is designed so that each level of planning can be related to each other to retain consistency, but monitored individually to retain local control'.

Point Two, 'Adopt the new philosophy', provides a focus for the reduction of waste and teamwork:

'Waste movement is reduced by repositioning the worksite. Waste overproduction is stopped by using the pull system for all processes. Waste of poor quality product is reduced by not allowing sub-standard work to pass on to the next point. Waste of waiting is reduced by carefully balancing the workload in each area'.

'We have a system for management initiated improvement teams, or Jishuken teams. One such example is found in the paintshop. We have two topcoat spray booths. Previously we used both booths to support a

production volume of up to 100,000 vehicles per year. Ultimately we wish to increase this to 200,000 vehicles per year capacity, necessitating each booth carrying 100,000. To achieve this a special team was set up to investigate all the issues relating to the significant change required; equipment capacity and maintenance, material usage, quality, implementation timing, manpower required and so on. The process was successfully completed in four months with no adverse effect on quality'.

Point Three, 'Cease dependence on inspection to improve quality' needs little explanation. Suffice it to say it is not a 'Utopia based on perfect parts and process stability and members who always precisely follow perfect work instructions' but the simple application of the established techniques of Just-In-Time management and Poka Yoke (defect prevention).

Point Four, 'End the practice of awarding business on the basis of price tag' has been achieved by working with suppliers and yielded enormous benefits (a 90 per cent reduction of defects in two months in one case) whilst Point Five, 'Improve constantly and forever the system of production and service' is achieved by standardising improvements to create new baselines of performance [not by setting targets -Ed].

Point Six, ' Institute training on the job' is self explanatory, with classic QC tools training being applied to specific actual problems, whilst Point Seven, 'Institute leadership' compels management and supervisors to adopt a supporting rather than a controlling role.

Point Eight, ' Drive out fear' is perhaps most important of all and is focused on breaking physical and mental barriers between management and workers:

'We have a system for extensive pre-negotiation of new ideas or changes to processes called Nemawashi, which ensures that all the affected areas are aware and are in agreement with the concept and the detail of the change. Ensuring everyone knows the effect of the change and what is expected of them drives out the fear of the unknown'.

Point Nine, 'Break down barriers between departments' is achieved through 'a dynamic dialogue between all departments involved' e.g. in exploring a cost reduction idea as described in the paper, whilst Point Ten, 'Eliminate slogans, exhortations and targets', although not followed strictly, ensures that measurement is used effectively and is not arbitrary .

Point Eleven, ' Eliminate work standards or quotas' enforces the principle of quality before quantity, and whilst the company uses 'standardised methods' these are clearly distinguished from 'standardised work' in which every element of a job becomes standardised.

Point Twelve, 'Remove barriers that rob the worker of his right of pride in his work' is clearly very important and the supervisors have an essential role:

'The supervisor's function is not one of witch-hunting, to point the finger and apportion blame, but one of support, to mobilise resources to help fix the problem quickly and effectively, and stop it happening again'.

Point Thirteen, 'Institute a vigorous programme of education and self improvement' is described at length and involves teaching tools and techniques as they are required, step by step teaching and various forms of specialised training. Point Fourteen, 'Put everyone in the organisation to work to accomplish the transformation' is reflected in Hoshin Kanri (policy management) which not only defines and measures the effectiveness of every function and member of the organisation but also provides everyone with the power to manage their own processes.

TOTAL QUALITY IN ACTION

Sheffield Hallam University hosted its Second Annual Conference on TQM on 8th and 9th July with the title this year being 'Total Quality Management in Action'. Again the event proved popular with some 230 attendees and 44 papers covering eight branches of TQM: 'TQM Principles and Practice', 'Community and Education', 'The Role of Self Assessment', 'Instructional Comparisons', 'Enterprise and Industry', 'Quality Methods', 'Continuous Improvement Process', and 'Quality Measurement'.

As with last year's conference *Quality Matters* selected eight papers for review, beginning with the Second British Deming Memorial Lecture by Brian L. Joiner of Joiner Associates.

Leadership in the 21st Century.

Brian Joiner's lecture had the above title, and as with Dr. Henry Neave's presentation last year, was largely different from the paper in the Conference Book, focusing principally on the subjects of customer complaints and innovation. This considered critically the assumed goal of most organisations to reduce customer complaints, questioning the validity of the assumption and pointing out why, in most cases, it represents a false goal, and introduced the Kano Method for implementing customer focused innovation.

Customer complaints were, he argued, largely no more than the 'tip of an iceberg' i.e. for each official complaint there are many more unofficial ones which are commonly heard but not recorded. Consequently, seeking to reduce these complaints in practice does little or nothing to improve the customer focus of the organisation. Rather the reverse is true, i.e. the goal of increasing the number of customer complaints, but with ever decreasing severity, will lead to a greater understanding of what customers actually value. This will then serve to reduce the "water level", which he argues is likely to be much more profitable:

"The customer who complains still believes there's hope for you".

Delegates were then asked, with the aid of a handout, to consider the case of a division of a company which manufactured cameras well, but urgently needed to increase sales if it was to survive. The approach adopted was one of Pareto Analysis of the pictures which their cameras produced, which highlighted three main problems: underexposure, out of focus and blankness of film.

By talking to the customer these problems were later solved by breakthrough innovation in the form of built in flash development and automatic loading and winding, as the problems were in fact with the film rather than with the cameras. Kano's Three Step method thus asked:

(i) What are our customers seeking to achieve that is in any way related to our product or service?

(ii) What barriers are they encountering that are in any way associated with our product and/or service?

(iii) What changes can we make that will help our customers achieve their objectives?

In his paper Mr. Joiner focuses on The Leadership Cycle which consists of challenging what is, imagining what will be, and then making it happen. He discusses each of these three elements in turn before concluding with a discussion of how leadership relates to democracy.

In 'challenging what is', readers are alerted to the concept of 'The moose on the table' i.e. issues about which everyone is aware but which nobody openly discusses:

'People will talk over, under and around the moose, but no-one says "There's a moose here that we have to deal with". Every organisation has a moose on the table though some have ignored it for so long that they've forgotten the moose is there. A newcomer soon learns that to mention the moose is to unleash a barrage of defensive abuse. All too soon a newcomer adopts the corporate myopia and joins the forces that attack other moose-sighters'.

It is argued that if an organisation is to make real progress it cannot continue in this vain i.e. we must be willing to examine the unexamined, discuss the undiscussable and challenge the unchallengeable. This leads automatically to an acknowledgement of the need for openness and honesty in an organisation, which is willing to welcome the bad news as well as the good in order 'to surface the truth', lest an organisation should become 'as sick as its secrets'.

There is firm emphasis on the need for dialogue to prevail over debates which often degenerate to the point of becoming battles for which there has to be a 'winner' and a 'loser' and on the need to understand customer needs and values, the technologies of the business, the use of data, and the concepts of teamwork and change.

In 'imagining what will be' the technique of scenario planning, adopted by the Royal Dutch Shell Company in the 1970s, is highlighted, striking a balance between imagination and knowledge. Creation of an environment in which curiosity and forward thinking are 'eagerly welcomed as part of everybody's job' is seen as crucial, and strong parallels are drawn between the knowledge and skills required for 'imagining what will be', and those needed for 'challenging what is'.

In 'making it happen' it is argued that the majority of change effort fails through poor quality of execution rather than poor design. For ongoing support, follow-up is an essential element of change management which should be fuelled with 'energy and excitement' from 'imagining what will be'. All too often people are left with broken dreams without ideas being used to generate a new vision. Characteristics of an environment which is supportive of making the desired changes are listed.

In 'leadership and democracy' it is suggested that, increasingly, there will be less reliance on formal organisational charts and a greater need for shared leadership responsibility. It is asserted that a greater balance is needed between formal and spontaneous organisations with space created in formal organisations 'to welcome, support and celebrate grass root initiatives'.

[Issue 103 (July 1997)]

THE CHALLENGE OF CHANGE

The BDA held its tenth Annual Conference at the National Motorcycle Museum on 14th and 15th May with the theme of 'The Challenge of Change'. There was as in previous years a varied set of presentations including welcome returns for Myron Tribus and Alfie Kohn, as well as a few newcomers such as Vic Forte and Ben Freedman.

Myron Tribus presented the first paper which addressed the topical subject of quality in education and in particular the action which the business community could take to improve it. He emphasised the fact that educational establishments were in practice industry's most important suppliers and with reference to the Secretary's Commission on the Acquisition of Necessary Skills (SCANS) Report of 1991 he outlined how the requirements of industry had changed away from a mere acceptance of quiet and obedient workers and towards a demand for entrants who are able to acquire new skills readily, understand systems thinking, develop thinking capability and engage in group problem solving:

'I have been told by a Motorola executive that when Motorola opens a plant in Asia, they interview two employees in order to find one who is qualified to learn what has been learned in their modern factories. In the USA they tell me they have to interview ten to fill a similar position. Motorola does not expect to find people already trained for the new jobs; no schools can keep up. Motorola is looking for people who fill the requirements outlined in the SCANS report'.

He argues that Western academia is currently way out of touch with these changing requirements and that in order to achieve the SCANS Report's recommendations schools will need to change not just the contents of their courses but also the ways in which they are presented. In short, he says 'there will have to be a fundamental shift in the way schools approach education', and that industry, for the sake of its survival, 'must help the schools to change'. This help, however, has to be applied with some caution:

'Before approaching any school it is important not to assume that since quality methods have worked so well in improving the performance of companies, they can be taken, unchanged, into the schools. There are some very important differences. Attempts to bring industrial practices to the schools, unchanged, will cause great anger among the educators, and justifiably so'.

He emphasises that the most important central process in a school is learning, with teaching a means rather than an end, and warned against the use of 'market metaphors' on the grounds that unlike in industry, the users of the service are rarely those who are actually paying for it. The features which are seen as being most desirable in the education system are summarised under the headings of 'knowledge', 'know-how', 'wisdom', and 'character' and nine practical steps are suggested for companies to follow to help the schools to improve. These include most notably the provision of release time (Re - half a day per week) for scientists and engineers to help in a classroom environment, the offering of opportunities for administrative personnel from the school to meet those in the company who have to perform similar functions (e.g. purchasing, payroll and accounts, maintenance and catering), and the creation of a 'school to work' programme:

'In Australia there are "E-teams" in which teams of students (usually seniors) are given an intensive training in quality improvement methods for one or two weeks after school. Then they are put to work on an improvement project in a local company. At the end they make formal reports to the company and to their fellow students'.

Alfie Kohn gave two presentations, the first entitled 'Why Performance Based Pay cannot work', the second entitled 'Quality as a Democracy'. He argued as in the past that punishments and rewards were in fact two sides of the same coin, supporting his arguments with evidence from numerous

528

research studies. He suggested that the quality journey and performance-related pay were incompatible, as the latter undermined intrinsic motivation as a result of outdated psychological assumptions:

"The more you reward people for doing something the more they tend to lose interest in whatever they have to do to get the reward and eventually you have to keep rewarding because the intrinsic motivation disappears".

Six fundamental reasons were given as to why rewards tend to fail in their purpose and he implies that quality organisations should abandon the associated principle of top-down control:

'Tell people that their income will depend on their productivity or performance rating, and they will focus on the numbers. Sometimes they will manipulate the schedule for completing tasks or even engage in patently unethical and illegal behaviour'.

The paper by Vic Forte describes how the Deming philosophy has been applied at Fortes Bakery Limited of Burgess Hill West Sussex which has around 90 employees' and specialises principally in supplying the airline catering industry. Entitled 'Learning from mistakes' it describes how real change has been achieved and lessons learned, beginning with the all important matter of listening to customers:

'I remember one seminal experience that happened when I visited a valued customer, after they had told us that they were closing the account. They told me about a whole history of complaints going back months. I knew nothing about them'.

'In the early days we did not listen to customers. Then we started listening to them, and that was the start of the trouble, because we did not know what to do with the information. So we just blamed people, and put pressure on our subordinates who were only doing their best. We did not understand motivation. We knew no better'.

The author explains why on watching a Deming video, he became quite angry, not least with himself:

'I cannot understand why we seem to have so little common sense. After a few years of listening to customers it became clear that most of the problems kept repeating themselves. A problem that we thought we had cured merely fell asleep for a while only to wake up a year later and grab us'.

'We were tremendously energetic about dealing with customer complaints. We would always make sure that someone got told off about it. Indeed I think we sacked a few people, often at the request of customers. Even now our customers ask us why we aren't sacking the person responsible for the mistake, but our managers no longer join the call'.

The reasoning is as follows:

'Management fails to understand that in a stable system, mistakes are part of common cause variation. To react only to the ones with serious consequences is to treat common cause variation as if it were special cause variation. If all mistakes could be reported not just the disastrous ones, then management would have a rich source of data that they could use as a base for improving the processes. They would work with the people involved in the process to find ways of error proofing, preventing and eliminating errors'.

To the converted this seems obvious, but to the vast majority it is not, and it can take a long time to convince the uninitiated, as the author found:

'For quite some time I thought that it was sufficient only to talk to people about this new way of managing. I thought that everyone would just buy into it. It was a while before I realised that every person is the result of his or her own history. Not everyone is the same. It became clear that words only communicate to people who are ready to hear them. They themselves have to go through the right experiences to enable them to accept the truth of those words'.

'Another bitter truth, which I must now face is that my past way of managing has been a significant fact in the experience of others around me. I have managed by command and control for a decade and a half, and a lot of my colleagues have been with me for nearly that long. It is simply not enough just to talk about casting out fear; actions are needed, and people need to be convinced that those actions are beneficial'.

This says the author, is 'the debt that may have to be paid, and he suggests that the biggest challenge which management now faces is that of self-awareness, along with the need to adopt systems thinking:

'Do I fight against the natural learning that goes on in the systems that I manage? Is this why problems constantly seem to return? Is it because the sub-systems are learning to optimise themselves, but doing so at the expense of the system as a whole? Perhaps the requirements of the sub-system are not being fully recognised by those who manage the larger system, so the sub-system "learns" in a way that harms the system. We all have our little sub-systems. Managers learn to save face, or to meet the budget at all costs. Workers learn to keep their heads down; keep a low profile and no harm will come to them. Middle managers learn to get the product out of the door today, and pay no attention to their longer term tasks. They know exactly what would happen if they did not get the product out by the end of the shift'.

'Because every system has its language, people who operate in the sub-systems must learn the language of the wider systems, those in the wider

must learn the language of its component sub-systems. This implies effective communication, a lack of fear on the one hand and a lack of snobbery on the other, in other words profound mutual respect'.

In the remainder of the paper the author explains why processes drift and argues the case for workers to be given a share in the strategic action by having some insight into and some influences on the processes in the higher level system:

'Sub-processes usually have shorter time cycles than higher level processes. This means that learning can happen faster which is useful but forgetting can happen faster too. A problem arises when the learning that takes place at the higher level is simply passed on as a command. Then there is a danger that the reasons behind the command will not be properly understood and its legitimacy questioned. Rarely will the instruction be totally ignored, but it may be allowed to drift over time if it is not constantly reviewed and checked.

Because the time cycle is longer in the higher level system, the frequency of the check can never be fast enough. It is inevitable that processes will drift before someone gets round to checking and that the sub-system will ask the question "if we got on OK for so long without doing this, why do we have to do it at all?"'

He defends ISO9000 on the grounds that it could, if correctly installed, help to counteract the phenomenon of process drift, just as Investors In People (IIP) can provide a basic structure for administering training and development, though he clearly endorses Alfie Kohn's comments by saying that 'badges and rewards are no substitute for a sense of purpose'.

Ben Freedman's paper describes the quality programme which was introduced at Robins' Cinemas (which was formed in 1990 and currently operates eleven cinemas and two other leisure attractions in the UK). The programme was introduced in 1993 and various employees describe various aspects of the programme, which was introduced by a 'Leadership Group' which took the form of a cross-functional group of influential people in the company. An employee attitude survey was followed by a company wide analysis and strategy event:

'After the leadership/visionary bit we brought in other perspectives of the survey, firstly through the eyes of the people who drafted and collated it and then the view of the front line staff....Arguably the ticked box in the survey gave us this information, but this can sometimes appear to be bland and academic. We wanted the tick boxes to come to life, to turn the survey into something more tangible with the reality of personal comment and raction. In order to achieve this we invited four members of staff from across the country to come in and verbalise the report to tell us how they saw the world.

This not only endorsed the survey findings but turned the report into something living'.

A participant's view of the large scale event is given, along with a short description of 'what happened next':

'The issues that came from the Employee Attitude Survey were collated and divided into five main areas: communication training, opportunities, understanding work at New Row (central office), pay, and a better system for listening to our customers. Three examples of initiatives that have come from this response include a newsletter, a new personal review system and a cross functional salary team'.

'The purpose of the review system is to help people to improve what they do and how they do it. We wanted to come up with a system that was consistent with the company vision of self-management and one where the review process focused on the customer of the person being reviewed rather than the person himself. We used many of Peter Scholtes' ideas in a paper entitled "an elaboration of Deming's teachings on performance appraisal"'.

MYRON TRIBUS GIVES EQF ANNUAL LECTURE

The Engineering Quality Forum (EQF) annual lecture was given this year by Dr. Myron Tribus before a distinguished audience of 120 (including a recently elected MP) on 26 June at the Institution of Mechanical Engineers.

Dr. Tribus chose as his topic "Engineering with Quality" (although his message applied beyond engineering) and expressed his knowledge with considerable experience of engineering at all levels. His view is that engineers have difficulties in seeing how to make use of the tools and techniques of quality improvement, which they see working in production, to apply in the design process.

He began by showing that the problems start in the technical education process where different activities are 'compartmentalised' into professional characteristics. These were illustrated in orthogonal arrays, as faces of a cube. The first compartment is scientific, and academic i.e. a studying process that is effectively devoid of people. The second, a 'doing' face involves others in the immediate vicinity (in a company) but only in a limited way e.g. designing, planning. A third level, again orthogonal, shows how the activity moves throughout society e.g. using communication and transportation etc.

Engineers move along these levels, but few experience the activity as a whole i.e. the multifaceted nature of engineering work is seen but gives the impression that the 'quality movement' is someone else's problem and opportunity.

Dr. Tribus explained that the Tools and Techniques of Quality are deceptively simple; there are 3 types, Problem Solving, Problem Formulation and Group and Management Methods. These were described. He says when he explains these, senior engineers are apt to dismiss them as trivial and say "IAKI". Not a Japanese word but 'I Already Know It'. This is unfortunate because when applied with co-operation and teamwork they can be very successful. Many quality tools cannot be applied by one person, hence the dismissal. According to Dr. Tribus "in modern management 'IAKI' is forbidden".

Comparisons were made (18 in all) between "Traditional Style" management and "New Style" which were quite enlightening.

He then followed with a redefinition of management which was introduced as a series of "One Liners"e.g. :

* People work IN a system; the manager works ON the system

* Leadership in transforming and maintaining a culture is essential -Assent is not enough

* To increase productivity: increase quality. To push productivity will decrease quality

* Variability is like a virus, it infects all processes, even those which appear to be remote

* If you want to improve the product improve the process that creates the product.

* Whenever there's a problem the odds are 20:1 that it will be in the system, not the individual worker.

* You will get better products at lower prices if you do not force your suppliers to compete for your business.

* Engineers do not know how to compete for power (nor should they want to) hence engineers do not easily make senior management

* The Enemy is UNCERTAINTY i.e. Variation is an enemy.

Dr. Tribus concluded the lecture with a case application of Flowcharting, illustrating that this technique has greater potential for the improvement process than just plotting a system e.g. can be used to monitor changes. He encouraged all engineers involved in a project to start applying Quality techniques as soon as possible and the place to start is with a Flowchart. He once asked Dr. Deming "What does it take to succeed?". The reply was "A critical mass of people who understand and who work together consistently".

Question time raised some interesting points. –

Roy Scruton of I.Mech.E. pointed out that the lecture had an orientation to large companies. How does it apply to small companies? Myron Tribus believes 'it's not the size of the company but the spirit that matters. Large or small you just get on with it'.

Another delegate asked "how do standards like ISO9000 fit in with the lecture philosophy?" The response was that 'when BS5750 started a lot of harm could be done. As with Baldrige it all depends on the way that you do it'.

A follow through question on ISO9000 asked 'Why has the Quality profession gone in this direction when all the "gurus" have been against it?' The reply was that "there is no consensus in the Quality profession, indeed in many respects it is not recognised as a profession. Gurus' ideas are infiltrating in many areas . The solution is when older management and government decline and younger managers take over".

Myron Tribus ended on this theme with a memorable 'one liner' i.e. "Concentrate on training the young and progress will be made one funeral at a time".

[Issue 104 (August 1997)]

THE QUALITY JOURNEY

Sheffield Hallam University hosted The Second World Congress for Total Quality Management from 30th June to 2nd July, attracting a total of around 300 delegates over the three days.

The theme this year was 'The Quality Journey' with a strong focus on teamwork and self-assessment and a varied set of around 77 papers.

A general presentation on 'Data and Teamwork' by Brian Joiner on the opening day stressed the need for staff at all levels to be trained effectively in teamwork and the use of data in order to avoid the pitfalls of obtaining one set of improvements merely at the expense of another and of distortion of figures through 'eventive accounting'.

He argued that where data is used for reward and punishment rather than as a means of working on processes to generate improvement, there would be an inevitable decline, and with the aid of practical exercises for delegates he demonstrated just exactly what this meant. The misuse of data was, he said, 'a common and major problem which serves to destroy teamwork' .

Transforming an Enterprise.

The Deming Memorial Lecture this year was presented by Myron Tribus and had as its theme transforming an enterprise 'to make quality a way of life'. He spoke of the "extraordinary damage" which business schools have inflicted on enterprises through their assumption that work is essentially non-rewarding and that people must somehow be driven to do it, and of the current challenge of management to change its style in a collective effort to make work a more rewarding experience. He condemned "the extraordinary contesting for power" which exists in some large organisations and argued strongly against the case for quality audits, in favour of a strategy based on asking "how is it going?" and when improvements are made he recommended that the "lowest person" should present the story to the highest level.

In his paper he lists seven questions which may be used as a starting point for leading the transformation of a culture:

(i) Do you believe that when you have a problem no matter what it is, that you should begin by defining what it means to have a high quality solution? In other words, do you believe that quality is the answer to your most pressing problems?

(ii) Do you believe that it is possible to change the culture of an enterprise so that the people working in it treat quality as a way to solve problems?

(iii) Do you believe that this enterprise, your enterprise, can be so converted?

(iv) Do you believe you know how to lead the transformation or, if you don't, that you want to learn how to do so?

(v) Do you believe that it is sufficiently worthwhile that you are willing to commit yourself to lead?

(vi) Do you really want to do it?

(vii) Do you believe that the people on whom you rely to support you as you continue in your job will also continue to support you as you lead this change?

He suggests that if it is not possible to answer yes to the first six questions then one should not expect to succeed, and that if the seventh causes a problem then developing support will be one of the challenges which will accompany the assumption of a leadership role. He then lists the essential elements which exist in a chain of transformation (eleven in all) and some of the consequences which are likely if the essential link is not present. For example, lack of a visible strategy is likely to lead to false starts whilst lack of organisation and communication tends to result in non co-ordination of effort:

'If improving quality is everyone's job, it should be easy to keep a run chart on what fraction of the employees are engaged in an improvement effort, month by month. Training given should be tracked to see if it is actually applied and with what results'.

'The short-range goals should be developed as part of a process that makes it certain that the goal setting is not done in a vacuum, that people who are to carry out these goals are involved in the goal setting. The long-range goals should be accompanied by a strategy which describes what needs to be done to achieve them'.

'When people are asked to do something they feel unprepared to do, they get anxious. To be tried and found wanting is a humiliating experience for all people. Experience has taught me that people learn best when they feel the need to know. Therefore, training should be made available on a "just-in-time" basis. Training should be organised around teams working on real projects, of interest to the company. In my opinion it is a waste of time for people to stop their work and practise a quality improvement technique on a problem just made up for training. This sort of thing is done all the time in academia, which is why I refer to myself as a "recovering academic"'.

Following the presentation one delegate asked where he felt the UK stood on leadership and in reply Myron Tribus explained how he had been invited into one British company which boasted having more ISO certificates than any other, yet had found that it had made no difference to the quality of their work. He questioned the view that ISO9000 made a satisfactory starting point and called for some data to verify if indeed this had been the case. Professor John Oakland contrasted Britain's "outstanding lead" in ISO9000 registrations with its apparent failure to engage senior management in the essential culture change, though he said that he was "still hopeful".

THE CHALLENGE OF CHANGE (Case Studies)

Driving out Fear

The BDA was pleased to welcome Dan Oestreich, President of Cultures for Quality Inc. of Seattle, Washington USA, and author of two recently published books, 'Driving Fear out of the Workplace' and 'The Courageous Messenger' to address the conference with a paper entitled appropriately 'Driving Fear out of the Workplace'.

This outlines some of the symptoms of fear in the workplace, such as industrial relations problems, poor morale, lack of suggestions for improvement, people behaving "politically", poor decision making, resignation of high quality personnel, and 'eleventh hour' reports admitting that projects won't work or that there will be serious problems with costs or schedules. It then highlights the sources, which are commonly intertwined, and generally relate to actual events, the stories of others, private interpretations of the motives of others which result in unshared negative conclusions, and negative cultural stereotypes such as "the tyrannical boss" and "the irresponsible employee":

'Fear has been heightened at the very time that organisations need full energy, new ideas, and commitment to service from every member. It is therefore vitally important that people understand how to reduce its destructive effects as the processes of change proceed. Leaders in particular, who are responsible for initiating improvements and reductions in cost need to understand the dynamics of workplace fear and what they can do about it. Without this knowledge leaders will stumble, their good intentions undermined by an invisible, intangible barrier'.

The paper describes how 260 people from 22 different organisations representing service, manufacturing and government were interviewed as part of a research project into the causes and effects of workplace fear, conducted by the author and two of his colleagues, George Orr, and Ms. Kathleen Ryan:

'In each organisation we made an effort to interview a vertical slice extending from senior management to front line employees. We asked people what they had not talked about in the last five years of their work experiences, why they had not done so, and what impact that had on their work. In the course of these interviews we also gained data on the kinds of behaviours exhibited by managers and supervisors which caused people to be afraid'.

The author introduces the concept of the 'undiscussable' (a problem or issue that someone hesitates to talk about with those essential to its resolution) and reveals that approximately half of the 'undiscussables' related to management practice (opinions of how management or specific supervisors were conducting business and, in particular the interpersonal styles of specific supervisors), He highlights the fact that sometimes an 'undiscussable' can become spread across a whole organisation:

'In one firm we interviewed many people who had been touched by a top-down reorganisation that involved layoffs and a shift in business philosophy. Not only was the new business approach something which could not safely be questioned, but top management's decisions and methods for implementing it were also undiscussable, including the dismissal of people and how the "survivors" were expected to cope with increased workloads'.

Findings, however, showed that the fear of losing one's job was not the greatest fear which individuals cited. For some 70 per cent of respondents it was fear of repercussions given as a reason for being hesitant to speak up.

When they were asked about these 'repercussions' it was 'fear of loss of credibility or reputation', or 'fear of negative effects on one's career' or 'damaged relationships with a boss which could result in either subtle or overt harassment' which featured most highly:

'Once the relationship with the supervisor had been damaged people worried that the interpersonal communication would change, that there would be put-downs and insults over or under management or other direct repercussions for "stepping out of line"'.

The costly nature of the impacts of fear, for example through people making and hiding mistakes and indulging in a variety of 'performance impairing negative emotions, are highlighted, and whilst they are not necessarily measurable they are seen to present 'dramatic testimony to fear's costly influence' as evidenced by a quote from one banking professional:

"The bank has changed its relationship with its employees. Loyalty, trust and the family sense are gone. It's them and us – they would certainly lay you off tomorrow if it fitted a corporate interest. This certainly has reduced loyalty in return. I wouldn't recommend this bank to a friend".

Several behaviours that create fear are identified and discussed whilst in his speech Mr. Oestreich stressed the need to be mindful of subconscious arrogance:

" It's extraordinarily easy to become arrogant and assume someone else is the bully. Stop and reflect – what you may be talking to is a small part of yourself".

The paper concludes with seven strategies for reducing fear in the workplace, along with a blueprint for 'The Courageous Messenger':

'Often when speaking with managers or employees I find there is a natural desire for people to explain that they would like to make change in their organisations but can't because of the behaviour of those above them who would not accept or support this work. This is an awful reality to live but I am convinced it is not at all uncommon. My advice, which I am sorry to say is incomplete, is to do what work you can in the arenas in which you have the most influence. If there is work to do with those who report to you or with team-mates in building trust, in dealing with undiscussables that involve you and others, you can start there'.

Some more Deming Successes.

No BDA conference would be complete without some examples of how the philosophy is working in practice and this year was no exception, with the evidence of success being presented by Paul Hollingworth of Tetra-Main Limited in his paper 'Does it work? -The Truth is out there'.

Six case studies are presented illustrating the application of control charts. These challenge in particular the supposition that 'Quality means conformance to specification':

'Specifications are not wrong as such, but they do create a barrier to improvement. With an appreciation of the concept of loss function and armed with a simple XmR control chart, we may peer beneath the surface of pass/fail testing to discover the variation within'.

In the first example a sample of clay paving blocks were always measured in their pre-fired state to ensure that none breached their specification. None of them did so all appeared satisfactory until a control chart was applied which revealed that in practice there was a lack of statistical control with two working shifts producing decidedly different results:

'During the day the product has less variability and is closer to the nominal value. The night shift, on the other hand, will produce a small proportion of pavers below the minimum length -even though none were observed in the sample'.

The operating procedures for the two shifts were subsequently standardised with the process monitored by means of a control chart maintained by the operators, and the result was a significant reduction in overall product variability at no capital cost.

The second example concerns a bought in chemical manufactured in 100 tonne batches and purchased in 20 tonne shipments. Use of a control chart to plot the proportion of an undesirable element in twenty supplies showed that what had hitherto been assumed to be mere batch to batch variation actually had a pattern prompting further investigation. It was found that although there was a single manufacturer the purchasing company was in fact being supplied from two different plants. This was, apparently, a 'revelation' to the supplier who had for the last five years maintained 'a zero defect status of supply'. The customer meanwhile tightened the specification to the level achieved by the better of the two plants.

In the third example a concrete product has a specified range of 15.7 to 19.4 per cent limestone. Its manufacturer is keen to maintain the limestone content high as it is a cheap ingredient (by weight). Automated batch weighing equipment set to produce a mean limestone content of 17.5 per cent generates a print out each day showing the proportion of each ingredient in each batch. A curious employee plotted a control chart using this data, calculating control limits on a month by month basis and observing the effect of recalibration on the weighing equipment. Examination of the control chart from January to August showed that recalibration was only effective for six weeks, yet it was performed just four times a year. Investigation revealed that recalibration was only effective for six weeks because dust and debris accumulated in the equipment. The solution, rather than to increase the frequency of recalibration at a cost of hundreds of pounds, was to supply operators with a brush (cost £1 each) and request that they clean the load cells every day (an operation which took all of two minutes):

'This improved predictability, and enabled the company to increase limestone content by 0.7 per cent with total confidence. From September, the result is improved concrete mix consistency, producing a better quality product at a lower cost'.

Example four involves the production of concrete walling blocks, and illustrates the concept of 'tampering' as exemplified by Dr. Deming's well known 'funnel experiment'. Two XmR charts show how 'normal operator intervention' actually causes out of specification production whilst an absence of tampering enabled detection of a subtle change in a process variable (water pressure drop due to action by Yorkshire Water).

The subject of the fifth example serves to illustrate, if nothing else, that the Deming Management Method can be applied to anything. The sixth and last example examines every Deming practitioner's pet hate, of league tables for sales personnel:

'Why do Gill and Hazel out-perform the other operators? This question would be unlikely to get asked in the environment of fear that the league table helps sustain, but armed with the right question the answer emerged. It seems that when the Telesales office was set up, the switchboard was programmed with a 'hunt group' which would seek out the first free line in a set sequence. When all lines are busy (Barbara's included) the number of calls handled per operator will be influenced by the skill speed of the operator. At off peak times the system will always favour those extensions highest in the hunt group'.

[Issue 115 (July 1998)]

BDA TRANSFORMATION FORUM

The BDA held their eleventh Annual Conference at the University of Loughborough on 16th and 17th June. With a new venue and a slightly amended format the event attracted around 200 delegates who heard case studies from the Driver Vehicle Licensing Authority, Marshalls plc., The Body Shop, ICI, White Rose Line, J.Sainsbury's plc., Rover Group, and Tameside Metropolitan Borough Council, as well as presentations from the ever popular BDA speakers Myron Tribus, John Carlisle, John Norrie, and Hazel Cannon. A warm welcome was also given to Dr. Derek Roger of the Work Skills Centre at the University of York who spoke about 'Adaptation and Change: What Stress is all about'.

The conference proceedings incorporate fifteen papers some of which formed joint presentations, namely 'Co-operation and Continuous Improvement – The Missing Link' by John Carlisle and Charles Johnston, Director of Construction and Facilities Management for Sainsbury's, and the twin papers 'The Role of Standardisation in Improvement' by Terry Weight of Process Management International and 'The Application of Standardisation within Rover Group' by Gordon Vickers and Justin Bull.

Co-operation and Continuous Improvement – The Missing Link

John Carlisle spoke at length about the cost of non-co-operation in the UK construction industry which has been 'catastrophic' over the last twenty years thanks to a 'conflict-ridden culture revolving around competitive tendering (aided and abetted by the last Conservative government) and adversarial working relationships up and down the supply chain':

'In 1995 it was estimated that in a typical year there were over a thousand writs issued, claims of £500M,- of which 80% are settled out of court. In addition there is a current trade deficit of £1.8 billion in the import of construction materials and components alone'.

The consequence of this has been that legal and conflict costs have accounted for around 7% of turnover in this industry in the UK whilst average profit margins have remained stubbornly below 1 %. In Japan the figures are reversed. Similarly, the loss of 500,000 jobs between 1991 and 1996 has created "unknowable losses" in the form of lost expertise, the demise of training and apprenticeship schemes, and "an itinerant workforce with loyalty to no-one". Unfortunately the story does not even end here, for when the mechanical and engineering sector is included it is found that around 40% of service time is wasted, which is around double that experienced in Sweden and over 30% as much as in Germany, not to mention Japan. Suffice it to say, 21 of the world's top 50 construction companies are Japanese.

Turning to the retail sector, which spends around £2.5 billion each year on construction, the speaker argued conclusively that the industry could not afford to continue this way. The missing link is the mindset or mental model which the people with power have formulated about how an organisation works:

" If we moved management to systems thinking, from command and control thinking, the feeling of control goes ".

This, it is suggested, lies at the heart of the problem which in its ultimate has become "a vote of no confidence in the construction sector by investors". Fortunately, however, there are signs that change is on the way:

'On the supply side, construction companies like Morrisons and Thermal Transfer, who have been working collaboratively for some years, have profits of 5% and more, and a growing demand for their services. Symons and Willmott Dixon are also investing in a 'collaborative' and are getting real pay-offs up and down their supply chain. And special mention must be made of Brown and Root, some of whose managers' understanding of partnering is second to none. The bigger companies like Bovis, Birse, Tarmac, Laings and, latterly, Balfour Beatty, are making attempts to become more collaborative; but it is a slow process, despite the sterling efforts of Sir Michael Latham, The Construction Industry Board and the Universities of Reading, Salford et al'.

Further examples of these 'pockets of excellence' are mentioned in the paper, but it is the Sainsbury's case which is described in detail.

Sainsbury's currently build around 25 supermarkets a year using the principle of Strategic Partnering which has brought numerous benefits including a cost reduction of 35% on mainstream stores, reduced typical construction timeframes from 42 weeks to 15, and a 10% improvement from 70% to 80% in the delivery of zero defects at handover since 1990.

Their story begins in 1994 when, following a price war with other supermarkets, Sainsbury's Property division downsized from 240 to 80 staff, whilst at the same time the Department of the Environment 'virtually stopped giving planning permission for out of town stores':

'Sainsbury's strategy for maintaining its share prices had been to increase the size of the sales area each year, but it had no existing planning approvals and no land bank. The decision was therefore made to extend existing stores. This effectively involved more work per square foot than when it built new stores, and Sainsbury's Property Division now had fewer staff to do it. These factors forced Sainsbury's to outsource more of its work, which in turn meant it needed to work more closely with its suppliers'.

They began to focus on their long standing suppliers as they were largely aware of their strengths and weaknesses. The number of architects, for example, was reduced from 36 to 6 firms and three contractors were engaged in place of the previous 32, although four new construction management firms were engaged to satisfy the recognised need to acquire new management skills. In parallel with this internal partnering was adopted to remove waste from bureaucratic elements within the organisation:

'A strategy document was presented to the Main Board based on one project where it had saved £1,000,000 by getting the project team to co-operate in a joint search for savings. The document recommended that Sainsbury's changed the way it procured its buildings and partnering was put forward as the answer for the future. One of the reasons was that, although performance was improving at that time, it was variable. A model project was developed to make a 30% reduction in cost. Of the previous ten stores it had built, the target costs for elements were achieved on about half the projects, but only two projects were within overall model costs. The model produced a construction period of 28 weeks'.

Involvement with John Carlisle Partnerships (JCP) began in January 1996 when they were brought in as independent facilitators for the Savacentre project in Leeds. The concept of 'value engineering' was introduced and led to savings of around £750,000. Formal partnering workshops were then introduced on all projects whilst training was instituted for all staff which fostered partnering attitudes:

'Due to the success of the Leeds project, Sainsbury's employed the John Carlisle Partnerships to help it get the Partnering message across its own organisation. Workshops were held with project managers and senior managers. This is still continuing and it is successfully bringing internal people on board'.

'Sainsbury's specialist contractors are all encouraged to improve their technologies and are prepared to do so at their own cost because of the benefit of repeat business. IT initiatives to improve the cost management system are also on hand which will allow project teams to access information from other projects. This avoids people "reinventing the wheel" – developing expensive answers when better or cheaper ones already exist. Sainsbury's staff are setting their own performance goals as part of its Total Quality approach. Tough and steadily improving costs, time and quality targets have been established and new benchmarks are being developed jointly with the British Airports Authority. Both companies are also looking at sharing feedback and finding common solutions'.

The Role of Standardisation in Improvement.

Terry Weight in his paper describes standardisation as 'a very poorly understood and practised element in the cycle of continuous improvement' which 'sets up negative reactions in those who pride themselves in their ability to solve problems and act on their own initiative':

'We envisage red tape, unreasonable rules imposed from outside by those who don't really understand the real world in which we work. The consequences of this aversion are increased process variability, cost, hassle, stress and the waste of time and materials. The organisation's ability to learn and improve is impaired'.

This need not, however, be so:

'Within Kaizen, standardisation is seen as key with the additional insistence on 'the Japanese 5Ss' which are: keep only necessary items, maintain order at the workplace, keep machines and the environment clean, keep oneself

"clean", and maintain the self discipline of keeping to these habits. Some of the prescription goes too far for us; we are then tempted to reject much of the approach because of its "regimentation". This tempts us to believe the Japanese to lack innovative ability though this is not supported by their Patent history'.

It is argued that work improvement teams should start and finish with standardisation as 'this would release time and energy for creative and enduring improvement work'. Consultation and voluntary compliance, as advocated by the late Dr. W. Edwards Deming, are, however, essential if this approach is to succeed.

The following definition of standardisation is suggested as a starting point:

'Formally agreeing, describing, and then implementing the methods to be used to achieve the best currently known balance between effectiveness, efficiency and adaptability'.

Next, a study of variation is recommended along with the application of a modified form of the PDSA cycle, known as SDSA. (Standardise-Do-Study-Act):

'There is variation in the output which results from variation in both the set of inputs and the transforming activities. We can only reduce the variation in our output and get closer to target by finding the key sources of variation and reducing these. This implies standardisation. Why would we discover the key sources of variation only to allow them to continue to vary?'

A few basic rules for standardisation are then put forward:

(i) Efficient and effective standardisation involves specification for all of the factors known to have an important influence on the important outcomes but no other factors.

(ii) The people working in the process must be enabled to feel significant influence on the process they work in. This will encourage the process discipline needed. Where there are too many to involve, and for new starters, the training needs to include the "why" as well as the "how" and "what" of doing the job.

(iii) Managers and technical experts have a new role helping the workers in the process, to exercise their process responsibility effectively. This means helping them develop and maintain good process understanding and agreement on the process purpose, and facilitating when necessary their improvement work.

(iv) The purpose of process audit should be "to assist people in the process to work to and improve the standardisation process". Who carries out audits and how the results are used should reflect this purpose. Managers have an important enabling role here.

(v) The nature of this task clearly affects both what and how you should standardise.

The timing of standardisation should be:

- upon initial process definition

- upon subsequent improvements to the process

- upon changes in customer requirements

- upon changes in supplier capabilities

The paper by Gordon Vickers and Justin Bull describes the application of these principles first of all to the rear door assembly process on the Land Rover Discovery product built at the Solihull plant, and second to the Rover 600 Window Regulator Setting Process.

The first example illustrates how a process can be improved purely by focusing on the process elements rather than opting for the more usual and costly alternative of re-designing the physical parts. It follows from a policy by Land Rover Vehicles of adopting process standardisation following the training of internal consultants and the subsequent initiation of the Process Improvement Department.

Discovery was chosen as the product owing to its high volume and world-wide market appeal, and the interior trim fit cell then selected as a result of the high visual customer impact possessed by the parts within it. A matrix was then deployed to identify the rear end door seal as the process for the pilot standardisation exercise:

'Both a Process Improvement Consultant and a Process Improvement Manager were used in a full-time capacity to facilitate all activities, work together and share our learning. The standardisation team consisted of members from Production, Assembly, Manufacturing Engineering, Trim and Hardware Design and Technical Support -All full-time team members. Part-time members also joined the team from Product Audit, Water Test, and other Production Cells as required. In order to try to create the necessary team spirit, the PMI "Team Start up" process was conducted. Here the team members were introduced to each other, the specific goals were highlighted, the process constraints identified and their level of awareness of process raised'.

A review of current process knowledge followed by documentation of current ways of doing the work showed that four different operators applied four different methods of working with regard to tooling methods, transportation routes, direction of fit, and force of hammering onto body flanges. Each operator was aware of a written process for performing this work, but none had actually seen a copy. They had never been part of the development process.

Each operator tested each method at the weekend so no delays to normal production occurred. They then discussed amongst themselves which method should become the standardised process. Each operator then tested the new agreed method until content with it and as a result they became committed to performing the work in a new uniform single manner:

'This standardisation example had the major benefit of identifying very costly and totally unnecessary re-work at water test. Seals were being replaced and damaged, with all the problems being fed back to the seal assemblers. This had previously gone unnoticed'.

The second example, by contrast, stemmed from customer problems discovered in the market place i.e. front door glass judder during up/down operation. It was considered to be an ideal process to which to apply standardisation since all aspects of the customer problem pointed towards variation in the process and the process output was quite measureable:

'The customer complaint was easy to replicate and hence was built in to the dynamic product audit. A three month in-service warranty claim rate of 0.08-0.15 faults per vehicle meant the problem was consistently in the top 20 list of customer problems'.

Again a process improvement team was established, with their main task this time being to translate customer concern into a product problem. The team brainstormed all sources of variation in both the process and the product:

'One source of variation was levelled at the different methods employed by the manufacturing associates in setting the regulators. Specifically this meant setting the rearward and forward window regulator bolts at differing heights. An extreme case of poor setting could cause the glass to fall out of the door seal.

A number of tests were first run by the team to establish the nominal position for the regulator bolts. The nominal position was then measured to establish a known position. The position was then compared to a number of examples from the manufacturing process. At this point the team could establish that it was not only distance away from the "nominal" position that was critical, it was the overall process variation which could affect the number of problems which the customer might see.

A number of alternative methods were then developed by the process improvement team to discover the best way of setting the bolts to the nominal condition. The various methods were then trialled, with the bolt positions being measured at the end of the process'.

The step which was observed to be the prime contributor to the variation was that of tightening the regulator bolts. Process instructions did not define the exact method of assembling and setting the window regulators therefore torque settings were validated infrequently on rechargeable power tools. An improved standardised process has rectified this, and resulted in fewer warranty claims, the elimination of product audit defects, reduction of reliance on rework and improved cost performance.

[**Quality Matters comments:** It can be seen, from the above detailed reports that the initial driving force for change can be quite different, but the application of a 'Philosophy of Change' in the above using Deming principles, whether in the boardroom or on the shopfloor, is essential for success. The traditional management exhortation 'call for more steam' or 'new targets' in such circumstances without a 'Philosophy of Change' has been the ruin of many otherwise good companies].

[Issue 116 (August 1998)]

APPLYING DEMING TO LOCAL GOVERNMENT

The Tameside MBC (outer Manchester) case study given at the BDA annual conference is interesting as it provides what is probably the first really serious attempt to apply Deming principles in British local government. The Chief Executive of Tameside MBC, Mr. Mike Greenwood, explained how it has been done and what some of the early benefits from this approach have been.

The Authority had been seeking to change its organisation and culture since 1990, but appeared to lack any strategic direction until 1995 when the phenomenal benefits which the Deming Management Method was beginning to bring to the private sector started to be noticed by senior management of the Council:

'The approach which Tameside has taken firstly involved ensuring understanding of the ideas amongst senior management. Following work with the Management Team, a series of one-day introductory seminars led by Henry Neave was offered and around 200 middle and senior managers attended. In parallel with this, the Council made use of the OED three day continual improvement simulation. About 800 staff have had the benefit of this very valuable learning experience.

As staff completed the course, they were encouraged to form CI groups in the workplace. The initial approach was one of empowerment and encouragement from management; to capture the enthusiasm which the course developed in individuals to apply it directly in their own workplace. The experience from this was interesting and variable. Some managers and work groups quickly grasped the issues and used the new techniques and learning to embark upon active improvement of systems and services. In other parts of the organisation things did not proceed as smoothly. The areas where more problems arose tended to be either those where the systems were inherently more complex or where management leadership was still locked in the old paradigm. The latter point is being addressed through the Council's Management Development Programme'.

The most successful improvement activities have been identified as those in which there have been total ownership and commitment from the work groups themselves. Specific benefits have included:

- Debt recovery (£4.9 million debt in 1995 reduced to £2.3 million)

- Improvements in reliability of council tax bills and the time taken to produce them (from 9.0 days to 1.2 days, described as "a very pleasing project" after three PDSA cycles).

- Reduction in the time taken to supply library requests from 32 to 20 days following two PDSA cycles and a partnership with The British Library to improve the total system.

- A "breakthrough" in social service provision directly attributable to the successful deployment of control charts.

Departmental business plans currently ensure that all work groups have clear measures of their activities, flowchart their procedures, and understand inputs and outputs to and from their systems. Improvement against the measures is tracked, but the emphasis is very much on the empowerment aspect.

Following the presentation Mr. Greenwood was asked if he was aware of any other UK local authorities that were applying the Deming philosophy and he referred to early efforts by both Walsall and Barnsley councils where there has been "thinking of Deming at a senior level".

He advocated the benchmarking of best value as a means to establish a network in this area. Meanwhile Myron Tribus described the presentation as "one of the best that I have heard" and called for what had been said and written "to be made more widely available".

TRANSFORMATIONAL LEARNING ON THE INTERNET

The task of bringing the benefits of the Deming approach to the attention of a larger audience can only have been enhanced by the launch of the Deming Electronic Network (DEN) on the Internet.

A paper by Alan C. Clark given at the BDA annual conference describes the DEN and its background as well as how it may be accessed and used as a vehicle towards the formation of 'a virtual Deming community':

'Visions are emerging within the BDA of it as a virtual organisation. One early manifestation is in the BDA Alliance of Consultants who have begun parallel circulation of notes from its meetings using e-mail. On the world scene some Deming groups are posting announcements of meetings and notes from meetings on the DEN'.

The DEN at present comprises two components, a mediated discussion list based on e-mail and a Web site. The Web site contains, amongst other things, an archive of all of the postings to the discussion list. It is a volunteer-based, non-commercial electronic communications resource which is available internationally to individuals and organisations. Its stated aim is as follows:

"To learn, apply and extend the teachings of Dr. W. Edwards Deming and to help others do the same".

The 'learn' component is grounded in Dr. Deming's writings whilst the 'apply' component is grounded in personal experiences and the 'extend' component is grounded in individuals' unique perspectives:

'Many come to this list with a basic understanding of the Deming Philosophy, but want to know either how to actually apply it personally or how to encourage others inside or outside their organisations to apply it. In this area of our dialogues, we often offer anecdotal evidence and personal perspectives'.

'Whether they are universally applicable or based on a specific Deming teaching is not as important as the ability to perceive that a Deming principle has been applied'.

The DEN discussion list is moderated by Jim Clauson of Kingston, Tennessee and currently has around 700 subscribers in 20 countries.

Discussion topics are varied and there are two subscription options: Normal Messaging and Digest Messaging. Normal Messaging will typically yield between 10 and 20 messages per day whilst Digest Messaging produces a single daily message with an index derived from a set of daily messages.

[Issue 127 (July 1999)]

B.D.A. TRANSFORMATION FORUM

The twelfth annual British Deming Association Forum, held for the second time at Loughborough University from 16th to 18th June, featured a welcome return by Jim McIngvale ("Mattress Mac") President and owner of the Houston based furniture retailers Gallery Furniture, along with fellow American speakers Peter Scholtes, Myron Tribus and Linda Borsum.

This year he described the situation six years on, with the predictions of some that his decision to follow Dr. Deming's advice would result in the ruination of Gallery having been proven to be completely erroneous. His presentation is reviewed below along with those by Andrzej Blikle (owner of Warsaw based luxury pastry manufacturers A. Blikle and Professor of Mathematics and Computer Science at the Polish Academy of Sciences), BDA Director of Research Professor David Kerridge and Nick Baxter (General Manager of Cornerstone Community Care, Aberdeen), and the team of Marshall's plc (formerly Yorkshire Brick).

Gallery Furniture Six Years on.

Gallery Furniture's sales topped $100 million in 1998 and in explaining how this was achieved "Mattress Mac" outlined how his company had radically altered the profile requirements for sales people with particular regard to recruitment, in favour of individuals likely to be loyal and sincere. Also they removed the payable department, introduced the "memorable experience" concept to customer service, has become a major sponsor of sporting events (tennis) in the US, and is now exploiting information technology to the full in both marketing and distribution.

This explanation included a description of "Personalysis" (the pre-hiring employee evaluation principle used to ensure that the right people are recruited for sales, deliveries and finance), and various aspects of "fun in retailing" which has involved such initiatives as free snacks for customers, promotional basketball dispensation, the construction of sports memorabilia areas and even a "tropical rainforest" built into a store so that furniture retailing is no longer "about as exciting as going to the dentist". Most impressive, however, is perhaps the diversification into tennis sponsorship and the innovative use of IT.

The company's involvement in tennis began in 1995 with a deal with the organisers of a women's tennis tournament at a time when many clubs in the US were experiencing great financial difficulty. This led to some high level publicity for the company which culminated in the involvement of Steffi

Graf in a schools project in which she played barefoot alongside youngsters, with a highly desirable impact on society resulting. This was in stark contrast to the many US tennis clubs that were going out of business largely, according to the speaker, because the system under which they operated was strangely reminiscent of Gallery's pre-Deming days i.e. it revolved entirely around the commissions paid to professionals. Mr. McIngvale then outlined how his organisation subsequently came to acquire all four US Grand Slam tennis surfaces and to operate "the most profitable tennis club in the US" with salaried rather than commission based professionals. The free lessons and clinics were, he said, "loved by members".

The abolition of sales commission has likewise offered a new marketing advantage in that it has enabled advanced selling on the Internet to become a reality, with customers and potential customers able to control in-store cameras to select their purchases. He said:

"If salespeople had commissions they would have fought Internet selling tooth and nail. Instead we have had over one million hits this month alone and complete co-operation".

Likewise in distribution the Internet is being used to allow customers to keep track of their consignments through a network of distribution centres whilst an in-house rather than an outsourced delivery fleet which enables the customer interface to be managed without hassle.

In his conclusion "Mattress Mac" acknowledged that he still had challenges to face, including good competitors who were well financed, although the greatest challenge, he said, was to stay on the Deming course. He assured delegates that his company was "going to stay the course".

"Mattress Mac" was clearly going to be a popular speaker and in view of this a special 50 minute questionnaire answer session was arranged for delegates which was well attended. In this session he was asked a range of questions which covered subjects such as supplier assessment, evaluating the performance of sales staff, dealing with customers who make purchases that they cannot afford, the status of competitors and staff turnover. He explained how the company's 40 suppliers were "critical", "managed very carefully", and not cut off but helped in the event of a problem. He did, however, engage in dialogue with other furniture people around the country to raise questions about reliability. The performance of salespeople on the other hand was more behavioural than numerical:

"We can watch and study them. If they hide in the bathroom all day then we know that they have to go".

Awkward customers, he acknowledged, did also arise, but were usually dealt with by a full refund. "It is not worth fighting over $200", he stressed, as the company's reputation was far more important, along with an understanding of the true cost.

He was asked whether any of his competitors were seeking to follow his company down the Deming road or whether they were largely still old-style. In his reply he suggested that the old-style still prevailed and that all of them still struggled with a three to four week delivery schedule which was afar cry from Gallery's "unique selling point" of the "immediate delivery". He did, however, express some interest in the activities of Ikea in Sweden, particularly with regard to design and production of furniture in which he had identified a leading role not currently practised by Gallery.

On the subject of staff turnover he acknowledged that the company's current rate of 15% was higher than he would have liked, although it was not at all negative as this sort of level does allow for an input of new people who may have fresh ideas and be able to solve problems in a different and beneficial way.

Applying Deming in Eastern Europe.

The presentation by Andrzej Blikle entitled 'The unsweetened history of a small fast-growing company in a medium fast-growing country' traced the outline of his family owned business from 1845 and whilst slogans like "All One Team", "quality over Profit" and "Salaries not by Incentives" could, he suggested, easily be mistaken for direct quotes from old Communist Party posters, delegates soon discovered that the interpretation was quite different.

Like "Mattress Mac" Professor Blikle also had a nickname ("The Doughnut Man") which derived from his relations with border police as his high quality luxury pastries and doughnuts were exported regularly to Germany and other Western markets, and delegates soon warmed to his frank confidence building presentation style using immaculate English. It was soon recognised that whilst the business was small (just 270 employees in ten luxury pastry shops and one luxury café-restaurant, and a sales revenue last year of around $5 million), it was quite possible to apply the Deming philosophy even in a country where front line workers still cannot afford to rent even a modest flat. Thus, if you think you can't do it "The Doughnut Man" will assure you that you can.

The Deming journey began in 1995 when the speaker became inspired by the work of Brian Joiner (Fourth Generation Management) and later Alfie Kohn (Punished by Rewards). Implementation of the 'Joiner Triangle' followed with a philosophy of continuous improvement based on systematic thinking and a 'one team' concept. A 36 hour course given by the speaker based on the teaching of Brian Joiner kick started the process, supported with a two day course led by consultant Jim Murray. A series of 20 seminar lectures were then given to staff which included a version of *'Punished by Rewards'* which had so impressed Professor Blikle at the 1994 BDA Forum and *'In*

Pursuit of Quality -The Case against ISO 9000' by John Seddon (see Chapter 1).

At top management level private interviews with a core of 15 people assisted by consultants have led to the production of a "consolidated report" which has revealed "many underground problems". More importantly, this report has been made public to these 15 people resulting in a "breakthrough in communication". In addition flowcharting has been deployed to ease the understanding of procedures, which currently number around 60, whilst for sales staff there has been a complete reconstruction of the remuneration system along the lines advocated by Alfie Kohn and exposure to life in other departments, particularly production where they see and experience the problems encountered by their internal suppliers:

"It took six months to prepare the new remuneration system following the fifteen managers' discussions. There is now no remuneration based on closing balance sheets and all work that is predictable, unless it takes extra hours, does not give rise to extra payments".

There is now a weekly workshop for senior management which avoids technical managerial problems and focuses on important general matters, such as 'Four days with Dr. Deming' which has now been translated into Polish. Other initiatives include the 'job instructor' concept borrowed from the Japanese which has overcome the personnel problems which can arise when someone perceives a competitive threat from those whom they are training [very important -Ed].

The business results which have accompanied this small company's transformation over the last five years are impressive by any standards and are clearly shown in bar chart form in the conference proceedings. Basically they show a three fold increase in employees, a five fold increase in sales revenue and an increase in average sales revenue per employee from around $12,500 to around $20,000.

The conference literature also lists some of the company's problems and achievements and displays a matrix showing how the company's achievements link in with 'Joiner's Triangle' and the actions which have accompanied those achievements. For example, achievements have included no more misleading financial analyses, more competence delegation and quality improvement of some products. Actions have included control cards and Pareto in financial management, no penalties or rewards either in remuneration by incentives and the establishment of quality circles.

The presentation attracted a number of questions which included notably the subjects of the company's influence on others in Poland, and the success of quality circles. In his replies the speaker explained how, at least in the pastry making field, others appeared to be reluctant to talk, although when he organised a monthly open seminar of four hours' duration he had had some interest from other industry sectors, such as banking and telecommunications, with interest sufficient to enable Poland to host its first Deming Forum this October with Jim Murray as Keynote speaker. In describing his success and continued support for quality circles he said the following:

"The café was once a difficult area. People were afraid to discuss quality issues, but since the introduction of quality circles people have become much more enthusiastic and real success has been seen from them. The first results of the implementation of Deming can be seen in four to five years and we are now at around this region".

Achieving Transformation in Community Care.

Transformation in community care was "something different except for the external pressure to cut costs" according to David Kerridge, who is Aberdeen based and was approached by Nick Baxter in 1994. It was different since unlike Gallery Furniture the customers were not the people who were paying and better quality would not necessarily mean increased profits. This did not mean to say, however, that business results could not be achieved, and indeed they have been.

The Cornerstone case study provides an excellent example of how the Deming Management Method can be applied outside a manufacturing environment in an area where the potential gains are almost entirely intangible, yet clearly measurable by the naked eye. "There were no easy visible gains at shopfloor level", and "improving processes does not necessarily save money", said David Kerridge, but there were some very definite "invisible and heavy losses".

Training in the System of Profound Knowledge took about a year, and this was supported with a series of continuous improvement seminars from another consultant, Gordon Hall. Meanwhile David Kerridge visited houses, examined potential areas of conflict and antagonism and mapped out a system. This highlighted particularly the issue of 'tampering' with stable processes and the high volume of the Chief Executive's time that could be saved by eliminating it.

Nick Baxter explained how control charts were later introduced systematically, first with his own 'General Manager's Arrival Times' which proved to be "a useful exercise that gave confidence", and then with financial activities such as cheques issued per month and payroll queries. He explained how now he only signs around four cheques per month after asking the question "do I need to sign all these cheques or could someone else do it?".

In describing some of the achievements over the past year he confessed to having been initially "confused" and "disorientated" by the Deming philosophy in a manner that "felt cult-like" but accepted that without it would not have been possible to maintain the same quality of service for less cost without having to cut costs or rates of pay. Some of the benefits listed were:

* the opening of six new houses

* the achievement of a British Safety Council Five Star Award

* the achievement of the UCB 1998 Care Home of the Year Award

* continued growth (19%)

* financial results with an estimated value of £500,000 .

Cornerstone Community Care was established as a voluntary agency in 1980 and provides services principally to people with learning disabilities in North East Scotland. Their turnover is currently £5.9 million and they employ 300 staff in 50 service settings.

Improvement through Office People.

At the 1994 BDA Forum Alan Winlow of Yorkshire Brick presented a paper entitled 'Quality, Productivity and Environmental Position' which described the company's early application of the Deming Management Method in the production area. Savings of £390,000 were reported from waste reduction whilst improvements in energy utilisation led to annual savings of £35,000 and water consumption was reduced by 80%. Later that year Barnsley based Yorkshire Brick was acquired by Marshall's plc. Who are a leading manufacturer of building products based in Halifax who employ 2,800 and operate 33 sites all over the UK.

The acquisition, however, did not result in a compromising of Yorkshire Brick's Deming principles. Indeed the reverse is true and at this year's BDA Forum Group Office Service Improvement Manager Assunda Zito described how the Deming principles adopted for production at Yorkshire Brick have not only been continued by Marshall's in their production activities, but also taken a stage further into that often troublesome area of Head Office.

Marshall's Head Office is known as Brier Lodge and has around 2000 employees, and as Yorkshire Brick was transforming its production this place retained an antiquated management structure with unclear lines of communication, teams (or what passed for them) working in isolation from one another, and an outdated deployment of extrinsic motivational methods:

'In 1995 things had come to a head and the directors were toying with the idea of bringing in one of those "do as I say and everything will turn out wonderful" business renewal experts. Fortunately, Graham Holden (Finance

Director) suggested that instead we give the office a try at continuous improvement (up until then it had only been recognised as a factory initiative). The key differences between what we tagged as a "do as I say" business renewal expert and a continuous improvement coach and facilitator are considerable. The first uses his own knowledge and ideas to initiate change and the second listens to the company experts and helps to facilitate the employees' knowledge and ideas. Paul Hollingsworth, the management development consultant from Tetra-Main, was deemed the man for the job and there began the transformation of Brier Lodge'.

The paper explains how Mr. Hollingsworth enlightened the management with 'Fourth Generation Management' theory and Beckhard's formula for effective change i.e. multiply dissatisfaction, vision, capabilities and first steps together to overcome resistance to change. It follows that in the latter if any of the above four components are zero then nothing will happen:

'We decided to establish the level of dissatisfaction within the office. We asked for and immediately received hundreds of problems which were then categorised into 80 common areas. In addition we asked the following question: 'How would you describe the ideal Brier Lodge in the year 2000?'. The results were then categorised into twelve areas to form a vision statement'.

The paper explains how a large proportion of the original 80 problems were connected to Hertzberg's so called "Hygiene Demotivators" and this prompted a thorough refurbishment of Brier Lodge using the company's own products. Next, a team was formed by Graham Holden to lead the Improvement through Office People initiative whilst Tim Downes and Ken Fleming (special project manager) acted as facilitators:

'People were nominated to represent every one in four employees and these representatives were also trained on how to use the 10 Stage Model and in customer care. This was followed by tools and techniques training, to put theory into practice, run by our now legendary CI trainers Damien Duxbury and Alex Ross. Since then, the floodgates were opened with numerous training courses taking place. These ranged from effective sales negotiation to David Train and his Bell Boats'.

The new leaders were coached using an Office Leader Purpose Statement which was formulated by all office leaders as a guide. An effective multi-levelled meeting structure was then put in place enabling each team to develop its own improvement strategy. These strategies are combined in a series of system improvement meetings. In addition a cross-functional team was formed from all levels of the company to develop a Statement of Values and Principles, excerpts from which are included in the conference literature. The paper then describes how David Train's Bell Boat concept was applied at Brier Lodge:

'Each boat had members of each different Brier Lodge team in it to encourage the feeling of all one big team. This was followed by learning about the value of co-operation as the teams made their own paddles (the first thing some people had made for forty years). This was rounded off by a brain storming session where the people compared what they had learnt with what happened at the office'.

Since then cross functional teams have been formed to take forward many varied projects and Belbin's theory has been added to aid the teambuilding process. The benefits are illustrated with reference to three troublesome areas (contract sales, customer advice, and stockist sales) where abandoned calls were adversely affecting customer service and doing untold damage to the bottom line.

In contract sales in 1998 it was not unusual to have 17% of calls lost in a day. The team worked to improve the process along with their colleagues in external sales and by 'almost eliminating the stop/start element that affected throughput' they managed to reduce the mean abandoned call rate from 14% to 7.2%.

In customer advice the team identified the factors which caused calls to be lost:

'They freed up one of their five telephone advisors to work full time on improvements. Then, as a team, with the improvement facilitator co-ordinating matters, they tackled the reasons that were within their control. The simplest of the changes, which was channelling all administrative duties through one person, had the greatest bearing on the outcome'.

'By adopting this new procedure, the advisors were more able to receive incoming calls and the after call time decreased as a consequence. The results were impressive. In every month the number of abandoned calls decreased whilst the levels of calls increased. The mean abandoned call rate has reduced from 15.6% in 1996/97 to 7.5% in 1997/98. The idea of appointing a recognised improvement facilitator has since been adopted in several teams.'

In stockist sales control charts were used to track incoming and abandoned calls which led to actions to staff the team according to peaks and troughs i.e. matching customer requirement with resource. The result was a drop in mean abandoned calls from 9.2% in 1997 to 2.9% in 1998 and a reduction in variation from 17.5% in 1997 to 6.6% in 1998 i.e. improved consistency in customer service.

More recent initiatives have included the flowcharting of current and future procedures with a view to adopting Best Office Practice at all sites, the introduction of a new Dispute Management System (invoice query resolution) which uses software created in-house by a leading administrator from which 'feedback from both internal and external customers has been very encouraging', and the second stage of Improvement Through Office People at the company's second largest office (Sandy in Bedfordshire). Also, a new area is being looked at - innovation of product and service.

In addition to the paper the conference literature includes 'The Vision of Marshalls' Offices in 2003', 'The Office Leader's Purpose Statement', 'Marshalls' Attitude to Work Survey - Brier Lodge', and a fish bone diagram detailing all of the activities and changes that took place at Marshalls from 1995 to 1997.

Further Information.

The last BDA Forum of the twentieth century attracted around 185 participants. It was recorded in its entirety and the 22 audio cassettes may be purchased from: QED Recording Services Limited, Lancaster Road, New Barnet, Hertfordshire EN4 8AS. Telephone: 0181 441 7722.

[Issue 128 (August 1999)]

FOURTH SHEFFIELD WORLD QUALITY CONGRESS

The Fourth World Congress for TQM at Sheffield Hallam University from 28th to 30th June had as its theme 'Integrating for Excellence : Achieving Customer Loyalty'. It was opened by the University's Vice Chancellor Professor Diana Green who outlined proposals for a pilot scheme to be led jointly by Sheffield Hallam University and the University of Durham which will test the application of the EFQM Business Excellence Model in the UK's Higher Education sector.

The New Competencies of Leadership

The Deming Memorial Lecture this year was delivered by Peter Scholtes and had the above title. It consisted largely of an adaptation of part of his latest book entitled' The Leader's Handbook' which was published last year which elaborated on six 'competencies of leadership' based on Deming's System of Profound Knowledge. The six competencies are listed as follows:

    (i)   The ability to think in terms of systems and knowing how to lead systems

    (ii)   The ability to understand the variability of work in planning and problem solving.

    (iii)   Understanding how we learn, develop and improve, and leading true learning and improvement

(iv)   Understanding people and why they behave as they do

(v)   Understanding the interdependence and interaction between systems, variation, learning and human behaviour: knowing how each affects the others.

(vi)   Giving vision, meaning, direction and focus to the organisation.

Of these particular attention was paid in the presentation to the second and fourth competencies, with notable regard to common misunderstandings concerning motivation and the application of perceived simplistic solutions to complex problems:

'Leaders who fail to master the concept of variation will see trends where there are no trends and will miss trends where there are trends. They will blame people for things beyond their ability to control and give credit for things equally beyond control. Those who do not understand variation will have simplistic -almost superstitious -explanations about past events and they will have no understanding about what to expect in the future. When revenues fail to meet expenses, the simplistic manager will declare "Costs are out of control".

Often, there are no data for this assertion and the impetuous decisions will be to cut costs in ways that may damage the future of the enterprise. How much cutting to do and where to cut may well be a product of the manager's unease (or, perhaps better stated, the manager's disease)'.

Understanding human behaviour was described as 'the greatest shortcoming of managers' and the speaker condemned wholeheartedly the " cyclical premise" behind performance appraisal which results in "people withholding effort and waiting for it to be bribed from them". He described the managers who advocated the concept as "mean spirited" and called for them "to stop doing it and stop others from doing it":

'Too often our only purpose is that of profits. When we are driven by profits alone, then our goal and purpose are to make money. Our measure of success is profits and our performance is evaluated by profits. But if the purpose of our system is to take care of our people, then our actions will be aimed at that end. We will be profitable because without this, the system's purpose, taking care of people, would not be attained. But this larger purpose requires so much more. It does not involve making deals as much as building an interactive, interdependent community'.

With regard to the fifth competency (Interactions and interdependencies) Mr. Scholtes explained 'the pinball effect' whereby the development of ideas and inventions 'carom off each other' rather than developing linearly, and 'the tipping point' whereby an event or condition changes the balance of forces and affects the equilibrium:

'A Scotsman named Bell, whose wife was also deaf, was an advocate for voice training for the deaf. Their son, Alexander Graham Bell, developed a mechanical device to convert sound into electronic signals so that the deaf could "see" the sounds. This quickly evolved into the telephone. The path of inventiveness, thus, is carved by combining a desire to solve a problem with unique knowledge and know-how; and the inventiveness takes different twists as different people with different resources become involved. The message of the pinball effect: sometimes the answer comes from the places we least expect. We can nurture among ourselves a readiness for the unexpected possibilities.

'New York City's crime rate is now lower than that of, some smaller cities, such as Boise, Idaho. This did not happen by accident. It has taken nine years of carefully planned efforts to reduce the crime rate in New York City. Most of all, it has taken leadership, people in positions of influence to exert a persistent, concerted and thoughtful effort. The pinball effect and the tipping point concept are but two ways of rethinking the leader's need to see things in the larger context and to consider the interactions and the interdependencies. Leaders need to ask themselves "And then what?", "What's next?", "What are the possible implications?"

The paper concludes with a seven stage methodology for planning and breakthrough improvement.

Further Information

'Proceedings of the Fourth World Congress for Total Quality Management: Integrating for Excellence' Edited by Gopal K. Kanji (ISBN 0954-4127)

[Issue 130 (October 1999)]

TRANSFORMING CALL CENTRE OPERATIONS

Britain's call centres have gained a bad reputation in recent years and have been likened to the 'sweat shops' of the 1920s. This, however, need not be prolonged according to occupational psychologist and Managing Director of Vanguard Consulting John Seddon whose recently published 'Guide to Transforming Call Centre Operations' maps out a course for transformation based on Deming principles which he believes could be an industry standard in five years' time.

According to John Seddon a call centre's purpose is 'to allow customers to pull value from an organisation' but recent studies such as Teleculture 2000 undertaken by the Henley Management Centre suggest that call centres 'vary enormously in their ability to deliver customer satisfaction' whilst

Vanguard's own research has shown that closure at first attempt rarely exceeds 65% and in one financial services organisation was just 21 %:

'Sometimes closure at the first attempt looks high on a first impression, but when you dig down to the detail of the workflow you often find the first impressions to be unreliable. For example, measures of closure at the first attempt might ignore successive handovers within the call centre or transferring messages to another part of the organisation. Managers often become adept at massaging their measures'.

It follows that a call centre does not necessarily result in improved service and lower cost to the organisation and Mr. Seddon offers the following reasons as to why so many call centres have become 'sweat shops':

(i) Measuring call activity ignores variation (people can get adverse work measurement numbers when the causes of variation are outside their control).

(ii) Managers pay attention to people for the wrong reasons (particularly service agents as a result of being unaware of the extent of variation attributable to the system).

(iii) Managers are focused on internal issues (Managers are primarily concerned with matters of productivity and as a consequence service agents lose sight of their purpose and managers become out of touch with opportunities to make significant improvements in productivity).

(iv) In order to survive in such an environment people learn to cheat (It becomes the only way to avoid adverse criticism).

(v) Managers focus on people inappropriately instead of on the work design (For example seeking to 'cope with poor performers' and 'keep the good performers motivated' rather than acting on the system to improve morale and reduce staff turnover).

With this background Vanguard Education, of which John Seddon is Managing Director, hosted a one day conference on 21st September with the help of speakers from ICL, HSBC Midland Bank, and Virgin Train Line outlining the Vanguard approach and demonstrating the potential benefits. These are reviewed with other case studies and examine the essential role of information technology with particular regard to Interactive Voice Response (IVR) on which so many call centres now rely.

Case Studies in Call Centre Management.

A central feature of all the case study presentations was the distinction that was made between value demand (what the call centre exists for to do for customers) and failure demand (demand caused as a result of failure within the call centre or its host organisation to get something right for the customer). According to John Seddon at least 30% and in some cases as many as 75% of calls received by a call centre will constitute failure demand. He referred particularly to police call centres where the nature of calls "were often ignored" and failure demand "is designed in".

Stephen Parry, Head of Corporate Operations for the Operational Services Division of ICL, explained how in his organisation the ratio of value demand to failure demand has been used as a measure of the company's health whilst front line staff were taken through the concept of viewing the organisation from the customer's point of view. The involvement of managers was kept to a minimum in order to avoid contamination by their preconceived ideas and when management was presented with a systems map of the organisation which had hitherto been unseen they "were shocked". The 'make and sell' approach of the past whereby customers talk to marketing groups and then compile a model from which targets are derived gave way to a 'sense and respond' approach which was iterative and used real operational information to influence the design of services. Examples of calls that have satisfied a particular type of demand in the past are tracked so that a control chart can be used to predict what they will do when the same type of demand recurs.

Chris Jones, Centre Manager for the HSBC Midland Bank Customer Service Centre in Swansea, explained how the 'mass production approach' which implies that everyone should be treated the same when it comes to call centre operations was a recipe for disaster. He asserted that all customers are individuals and that it is simply not possible to supply good quality customer service by treating them all the same. A keen advocate of the EFQM Business Excellence Model, Mr. Jones stressed that call centres should be used as "catalysts for change" because their staff are frequently much more customer focused than those elsewhere in the organisation and that the key to making this profitable was *"to make the important measurable rather than the measurable important"*.

Often, he said, organisations prefer the easy option of measuring how long calls take and of giving these measurements undue priority over the real measures i.e. what the customers measure. In this regard he quoted the nature and type of demand as a crucial measure and explained how HSBC Swansea's current failure demand rate currently stood at around 20%. At HSBC the ability of staff to understand customer requirements is used as a barometer for the Business Excellence Model's customer satisfaction criterion whilst traffic volumes are divided into six types in order to segregate value calls from failure calls.

Alan Meekings, Vice President of Gemini Consulting and Account Director for Virgin Train Line described how last year his organisation quadrupled capacity and doubled productivity in six months largely as a result of ceasing to focus on average call duration as a measure of productivity. He stressed the importance of enabling front line people to step into the minds of customers in order to ascertain what really matters to them and of making variation visible. "If you merely look at the number of calls handled how can you evaluate them if you don't understand their nature?", he asked delegates. He acknowledged Virgin Telesales' past reputation for poor customer service with customers frequently waiting half an hour to get a response, and the need of management to do something about it, but equally hoped that the benefits of the new approach would serve as an example to others i.e. 4% of calls unanswered instead of 77% and a maximum wait of 3 minutes instead of half an hour. They are currently working on a web-enabled contact centre with the aim of enlarging the breadth of customers served.

A further presentation by Barry Wrighton, of Vanguard, described a further case study from Ireland involving computer maintenance which entailed placing diagnosticians and resourcing controllers on a front line team to ascertain from customers what mattered to them so that they could create value. He described how they went to a call centre for one week to listen to types of calls rather than checking up on call centre staff and how this subsequently generated a dialogue about types of demand within the call centre. It was found that a major cause of variation was the quality of the diagnosis and this data was used first to re-educate management and then IT providers. Total Elapsed Time was reduced from six days to eight hours.

These presentations are augmented by further case studies in telecoms, described in the Guide, and retailing (Staples Direct) which is available on a special audio cassette.

The Guide states:

'A telecoms service provider improved its bottom line by millions of pounds in six months. One of the actions which made a significant contribution was to find out what was predictable in terms of customer demand and restructure the organisation to put all of the necessary skills into the call centre. In practice it meant moving whole departments into the front line. The purpose was clear to all and very simple; they set out to learn how to answer all calls at the first point of contact. The leader recognised that good service would be cheaper and would keep more customers'.

Ms. Janine Myles, Former Call Centre Manager for Staples Direct states:

'We had a traditional call centre at Staples Direct. We had the telesales people and when they were really good at telesales we promoted them to take service calls and when they were really good at service calls we put them in the complaints department because they could handle the stress of all the complaints. The only way you could get promoted through that organisation was for the business to get more and more wrong so that there was a bigger complaints department. I knew something was wrong but I

didn't know what was wrong. This approach of thinking of the organisation as a system has given me the opportunity to see where things were going wrong'.

'We had a lot of customer complaints at Staples Direct and a lot of compensation. We were losing customers and there was lots and lots of failure demand -66%. The morale within the team was poor and we had a very high staff turnover so one of the things we thought about doing was increasing the pay rates because we were losing the best people and they were going to better salaries. So we thought that if we increased the salaries of those people maybe they would stay with us. So we increased the salaries of those people and it worked -for a week. They all put in a lot of extra effort and thought it was great place to work for a week. Then, everything went back to normal again'.

With the Vanguard approach Staples Direct doubled sales and reduced staff turnover and in the case study Ms. Myles describes how her job changed from being a 'solution provider' to one of an 'obstacle remover' and how it led to both 'some tremendous personal development' and customers who were 'over the moon'. She concludes:

'Given the right organisational development this has amazing potential. A recent survey by the LNR Marketing Group said that 60% of call centre managers agree that there is no time and no resources to accommodate staff development. If only they were here today they would see that the resource is already there. They are alreadyemploying these people and the time is already available, but it is being wasted on failure demand. All they need to do is view the organisation as a system and they are there'.

[Staples Direct's Birmingham call centre is currently being developed as a US "Centre of Excellence" for their European operations and Ms. Myles is now helping to transform call centre operations at Royal Mail – Ed].

The Role of IT.

The Guide describes at length what IT can bring to a call centre, but also warns how IT can hinder a call centre's achievement of purpose if misapplied. One particular area of IT that is causing concern is that of Interactive Voice Response (IVR) which effectively allows customers to route themselves through a call centre by pressing a series of buttons on their telephone. It is of concern because experience suggests that customers more often than not find such systems to be both confusing and frustrating. They have to work out what to press to get what they want and they find themselves confused about how to choose the best option. The Guide argues that call routing systems of this type will only work well when one can predict the nature of customer demand in customer terms with the customer able to actually control the service delivery. Unfortunately, however, this is all too often not the case:

'In most applications we find managers focusing on internal (cost reduction) preoccupations and what is possible in technological terms. When one looks outside-in – the nature of demand and what matters to customers – one often finds the IVR "solution" to be causing costs as well as, at some level, reducing costs. In the worst cases organisations are creating revenues from customer queues, putting high charges on Call Centre lines. Provided the customer perceives the service received as valuable this may not be a problem, but if service is poor and high cost customers will inevitably go elsewhere'.

The good news is that IVR can be and has been applied successfully:

'In a Government service organisation managers learned about the nature of customer demands by sitting next to service agents and listening to calls. They found eighty or more per cent of the calls to be for five simple reasons. In each case answers could be easily provided by a recorded voice. When the managers then designed and implemented their new IVR system they kept listening to calls. While the new system worked very well a few customers did not get their needs met. The managers listened to what was required and re-designed the recorded messages.

Throughout their work and to this day the managers gave customers an early and immediate routing to a "live" service agent if the customer so desired. Productivity has improved remarkably because they learned to focus on quality -starting with the demands placed on them by customers. This organisation takes many more calls than it did five years ago with the same number of staff. They have minimised the costs of transactions with customers without diminishing value to the customers; customers are able to get what they want'.

The Guide also discusses the pros and cons of Computer Telephony Integration (CTI).

Making Transformation happen.

The starting point for the achievement of transformation is identified as understanding the type and frequency of customer demand through sitting with people who work on the telephones, working through a series of iterations, and then listening and classifying. At the start of such exercises managers often claim that their calls will be entirely unpredictable, but in practice every call centre's work has been found to be largely predictable. The Guide proposes the following five step methodology for conducting a performance assessment:

(i) Understand nature of demand from the customer's point of view.

(ii) Understand the value created for the customer by type of demand.

(iii) Understand flow i.e. how customer demand is dealt with by the organisation.

(iv) Understand the system conditions and how they affect performance.

(v) Understand how managerial thinking has led to the creation of the current system.

Further guidance is given on assessment team selection, presentation of assessment findings and proposed actions, and redesign of the measurement system.

Vanguard claim that in every case where this programme of transformation has been followed, action on the system "has produced outstanding results". John Seddon says:

"The results of such a transformation always go beyond improvements in service and efficiency. As managers and service agents learn to conceive their roles in terms of purpose and are enabled to contribute to improving performance against performance, they become highly motivated. Improved service and reducing costs are not the only desirable outcomes: learning, pride and enhanced contribution are also natural consequences of managing a call centre as a system. Indeed the ease and speed of change is a lesson for all organisations stuck within the mass production mould".

[Issue 134 (March 2000)]

QUALITY CULTURE

At *Qualitex* at the Hammersmith Novotel on 14th and 15th March two of the eight seminar sessions had the theme of 'Quality Culture'.

Using Deming Principles for Strategic Change

Ian Graham of PRISM-TBM, and founding Director of the BDA, provided two classic case study examples to illustrate the kinds of real benefits which are there for the taking for organisations with the courage and determination to pursue the Deming route.

The first example is that of a department within NatWest Bank known as Document Solutions. This department's job is to send out bank statements and other paper communications to customers. A team was established with the objective of improving the efficiency with which circulars were despatched, including a reduction of the cycle time for circular production and despatch. In order to do this they took a systems view and applied the Deming philosophy under the guise of 'Fourth generation Management'.

566

They sought to improve their internal processes along these lines and establish closer partnerships at both ends of the process.

Ian Graham stressed the fact that the team viewed suppliers as if they were customers:

'One of the key parameters of performance is the editing time for the production of circulars and this was shown graphically in a slide. This picture extends over a considerable period encompassing several months. It is possible to identify some improvement going on but it can be seen that the amount of variability that is shown makes it difficult to visualise the actual level of performance at any one time. This is the secret of applying the theory of variation by using charts and graphs like this in order to get a firm appreciation of "process capability". This is moving strongly away from the naive and simplistic approach of comparing performance with targets, both in terms of arbitrary targets themselves and also against arbitrary time scales. This is looking at data over time so that it may be used for the prediction of performance in the future'.

'The team discussed barriers that would prevent them making progress and in particular identified a key. problem that is affecting the process of the difficulties faced by the writers of the circulars. They decided to collect data on the factors affecting the writers and conducted a survey to look for the most frequently asked questions from them. From this they developed theories, in particular that difficulties enter the system from upstream due to the variability of the standard of writing of presentations. In order to reduce variation they identified the need for much more standardisation and uniformity, both with the customers and with the partners in their own internal organisation'.

The slides illustrate the dramatic improvements in circular editing time that were realised over a period of just a few months. The improvements are ongoing with latest developments including the establishment of a 'proof reading area' on the Intranet which enables customers to check their work electronically.

The second example given by Ian Graham is 3M Electronics Products Europe. (This is the company of David Taeger who chaired the BDA so it is not surprising that they should look to Deming when they identified a need for breakthrough improvement in their supply chain efficiency):

'The initial situation is shown numerically and many organisations will probably recognise the kind of levels of performance that are shown. The approach they took was to form a cross-functional team. This is critical because processes do work cross-functionally, not up and down the system. They formed a team from sales and marketing, logistics, finance and quality. They identified the appropriate performance indices and developed policy statements to ensure understanding across the board. Interestingly, they also

identified the need for process ownership and senior managers took on this role. They conducted process improvement using the PDSA cycle and this enabled them to prioritise action. In 3M everyone is using Control Charts (or "Process Behaviour Charts" as we often call them now) to understand data and it is excellent to see management data being presented in Control Chart form. This allows movement from simplistic measurement against targets and arbitrary periods of time and more into understanding the history of the process and being able to predict the future with confidence'.

'Two examples are given here from the key priorities that were set by the team. The first is logistics costs which, as can be seen, have been driven down continually over a considerable period of time. The second shows the results of changing the policies with respect to the number of direct accounts handled by 3M compared to its third parties. There is a dramatic fall in the first place down to the design level that is then maintained over a long period. The advantage of using Control Charts is that one can see and have early warning of any possible change in the desired situation whereas this cannot be done with summary data over, say, one year'.

The speaker pointed out that when all management data is presented in Control Chart form it can give rise to a very different agenda for discussing data than that which otherwise may be adopted. This can have many advantages provided that the Control Charts are used appropriately and the underlying techniques have been correctly taught, so as to avoid the pitfall of accumulating mountains of Control Charts. Mr. Graham concluded:

"Working on processes is the key to the future and there is clear indication in both NatWest and the 3M company that this is precisely what these organisations are setting out to do. If they are successful with this in the longer term real breakthrough performance will come".

BDA DISCONTINUES

With great regret this month we have to report the discontinuance of The British Deming Association. The demise follows in the wake of a fraud investigation (the employee perpetrator ultimately given a prison sentence) but the result left the Association unable to meet its financial commitments despite major efforts from many individuals.

The Alliance of Consultants will continue and the books/video business is expected to be sold as a going concern. A UK Deming Newsletter (ISBN 1470-5672) has been established to keep members informed of present and future developments and a number of regional events have been planned for late June/early July to replace the Annual Conference. A meeting of the liquidators is arranged for 29 March in Salisbury. [This sad event would surely have made the esteemed guru, whose personal philosophy was based on management integrity, show great remorse-Ed].

568

DEMING TRANSFORMATION FORUM

The demise of the British Deming Association at the turn of the millennium left many individuals stunned, and saddened that the Association that had hosted some of the nation's finest conferences, should have collapsed in the tragic circumstances which it did. Many of its former members naturally were and still are passionate about the Deming philosophy and the marvellous results which its application has achieved in all areas of society, industrial and non-industrial, political and non-political.

It follows logically that in the aftermath of the liquidation of the BDA a number of members should be sufficiently moved by what has occurred to be inspired to do something at least to instigate a revival and, if possible, a new lease of life to the Deming representation in the UK. In February, therefore, Hazel Cannon, a founder member of the BDA, met with colleagues Alan Winlow and Martin Malpas to discuss future possibilities and on 1st March a legal entity known as The Deming Forum was established with headquarters in Milton Keynes. This subsequently provided a rescue package for the Deming voice in the UK, providing the means for volunteers to arrange and optimise the learning and application associated with the Deming philosophy.

The aims of the Deming Forum, which has been formed as a limited company, have been established as follows:

* To provide and enable learning opportunities for those who wish to learn and deepen their understanding of the Deming philosophy in the UK.

* To act as a focal point and information service for those who seek knowledge and support in applying the philosophy and principles of the late Dr. W. Edwards Deming.

* To act as a link with other Deming bodies outside the UK.

* To act as a liaison for those who wish to network and support the Deming philosophy in the UK.

* To act with integrity to optimise the Deming community for the benefit of all.

In keeping with these objectives one further aim was then to take stock of the resources available with a view to planning and organising the Transformation Forum 2000 which the BDA had scheduled at Loughborough University. The resulting discussions concluded that some kind of event was certainly possible and indeed desirable, although some careful consideration was needed to determine which dates and venue, or venues, would be most appropriate. The final decision was to stage two one day events in Birmingham and Brighouse on 28th and 29th June.

With the amount of effort and short timescale involved few would perhaps have expected the Deming Forum to have been in a position to report a combined attendance for the two days of over 200.

Hazel Cannon provided delegates with the following assurances about the Deming Forum, membership details of which are still being finalised:

"The Deming Forum will not be bureaucratic or restrictive. It will be inclusive, welcoming and embracing the future. Deming is a culture not a cult and we must build on this phenomenal theory and continue to develop it and make it pertinent to everyone in the future. The Deming Forum will not, however, tell the market what it will deliver".

Dr. Deming's daughter Diana Deming Cahill, flew over to the UK to support the Forum's inaugural event. She told delegates:

" I am delighted that the philosophy and learning has a voice in the UK and I'm sure my father would be heartened to know it was in safe hands".

There were 19 presentations over the two days, some of which were repeated at both venues. These included Myron Tribus, who spoke about 'The implications of brain science for leaders' and stated the need for leaders to recognise the fact that the unprecedented rate of change in technology, as well as social, economic and political structures, creates a new distinction amongst people i.e. those who know how to learn and others.

He predicted that as a consequence there would be no future jobs for people who did not

(a) Know how to learn quickly

(b) Enjoy being continual learners

Furthermore, education systems which do not teach people to enjoy learning on their own were "menaces to society's survival". In this regard he called for the governance of the education system to be changed, putting quality first, and for the basic paradigm of education to be changed from teaching to mediation i.e. autonomous learning.

Other well-known speakers included Prof. Henry Neave who offered a second chance for delegates to hear his Professorial Inaugural Lecture as W. Edwards Deming Professor of Management at the Nottingham Business School, Nottingham Trent University, which was first given on 2nd March. To the best of our knowledge only one other person (Barbara Lawton of the University of Colorado at Denver) has the honour of being granted this title, which has to be a fine tribute to the UK's leading academic expert on Deming application and practice. In his paper he summarises Dr. Deming's teachings to top management and engineers in Japan, and recites some of his experiences with the man and his message, and poses the following question:

'As the world grows ever more complex, and often more cruel, and as technology increasingly provides opportunities to do greater good but, if misused, can also do greater harm, do we not increasingly need the help of the Deming philosophy -its values, its principles, its logic, its practical guidance?'

He refers to Deming's work as 'a real source of help and hope for making a better future materially, socially and mentally'.

Chapter Eight

Quality Methods and Tools

The Quality Methods Association (formerly The Taguchi Club) has been the principal member organisation in the UK for the application of the methods and tools used for quality improvement. Various special interest groups were active within the QMA throughout the 1990s, although the Research and Development (R and D) Group formed the main core largely through its links to the former Taguchi Club of the 1980s.

In the first half of the decade the annual QMA conferences were popular and well attended and were reported in Quality Matters from 1991 onwards. Sadly, however, budgetary constraints took their toll and during the second half of the decade events tended to concentrate on smaller, more specialised activities, of which a number are reported.

In addition to the subject of Taguchi Methods, which are now actively promoted by ASI Quality Systems, the compilation below includes articles on tools which have enjoyed moderate popularity during the 1990s, most notably Quality Function Deployment (QFD), Design of Experiments, Total Productive Maintenance (TPM), Process Mapping and Statistical Process Control. In the latter part of the chapter there is a focus on the tool which is currently proving to be most popular, namely Six Sigma. It is yet to be seen whether much of the present day investment in this specific methodology, which began in the U.S. in the mid 1990s and is now in evidence in the UK, will prove to have been worthwhile. The reader's attention is drawn particularly to the penultimate article of the chapter and the associated 'point and counterpoint' discussion.

QUALITY METHODS ASSOCIATION ANNUAL CONFERENCE

The year of 1991 has shown a number of changes in the approach to Quality, and one of them has been the first full year in which the Quality Methods Association, formerly the UK Taguchi Club, has been active, casting away their image as a single country single guru 'club' and becoming an all-embracing users group dedicated to quality and productivity improvement generally, as a means of securing competitive advantage and customer satisfaction.

The Association provides UK management with a network and forum for the sharing of ideas and experience without the constraints often imposed by professional bodies and certification agencies. Under the chairmanship of Professor Tony Bendell, head of mathematics, statistics and operational research at Nottingham Polytechnic, three study groups have been formed in the specialist areas of quality management, quality methods and tools, and research and development. There has been an active programme of seminars and workshops covering such subjects as software for quality improvement, measuring a caring culture and measuring customer satisfaction (common problem areas for management right across industry).

The year has culminated with the staging of the Association's first Annual Conference at the Bath Hilton Hotel on 22nd and 23rd October, where over 60 delegates convened to hear a selection of papers from 21 speakers.

Taguchi : the Ultimate Quality Improvement Technique?

John Disney, Research Fellow at Nottingham Polytechnic, questioned whether much of the 'hype' associated with Taguchi's methods really has been justified. Consultants, he said, have made 'goldmines' out of these latest Japanese methods, but no one of these 'gurus' have the answers to everything and people don't really know where to apply the techniques.

Taguchi was an engineer and has made statistical methods acceptable and accessible to engineers. He has revitalised experimental design and the extremely powerful technique of brainstorming. ITT in the United States are amongst examples of companies that have saved millions of pounds in the last five years by applying the techniques of Taguchi methods. But for all this the techniques have been overmarketed and hyped. There has been an overcomplicated use of statistics and the orthogonal arrays so often associated with Taguchi were in fact the innovation of Finney in 1945.

People need to recognise that Taguchi adapted statistical techniques rather than having personally invented them. The case of the signal to noise ratio was raised, and the speaker pointed out that whilst there were in practice some 47 of these ratios, popular literature only focused on four.

It also needed to be recognized that Taguchi methods may not be the most appropriate tool in some cases, for example Taguchi's Accumulation Analysis is weighted towards finding location defects rather than dispersion defects. Likewise linear graphs do not always lead to the highest resolution of design and can lead to unnecessary confounding.

Taguchi can complement Deming, according to the speaker: Deming has the aims, Taguchi the tools. But the only 'real guru', he said, was Ishikawa, whose seven tools of quality control were 'under used' and contributions 'under rated'. The concept of quality circles, which he founded, have been a disappointment in the West largely because they have not been introduced properly.

So, is Taguchi the ultimate quality improvement technique? Answer -no, it's just part of the engineer's tool box.

Taguchi -a robust yet simple Alternative

A second presentation on Taguchi was made by Dr. Malcolm Moore, consultant statistician for BBN UK Limited, who proposed an alternative to Taguchi which was said to overcome four of Taguchi's prime weaknesses:

(i) Saturated designs use no Pareto principle to sort causal effects from random effects.

(ii) Some factor combinations in experimental design are impractical resulting in excuses to 'rubbish' experimental design principles and compromise objectives.

(iii) Environmental factors are assumed independent of the experimental design. They may not be and in fact probably won't be. The result is a biased estimate of variation.

(iv) The empirical style of Taguchi attempts to remove effects of causes rather than identifying causes of effects.

Taguchi methods, he said, gives erroneous results in 20 per cent of cases where they are applied but people are still using them because no-one has yet provided a simpler technique. A D-optional design model was therefore proposed with multiple regression extended to include quadratic terms. It is anticipated that this will soon be available commercially.

MAINTENANCE 91 CONFERENCE

The Maintenance '91 Conference took place over three days at the Hotel Metropole, Birmingham, adjoining the National Exhibition Centre, from 8th to 10th October, and was divided into three sections: Best Demonstrated Maintenance Practice in UK Industry, Total Productive Maintenance, and Total Quality and Optimising Manufacturing Facilities.

1991 Maintenance Survey Results

Phil Upshall, Maintenance Practice Leader for Coopers and Lybrand Deloitte, presented the first paper outlining the results of a survey conducted by his company in association with *Works Management* journal into maintenance issues in British companies. Questionnaires were sent to 5000 manufacturing sites employing over 100 people, half of which were sent to Directors, half to maintenance managers. Approximately 450 were returned, equating to some 5 per cent of British manufacturing industry.

One of the most interesting questions asked whether people were happy with the performance of their maintenance department and less than a quarter said that they were, representing a fall of some 15 per cent on a similar survey, conducted in 1983. Some 29 per cent of directors said that they were not satisfied as against 19 per cent of maintenance managers, with 46 per cent of directors sometimes satisfied and 56 per cent of managers sometimes satisfied. Around 1 per cent did not respond.

Findings revealed that satisfied sites were more likely to set maintenance objectives, discuss maintenance at board level, monitor all downtime, have an effective maintenance improvement programme, use predominantly preventive and predictive maintenance, have maintenance skills that match needs and rarely suffer from conflict with production.

Whilst these differences sound plausible, many maintenance professionals may feel that in recessionary times these items are an expensive luxury, and if money is not available, is there any point in discussing it at board level? It would appear not, but in practice the satisfied sites spend a third less and have less than half as many maintenance employees suggesting that effective maintenance does not necessarily mean expensive maintenance.

The causes of dissatisfaction have changed little since the surveys of the mid 1980s with lack of preventive maintenance still being predominant. From the table presented in the paper, it is evident that conflict with production has worsened since 1983, with other causes such as poor staff ability, lack of spares, lack of information and slow responses having fluctuated only marginally.

The paper describes the causes of dissatisfaction as remarkably similar for both directors and maintenance managers with two notable exceptions: directors are nearly twice as likely to blame lack of management ability whilst maintenance managers are twice as likely to blame lack of staff.

Satisfied sites are much more likely to be using preventive maintenance as the predominant maintenance philosophy, but it is pointed out that sadly, the proportion of sites relying primarily on breakdown maintenance is about the same as it was in 1983 (40 per cent of satisfied sites, 79 per cent of dissatisfied sites).

In answer to the question do maintenance department skills match needs, 78 per cent of satisfied sites said 'yes' as against 37 per cent of dissatisfied sites. Maintenance managers and supervisors have apparently received more training over the past twelve months, but it is noted that in the satisfied sites the craftsmen receive more training than in the dissatisfied ones, and it is suggested that the training of managers and supervisors may have done little to improve performance -anecdotal evidence indicates that management training is frequently offered as a reward rather than having a business need.

Computerised maintenance management systems are in use in over half of the sites, but functionality is said to be not used well and lack of information is growing as a cause of dissatisfaction in the maintenance department.

An interesting observation is that satisfied sites appear to have older equipment even though maintenance managers in the UK anticipate maintenance costs to rise with age and reliability to fall. The Japanese, by contrast, expect reliability to increase with age on the grounds that their continuous improvement programmes will eliminate design weaknesses.

Total Productive Maintenance and Total Quality

Peter Willmott, Managing Director of Willmott Consulting Services, described how Total Productive Maintenance fits in as 'a practical sub-set of Total Quality in action'. There is nothing 'earth shattering' about it, it is just Total Quality Management working in practice at the sharp end of the business.

It is, however, about changing attitudes, teamwork, and enhancing individual skills, making continuous improvement a 'habit' aimed at plant availability and reliability, continuity of production, and the quality of the process and hence the product. It embraces and impacts on aspects such as health and safety and environmental concerns. The TPM teamwork philosophy capitalises on known maintenance techniques such as reliability centred maintenance and condition based maintenance.

This year in the UK, companies will spend something approaching £14 billion on maintaining manufacturing and process industry assets. This level of spend is equivalent to twice the UK trade deficit or around three times the annual value of new plant investments. A study of maintenance throughout the EEC, carried out on behalf of BRITE/EURAM has, however, shown that most companies have failed to develop maintenance strategies in line with their investment in advanced manufacturing technology, with the result that maintenance practices lag behind the advances in technology.

One of the main reasons for this is that maintenance is not usually considered at board level. Most companies do not know the cost of downtime, or what the overall financial effect of unusable machinery is on their business (especially in terms of lost sales opportunities), and only a minority have thought through a reasonable machine availability target, so providing a realistic starting point for the determination of a maintenance strategy and policies:

'In a typical factory many pieces of equipment are poorly maintained. Chronic loss is a product of this neglect, and maintenance personnel spend much of their time trying to find and treat its causes'.

Historically, in the piece part manufacture and assembly industries, there has been little pressure to place the maintenance function under the microscope. Excess stocks could be built and carried, overtime and extra shifts could be worked, and spare capacity could be arranged (as extra machines or quick off-load sub-contract). The future for these industries' maintenance is now, however, fundamentally different, and there are signs of a gradual realisation that the competitive advantage obtained from expensive and complex machines and systems is only as good as the company's ability to ensure maximum availability of the manufacturing process when it is needed.

TPM examines ways of avoiding or reducing the need for maintenance and can yield immense benefits through improvements in overall equipment effectiveness and productivity, but it is no quick fix and companies should allow two years for the changing of their maintenance culture. It involves asking the question 'why are we having to maintain plant and equipment?' And yields answers like the simple fitting of a guard over a bearing housing to prevent the ingress of dirt and lengthen bearing life.

Five action points are recommended as a starting point:

(a) Maintain autonomously

Operators share responsibility with maintenance crafts people for machine availability and condition of equipment. Attune operators to deviations from standard that adversely affect productivity and unit costs to free maintenance personnel from the burden of trivia.

(b) Practice quality maintenance

Identify plant and equipment vital to the process and critical in terms of breakdowns. Subject each item to a detailed condition appraisal outlining actions needed to bring it to target performance level. Operators and maintenance staff jointly develop routines to keep plant at this level. This encourages operator ownership.

(c) Improve equipment

Constant vigilance and investigation of plant performance will lead to modifications which will raise reliability. But note: if TPM is used as a means to reduce staff and plant availability remains static the programme will fail and the potential contribution of better maintained plant lost.

The impact on design can be considerable: Japanese purchasers frequently visit suppliers to see how equipment is built, and may even send their own people to help assemble it and improve understanding. When it arrives on site they may strip it down, add modifications and rebuild it. Message: why wait until the equipment breaks down before you learn how to fix it?

(d) Communicate improvements

Firms operate across sites and between shifts. The chances are that solutions found in one area can also be used elsewhere.

(e) Train and make people aware

The cultural change brought about by TPM is doomed without education and training, and a three-tier approach is suggested. First, a one-day awareness module explaining TPM and how it fits in with business goals. A four or five day course for team leaders may follow, backed up with individual skill enhancement covering detailed training on techniques used and 'on the job' machine specific single point lessons.

[Issue 44 (August 1992)]

MAINTENANCE MATTERS

The annual shutdown provides the ideal opportunity for an annual overhaul of plant and equipment. For some companies recessionary times may present opportunities for a higher profile for cleaning and maintenance with redeployment of staff into housekeeping roles enabling key staff to be retained in preference to lay-off as well as providing a foundation for future prosperity and cultural change. An important consolidation phase in the company's development is therefore enabled to occur.

which provides a service and there is a move towards providing Production Managers with direct control of the Maintenance Cells.

Photographs illustrated how Improvement Groups have made progress with the environment as well as with equipment, and how the all-important breakthrough in the traditional Assembly areas (classically seen as a machine tool issue) is yielding significant quality improvement benefits with the potential for more.

At Volvo TPM principles were gradually introduced in the 1980s and in 1985 the maintenance function was redefined, becoming more integrated. Maintenance operators were trained and educated to a higher level of responsibilities and were formed from single-skilled to multi-skilled 'Volvo technicians'. Maintenance staff became involved from the drawing board onwards and a preventive approach with the introduction of condition monitoring has taken the place of breakdown maintenance.

Integration between Production and Maintenance took place in 1987 and, with further development by middle management this was expanded in a first step towards the quality department, and ultimately into total involvement of the whole organisation.

Around the basic integration idea a new working structure called VEC-TEAM (V – Volvo, E- Europe, C – Cars) was created, whereby self-managing teams of 10 to 15 operators acquired responsibilities for maintenance activities such as cleaning, check-up and front line maintenance operations, quality control techniques and some small materials handling activities. A special 'VEC-TEAM interdepartmental supporting group' helped in organising training and education to meet the revised job contents and a special 'VEC-TEAM organisation' guided and supported the new ideas to be implemented in the day to day reality, supported with overlapping small group activities.

Three years later there was integration of the VEC organisation into the Volvo Car Corporation product development, marketing, component delivery and after-sales departments.

A 'positive trend' in the company's 'Quality Index' was shown graphically and is attributed mainly to ' a changed mentality of people towards the company and the job, as well as self-confidence and a strong belief in our growing culture'.

TPM in Steelmaking

The steelmaking industry was represented from the UK by Paul Tucker, TPM Facilitator for Allied Steel and Wire Limited, and John Griffiths, Shift Works Manager for Tremorfa Steel Works (the steelmaking division of Allied Steel and Wire), and from Germany by Gerd Phillipp, Superintendent,

Mechanical Maintenance for Badische Stahlwerke AG in Kehl, on the River Rhine.

The case of Allied Steel and Wire is a classic example of a turnaround, from losing £1.5 million a month in 1981 to now selling reinforcing steel at 1985 prices and still managing to make a profit.

The company was guided on a Total Quality route from 1990 by Mike Robson Associates who coached two senior managers who were then in a position to pass on the message to (approximately) 300 middle managers and hourly paid workers. 'Health Check Teams' were set up and TPM was seen as 'able to provide the framework for measurement of continuous improvement' as well as fitting in well with the Total Quality philosophy.

With the aim of ensuring that all work done in the TQ/TPM field is seen to have the strong support of the company's executives, TPM related work is co-ordinated by the company's Plant Performance and Reliability Group which comprises a senior manager from each of the company's Business Units, and reports directly to the Managing Director.

TPM or 'Team Maintenance' became Total Quality applied to people, plant and equipment. The company advertised for 27 team leaders and there were 90 applicants all of whom were given the opportunity to undergo the team Leader training programme. Around a third of the company's workforce attended a one day TPM Awareness session led by Peter Willmott.

Production operators were apparently very willing to take on the additional responsibilities that TPM was going to require (as opposed to being suspicious).

The authors describe the reasons behind the application of Overall Equipment Effectiveness as a key business driver and how a pilot study was undertaken to develop a measure of OEE for the two furnaces at Tremorfa, which have been identified as 'bottleneck items of plant' and clearly an area where performance needs to be quantified 'in true TPM fashion in order to highlight areas for improvement'.

Gerd Phillipp also drew an analogy between Formula 1 Motor Racing and the activities of production and maintenance crews. In both cases an excellent driver, superb maintenance and modern equipment make a winning team, whilst spontaneous patchwork leads to losing laps and may cause accidents and wrong spares 'entail enormous consequences'.

He explained how maintenance has become 'a decisive factor of profitability for many industries' and how in his company good maintenance 'contributed substantially' to their survival in the early 1980s. The maintenance principles adopted are those of preventive, scheduled maintenance; decentralisation of maintenance; production-integrated maintenance and permanent personnel training.

On-site maintenance crews were formed headed by assistant superintendents who report to the production superintendents of each department. The superintendent Central Maintenance retained responsibility for the repair shop and warehouse, and for major preventive actions. This is said to have yielded benefits in the understanding of each other's problems, removal of departmental borderlines, improved co-operation between production and maintenance, fostered decision making with shorter implementation time, and joint responsibility for the condition and availability of equipment on-site.

The central department defines the inspection and maintenance intervals which are strictly observed on-site, and prepares performance files on equipment and new work schedules. With the aid of operational delay records a 'realistic picture of the weak points of the equipment' emerges enabling systematic corrective action to be taken to achieve the objective of high equipment availability.

The impact of equipment availability on plant performance has 'greatly increased the influence of maintenance experts on the purchase of new equipment' and serviceability and ease of maintenance are 'important criteria for the selection'.

From day to day operating experiences, engineering objectives have been defined and subsequently built into the company's equipment (a lot of the company's older equipment has been redesigned and re-engineered within their own engineering division). As a result, whilst much of the company's equipment is 'sophisticated and highly advanced', it is also 'simple and reliable and easy to maintain'.

Questions and Answers

The conference afforded the opportunity for a range of questions to be asked on the content of the papers presented.

Allied Steel and Wire were asked what they were doing to get fitters and operators involved and Mr. Griffiths replied by saying that they were currently working on training multi-skilled teams which incorporate traditional maintenance personnel into production teams.

When tackled on the 'failure' of quality circles Mr. Willmott emphasized that TPM 'uses the best bits of Total Quality' and 'underlines the ownership of tangible pieces of equipment'. TPM was successful, he said, 'because it is practical, recognizable, and allows people to see improvement, but it requires commitment'. The reason some quality circles may have failed in the past was, he suggested, because these features had been largely lacking.

Another delegate questioned the feasibility of gaining ownership of large kit and Mr. Griffiths accepted that this was 'a sixty four million dollar question', but he said that at the end of the day it amounts to pride of workmanship. Mr. Willmott agreed, and added that he felt that it was vital to get operators interested in pride of workmanship. They like to be asked their opinions and he said that he was very encouraged to hear a fitter say after 25 years service 'I want to contribute something positive to this company'.

Finally, the panel was asked to comment on whether it felt that TQM was a prerequisite to the success of TPM and Peter Willmott said that he could think of only one in fifteen of the companies he was helping that hadn't taken TQM on board. Most see TPM as an application of TQM.

[Issue 45 (September 1992)]

A TRADE UNION VIEW OF TPM AND INDUSTRIAL CHANGE

A trade union perspective of TPM was provided by Lynn Williams, National Organiser for the EETPU based in Kent. He said that he felt unions and management in practice had a lot in common, but more needed to be shared and there should be more dialogue on how to achieve both quality and more secure employment.

TPM, he said "allows maintenance to become on a par with the 'sexy bits' of the organisation, but we have to break down the 'industrial apartheid' whereby maintenance was suspicious of the shopfloor and vice-versa". People need to become more involved in processes which drive out fear in organisations, and in Mr. Williams' belief any company should be well equipped to incorporate an industrial relations clause that stipulates that there will be no compulsory redundancies as a consequence of the introduction of TPM.

Computerised maintenance was criticised as 'often not programmed for its task' and where training was offered off-site it should be to nationally agreed standards.

The common craft rate he said 'had outlived its usefulness and contributes to the confrontation between maintenance and production', and he condemned the practice of engineers keeping reference books and manuals locked away, denying the craftsman of a right of access.

The need for direct supervision in organisations was heavily criticised, and it was emphasised that in many cases there were a number of alternatives to hard cash that should be considered amongst the aspects that are open to change notably manning levels, job boundaries and content, hours of work, the structure of working hours, work allocation, and systems of payment:

"People often actually want to move into new areas of technology and can be rewarded by training opportunities as well as cash".

Craftsmen, he said, particularly welcomed such training opportunities, and frequently want to be part of a change, so long as those changes are not thrust on them.

In his paper he explains how joint problem solving has proved effective in many companies where Joint Working parties have been set up to enable changes to occur in working practices, and as part of a 'Model Agreement' for bringing about change he recommends a Joint Problem Solving Forum rather than a negotiating forum, open to all parties to investigate the potential for change.

A set of model clauses for a transition agreement leading to flexible working practices is reproduced in the text of his paper. He recommends, for example, a short Education programme to raise the awareness of Shop Stewards/Working Party representatives involved in the process of changing working practices and the implementation of the agreement. Also technical and practical training for all employees, but with recognition of the fact that some may not wish to participate and assurance of such employees' security of employment. Employees failing to meet the standards should be offered the option of further training or revert to their original jobs.

The union currently provides an advice service at Cudham Hall where on-site presentations are given to EETPU members, and members of other unions and managers, who are 'not beyond this advice'.

Lynn Williams was asked what training he was doing for his own people and he explained how they had been educated to a point where managers regularly produce bulletins for the shop stewards' newsletter. A minority of union officials 'don't accept advice' but the majority do. Another delegate added that he felt that the district officials of some unions behaved as 'blockers'. It was generally accepted that some unions would ultimately have to get to grips with this, but Willy Poppe suggested that the Japanese were setting a good example here, and explained that union leaders from his company had visited Japan and learnt from their example.

Mr. Williams was also questioned over whether it was 'realistic to ignore the up-front payments'. He replied by saying that up-front payments were 'a bit traditional':

"Most craftsmen will say that training is more important to them than money. Money is not the motivating factor. Opportunity for training and responsibility are becoming increasingly more important".

He explained how lately there had been much more of a desire to experiment in evaluating total packages with cost-benefit analysis.

SPC COMPANY WIDE IMPLEMENTATION

An interesting account of how company wide application of Statistical Process Control (SPC) techniques have been successful in driving down quality costs was provided by Bob Pigram of York International, the world's largest independent manufacturer of air conditioning and refrigeration equipment, based in York, Pennsylvania.

The presentation to the Quality Methods Association annual conference described how the SPC training package produced by Futuremedia had been assessed and purchased, and subsequently used by the company to realise substantial savings, notably in the finance section where personnel who had previously felt that TQM did not apply to them, were able to be convinced otherwise in a language which they were able to understand.

The 'Lasermedia' interactive disc package was found to work best when two individuals worked together and after pairs of senior managers had familiarised themselves, volunteer facilitators from groups of 15 to 18 worked step by step through the ten hour package, spending two hours per week over a five week period, with the assistance of the speaker and other senior managers.

To date some 21 SPC cells have been established, which have begun to work on projects which they have largely decided upon with minimal input from senior management, and, of the company's 9000 employees, around 250 have participated in all or part of the ten hours of interactive video training.

For every manufacturing cell trained (approximately 15 people) a supporting department cell was trained, and as each cell's training is completed, each cell, with its facilitator, decides which of their own processes will be measured to implement improvements. Support is given by the Quality Department in devising measurements and the appropriate techniques to obtain the best from SPC.

On a three monthly basis each active SPC team makes a presentation of typically five minutes' duration but sometimes up to 20 minutes, to senior management, with typically 4 to 5 groups presenting in one session. It is noted that after some initial nervousness 'many employees have shone with both results and professionalism'.

Successful projects include: reduction of copper scrap from a machine of £255 per week to around £70 per week; savings of around £400 per 6 units of aluminium foil purchased, by decreasing tolerance values (since buying by weight at the top limit of thickness resulted in sub-optimal supply); resolving a problem of pressure variation on an air circulation system; and significant savings in hassle through streamlining of administration e.g. by improving the processing of expense forms.

The discipline of SPC is said to be 'giving the responsibility and authority of measuring quality to every member of the company' and the Futuremedia package, purchased for £10,000 including the p.c. was described unanimously as a 'fantastic way to learn'.

[Issue 54 (June 1993)]

PROCESS MAPPING SYSTEM LAUNCHED.

The simple technique of linear flowcharting, most commonly associated with manufacturing and computer industries has, in recent years, evolved into a powerful general management tool. Previous application problems have been that the stimulus for it has arisen from the need to pay greater attention to detail and reduce error, rather than to combine ideas from many brains and knit them together into one unified and agreed representation of a process.

In order to address this, David Howard founder of Management New Style and a European chartered engineer with over 20 years of practical project and process management experience within construction, service and manufacturing industries, has devised a system of process mapping. This is equally applicable to service or manufacturing industries and builds on the work of Dr. W. Edwards Deming and Myron Tribus to form a basis for process oriented management, leading to measurable improvement.

The method uses traditional flowcharting symbols as indicators of activity and orders them against the people involved and the relevant time sequence. The process map thus formed is then used as a datum from which to substantiate further improvement.

Anyone familiar with computer systems should 'be at home with the technique if not the consensual method of its application' whilst for those who are not familiar with computers the technique 'will be readily assimilated'. One should not, however, be misled by the simplicity of the technique which, if used properly, is said to benefit companies, managers, suppliers and customers.

David Howard says:

'Excellence in performance, contribution of value and reliability through attention to detail all combine to create a product or service that attracts a customer's preference. It is the ability of process mapping to contribute to improvements across all three of these co-ordinates that makes it such a powerful tool in managing for quality'.

It is emphasised, that for the technique to be successfully undertaken a preparatory and thorough understanding of its purpose must be communicated to all participants, because so long as there is a perceived fear of arbitrary action being taken by management as a result of the outcome of the process, mapping the full benefits of the technique will not be achieved. In particular any manpower savings that might become possible as a result of efficiency improvements must be seen by top management (and understood by all employees) as providing opportunities for process improvement training; an assignment to another position; opening up new added value processes; or expanding the business i.e. there must be no irrational fear of a hidden agenda concerning job reduction.

The role of the chart leader is described, and several sound reasons given as to why the chart leader should be appointed from outside of the working group, notably avoidance of pre-occupation with internal politics, over-burdening with 'crowded thinking' and apprehension of asking what could be perceived as self-evident questions by the group members.

Practical examples are given to show how the technique may be applied and to illustrate the kinds of benefits that may potentially be achieved. These include a trade debtor example where flow mapping of sales and distribution processes led to a reduction from 185 box errors (equivalent to 4,100 parts per million), to less than 10 box errors (150 ppm) after one year by the operators themselves, once they had learnt the techniques. The cash benefit was a reduction in trade debtors from 5.5 weeks to 3.5 weeks, saving £300k in interest cost alone. Also the case of a hospital outpatient process where the application of deployment flowcharts can be seen to lead to considerable time savings by mapping changes and representative times.

The changes that are made are grouped into four headings: Acceleratlon, Simplification, Clarification and Innovation.

Accelerating the rate at which value is added to the process inputs, and therefore the efficiency and productivity of the process, involves locating bottlenecks or log-jams (points where work builds up because of a restriction in handling capacity down stream), and the reduction and removal of rework loops. It may result in the amalgamation or elimination of certain tasks that inspection show to be redundant to the primary needs of the process.

Simplification opportunities become more readily apparent by inspecting the flowchart than from reading procedure statements, for example unnecessary authorizations often become apparent for the first time as a result of flowcharting.

Clarification of process tasks 'is a natural benefit of flowcharting and the subsequent analysis of the completed chart' and an inability to clarify a work process i.e. a transformation which adds value 'suggests the existence of confusion and therefore costly waste'.

Innovation opportunities, described as most valuable long-term benefit of process mapping' are achieved as regular concentration on the detail of the process by the people who are part of the process 'naturally generates a large number of small improvements over time'.

The Flow-Map system has been welcomed by acknowledged leaders in the field of quality, e.g. consulting engineer Myron Tribus, and Homer Sarasohn (who is noted for his contribution to the re-establishment of the Japanese electronics industry after 1945 and served as the exemplar for Japan's industrial and economic successes over the following 45 years).

Tribus says:

"David Howard has made an important advance in quality management instruction by developing his kit for deployment flow charting. In my experience, when faced with the challenge to produce a flow chart, most beginners find excuses to do something else. The handy templates and magnetic boards make it difficult to resist making that first try. Anything which overcomes a barrier to actually applying the tools of quality management to a real situation has to be reckoned to be a positive contribution".

Homer Sarasohn comments:

"The text under the title 'Process Oriented Management' is especially impressive. This is what I taught the Japanese. It is what American (and British) managers must still learn....".

The FlowMap System comprises both Team Kits and Management Kits.

The FlowMap Team Kit is based on linked A2 and A4 scale process mapping modules. They encourage participation by all process team members. These modules capture process detail using large scale A2 magnetic symbols which encourages participation and allow for convenient changes and editing. The A4 scale components facilitate photo-copying of results at the end of a mapping session and provide participants with a valuable record of progress made.

The FlowMap Management Kit is based on process mapping software derived from a successfully proven professional flowcharting programme developed by Aeon Software. The FlowMap software operates on PCs (286 and higher) with Windows 3.1. It creates 3D matrix flowcharts. In addition to the software user-guide the kit contains comprehensive documentation on process mapping. Worked examples, both in the guides and in the software, demonstrate the versatility of process mapping. FlowMap software provides not only an operational basis for continual improvement but also a versatile planning tool.

MANAGING CHANGE: USING SPC FOR SERVICES

An example of how change may be achieved by applying the methodology of SPC was described by Mervyn Nutbourn of the internal consultancy department of the Woolwich Building Society at the IMS Financial Services meeting (Quality Matters issue 56). His presentation entitled 'Railroad to Success' looked at how S.P.C. has been implemented within the Eastern Region of the Woolwich as part of an overall quality initiative.

In July 1990 the Eastern Region was in the unenviable position of being at the bottom of the company's regional performance league tables. Whilst it was accepted that these could be 'a bit misleading', it was clear that change was needed. The league table position merely reinforced this need.

Chastisement of the branches was clearly not the answer, but rather 'a journey in a positive direction with many stops along the way', hence the analogy with railways. In the autumn of 1990 a project board was set up consisting of the of the Regional Manager, a number of senior District Managers and a member of the Internal Consultancy.

Customer and team research, confirmed that this was the way to proceed. A pilot project followed in which process maps were produced for processes such as mortgage processing and balancing a till. The 'Customer for Life' pilot course commenced in March 1991, which highlighted the actions, attitudes and philosophy required to exceed customer requirements.

A 'Lending Group' was inaugurated involving a number of the District Managers and the regional Credit Manager. This group agreed new standards for underwriting, arrears, reporting/management, and possessions management. Two Roadshows indicated both interest in the project and high expectations for the delivery of promises by the project board on the part of branch staff.

Further 'Customer for Life' courses followed, and extensions to mortgage applications, telephone standards, referrals standards and the arrears process were mapped in the autumn of 1991.

In December 1991 the Great Eastern was aligned with the rest of the Society's 'Vision and Values' of quality of service, innovation and organisational effectiveness. Whilst process maps were being produced and attitudes were changing, some proof was needed of the rate of change i.e. a measurement system was required.

It was concluded that without measures there is no focus, whilst ownership of measures for improvement should be with the people who do the work.

The use of measures to drive improvement, however, starts with people thinking differently. Another conclusion was that managing by attention to output often leads to an incentive for people to cheat, whilst making changes on the basis of inadequate information can lead to costly mistakes.

These principles, coupled with a number of fundamental quality principles, like process measurement being a prerequisite for improvement, led to a decision to implement SPC as part of the change process. This provided a common language for discussing process performance and allows for testing of any change in the process.

Statistical Process Control was applied to the regional and branch 'strike rates,' a weekly performance measure. Historically the Regional Manager reacted to 'strike rates' either by praising or chastising the District Managers. In practice the District Managers did little of difference from one week to the next, and so took little notice of the Regional Manager's comments.

With SPC, control limits were set which prompted the Regional Manager only to react when control limits were breached, as he could now see if the process was in control. It did not improve the process but staff could now see a senior manager producing an SPC chart and maintaining it publicly. This was seen as a clear change for the better, and so the use of SPC was extended.

Two processes owned by the staff: Till Balancing and Mortgage Processing were selected for SPC attention. Branch staff were 'very suspicious of the motives' since 'this cultural change was not part of the usual managerial style employed in the Society'. Staff grew to 'appreciate the extra responsibility', especially when given the opportunity to take action in the case of 'special causes'.

The methodology of SPC was later extended throughout the region.

Monitoring of the development and maintenance of SPC charts for a range of processes is being achieved in two ways. District managers send copies to their regional office within a set period and the Regional Manager incorporates SPC chart inspection into his programme of visits, and questions chart 'owners' where appropriate e.g. when special causes are apparent.

Since the introduction of this programme the Eastern Region has won the 'Region of the Year' Award, and a decision has been taken for all of the regions to follow this 'quality route' using SPC.

QUALITY IN PROJECT MANAGEMENT

The management of projects and in particular R and D is critical for many industries to survive. Recently there have been several examples of spectacular failures to reinforce the issues involved.

An axiom of quality is 'if you want to get it right in the end, then get it right in the beginning'. In industrial practice this means attention to the R and D phase and Project Management. This was addressed by the QMA R and D Study Group meeting at the Esso Engineering (Europe) headquarters in Leatherhead on 3rd March.

The subject of the event was 'Managing R and D Projects' and six papers were presented.

Uncertainty Mapping for R and D

Research by the Manchester Business School examined, amongst other things, the influence of TQM initiatives on current project management. Their report was presented by Jeff Butler of the R and D Research Unit. He traced the various stages in industrial development from the establishment of basic cottage industries and presented a graph which showed how the rate of innovation varied with industrial maturity. The resulting product and process innovation curves showed how TQM has affected process innovation in recent times. This is in marked contrast to product innovation which reached its peak in the nineteenth century. With improvements to process innovation being a characteristic of leading companies throughout the 1980s, it is seen that there has been a lot of progress in this area, streamlining administration procedures, and reducing superfluous documentation and workflow. The Japanese in particular have made great advances in process improvement over the years. However, many are now examining what lies beyond world class performance and it was hinted that perhaps for some at least, the rate of process improvement may have approached saturation level. The requirements of future prosperity have distinctly shifted in favour of innovativeness and the further improvement of product design, using techniques such as Quality Function Deployment (QFD).

This led to a consideration of measures of innovativeness i.e. measurement of the frequency of innovation and the effects of it on established styles of project management. In this connection the need to recognise the knowns and unknowns of project management was highlighted. He pointed out that in traditional project management the schedules relating to aspects such as costs and resources tend to be known, but not the scope for new ideas or new technology which could potentially render an expensive project redundant and at worst put the company out of business. He asserted:

"It's usually what we don't know that causes things to go wrong rather than what we know".

The Manchester Business School has been actively involved in the development and promotion of techniques to help companies to identify where their projects are most vulnerable to such unknowns, and how they might become better able to protect themselves against the potentially devastating effects that they can cause, as well as enhancing them so that they can be used to help the company rather than to its detriment. Improving the flexibility of projects is clearly an issue and to this end the School has pioneered a technique of 'uncertainty mapping' building on a concept which was conceived four years ago by the R & D Unit's Director, Alan W. Pearson.

The technique utilises a two by two matrix by which projects may be classified in one of four quadrants according to the level of uncertainty associated with its ends and the level of uncertainty contained within the means to its ends. It is noted that a project's classification may change with time or be made to change with time as various uncertainty factors are identified and removed.

The first quadrant is characterised by high uncertainty in both the ends and the means and is where many projects have to be placed at the exploratory idea formulation stage. Here freedom of the innovators and good communications are important.

The second quadrant has typically a lower uncertainty in its ends, but the means are still high. Projects in this quadrant are classically engaged in development engineering and it is suggested that a project may benefit here if known or simpler technology is applied.

In the third quadrant things are the other way around, and this typically occurs in application engineering where there is a clear need to be selective and avoid the temptation to work on too many projects at once.

In the last quadrant new and innovative combinations can be developed with high levels of control since the risks are low on both counts. The use of process plans in the chemical industry to make new compounds was used as an example.

Automating Project Management

The subject of automating project management was discussed by Gerald Kelly, Director of microcomputer consultants Leading Edge Computers, who suggested that the notion that the 'blue sky research' of the first quadrant above rendered it inappropriate for software application 'was a mistake'. Software was, he said, 'a recording device by which to later analyse the way you work'. He made reference to several cases where it had been used to great effect to identify at an early stage resources which in practice were not needed, as well as pinpointing where important resources had been omitted. Software can therefore greatly assist the company as an enabler to resource adaptation.

In later stages the advantages of using software continue as it shows the amount of resources used, and enables identification of situations where rental may be preferred to purchase.

Where there are multiple projects, software can assist the company in ascertaining the optimum method of sharing resources between projects, and provides a means of levelling resources in cases of resource conflict. Particular attention was drawn to cases where overloads which had not been apparent had halted the project, and how particular software may be used to prevent this by means of an 'overload finder'.

Further benefits include the ability to attach notes or spreadsheets to a project during the course of its development (for example to describe an outline to a task, and the ability to effect improvements to scheduling and tracking).

Modern packages based on graphical interfaces are noted to be 'easy to use and easy for guiding someone whose interaction with software is limited'.

Mobile Radio Project Development

The first of two presentations from Roke Manor Research was given by Paul Smith, Principal Group Leader for their Radio Communications Department, who provided a practical example of project development in the field of telecommunications.

This concerned the development of an RF subsystem for a mobile telephone over a timeframe of two years by a team of seven which later rose to ten. It was a 'fast track and high risk' project because it involved designing for frequencies which had hitherto not been considered for exploitation by a mass market. Its lifecycle consisted of a research phase of one year's duration which included demonstration building and testing, followed by a development phase incorporating revision of the original design and later manufacturing and testing, and finally a product support phase that ensured continued attention to quality post manufacture.

The research phase was characterised by a high degree of freedom for the team [Deming: Innovation comes from freedom -Ed], and attention to risk assessment. Risk assessment was critical here because components had to be designed in for manufacture two years hence, and the company had to decide whether to use a defined module, the supply of which had been promised by a competitor, or whether to use 'a discrete replacement for this module'. Application of risk assessment techniques showed that the latter choice was preferable. In this connection the speaker referred to the need always to question results that have not been proven or validated.

The development phase was characterised by rapid design iteration and there was much attention to the critical assessment of the quality of external data. There was a need for attention to good communications to ensure information flow (particularly if the information is subject to change and arrives from abroad in a foreign language), and the need for effective contingency planning. It was noted that it is not always the same team that progresses from research to production, and that 'the value of reviews should not be underestimated'. The need for an understanding of the purpose of reviews on the part of all was also emphasised, so that they will stimulate positive contributions. Lots of people, he said, come to a review without understanding its objective and consequently a lot of time can be wasted. It was therefore imperative that the project manager ensures that the purpose of a review is stated:

"Reviews often happen when you least want them, but it is better to have a late review than none at all. This can be difficult a when engineers are anxious to get the job out of the door".

Discussing testing the author explained technically the importance of knowing the purpose of a test i.e. what is the test for? In this case 100 per cent testing was not realistic as there were 300 possible operating channels with 10 possible power levels and 3 temperature specifications making 9000 combinations for which the timeframe for testing was not sufficient. [A classic case for the use of Taguchi techniques –Ed].

The product support phase was characterised by close communication with the customer, which according to Mr. Smith 'is one of the most important things for the project manager'.

He said:

"Poor and distant relationships with the customer impede the management of problems, and we always keep a close watch for organisational changes in the customer's company".

He also highlighted the need to continually check customer expectations since they can change and if one is not careful they can soon differ from what one's company is producing.

In his conclusion he suggested that management emphasis has, of necessity, to differ between the research and development phases whilst the intelligent use of reviews throughout all project phases was essential. Also recommended was a clear test philosophy, with a clear understanding of it and its limitations, and on continual checking to ensure that small concerns do not develop into major problems.

The speaker was asked to elaborate on the company's contingency planning, and he described how several iterations had been planned into the development phases, but when it was seen that part of the development was not going as well as planned, a number of parallel activities were devised 'to aid options later'.

The second presentation from Roke Manor, by Dave Woodcock, focused on the improvement of quality and suggested that there were 'far too many quality staff who have never managed a project in their life'. For those who have tried there is a recognition that project managers typically have little control over their projects. This is unfortunate because often the senior management sees only the business perspective i.e. increasing the rate of generation of profit, minimising the amount of money invested or minimising operational expenses (cost cutting). This approach commonly leads to a desire for example to reduce testgear, sub-contract at the expense of one's own in-house facilities, employ lower skill based staff, minimise salaries and cut back on training. It follows that a dilemma exists in the ways in which quality is perceived and to help avoid this business management, quality management and project management have of necessity to be integrated.

Three parameters that were identified as being key to the success of a project are staffing, initial project costing and estimating, and experience, all of which are never fully under the control of the project manager. Project managers are, however, slowly realising the extent of the added value accruing from meeting hidden customer requirements rather than merely conforming to specifications. The speaker called on all Quality Managers to look more deeply at project objectives as distinct from focusing exclusively on traditional areas like BS5750 and TickIT. Project managers, he said, had of necessity to own their systems and be able to feel that business is capable of being within their control.

[Issue 71 (November 1994)]

DEVELOPING STANDARDS FOR R AND D

The QMA R and D Special Interest Group met in Swindon on 8th November to discuss the subject of standards development in R and D. This included five excellent presentations which covered health and safety standards, environmental standards and the integration of standards in the context of R and D, along with two highly informative case studies.

Health and Safety Standards for R and D

The first, and perhaps the most important essential set of standards to be addressed were those of health and safety, and these were outlined by Joe

Microwave Integrated Circuits. This illustrated how attempts to transplant standard statistical process control (SPC) techniques into a batch processing wafer fabrication line can lead to difficulty through the incorrect interpretation of detail, false yield information and gross costing inaccuracies.

The case study in question was noted to relate to a leading edge state of the art form of manufacture which is finally taking off after years of prediction. An example application is in the radio telephone industry. It was a 'classic' in the electronics industry with sample measurements taken from each batch (from one or every wafer, or several wafers) rather than at intervals from a continuous product flow with the consequence that standard SPC control limits are frequently violated. Since SPC ordinarily requires a process to be stopped and investigated at each violation, it follows that the technique either tends to be abandoned in such cases or else control limits are set which 'look about right' but have no statistical basis.

It was emphasized that what in practice was required was a system which would halt production, but only after genuinely abnormal events. A solution to this is to adopt a moving range chart. It was explained how this led to a saving of £40,000 in six months.

He then explained the attributes of the Cusum (Cumulative sum of deviations from target) chart in picking up transition points):

"If a process suddenly slips out of control standard control charts will pick it up after two or three runs, but if any process is drifting it may take twenty to thirty runs. Small process shifts can be detected much sooner with a Cusum chart".

In addressing the complex statistical design of experiments it was explained how in an etching process a student had used an RS1 computer system to perform 27 process runs with a range of parameters which gave "wonderful response circuit matrices optimising etch rate uniformity", but which did not account for the fact that uniformity already exceeded 6 per cent, nor the fact that the etch rate was not critical. The result was that a £15,000 computer led design failed to address the variables which were critical and in the end delivered improvements which 'weren't really needed'.

Consequently the speaker justified his preference for simple design of experiments, and urged delegates to consider:

(i)   if parameters are critical

(ii)   if they can be accurately measured

(iii)   if they are being correctly charted

Professor Bendell complimented Mr. Lindsay on the high standard of his presentation, adding that in the components industry these sorts of problems are very typical. He said:

"Often SPC is a technique that has been put in on a half baked idea of application and the state of application in the UK is appalling. The service sector is making the same mistakes as manufacturing".

Chairman's Report

In his Chairman's Report this year Professor Bendell pointed to 1994 as having been 'a year of challenge', and whilst attendance at meetings 'had dropped off slightly' he said that by and large the Association 'has done well in maintaining its momentum' with membership 'holding up well under recessionary pressures'.

[Issue 89 (May 1996) First Leicester Conference on ISO9000 and TQM]

Training Needs associated with SPC

At the First Leicester Conference on ISO9000 and TQM three presenters from the University of Edinburgh (Claire Hewson, Peter O'Sullivan and Keith Stenning), focused on SPC with particular reference to training where there is considered to be a huge potential for improvement on the part of British industry.

The paper describes the approaches taken by four companies, a plastic injection moulding company, a forging and pipe extrusion company, a brewery, and a bolt manufacturer. Each was identified as being at different stages of SPC implementation. The experience in applying SPC varied from over ten years in the case of the forging and pipe extrusion company to four months in the case of the brewery.

In all of the companies the implementation of SPC involved both quality control managers/teams and machine operators, but the degree of involvement and responsibility varied. In the two advanced companies (the plastic injection company and the forging and pipe extruder) there was noted to have been a shift of responsibility toward the machine operators and away from the quality control group:

'The injection moulder divided the production line into three cells, giving each cell responsibility for taking measurements and inputting data to the appropriate p.c. The actual measurement and input of data was carried out by the machine operators; output was monitored by an appointed cell leader who was given the responsibility of acting upon this information if necessary. Cell leaders were required to report to team leaders, whose responsibility it was to co-ordinate the cells across shifts'.

'A similar move of responsibility was observed in the company engaged in forging, which made the machine operators responsible for taking measurements, performing elementary statistical analysis on these measurements, and making preliminary adjustments (by referring to an action list) if the process appeared to be going out of control. If a problem arose which could not be corrected by reference to the action list, the operators were required to notify supervisory staff; such problems were then tackled by a corrective action team put together by senior management'.

In the other two companies operators took measurements and recorded them but did not perform statistical analyses or interpret information. This was left either to an inspector or the quality department. Not surprisingly these two companies, when questioned, were found to 'give little or no training to the shop floor personnel' in stark contrast to the advanced companies:

'The injection moulder employed a training scheme with several stages; in one stage all shopfloor workers were shown an SPC video (produced by Mitutoyo) and given a short introductory talk by the quality manager. Stage two involved on the job training which took place on the shopfloor and covered the use of measuring tools and SPC software; stage three consisted in sending the nine cell leaders on a two day Mitutoyo course which demonstrates the uses of Statpack and also presents some theoretical concepts related to statistical analysis.

The approach to training the process operators in this company was to keep things as non-technical and unintimidating as possible, and to emphasise application of the theory. Training was directed mainly at the shop floor personnel once it was noted that here the knowledge gap between existing skills and required skills was greatest'.

All of the companies apparently reported benefits from the use of SPC. These were quoted as; improvement in the location of problems in the production process, reduction in the number of problem components returned by the customer, reduction of scrap due to machining errors, and improvement in the measurement of machine capability. For the brewery; reduction in the number of beer losses, and reduction in variation around target specific gravity. The deficiency in training, however, in the lesser developed companies is clearly seen to be an inhibitor to the desire of these companies to improve and increase their use of SPC. [The rich get richer - Ed].

The bolt manufacturer 'reported problems relating to a lack of SPC skill, and lack of motivation, in shop floor personnel', whilst the brewer's operators 'were not encouraged to become very involved in the implementation of SPC and in particular were not encouraged to interpret and act upon SPC data'.

The authors highlight the need for operators to acquire at least some minimal understanding of the principles that underlie the data analysis techniques being deployed, and learn to both interpret and act on the data that they collect, since even in the advanced companies 'operators were failing to engage in problem solving behaviour and carry out corrective action'.

The authors conclude that:

'A fundamental element in the skills required by operators is the ability to apply theoretical statistical concepts to real processes and conditions in the workplace. A more detailed specification of particular types of problem skills relevant to the use of SPC in manufacturing processes, as well as data from a larger sample of companies using SPC would be beneficial in guiding the development of SPC training materials'.

The development of computer-based learning environments is advocated on the grounds that they incorporate graphical reasoning methods which ease reasoning by reducing computational load and demand on memory, as is a fuller investigation of the specific training materials that are currently being presented to operators.

[Issue 93 (September 1996)]

TPM at Harris Ireland

At the TQM in Action conference at Sheffield Hallam University Dr. Rodney McAdam and Anne-Marie Duffner of the Ulster Business School considered how TPM can be implemented once TQM is in place and how it may be driven subsequently through the application of audits based on the criteria of the Baldrige Award model.

The paper describes a case study, that of Harris Ireland, a Subsidiary of the Harris Corporation in the USA which manufactures Metal Oxide Varistors (transient voltage suppressors comprising of sintered metal oxides), and has annual sales of the order of $30 million. It has 275 employees, is situated in Dundalk, and introduced TQM in 1991, in line with the corporate strategy of the Harris Corporation. This brought about 'substantial business improvement' with losses turning to profits in 1993, but at the same time a recognition of the need for further improvement if the momentum was to be sustained.

In the USA Harris had already established as a corporate goal the objective of winning the Malcolm Baldrige Award by 1999. To this end they established a Total Quality Systems Review consisting of a team and a measurement system.This team conducted structured interviews with a cross section of the workforce and makes observations and recommendations.

Such interviews were undertaken at Harris Ireland in May 1995. These revealed that a clear majority of groups practised ongoing improvement as part of their job when they were questioned on their application of the

Japanese '5S' model as part of their ongoing commitment to TQM. At the same time, however, the performance of existing equipment within the organisation was rated as low and the resulting conclusion was that implementation of TPM was needed:

'The majority of groups see machine performance as critical, yet perceive the maintenance of equipment as occurring only sometimes. This data reveals a gap that can be narrowed through the implementation of TPM'.

In order to facilitate the introduction of TPM they benchmarked two companies, Short Brothers plc and NEC Semiconductors Limited, which already practised TPM. This exercise confirmed the fact that for implementation to be successful each company needed to develop its own plan, customised to its own needs and problems as well as the type of industry, production methods, equipment types and conditions used. Each overall implementation plan, however, will also have some similarities with the other.

[Issue 108 (December 1997)]

NEW WEBSERVER S.P.C. SOFTWARE

What is said to be the first true web version of any statistical process control (SPC) software has been launched by Adept Scientific plc. The NWA Quality Analyst Webserver Edition provides dynamic access to quality analysis data to users across an organisation including customers via corporate intranets or extranets.

Previously SPC data has only been accessible over the web in view-only form as grabbed bitmap images, but now anyone with access to a company intranet can view and dynamically interrogate quality information.

This means that internal staff and customers can check the quality documentation associated with any item at any time without having to go through their own inspection procedures. It also brings to the PC platform 'unmatched functionality, absolute precision and unparalleled ease of use' offering 'virtually every variable and attribute control chart needed by quality management professionals'. In addition the NWA Quality Analyst Graphics Viewer coffers functionality not available with a standard web Browser':

Users can accumulate several charts (more than 100 at a time) and format them into multichart page layouts for display and printing. This makes it easy for them to compare charts from multiple products, processes or locations. Users can control the appearance of charts and, by clicking on data points, can view descriptive information (such as date/time, shift, lot number etc) associated with the data point. They can then save charts in a format that can be easily shared with other NWA Quality Analyst users'.

QUALITY IN DESIGN AND PRODUCTION

Quality in Design and Production (QidPro) formed the centrepiece of the 1997 Inspex exhibition at the National Exhibition, Birmingham, from the 4th to 6th November. Organised by Mitutoyo and placed strategically between the supporting exhibitions of Tooling and Manufacturing Week QidPro reflected the emphasis on measurement and testing for design and production which characterised the exhibition as a whole which featured around 150 companies.

Breakthrough in Raster to Vector Conversion

With the growing popularity of low cost scanners, many electro-mechanical engineers want to scan paper-based drawings into their computer aided design (CAD) program as an alternative to the time consuming task of redrawing them.

In practice, however, the scanned raster images first have to be converted into editable vector (DXF or DWG) formats before changes can be made in their CAD program and the conversion process has been notoriously unreliable as well as very expensive. It has not been unusual for example, for investments in software of the order of £3,000 to be made only to find that the resulting vector files were of little or no practical use. Drawing elements, i.e. lines and arcs are often made up of many short lines which make editing difficult or even impossible. For many CAD users there is no advantage in editing drawings converted in this manner.

In an attempt to offer a solution to this dilemma Softcover International have released a keenly priced raster-to-vector convertor which enables CAD users to quickly edit scanned images in any CAD programme. The Scan2CAD v 4.5, which is priced at around £199.00, identifies the optimum method of creating accurate vector lines and arcs such that conversion results, according to the suppliers 'beat or at the very least match each and every one of the market's high profile packages'.

Changing trends in Rapid Prototyping.

Selective Laser Sintering (SLS) is a unique computer integrated high precision manufacturing process which rapidly builds durable and fully functional 'protoparts' and even instantly useable soft tools. Pioneering work with Kango, worldwide leaders in industrial power tools, led to savings of the order of three months of time in the design and testing of its new 760 industrial hammer drill.

The pioneers, AMSYS, Rapid Prototyping and Tooling Limited of Sunderland, are now confident that this technology will very soon replace traditional Stereolithography (SLA) as manufacturing industry's preferred choice for rapid prototyping and rapid tooling applications.

Commenting on the applications to date Daniel Tramontana, Design Engineer for Kango says:

"SLS technology speeds up the whole design and production process. On the 760 project AMSYS was able to take our design specifications and produce the first model prototype within a matter of days rather than the normal weeks".

This is now being extended to rapid tooling technology with the aim of reducing the product design-to-market lifecycle:

"We're currently examining the opportunity for reducing our production tooling times. Amsys' technology could potentially provide us with final production tooling in just two months as opposed to six. This would deliver significant savings in tooling costs, faster product to market times and, ultimately, faster pay back".

Managing Director of Amysys Mike Hartley adds:

"SLS already scores over SLA when it comes to toughness and durability – the advantages here are well known. However current advances in new materials such as DuraForm, tooling and finishing, enable us to provide SLS prototypes that match and even exceed the aeshetic quality provided by SLA. This will negate SLA's claimed key advantage and probably lead to SLS becoming the universal choice for all rapid prototyping applications".

The company, following its £1million management buyout from The University of Sunderland, has invested around £0.5 million in two new SLS Sinterstations.

Polymer Technology yields savings in Rapid Prototyping

The need to develop expensive silicone tooling and mouldings in order to produce models of new parts for pre-launch testing may soon be a thing of the past following the development of new polymer technology by Amysys. The new technology known as FlexForm is said to allow for savings of up to 40% to be made in the engineering and manufacturing of fully functional rapid prototype parts such as seals, gaskets and mouldings where 'rubber-like' compression features are required and applications where strong resistance to high temperatures (up to 159 degrees Celsius/307 degrees Fahrenheit) are needed at the trial stage.

Sales Director Dion Griffith comments:

"FlexForm is a truly unique and innovative product. No other rapid prototyping material can produce the concertina-effect that is a key feature of many parts, notably those produced in the automotive industry".

New Standards for Taguchi Software

New standards have been set for Taguchi Design of Experiments software with the addition of Dynamic Characteristics and the automation of orthogonal array design by American based Advanced Systems and Designs Inc. The ANOVA™ Graphical User Interface is said to eliminate difficulties such as trying to remember programming commands and syntax, the necessity of going through multiple steps, and the limitation of displaying just one file or experiment or chart at any given time.

The Design Array for Windows ends the hassle of leafing through pages of linear graphs and modifiying them to create the right design, and of the transcription errors which tend to occur when creating multi-level factors:

'With Design Array for Windows the user just enters the number of levels for each factor and the interactions to be studied, Design Array automatically selects the appropriate array, allocates factors and interactions to columns and modifies the array to cater for multi-level factors. Design Array also allows the user to nominate the columns for each factor.

This gives the user the flexibility to do their own thing, but with the confidence that the design is technically correct. Design Array's intuitive layout and on-line documentation help the user to create powerful designs with a minimum of fuss'.

NEW TAGUCHI METHODS USER GROUP

Milton Keynes based ASI Quality Systems, the UK representatives of an international organisation, have announced the formation of a new Taguchi Methods User Group for those who may be interested in sharing experiences of application. The Group will run in a similar way to the format already followed by ASI's QFD User Group and its main purpose initially will be to promote the implementation of Robust Design with the emphasis on the provision of practical support. The unique relationship between ASI and Dr. Taguchi ensures that members of the Group will benefit particularly from learning about up to date methodologies.

[Issue 115 (July 1998)]

QUALITY FUNCTION DEPLOYMENT

Quality Function Deployment (QFD) is a notoriously underutilised management tool in UK manufacturing industry yet it offers potentially enormous benefits through minimising design changes, improving

610

communication, dramatically improving customer satisfaction and generally reducing the length of the product development cycle. Time and again management is accepting that it must listen to its customers if its businesses are to prosper. However here is a golden opportunity which would appear to be all but going to waste, for QFD not only captures the 'Voice of the Customer' but also helps it to be understood throughout the organisation and indeed translated into Business Results. It is arguably a must for any manufacturing organisation today and Quality Matters is pleased to report on an event which provided a rare insight into this little used but powerful weapon in the quality armoury.

The event was the 1998 European Product Development Symposium hosted by ASI Quality systems, currently the centre for QFD and Taguchi Methods, at the Hanover International Hotel, Daventry on June 24th and 25th. It featured some 14 presentations including case studies from four organisations which have each benefited considerably from the application of QFD. The papers are reviewed below, together with the introductory presentation by Simon Barnard of ASI Quality Systems. The guest speaker Jim Wilkins of the American Supplier Institute explained how QFD effectively integrates with both Taguchi Methods™ and the Theory of Inventive Problem Solving or TRIZ which has now become the subject of some debate. First, however, an overview is given of the concept of QFD to assist those who may not be too well acquainted with it, using ASI Quality Systems' Module Guide as a reference.

The Concept of QFD

The concept of QFD derives from three pairs of Japanese characters, namely Hin Shitsu (quality features attributes qualities), Ki No (Function mechanisation), and Ten Kai (Deployment diffusion development evolution). It is defined as follows:

'A system for translating consumer requirements into appropriate company requirements at each stage from research and product development to engineering and manufacturing to marketing/sales and distribution'.

It may be considered as 'the act of taking the voice of the consumer (or user) all the way through product development to the factory floor and out into the marketplace'. As such it should not be regarded purely as a quality tool but also as a planning tool for the introduction of new products as well as the upgrading or improvement of existing products. Used properly it should drastically reduce the waste of time, effort and money that commonly results from a need to redesign as a result of poor planning or poor product definition, and help to solve problems with multiple causes which have historically defied solution.

Central to the QFD concept is the so-called 'House of Quality' chart which is so named because of its roof-like structure and 'rooms' which may be 'toured'

[rather like moving round a Cluedo board -Ed]. This chart is derived from a list of objectives or 'WHATs' which take the form of spoken customer requirements which are termed 'performance quality' non-verbalised customer wants such as 'hidden components and assemblies' which are termed 'basic quality', and unspoken 'excitement features' which are termed 'excitement quality'.

A Kano chart is used to visualise customer satisfaction versus degree of achievement for each of the three types relative to time. One or more 'HOWS' are then generated for each 'WHAT' so that customer requirements become translated into global characteristics which in turn become 'design requirements'. These are usually measurable characteristics which can be evaluated on the completed product.

Some of the 'HOWS' inevitably affect more than one 'WHAT' and may even adversely affect one another. To overcome the difficulties which this may present the 'HOWS' and the 'WHATS' are turned perpendicular to one another and a Relationship Matrix constructed using symbols to illustrate strong, medium and weak relationships. Even complex relationships can thus be both depicted and easily interpreted. Blank rows and columns will serve to indicate areas where the translation of 'WHATS' into 'HOWS' has been inadequate.

With this matrix in place a set of measurements for the 'HOWS' can be introduced which indicate the performance levels that are required to provide customer satisfaction. It is stressed that these measurements will not necessarily reflect current performance levels, indeed they probably won't. These 'HOW MUCHS' then serve as a guide to subsequent design and allow for an objective assessment of progress, minimising so-called "opinion-eering".

In addition to the 'HOW MUCHS' the 'HOWS' may also have attached to them a Correlation Matrix. This takes the form of a triangular table or 'roof' which establishes the correlation between each 'HOW' and identifies areas where trade off decisions and research and development may be required. Symbols are again used to indicate the relative strengths of the relationships between the 'HOWS', showing whether they are strong positive, positive, negative, or strong negative. Those 'HOWS' which support one another, and those which oppose are thus clearly revealed and visualised.

Positive correlations enable resource efficiencies through the avoidance of duplicated effort to achieve the same result. Negative correlations will highlight the trade-offs which almost invariably characterise a well optimised product. The Guide suggests that there should be no negative correlations. If there are some then there has most probably been at least one error in the construction of the chart. It also suggests how trade-offs should be approached:

612

'Our first response to a negative correlation should be to seek a way to make the trade-off go away. This may require some degree of innovation or a research and development effort which may lead to a significant competitive advantage. Frequently, negative correlations will indicate conditions in which design and physics are in conflict. When this occurs physics always wins. Such trade-offs must be resolved. Trade-offs which are not identified and resolved will often lead to unfulfilled requirements even though everyone has done their best'.

'Some of the trade-offs may require high level decisions because they cross engineering group, department, divisional or company lines. Early resolution of these trade-offs is essential to shorten programme timing and avoid non-productive internal iterations while seeking a non-existent solution'.

'Trade-off resolution is accomplished by adjusting the values of the `HOW MUCHs'. These decisions will be based on all the information normally available: business and engineering judgment as well as various analysis techniques. If trade-offs are to be made, they should be made in favour of the customer and not what is easiest for the company to perform'.

Trade-off decisions may be simplified with the aid of Engineering Competitive Assessment, Customer Competitive Assessment and Importance Ratings. The Engineering Competitive Assessment is a competitive assessment of the 'HOWs' utilizing the best engineering talent to analyse competing products. The Customer Competitive Assessment is competitive assessment of the 'WHATs' and represents the customer's perception of a product relative to the competition. Both take the form of graphs which depict item for item how competitive products compare with current company products. 'WHATs' and 'HOWs' that are strongly related will normally exhibit a relationship in the competitive assessments, providing a cross check and highlighting gaps in engineering judgment. Importance Ratings for the 'WHATs' and 'HOWs' depict the relative importance of each 'WHAT' or 'HOW' to the desired end result. The 'WHAT' Importance Ratings are established through genuine customer assessment whilst the 'HOW' Importance Ratings are calculated by assigning weights to the relationship symbols:

'The Importance Rating for the 'HOWs' provides a relative importance of each 'HOW' in achieving the collective 'WHATS'. These values have no direct meaning, but rather must be interpreted by comparing the magnitudes to each other. If a trade-off decision is necessary between the 'HOWS' with the 89 and 9 Importance Ratings, greater emphasis should be placed on the 'HOW' with the 89 rating'.

The 'rooms' of the 'House' are now in place. They are, however, separated by 'corridors' which reflect information commonly used to facilitate the product development process. Examples are as follows:

- Service complaints

- Organisational difficulty (relative difficulty in accomplishing HOWs)

- Service repairs and service cost

- Control items such as regulatory requirements

Movement around the 'House' to drive the voice of the customer through the organisation may now be accomplished using a four phase process in which the 'HOWS' of one chart become the 'WHATS' of a new chart until each objective is refined to an actionable level. The Pareto principle determines which 'critical few' HOWs are selected for the next phase of the QFD. The four phases are, respectively, Product Planning, Design Deployment, Manufacturing Process Planning, and Production Planning.

In the first phase company measures are derived from customer requirements. Some of these measures are then carried on to the next chart to establish the best design and its part characteristics. In the second phase the 'HOWS' take the form of part and part characteristics of the design effort whilst in the third the 'HOWS' are the critical process parameters which, when controlled, "provide" the critical part characteristics. The last phase is then concerned with day to day production controls and making sure they are in place.

The Guide suggests that the complete QFD process typically will involve around 50 to 60 hours of team meetings and team work for each member with most of the work being undertaken outside of the meetings. The team meetings are principally for the purpose of co-ordinating activities, updating charts, analysing information and deciding on the information which needs to be gathered by individual team members:

'While it is possible to achieve substantial gains by implementing QFD only down to the part characteristic level, the greatest gains are realised only when taken down to the most detailed level of production requirements. The QFD process is well suited to Simultaneous Engineering in which product and process engineers participate in a team effort. QFD may be thought of as "blueprint" for the operation of such product development teams'.

Applying QFD.

Four organisations which have applied the above concept and clearly benefited from it are Nissan, Pirelli-Cables, Mars and Kawneer UK. At the conference Roy Steel explained Nissan European Technology Centre's Integration of QFD into the Development process, Nigel Fishlock explained the role of QFD in the Development of Fibre Optic Cable by Pirelli-Cables Limited, and John Cooke of the Four Square Division of Mars explained the application of QFD within a specific project entitled The Flavia Vendor Project. The QFD Success Story of Kawneer UK was explained by Simon Barnard of ASI Quality Systems.

Roy Steel's presentation described how NETC has applied QFD to new vehicle development. Specific examples include seat belt installation for which a 'House of Quality' chart was shown, and Passenger AirBag Deployment for which the company has chosen to apply 'the essence of QFD'. He emphasised how every system development planning paper through QFD, necessarily includes an element of the customer voice, although it is accepted that QFD may not be appropriate for every component. As a generator of process control characteristics QFD forms an important part of design control, an aspect of quality which proves so often to be troublesome for manufacturing organisations. Nissan is currently leading the way in DTI funded research to examine methods of 'grabbing the unsaid customer voice' under the acronym CUPID (Customer Satisfaction Processes in Design).

At Pirelli QFD has been introduced into a completely re-invented Time To Market (TTM) process for new products, which has subsequently been used to develop a revolutionary fibre optic cable:

'A cross-functional team (referred to as the TTM process review team), including representatives of the Engineering, Manufacturing and Commercial functions was established to improve the process. Additionally, there was a strong high level managerial commitment with the Chief Engineer, the Manufacturing Director and the Business Director all contributing strongly'.

The QFD concept was applied at each of the three stages of the resulting improved TTM process i.e. Justification (assessment of commercial viability, technical risk and product definition); Design, Develop and Test (using predictive technologies to mathematically model the performance of the product and verify cable design); and Product Launch (information dissemination, training of manufacturing operatives and longer term capability studies to confirm yields, machine speeds and other significant process parameters):

'A new customer requirement was established for a Limited Fire Hazard (LFH) patchcord cable. A cable specification existed, based on previous cable designs. The previous cables were manufactured as a tightly sheathed cable construction and were compliant against the relevant specification. A prototype LFH patchcord was designed and manufactured based on the specification and previous design knowledge. The cable was fully compliant against the requirements of the new specification including temperature, tensile, crush and bend testing. However, problems were encountered during termination and temperature testing of the patchcord assembly. After a lengthy investigation it was found that the sheath tightness directly affected the performance of the connectorised product. After carefully reviewing the test results the TTM process review team decided it was necessary to apply the TTM process to progress the project'.

An inter-company team established between the cable manufacturer, end user and connector house resulted in the identification of five key design parameters derived from the accurate definition of the functional requirements of patchcords. The QFD concept was then used to establish the relationship between the design parameters and process parameters and a pre-planning matrix (simplified version of a QFD chart consisting of customer requirements, importance ratings and competitive assessments) devised as a precursor to full QFD. The chosen process parameters were then investigated to ascertain their effect on the design parameters.

The Flavia Vendor Project involved the development of critical functional parts for use in a new Japanese hot and cold drinks vending machine. Working in a joint development for the first time with two Japanese partners (National Panasonic and JVS/APEX, the second largest vending distributor in Japan), Four Square realised the very demanding quality and performance expectations (five times improvement in reliability over the system that had been used before) necessitated an approach that breached traditional Western management thinking. Fortunately Four Square had used QFD since 1990 and it had 'proved effective in the management of a number of previous product developments', at least to the extent of knowing that the demanding challenges that were being posed were attainable:

'In parallel with the convergent design activity, the QFD was taken to the next stage with a Phase 1 matrix (shown as Appendix 4 in the paper) prepared for the Flavia Vendor "Core Parts" as the pump, filterpack handling mechanism and Cup Door Assembly were known. Phase 1A matrices were then prepared for the pump and filterpack handling mechanism to give more detailed objective definition for subsequent design, development and qualification activities.(These are shown in Appendix 5 in the paper).The Phase 1A matrices linked into the earlier functional analysis work by making use of measurable Quality Characteristics which directly related to the functions performed by the mechanisms. These characteristics linked into several TaguchiTM optimisation experiments which were used to assess robustness and performance of the concept solutions and to aid the selection process'.

'As we prepared the detail design of the first stage proof-of-principle prototype (M1), our major effort went into ensuring that there were no negative interactions between functions. At this stage in the project there were still a number of areas of uncertainty which needed to be checked in development testing. The prototype parts used during this time did not reflect the final manufacturing requirements being machined from solid and fabricated'.

The Phase 2 QFD matrix provided an important prompt to gain information on critical parameters in the design and priority areas for the designer and toolmakers to focus their attention.

'When design work was completed for the M1 prototype, the design team started to consider how to make the assemblies and components consistently. Several Design For Assembly (DFA) sessions were held with involvement from Four Square production associates and suppliers. The primary focus of these meetings was to eliminate risk of mis-assembly through the assembly process. Through this activity the production associates started to take ownership for the design and could consider line fixturing and test requirements. As the detailed design of parts progressed to the point where final production representative parts could be prototyped, design release checklists were used to ensure all the right design checks had been made. Maintaining the focus on functionality, the checklists were used to check that that the designer had considered part function and had specified critical characteristics from the Phase 2 QFD chart and Failure Mode and Effect Analysis (FMEA) work'.

Benefits achieved include the following:

* Overall machine reliability and, in particular, the performance of Four Square Modules, has exceeded expectation since launch.

* The convergent Design process which allowed the best parts of both existing technology and new concepts to be combined so as to produce a total solution that is superior to any of the contributing designs, allowed Four Square to maintain a focus on design for manufacture without any change in concepts.

* The Flavia core parts project plan remained in line with the overall agreed plan throughout the project.

*Early supplier and production in the project which resulted in comprehensive quality control plans throughout the supply chain which were related to customer requirements.

*High levels of consumer acceptance for the product which resulted in drinks sales which were 15% higher than anticipated.

Kawneer UK manufacturers of window systems, applied QFD in 1995 with a brief to make 38% of their total product range obsolete and introduce a completely revolutionary window system in its place. With help from ASI they recognised that the key to success was driving the voice of the customer i.e. that the product range had performance over and above the existing window range at no extra cost. Architects, who had responsibility for devising window specifications, were attracted to events where they discussed in small groups what they liked or disliked about current products. A lead team of senior managers from design, production and marketing was formed to provide senior level commitment to QFD whilst support teams involved managers from all other departments. The 'House of Quality' was used to gather the voice of the architects and translate it into new specifications:

"The teams worked through the chart which revealed that a critical area was hardware (locks, hinges, trim etc.) and that a problem area was that they had many hardware suppliers from whom they were purchasing very small amounts at high cost. Separate QFD charts focused on hardware and propelled the organisation towards single sourcing based on partnerships".

Phases 2 and 3 of the QFD were conducted in parallel, facilitating communication between design and production and ending the history of antagonism which had existed between them.

The QFD application resulted in a set of prototype dies which were fed through production and back to design, along with a window range which was launched in November 1996 and reached its annual budget by June 1997. With these early successes Kawneer is now adopting QFD in all its divisions throughout Europe. [This last case study is an astonishing story which potentially could be repeated many times throughout British industry- Ed].

Integrating QFD with TIPS and Taguchi Methods™

Whilst the QFD concept clearly has much to commend it with regard to providing desirable products, delegates were cautioned against the temptation to simply apply it to everything. Instead Simon Barnard and Jim Wilkins recommended that it be integrated with the Theory of Inventive Problem Solving and Taguchi Methods™ so that as well as being desirable, products will also be innovative and robust in design. Together the three concepts combine to produce Total Product Development in which the most innovative solution is one which solves a physical contradiction, that is to say one which sounds impossible in nature, for example something which must be both hot and cold.

Using the simple example of a child's water pistol, the two presenters sought to demonstrate how the separation principles incorporated into TIPS, such as time, space, or mode of operation, identify concept ideas from which the best can be selected using appropriate convergence criteria. The following methodology was advised:

"Place the concept ideas across the top of a matrix. List the criteria for selection. Take one concept as a datum, then look at concept two and ask

yourself if it is better than concept one for each criterion. This should help you to converge on a final design".

"TIPS recognises the fact that innovation solves contradictions. It can avoid a trade-off and give you the best of both worlds. So start by defining the contradictions where they occur. The House of Quality correlation matrix can then be used to examine all trade-offs".

Attention was drawn to a TIPS database to which reference may be made in order to determine which scientific effects to apply in the TIPS process.

On the subject of robust design delegates were urged not to rely on traditional measures of robustness such as reliability testing, customer complaints and warranties as these measures occur much too late in the product development cycle. Instead a single measure known as the signal to noise ratio, that is to say the energy transformed to perform the intended function, divided by the energy transformed to perform other than the intended function, was recommended. This measure can then be increased in value through optimisation of the engineered system which is achieved through the application of control factors to reduce the waste creating noise factors. These control factors are ideally insensitive relative to noise factors. "It is low-tech to adjust a process average instead of variability", delegates were told.

This theme was continued by Shin Taguchi (son of Genichi Taguchi) who is currently the President of ASI. He said the following:

"In the customer's world there is only signal and noise, such as the environment, ageing and manufacturing variability. It is not that noise factors cause problems, but that they cause variability in energy transformation, and this variability produces output other than that intended, that is to say symptoms".

Merely focusing on symptoms, however, constituted "very inefficient engineering" as it allows only for measurement at the downstream stage. In place of this delegates were advised to consider a two-stage optimisation process consisting of reducing functional variability and adjustment of sensitivity i.e. once a concept has been developed and selected, optimise for robustness by trying many designs within the design space by measuring energy transformation and testing under selected noise conditions, taking advantage of interactions between control and noise where they occur:

"Seventy five per cent of an engineer's time is typically spent fire-fighting. Noise factors cause this fire and the fire starts because people measure symptoms. The robust function is fire prevention at the upstream stage".

Unfortunately such concepts have had a low uptake in the West, as Research and Development in countries such as the UK "almost never study robustness let alone try to optimise it". Furthermore, measurement technology may have to be specially developed, which requires exceedingly strong project management which, sadly, is often lacking.

[Issue 125 (May 1999)]

PROCESS CONTROL MATTERS

The subject of process control is frequently viewed by management as the province either of the advanced statistician or of the specialist engineer, each of whom has traditionally been 'compartmentalised' by industry. Consequently the discipline has all too often not been afforded either the respect or the recognition that it rightly deserves in modern Western societies. In academia, however, an appreciation of the fact that by making a few key improvements in this area an organisation large or small can greatly enhance its competitiveness is beginning to emerge.

This was reflected in the content of the Second International Conference of the Control of Industrial Processes on 30th and 31st March at the University of Newcastle upon Tyne which paid tribute particularly to Alan Winterbottom, Visiting Professor and former Head of Statistics at The City University, London for his contribution to the improvement of quality in industry through the application of statistical methods.

His work as a member of The Royal Statistical Society's Quality Improvement committee in connection with the need to merge the minds of statisticians and engineers for the better control of industrial processes formed the basis for the first and now the second conference devoted to this purpose.

The conference featured some 44 presentations, four software demonstrations and a tour of the Nissan automotive plant at Sunderland where plans are currently being finalised for the launch of the new Almera car in January 2000.

Developing a Control Strategy.

This presentation by Hugh Melvin described Trioxide's 'Control Journey' from 1993 which was inspired by a recognised business need with lots of learning in an industry where a difference of 4 parts per million of Chromium in the final product can mean the difference between success and failure. Beginning with the statement that "In a World Class Company Process Control is a strategic competitive weapon and should be used as such throughout the business" the speaker explained how by applying sound basic process control engineering with the aid of networked engineers a 'marriage between statistical and process control methodologies' was achieved which yielded significant benefits in terms of throughput, availability and quality:

*'By comparing Trioxide performance against accepted "World Class"
standards we can quantify both the total shortfall and also provide an
educated guess as to the contribution that Process Control can make. By
doing this we find that an achievable benefit on the bottom line in excess of
£20 million is available and this is the incentive against which our
performance is measured. Annual analysis of Applied Control project
activity purpose around the Group is directly linked to financial benefit. This
is an incentive to the engineering community and a measure of progress to
management'.*

Crucial to the success of such a strategy is an understanding of variation as
this enables process performance over time to be brought as near as possible
to process capability. This is achieved first and foremost by reducing
disturbances and eliminating 'assignable cause' variation. This is then
supported by a 'conformance' measure for processes which are infrequently
sampled and which are subject to manageable disturbances:

*'Conformance is a "user friendly" measure of determining and monitoring a
process against demonstrated performance. The method results in a simple
measure of "percentage in conformance" which is directly related to the
mean and standard deviation of our key quality parameters. We are finding
that our factories support this analysis as it gives them a practical and non-
threatening tool for assessing their own performance. Review sessions are
an essential part of the process and the reasons for any difficulties in
achieving 100% conformance are discussed and acted upon by the
operations staff. They therefore "own" the analysis which is a vital
ingredient for the improvement cycle'.*

The speaker was keen to stress the importance of the three control steps of
networking, maintenance and monitoring to the control engineer and of the
need to ensure that factory information systems and tools such as Lotus
Notes are fully utilised:

*'Completing a control project is only the first stage in getting the expected
benefits. Sound training of maintenance crews, together with efficient handover of projects, is essential and this falls within the control engineer's
remit'.*

The tools of process control which Trioxide has adopted include an
Improvement Matrix derived from the work of Joe Shunta of DuPont [who
also spoke at the conference -Ed], which has been published in a book
entitled 'World Class Manufacturing through Process Control'. This
comparatively simple tool is adapted to skew distributions and enables the
control engineer to assess the often conflicting situation of whether to
improve control or change the process.

It is supported by means of a Process Control Index originally conceived at ICI which the speaker admitted was initially somewhat unpopular with Trioxide's staff, but was soon accepted once its benefits were seen in conjunction with sensible application. This is essentially an audit technique which gives each factory a rating against seven control steps and 'is useful in focusing attention on the benefits of control as well as the method of achieving it', but there is "no points scoring" between factories nor any discussion of any individual factory's Index with other factories [i.e. it is not a league table-Ed].

In his conclusion the speaker described a full process simulator briefly, commenting that it "could be a worldbeater" with its hands-on control facility which can introduce variables such as noise and disturbances. This, he explained, would most probably be marketed outside Trioxide from the beginning of next year as it fills an important gap in the skills training market.

Reducing Changeovers in Continuous Operations

The Single Minute Exchange of Die (SMED) technique has been applied successfully by the automotive industry for some years now, offering substantial benefits to batch production. This presentation described how the technique has been taken a stage further and applied to single stream continuous plants with bottom line benefits running into millions of pounds.

Brian Hull of ICI explained how a five step improvement process was initiated inspired by a desire to improve the uptime of plant. Cleaning operations provided a clear application area for SMED. A teamwork approach was initiated following identification of critical success factors which later revealed how furnace downtime as a consequence of coking up created a bottleneck that affected plant throughout and how water wash was then pinpointed as an area for improvement. Training in SMED (techniques for reducing changeover time) then followed with the aid of a full time facilitator, and the five steps process analysis.

Application of SMED led to the development of a model for water wash with the contractor working the critical path incorporating 24 hour working. This had never been asked for before, but was accepted once the full extent of the benefits to ICI were appreciated.

Measured gains were:

* reduction of seven day turnaround to five days.

* savings of £2000 per hour for 50 turnarounds per year (£2 million).

* further savings from a reduction in the number of water washes required.

In his conclusions the speaker said:

"SMED is applicable to the process industry and there is much scope in continuous as well as batch plants. The key is a multidisciplinary team involving suppliers and a good hands-on training tool to get operators feeling comfortable".

Following the presentation he was asked whether the assumption that with SMED one invariably desired increased output was correct. In reply he advised that whilst one may desire to have increased output this may well be of secondary importance to the desire to achieve a more flexible turnaround so that customers can be given greater choice, for example, through an improved range of colours, with lower rather than greater stock holdings.

The Role of the Internet in SPC

This presentation by Mike Thelwall of Wolverhampton University explained how the Internet is beginning to impinge upon the work of the quality engineer and his SPC tools. It outlined how a DTI funded programme (Internet learning Communities within the UK Automotive Components Sector) is providing a set of web-based materials for training the SPC engineer on-the-job:

'This Internet-based training programme provides an on-line managed learning and support environment where the Machine operator or Quality Engineer can improve their knowledge and skills in applying SPC techniques and can obtain on-line support and assistance with queries and problems via a mediated forum'.

Such initiatives are envisaged by the speaker to result in " a significant move away from centralised SPC systems towards a much more customer led, decentralised one" and " an increasing orientation towards Internet technologies from SPC software designers". Some of the packages currently on offer with Internet capabilities were then outlined:

'Products such as StatSoft's STATISTICA Enterprise Wide SPC System, Western Thunder Inc's ONQuality with Web Feet, PC Engineering's Improvit 4 and Advanced Technologies' AT Sigma Internet Reports for AT Sigma SPC allow users to access SPC information with a web browser through an Intranet or even Internet connection. Some of these also include additional enterprise tools such as the ability to email reports and other control information. Western Thunder cite a car parts manufacturing division of Ingersoll Rand as one organisation implementing SPC through an Intranet.

The speaker stressed, however, that an SPC package does not necessarily have to possess Internet functionality in order to have its information accessible over the Internet as long as its database is visible to software that can link to the Internet. A model is thus proposed which would potentially render the tasks associated with the distribution of SPC charts and reports unnecessary:

'The stabilised data arising from the processes will be automatically transmitted to a central database via a simple suitable factory wide network. The data is then incorporated into a database, often held on a conventional PC. This database is provided with a suite of suitable extraction, reporting and analysis software. The database is then used by the Quality Engineer to produce reports for internal use and for use with the customer (for example, many customers of steel insist that an SPC chart be supplied with the physical product as an annex to the usual certificate of conformance). The SPC data would be stored as an MS Access or SQL database mounted on an Internet server, connected to the Internet via a route or gateway (Internet Service Provider)'.

The remote customer would use a conventional Internet Browser such as Navigation Explorer to access the Server at the supplier via the Web, and data downloaded into their Quality Audit database.

The use of the Internet as a means of distributing SPC data from supplier to customer is envisaged to offer the following benefits:

* Reduced suppliers' handling costs in extracting and distributing SPC data to the customer.

* Improved responsiveness and level of customer service.

* Fewer errors and mistakes such as SPC charts being sent to the wrong customer or not being sent to the customer.

* Improved corporate image of supplier.

Improving Process Control with Designed Experiments.

This presentation by Marion Gerson of Newcastle University argued the case for the use of experimentation as a means to investigate production processes with the aid of two examples both of which yielded impressive results. The first concerned a plant which made a product the main impurity of which was water for which the specification stood at 1 %, but for which there would be a major competitive advantage to be gained from a reduction to 0.2%. The second concerned an extrusion process for which the number and inter-relatedness of process factors identified as affecting the product profile and strength was so great that the company was unable to produce consistent output.

In the first case the key production stage was the final distillation column where product was distilled into a storage tank leaving water as a heavy impurity at the base of the column. The level of impurity could be reduced either by reducing the temperature of the column or by increasing the reflux ratio (proportion of product vapour recycled into the column), but either action would compromise throughput. Before a decision could be made about taking either action some quantification of the improvement in purity relative to cost was needed. This scenario was ideal for the application of design of experiments theory, although as the speaker stressed, the plant management did need some convincing.

Further investigation revealed significant background variability stemming from two pieces of equipment normally used for sampling and this was overcome by selecting the single most reliable piece of sampling equipment. Investigations in the laboratory also 'led to a major programme of estimation and improvement of analytic errors' which 'had beneficial consequences for a whole range of other processes'.

With further background variability reduced by making timescale adjustments to the sampling process to eliminate extraneous and uncontrolled variables as much as possible the experiment was conducted as follows:

'It was agreed that, once changes in temperature or reflux ratio had been made, the process would settle down within 1.5 to 2 hours. So it would be possible to set up and measure four sets of conditions within an eight hour shift. For practical reasons it was decided always to use the same shift team, and only when they were on the morning shift'.

The outcome was described as "spectacularly successful" with subsequent information not only leading to the desired reduction in specification but also 'a desirable blueprint for many other investigations'.

In the second example a screw extruder had seven heating/cooling zones as well as a rate of extrusion, a haul off speed and five further heaters in a de-stressing unit. There were then 48 dimensional measurements of the output profile combined with a residual stress measurement. A Principal Component Analysis of the 48 dimensional measurements provided a guide to three linear combinations of the measurements with straightforward physical interpretations. These were namely overall size, a measure of the height to width ratio and a measure of edge distortion:

'During the experiment we retained all 48 measurements but demonstrated very clearly that in future three sensible combinations of 12 measurements would be satisfactory for all QC control charting and other purposes'.

Discussions eventually suggested that extruder speed and the ratio of haul-off rate to extruder speed were the critical factors. This latter decision turned out to be valuable:

'Not only did it make for much greater acceptance of the experimental design, but the experimental results showed that some output parameters were affected only by the speed and some only by the ratio. Understanding and decisions on further action were greatly simplified as a consequence'.

The results were described as follows:

'Many of the implied theories turned out to be correct, and the experiment provided good estimates of the size of the effects. This was very valuable. However there was also one quite unexpected conclusion which, once revealed, explained much of the company's previous inability to produce consistently good product. This was an interaction effect which would not have been revealed by a simplistic or (probably) by a less well thought out experiment. Its discovery more than justified the effort put in during the planning stage. The result was a reduction in rework and greater market share for the company and much better understanding and control for the process operators'.

The speaker concluded that "the commercial value of experiments like these often greatly exceed the inputs of time and money", but as the second example illustrated "Taguchi designs are only a small subset of design of experiments and may not be robust designs for big plants and some applications".

[Issue 127 (July 1999)]

SIX SIGMA QUALITY

In addition to Dan Reid, the Elmia Qualitec '99 conference in Jonkoping also featured a half day seminar from Dr. Noshir Khory, Manager of Supplier Training and Development for Motorola in the USA. Motorola are perhaps best known amongst quality practitioners for the development of the Six Sigma technique and in the seminar, entitled 'Design for Manufacturability' delegates were introduced to it under the heading of 'Analytical Concepts essential to the Design Process' which also dealt with the relationship between Six Sigma and robust design.

At the seminar Sigma was defined as 'a measure of how well the data is clustered (or spread out) i.e. a measure of the "fatness" of the distribution'. Thus a small sigma implies tightly clustered data and hence small variation whilst a large sigma implies that the data is loosely clustered, i.e. that the level of variation is high. It follows that under normal conditions the ideal situation is zero sigma as this represents zero variation in the data.

Process capability may be defined by the three sigma limits on either side of the mean or target, which encompass 99.74% of the total area under the normal or "Gaussian" curve. The associated. Capability Index may be calculated by dividing the specification width (difference between high and

626

low spec values) by the process width (defined by the process capability and ideally a small value).

The Capability Index indicates how well the process width matches the customer's specification width and ideally has a high value. The Capability Index thus provides a measure of the "Design Margin" of the product. The Six Sigma concept applies this principle by setting the specification levels at plus or minus six sigma either side of the mean or target so as to build in a Design Margin. This concept was simply illustrated by the speaker with reference to the experiences of Ford in the US in the early 1980s when a bad winter revealed a massive difference between the performance of transmission systems sourced in the US and those supplied from Japan. It was found that 85% of returned transmissions were of US origin whilst only 15% were of Japanese origin. This was a consequence of the superior Design Margin of the Japanese product.

Motorola decided they wanted to follow this example in order to safeguard themselves against potential shifts in their distribution curves due to unforeseen conditions such as the one Dr. Khory described where a dock strike resulted in total failure of a consignment of police radios due to three months' exposure to 90% humidity, high temperature and a salt laden atmosphere.

Further applications of Six Sigma were described at the Quality Methods Association seminar at Renishaw plc, Gloucestershire on May 25th. This was chaired by leading UK consultant David Hutchins who in the Spring 1999 issue of the QMA Newsletter "*Tell me*" explains the training methodology currently being adopted for teams wishing to use Six Sigma and some team related projects to which it has been applied:

'In the early stages, the tools which people are trained to use are relatively' simple. They include techniques to collect and analyse data, diagnostic tools for cause analysis and the means to implement solutions and to hold the gains. Using terms borrowed from the martial arts, teams that have demonstrated the ability to use these tools effectively for the solution of real work related problems are said to have achieved "Green Belt" status.

However, as progress is made, new techniques are introduced to enable the maturing teams and individuals to tackle more complex problems. When this level is reached the teams are regarded as being "Black Belt". Achievement of this status is a strong motivator for the teams'.

'One of the attractions of Six Sigma is the fact that the most important practical and usable techniques are usually quite simple even for those who are not mathematically inclined. This is true even at the Black Belt level. Only the most sophisticated of the techniques employed require a degree in mathematics to obtain their benefits. The need for these is relatively rare and in such cases outside assistance may be sought if these are required.

Experience indicates that even the crudest application of the simplest concepts can produce stunning results'.

At the seminar Shane Yenvin and John Pollock of Motorola of Swindon explained how their organisation is currently applying Six Sigma to improve customer satisfaction. They were joined by Director of Catalyst Consulting Limited Vince Gant who explained how the Six Sigma concept aligns with the Business Excellence Model. These presentations were supported with case studies from Rexam Plastic Packaging Ltd., Invensys Intelligent Automation and Kodak Ltd. The above presentations and case studies are briefly summarised below.

Six Sigma and the Customer.

Shane Yenvin and John Pollock work in the Network Solutions section of the GSM Division of Motorola which occupies an area of 250,000 square feet in a one year old building. Between them they have a total of eighteen years' experience in the Six Sigma methodology making them well placed to describe how its relevance and application impacts on customers in the telecommunications field.

In introducing Six Sigma they stressed that it should form part of a programme rather than be implemented as a programme in itself and that its primary aim should be to improve reliability i.e. ensure that the product works first time, stays in service and is "plug in and go".

A key measure of this reliability is the failure rate in the field, which is thus the driving measure for the Six Sigma focus. The starting point for failure in the field is the percentage return rate per month.

Correlation tests were undertaken between the percentage return rates per month and various internal quality measures (in particular the factory ppm, defects per unit and first time yield), as well as measures of product and process complexity. These provided "snapshots in time" with some important messages. John Pollock commented:

"With any Six Sigma programme you have to make sure that the measurement is important to the customer. Does the customer really care about the ppm rate in the factory? The ppm may be good for internal process measurement but is not necessarily the only measure that is needed for the customer".

The correlation tests showed that reduced product and process complexity tended to result in a lower ppm, but defects per unit and first time yield both showed a better correlation with the percentage return rate than the ppm. The advice given was therefore "keep the product and process simple and then drive the ppm", and "reduce the number of connections and opportunities for error in parallel with the ppm drive".

Motorola are currently using the Six Sigma technique to improve the reliability prediction of products before shipment.

Six Sigma and the Business Excellence Model.

Vince Grant pointed out that as well as being the architects of Six Sigma Motorola had also been a Baldrige winner, which served to illustrate how the Six Sigma concept and the Business Excellence Model "are complementary and work well together". He explained how he had been "very struck" at this year's EFQM Learning Edge conference in Geneva with the large number of comments that were voiced about Six Sigma and the desires of many attendees to have it established within their supply chains.

The speaker stressed that the new version of the Business Excellence Model places much more emphasis on customer facing processes in Criterion Five and that Six Sigma was relevant to this as it provides a specific approach for the design of new processes. The real challenge, however, will come from the translation of business problems into statistics and back i.e. the coding and decoding of the problems themselves rather than the complexity of the statistics. Selection of the right projects will also be important, driven by policy and strategy which, in the new Business Excellence Model, incorporates the old Criterion 5a (requiring evidence of how processes critical to the success of the business are identified).

Both Six Sigma and the Business Excellence Model rely on measurement with, the speaker suggested, the Plan-Do-Check-Act methodology being common to both. The Sigma measure was, he said, "about a commonly understood measure of processes" and "measurement that is appropriate to the problem".

By contrast the Business Excellence Model Radar Chart "measures how good processes are and the results" and "shows what the process part of the Business Excellence Model actually represents". His advice was that the Business Excellence Model should be used to gain a strategic understanding of the management system. Then, once one has identified those processes which need to be improved, the Six Sigma technique can be used to achieve continuous breakthrough in process performance i.e. use both continuous and discontinuous improvement "to break through the barriers at four to four and a half sigma". This should then "help the organisation to focus on process rather than function".

In his presentation Mr. Grant made reference to his work with GE Capital's Six Sigma programme and to their associated training which has involved the training of so called 'Master Black Belts'. In the questioning which followed he was asked to elaborate on this and he gave the following response:

"In GE Capital the Black Belt is a full time project leader responsible for two or three or even up to ten people. The Black Belt leads the improvement team. The Green Belt is part time for twenty to twenty five per cent of the time and is only responsible for leading one project. The Master Black Belt is the internal consultant that trains others with a specialist role in training, benchmarking or similar. Black Belts report to people in their own departments whilst the Master Black Belt reports to the quality leader in the organisation".

He urged delegates to exercise some caution with the use of this terminology, however, as one of his company's clients uses the term 'Black Belt' to mean what is really a hybrid between a conventional Black Belt and a Master Black Belt.

The Six Sigma Implementation Roadmap.

The Rexam case study was delivered by Group Continuous Improvement Facilitator Ms. Harriet Elfers and consisted essentially of a 'Roadmap' approach based on five key success factors:

* Organisation and staffing (which includes Six Sigma behaviour in performance management, clarity around roles and responsibilities for accomplishing change and a critical mass of people doing projects).

* Training (includes a quick roll-out of Six Sigma to create the critical mass, sponsor training on project selection and review techniques and application of 'train the trainer' concept).

* Communication (clear and continuous with every available technique used to learn, inform, persuade and inspire and assist others to do the same).

* Project selection (includes time spent with management on the link to strategic business targets, building savings into budgets and generating the baseline for the most important processes and critical areas to focus on).

* Measurement (includes determining how to evaluate progress, integrating report-outs in the established review structure, changing traditional reporting formats and avoiding reaction to so called 'one point' measurements).

In her presentation Ms. Elfers explained how the 'Roadmap' and critical success factors had been derived from the change management model adopted by General Electric (GE) and developed with the aid of US based consultancy 'Six Sigma breakthrough Technologies' who presented it to senior management and subsequently provided the training. The key to success with Six Sigma was, she said, in the way training was conducted i.e. in twelve to twenty days in four modules, entitled 'Measure', 'Analyse', 'Improve', and 'Control'. This is then followed with the first project which is typically designed to be manageable over a time frame of around five to six months. She stressed that Six Sigma is a culture change type of initiative and shared with delegates the following common pitfalls:

- Insufficient time devoted to project selection and lack of appreciation for the need to train people how to do it.

- Too much emphasis on the concept and not enough on the way i.e. measuring the number of Green Belts and Black Belts trained such that Six Sigma merely becomes a goal in itself.

- Rewarding of Black Belts with stock options [very dangerous – Ed]

- Initiative fatigue stemming from attempts to implement more than one different initiative at the same time.

- Management preaches the change but doesn't "live it".

- Black Belts remaining responsible for fire-fighting as a result of poor allocation of procedures for Six Sigma projects.

- A continued focus on bottom line and productivity measurements rather than allowing Six Sigma to focus on customer satisfaction which, although it may not appear to save much money by direct savings, is vitally important for success.

- Timewasting on 'jargon discussions'.

Following the presentation she was asked what she would most choose to have if she could have just one thing assured in all of this i.e. the most important thing to have. Her reply was "a shared vision by management".

Typical Six Sigma Projects

Paul Tempest, a Master Black Belt responsible for the co-ordination of Six Sigma projects at five sites of the global control and instrumentations company Invensys, provided an insight into some of the projects to which the Six Sigma methodology was currently being applied. He explained how the Intelligent Automation Division currently had 27 Master Black Belts, 181 Black Belts, 560 Green Belts and 1300 live projects, with so called 'transactional projects' representing over half of Invensys Intelligent Automation's potential benefits. These projects include areas such as invoicing, credit control, order handling, accounts receivable and software debugging, all of which are prime sources of waste i.e. things which the customer is not happy to pay for. Other project areas are engineering design, and manufacturing and installation (such as field returns, cost and cycle time reduction, in-time travel distance reduction and packaging, the latter having recently been the subject of a £50,000 saving arising from the changing of a hitherto overlooked wood specification).

Sources of projects were listed as follows:

* Customer surveys and feedback

* Internal audit reports

* Process studies

* Process frustrations

* Improvement drivers

* Critical to quality (CTQ) issues (such as high maintenance or operations costs, high rework levels, recurring problems or unpredictable process performance)

A Project Desirability Matrix is used to identify which projects

(i) have a high potential business impact

(ii) require the least effort

(iii) have the highest probability of success

These criteria are weighted and compared with the "ideal project" scenario which essentially has the following characteristics:

*Problem significantly impacts on cost and/or productivity.

*Has direct or indirect impact on the customer.

*Has a documented history and a reliable measurement system associated with it.

*Is linked to the bottom line.

*Involves minimum reliance on other divisions.

*Is "bite sized" and achievable.

*Improves the process as well as reducing costs.

Projects such as creating or revising a report, improving a supplier s performance without any arrangement to share the benefits, or reducing the cycle time of a non-bottleneck operation would therefore not be typical candidates (little or no business impact). Likewise installing a new computer system improving profitability of an entire product line or channel or "fixing" the annual planning process would not (high effort needed), nor a project which depends on the completion of other risky projects.

The speaker explained how the Six Sigma structure runs in parallel with the line management structure with Black Belts making a point of challenging conventional management thinking as well as using and teaching Six Sigma concepts. They act both as technical managers and internal consultants. The Green Belts by contrast spend around 30% of their time on Six Sigma projects, are mentored by their local Black Belt and either run their own projects or act as senior team members.

Benefits associated with Six Sigma based projects have included:

* Improved understanding of the needs of each department.

* Improved communication and information flow.

* Closer co-operation between departments during design stages.

* More consistent working practices.

* Logging of problems for future improvement.

* Monitoring of new procedures.

Sometimes, emphasised the speaker, a "whole raft of problems" may be eliminated by one simple act, as was the case when carriage charges, which accounted for 20% of all invoice queries, came under investigation and were later scrapped for normal next day delivery and replaced with a standard flat rate for express delivery. Previously the manual calculation of these charges had consumed a lot of time and different agreements with different customers had been "very confusing".

The Kodak Black Belt Programme

This was described by the Quality Manager for Kodak UK Manufacturing Ms. Jilly Brown who is responsible for three sites at Harrow, Annesley (East Midlands) and Kirkby on Merseyside. For them the Black Belt approach is merely one of the more recent of a chain of quality initiatives which have included MRPII Class A, ISO9000, ISO14001 and the Japanese inspired 5S management system.

The purpose of the Black Belt Programme is 'to accelerate the rate of improvement in defect reduction, cycle time, and product/process capability, and is supported by an overall improvement goal of '10X improvement in cycle time reduction and defect reduction every three years'. In describing it

Ms. Brown explained how her company had learnt from experience the turn off effects which can arise from attempting simply to train everyone in SPC techniques and had consequently realised that it needed to be much more selective in providing the expertise that was necessary to tackle certain types of project. She then outlined the Black Belt training itself which essentially has two forms:

(i) Management Black Belts for line managers with enough knowledge of quality concepts and tools to provide effective leadership, role modelling and reinforcement of 10X improvement initiatives.

(ii) Black Belt Practitioner for users and teachers of Six Sigma tools assigned to key improvement projects who are expected to produce predefined business and customer results.

Management Black Belts typically undergo five days of classroom based training before becoming owners of the 10X improvement strategy and plan, as well as of some improvement projects. They will typically select projects which potentially have at least $100,000 and may have between 500 and 800 staff working for them. Black Belt Practitioners, by contrast, undergo five weeks of training over five months, four of which are spent on quality tools and one on interpersonal skills.

All of this is project related and they are assessed on Six Sigma tools, change agent skills, project results and class participation. Some of them are positioned to go anywhere to solve problems, but as the speaker explained, there are as yet insufficient people to allow everyone to do this.

Projects have a one year limit and have to be part of the portfolio supporting the business strategy. They must have one or more of the following objectives:

* Improved customer satisfaction.

* Defect reduction.

* Cycle time reduction.

* First pass yield improvement.

* Lead time reduction.

* Variability reduction.

* Optimisation of product or process performance.

* Cost reduction.

* Reduction of Cost of Quality.

* Improvement of delivery.

The speaker stressed the importance of avoiding duplication when allocating projects which necessitates that people have a view of the whole business and are able to "move barriers". She then explained how a worldwide database of projects based on Lotus Notes had been established and made open to all Black Belts, as well as a quarterly network in the UK to maintain the team spirit within the British Black Belt Group.

The term 'Green Belt', however, was "not used", although it was pointed out that her company's equivalent was that group of people who had undertaken five days of advanced quality skills training.

Latest developments at Kodak include the establishment of a specialised version of the Black Belt programme for non-manufacturing areas where Ms. Brown said "there is a huge potential impact for the Six Sigma concept".

[Issue 128 (August 1999) 4th. Sheffield World Quality Congress]

Implementing SPC in Sweden.

As in previous years there was a strong Scandinavian presence at this year's Sheffield World Quality Congress (28th to 30th June) as nine out of the fifty published papers were by Scandinavian authors. From these nine 'The Implementation of SPC and Process Capability Studies' was selected and then presented by Ann Brannstrom-Stenberg as one of four papers devoted to Process Management and Measurement.

She described a survey undertaken in 1997 to ascertain why companies in Sweden chose to implement SPC and process capability studies. A questionnaire was compiled which yielded 83 responses:

'The study population included all members of the Swedish Association for Quality belonging to the section of Statistical Methods, SFK-StaM, and persons who had participated either in courses on Total Quality Management given by the Association of Swedish Engineering Industries, VI, or the course "Quality Leadership" given by the Department of Engineering Sciences, Physics and Mathematics at Karlstad University.

These three populations were chosen since they were considered to be representative of the target population. A total of 491 questionnaires were sent and 155 were filled in and returned. Of these 155, 83 reported that they used statistical process control and/or process capability studies'.

'Most of the 83 organisations had between 100 and 500 employees. A few organisations had more than 4000 or fewer than 100 employees. It is obvious that statistical process control is mainly used within large organisations. Seventy five percent of the larger organisations that answered used it. Process capability studies are equally common in organisations with fewer than 100 employees as in organisations with 100 employees or more'.

Findings showed that 65 organisations used SPC with 40% of them electing to do so because their external customers required it. The rest had done it of free will because they wanted lower quality costs, fewer rejects, less inspection and better knowledge of processes. Of those which had implemented it due to customer requirements, most were in the car industry. Very few were in processing and service.

The speaker discussed the advantages and disadvantages experienced with SPC depending on the cause of implementation. The advantages are shown diagrammatically in the conference proceedings and essentially show that amongst the organisations which had implemented SPC the main advantages were in the form of process or product improvement and increased opportunity to control processes. For those organisations that had undertaken SPC voluntarily the main advantages were lower rejections and quality costs followed by process and product improvement:

'Organisations that have implemented statistical process control of their own free will experience advantages to a greater extent. Such advantages are lower rejection rates, lower quality cost, quality insurance and/or higher traceability. Organisations that implemented the method due to requirements from external customers did not experience these advantages to the same extent. Advantages such as higher motivated workforce and lower inspection activities were experienced by organisations that implemented the method voluntarily'.

The analysis of the disadvantages on the other hand revealed that organisations that were required to implement SPC because of customer pressure experienced disadvantages such as heavy investment and SPC not fitting the organisation's processes to a greater extent, but did not experience much difficulty in establishing control parameters:

'Organisations that implemented statistical process control voluntarily mentioned that it was difficult to find parameters that were to control the process. None of the organisations that had implemented the method because of external requirement mentioned the problem. The reason for this may be that when the organisations have external requirements the customer also specifies the parameters to be controlled. It is only organisations that have implemented statistical process control of their free will that report that they cannot find any disadvantages using the method'.

The remainder of the study examines the link between SPC and process capability studies. The speaker argued that 'a proper use of capability studies requires that the process is stable' and she therefore described it as 'quite surprising' that some organisations insist that a process be capable before SPC is applied. This view appeared to find favour with the audience with one delegate commenting:

"I am not surprised some organisations are doing capability indices first. Customers often demand suppliers achieve a given capability level so it becomes a target. I have heard stories of companies choosing the right data in order to get the right capability number to meet the target. This is not what SPC is about. We must change this philosophy of understanding".

[Issue 129 (September 1999)]

SHEFFIELD WORLD QUALITY CONGRESS (PART 2)

The Six Sigma Debate.

A key feature of this year's Congress was a 'Point and Counterpoint' discussion of the merits and demerits of adopting the Six Sigma methodology as part of an ongoing quality management programme. The discussion, which included two short case study presentations from IBM Italy and Sony UK in support of Six Sigma, was moderated by leading US expert Hans Bajaria who introduced various thought provoking counterpoints based on experiences in the US where Six Sigma has enjoyed something of a rejuvenation following recently reported successes by General Electric.

The discussion was not so much a debate about "for Six Sigma" versus "against Six Sigma" but rather an exercise in striking a balance between "the much talked about side of the coin" and " the other side of the coin". In all a total of fourteen 'points' and 'counterpoints' were raised, urging delegates to think carefully before necessarily choosing to follow the potentially highly expensive examples currently being pursued across the Atlantic. The fourteen 'points and counterpoints' gave rise to the following fourteen recommendations:

* Treat every new quality initiative including Six Sigma as a two sided coin so points and counterpoints can be examined before one becomes too deeply committed.

* Solve problems rather than becoming overly concerned about reporting the Sigma level of progress and use before and after pictures to demonstrate progress.

* Avoid desensitising problem conditions by allowing for target shifts (amount of shift and type of shift are a matter of discovery not assumption, and one should not therefore assume that a plus or minus 1.5 Sigma shift will necessarily result in 3.4 PPM).

* Measure operational excellence efforts by measuring uniformity around a target independently from specification range.

* Make distinction between variable and attribute data for selecting a problem-solving tactic (for variable data target shift and variation are independent whereas for attribute data they are dependent and converting attribute data into an equivalent Sigma level forces solving variation as a problem condition – if a target is solved as a primary problem variation could be changed as a side effect or vice-versa).

* Divide variability into the three problem components of instability, variation and off-target (if variation is taken as the only component one could end up working on the wrong problem condition which could undermine the whole problem solving process).

* More attention should be paid to developing robustness than to reducing variation because robustness can eliminate the need to reduce variation.

* Develop a larger collection of strategies and methods to support conventional Six Sigma methodology because reliability methods, multivariate methods, observational studies and robustness concepts are frequently omitted.

* Develop and execute statistical thinking to resolve transactional problems (a large number of cases require countering of the problem rather than determination of the root cause).

* Create breakthroughs by attacking 'industry money gobbling evils' (industry spends a lot of money trying to control key characteristics when the process of determining them is poorly defined and executed; using statistical control charting instead of defining problems; inefficient selection and execution of Design of Experiments; and so called 'reliability tests' which are actually durability tests).

* Minimise investigation costs by using statistics as a science of indication rather than of confirmation as Six Sigma often tempts (problem solvers need to evaluate a series of indications until they arrive at the final solution which only then can be confirmed).

* Place primary emphasis on engineering strategies supported by statistical breakthrough strategies (Six Sigma is only a statistical methodology which has to be combined with engineering strategies to successfully solve problems).

* Use vertical systems to resolve problems and horizontal systems to hold the gains (Six Sigma is a vertical system i.e. it starts with a situation to be resolved and ends with a permanent solution, but the creators of Six Sigma never discussed the difference between such a vertical system and the

horizontal ones which improve working efficiency without necessarily solving problems).

* Beware of Six Sigma success stories (documented case studies are often presented as the strongest evidence for Six Sigma success but the case studies illustrated on websites are sketchy and there is no mention of any specific Six Sigma methods that were used to resolve the problems).

Hans Bajaria concluded as follows:

"Collectively these counterpoints issue a warning to the potential users of Six Sigma methods. The usefulness of the Six Sigma philosophy, methods and breakthrough strategy can be realised only if we are conscious of the counterpoints. There is no doubt that industries need a vertical system such as Six Sigma strategy to solve complex problems. However, pursuing Six Sigma strategies without the comprehension of counterpoints is a potential disaster in the making. If we make the Six Sigma strategy yet another fad, it will be a reflection on our culture rather than the quality science".

[Issue 137 (June/July 2000) Deming Transformation Forum, Brighouse, June 2000]

Deming and Six Sigma Improvement.

An insight into how Deming's teaching could greatly improve the potential benefits of the methodology of Six-Sigma was provided by consultant Ian Graham with the help of Martin Gibson of Motorola at the Deming Transformation Forum. In the joint presentation Six Sigma was viewed as an important concept in that it allows for quantification of defects providing a common language for the whole business to compare themselves and work towards a common goal, but flawed for the following reasons:

* it still relies on specifications to define quality

* it accepts process drift as inevitable

* it uses rigorous mathematical statistics which can be based on false assumptions about the properties of a normal distribution

* it can become the province of the so called "Black Belts" rather than providing a means for everyone to use and understand control charts

* it places a heavy reliance on techniques often at the expense of the people dimension

Thus, whilst Six Sigma compels people to understand the data of processes, which is "a giant leap forward" there is a danger that one could end up merely "playing with numbers" and "counting defects". With Ford Motors now demanding that all of their suppliers have Six Sigma Black Belt training programmes, and others presumably set to follow, these dangers are seen as being something to avoid when it comes to application, and the presentation explained how they could be avoided by:

(i)   Learning Deming theory and challenging prevailing theory that gives precedence to specifications rather than the far more meaningful 'Loss Function'.

(ii)   Using the Shewhart practical approach to statistical process control.

(iii)   Teaching the theory of variation at a level that all people can apply.

(iv)   Teaching tools simply and within the context of learning, experimentation and innovation.

(v)   Paying attention to psychology, IT and public sector initiatives.

Chapter Nine

Measurement and Reliability

Measurement has always been an essential component of successful quality management and it has been said that if one cannot measure one cannot manage. It has been a neglected area for many years representing the more traditional side of quality often seen as the province of specialist engineers and only really relevant to manufacturing. As the decade progressed, however, there has been a renewed focus which culminated with the launch of the DTI's National Measurement Partnership Programme (NMP) by the then Secretary of State for Trade and Industry the Rt. Hon Peter Mandelson MP in November 1998. This was later followed through with the 'Competing Precisely' programme run by the DTI in conjunction with the National Physical Laboratory and the staging of the First National Measurement Conference at the end of 2000.

Earlier in the decade the Quality in Manufacturing Exhibition and Conferences sponsored by the journal Quality Today, with whom Quality Matters enjoyed a healthy and co-operative relationship, acted as a focal point for measurement related issues and the compilation below includes the Quality Matters reviews of the events in 1997 and 2000.

The more general but related subject of reliability was addressed through the biennial European Safety and Reliability (ESREL) conferences which essentially took over from the National Reliability conferences in 1991. In 1995 the ESREL conference was held in the UK under the joint sponsorship of the IQA and the Safety and Reliability Society. In 1997 the event moved to Lisbon and the Quality Matters reviews of both of these events are included below. The 1999 event in Trondheim, Norway was not covered.

Other notable developments in the 1990s include the growing recognition of the phenomenon of electromagnetic compatibility and its associated legal issues, the increasing importance attached to the techniques of risk assessment in order to measure reliability, and the technological advances made for example in temperature compensation for co-ordinate measuring machines (CMMs).

THE SURFACE MOUNT CLUB

The electronics industry has been through its customary revolution with the introduction of Surface Mounted Components onto Printed Circuit Boards. Design engineers welcomed the increased packing density on the boards and flexibility, particularly using Computer-Aided Tools for Design.

Less enthusiastic were the electronic production engineers who found themselves with unfamiliar problems to solve. This particularly applied to those only electronics trained, and many problems were found to be mechanical or chemical in origin. In a fast-moving industry these problems had to be solved quickly and expert help sought.

This was the climate for the foundation of the Surface Mount Club where scientific help was available from the National Physical Laboratory. Companies seeking the help joined together and funded further research for their common good. *Quality Matters* found that some of their contributors were founder/early members of the Club. Over the last few years the techniques have stabilised, but there have been some spectacular failures on the way, notably the American Department of Defence radio project Sincgars V, where the new technology was used "in a hurry" without proving the techniques and with disastrous results. This retarded the project by years rather than months.

Process Control and Quality Standards

Surface Mount Club News (Issue 8: November 1989) contains a useful feature on process control and quality standards of surface mounts. This describes success in achieving process control in the soldering of surface mount assemblies as an important target for the UK electronics production workforce' and explains that 'perfection to the point of omitting 100 per cent visual inspection' is still some way off in most applications. Various reasons are given for this including:

* designers of surface mount circuits are still on a steep part of the learning curve.

* 'underdeveloped' surface mount component structures and termination designs are passed down to users as international standards as a result of 'commercial pressures and weaknesses in the system'.

* supply of certain components and process equipment known to have quality and reliability problems in the field such that 'when things go wrong there remains enough room for component suppliers, equipment manufacturers and assemblers to argue about the causes'.

* marginal solderability of components used for reflow techniques which have 'negligible mechanical agitation to assist wetting, coupled with absence of suitable standard methods of solderability testing.

It is noted that 'yesterday's solderability standards for wave and hand soldering of leaded components have been arbitrarily applied by their manufacturers and distributors to surface mount parts', whilst 'unnecessarily stringent requirements for surface mount joint meniscus contours' coupled with 'desire for cosmetically immaculate component orientation' on the part of original equipment manufacturer (OEM) quality organisations could be 'counter-productive'.

It suggests that whilst the validity of recommendations for visual standards of solder joints should be based on test results for adhesion, shock, vibration and acceleration at severity levels appropriate to the application), in practice they tend not to be, and notes that those who care to attempt validation of visual standards by means of push tests 'will be surprised to find factors of safety approaching ten times for joints which they may previously have regarded as being rejectable due to insufficient solder' .It also suggests that 'touching up joints to improve alignment or solder quantity can reduce reliability' because of the reliance on operator skill.

[Issue 74 (February 1995)]

NATIONAL ACCREDITATION BODIES MERGE

It has been announced in Parliament by the Trade and Technology Minister Ian Taylor that the National Accreditation Council for Certification Bodies (NACCB) and the National Measurement Accreditation Service (NAMAS) are to merge into one accreditation body.

Interestingly the new body will be in the private sector, non-profit making, and will take over the staff and functions of existing services from the DTI in 1995.

The NACCB and NAMAS are the overseeing authorities on behalf of the government to ensure that the standards of the certification bodies are correctly set and maintained. In the past the consistency of assessments, not only between certification bodies but within them, has been a controversial issue, and these national authorities are responsible for ensuring 'a level playing field'.

The new company, (limited by guarantee) will carry out assessment of certifying organisations for laboratories, test houses, certifying bodies and include environmental verifiers and future related fields.

The symbol of accredited authority (appearing on all accredited sources) of the Tick and Royal Crown will be maintained by the merged company.

Last year *Quality Matters* reported (Issue No.66) the merger between the Western European Calibration Co-operation (WECC) and the Western European Laboratory Accreditation Co-operation (WELAC) where measurements made in Europe could be harmonised under one authority. It was predicted that other mergers would follow as various National Authorities realised the benefits of harmonisation, particularly where the activities are technical and can avoid the controversial nationalistic commercialism. [A problem often associated with the EC Directives- Ed]. The merger of NAMAS and the NACCB is a typical case in point.

[Issue 79 (July 1995)]

RELIABILITY MATTERS

There has been renewed interest this month in the subject of reliability. Sir John Harvey Jones in his well known 'Troubleshooter 2' series (BBC2 21st June) showed how reliability (or rather the lack of it} has impacted on British manufacturing industry , with the example of Triumph motorcycles compelled to manufacture components internally at great cost to achieve the reliability they required without recourse to foreign suppliers.

So how can British manufacturing retrieve some of its lost markets by achieving levels of reliability which are world class? Investment in state-of-the-art manufacturing equipment would appear to be essential, supported also with an understanding of scientific developments in the field.

These scientific developments are frequently mathematical in nature, and rarely understood fully by quality practitioners, yet their impact on subjects such as design for manufacture can be considerable.

This month *Quality Matters* concentrates on these scientific developments, providing an outline of some of the latest pioneering developments in the UK. These were presented at the recent ESREL '95 Conference in Bournemouth (26th to 28th June 1995}, sponsored jointly by the Institute of Quality Assurance and the Safety and Reliability Society.

A total of 69 papers were presented plus a Keynote Address from Dr. P. Kafka, Chairman of the European Safety and Reliability Association (ESRA), a non-profit-making international association (launched in 1990) aimed at the advancement and application of safety and reliability technology in all areas of human endeavour.

The Keynote Address focused on the role of ESREL conferences in promoting information relating to technological challenges and innovation in

Europe i.e. the 'high tech potential' of countries developed through European wide R and D Framework Programmes.

The paper outlines the objectives and scope of the Channel Tunnel Safety Case (CSTC), which represents the first application of the Safety Case Concept to a bi-national project in rail transport. Also how various automotive manufacturers, electronics companies and part suppliers have co-operated through a working group, called 'Vehicle Safety and Dependability' in a common project known as the 'Iterative safety design process -as an approach towards safety analysis and assessment of future vehicle systems'.

From the remaining papers *Quality Matters* has selected eight for review.

New Approaches to evaluating Fault Trees

This paper, by R. M. Sinnamon and J. D. Andrews of the University of Loughborough (presented by researcher Ms. Ros Sinnamon), focuses on the application of new computer techniques to the already established technique of Fault Tree Analysis, known as the Binary Decision Diagram Method.

The paper describes the origins of Fault Tree Analysis (H.A. Watson in 1961-2 for the Launch Control system of the Minuteman Intercontinental Ballistic Missile) and explains how it has subsequently become a widely accepted technique for the assessment of the probability and frequency of system failure in many industries. It is limited, however, by the many hundreds of thousands of combinations it yields as the potential cause of system failure.

These combinations (termed minimal cut sets) are tedious to handle, even with modern day high speed digital computers. With computerised analytical techniques now already highly sophisticated it is envisaged that even with further refinement traditional techniques are viewed as unlikely to be capable of reducing the amount of computer time required very substantially. A completely new approach is therefore required.

Fault Tree Analysis has essentially two components (qualitative in which the minimal cut sets are obtained, and quantitative in which the probabilities and frequencies of system failure are calculated). This paper focuses on the qualitative part and argues that whilst most analyses work directly with the system fault tree structure, which is acknowledged to provide 'a very good representation of the system failure logic', this may not in practice be the most efficient method. Certain 'new algorithms for fault tree analysis' may be far more efficient:

'The task of obtaining the minimal cut sets of a fault tree can become computationally intensive if the logic equations produce many cut sets. If a large expression is obtained then applying the reduction rules can take a long time on a computer to make the expression minimal. Also storing all the

logical expressions for each gate in the tree can make extensive demands on memory space'.

The new approach advocated in the paper uses instead a 'directed acyclic graph' or Binary Decision Diagram (BDD) in which all paths terminate in either a 1 state (system failure) or an O state (system success), making the cut sets (all 1 state) readily identifiable. A technique called 'special ordering' is deployed to reduce the number of redundant BDDs when the fault tree contains repeated events, and as trees increase in size this technique yields increasing benefits.

The paper concludes:

'The BDD form for the Boolean equation seems to provide an alternative technique to efficiently analyse fault-trees. Also by considering the ordering of basic events the BDD can produce minimal cut sets without having to eliminate redundant cut sets as is often the case with conventional techniques.

The trade off for this is the effort taken to convert the logic from the fault tree structure to the BDD form. However, early work indicates that for large complex trees this can produce a substantial reduction in computational effort'.

Following the presentation Ms. Sinnamon was asked how many groups were currently creating very large fault trees and stood to benefit from this development. In reply she pointed to at least one large fault tree currently being evaluated in the nuclear industry which was incapable of being analysed by traditional techniques, but which had been successfully analysed using the technique described.

Risk Assessment Methodology in British Gas.

The paper by H. F. Hopkins and M. A. Fishpool of the Gas Research Centre at Loughborough provides a case study of the development of risk assessment in British Gas with particular regard to plant and pipelines. The aim is to make quantitative risk assessment more consistent and accessible so that it can make an increasing contribution to the design and operation of installations.

The paper points to the increasing use of risk assessment methodology in notably, planning matters relating to storage and process plant. Also considered is pipeline design where recent codes and standards such as BS8010 (Draft) Pipelines: Part 2 Design, Construction and Installation of Pipelines on Land; Section 2.8 Pipelines in Steel for Oil and Gas; here risk assessment has been used to reassess the restrictions imposed by earlier more prescriptive codes.

Research into the failure modes of pipes and vessels and into the consequences of releases of flammable substances from Liquified Natural Gas (LNG) sources and high pressure natural gas pipelines has been necessarily predictive with additional supporting data supplied from physical modelling techniques such as wind tunnel studies. In addition the range and complexity of computer models has been extended enormously with more models being based on the physics of processes, as against being empirical.

As risk assessments have become more complex, particularly in the case of pipelines, separate computer programs have had to be developed for each assessment and problems have arisen with consistency. Analysis led to a decision to adopt a packaged management system development organised as a joint project between the producers and users of hazard and risk assessment methodology. This later highlighted the degree of expert judgment and simplifying assumptions that had been made previously.

Expert judgment has therefore been 'formalised' for standard situations so that safety engineers can concentrate on the non-standard or site specific aspects of a location. Also simplifying assumptions have been frequently eliminated by the specifying of a software procedure which transfers many of the more time consuming tasks to software. A knowledge base then defines which software models will be run, and their input, output and data handling requirements.

The first package to be developed in this way was the TRANSPIRE risk assessment package for transmission pipeline risk assessment, which is now in routine operational use and is said to have enabled risk assessments to be carried out 'quicker and more consistently, with the derivation of the results being more easily understood by operational managers and by regulatory authorities due to the improved structure and accessibility of the methodology'.

The paper highlights the similarities involved in developing a methodology for the assessment of each plant type, and lists five general stages of assessment procedure each of which contains elements from a generic set or sequence. It is anticipated that a knowledge base for assessment will result, which accesses appropriate models from a library rather than a dedicated set of calculation procedures. Common databases will be available to access released material properties and weather data etc.

Presenter Harry Hopkins commented :

'At the present time methods are being investigated to interface models and systems which are outside our direct influence. These include CAD interfaces to assist with offshore platform design databases for storing and retrieving frequently accessed information such as gas properties or meteorological data, and applications implemented in other proprietary software '.

Remote Diagnostics for Manufacturing

The paper by Dr. K. Clements-Jewery and Mr. Peter Dunlop of the Department of Engineering at Glasgow Caledonian University entitled 'the use of remote diagnostics in manufacturing industry' describes recent developments in the field of remote diagnostics i.e. systems which can remotely monitor and diagnose machine or process faults without the need for a specialist 'expert' to be on site.

It highlights the increasing number of UK companies which are now using Remote Diagnostics Systems interfaced with programmable logic controllers to control various types of plant and machinery .The attraction is the potential for reduced costs and improved speed of rectification attainable by allowing information to travel to the expert rather than vice versa:

'The adoption of these remote diagnosis systems is potentially attractive to a company since they do not have to have their own highly trained staff on-site nor wait for the contractor to travel to the plant'.

The technology, however, is relatively new and as yet there is little quantified data available about the efficiency and safety in use aspects of these systems. Information at present would appear to be limited to a Draft Guidance Document entitled 'Safety in Remote Diagnosis of Manufacturing Plant and Equipment' recently released by The Health and Safety Executive (HSE), and as far as the investment is concerned companies can do little more than hope that the potential benefits will be greater than any potential operational or safety problems that any maintenance staff might encounter.

In order to try to make at least a first attempt to remove some of this uncertainty Glasgow Caledonian University has undertaken a limited evaluation of one commercially available system that is currently supplied by Siemens plc, with the aim of later selecting areas for further research.

An experiment was designed in which a remote diagnostic system was compared with a 'normal' controller-machine system with faults introduced into both for diagnosis and evaluation of maintenance efficiency and operational safety. A quantitative comparison was made with the aim of providing a guide for a subsequent cost-benefit analysis.

Four young engineers assumed the role of 'guinea pigs', and were timed as to how long it took them to diagnose six faults which were graded in order of perceived difficulty.

The results (shown graphically) illustrate that good local diagnosticians are just as efficient as a remote expert diagnostician, suggesting that remote diagnostic systems do not appear to offer any real advantage in use, mainly because clues and information not displayed on the remote site p.c. (e.g.

feeling if a solenoid is warm when energised) removes a very important part of the information needed by the diagnostician. The skill level of local technicians can vary greatly, however, which can affect the diagnostic time.

In conclusion the paper lists some important considerations for companies considering using remote diagnostics, not least the existing skill and knowledge levels of their own maintenance staff as well as the competence, costs and availability of the expert remote diagnostician. There would appear to be a trade off in safety i.e. enhancement of safe working practice during maintenance through elimination of or reduction in the use of trial and error methods of local maintenance staff who are exposed to danger by 'unthinking' operations versus the potential for new or unknown safety problems which may arise when active control of a machine is in the hands of a remote diagnostician.

The paper accepts that 'the potential saving of maintenance costs is very considerable' though suggests that at present the best use of remote diagnostic equipment probably lies as status indicators, informing central control room technicians of the status, for example, of fluid levels in tanks:

'Systems as described in this report, even these simple) ones, are not easily diagnosed using remote systems. In the more realistic industrial scene where the machines and plantare much more complex the remote diagnostic task would be much more difficult and could only be justified where the remote diagnostic facility is shared with many users each with identical plant such as is found in the computer industry where a national centre of expertise can diagnose mainframe machine faults in customer plants throughout the UK'.

No Fault Found: Loughborough investigates.

The phenomenon of 'No Fault Found' i.e. where an initial fault at system, subsystem or component level cannot be properly identified, has been a headache for the electronics industry for some time. There has been little serious research into its causes, and so far no-one has really contributed any ideas for improvement. There has, however, been at least one serious attempt to collect data and make at least a few observations, and the paper by J. A. Jones and J. A. Hayes of the International Electronics Reliability Institute at Loughborough University entitled 'Investigation of the No Fault Found phenomenon in electronic equipment' prompted considerable interest from delegates.

The paper introduces the principal types of 'No Fault Found' and then explains how the team at Loughborough have collected and analysed field information from a wide range of electronic equipment over a period of around ten years. Thirteen separate data sources covering five environments have been input to the database with all information coming direct from the field following commissioning and test so that it represents actual field failure as experienced by the manufacturer's customers.

650

The types of 'No Fault Found' are classified in three ways:

*equipment level NFF (operator experiences equipment failure but test engineer later finds no fault)

*board level NFF (as above but test engineer finds a problem, removes a board for test, but subsequent laboratory testing finds no fault)

*component level NFF (as above except the lab test now identifies a faulty component which when tested shows no fault)

Research has shown that when equipment fails in the field, in around 40 per cent of cases it is due to an NFF situation of one of the above kinds. This is regardless of the source, though when 'No Fault Found' is expressed as a percentage of replacements i.e. percentage of the repair budget that is 'wasted' by not finding a true root cause of failure, the figures vary from 18.5 per cent to 53.3 per cent across six sources. A table is then presented to illustrate the frequency of NFF recurrence i.e. when a given board fails again, once a previous NFF almost as frequently as a real failure is identified.

The findings were analysed in three ways, examining respectively the relations between NFF incidence and other component types, NFF incidence and the level of equipment usage, and NFF incidence and equipment complexity. Scattergraphs show plots of numbers of connectors per board versus number of NFFs, number of complex components per board versus number of NFFs, and numbers of boards per system versus number of NFFs per system. A pie chart also illustrates relative numbers of NFF for various bands of equipment usage.

The analysis showed that there appears to be no relationship between the number of complex components on a board and the number of NFFs, no correlation as yet between specific component types and the number of NFFs, that boards which experience the highest levels of NFF have usage levels of between 10 and 49 per cent and account for almost half of the failures, and that there is no apparent relationship between equipment complexity and the number of NFFs.

Given these results it is suggested that further research is needed investigating, e.g. software faults and transient effects since some of the commonly held beliefs about NFFs (that they are a function of numbers of complex components, corrosion of connectors or familiarity with equipment) would appear to be unfounded.

The IERI Database on 'No Fault Found' currently contains details on 35,000 systems, 20 million components and 221 billion component hours.

The presentation prompted a number of questions and comments from delegates which suggested some possible new lines of thought for the investigation of NFFs.

One delegate, for example, suggested that marginal design using close to boundary tolerances could be a factor whilst another suggested that multiple replacements (which are around 40 per cent in the Royal Air Force) are a probable cause. Another delegate suggested that one cause could be test rigs which do not adequately reflect true working environments, particularly with such effects as filament growth in pcbs, which is known to be affected by vibration at certain frequencies.

A further delegate asked about database availability and the speaker (J. A. Hayes) described how it was the intention to establish a 'reliability club' which would most probably operate by subscription. He later acknowledged that getting people to collect, keep and use NFF data was not easy. When the Institute attempted to create a file specifically for component level NFFs the threat of legal action caused complications and this had to be abandoned at least for the present.

[Issue 80 (August 1995)]

ESREL '95 (PART 2)

Validation of Human Reliability Quantification Techniques

The second review of ESREL '95 in Bournemouth begins with the paper by B. Kirwan, R. Kennedy and S. Taylor-Adams entitled 'A validation of three human reliability quantification techniques: THERP, HEART and JHEDI' which was presented by Barry Kirwan of the University of Birmingham on behalf of the co-authors.

This informative paper describes a validation study of the well-known single assessor Techniques for quantifying Human Error Probabilities (HEPs), notably the Technique for Human Error Assessment and Reduction Technique (HEART) and the Justification of Human Error Data Information technique (JHEDI).

Of the three THERP is the oldest, dating back to 1981 whilst HEART, developed by the CGEB in 1986 is the most popular, being quicker and less resource dependent. The third technique, JHEDI, is more recent, being developed by BNFL in 1990, and is thus more of an 'unknown quantity'.

The authors point out that for some time now there has been a shortage of reliable data in the field of human reliability assessment, although there have been a number of attempts to generate human error databases which have subsequently been abandoned for one reason or another.

Each of the three techniques has its own specific characteristics, for example with THERP a key issue is accuracy whilst with HEART it is especially desirable to know whether the calculation process produces realistic human error probability (HEP) predictions relative to known values. With JHEDI the key factor would appear to be its performance relative to other techniques. For all three techniques it is desirable to establish how consistently assessors apply the technique, e.g. do they select the same table for a particular error from the THERP handbook, or select the same generic error probability category when using HEART, or select the same task type and error descriptor for the same task with JHEDI.

Some 30 real HEPs were selected whilst a pilot study using THERP, the most resource intensive of the three techniques, determined that each assessor would work for two days maximum on their validations to prevent negative fatigue effects from disturbing the results. Nine experimental sessions, including three pilot studies, were held in different locations on different days with 'experimenters' acting as invigilators so that discussions between assessors did not introduce any uncontrollable bias to the study.

Results showed that 23 of the 30 assessors, which represent 'a relatively large proportion of the active assessors in this area in the UK today', showed 'a significant correlation between their estimates and the real HEPs, supporting the predictive accuracy of the techniques'. Some variation in the usage of the techniques by the different assessors is reported and the assessor calibration results 'suggest there is room for improvement'. At an individual level the JHEDI technique is noted to 'have more correlations than the other two techniques' as well as being the least optimistic technique, though this result 'is believed to be marginal and not significant'.

As the HEART technique has currently the most widespread use in the UK, with use' of the other two techniques being confined largely to the nuclear industry, it is perhaps not surprising that the speaker was asked to comment on how confident he was in the HEART database as far as engineers were concerned. In his reply Mr. Kirwan pointed to a lack of guidance in its use for which assessors were "crying out" and a substantial amount of variability in the way data is used. However, he said that he thought that present evidence suggests that engineers could produce valid results using the technique once this internal consistency is improved.

Computerisation of Human Error Assessment

In a related paper Kirwan et al describe how one of the main drawbacks of HEART, namely that it is paper based, has been overcome through the development of a DOS-based prototype of the technique which has been subsequently evaluated to produce a Windows-based format.

The paper points to a number of key benefits which computerisation of this technique is envisaged to bring, namely improvements in assessment speed and ease of use, reliability both for calculation and intra-assessors data storage reference, and documentation, guidance and auditability.

In the light of feedback, the HEART system was computerised using Visual Basic (Microsoft Professional Version 3.0).

All of the standard functions of the paper-based technique were retained whilst new functions were added, in particular extensions and modifications to the examples provided to guide assessors and incorporation of Windows gives ease of use.

Results from usability trials suggested that the overall reaction 'was very favourable' and that what problems there were were due more to lack of familiarity with HEART than unfamiliarity with the system in question. The conclusion was therefore that more training in the use of HEART would possibly enhance the usefulness of the system.

The paper concludes with some suggestions for future work notably incorporation of task dependencies, a five point anchoring scale rather than three point one to improve assessor guidance and further reduce intra-assessor variability, a means for assessors to edit choices, during an assessment, and a means for calculating upper and lower confidence bound probabilities for generic categories.

Safety and Dependability in Engineering Design

Of the 69 papers presented some 32 featured overseas contributions and one of these which was of particular interest was that with the above title, by M. Ransand and T. Osteras of the Department of Production and Quality Engineering at the Norwegian Institute of Technology in Trondheim, which was presented by Trond Osteras.

The paper focuses on the issue of standardisation in Europe and in particular the requirements of the Machinery Directive which made it illegal to sell a wide range of machines and associated units without the CE Mark from January of this year. It highlights the 'hierarchy' of technical standards associated with this Directive' and proposes the adoption of concurrent design philosophies. This required full integration of safety and dependability engineering disciplines with the other engineering disciplines of the product development process. To meet this challenge relevant standards and directives are to be considered early in development. Also design deficiencies conflicting with them are to be pinpointed early whilst the product is most flexible to design alterations.

It is noted that some 600 harmonised standards are currently being drafted to accompany this one directive:

'If a manufacturer can find a C standard that is applicable for his product, he may design his product according to this standard, and thus fulfil the safety requirements of the EU Machine Directive. Many of the C standards will, however, give references to higher order standards (A and B) when dealing with special hazards or special safety topics or equipment. The manufacturer therefore has to check the requirements in several A and B standards in addition to the C standard. During the first few years he will most likely not find an applicable C standard and will therefore have to verify compliance with the Directive either by going directly to the essential requirements of Annex 1 of the directive and/or through a risk assessment based on the A standards'.

Three key A standards that are identified are:

* EN-292-1 "Safety of machinery –basic concepts, general principles for design Part 1: Basic terminology, methodology" (CEN,1991).

* EN-292-2 "Safety of machinery –Basic concepts, general principles for design Part 2: Technical principles and specifications" (CEN,1991).

* pr EN-1050 "Safety of machinery -Principles for risk assessment" (CEN draft standard, 1994).

Various standards have so far been produced covering dependability and dependability attributes, including BS5760: Reliability of systems, equipment and components (1985), which reflect the status of dependability engineering at the time when they were developed. However, they do not reflect the 'state-of-the-art' and 'may harm the harmonisation effort'. The authors clearly favour IEC300-1 Dependability Management Part 1: Dependability Assurance of Products (1993) as 'the preferred standard for dependability engineering management' arguing, that it focuses attention on dependability activities throughout all life cycle phases (not just product development). It also specifies general dependability management responsibilities and connects quality management to dependability engineering through a linkage with ISO9001:

'Influenced by the ISO9000 standards the IEC 300-1 standard introduces requirements to quality control of the dependability engineering process in line with other engineering activities related to the product development. This shows that also dependability engineering is affected by the massive focus on total quality management seen in recent years. Dependability engineering procedures will, for example, be subject to review in order to gain ISO9001 certification'.

Whilst this standard is clearly favoured, however, it is not specific regarding the implication of design practices to ensure the development of dependable products. A set of design practices are therefore proposed to prevent design inadequacies from contributing to safety and dependability problems in operation. These include, for example, recommendations for design for interaction with other systems (e.g. support systems), internal interaction (so that parts operate properly together) and all life cycle conditions of the product (such as transportation, storage and disposal as well as operation).

A general procedure for developing safe and dependable products is outlined which addresses the preconcept, concept and design phases of product development and diverts attention away from verifying compliance with safety and dependability targets and towards meeting the requirements of quality philosophies which have zero defects in design as their aim. Quality Function Deployment (QFD) is advocated throughout the design process to analyse more detailed design and component characteristics against the same set of requirements. It is not referenced in any dependability engineering standard, along with Failure Mode and Effect Analysis (FMEA) as a focus for identifying potential failure modes and their causes in a proactive way.

A methods and tools section then describes a simple approach for meeting the safety requirements of the directive based on the hazard analysis requirements of EN-292-1. This highlights the requirement of the directive to document that all essential health and safety requirements specified in its Annex 1 have been fulfilled, and identifies various hazards as listed in pr EN 1050.

Measuring In-service Reliability

The final paper selected for review is 'The measurement of in-service reliability in the British Army by Major (Retired) P .J. A. Britton, Equipment Support 21 b, Headquarters Quartermaster General, Ministry of Defence (Army). This describes the Army's new reliability data collection and analysis system called Battlewinning Equipment Reliability Return (BERR). The system was trialled in 1988, following a House of Commons Defence Committee inquiry which highlighted the inability of the armed forces to quantify the reliability characteristics of in-service equipment. BERR became live last year.

The paper describes how reliability trialling used to be done on a sampling basis:

'A team would descend onto a unit, disrupting normal day to day activities, and either demand that the crew and maintainer record every unusual incident in minute detail, or a team of recorders would follow every equipment around noting every event, all usage and every aspect of environment. On some occasions, the units were directed to exercise their equipment as close as possible to the battlefield mission for which the equipment was designed. Every incident was "scored" by an incident sentencing committee to ascertain the relevance of the failure'.

This resulted in commanding officers finding every excuse possible to avoid being the unit selected for trial, as it tended to be 'totally disruptive to the unit', and frequently interfered with training as well as being costly.

In 1988 a House of Commons Defence committee was charged with the task of investigating the high cost of equipment maintenance in the armed forces. Subsequently the Army and the other forces were obliged 'to raise the profile of reliability, both during procurement and in service'.

[A complementary paper by Colonel Barry J. Hodgkiss of the M.o.D. Directorate of Reliability, (which was formed the following year), describes some of the problems arising in procurement through the application of the flawed cost plus system of contracting and steps taken to redress this- Ed].

In consequence the Army abandoned its previous methods of measuring in-service reliability and instead has sought to measure the reliability of all Army equipment throughout the time it is in service using the BERR system. This uses a SuperCalc computer program and was trialled in a tank unit in Hampshire.

Results of the trial showed that the project 'was on the right lines' and led to a number of improvements, notably in the format of the form used to collect data, and with the method of collecting data:

'One of the biggest problems with collecting data is that unless the data collector has an interest in the output of the data collected, then he will not record the data with any enthusiasm, and often make mistakes or not collect it at all. Reliability is of no immediate interest to the user, but the operational availability of the equipment is of vital importance to the commander of the unit'.

'It was quickly realised that if the date of the failure and the date that the equipment was returned to the user were recorded, then the availability of the equipment could also be calculated. This was an important step'.

Important information supplied by BERR include reliability figures for sub-systems which can provide early warning of problem areas and highlight where money would be best spent on modification; "Days available per Fail" which gives a measure of logistic support:

'Although there is a relationship between availability and reliability, when equipment is little used availability is almost entirely a function of logistic factors such as spares availability. Where there is high usage coupled with low reliability, the achievement of a high availability indicates that logistic resources are large and effective. The converse is also true; high reliability with low availability show poor logistic support'.

657

[Japanese electronic equipment design took this route to achieve exports - high reliability masked their early inability to service equipment from Japan to USA and Europe -Ed].

Introduction of BERR last year was not without its problems; of the 80 sets of the program and accompanying p.c. and laser printer despatched to units in the UK around a third were found to be faulty whilst of the 70 deployed in German units there was only one faulty set. The turnover of operators was also unprecedented; over half of those who had been trained on two day courses left within six months, and there were some problems with usage data:

'Some operators had entered the start states as zero. After all it was the start of the system. At the end of the month they entered the meter readings with some startling results. For instance, it showed that every vehicle in one fleet of armoured vehicles travelled an average of 50,000 miles in the month, an average speed of 70 mph for every hour in the period. This error was not picked up for two months. The error occurred in spite of warning messages built into the program. No program is soldier proof'.

Most of the bugs have, however, been reportedly removed from the program and Commanders 'are beginning to trust the outputs'. A new version of the software is currently being produced and work is in hand to link all the computers by modem and introduce a system of automatic usage recording. A number of I.T. systems which collect similar data are currently being assessed for their suitability for feeding BERR by dynamic data transfer. In the future it is envisaged that data will be sent automatically by radio to a central computer in a manner similar to that achieved by British Rail's Total Operating Procedure System (TOPS).

The paper concludes:

'BERR is a unique system, in many ways a world leader. Although it is now well known within service circles, it is hardly known outside the Ministry of Defence. Once it is fully developed it will have potential in many areas as well as the defence industry'.

[Issue 100 (April 1997)]

NEW INFORMATION PAPER ON ELECTRICAL INTERFERENCE

The Building Research Establishment (BRE) has produced an Information Paper on the effects of electrical interference following a series of investigations into the effects of magnetic fields arising from the use of building services equipment.

Findings have shown that equipment such as busbars, transformers, lift gear and HV AC plant in non-domestic buildings can produce fields which extend for up to 5 metres before returning to normal background levels, with consequent interference effects on computers and other electronic equipment. Typical symptoms include the phenomenon of 'VDU wobble'. The Paper explains how electrical interference may be avoided.

[Issue 102 (June 1997)]

QUALITY IN MANUFACTURING

The 1997 Quality in Manufacturing exhibition (QM97) took place this year in Manchester, on 3rd and 4th June at The Bowler's Centre in Trafford Park. A small but select group of around 50 exhibitors reported a quiet event.

Innovation in software engineering was in evidence from Gimlet Product Outfitters who were demonstrating how their already proven System 9000, which supports ISO9000, QS9000 and ISO14000 has been adopted widely in the automotive field (e.g. by Chrysler and General Motors) as well as other leading worldwide organisations such-as Unisys and Visa.

This has now been successfully introduced onto the Internet. Likewise an alternative approach to applying and exploiting Design of Experiments which exposes a number of weaknesses of Taguchi techniques, was unveiled by Scottish based RSD Associates who, in promoting their Matrex for Excel 5.0. were keen to compare their 'non-linear programming tools' with Taguchi's approach of using a signal to noise ratio, claiming that their method, was 'a more powerful method for robust design' which 'is straightforward to implement'.

Two further products which were featured, both of which have recently received prestigious accolades, were Triangle's Q Achiever Plus, and the Saphir co-ordinate measuring machine (CMM) from CE Johansson which Won last year's Metrology Innovation of the Year Award.

Triangle made history by becoming the first non-US company ever to win a Beacon Award at Orlando, as well as being the first company in the world ever to win the Best Business Application Award in both the US and Europe in the same year. The product, The ISO Achiever Plus, provides a clear and comprehensive framework for a company's quality management documentation, helping to gain and maintain ISO 9000 certification, saving companies time and money by freeing them from the burden of maintaining cumbersome paper-based quality management systems. They say: -

'Business and quality managers can take advantage of the Notes workflow functionality to reduce lead-time in cycling documents for approval and distribution, allowing the system and its users to collaborate proactively. The product has been used in companies of all sizes and from all industry sectors'.

659

The Johansson Saphir 'rewrites all the rules CMMs so that companies can use them as an integral part of production and manufacturing, not enclosed in a separate room'. It is claimed that the product 'will measure components in half the time of conventional CMMs yet with full accuracy, even under varying temperature conditions'. New ideas have been used throughout, from bearing design to structural mountings and materials of construction (aluminium) as well as with the software, such that there is no dependency on conventional error mapping to achieve accuracy when the machine is calibrated. Instead a patented thermal compensation system is applied which continuously monitors and changes the machine's geometry in real time. The manufacturers say:

'Johansson Saphir is one of the fastest co-ordinate measuring machines available today. Measuring at a rate of more than a point a second, it can even operate alongside most production equipment. Johansson Saphir can provide both rapid first-off inspection and statistical process control (SPC) providing direct feedback to the machining process. Measuring in process allows manufacturing to tighter tolerances, entirely free from systematic machining errors and the associated scrap costs'.

The exhibition was supported by twelve seminars, mostly of half an hour's duration, which were free to attendees. These included 'ISO 9000 Document Control through the Internet' by Gimlet, which included a free demonstration CD-ROM for delegates; 'Temperature and CMMs -a problem for shopfloor measurement?' by Johansson; and 'CMMs and CAD interfacing using a DMIS Approach' by LK. The seminar 'Document Control and cutting Costs using Quality Management Software' by IdeaGen, described how RAF Henlow cut the implementation time for ISO 9000 from 18 months to six using their Quality Workbench software. Jungheinrich published an Internet version of their quality manual; and 'Developments in Software Metrology' by Mitutoyo explained how traditional problems associated with 3 axis CMMs (software reporting, lack of interaction, and poor interrogative facilities of software), have now largely been overcome. Speaking on behalf of Mitutoyo David Coughlan said:

"We live in a very exciting time and in the next few years laptops are going to allow for the importation of real life models for manipulation".

Improving the Performance of CMMs.

Eley metrology achieved a notable quality first earlier this year when they became the first company in the UK to gain accreditation to ISO10360, a new standard launched last year which is regarded by many as representing an important step towards the international standardisation of performance verification and traceable certification of CMMs. Now, having achieved it, they are keen that others should follow, arguing that the manufacturers of high quality CMMs no longer have the excuse that tedious measurements and analysis of data is required in order to guarantee compliance with an internationally recognised performance standard.

In outlining the background to the new standard they explained how until about seven years ago there was no officially recognised standard verifying the performance of a CMM, save for a Code of Practice for Machine Verification based on the US standard B59, which suffered the drawback of a lack of calibration procedures and consequently a lack of traceability to a nationally recognised length standard. This was addressed in 1990 by The British Standards Institute (BSI) who produced the then revolutionary BS6808 which used end bars or a step gauge which did provide traceability to national length standards, but required the user to take around 4000 measurements and subsequently analyse the data in a way which was considered to be so time consuming as to be not worthwhile, other than to a select few. The result was poor uptake of a standard which, apart from its somewhat strict and onerous requirements, was good in principle.

In recognition of this the International Standards organisation (ISO) sought to develop a more popular standard which would fulfil the same role, and the result was ISO10360 which uses five bars measured three times each in each of seven measuring lines which gives a total of 115 measurements (as against five bars measured ten times each in eight measuring lines). Furthermore, unlike BS6808 which allowed for up to two results out of 50 to be outside specified tolerance levels, under the new standard no results were to be permitted to be outside tolerance levels, so ensuring that sub-standard or 'borderline' machines would not be passed as compliant.

Following the release of the new standard Eley argue that it now takes substantially less time to test a machine than formerly, and the analysis is much less onerous. Consequently a good machine will pass off quickly and only where a machine is sub-standard will the number of measurements and time taken approach the levels required by BS6808. But whilst the new standard is envisaged to create more of "a level playing field" amongst the manufacturers and suppliers of CMMs there still remains a requirement for a Code of Practice for training and education in relation to the new standard in order to encourage its uptake by businesses. This is, however, being addressed by Eley who have devised a series of seminars to provide what they see as essential basic training in the application of the new standard.

[Quality Matters comments: Standards for the calibration of CMM's traceable to National Standards have been around for decades, and the *Quality Matters* Editor was involved in the development of a Ball plate Area standard at NPL 25 years ago for such a purpose. Eley, however, are correct in that such standards did not achieve international recognition, not because of the need to measure so many points (not a problem) or relationship to the standard Metre, but that there were no standards of AREA (which takes into account Squareness i.e. the alignment of axes of the CMM). It was, at the

time, a weakness of the Americans (and in other parts of the world) to measure Angle with sufficient precision (fractions of a Second of Arc) to accept this solution. It was in their interest to concentrate on length standards internationally where a great debate was raging on the cost to countries of Metrication.

International recognition of standards is not necessarily technical (metrology) but a consensus of acceptability. The problem became more political e.g. who should control the standards used by NATO. Sales of CMMs were banned to Eastern Europe but the British were selling 'Buses to Cuba' at the time! Mainly due to these difficulties, the programme for a technically acceptable 3 dimensional calibration standard traceable to national standards at NPL was abandoned. However, the world progresses e.g. Software is now more adaptable to make compensations for current applications.]

The Case for Dynascopes

The seminar by Vision Engineering was presented by their Sales Manager Howard Potter and was centred around the need for non-contact measurements of parts which are troublesome by virtue of their size, the fact that they may be easily deformed, the ease with which they may be damaged or contaminated, or the necessity to obtain a qualitative rather than a quantitative assessment. For these applications the choice of optical head can be, he said, "a nightmare" as each option invariably requires a trade off between attributes.

Several of the options which are currently available were discussed in turn with their positive and negative attributes highlighted and compared. First, the simple monocular microscope was noted for its good quality image, low cost and ease of use, weighed against its requirements for a still eye and consequent neck strain if used for prolonged periods. Then, the binocular microscope was considered, which again gave a good quality image at low cost and was easy to use, with the added advantage of providing an image which could be seen with both eyes. This system, however, still required the head to be maintained in a steady position and even when wide field eyepieces were used to compensate, the advantages were seen to be minimal.

More elaborate systems included various types of projector and closed circuit television (CCTV) apparatus. The projectors scored on their ability to provide good contrast without eye strain but were clearly limited to certain types of applications and materials. Black plastic components, for example, were not well suited to these systems. By contrast CCTV worked well with little light and had the added benefit of allowing digital processing of signals, but they were seen to have limited camera resolution and be prohibitively expensive unless there was a really high throughput requirement.

The speaker argued that when placed alongside these instruments the case for the Dynascope was good, it having no eyepieces, a high resolution image, correct posture in use, and ease of use even with corrected vision. Technically the instrument is an aerial projection system in which an image is formed in mid air i.e. there is no screen, and wherever the operator stands in the field of view the whole image, not just part, is visible. There is thus no parallax error as is the case with a microscope. Supporting literature describes the product as follows:

'A great all-rounder the Workshop Dynascope incorporates the functions of a bench magnifier, conventional and tool makers' microscope, profile projector and CCTV inspection system in one convenient unit. Options include surface profiling and photographic recording capabilities. In addition, straightforward measurement facilities can be added. All options are retro-fittable and can be upgraded in the field'.

'The ergonomic and highly accurate system provides up to 50x magnification at an extremely low cost. Of particular benefit to the inspector of precision engineered parts is the exceptional shadow-free surface illumination provided by the benchtop Dynascope. This feature offers a level of image brilliance, contrast and clarity normally associated with instruments many times the price'.

The new unit has apparently already found favour with engineering companies involved in tooling, toolsetting and tool alignment, laser cutting, ECM and conventional machining, and the manufacture of precision mechanical and moulded parts. The Workshop Dynascope is also said to be 'proving ideal for post-production and incoming goods inspection'.

A new precision measurement system (The Quadra-Chek 2000 which is a two-axis metrology package, comprising a versatile Smart-box Digital Readout with pre-defined function key to measure geometric features, and its variant the QC 4000 - a PC-based system operating under the flexible Microsoft Windows platform to provide semi-automatic measurement capabilities in two, three or four axes) can be integrated with the Dynascope, as can a motorised work-stage to facilitate automated dimensioning during inspection.

Vision Engineering were also a finalist in the 1997 Prince of Wales Awards for Innovation for which their 'Mantis' was nominated in the category of "the innovation that has already proved itself a commercial success". The 'Mantis' is the world's first eyepieceless microscope and bridges the gap between microscopes and bench magnifiers by providing advanced inspection features to increase productivity in the production environment. The linear magnifications offered are beyond the capabilities of traditional bench magnifiers, although the biggest benefit is said to be the reduction of operator eyestrain and fatigue by what is described as 'one of the most ergonomic inspection systems ever devised'.

CMMs on the Shop Floor

Jonathan Shaw of US based Fabreeka International described how whilst moving a CMM onto the shopfloor can expose such a machine to a variety of vibration hazards, neither the performance nor the throughput has necessarily to be compromised.

It was explained how perhaps one of the most underrated areas of vibration control is typically the low frequency end of the vibration spectrum:

'Many technical seminars, educational institutions, and industrial technology groups consider low frequency to be a vibration isolator having a natural frequency of 2HZ. Current industrial and scientific communities, however, now require solutions below 1 Hz when employing precision machines, metrology and seismic experiments. Due to dynamic excitations, unique solutions are required'.

Fabreeka, whose name has been associated with innovation in the field of vibration isolation and shock control since 1917, contest that low frequency vibration isolation 'may be viewed as a method of improving the current vibration environment to achieve a significant increase in precision manufacturing "throughout" or to offer a surface which approaches the "vibration-free" domain':

'Approaches which are slowly becoming obsolete are the proverbial "in ground pad" which supports a heavy load such as manufacturing equipment which induces shockforces and medium to high frequency vibration. It has been proven that a poorly designed pad tends to amplify rather than attenuate the intended dynamic inputs below 25 to 30Hz. Additionally the natural frequency of the concrete pad itself must be much stiffer than the frequency of isolation range'.

It is argued that vibration measurement by testing is the most accurate method of achieving useful results, but that this is not always practical or possible as, for example, when a new facility is being designed. In these cases a thorough dynamic analysis using computer programs such as NASTRAN or COSMOS is needed, and selection of the correct instrumentation is critical since the wrong choice can result in many unanswered questions leading to invalid assumptions.

The paper describes current state-of-the-art calibration attenuation techniques and introduces a case study involving a CMM:

'Ultrasensitive measurements were required in using the CMM, therefore decoupling of low frequency input was mandatory. Additionally a horizontal "beat frequency" of approximately 4Hz must be attenuated. This frequency

occurs when vibrations are caused by two sources usually designed to operate at the same speed'.

[Issue 103 (July 1997)]

QUALITY AND RELIABILITY

This year ESREL was held in Lisbon at the Fundacao Calouste Gulbenkian from 17th to 20th June, with the theme of 'Advances in Safety and Reliability', and the support of Instituto Superior Tecnico of the Technical University of Lisbon. It was a large event attracting around 465 delegates and featuring around 280 presentations from 35 countries under 67 specialised subject headings. Examples of subjects covered are: Risk Management Decisions Support Systems (10 papers); Software Reliability and Safety Critical Systems (13 papers); Industrial Safety (10 papers) ; Transport (25 papers) ; Offshore Safety (17 papers); Uncertainty Modelling and Analysis(10 papers); Maintenance (16 papers) ; Data Analysis (6 papers) and Reliability in Design (7 papers).

It can be appreciated that the wealth of information presented is considerable, with each of the papers having been fully reviewed by an international committee of specialists from various countries, industries and technical disciplines before being compiled into three hardback volumes totalling around 2,500 pages.

It is beyond the scope of *Quality Matters* to attempt to highlight all subject areas bearing in mind the highly specialised nature of much of the work, but a review of selected papers is given.

Safety related Fault Tolerant Systems in Vehicles.

With the largest single subject category being transport (25 papers covering railway, maritime and aviation safety, automobile reliability and ship equipment reliability), it is perhaps appropriate to consider this group of papers first, beginning with automobile reliability. There were three papers under this heading: 'The Intelligent Actuation and Measurement (IAM) Model and its Maintenance Relevance for Robotic Car Assembly by S.W. Zeig, Sweden; 'Using Semi-Parametric Bayesian Techniques in Reliability Validation Tasks by Messrs. Raoult, Gorget and El Khair (France); and the selected paper 'Towards an Architecture for Safety Related Fault Tolerant Systems in Vehicles' by various authors, the presentation of which was delivered by Thomas Thurner of Daimler-Benz Research, HPC : T721, D-70546 Stuttgart, Germany.

This paper introduces a framework for the application of safety related fault tolerant electronic systems without a requirement for mechanical backup (the so-called 'x by nine systems' where x denotes any particular safety related application such as steering, braking, powertrain, or suspension control).

These systems are envisaged to 'significantly increase overall vehicle safety by liberating the driver from routine tasks and assisting the driver to find solutions in critical situations'.

The proposed framework is a result from the Brite-EnRan H Project 'Safety Related Fault Tolerant Systems in Vehicles' which considered the replacement of mechanical back-up systems with distributed fault-tolerant mechatronic systems (steering wire, brake by wire etc) within theconstraints imposed by modern day mass production techniques:

'With present implementation strategies future safety increasing driver assistance systems or even just a subset thereof, cannot be realised within the typical constraints of mass production: low cost, reliability, system modularity, maintainability in the field whilst meeting the requirements for safety certification. At the moment it cannot be expected that cost-effective manufacturable x -by -nine solutions will rely on expensive mechanical backup.

However with no mechanical backup available, electronic reliability and demonstration of the safety of these new systems becomes crucial, especially under the given hard real time constraints in vehicles'.

'Because of big expenditure and outlay in advance, no single vehicle manufacturer has up to now introduced safety related fault tolerant systems without mechanical backup. In order to share research effort and to make mass production possible, the European vehicle industry has to offer European wide accepted solutions, and to set standards for x -by -nine systems to remain competitive. A common approach towards safety certification and clear legal requirements is necessary to avoid European fragmentation and unco-ordinated and parallel research. As a result a consortium has been established.'

The framework itself is based on a Time-Triggered (TT) Architecture developed at the University of Vienna which is seen to offer the combined advantages of composability, 'babbling idiot avoidance', and ease of certification:

'If a specified property holds for all components at component level the integration of these components should exhibit the same property at system level. Communications systems in the automotive environment always include several autonomous ECUs that interact via a real time communication service to achieve the desired system objectives. The complexity of such systems requires composability which allows the design of smaller subsystems and a following integration without any unintended side effects'.

'Error detection in the temporal domain is of critical importance in distributed real-time systems that use a shared communication channel. A faulty node that monopolises the common channel by sending high priority messages at erroneous points in time disrupts the communication between all properly operating modes and can thus cause a complete system failure.

A node that sends messages at the wrong point in time is called 'a babbling idiot'. A babbling-idiot-timing failure is the most serious failure of a node in a system with a shared communication channel, such as a bus system. Error detection in the temporal domain at the external node interface can only be performed if a priori knowledge is available about the intended time intervals, when a node is allowed to send a message. In a TT architecture this information is static and stored in the communication system independently of the application software in the host. It can be used to construct effective mechanisms for the detection from timing failures of the host'.

'TT systems guarantee a deterministic a priori behaviour because of the statically designed system parts. This property together with the composability aspect, allows for an easier safety certification'.

Further advantages are described in relation to the node architecture, in terms of efficiency, simplicity, and testability:

'By using the fail silent property as the underlying concept for fault tolerance, a clean architecture with a minimum of cross couplings and special circuitry is obtained. Two levels of dependability (a fail silent node or a fault tolerant node) are obtained with the same fundamental terminology and principals. Furthermore, the concept of a node that is either correct or silent is easy to communicate within the organisation and to sub-suppliers and partners'.

'The fail silence property is a testable property since it is well defined. The testing can be concentrated on verifying (by for example fault injection) the fault containment performance, i.e. test that a node doesn't violate the fail silent property. This type of property is well suited for experimental validation'.

Moving on to the system software architecture two departures from the traditional Object Orientated (O-O) implementation style can be noted:

'The traditional style is typically based on passive objects which are activated by passing control flow upon method activation. For Distributed Fault tolerant Real-time (DFR) applications the objects should be autonomously active. Such an active object is typically triggered by the progression of time where the object updates its internal state. For control applications concurrent activity should be possible between different active objects and within one active object (this is also a departure from traditional O-O implementation). The communication between these active objects should be carried out by means of state messages exclusively. In contrast usage of variables for object attributes in traditional O-O implementation does not support concurrency'.

The X-By-Nine consortium recommends the use of an ANSI C subset which requires both the exclusion of some of the ANSI parts and the addition of new functionality.

In conclusion the authors say the following:

'A common European x-by-nine development, which has the potential to become a European or even a world-wide standard, accompanied by a broad and fast dissemination of the results, translates into a significant strategic advantage for the European automotive, supplier and semi-conductor industry .The success of this project will put the European industry in a pole position in an important emerging high technology market. A direct benefit will be given to the vehicle customer'.

Following the presentation the speaker was asked how long he expected it to take for this new technology to be incorporated into actual vehicles and in response he said that he expected "spin-offs possibly in five years".

Assessing Railway System Service Quality.

There were six papers on the subject of railway safety entitled 'Safety Quantified Communications and Management of Railway Spaces Open to the Public', by Lilian Hall French (France); 'Application of a Quantified Risk Control Process by Messrs. Tong, Kwong and Ho (Hong Kong); 'Monitoring of Railway Vehicles Availability' by A. Hudoklin and A. Stadler (Slovenia); 'Reliability Centred Maintenance of Signalling on French Railways' by J. P. Dermengham; 'Quantitative Risk Analysis of Industrial and Transportation Activities in the Ravenna Area: A Second Report' by Messrs. Spadoni, Leonelli, and Egidi (Italy); and 'A System Reliability Model for analysing Performance of a New Railway' by various authors. The latter which was presented by Ian Muir of W .S.Atkins Safety and Reliability, Woodcoye Grove, Ashley Road, Epsom, Surrey, is reviewed below.

The subject of the paper is the Lantau and Airport Railway (LAR) in Hong Kong which provides a unique luxury express service in which passengers can proceed through a station in which their airport baggage can be processed relieving congestion at the airport, This experimental approach to customer service has been subject to assessment using a Railway System Reliability Model (RSRM) the development of which is described in the paper:

'At the overall Railway System level, the poor reliability of one system could be balanced by the superior reliability of another system. It can also be argued that a high reliability system has increased acquisition costs

although this could be offset by a reduced in-service maintenance cost during the railway system lifetime.

Railway systems and sub-systems are traditionally procured separately using different contracts with different suppliers. This prohibits the consideration of issues like System Reliability and System Performance during the contract phase to verify and confirm the likely Railway System performance, identify the under supply or over supply of equipment within contracts, and predict operational availability which determines the passenger carrying capacity and revenue generation, an overall Railway System Reliability Model is required'.

This model was developed in three phases:

* Failure mode and effect analysis (FMEA) with expanded consequence analysis

* Development of system wide reliability block diagrams (RBDs)

* Overall railway system performance prediction

The first phase of the project was carried out extensively using the spreadsheet facilities provided by Microsoft Excel. The other two phases were to be completed using an in-house developed software tool based on the same software package, but in practice it was found that the resources required to develop such a tool far exceeded the timescale and budget of the project and so an alternative was required.

Various requirements for a commercially available software package were laid down and eventually the AvSim package produced by Item Software Limited was selected:

'The additional processing of the simulation results generated by AvSim in order to estimate passenger delay minutes per year, overall system downtime per year, and other useful information, was done in Microsoft Excel using a number of purpose written macros'.

In the first phase the FMEA approach described in BS5760 was modified to accommodate the need to identify the consequences of a failure at railway service level and an example of the modified Leader of the FMEA table is shown in the text:

'Information gathered during the FMEA created the basis not only for the development of the RBDs within each sub-system investigated but also for the identification of the key service failure scenarios for which operational responses would be required'.

669

Formulae are outlined to illustrate how it is possible to calculate the number of trains and passengers affected by service failure and to estimate the mean time between trains for a reduced service. Excel Visual Basic macros were then used to calculate the number of trains affected by system failures in various identified situations. Finally a delay calculation example is provided using a real incident in order to validate the method described.

It is envisaged that the new model will:

*predict the likely future operational performance of the LAR

*determine those components/contracts which have the most influence on operational performance through the interrogation of the AvSim results.

*assess the variability of LAR performance over the lifetime of the railway through the specification of suitable wear-in-wear-out parameters in the input data files –subsequent application to the model will yield predictions of operational performance in the relevant life-cycle.

*identify the optimum maintenance requirements for the railway by adjustment of preventive and corrective maintenance policies thus resulting in identification of the most cost effective maintenance regime.

*provide a basis for the modelling of other railway systems.

At the conclusion of his presentation the speaker explained how it was hoped to develop a fully integrated model which would enable operators to assess the effects of changes in particular policy changes such as where to locate maintenance staff, as well as covering related systems such as escalators, transport interchanges and ticketing interfaces.

The presentation attracted a number of questions including whether the model could handle different types of performance trains such as a continuation of freight and passenger trains. In response he explained how the performance characteristics can be modified by the user, though he accepted that by train a specific reliability model may be needed.

Reliability Analysis of a Multi Exchange Telecommunication Network

In addition to the papers highlighted above there were also three case studies of systems reliability. The paper by various authors from Dep. Eng. Electrotechnica, FCTUS, University of Coimbra (Portugal) and Portugal Telecom, 1000 Lisbon (Portugal), presents a brief review of a methodology developed by the authors for assessing the reliability of a large circuit-switched multi exchange digital network based on an integrated evaluation of reliability and performance measures. This is followed with a description of a computer-based model for the reliability performance analysis of the Lisbon digital urban network which has been developed using the original methodology outlined, which has subsequently been implemented through a contract of collaboration with the Portuguese public telecom operator.

The basic methodology consists of the following:

- Integration of reliability analysis with functional network performance evaluation, translated into a unified approach of parametrisation of the reliability grade of service, based on the calculation (for each considered state of the physical network) of increments of lost traffic between each functional network pair of nodes.

- Definition of a failure prone physical network and of a functional network.

- Interactive selection, through a new algorithm, of the most probable states of the physical network depending on the estimated probabilities of failure of the physical network components.

- A biparametric traffic model that describes all of the node to node traffic flows in all of the trunks of the functional network, that is, including a complete description of the traffic flows in every trunk (marginal means, variances and blocking probabilities).

- Definition and calculation of a multidimensional set of performance parameters of various types, weighted by the corresponding state probabilities.

The analysis method is described followed by a specification of the network to be analysed:

'The Lisbon telecom network, in 1994-95, could be divided into three main areas: Urban, North Regional and South Regional. A model able of performing the reliability analysis for the whole Lisbon network would be too heavy and slow in computational terms as a result of the very high number of failure prone components and the computational cost associated with the performance evaluation of each failure scenario.

So it was decided that the study would focus on the Lisbon Urban Digital Area and that fictitious switching nodes should be used to represent the incoming and outgoing traffic from the adjacent areas.

A list of ten of the most significant parameters obtained by applying the computer based model is then given:

*Node to done blocking probabilities in the fully operational state.

*Average node to node blocking probabilities for every flow.

*Node to node lost traffic for every flow.

*Average call congestion in the network for every considered state.

* Cost of the average node to node lost traffic for every flow.

* Average network performance in monetary units.

* Upper and lower bounds for network average performance in monetary units.

* Number of times a flow disconnection occurs, and respective probability, in a given sample space.

* Identification of the failed components in states for which the node to node blocking probabilities exceed some pre-defined values.

* Identification of the failed components in states for which the call congestion exceeds a certain value, and corresponding probabilities.

A discussion of the results highlights the large number of node to node disconnections arising from the high value failure probability of the elements in the 'node' type of the physical network, as well as a means of identifying those trunks which most affect network performance.

In their conclusion the authors say:

This study highlights the application potentialities of the developed model which are related to its capability in calculating several sets of performance parameters at the network, traffic flow and trunk level, throughout the most significant failure scenarios. As an example of this capability we could mention the calculation of the probability of the grade of service for a pair of exchanges exceeding certain values or the assessment of the prospective influence of the failure of certain network components in the degradation of the blocking probabilities of a given traffic flow'.

[Issue 104 (August 1994)]

QUALITY & RELIABILITY (ESREL '97 PART2)

Technical Certification of Dangerous Equipment

The ten papers under the heading of 'Industrial Safety' at this year's ESREL conference included two from The Netherlands which were potentially of considerable interest to quality as well as safety practitioners. The first of these, by various authors from The Safety Science Group, Delft University of Technology, AEA Technology, Netherlands BV (25 14 AB Dan Haag), and The Dutch Institute for Working Conditions (1070 AR Amsterdam) was entitled 'Technical Certification of Dangerous Equipment: A Study of the Effectiveness of three Legally Compulsory Regions in The Netherlands'. The second, by J. H. Heeringsle Project Office for Research on Materials Production Technology at Apeldoorn, and J. Boogard, Chairman of The Dutch Quality Surveillance and Non-Destructive Testing Society at Geleen, was entitled 'Planning of Components Inspection: Developments in The Netherlands'.

The first paper presents the findings of a study commissioned to evaluate the effectiveness of the present certification and inspection regimes associated particularly with lifts, cranes and pressure vessels in the light of plans by the Dutch Ministry of Social Affairs to decentralise the certification process:

Changes in the European regulations for these three types of equipment, and a reconsideration of the role of the government in regulating safety led the Dutch Ministry of Social Affairs and Employment to reconsider the regulations in force in The Netherlands governing these inspection certification regimes. A research study was commissioned to evaluate the effectiveness of the existing regimes. In particular the Ministry was interested in the need for any changes in the criteria for certification and the organisation of the regimes themselves in the light of possible opening up of certification to competing certifying bodies in a free(r) market'.

In the study the actionees from each certification regime (the certifying body with a monopoly of the legal inspection, other certifying bodies doing similar work, manufacturers, users of equipment, and regulatory) were interviewed. In addition the records of the certification bodies were studied to extract data about the effectiveness of the regimes so far as this was possible:

'It is particularly worthy of note that none of the certifying bodies had their data available in a form which could be easily analysed; most was not computerised, and there was no consistent classification of the types of defects found during inspections. This necessarily limits the quantitative results which can be presented'.

The questions asked for each of the three types of equipment (a formative Check List) were as follows:

(i) Are all of the appropriate types of equipment covered by the legal requirements, based on how dangerous they are?

(ii) Is all of the required equipment registered for inspection and certification?

(iii) Are the inspection criteria appropriate: clear and covering the factors which lead to accidents?

(iv) Is the frequency of inspection appropriate and is it being kept to?

(v) Are the available expertise and methods of inspection satisfactory?

(vi) Are a significant number of (serious) defects found and corrected?

(vii) Are there accidents with the types of equipment which can be traced to the functioning of the regime?

(viii) What would the expected effects be of removing the inspection monopoly and introducing competition?

The results are summarised in tabular form and discussed. In particular it is noted that the overview of what equipment falls under the regulations will disappear with the loss of the
monopoly:

'Only at the time of compulsory user certification will registration take place with one or other of the approved certifying bodies and no system of reminders for certification will therefore be possible. The government appears to have no intention of requiring this despite the problems this may cause for tracking down equipment which may more easily slip through the net of inspection as a result. This was seen by interested parties as a negative effect of the removal of the requirement for inspection before equipment can be taken into use, coupled with the introduction of the CE Mark. A further concern in that respect was the adequacy of the European supervision of the uniform quality of independent inspection of new equipment carried out by notified bodies in all European Union countries'.

Another general concern was that removal of the certification monopoly could result in a loss of expertise and "loss of memory" for less frequent and older problems as well as concern about who should be permitted to certify equipment:

'The manufacturers of lifting equipment felt that the technical expertise of engineers not employed by them could never keep up to date with new developments as well as they could. On the other hand others doubted the independence of manufacturers. In the area of pressure vessel inspection a similar concern about the role of user inspectorates was the subject of strong debate. The independence of their inspections is currently guaranteed by supervision of their programmes and reports by the certifying body'.

The paper points to 'a remarkable degree of satisfaction with the current regimes for technical certification', highlighting 'the relatively high percentage of defects found by the regime and the low numbers if not absence of accidents from technical failures in the three types of equipment', and the frequent mention of 'the preventive working' of the compulsory regimes which have led to 'more voluntary inspection and corrective actions so that equipment was not laid still at the legal inspection'. It is noted, however, that the satisfaction 'seems to be based almost entirely on qualitative and subjective assessments':

'None of the regimes could produce easily comprehensive data to prove the worth of the inspections; none could demonstrate clearly what types of defects were discovered, nor whether these had any implications for the design or use of the equipment. In other words the regulatory system currently has no systematic feedback and learning loop based on data analysis by which its effectiveness can be assessed, nor whereby proposed changes in it can be objectively evaluated'.

The authors conclude that:

'A national system of analysis of inspection data would be worth establishing, if it were computerised and gave rather more depth of causal information. The incipient removal of the monopoly of periodic inspections will make this more difficult to set up, since more certifying bodies will have to be persuaded to collaborate'.

Reliability Data Banks

Four papers were presented under the general heading of 'Reliability data banks' outlining the role and function of the European Safety and Reliability and Data Association (ESReDA), a non profit making organisation dealing with data collection in the fields of safety, reliability and risk and its associated databases (EnReDatA). To conclude the review of ESREL '97 an overview of each of these is presented.

The first paper, entitled 'The European Industry Reliability Data Bank' by H. Procaccia, P. Anforl and S.Arsenis, describes how EnReDatA (The European Association of Data Bank Owners) was formed in 1973 and gained the support of the Joint Research Centre of the Commission of the European Communities in 1978.

It describes EnReDatA's goal, to provide its members with a reference base of generic reliability data gathered from various sources, and the progress made to date (the Component Event Data Bank associating the contributions of European Electricity Utilities, the Mechanical Valve Reliability Data Handbook mixing for the first time data from electricity and oil companies, and the EIReDA volume 1 data base containing the reliability data of the French probabilistic Safety Assessment (EPS1300): data recorded by Electricite de France from 1977 to 1987 in 34 nuclear power plants).

675

It then describes how EnReDatA merged with the European Safety and Reliability Research and Development Association (ESRRDA) in 1992 to form EnReDatA, which currently holds data on around 120 families of components, including mechanical, electrical and instrumentation components.

The second paper, entitled 'The ESReDA Guidebook on the Effective Use of Safety and Reliability Data with particular reference to '"Intelligent" Selections from Raw Reliability Data' by S. Arsenis summarises the topics covered by the above Guidebook which was published in 1995 and then focuses on one particular topic: a method for sampling from databases storing raw reliability data for estimation of and testing for reliability parameters:

'Subject matter experts define the relevant variables. The definition or samples where estimation or testing is to be done is then made by "intelligent" selections on the relevant variables: for each variable, the essential categories where most data lie are selected against those of a few heterogeneous components and consequently infrequent combinations of the essential categories are dispensed with.

The procedure results in a relatively small number of taxa where most data lie. The dependence of component variables makes the procedure economical with regard to the exclusion of data and relevant to the identification of errors in the collection or storage of the data. The procedure has been applied to form a taxonomy for electric motors'.

The third paper, entitled 'Data Bank Quality' by Lars Petersson, Chairman of the ESReDA Working Group on Data Bank Quality' highlights the role of the ESReDA Working Groups (formed to address ideas or problems common to some members and typically existing for two to three years) and then describes the progress made by one of them [the Working Group on (Reliability) Data Quality]:

'We just had a Data Handbook Working Group finishing its work and increased Data Quality may be seen as a natural continuation of that work. Consequently a Data Quality Working Group was established in April 1996'.

The work of the Group is divided into three phases:

(i) Study existing definitions and standards, make a RAMS bibliography, plan for phase 2.

(ii) Recommendations on applicability, definitions, collection, storing, use, methods, software etc.

(iii) Compilation of the material and results into a book to be presented at a seminar.

The work of the Group includes the following:

'There is a Draft standard ISO/CD 14224 "Petroleum and Natural Gas Industries –Collection Reliability and Maintenance Data for Equipment". This is based on experience from the OREDA data collection project. To get a measure of the usefulness of this draft we made a test within the Working Group. We selected information from some 20 reports on 3 groups of Components (Valves, Pumps and Gas Turbines). These failure descriptions were sent to a number of people in the WG and some others.

All were asked to classify for Failure Modes and Failure Descriptors according to the Draft standard. All were given the same material, asked to do the same thing'.

In this connection the paper concludes that 'the classes used in the draft standard are not sufficiently well defined or organised'.

The fourth paper, entitled 'Development and use of a Directory of Accident Databases involving Chemicals' by P. Pineau, outlines the content and possible application areas for a recently published directory of accident databases involving chemicals, and the reasoning behind its production:

'Many databases on accidents implying chemicals are in existence and data is shared between database developers and end users. The reliability of data is strongly related to the quality of data collected from accident investigations and their subsequent analysis. Many frameworks for collecting, recording, and enduring quality are in existence but there is a need for harmonisation. Since 1993 a working group of ESReDA "Accident Analysis" is dealing with data collection, quality, reliability and networking of accident data'.

'A preliminary analysis of existing databases led to the conclusion that they are generally all "abstract" databases and result from an aggregation process of existing information. During this stage, some form of "filtering" and coding of this information originating from various analysis occurs. Even in a direct collection of data by database operators, the interpretation of the initiating events, the sequence of subsequent events and the effects and causes may be difficult owing to the large variety of involved materials, plants, processes and causative factors. A methodology for direct investigation of accident was developed elsewhere and implies four main steps: gathering evidence with a search for information, exploring possible scenarios, investigating the scenarios, and performing the validation of assumptions'.

The basis of the directory is a description in four sections: identification, technical aspects, access conditions and use, and database details.

Further Information.

The annual ESREL Conferences stem from a European initiative merging several National conferences into a Pan-European Safety and Reliability Conference under the auspices of ESRA, the European Safety and Reliability Association which was established in Brussels in 1992. The proceedings of this year's event are in three hard-back volumes as edited by C. Guedes Soares of the Technical University of Lisbon. They are published by Elsevier Science (ISBN 0-08-042835-5)

[Issue 105 (September 1997)]

DEPENDABILITY OF INSTRUMENTATION AND CONTROL SYSTEMS.

Six papers were presented at ESREL '97 on the subject of reliability of power engineering systems, titled as follows : 'Power System Reliability Assessments'. A Review by R. U. Allen (Manchester Centre for Electrical Energy, UMIST UK); 'Reliability Analysis of Distribution Systems considering Sub-unavailabilities' by Messrs. Ubieda and Abbad (of Spain); 'Liability for Electrical Accidents: Safety and Risk' by R. H. Stillman, Australia; 'The New V DEW Statistics of Incidents -A Source for Component Reliability Indices of Electric Power Systems' by various German authors; 'Different ways to process failure Statistics for use in Reliability Analysis of Electric Power Systems' by Messrs. Lovas and Opskar (Norway); and 'Deterministic and Probabilistic Approaches to the Dependability of Instrumentation and Control Systems: Two Complementary Assessments in Compliance with IEC 1069' by G.Allain-Morin and R. Hausberger of Electricity de France (Clamont and Moret/Laing).

The latter paper introduces the IEC standard 1069 entitled 'Industrial process measurement and control -Evaluation of System properties for the purpose of system assessment' and in particular addresses part 5 of the standard on 'Assessment of system dependability'. It is noted that this standard will eventually comprise of eight parts, the first two dealing with general considerations and the methodology to be used, the remainder respectively with the evaluation of functionality, performance, dependability, operability, safety, and "non-task related" system properties of an industrial process measurement control system.

The paper outlines how to construct an evaluation programme based on Parts 1 and 2 of the standard before focusing on Part 5 and its two complementary' approaches (a deterministic approach for evaluating system credibility and a probabilistic approach for evaluating system availability and reliability) :

'To design the evaluation programme, the objectives of the evaluation and the demands and specifications of the system must have been defined beforehand. The main stages in an evaluation scenario are given in figure 2 in Part 2 of the standard. To sum up, this scenario demonstrates that it is necessary to have beforehand identified the evaluation objectives, which may be connected but very different, and to have provided an evaluation benchmark (specification and technical characteristics) which meets these objectives.

'The evaluation benchmark includes the specifications for the system and its technical characteristics which present system missions, the conditions of influence associated with its operating environment (natural equipment and human environment) and demands concerning each property expected. The major difficulty is structuring the information in this benchmark so as to best prepare the evaluation actions which can reply to different objectives. Often there will be only a specification which supposedly caters for multiple expectations. This structuring must allow for easier triggering of assessment or evaluation actions by allocating different properties to the internal functions (or tasks) of the system'.

In discussing the evaluation of dependability the authors define the key terms of Part 5 (dependability, reliability, maintainability, availability, integrity, security, and credibility) and illustrate its dependability hierarchy using a block diagram reproduced from the standard. It is seen that Part 5 requires two evaluations, namely availability (probabalistic component) and credibility (deterministic component).

The valuation of the probabilistic component consists of three degrees of evaluation, i.e. evaluation of the Dependability policy of Electricite de France (EDF) manufacturing partners, critical analysis of the indicative probabilistic studies carried out by EDF partners, and the performance of specific indicative probabilistic studies on critical systems and parts thereof by EDF:

'An evaluation of the ability of system Suppliers to build systems and evaluate their probabilistic dependability can be carried out. It could, for example, be based on an examination of a supplier's industrial references in the energy sector, on study of the quality of his collection of dependability data and of his data analysis system, on study of his organisation, his Dependability policy, and his maturity in Dependability evaluation actions, as well as on analysis of his ability to supply top quality software (for instance by applying existing evaluation models and normative benchmarks such as IEC 880)'.

'EDF has already carried out critical analysis of dependability studies performed by manufacturers, as part of the above-mentioned experimental global evaluation programme. The main criteria for analysis were as follows: legibility, structuring, and coherence of the study approach, traceability and coherence of assumptions, pertaining to analysis, modelling, and calculation'.

'The evaluation of the systems studied is based on an analysis and modelling process generally always comprising the same steps which are more or less formalised and predominant, depending on the studies. This process (Illustrated) aims at obtaining quantified probabilistic results. It includes a preparatory phase of qualitative analysis which is important and necessary for tackling the failure modelling phase and qualitative processing'.

The evaluation of the deterministic component involves two steps, first an analysis of the data available from the manufacturer which includes a comparative examination of the main requirements of the specifications and the information released by the manufacturer (constructive data test or study results, operating feedback etc):

'During this step attention is also paid to more generic aspects such as the quality of electronic components (examination of the parts lists of I and C electronic components and of sources of supply in order to obtain the best possible guarantees with respect to the reliability of the I and C system and the durability of supply). The evaluation is thus not restricted to just evaluation of the product but also included evaluation of the manufacturer, which is seen to be indispensable in light of the constantly increasing complexity of such systems'.

This is followed by additional tests and analyses:

'In terms of evaluation of integrity there is no standardised IEC tool because this property has not always been precisely identified by manufacturers or users, and because the probabilistic approaches associated with the introduction of information technology into I and C has often got the better of deterministic approaches. To check the integrity of an I and C system, IEC standard 1069-5 using Fault Injection Techniques, something EDF has extensive experience in. The thinking underlying fault injection tests is as follows: an I and C system with "integrity" must exhibit no failure in the correct accomplishment of its mission despite the failure of a component within it. To check these aspects, faults are created (for instance a PCB is disconnected) and the resulting behaviour of the I and C system is observed (messages given and status of output).

[Issue 108 (December 1997)]

MAKING MEASUREMENT PAY

Sira Test and Certification Limited have released a new calibration video on behalf of the DTI, entitled 'Making Measurement Pay'. It explains why calibration should not be viewed as a financial burden but rather as a positive contribution to the overall quality of the final product or process.

It features interviews from a wide range of industrialists and representatives of trade associations and provides answers to questions such as: 'How do I ensure my measurements are traceable to fundamental standards?', 'Should I choose a NAMAS accredited laboratory or a company, with ISO 9000 offering a calibration service?', 'How do I specify my calibration certificate?' and 'Does going to a laboratory holding an accredited ISO 9000 certificate for its quality management system provide assured calibrations?':

'Be careful you are not deceived by a certificate that includes a statement like "traceable to NAMAS". This is usually a sign that it's not an official NAMAS accredited certificate. The problem with a statement like "traceable to NAMAS" is that a genuine NAMAS certificate guarantees a great deal more than just the traceability of the measurements. It also guarantees that the personnel, the equipment, the procedures and the environment in the laboratory conform to NAMAS quality standards'.

[Issue 111 (March 1998)]

NEW TOOL TO REDUCE HUMAN ERROR

Rolls Royce and Associates Limited have pioneered a new approach to the reduction of human error which has culminated in the development of a tool known as the Assured Standard Error Reduction Technique (ASSERT). This defines human error as 'an out-of-tolerance action in a work process where the limits of tolerable performance are defined by customer requirements' and introduces a set of Performance Influencing Factors (PIFs) which have been found to influence the probability of a given error occurring.

Error identification is achieved using task analysis in conjunction with an error classification scheme as well as through the collection and analysis of data concerning past errors. Task analysis provides a systematic representation of operator decisions and actions in the form of a diagram or table. A team-based implementation process which is consistent with employee involvement is then applied enabling the tool to be used both to reduce errors in existing work processes as well as errors in proposed work processes -where ASSERT functions as a process design tool. David Clarke of Rolls Royce Associates Ltd. of Derby comments:

'In today's business environment continuous improvement is required for success. Human error leads to defects in products and services and a failure to meet customer requirements. ASSERT contributes to quality improvement by reducing human error in work processes. Error reduction is achieved through the use of a structured method carried out in a team setting'.

[Issue 119 (November 1998)]

TEMPERATURE COMPENSATED CMMs FROM MITUTOYO.

A new unique range of temperature compensated co-ordinate measuring machines (CMMs) has been launched by leading measurement technology specialists Mitutoyo. The new range, known as Euro-C Apex, features both machine and workpiece temperature sensors and uses software to ensure that the stated accuracy of the CMM is true across a range of temperatures rather than only at one specific temperature. The manufacturers state the following:

'The CMM's high standard of accuracy is no longer affected by ambient temperature fluctuation or internal sources of heat, which would have meant that the CMM would previously have to have been operated under controlled temperatures. Geopak Win CMM measurement software allows the operator to input the coeffect of expansion of the material being measured and uses the temperature difference, actual temperature and thermal properties of the materials involved to calculate and maintain measurement accuracy between 16 to 26 degrees Centigrade'.

[*Quality Matters comments*: This is a major contribution to high precision CMM measurements, which has been overdue for many years. Measurements are relatively straightforward at a constant fixed temperature, but temperature differentials with different co-efficient of expansion, between workpiece and machine scales give significant measurement errors. Mitutoyo are to be congratulated in tackling this problem].

[Issue 121 (January 1999)]

MEASUREMENT MATTERS

The oft quoted words of the eminent physicist Lord Kelvin (1824 to 1907) are:

"When you can measure what you are speaking about and express it in numbers you know something about it; but when you cannot measure it, when you cannot express it in numbers, your knowledge is of a meagre and unsatisfactory kind".

This highlighted the fact that even in Victorian times good measurement practice was fundamental to effective management. Yet measurement skill, it would seem, remains all too often a neglected and misapplied discipline of quality with many organisations apparently unaware of the potential benefits that are obtainable from having accurate and traceable measurement.

Recent studies, commissioned by The Department of Trade and Industry National Measurement System Policy Unit have revealed that:

*there is a very low level of awareness of the National Measurement System and its potential to support wealth creation in the UK.

*although measurement is considered vital, with an average of five different measurement activities undertaken during production in each UK company, only 38% of even the largest companies budget for the measurement function.

*lack of training and capital investment, stemming partly from low management commitment to measurement, are seen as major barriers to improved measurement performance.

*industry is not well informed of the access routes to the national centres of measurement expertise.

*knowledge transfer, technology leadership and dissemination of best practice are important means to realise the UK's investment in the National Measurement System.

These studies, coupled with a clear understanding of the importance of improved measurement practice in ensuring the future competitiveness of the UK manufacturing sector, have led the DTI to establish a National Measurement Partnership Programme which was officially launched on 5th November 1998 by the Rt.Hon. Peter Mandelson M.P., then Secretary of State for Trade and Industry. This three year Programme has the following objectives:

(i) To increase the uptake of traceable measurement in the UK.

(ii) To increase the UK skill base in measurement through formal training.

(iii) To increase industrial access to measurement expertise.

The principal strength of the Programme, which brings together for the first time all organisations with an interest or responsibility for measurement to champion better measurement practice, lies in the wealth of existing networks that are represented by its members. These networks will be used to undertake a regional awareness campaign under the banner of "Competing Precisely" which will feature case study presentations by local businesses that are able to speak from experience about the benefits of good measurement practice along with workshops on measurement issues that are relevant to specific UK regions.

Participants in the Programme so far include The National Physical Laboratory, The Laboratory of the Government Chemist, The National Engineering Laboratory, The National Weights and Measures Laboratory, The United Kingdom Accreditation Service, GAMBICA, The Institute of Measurement and Control, The British Measurement and Testing Association, The Gauge and Toolmakers' Association, The Worshipful company of Scientific Instrument Makers and the DTI. In addition some 130 calibration laboratories which represent the shop floor for traceable calibration in the UK have expressed an intention to participate in the Programme.

These laboratories perform many hundreds of thousands of calibrations per year for UK industry ' acting as local guarantors of measurement quality, and it is envisaged that a network of UKAS accredited laboratories will be established to promote the benefits of traceable measurement through accredited calibration laboratories which themselves will be promoted as regional centres of measurement excellence. As part of this a world wide website will be established detailing the services provided by every accredited calibration laboratory, and a National Conference of UKAS accredited laboratories organised to provide a forum for the debate of UK measurement issues both at technical and policy level.

The national training need for skilled measurement technicians will be addressed by Brunei University who will work with colleges and companies to establish regional training centres which will offer a National Vocational Qualification in measurement. The first of these regional centres is likely to involve a partnership between Coventry Technical College and Mitutoyo. It is anticipated that around 100 students will register for the qualification over the next two years. In the meantime Loughborough University, Loughborough College and Rolls Royce have joined together to compile a level 3 NVQ, accredited by the Engineering and Marine Training Authority (EMTA), which will develop and recognise the skills of technicians involved with measurement and calibration.

Teaching syllabuses for this in the major measurement fields are currently being developed by the Edexcel Foundation who are also developing a nationally recognised Professional Development Qualification (PDQ) in measurement and calibration.

The "Competing Precisely" campaign will be promoted by NPL who will provide funding for selected local measurement focused events and act as the centre for a National Measurement Helpline which will provide a single point of access both to the many hundreds of scientists at the national laboratories and to other experts in universities, accredited laboratories and trade associations.

At the launch Peter Mandelson commented:

"If there is one branch of science and technology that is totally dependent upon good teamwork it is measurement. Good measurement means getting to grips with product quality, but measurement can only deliver results by a process of comparison, ultimately to standards established at the national level, and comparison is only possible through collaboration and partnership between a very wide range of players in the measurement field. I am pleased to see that today marks the launch of the National Measurement Partnership, a programme which will strengthen still further the cohesion of all organisations in the UK's measurement infrastructure".

Implementing good Measurement Practice.

At the heart of the "Competing Precisely" campaign is an assessment schedule for companies whereby managers evaluate their company's measurement performance against various market requirements and then compile an action plan for improved performance. Six guiding principles, originally established under the DTI's Valid Analytical Measurement (VAM) Programme, are used to help to define the policies and practices that could be adopted in order to ensure that measurement in one's company reflects the demands of the market. The principles are as follows:

(i) Choose the right measurements (measurements should only be made to satisfy agreed and well specified requirements).

(ii) Select the right tools (measurements should be made using equipment and methods which have been demonstrated as being fit for purpose).

(iii) Employ the right people (measurement staff should be appropriately qualified, competent and well informed).

(iv) Conduct regular review (there should be both internal and independent assessment of the technical performance of all measurement facilities and procedures).

(v) Ensure demonstrable consistency (measurements made in one location should be consistent with those made elsewhere).

(vi) Adopt the right procedures (written measurement procedures should be a central feature of the quality management system).

The assessment consists of a series of statements grouped according to the six principles. Typical examples of these are as follows:

*we define measurement requirements in terms of the customer's needs and seek to agree our measurement approach with the customer -always, sometimes or never?

*our choice of measurement method drives our selection of measurement equipment rather than vice-versa -always, sometimes or never?

*we continually refresh the technical training of measurement staff -always, sometimes or never?

*we record and regularly review our performance in meeting measurement requirements, and take any necessary remedial action -always, sometimes or never?

*we work with our customers to ensure that our measurement quality is consistent with their needs -always, sometimes or never?

*we have written procedures in place to ensure we are implementing requirement driven selection of measurement methods and equipment - always, sometimes or never?

Actions which may subsequently be taken to improve performance may include:

*identification of a suitably qualified person on the management team to review product specification with customers to ensure that everyone is aiming at the same target.

*relating the customer's need for a particular specification to the measurement approach that will demonstrate it with due attention to the level of accuracy or tolerance required.

*analysis and recording of staff competences required to meet measurement objectives.

*ensuring that the staff involved in measurement understand the factors contributing to measurement errors and inconsistency.

*establishment of a programme of inter-comparison for measurements with customers and suppliers.

*development of simple step by step procedures to ensure that the correct equipment and methods are used for each measurement task.

A Measurement Advice Chart assists participants seeking advice for each of the actions identified under the Six Principles of Good Measurement Practice. In some cases intermediary bodies are listed pointing to other sources of help more precisely tailored to specific needs.

Benefits of good Measurement Practice

Organisations which have achieved notable commercial success from the adoption of the above approach include Vauxhall Motors, Scottish and Newcastle plc, Stewart Grand Prix, clothing manufacturers J.Barbour and Sons, Linx Printing Technologies plc, and pharmaceutical packaging specialists Rexam Containers Limited of Portsmouth.

At Vauxhall the alignment of body shell parts is a key quality objective. The so called 'fits and finishes' are critical measurements and whilst body gaps (between doors, bonnets etc. and body frame) of 10mm were considered to be acceptable in the 1970s this is not now the case. There is intense pressure now for meticulous accuracy in the fit of the sheet metal parts of the body shell and when the Vectra came on line in Luton in 1995 a new bonnet/rear-view mirror design which formed an important innovative characteristic of the vehicle required an exact alignment of 'winglets' to door mirrors. This required an investment in state-of-the-art measurement equipment which utilised laser technology to provide 100% inspection of body shells in 18 dimensionally critical areas. The investment led to scrap rates of bodies being reduced by 80%, dimensional variations being reduced by 50%, and reductions in the amount of rework required on panel fits. Early successes prompted further investment in measuring equipment to measure the tailgate aperture of the Vectra Estate introduced in September 1996 and to extend the measurement techniques to the measurement of the apertures of all front and rear screens. Interacting with assembly robots the laser measurement communicates the correct position of the glass in relation to the aperture. Measurement by this method is a major contributor toward the elimination of water leaks and misalignments.

At Scottish and Newcastle a simple but effective calibrated measurement gauge has improved consistency of the manufacturing process, improved the consistency of product quality, increased manufacturing efficiency and reduced rework costs. With the Newcastle Brewery producing 40,000 bottles an hour 24 hours a day, five days a week a rapid and effective check system is needed to ensure that the bottling process always runs within its defined control parameters. This includes a requirement for the metal caps or 'crown corks' to be crimped on correctly and consequently it is critical that the dimensions of the 'crown' once crimped onto the bottle lie within certain specific measurements. The gauge system used is regularly calibrated against traceable standards and trend analysis of test results enables the required frequency of planned line maintenance to be ascertained.

Significant capital investment in state-of-the-art measuring equipment at Stewart Grand Prix has been critical to their ability to quality check supplier components, design and check original components, ensuring components meet stringent internal and external design requirements, and for undertaking accurate in-house design modifications. Ford supply their Zetec-R V10 engine but Stewart Grand Prix design their own gearboxes which are difficult and expensive to cast in magnesium. Modification of these gearboxes for interim testing of development Ford Zetec engines was vital. Mitutoyo 3D co-ordinate measuring machines (CMMs) were purchased which enabled the gearboxes to be re-tooled for testing with important consequent time and money savings. A 50% scale model of their car was constructed for wind tunnel diagnostics testing and the CMM offered important benefits here also, notably in ensuring that the car's shape complies with various sporting regulations such as those on the limits for the position tolerances of wing and body structures which have to be tested and constantly measured for conformity throughout the construction phases.

The manufacturing operations of J. Barbour and Sons is concentrated at six sites in Northern England and the need to achieve consistency between these sites led to a drive to improve measurement and in particular to improve control of the dimensions of fabric used to assemble garments. Dimensional measurements are critical for the measurement of incoming roll stock widths, computer controlling of lay planning and cutting, improving sewing precision, applying set tolerances to the manufactured product, 'first off-line' measurements to inspections and barcode control, and quality control checks in the form of defined product tolerances.

Specification of minimum dimensions and the measurement of roll stocks on receipt, for example, allows computer aided design (CAD) operators to use lay plans of standard width, so removing the need for re-planning lays. Where widths do vary the information can be fed directly into the CAD system and taken into account so reducing waste and improving cutting efficiency. In some areas a simple rule and tape constitute the measuring equipment, but their effectiveness has been greatly enhanced when supported by precise measurement techniques calibrated to standards at NPL. Benefits achieved include:

*improved material usage of Thornproof fabric from 70% to 90% following the introduction of calibrated measurement techniques.

*improved consistency of cut material on sewing and assembly lines where calibrated market templates have improved the consistency and accuracy of assembly.

*reduction in rework by a factor of seven following the introduction of measurement procedures at mid-line and final inspection.

Linx Printing Technologies plc has contributed to the refinement of a non-contact printing technique known as continuous ink jet printing (CIJ) and manufactures a range of CIJ printers and inks. The process is non-contact producing characters or graphics from individual electrically charged droplets of ink. The printers print variable information such as sell-by dates, serial numbers and other codes onto products and product packaging at high production line speeds (lines running at over 7 metres per second). High reproducible control of each ink droplet, through measurement, is required. Crucial to this is a 62 micrometre circular orifice through which the ink flows for which the dimensions must be exact. The orifice is ground into a synthetic mineral crystal with a low thermal expansion. Stereoscopic microscopy equipment supplied by Zeiss of Switzerland is used in conjunction with video monitors to provide first rate quality control for the manufacture of these critical components.

The orifices are inspected and measured at 500x magnification to ensure that dimensional tolerances and circularity are within specification and to confirm the absence of damage or contamination. During the inspection process defects of sub-micrometre magnitude will trigger rejection of the component. A diffraction grating method is also used to check the depth of the orifice, which is another key parameter. The images and measurements generated during inspection then travel with the printhead and ultimately the printer as the assembly progresses. By measuring critical parameters of the crystals Linx is able to detect potential problem components before they become built into the printhead, eliminating rework which otherwise would create a major cost.

At Rexam Containers investment in accurate measurement has brought benefits in all process areas including the quality checking of incoming new materials, the quality checking of manufactured goods to stringent customer specifications, and the early identification of potential tooling problems. The requirement for high specification packaging products with tight tolerances has meant that non-destructive dimensional measurement is a crucial element of process control, since destructive testing of moulded containers does not always reveal true dimensional information owing to stress relief in the plastic.

A DEA Swift Co-ordinate Measuring Machine has been used for non-destructive testing in the quality laboratory for many years, but it has been found to be inappropriate for certain types of routine quality measurements, such as the routine evaluation of certain crucial production parameters like the wall thickness of containers. Investment in an alternative technique utilising a device purchased from Electro-Physik GB Limited and applied in conjunction with a TSB Metrology Wedge Software data collection programme has improved the efficiency and reliability of the quality checking procedure. In particular it has allowed for several single point measurements to be made for each container i.e. simple quality control measurements in line with immediate report generation with the reports accompanying the product through the rest of the production process. Faster and more accurate results have resulted.

[Issue 126 (July 1999)]

ELECTROMAGNETIC COMPATIBILITY MATTERS

Since 1996 it has been mandatory in the UK for manufacturers of electronic equipment to guarantee that such equipment contributes no more than a defined amount of radiated or conducted interference (based on type of equipment) and that the operation of the equipment is not compromised by interference generated in other electronic equipment. The range of frequencies concerned spans the range from 150KHz to 30MHz for conducted interference and 30MHz to 1 GHz for radiated interference. In the UK the regulations governing these requirements are the Electromagnetic Compatibility Regulations 1992, the Electromagnetic Compatibility (Amendment) Regulations 1994, and the Electromagnetic Compatibility (Amendment) Regulations 1995 which came into force on January 1st 1996.

Electromagnetic compatibility or EMC is thus seen to be predominantly a legislation driven issue somewhat akin to health and safety, and similar terminology such as 'declaration of conformity' and 'due diligence' is used. The legislation contains some 100 clauses plus schedules making it a complex area both legally and technically, particularly in industry sectors such as information technology where there is a tendency for manufacturers to apply many integrators using CE marked sub-units, and to subsequently believe (falsely) that no further testing of the product or system is needed. In the UK two such manufacturers have recently been brought to court and fined.

In this issue of *Quality Matters* two aspects of electromagnetic compatibility which are likely to be of most interest to readers are discussed, namely the CE marking issue referred to above, and the Simple Legislation for the Single Market (SLIM) report on the European EMC Directive which will effectively modify the Directive.

Problems with CE Marking

This is the subject of a recent seminar paper presented by Eurling Keith Armstrong, a partner of Cherry Clough Consultants, at the EuroEMC Exhibition held at the NEC, Birmingham, on 14th and 15[th]April. In it the author argues that Declarations of Conformity and CE Marks cannot be relied upon as a guarantee of due diligence for EMC compliance for the following reasons:

(i) When they sign their Declarations of Conformity and affix a CE Mark some suppliers lie, do not in practice use the due diligence their customers require, or make serious errors.

(ii) Suppliers of items intended for incorporation into final apparatus often apply the standards which make it easier for them to affix the CE Mark rather than the somewhat tougher ones that their customers need to apply to their final apparatus.

(iii) The installation of an item in the field may be so different from the way in which it was configured for EMC testing as to make the test results meaningless.

(iv) Test laboratories Competent Bodies, and Notified Bodies can all make mistakes when they assess EMC.

(v) There can be a cumulative effect of emissions, for example, a fully EMC compliant motor drive may have emission levels that are just below the limits in the appropriate test standard, but when two or more are configured together the combined emission exceeds the limit for the final apparatus.

(vi) A CE Mark may be affixed legally to an item designed for incorporation into another apparatus on the basis of compliance with the Low Voltage Directive or the Machinery Safety Directive, which may be irrelevant for EMC compliance.

(vii) UK case law indicates that a successful defence of due diligence cannot be assured where the manufacturer, assembler or user has merely relied on statements by suppliers.

Further to this the paper states the following:

'Industrial control panels are often constructed of CE marked power suppliers, PLCs and/or computers, motor drives, displays and control panels etc, but test laboratories all over the country report that when they do test such equipment for compliance to the relevant EMC standards they almost always fail'.

All of this can be bad news for a manufacturer since liability for non-compliance may not be easy to pass on to the supplier of a non-conforming item and even if it is it could be a difficult matter to recover from suppliers or their insurers. The enforcement authorities, however, are likely to take action against the final manufacturer should the apparatus concerned be found to be non-compliant by virtue of an incorporated item or items.

In order to attempt to overcome some of these problems the author therefore recommends that manufacturers cease to rely on CE marking and instead take steps of their own to ensure that their engineering performance in respect of EMC is at least adequate. For this the author offers the following recommendations:

* Decide which EMC standards and levels the final apparatus needs to comply with, considering its likely or possible electromagnetic environments.

* For the EM performance of non-critical functions it is enough to consider the normal operating environment of the apparatus but for all critical functions (whether safety or mission critical) it is necessary to consider all reasonably foreseeable situations even if they have a low probability, including foreseeable misuse such as an operator or visitor using a mobile phone in a banned area.

* Analyse the functions that the item performs or which depend on its correct operation, for criticality and ensure that no safety functions are allowed any significant degradation of performance over the entire range of electromagnetic threats.

* The complete engineering specification for engineering EM performance of an incorporated item should include all the EM stresses it is to withstand,

the amount of functional performance degradation allowed during the application of those stresses, and the amount of electromagnetic emissions it must not exceed.

* The specification should be sent to the favoured item suppliers for their replies, the company pointing out that the actual independent evidence of conformity with the specification will be required from the successful tenderer.

* Make sure that the agreed EMC specifications and the agreed requirements for evidence that they have been achieved are written into the purchasing contract accepted by the supplier of each item.

* Items for which the necessary evidence is not available (for whatever reason) should not be purchased unless it is intended to put the final product through EMC compliance tests and unless contingency costs and timescales have been allowed for remedial work and re-testing that is usually required in such situations.

* If potential suppliers claim design secrecy issues as a reason for not providing evidence, insist 'on a trusted third party report which confirms that the item meets all the EM engineering specifications without revealing any of the suppliers' supposed secrets.

* Scrutinise Declarations of Conformity to see if they list the EMC standards required by the engineering specification for the item and for suspect standards such as EN 61131-12 for PLCs which cannot be applied to the final apparatus.

* Check that all Declarations of Conformity actually cover the item concerned and are clearly signed and dated by the supplier's Technical Director or equivalent, with attention being given to any recent dates being applied to items which have been on the market for some time.

* Suspect any inappropriate or unreasonable warnings, limitations to use, or attempts at disclaimers.

* Beware of EN 55022 in the IT sector as it is often misapplied particularly when staff are integrating computers and computing devices into industrial control systems, printers and displays.

* Avoid suppliers that don't provide detailed assembly and installation instructions and ensure they are followed as many modern best EMC practices for installation directly contradict traditional practices.

* Scrutinise suppliers' instructions for inappropriate or vague limitations or instructions and for any requirement for expensive or exotic cables, connectors, filters, shielding or bizarre environmental conditions.

692

* Ensure test laboratories are accredited for all the tests covered by their report and confirm all certificates with the issuing laboratory regardless of protestations from salesmen.

* Compare performance as shown by test reports or certificates with the agreed engineering specifications for the item concerned.

* Beware of so-called Technical Construction Files (TCFs) as they may contain warnings where an assessor has not been able to declare a product as non-compliant but has serious concerns e.g. regarding specific installation requirements or limitations in usage.

* Suppliers with ISO 9000 should have their quality manual scrutinised with regard to procedures for maintaining the specified EM performance in production.

[In essence the principle is that on system integration it cannot be assumed that the original assessment of compliance continues from equipment(s) to system e.g. interconnecting cables may radiate. -Ed].

The full version of the paper, entitled 'CE plus CE does not equal CE: What to do instead' may be obtained from Cherry-Clough Consultants, Cherry Clough House, Rochdale Road, Denshaw, Oldham OL3 5VE.

The SLIM Initiative

In September of last year a long awaited Simple Legislation for the Single Market (SLIM) report on the EMC Directive was released for public comment. This sets out a total of twenty recommendations for the revision of the Directive which the European Commission is currently considering with a view to publishing a 'communication' which will be submitted to the European Parliament for approval. Some of the principal recommendations are as follows:

* that both emissions and immunity remain within the scope of the EMC Directive in such detail that only specific technical questions are left to standardisation .

* that immunity requirements should be more fully addressed in the EMC Directive to prevent new national legislation.

* that installations and large machines be permitted, provided no complaints have arisen, to be put into service without EMC assessment.

* in cases where such assessment may be required the methods of "in-situ" testing along the lines of EN 55011 should be used (radiated emissions

performed at a distance from the installations perimeter, and conducted emissions at the utility supply connection point).

* that definitions for large machines and installations, as well as small machines and networks, be added to assist manufacturers in determining the applicability of the Directive to their equipment.

* that installations may be manufactured from CE marked and/or non-CE marked components and only in the event of a 'challenge' would appropriate measures need to be performed to bring the installation into compliance.

* that a panel consisting of European Commissioners, standardisation experts, industrialists, CENELEC and ETSI members be established to take a 'critical' look at the relevance and applicability of all standards, as well as the future of standardisation, with a view to reducing the number of standards produced and increasing their ease of use.

* that the EMC Directive be revised to accommodate some of the text of the European Commission's EMC Directive Guidance Document particularly in the areas of definitions of components and so-called EMC passive equipment, the EMC analysis process, the application of the Directive to installations, and 'other areas which could be fully transferred'.

This latter recommendation is significant as the EC Guidelines, which were published in April 1997, placed a different interpretation on the original Directive which in some cases conflicted with national legislation. Acceptance of the SLIM Initiative and the issue of a new Directive is thus likely to end some of the ambiguity which currently exists and create an opportunity to improve the way the rules are interpreted in the light of experience.

The panel mentioned in the recommendations is also important as it is expected to address whether there is a need to redefine certain EMC environments [a controversial area -Ed] and to examine specific standards, notably EN 61000-3-2 and EN 61800-3 which have given rise to concern.

One further issue which has significance although is not specifically referred to in the recommendations is that of alignment between the EMC Directive and the Low Voltage Directive through a system of Module A (self certification) to compliance. This was actively discussed by Member State Authorities, industry representatives and others at a special meeting convened by the European Commission on 24th and 25th February and now appears to have been shelved i.e. there was a balance in favour of retaining third party certification for EMC.

Further Information on Standards

In the telecommunications field there are currently no CENELEC EMC standards harmonised to the Telecom Directive. The European Telecommunications Standards Institute (ETSI) is, however, presently developing a range of standards for radio and telecommunications equipment with most of the work being performed by two sub-committees or working groups namely Equipment Engineering or EE4 which is considering general requirements and Radio Equipment and Systems or RES9 dealing with wireless communications. Some ETSI standards will be published as EN standards harmonising with the EMC Directive.

A new complete list of standards harmonised with the EMC Directive was published in the Official Journal of the European Communities on February 27th and this includes most of the standards published on April 3rd 1998 plus forty new standards and amendments. The complete list covers 110 standards with many including references to amendments. The list now includes 23 EMC standards from ETSI.

S.G.S. EXPANDS EMC LABORATORY NETWORK

Certification body SGS has expanded its EMC facilities with investment in London, China, and Korea. The London facility will serve as a satellite to the well established facility in Durham, and, along with the other laboratories, will provide compliance testing for a wide range of household and similar products as well as pre-test and debugging of computer and industrial products. Commenting on the expansion John Whaley, General Manager of SGS International Electrical Approvals said:

'The new facilities will allow manufacturers and importers in these areas the ability to obtain cost efficient EMC testing on their doorstep. The reputation of SGS in this field of testing will make the new facilities a welcome first port of call for many electrical and electronic manufacturers'.

FIRST U.K.RADIO EQUIPMENT CONFORMITY ASSESSMENT BODY ANNOUNCED

Radio Frequency Investigation has become the first organisation in the UK to announce its appointment as a Radio Equipment Conformity Assessment Body (RECAB). The RECAB has full authority to issue type approval certificates under Section 84 of the Telecommunications Act 1984 in respect of radio equipment for which the Radiocommunications Agency is responsible. As a result manufacturers of radio equipment should enjoy a greatly reduced time to market as a result of a new streamlined Radio Type Approval procedure for products ranging from short range devices such as keyfob transmitters to GSM basestations.

In line with guidelines from the Radiocommunications Agency, RF's RECAB department has been established independently of its test laboratory as part of its regulatory and Technical Support service (RATS).

Under the new procedure a manufacturer whose product has passed Type Approval testing at RFI will submit the test results and application forms to the RFI RECAB which will issue a Certificate of Type Approval within a few days.

In the past the results and applications had to be submitted directly to the Radiocommunications Agency, a process which typically took four to six weeks to complete.

Certificates issued by RFI will be valid in the UK and in all other European countries that have signed up to both ERC/DEC/(97) 10 on the mutual recognition of conformity assessment procedures and the relevant product standards (such as ETS-300-220 on short range devices). This also means that suitably qualified laboratories outside the UK will be able to submit their test results to the RFI RECAB for assessment.

Radio Frequency Investigation Limited is an independent test laboratory providing testing, consultancy and training services for manufacturers, importers and exporters of electrical and electronic equipment. Specific areas of expertise include electromagnetic compatibility (EMC) testing, radio and microwave type approvals and the testing of cellular radio mobiles and basestations. RFI is accredited by UKAS and RFI's reports are accepted by many regulatory authorities around the world.

NEW ANTENNA COMBATS ELECTROMAGNETIC STRESS FROM MOBILE PHONES

A new type of antenna known as the Techno AO has been designed to combat some of the adverse effects of so-called mobile phone radiation or 'electromagnetic smog'. Its essential element is a crystalline solution reservoir which has been electromagnetically treated to ensure the constant emission of a low frequency oscillation which acts as a 'pacemaker' for the natural alpha rhythms of the human brain such that its even and uninterrrupted signal provides a focal point or 'tuning fork' amongst the multifrequency 'electronic smog'. The result is a resonance effect which is said to 'balance all stressful artificial emissions against the natural wavelengths of the brain'.

The new antenna is said to be 'non toxic, non-iodising, non-radioactive, does not require a power supply or battery and does not interfere with the operational functions or performance of the equipment it is fitted to'. It carries a CE mark and is protected by an international patent.

NEW WORKING GROUP TO INVESTIGATE MOBILE PHONE HEALTH AND SAFETY ISSUES

Tessa Jowell, the Minister for Public Health, has ordered the National Radiological Protection Board to set up an independent expert working group to investigate the health and safety implications of continued mobile phone use following concerns which have been highlighted by current research. The exact form of the group is yet to be confirmed but it is expected to be drawn from relevant scientific fields, consumer groups and the industry.

Recent research at Bristol University has shown that there can be a small but significant change in reaction time when people are subjected to certain frequencies and RF radiation associated with prolonged mobile phone use whilst at Montpellier University in France a similar exposure to radiation was found to increase the mortality rate of chicken embryos from 18% to over 72%.

NEW COMPUTERISED TELECOMMUNICATIONS FIELD TEST SYSTEM

A revolutionary computer based hardware/software combination for telecommunications field service testing has been launched by National Instruments. Known as the N 16830 ISON Basic Rate Tester it is based on a PC Card (PCMCIA) that plugs directly into a laptop and verifies voice and data services at the subscriber's location, performs bit-error-rate tests to verify physical layer integrity, and troubleshoots problems, with the U and S/T interfaces.

The unit's ready-to-run Windows 95/98-based software leverages the power of the portable PC for processing speech, results display, analysis and date storage, and incorporates a test sequencer which automates the ISON test process and stores results. This is said to offer distinct advantages in test speed, size and costs over comparable field-portable products. Commenting on the launch Dr. James Truchard, President and CEO of National Instruments said:

"The trend for field service and test is moving towards portable computer-based solutions. We are excited to offer telecommunications service companies the ability to leverage the portability of notebook computers with our productivity tools to expand the range of measurements engineers can make".

The NI6830 is suitable for testing in numerous ISDN protocols including the Euro-ISDN, National Implementation One (NI1), AT and T Custom, Northern Telecom DMS, British ISDN 2, French UN3, and German variations. With the N 16830 users can integrate ISDN testing with other test and work management programs and can create a suite of tools for telephony field tests using a standard laptop or hand held PC.

NEW SOFTWARE FOR FACILITIES RISK MANAGEMENT

A new software package for facilities management risk evaluation and service monitoring has been launched by BWA Facilities Consulting. Known as Frisque (Facilities RISk and QUality Evaluation) it enables management to dynamically evaluate their core business susceptibility to variation in premises and support service performance relative to the levels and costs of service needed to maintain specified performance targets. It also deploys two complementary indices, the functional performance index (FPI), which calculates the risk level for the core business of each individual facilities operation from catering and porterage to electronic communication and IT, and the Service Level index (SLI) which measures the level of resources needed to achieve given FPI levels and allows financial directors and others to view at a glance the cost and service quality implications of varying these levels.

Commenting on the launch Bernard Williams FRICS, Senior Partner in BWA, said:

"The conventional approach to the establishment of service levels is shaped by perceptions of affordability which are induced by a tug of war between the push of budgetary constraints and the pull of user satisfaction demands. This is the wrong way round. The process should begin with the risk which inadequate facilities present to the core business and then work back down through quality and functional performance levels, user satisfaction, service levels and finally the resulting, and of course value engineered, cost. This is the only realistic way to establish true affordability and Frisque gives managements, for the first time, an easily comprehensible way of managing the process to suit their own needs".

NEW CERTIFICATION SCHEME FOR ELECTRICAL AND ELECTRONIC PRODUCTS

A new Electrical Product Certification scheme designed to encompass all relevant European Directives and associated regulations has been launched by certification body SGS.

In particular it resolves the issue concerning separate national approvals and offers a universal approval mark for electrical goods entering Europe.

Under the scheme each product and its process is reviewed to identify areas that are critical to the product's performance. The product is then Type Tested to ensure that it meets the technical aspects of all regulatory requirements. Where it is in series production the manufacturer's assembly site is assessed to ensure that the product meets the requirements.

For organisations which have achieved ISO9000 certification all that will be required will be an assessment of the quality plan and an audit of the manufacturing process and it should be possible to combine the surveillance visits.

Where products are assembled at a customer's premises the scheme may also be appropriate but the resulting Certification Mark would only remain valid so long as the product continues to be assembled there.

[Issue 129 (September 1999)]

QUALITY AND RISK

Risk was the theme of this year's annual conference of The Royal Statistical Society at Warwick University from 12th to 15th July, making it particularly relevant to quality, environmental and health and safety practitioners for whom risk assessment is an ongoing requirement.

There were around 78 presentations grouped roughly as follows: Public Risk Perception (4 papers), Health (20), Environment (6), Finance (14), Education (2), Nuclear Industry (2), Change Point and Related Methods (8), Water Engineering (one paper on 'Reliability Modelling and Risk reduction in Distribution Systems'), and 21 general presentations covering, for example, 'D-optimum Experimental Design in Adaptive Optimisation', 'Modelling and forecasting for Physical Phenomena using multi-level Computer Codes', 'Dependency modelling in Engineering Risk Applications' and 'Proactive Risk and Decision support for Local Government Managers'.

The event was opened by Professor Jerome Sacks of the National Institute of Statistical Sciences in North Carolina, USA, who gave a lecture entitled 'What's at risk?' with reference to the nuclear waste legacy of the Cold War, the health effects of electromagnetic fields, and the risks to health posed by air pollution and particulate emissions. With regard to the latter he drew the audience's attention to a US court ruling which countered a revision of the US Ozone Standard by the US Environmental Protection Agency (EPA).

The court, said to have been one of the most conservative in America, accused the EPA of applying "no intelligible principle" in their standards setting when they "should be capable of developing the rough equivalent of a generic unit of harm that takes into account the population affected, the severity, and the probability". In other words, said the speaker, they should have been able to do a risk assessment, and the outcome of this case has resulted in "a very troublesome situation" as statistics have "pushed the courts into play". Furthermore, through this case there was "a very strong reflection of a political environment" which has created an interaction between politics, risk and science that "cannot be ignored". He commented as follows:

"The ambiguity in the use of statistics almost has an equation. If we want action we have to account both for the risk and the political issues surrounding it. In other words, action equals risk plus politics".

Elsewhere in his presentation he referred to the weaknesses of statistical models in areas such as the prediction of colloidal transport on nuclear waste sites and the "damned few statisticians" who were currently involved with models that were "very wrong". He illustrated the point with reference to the Nevada nuclear legacy where Plutonium was discovered in groundwater 1.3 km from a nuclear test site, indicating movement that the models "did not predict".

On the subject of electromagnetic fields he drew attention to a recent report by the US National Institute of Environmental Health Sciences which pointed to weak epidemiological and zero scientific evidence to support the case for aggressive regulation in this area. "'Should we beware of epidemiology or beware of advocacy groups?" he asked.

In the questioning which followed one delegate suggested that human sensitivity to electromagnetic field risk varies considerably between one individual and another and that consequently those who were most likely to be at risk would be those who were hypersensitive. He asked if this possibility had been considered by statisticians.

In reply the speaker said that there was "no concrete evidence of characteristics which make some people more sensitive than others", although he accepted that there could be some information in the report which he cited. His concluding remarks were:

"Statistics must be able to present themselves so that they are understandable. The understanding of risk and the use of risk is what's at risk".

Normal Accidents: A Statistical Interpretation

From the remaining general presentations four which are considered to be of particular relevance to quality practitioners have been selected for review, beginning with the paper with the above title by Tony Cutler of Aegis Engineering Systems. This builds on the theory of American sociologist Charles Perrow who coined the phrase 'normal accident' in the 1980s and applies the teachings of W. Edwards Deming to understand, minimise and manage risk through the use of process thinking:

'In the wake of Three Mile Island and other incidents with global impact Perrow observed that many major accidents were inevitable consequences of the way that systems were designed and routinely operated. Because of a failure to link day to day process variation with possibly catastrophic

outcomes, operators were unable to foresee, mitigate or otherwise manage the risks'.

'Normal Accidents' have the following characteristics:

(i) Unexpected and complex interactions between faults that are tolerable individually.

(ii) Tight coupling that allows little opportunity for mitigation or defence once a fault has occurred.

These characteristics are illustrated practically with reference to last year's report by the Department of the Environment Transport and the Regions into the sinking of the MV Derbyshire:

'The ship ultimately foundered when a critical hatch cover failed under severe dynamic loading from high waves crashing onto the deck. Water entering through the damaged. hatch led to sudden and catastrophic flooding. None of the individual faults (hatch cover unsecured, inability to secure hatch cover subsequently, non-conservative design of critical hatch cover) would have resulted in disaster. It is most difficult to foresee such interactions at the design stage. The speed with which the flooding occurred and the prevailing weather conditions ensured that the failure would inevitably lead to fatalities. Such is the meaning of tight coupling between a failure and its catastrophic consequences'.

Mr. Cutler asserts that 'Normal Accidents' 'have a rigorous meaning and great significance' when interpreted in terms of common cause variation and process capability, and argues that accidents are outcomes of a system and that we cannot work purely on outcomes:

'Many organisations fail to obtain real value from much of the engineering analysis that is performed on systems at the design stage. Techniques such as fault-tree analysis are sometimes seen as providing a definitive and final answer to the safety question. In a process conscious organisation they are most effective in establishing the criteria by which system safety effectiveness and efficiency will be improved over the whole life and disposal of the asset'.

'Once we see that some accidents are the result of common cause variation there are inevitable implications for how we investigate them and work for improvement. We often look at the events that surround an accident without understanding the full context of what was happening in the accident free periods. This can lead us to treating common cause variation like special cause variation and degrading system performance still further'.

He explained with the aid of a railway signalling example how whilst historical data may suggest that common cause variation is within a safe limit, the past may not always be representative of the future:

'The fundamental attribution error may lead us to miss root causes of failure within the system design and to ruin individuals who have displayed nothing other than normal carelessness. There is a further danger that investigations spawn recommendations founded on happenstance data and lead to tampering with the system'.

[Deming practitioners will be familiar with the concept of tampering and variation -Ed].

Mr. Cutler contests that just as there is chance-cause variation in electromagnetic interference so also is there variation in all aspects of human performance, and he suggests that the same sorts of capability pictures can be used for each i.e. we can create models of human perception, attention and diagnostic ability even through there is presently no simple method of quantifying these characteristics. In the latter part of his paper he argues the case for a programme of continual monitoring and improvement based on the following six principles:

*Develop the voice of the customer.

*Develop outcome measures.

*Develop process measures.

*Assess stability.

*Assess capability.

*Institute continual monitoring, learning and improvement.

Project planning Risk

The paper by Brad Payne of Nottingham Trent University and former Quality Methods Association Chairman Tony Bendell [now at Leicester University -Ed] provides a critique on today's project management techniques, in particular the Performance Evaluation and Review Technique (PERT), and proposes an extension to classical theory which takes into account the dependencies which exist between time, cost and quality. Brad Payne, who gave the presentation, warned delegates to beware of the "biased results" that can arise from the application of PERT and critical path analysis which he says "have been over-used for determining project risk".

'The construction industry is a major user of project management techniques for scheduling, resource allocation, time management and cost management. However, such techniques are typically applied in a univariate way with time, cost and quality measures and influences not considered together if at all. Motivation for the development of a generalised model by the authors is

from concerns in the construction industry where time, cost and quality are indicated as key measures reported in the recent literature'.

The model is based on the standard BS 6046 which recognises that

* No two projects are the same.

* A project is made up of phases.

* A project contains uncertainty and risk.

* The conduct of project phases often affects the operation of the project outcome.

The model attempts to overcome some of the difficulties associated with quantifying quality through the use of a project quality indicator that shows how well a project is performed. This considers the loss in quality rather than simply analysing how much of the project is done correctly. A transformation from cumulative quality loss to project quality is applied:

'In general, assuming that the quality loss measure indicates how well the project is performed, the operation of the Project Outcome may be related to it. Including such a concept extends the classical project model since operational measures, such as reliability, availability and output may be considered in the planning process. Our project formulation has two distinct stages. We define the Performance Phases to include all activities from project commencement to the point of operation, which may include planning, testing and burn-in procedures. The subsequent phase, where the Project Outcome is put to use, is defined as the Operation Phase. Key measures at the end of the Performance Phases will be accumulated time and cost, which are assumed additive over phases and accumulated quality loss'.

The reliability of the Project Outcome is defined as the probability that the Project Outcome is performing as required:

'Project outcome reliability provides an indication of the time to failure of the project outcome. The definition of failure in this application is debatable and project dependent and may result in various alternative risk measures'.

The paper concludes:

'The classical approach to project planning, where typically a univariate independent measure such as time and cost is modelled, is insufficient to model the risk measures associated with the performance of the project and the operation of the project outcome. In this paper a general model is formulated which overcomes the modelling restrictions and computational difficulties associated with the classical approach. The measure of project quality developed enables the operational measures of reliability,

availability and output of the Project Outcome to be related to the conduct of the project. Implementation of the model will provide the ability to assess the operational performance based on various project performance scenarios and thus influence early planning decisions.'

Disaster Risk: issues of Measurement and Management.

Professor G. Alex Whitmore of the McGill University in Montreal spoke about disaster prevention and mitigation with an emphasis on measurement, He spoke at length about the conduct of risk audits and the need for risk itemisation, arguing that if a disaster mode is missed in a risk audit then the chances are that it will not be subject to a risk management action.

He explained how about a year ago he had been "truly shocked" at the level of impact of disasters on the Chinese economy (30% of Government spending and 3% of GDP) and how this had prompted him to take along hard look at what constitutes a disaster (an intersection of contributing events) and what can be done regarding prevention and control as against merely spending on firefighting afterwards. He then drew on the analogy between disaster management and reliability analysis of a general system and described how an unanticipated disaster event would frequently have more severe consequences than one which had been anticipated i.e. taken into account in the audit.

The speaker was notably critical of the current focus of much modern literature on the purely economic aspects of risk management, describing it as "unfortunate" since "the consequences of a disaster are only partly economic". Whilst he did accept that "an economic incentive may encourage people to reduce or avoid risk", he clearly advocated a much stronger focus on risk reduction through the use of containment strategies. This approach he said "can minimise the impact and stop the propagation of consequences" and hence was "rich in possibilities".

He urged delegates to consider carefully the risks posed by integrated and interdependent systems as well as those posed by economies of scale, and suggested that greater use should be made of planning for disaster containment in the planning phase. He then proposed the construction of a disaster risk portfolio as part of a methodology to design systems to be robust against unforeseen disaster modes. In particular he stressed the need to consider the phenomenon of "parameter drift" i.e. the possibility that the probability of a disaster occurring may be unstable with respect to time and he advocated the use of statistical tools which took this into account by allowing the evidence of the past to decay by using weighting factors which favoured the current and the recent.

In his conclusion he called for greater public education about risk management and greater use of disaster planning by households, organisations and government. He said also that he strongly suspected a

704

positive correlation to exist between well conceived green policies and a reduction in man-made disaster risks.

Risk Management at Unilever.

An interesting case study in risk management was presented by Phillip Whittall of Unilever, who explained some of the reasoning behind his organisations's relatively advanced risk management programme which came about largely as a result of 'learning the hard way'.

The speaker explained how two to three years ago his organisation had launched a new brand of washing powder called 'Persil Power' which had had a very high research and development cost, but later turned out also to have "a well publicised flaw which cost the company dear". The company's good name was affected in addition to the product being a write off both at home, where the organisation enjoyed a 25% detergent market share, and abroad where further launches were found to be costly.

The experiences with this particular product led to risk management receiving a much higher priority in Unilever and Mr. Whittall described how consultants were imported from Eindhoven to ensure that an effective risk management policy would be in place for all future product launches where the company's reputation was at stake. He introduced the concept of a "type three error" i.e. type 1 is where you think something is important but isn't, type 2 is vice versa, and type 3 is where you don't ask the right question in the first place and so miss the critical issue. Such errors, said the speaker, were most important in risk assessment.

Open ended non-threatening interviews were held involving one team member, one interviewer, and a scribe [recorder who may contribute -Ed]. These lasted from between one and one and a half hours and discussed such matters as risk aversion (confirming to each team just exactly what must go right). A risk management plan was drawn up and rehearsed, since a rehearsal "can make a huge difference should things go wrong" and "teams will come to better decisions if they have already talked something through". Thus there was a contingency plan for everything such that if something goes wrong the chances are it has already been discussed at some point.

Decision trees were used to introduce project teams to the often difficult area of risk aversion and great importance was attached to ensuring that any risk related issues that were surfaced in interviews were not ignored. It was noted that often the most interesting information was revealed in the last few minutes of an interview, and the speaker emphasised the importance of maintaining active listening during this period especially.

The presentation concluded with a description of a more recent product launch of detergent tablets which, like Persil Power, was risky, involving an investment of the order of £10 million in tabletting equipment. This was an opportunity for the organisation to put into practice the new risk management policies and make up lost ground. In all 27 team members identified 145 risk issues, some of which occurred in practice but this time the whole team "had a clear view of the issues and actions required". The result was a seizing of 10% of the market during 1998, which of course is still ongoing.

This popular presentation attracted a number of questions from the audience which included an enquiry about the position of competitors in the decision tree and about whether there was any post-event auditing carried out following the tablet launch. In reply to the first of these subjects Mr. Whittall explained that the activities of competitors did indeed feature in decision trees because in his business one knew only too well the importance of being first to market. There was no secret to the fact that Proctor and Gamble were also seeking to be first to market whilst major supermarket chains had a time lag of around six months. "Modern technology means you have much less time to make money when you have got an innovation", he said.

With regard to the second question he confirmed that as yet there had not been a post-event audit on the tablet launch, and agreed that to do so "might be a good idea". He explained how the consultants had used "trigger lists" of issues that tended to affect product launches and that the interviewers had used these as "crib sheets" during the course of their interviews. He offered the following advice to delegates:

"If you have a brand that is failing, do anything. If you have one that is successful then make sure you really know what you are doing before you do anything".

[Issue 130 (October 1999)]

IMPROVING QUALITY IN ELECTRONICS MANUFACTURE

Four innovations designed to improve quality in electronics manufacturing operations have been announced by automated solutions specialist PMJ. These are (a) stress-free depanelling cell designed to overcome damage to delicate components when they need to be broken apart, (b) specialised Odd-Form Assembly Cell designed to overcome problems of misplaced or omitted components and wrong component values associated with manual insertion of so called odd-form components, (c) labelling cell designed to eliminate identification and traceability problems, and (d) an automated Final Assembly system that is said to achieve dramatic quality and throughout gains whilst at the same time yielding a maximum return on investment. The suppliers state the following with regard to the four innovations:

'Most PCBs contain a number of odd-form components. For many devices such as switches, customer connectors, SIPS, DIPS and relays, hand

assembly is standard practice as their shape and complexity makes automation difficult for conventional placement machines. The HiSAC Assembly Cell is an automated, flexible, modular unit with a small footprint that fully integrates into the production line. This maximises throughput, increases quality and reduces overall assembly time and costs. It also provides considerable savings in factory floor space, when compared to multiple workstations'.

'Virtually any shape or size of component can be handled as the Cell uses a servo-driven "gripper" that can open and close to suit any size. The gripper automatically changes its tooling or "fingers" to accommodate an exhaustive range of odd-form TH and SMT component body shapes. As part of an integrated manufacturing line, product quality and consistency are improved, uptime is maximised and labour costs are reduced. The Cell's capabilities and flexible modular configuration ensure future proofing, as it is compatible with a vast range of devices, board designs and line configurations'.

'Automatic product identification and traceability through bar coding is essential in many modern in-line assembly processes to maintain high throughputs and yields. Yet while most manufacturers are willing to invest in expensive assembly machinery to achieve the highest levels of print or placement accuracy, the costs of unnecessary downtime and assembly errors due to board labelling problems are often overlooked. A wrongly placed or damaged label can bring an entire manufacturing line to a halt if, for example, the bar code reader on a placement machine cannot match a PCB's product code with the correct placement programme. Even the wrong orientation of a label can prevent a machine from being able to read it. An apparently "simple" fault can therefore result in thousands of pounds worth of lost production and downtime. All these problems can be avoided with the HiSAC labelling cell'.

'The HiSAC labelling cell guards against labelling errors by immediately placing a bar code label onto each PCB as it enters the assembly line. It also verifies that the label is readable both before and after its placement on the board's surface by using a bar code reader on the pick-up head itself. This guarantees that the label is in good condition, correctly printed and is positioned in exactly the right place on the board. This ensures that any bar code readers further down the assembly line will be able to read the label without difficulty. The fully automatic labour saving cell is so effective it often eliminates the need for an operator. When used in a typical three shift operation the PMJ cell can pay for itself in less than a year'.

'Although the final assembly of the vast majority of products is still performed by hand, most manufacturers would automate the process if a suitable solution existed. Traditional attempts to provide such a solution have often been extremely costly and complicated and suffered from an inability to replace manual assembly's flexibility to accommodate new product designs. These barriers are eliminated by PMJ's highly adaptable

HiSAC 1500 FA -final assembly cell which can perform a vast array of final assembly functions. These range from labelling and screw driving to component calibration. To ensure maximum uptime on a line PMJ's final assembly cell can be reconfigured for product changeovers within minutes. This is achieved through a series of unique features designed to make the machine as flexible as possible'.

'One sector where PMJ's final assembly Cells are being heavily used is the mobile phone industry. Because high volume mobile phone production demands round the clock production the PMJ final assembly cells eliminate a host of traditional problems associated with manual assembly in such environments. These include staff coverage problems associated with, for example, manning late nightshifts or holidays, quality control problems due to variations in operator performance, and downtime stoppages stemming from unexpected absenteeism'.

[Issue 130 (October 1999)]

NEW MEASUREMENT HELPLINE LAUNCHED

The first fully comprehensive measurement helpline in the UK, the National Measurement Partnership Helpline, has now been launched. The special number 0208 943 7070 has been established to provide a fast response service to callers with measurement queries and builds on the expertise of the existing Helplines of the national laboratories and UKAS. Open from 9am to 5pm the Helpline will answer queries immediately if possible. Otherwise it will provide the name of an expert for the caller to contact or take details of the enquiry and pass it to an appropriate expert. The National Measurement Partnership also has a website at www.nmpuk.co.uk. which can be used to access measurement advice and Helpline services.

[Issue 132 (December 1999)]

NATIONAL MEASUREMENT SYSTEM UNDER REVIEW

The DTI has commissioned P. A. Consulting Group to study the rationale for and benefits of the National Measurement System, the national infrastructure launched last year to support the UK's measurement standards.

P .A. Consulting will lead a consortium with representation from the London Business School, Surrey University and the Manchester Centre for Research on Innovation and Competition (CRIC), as well as specialist advisors on small and medium sized enterprises.

The study will examine in particular the potential value of having either a more centralised system or a more distributed network of national laboratories.

COMPETING PRECISELY

The National Measurement Partnership Programme (NMP) was officially launched on 5th November 1998 by the Rt. Hon. Peter Mandelson MP, then Secretary of State for Trade and Industry. As part of this programme the DTI and the National Physical Laboratory (NPL) have co-ordinated a measurement awareness campaign entitled 'Competing Precisely' designed to promote and support good measurement practice throughout UK manufacturing industry. The Competing Precisely' campaign

* demonstrates the business benefits of accurate measurement for improving a company's competitiveness

* presents the importance of measurement for demonstrating compliance with industrial specifications, standards and legal requirements

* supports the development of good measurement practice by providing a practical 'toolkit' to assist companies in the improvement of measurement quality

* provides access to local and national sources of measurement expertise and services

* promotes the use of accredited measurement suppliers for crucial measurements in the UK.

At this year's Quality in Manufacturing Exhibition at the National Motorcycle Museum in Solihull on 12th and 13th September one of four seminar streams were dedicated to the Campaign and its achievement and benefits.

Speakers from NPL, the United Kingdom Accreditation Service (UKAS), Huddersfield Centre for Precision Technology, Concentric Pumps Limited, and Coventry Technical College were introduced by Paul Roberts, Business Manager for Applied Technology for Fluke Precision Measurement Limited (formerly Wavetek-Datron).

The papers by Paul Roberts and the joint presentation by Richard Freeman of Huddersfield Centre for Precision Technology and Steven Banks of Concentric Pumps Limited were essentially case studies of measurement in practice which yielded impressive bottom line results. Below we review the remaining papers by Ms. Glenis Tellet and Malcolm Loveday of NPL, UKAS Accreditation Manager, Ms. Carole Atkinson, and Clive Bringloe, Senior Project Manager for Metrology at Coventry Technical College.

The National Measurement Partnership Programme

Ms. Glenis Tellet explained how the NMP was bringing "real benefit" to the UK measurement infrastructure by bringing together industrialists from different sectors to discuss issues related to measurement. The measurement infrastructure currently has a budget of around £40 million a year and through the NMP individuals are now able to influence how most of this is spent with "real knowledge sharing".

According to the speaker measurement currently has a £5 billion positive impact on the economy (0.8% of GDP) with good measurement practice providing a means of demonstrating certainty about the accuracy and consistency of measurements. She explained how underpinning most areas of measurement was a chain of traceability which provides an unbroken and demonstrable link between the measurements that companies make and the national standard Accuracy, however, diminishes along the chain, hence the need for calibration. The current knowledge sharing initiatives are aimed at addressing the following identified problems:

(i) The commercial benefits of good measurement practice are not always understood (especially low awareness of the issues in top management).

(ii) Measurement is often viewed as a cost rather than a driver of the bottom line.

(iii) Capital costs present a serious barrier to good measurement practice.

(iv) Only 38% of companies identify a budget for the measurement function.

(v) Historically, measurement has a mature infrastructure and is a "low adrenalin" issue.

(vi) 94% of companies in the UK are unaware of the National Measurement System even though they are heavily reliant on it.

Simplifying the Uncertainty of Measurement.

The second speaker from NPL, Malcolm S. Loveday of the Materials Centre, explained how currently there was an urgent need to simplify the uncertainty of measurement, particularly for engineers for whom the ISO publication PD6461 part 3 :1995- Vocabulary of Metrology -'Guide to the expression of uncertainty in measurement' was "totally unintelligible". Drawing on information compiled by Dr. Stephanie Bell of NPL he outlined how the evaluation of measurement uncertainty could be reduced to eight simple steps:

(i) Decide what you need to find out from your measurements and decide what actual measurements and calculations are needed to produce the final result.

(ii) Carry out the measurements needed.

(iii) Estimate the uncertainty of each input quantity that feeds into the final result and express all uncertainties in similar terms.

(iv) Decide whether the errors of the input quantities are independent of each other -if they aren't then additional calculations or information are needed.

(v) Calculate result of measurement (including any known corrections for things such as calibration).

(vi) Determine the combined standard uncertainty from all of the individual aspects.

(vii) Express the uncertainty in terms of a coverage factor together with a size of the uncertainty interval, and state a level of confidence.

(viii) Write down the measurement result and the uncertainty, and state how they were arrived at.

In the publication 'A Beginners Guide to Uncertainty of Measurement' (ISSN 1368-6550) Stephanie Bell of NPL's Centre for Basic, Thermal and Length Metrology, emphasises how the use of good practice such as traceable calibration, careful calculation, good record keeping and checking can reduce measurement uncertainties quite considerably, and stresses that it is generally just as important to minimise uncertainties as it is to quantify them.

The Guide explains simply what is and is not a measurement uncertainty, taking care to distinguish between an error (difference between a measured value and the 'true value'), and uncertainty (quantification of the doubt about the measurement result). The subject is noted to be 'widely misunderstood from the factory floor to the highest academic circles' and the Guide explains the main steps involved in calculating the uncertainty for a measurement with the aid of easy to follow examples.

The Guide is particularly recommended for technicians and managers in testing and calibration laboratories, technicians and managers in manufacturing, and technical salespeople:

'When conclusions are drawn from measurement results, the uncertainty of the measurements must not be forgotten. This is particularly important when measurements are used to test whether or not a specification has been met.

Sometimes a result may fall clearly inside or outside the limit of a specification, but the uncertainty may overlap the limit'.

ISO9000 Measurement and Calibration.

Ms. Atkinson's presentation provided an overview of the measurement and calibration requirements of ISO9001/2 and a look ahead to the new ISO 9000:2000 standard and how it incorporates the current measurement and calibration requirements.

The speaker emphasised the need to decide at the contract review stage what measurement and calibration system is going to be applied with the manufacturer being made to ensure that they have the capability to deliver. The selection of any external calibration source was, she said, "absolutely critical", since without calibration measurement "is not meaningful". In particular when equipment is used there must be a known uncertainty which is consistent with measurement requirements so that it is capable of delivering to the level of accuracy agreed.

For real guidance on calibration ISO10012, which is mandated by ASCS Aerospace, was recommended. Then, three common risks associated with certification were highlighted, all of which can be reduced through UKAS accredited certification:

(i) Samples taken during the certification process may not be representative.

(ii) Selection of an inadequate quality certification body.

(iii) Identification of inadequate sub-contract resource to conduct calibration, measurement and test.

With regard to the last problem delegates were reminded that reliance solely on the expectations of an organisation with an ISO9001/2 certificate may not be enough, i.e. UKAS accredited quality system certification is not a substitute for, nor is in conflict with, UKAS test/calibration certificates. Either scheme will complement the other.

Turning to ISO9000:2000, which is due for release next month, the speaker explained how one "needs a magnifying glass" to find the calibration requirements, but they are still there in Clause 7.6 which specifies a traceability requirement to meet customer satisfaction. This is augmented in the 'terms and definitions' sections which also introduces a requirement for the uncertainty of measurement to be addressed.

New NVQ for Measurement and Calibration.

Clive Bringloe outlined the content of the level three National Vocational Qualification and BTEC professional development qualification for measurement and calibration personnel.

Developed by Loughborough University, Loughborough College and Rolls Royce, and accredited by the Engineering and Marine Training Authority (EMTA) the new NVQ provides for the first time a specialist qualification for inspection and measurement technicians. This, said the speaker, recognised the lack of people in recent times who had been able to follow through the traditional inspection apprenticeships, as the speaker had done since his time at Bristol Siddeley.

Rollout of the new NVQ is being managed by Coventry Technical College, in conjunction with the Centre for Manufacturing Metrology at Brunel University and Mitutoyo (UK) Limited.

MEASUREMENT CASE STUDIES

The Competing Precisely seminars at Quality in Manufacturing 2000 at the National Motorcycle Museum on 12th September included three measurement case studies. Two of these were presented by Paul Roberts, Business Manager for Applied Technology for Fluke Precision Measurement (formerly Wavetek-Datron). The third was presented jointly by Richard Freeman from the Huddersfield Centre for Precision Technology at Huddersfield University and Stephen Banks, Manufacturing Quality Manager for the case study company, Concentric Pumps Limited.

The cases presented by Mr. Roberts were first an aluminium smelting example from Holland and second an example of confectionery weighing. In the first case measurement of smelter cell anode voltage was used to automatically control the smelting process by varying electrode depth and thereby control the purity of the metal produced and optimise energy usage.

In this case measurement accuracy directly impacted on both quality and productivity by influencing the yield, determining product quality and determining energy consumption. In the second example chocolates were automatically weighed prior to packaging and a transducer used to provide an electrical signal representing weight.

A precision digital voltmeter measured the weight transducer output and individual chocolate weight information used to control the amount of chocolate poured into the moulds and thereby ensure that the final package weights were correct. The cost structure was as follows:

* 30% margin for distribution and retail

* 50% margin for manufacturer

* 20% of product cost is packaging

* ingredients are 50% of individual chocolate cost

A 57g package contains 11 chocolates retailing for 30p and the product line turnover is £12 million per year at a production level of 60 million packages. Each chocolate weighs 5.2g and the ingredients cost 0.38 pence. For each 40 packages produced 39 must meet the legal minimum weight of 95% of package nominal.

The company invested in a £5000 measurement kit which had a payback period of six months. It was found that by saving just 60 microgrammes of ingredients per individual chocolate (0.1%) it was possible to recover the £5000 investment in six months purely as a result of improved accuracy in measurement.

Bearing Journal Nightmare.

Concentric pumps are in most engines and this presentation provided an excellent example of how a highly competent manufacturer managed to solve a serious recurring problem using measurement techniques. Transmission pumps fail when no oil or transmission fluid is pumped and this is very important to the end user. This happened when a lining 0.5mm thick wore down to its base within minutes of operation.

The pumps had been manufactured for ten years and an Ra Surface Measurement had been used. Changes in the production process had, however, caused a series of serious failures. A total of 800 man hours was spent measuring parts to seek out the error whilst production reverted to the laborious tool room grinder which gave a good finish but was slow.

After a period of ten months working with the customer, the measuring department and grinding staff, a return was made to the production grinder in March 2000, but in May the problem returned. Reducing the Ra Surface Measurement had not been effective and production had to revert yet again to the tool room grinder. Advice was then sought from Huddersfield University who undertook measurement of toolroom grinder, production grinder, and 1998 pre-problem output.

Findings showed that the measurement system being used did not tell the whole story. All three surfaces were found to have the same Ra value. It was only when three dimensional measurement was used that the 'waviness' which had led to failure was revealed. Once it was revealed, however, it was possible to take action which involved the purchase of a CNC grinding machine which could be used to meet a three dimensional specification. This equipment allows for specifications to be incorporated into the drawing in far more detail to control the process.

Key learning points from the presentation were as follows:

(i) Never apply a drawing tolerance without considering the manufacturing process, including the gauging process.

(ii) Always review the tolerance after process and gauging capability studies.

(iii) Always re-check the tolerance requirements during initial process qualification.

(iv) It took just 24 hours to obtain the data that led to the solution.

The UK Forum for wear testing is currently working with the DTI on methods for assessing Ra technology.

DTI Measurement Case Studies

In addition to the above the DTI has also produced a series of case study sheets on good measurement practice as part of its 'Competing Precisely' campaign. Recent examples include the following:

* Cinch Connectors who have achieved zero defect manufacturing rates for their H-3 Contacts as a result of investment in a new vision inspection system.

* F. G. Wilson (Engineering) Limited who greatly improved the consistency of cable termination by focusing on the accurate calibration of crimping tools.

* Integrated Sensor Systems (iSS) whose vision system for weld head positioning has led to decreased process time, improved process quality, reduced rework levels and increased productivity in pipe and pressure vessel welding.

* Rexam Containers Limited whose recent investment in and in-house development of accurate force measurement equipment has enabled them to determine the penetration resistance of their sharps containers and gain a Kite Mark for the certification of goods to BS 7320: 1990.

NEW QUALITY SCHEME FOR RADIO INDUSTRY

A new quality assurance scheme designed to complement the Radio and Telecommunications Terminal Equipment (R and TTE) Directive which came into force in April has been launched for the radio industry .

The Radiomark, proposed by Radio Frequency Investigation Limited, introduces third party certification for radio equipment to ensure the performance of such equipment in its intended electromagnetic environment and, in particular, against interference from other transmitters in its vicinity.

Radiated immunity testing will be applied at varying severity levels and a choice of procedures is offered to manufacturers. It is anticipated that the new scheme will help to reduce the burden on manufacturers of declaring product conformity and subsequent liability as well as countering the threat of 'inferior' products deriving from the freedom from type approval which is afforded by the Directive.

The Radiomark scheme will thus provide a means to distinguish products which genuinely comply with the Directive.

Chapter Ten

Customer Satisfaction

No book on quality would be complete without some mention being made of the importance of customer satisfaction, as this forms the essence of quality. It is the most heavily weighted of all the criteria of the Business Excellence Model and even ISO9000, which received criticism in the early years for its apparent lack of customer focus, now incorporates a requirement for customer satisfaction to be measured at least to some degree, even though critics might still argue that it does not go far enough. Other notable developments have included at European level the establishment of a Customer Satisfaction Index in 1998, mirroring a similar initiative in the U.S. in 1994, the launch of an apprentice scheme for customer service in the UK by the Customer Service Lead Body in 1997, and the launch in 2000 of a new International Foundation for Customer Focus led by Sheffield Hallam University in conjunction with the Aarhus Business School in Denmark and the Stockholm School of Economics.

In addition to the above the compilation below includes case studies from the chemical, travel and telecommunications industries and concludes with a book review on how to measure customer satisfaction.

ASSESSING CUSTOMER SATISFACTION IN TQM PROGRAMMES

A conference which focused on customer satisfaction in a TQM environment with an emphasis on the chemical industry, was held at the Cafe Royal, London, on 18th April. It was chaired by Graham Webb, Chairman of the Chemicals Group of the Industrial Marketing Research Association.

Customer Perception and Customer Satisfaction

The first presentation was by E. J. Henshall, Statistical Methods Specialist, Ford Motor Company, and examined customer perceived quality with reference to the model of Dr. Noriaki Kano, and the application of Quality Function Deployment.

Kano distinguishes three types of customer perceived quality: Basic, Performance and Excitement, each of which may be classified as spoken or unspoken. Basic features are those a customer takes for granted and will not even demand if asked (e.g. a car fuel pump). Performance features are those a customer will talk about (e.g. fuel economy, passenger comfort). Excitement features are those which may provide an unexpected pleasant surprise (e.g. Radio Data System which scans transmissions of a given radio station and automatically switches the receiver to the strongest signal, helping to overcome problems with FM signal reception).

Most current market research is directed at performance quality and violations of basic quality. More effort is required in the area of excitement quality. The act of asking customers for a solution is impractical since it would result in the feature no longer being unexpected. What is required is a 'listening' to the 'Voice of the Customer', understanding what is being said, but not expecting solutions.

A telephone survey was conducted by an external agency amongst a sample of car owners of three makes of car, including Ford. The cars were of comparable age and had all recently been back to the dealership for servicing. Around 40 aspects of the service process were assessed with customers asked if the level of performance was better than, equal to or worse than expectations using a rating scale. Examples included number of visits required to fix a vehicle fault, courtesy of service receptionist, time waiting to speak to service receptionist, and availability of weekend service.

Analysis of the findings enabled the most important aspects of the service process to be identified, which were then used to compile a Customer Competitive Assessment, assessing the company's performance in terms of customer demands in comparison with competitors' performance, and an Engineering Competitive Assessment whereby the company's performance is assessed from an engineering viewpoint in terms of substitute quality characteristics such as availability of tools and parts (shown graphically indicating the strength of relationship to customer demands).

It was pointed out that the Customer Competitive Assessment and the Engineering Competitive Assessment may be in conflict for particular customer desires.

Measuring Customer Satisfaction

The next presentation, by William Bowyer, Quality Manager, Shell Chemicals U.K., and Edwin Smith, Managing Director of I.F.F. Research, explained how traditional techniques for measuring customer satisfaction rely heavily on rating performance against a series of factors using scaling techniques, and these techniques may not be entirely in focus with the customer focus objectives of T.Q.M. They stem from an era where more distant relationships existed with customers, and management 'was preoccupied with corporate aims rather than customer needs'.

Mr. Bowyer explained that whilst companies in the electronics and automotive industries have faced extinction the chemical industry has not. To many in the industry there has appeared to be little need for improvement. The quality messages which stemmed from the D.T.I's quality drive in the late 1980s were frequently understood by production managers and staff but seen as 'irrelevant, or even worse, hindering' by sales and marketing staff. The speaker referred to an 'air of disappointment' because BS5750 has not delivered companies to 'the promised land'.

Amongst the reasons for the industry's reluctance to consider the customer, he suggested, is the fact that customers were often also competitors and there was thus a reluctance to talk to them, but more likely it was due to a combination of arrogance and fear, stemming from economies of scale in manufacturing which made companies product orientated, and fear of price erosion.

Mr. Smith described the evolution of customer satisfaction research, noting that rating scales tended to persuade customers that further dialogue on the issues discussed (or peripheral issues) was 'out of bounds', caused management to impute how customers feel about the company with little direct evidence to go on, and perhaps worst of all, in the move towards a TQM regime, could give customers completely the wrong impression about the company's customer focus capabilities.

He spoke of the tendency to confuse customer satisfaction with corporate image and purchase decision-making enquiries and of the 'common pitfall' which can arise from the desire to measure performance against competitors:

"When the results show that he (the company) is doing better than his competitors he relaxes in a warm glow. No end of analysis of by sub-groups in terms of customer loyalty can compensate for the fact that his data-base is probably deficient in his competitors' most loyal customers".

He then spoke of sales reps listening to customers with the objective of optimising how they position their company's offer, but ignoring other messages being given out by the customer, and even when they do not, only the acceptable parts of the customer viewpoint are filtered through to management. He emphasized the need for constant re-appraisal of the research methods being used, as in implementing a TQM regime, companies will be putting even more aspects of their customer servicing under the microscope than previously.

Roche Products Customer Focus Study

G. K. Webb, Marketing Services Manager, Roche Products, and C. T. Talbot, Marketing Consultant, gave an interesting presentation of a study undertaken by R.S.L. on behalf of Roche Vitamin and Chemical Division to ascertain the relative position of Roche and competitors in the free market sectors of Feed Additives, Food Additives and Pharmaceutical Raw Materials. The sample was to cover purchasing decision makers and influencers among customers and potential customers.

Letters were sent to each respondent preparing them for a call from an executive interviewer, who had been briefed. A summary report was offered to each respondent and complete confidentiality was guaranteed. There followed 43 face-to-face interviews from a sampling frame of 70 establishments, and at the end a self completion questionnaire about the perceived attributes of suppliers was given. In order to ensure complete coverage on key issues, 52 telephone interviews were also undertaken.

A response rate of 62 per cent was recorded, which amounted to a total of 95 interviews (43 plus 52) from 153 establishments, and 66 of these were with a major decision maker. A table showed the breakdown of these.

Results showed that:

*spot buying was favoured more in the pharmaceutical sector whilst annual contracts tended to be favoured in the food industry.

*the majority of interviewees said they asked suppliers for re-quotes where necessary.

*respondents that did not ask for re-quotes, maintained that they disliked bargaining and expected suppliers to give their best quote from the start.

*more than 75 per cent had a supplier assessment system of some sort, which tended to be reasonably formalised in the food sector but only four of the 16 respondents in the feed sector had a system.

*virtually everyone claimed to assess suppliers on quality of product and delivery service.

*75 respondents inspected suppliers' production facilities, the main reasons being to assess ability to maintain consistent quality and meet legislative requirements.

*78 per cent indicated a preference for suppliers to be registered under a total quality system, and the trend in the food industry 'was almost to insist' as it helped administration and minimised danger of product failure. However, the feed industry frequently preferred to assess suppliers by its own criteria.

*only 17 respondents claimed to have a just-in-time system of stock control, although most had computerised inventory or purchasing systems.

*the number of days stock varied; averaged 14 in the feed sector, 5 to 14 days in food, and 28 days in pharmaceuticals.

*lead times averaged 7 days in feed, 10 to14 days in food, and 3 to 4 weeks in pharmaceuticals.

*the pharmaceutical sector regarded it as important that a certificate of analysis arrived with the goods or soon after.

*75 per cent of those interviewed in-depth claimed to have designated 'key' suppliers with whom they had a good relationship and considered reputable.

As part of the in-depth interview respondents were asked to indicate the relative importance of various supplier attributes which would govern their choice of supplier, and to attribute scores to individual named suppliers for various aspects of their service. These are presented in tabular form in the conference report.

Findings showed that in 'feeds', Roche 'over performed' on punctual delivery and quality of service, sales personnel and sales literature, but tended to fall below expectations for frequency of contact. Quality of service was below expectations in the food sector, and availability of a financial package was below expectations in the food sector and the pharmaceutical sector.

A comparison was made with an American study in which respondents were asked to rate competitors from a list of six companies, and to comment on individual suppliers' strengths and weaknesses.

Customer Satisfaction Research: The Dow Chemicals Approach

The next presentation was by Phil Allen, Business Research Manager for Dow Chemicals, and focused on a customer satisfaction survey undertaken by Dow UK last year, with which he was personally involved.

The survey involved face to face interviews with 150 of Dow's top customers which represented around 80 per cent of business across eight business sectors. These were conducted by Dow's field sales force which had 'a very open and frank relationship' with the customer base and were accustomed to dealing with the respondents on a face to face basis. The subject matter for the questionnaire was formulated through consultation with the relevant commercial managers, notably the Customer Service Manager, Regional Commercial Director, Regional Sales Managers and Materials Management. Where possible questions were structured with pre-determined answers which merely involved ticking the relevant response.

In order not to pre-judge the service criteria which customers regarded as important, respondents were asked to list in descending order of priority the five most important service criteria which they use to assess and/or select their suppliers. This open-ended question could be easily coded and analysed so as to produce both a simple as well as an overall, weighted ranking of the criteria. Respondents were then asked to rank their best supplier and Dow against those criteria.

Following completion of the fieldwork, questionnaires were sent to an external agency for computer analysis. Data tables were produced from which an analysis and interpretation for commercial management was made by the Business Research Department.

A diagram in the conference report summarises the results, which essentially highlighted ease of contact as an area of high importance but the lowest rating. The speaker noted, however, the important observation that whilst it appeared that 98 per cent of deliveries were on time and manufacturing could not believe products were not delivered on time, they actually only looked at when the product left the works (if the shipment left the day before or the day after it was said to have left on time).

The survey was said to have given Dow UK a clear understanding of customer service priorities from the customer's point of view, indications of areas of service weakness and shortcomings, a basis for prioritising corrective action and remedial programmes, and a 'yardstick' from which to measure future changes in performance. Its shortcoming was said to have been difficulty, through use of their own sales force, in obtaining meaningful responses to questions relating to competitor performance. Several reasons are given for this.

Management reaction to the survey was said to have been positive and an intention to repeat the exercise has been declared.

For companies considering conducting similar surveys the speaker suggested that the questionnaire be piloted in the field, preferably with a selection of customers from outside the selected sample but covering the key business areas to be surveyed, and recommended that the work be conducted by an experienced marketing researcher familiar with aspects such as sampling, questionnaire design, data analysis techniques and code of conduct - otherwise call in an agency.

Following the presentation a number of questions were asked, one being on how one could assess customer satisfaction at operations level without becoming involved with the sales-customer interface. Mr. Allen asserted that a future survey may well cover the sales –customer interface and in that case salesmen would not be used as interviewers. He also assured that there was dialogue with both customers and the sales force to ensure that the interviews had been conducted properly.

The I.C.I. Experience

The next presentation was by Francis Evans, Commercial Development Manager, ICI Chemicals and Polymers, based at Runcorn, Cheshire, and looked at the implementation of T.Q.M. at ICI with particular reference to the company's customer and supplier base.

The paper explains how ICI claimed to be a 'Total Quality Company', if nothing else by the simple Quality Assurance measure for ICI Chemicals and Polymers of over a hundred ISO9000 registrations. He accepts, however, that if that was all they had, they would have achieved very little.

To achieve Total Quality top management had to be educated so that they could demonstrate commitment to and leadership of TQM from a knowledgeable base. Commitment, at its simplest, meant conforming to standards set for meetings and stating requirements of their people clearly and unambiguously with sufficient time for work to be completed, and whilst many managers did little more than this, the best do much more.

The paper explained how the external measures of supplier audits, complaints data and customer service surveys have been applied to ensure that the company is not reliant purely on internal views of systems which are subjective, may be biased and could be wrong. It is noted particularly in this context that a rigorous analysis of complaints information provides not only an indicator of current customer service performance but also clearly points to areas of weakness i.e. complaints are opportunities. Customer satisfaction surveys, however, if properly designed can be an invaluable source of data for improvement, although if badly conducted can produce misleading

723

information, resulting in inappropriate action as well as being a focus of irritation for customers.

The paper recommends use of an external market research organisation and sets out various objectives for a benchmarking customer service survey.

Customer Service as part of European Quality Management

The last presentation came from Joe Seydel, International Research Director for Rosslyn Research, and Roy Haworth, Market Research Manager for 3M UK. It described a customer satisfaction survey conducted on behalf of 3M which used 18,000 customer interviews to assess customer expectations as well as 3M and competitor performance, in 16 countries for 50 product groups. It was described as 'undoubtedly one of the largest research projects ever commissioned'.

The project involved face to face interviews in thirteen languages. In each country the sample was structured by size of customer, sales region and customer type. Data was presented at over twenty personal presentations at Senior European Management level, Worldwide Management level, European Product Management and Country Senior Management with additional written reports for Divisional and Product Group managers. A total 125 reports were written.

Companies ranged from those where 3M was a minor supplier to those wholly supplied by 3M, whilst the interviews themselves took around 35 to 40 minutes for 160 questions. These were not directed at nominated individuals, but at nominated directly involved job functions, i.e. those who were actually and directly experiencing the current level of service and could be best influenced by future action.

The survey sought specifically to address the current standing of 3M with regard to customer service, how this compared with service received from other suppliers, and the customers' expectation of really good service. Previous work by Mr. Howarth and previous experience of 3M customer service and customer care' surveys assisted in the formulation of the format, which covered overall vendor rating, vendor contact and accessibility, physical distribution and special and commercial factors. Fieldwork was done by 3M's UK fieldforce and sixteen European agencies who were given printed questionnaires, interviewer instructions and sample lists.

The project is said to have enabled 3M to know how their service is perceived by the customers in Europe by country, by business across Europe, and by business within each country. Perhaps the biggest bonus, however, was the unexpected observation that sixteen 3M companies were in fact speaking the same customer service language :

'There is now a common understanding about the terms used for customer service. Countries and businesses are learning from one another. Probably for the first time ever, the disparate elements of 3M Europe are being pulled together in a common direction'.

At country and business unit level teams have been established to work with the research, understand it and formulate tactical plans to address problems.

The company say that they are now 'researching the research' to determine what clients thought about the project and quality of information received and how they are using this information. It is then the intention to repeat the European Customer Service Survey to ascertain the effect of the company's strategies and tactics on the business, and refine the process by direct input from all those involved.

[Issue 40 (April 1992)]

BUILDING QUALITY IN CORPORATE TRAVEL

The Institute of Quality Assurance hosted a one day conference at the Heathrow Penta Hotel on 25th March, with the title 'Building Quality in Corporate Travel', which featured representatives from various sectors who help to comprise this important industry.

The opening address was given by the Rt. Hon. Lord Brocket of Brocket Hall, which he helped to restore and is now one of England's finest Georgian mansions. This has become a major executive conference venue with a reputation for high quality, hosting amongst other things, the EEC Foreign Ministers' Summit in 1981.

Some clients, he said, ask for impossible things, but it is those organisations that 'go the extra miles within bounds' that win. Some clients have to complain about something, but if the attitude is good the potential is there 'to completely take the steam out of the complaint'. People who are keen to please, he said, will be those who succeed in business.

Avis: trying harder to satisfy Customers.

Car hire company Avis Europe was represented by their Director of Customer Satisfaction, Ms. Linda Lash. Under her direction the company has built on its legendary 'We try harder' spirit, conceived in 1962, to establish the car rental industry's first and so far only totally integrated business approach to service excellence, which incorporates a Customer Satisfaction Tracking System. This surveys the opinions of over 175,000 car renters a year in 14 European countries and provides results monthly to around 600 stations for continuous improvement.

Her team also implemented the Avis Customer Response and Information System which records and tracks customer complaints and enquiries on-line for immediate preventative analysis, as well as sampling and reporting customer opinion of how well Avis has handled the contact and. how likely these customers are to use Avis again.

As Director of Training Ms. Lash led the introduction and training of the 'Wizard of Avis' computer system in fifteen countries, which later gained Avis the first National Training Award in the UK.

Her presentation focused predominantly on the issue of customer complaints and their relationship to customer care. Many companies, she says, have approached the topic of customer care by focusing on customer complaints as it is often the only numerical data available:

'If only 1 per cent or 2 per cent of a company's transactions end up as a complaint, then 98 per cent or 99 per cent of customers must be happy and service levels must be okay. Or, if the number of complaints is lower than last year, customer care must be getting better'.

Research on behalf of Avis from TARP consultants, however, shows that for every letter or call of complaint to the head office complaint handling units there were another five that complained to other sources such as the sales force, individual executives, or the point of sale. In addition, for every complaint received at head office there were ten more customers who had experienced a service problem and never complained, enquired or requested assistance (the 'tip of the iceberg' phenomenon).

Further to this TARP conservatively estimates that for many businesses one customer is lost for every fifty who hear negative word of mouth advertising. Research at Avis showed that of the customers who experienced no service problems 92 per cent use Avis again, but of those who experienced a problem but did not complain only 78 per cent chose Avis again. Of those who had a problem, complained, and were not satisfied with the way their complaint was handled 70 per cent intended to use Avis again. This compares with 91 per cent for those who had a problem, complained, and were satisfied with the way their complaint was handled. The conclusion is that profits come from doing the job right first time and from effective complaints management.

Avis uses mail surveys periodically to construct a Customer Care Balance Sheet (picture taken at a point in time which shows how much business is being lost from customers who do not complain and from customers who complain and are not satisfied with the way their complaint or enquiry was handled). This includes asking for an indication of how many people they may tell if they are not satisfied, and seeks to pinpoint specific problems that particularly irritate customers and cause them to leave.

726

The answers from these surveys provide the critical input for TARP's Market Damage Simulation Model which converts the results of the research into annual lost sales and revenue.

To support the Customer Care Balance Sheet ongoing measurement is achieved with a 'Customer Care Income Statement' derived from surveys using shorter questionnaires but still containing the critical question of repurchase intention. These provide over 1100 monthly reports of progress back to the individual Avis offices and departments that delivered the service and enable the results of their efforts to improve customer care to be seen.

This year Avis is surveying over 175,000 customers resident in 15 countries, varying from the once a year holiday renter to the weekly business renter.

[Issue 81 (September 1995)]

INTERNATIONAL QUALITY

[Part of the report on the 39th EOQ Annual Congress, Lausanne, Switzerland]

"What constitutes Customer Satisfaction ?"

Within the theme 'People for quality –quality for People' came a refreshing concept from Mike Gibson who is head of the Juran Institute operations in Europe, based in the Netherlands.

His paper 'Can't get no Satisfaction, suggests that it is not just 'customer satisfaction' that we should be striving for, but 'customer loyalty'.
He draws distinctions between the two, based on research in the USA into how customer satisfaction is measured. From a survey of 200 of the largest companies, over 90% are agreed that maximising customer satisfaction will maximise profitability and market share but only 30% were confident that "economic value had been added". Only 2% were able to measure and document increases in satisfaction level, as determined by the "bottom line".

Customer satisfaction values are not equated directly with increased sales or premium prices! There is no correlation between what customers say (often in response to questionnaires) and what they actually do! "Satisfaction" alone may be a false indicator according to Gibson. Price has been cited in about 80% of the cases studied, to be the first or second greatest element of 'Dissatisfaction' although when customers have shown a significant behaviour change (in their buying) price is never a significant factor. There is therefore considerable discrepancy in what the Chief Executive of the supplier believe is happening in his business, based on point of sale data, as annual survey etc, and what his bottom line might tell him. A customer can provide a high rating at one point and then exhibit 'disloyal' behaviour for factors not apparent or understood when data is assembled.

727

Such factors are: his share of the customer's budget; Consistency of purchase over time; willingness to pay premium prices; breadth of purchase etc.

Gibson sees this as a "customer satisfaction conundrum" and offers 'loyalty' as the key solution. This is defined as "a bond characterised by the target customers consistently spending the ENTIRE budget for the vendor's goods or service on that vendor!"

The length of relationship with an average customer is critical. The apparent aim is not to see how happy customers are, but why disloyal customers have become so. The focus is on behaviour. The process starts with "driverbased" interviews with customers who have clearly demonstrated unusual levels of loyalty or disloyalty.

[*Quality Matters comments:* The relevance of this approach in the UK is clear, but that does not make the task of identifying the factors any easier. There would seem to be plenty of work needed in the Marketing and Sales departments of many of our best companies. Perhaps award criteria have to be re-examined.]

[Issue 102 (June 1997)]

NEW APPRENTICESHIP SCHEME FOR CUSTOMER SERVICE

The Customer Service Lead Body (CSLB) has launched a new Modern Apprenticeship scheme for customer service following the successful development of a Framework in conjunction with North London TEC, a steering group of volunteers from TECs, Awarding Bodies, employers, and Organisation Development Limited (a group of consultants who managed the development work).

Under the scheme it is envisaged that TECs will register with the Customer Service Lead Body to offer the Apprenticeship, possibly offering funding to organisations wishing to put Apprentices (aged between 16 and 25) through the Framework, whilst employers will sign a contract with the TEC and the Apprentice to deliver the Framework Training. Providers and colleges may also assist the employer to deliver some aspects of the Framework and/or contract with the TECs to deliver the Framework themselves.

In order to achieve the Apprenticeship the Apprentice will be expected to fulfil an agreed personal development and training plan which will include an NVQ Level 3 in Customer Service; five Key Skills Units which must be separately certificated; certification in four additional units taken from Business Administration Level 2 or 3 and/or Information Technology Level 2; and an induction programme as required by the participating TEC and the employer.

An Apprentice who takes up the Apprenticeship shortly after commencing employment with a Customer Service focus will normally be expected to have the completion of a Level 2 Customer Service NVQ written into his personal development and training plan. Should this not be included then the employer and TEC should be satisfied that the Apprentice's previous experience and general level of competence in the delivery of Customer Service is sufficient to imply that demanding Level 2 would merely result in a cosmetic exercise in the collection of evidence.

A series of Regional Modern Apprenticeship Briefings have been scheduled during the summer. This will introduce participants to the scheme and re-launch the Level 2 and Level 3 Customer Service standards so as to extend understanding of them among key players in vocational training. Also it will provide an opportunity to promote understanding of how to construct a tailored personal development and training plan and how to use Key Skills mapping in portfolio assembly.

More information available from The Customer Service Lead Body, The Brackens, London Road, Ascot, Berkshire SL5 8BJ

[Issue 112 (April 1998)]

OPTIMISING SERVICE QUALITY IN TELECOMS

At the conference on 4th-5th March at the Regents Park Hotel organised by Vision in Business, entitled 'Optimising Service Quality to Exceed Customer Expectations in Telecoms', the attendance and lectures had a majority from European telecoms companies, particularly from companies around the Baltic whilst also prominent were American personnel and companies taking part in an expansion of their technology into the emerging deregulated PTTs. The emphasis of the conference was on Customer Service, how to determine the level of service expected, and how to measure and how to provide a culture which will respond to customer requirements.

Identifying Service Factors.

To commence the proceedings on Day One Swedish communications specialist Bengt Nordstrom, now working for Eircell in Dublin, advised the delegates that the best place to start was to "put yourself in the customer's shoes". The staff in the company best placed to do this are front line operators who talk to customers.

Measurements form a key role in the process of Customer Feedback (e.g. in ascertaining Call Response Time -not on looking just at Customer Complaints). Mr. Nordstrom then presented the Identifying Factors to measure from a Customer's viewpoint. These were:

- Ease of Contact

- Response Time

- Staff knowledge of customer issues

- Fault management

- Echo

- Delivery Times

- Service Reliability

- Accuracy of Billing

- Call completion rates

Measurements applied to the above enable the company to incorporate the customer's needs into the Service Development. A marketing programme is applied to gain an insight into the customer's future requirement and indicate the customer's perception of the company's Service Quality.

An important feature of the marketing programme on future customer needs is to curb any Sales promises for the future deliveries and development. This is achieved by placing the Service Manager who knows the company system and IT capability as a key decision maker and only agrees to what can be delivered. The teamwork operations using the above approach has developed confidence with the customers and allowed rapid progress in the company service quality delivery.

Measuring Customer Satisfaction.

Willem Willemson of Netherlands PTT Telecom explained how in 1989 his company historically had a 'Topdown' management which was replaced by a young management team who introduced both ISO 9000 and the Business Excellence Model. This changed the emphasis from Technology to Service and Functions to Process orientation. The effect of this was to change the Manager's role from a functional one to now being responsible for a Process.

The new management set an Agenda which put PTT Telecom in a context, with Quality Goals and Targets, Objectives and Performance. Focus groups of customers were formed to register their priorities from a customer viewpoint. This involved the use of the research technique SMART and benchmarking to find best practice. Once the priorities were set the objective was to obtain reliable data to measure customer satisfaction.

The surveys for critical processes by region were made by telephone, interviews and short questionnaires using the 'Cati' system i.e. asking the right questions only. The feature of measurement is to consider Sales to Billing as a Process. An assessment of Quality for the Process needs to have response at ALL levels i.e. have a measure for each step in the process. This is analysed each 3 months by Region (using a Business Score Card approach). However, all this work and good principles were not without difficulties.

In what was a very open presentation, Willem Willemson explained that setting targets and regional comparisons [League tables -Ed] brought about "cheating on data presentations and bonus hunting distorting information" goes on in ALL organisations and has a motivation of Fear [Deming point - Ed] or greed. Quality practitioners and management he said need to be aware of these effects and also to acknowledge the difference and relationship between satisfaction and performance. A key issue is the "following through of the WHOLE process and analysis for improvement". By examining step by step, the most common feature of where it goes wrong is found to be in the interfaces between steps.

A question from a delegate concerned Business Process Re-engineering where the speaker felt that BPR is a crucial investment where all must have training for change. He also paid tribute to the unions who gave constructive criticism in the process.

Another question asked about Rewards. The response was that Sales are a problem when they are bonus driven and the speaker wanted a Team Bonus but it has not yet been adopted.

Customer Satisfaction via a Complaints System

The next paper was by Peter van Varenbergh but due to illness was presented by Linda de Preester of Belgacom. The company Belgacom is 50.1% owned by the Belgian government and 49.9% is shared between Ameritech, Teledanmark and Singapore Telecom. For this paper to put in perspective the magnitude of Belgacom operations need to be considered. They have 26,000 employees, 4.7 million PSTN lines, 150,000 inward calls per day and 100,000 written customer requests per year. In recent years competition has increased and alerted Belgacom to ascertain to greater depth the views of customers.

In response to their replies Belgacom formally set up a Customer Complaints Management System in the Customer Service department which had the support and commitment of senior and middle management and the 'people in the field'.

731

The first step was to find out the problems, which originally came from Technical, administrative and support services who "seem to live in another world"; "never deliver on time"; consider Customer Service as "the enemy"; and where they understand "still don't care". With this background a 4 stage progressive programme was initiated to change this culture. Methods and Procedures were developed and ownership of them established. Details of the system were presented with the ultimate objective of giving empowerment to 'people in the field' and to encourage and train them to be "internal consultants".

For those considering setting up a comprehensive system some useful hints were given to decide on some benefits:

- Cost of retaining 5 customers = Cost of making 1 new customer.

- Selling to existing customers is 5 times cheaper than selling to new customers.

- 96% of all dissatisfied customers don't complain -they just leave.

- Solve the customer's problem and he might become your most loyal customer.

Improving Service through a Quality Culture.

In a lively presentation Nigel Parnell, of Cable and Wireless explained that changing a culture is one of the most difficult processes to undertake.

There were many truisms quoted in the presentation, many of which were not in the delegate notes. In Mr. Parnell's view the first priority must be commitment and belief, and to be convincing from the top management. There must not be hype or the extolling of change and one must recognise that there are no Prescriptive Answers. Whatever is adopted needs to be presented with style.

The best starting position is for the manager to become a listener; what are customers saying? What is the gossip around the coffee machine? etc. Encourage employees to speak up and have no fear of doing so [Deming point again -Ed]. Then face up to what they say. Explain so that they can understand their Role and Value in the company. It is important never to think someone is stupid because they have a low paid job –often they have the best common sense.

There must be a training programme which helps employees to appreciate their contribution and shows that management also appreciates that contribution.

Thus the culture starts with training. There is always an argument that if staff are well trained they will get poached -but if you do not train them-they will walk anyway. Also important is to recognise personal objectives (note people do not go to work to fail) so their training needs are reviewed often.

The time projected for this holistic approach is 20% Training, Team Briefing, coaching; 10% Leave and Sickness and 70% doing the allocated job. In creating the approach Teams are key and are Peer selected. They will then develop the culture. If management try to create a culture it has less chance of success. Note if this is done then you have to live with the result. The teams have to be self motivating and self focused, with Team Rewards (e.g. with Marks and Spencer Vouchers etc).

The session ended with Questions from delegates which included 'How do you integrate gossip into a culture? The response was that there were jokes at many levels in an organisation (Cable and Wireless have 6 layers of staff where discussion takes place and these are often used as discussion points.)

Next 'What is tolerated in a culture and what is not?' Here a background of selected types of culture, competencies, skills and styles which had evolved were mentioned.

Finally, 'What happens when companies merge and have different cultures?' Cable and Wireless had faced this problem and it was not an easy one to solve. They have tried to create a Global identity focusing on 'What is Wrong?' and promoting a culture of change. Mr. Parnell believed that in many large companies the culture is now becoming Global, not English or others. [Before this happens there is often a boardroom struggle in the Parent Organisation -Ed].

Service Level Guarantees for Quality

The challenge of deregulation and interconnect of German PTT on 1 January 1998 has been taken up by Siemens Nixdorf and Tony Kremer explained their approach.

Siemens Nixdorf intends to use its expertise both technically and of service gained internationally and in UK to become a major Service Provider in the new German system. The basis of the Siemens Nixdorf approach is:

(a) To examine customers' requirements (including their current dissatisfactions)

(b) Analyse the margins and scope of third party service

(c) Set up the service for satisfaction of customers' expectations by a series of independent Service Level Agreements.

The Service Level Agreements (SLAs) apply to customers i.e. what Siemens Nixdorf will supply and SLAs exist both internally and with partners.

The interconnect focus to customers to handle by Third Party Service Providers is an opportunity within the regulations to stimulate rapid growth with multiple entrants.

The SLA approach aims to provide variable level requirements but within a standard framework. The main thrust of the Siemens Nixdorf system is that clients will not be able to cope internally with the demands made to their current technical and IT systems.

When it became clear to delegates that the approach was only in the Planning Phase and that the work had not gone 'downstream' or matured the reception was mixed. SLAs were deemed by some delegates to be "too close to contractual Methods", but Mr. Kremer explained that they were flexible and at the outset they had defined the approach that the system must not be a constraint.

However, a delegate remarked later that with such a system, 'The devil would be in the detail'. Another said (sceptically) 'We will need to hear how they have got on in a few years' time before passing an opinion. We've all had good plans that haven't worked!'

Optimising Service Quality.

In a presentation which addressed the conference theme exactly: "Optimising Service Quality to Exceed Customers' Expectations", Spanish Business Operations & Quality Manager Jose Ruiz-Canela explained how AT and T Unisource had evolved from the AT and T (USA) Business Communication Services-Europe mission statement :

'To become the most responsive partner for business customers requiring seamless and integrated pan-European and global communications services".

They concluded that new business in telecomms (e.g. Global) cannot be carried out by any single company. Therefore partners are needed. AT and T Unisource was formed to cover Western Europe with partners from PTT Telecom (Netherlands), Telia (Sweden), Telecom+ (Switzerland), and STET/Telecom Italia (Italy).

This required a Comprehensive System with a Corporate Strategy. When 'Customer Satisfaction' in these areas was examined it was also recognised that within the corporate structure a Quality Strategy was needed because in this market place "Good performance is not good enough." Research showed the "40% of customers who perceive your quality as 'good' are subject to leaving". The research also found that in the top 6000 Multi National Companies (MNCs) (those having location in three or more European countries) the top 500 large MNCs account for 80% of revenue potential.

From these findings the Business Process had to be redefined. This redefinition began with the AT and T Unisource CEO Jim Cosgrove's commitment :

"We should begin each decision making process with the question 'How will this help our customers?'"

Jose Ruiz-Canela asserted that without CEO commitment TQM is 'just hype' which can only be used ONCE, i.e. no-one will believe it afterwards. He then explained how the system worked by:

*Integrating Quality management into the management system.

*Using process management as a way to manage the business.

This was achieved by a process methodology of Seven Steps (described) using cross functional teams. The 'Operational Model' for Quality showed that each area of Process Management went through a Quality Management System, progressing through ISO 9000, Continuous Improvement, with Benchmarking and TQM to achieve a goal of Excellence.

The detail of the methodology is given in the presentation literature through a number of diagrams showing how the process is developed. This is through training and discipline in the entire methodology with a pro-active approach to Continuous Improvement applied to the whole organisation.

The questions from international delegates showed an in-depth interest in the approach. A delegate from Poland asked 'How do you motivate the leadership chain?' (By defining Roles and Responsibilities -particularly that of the Team Leader); and When to Train and How to Reward? (Timing of both are important in the development of staff, decided by review).

A Norwegian delegate asked 'How did the process start?' The answer was that initially there was help from Consultants, who advised that the first Leader must be enthusiastic for training and that the first Project had to show some 'Quick Wins' (even though small) to show senior management that the approach could deliver.

"How do you get Partners into the Quality Process?" asked a delegate from Holland. Here the answer was specific in that the company had an 'Interlock Method', where initially the requirement was Legal and Formal, then later concentrated on Interfaces within the Quality Structure.

Cellnet drive Business Excellence.

On Day two Dave Rogers, Quality Systems Director for Cellnet Mobile Telecommunications provided an insight into how his company was getting to grips with the EFQM Business Excellence Model, thereby leading the way in their industry sector. The speaker admitted to being "tired" of ISO9000 which "was beginning to get mundane" now that the company had been registered to ISO9001 for nearly five years, although he later accepted that it could be "a great vehicle for finding out what is wrong".

Business excellence, by contrast, placed a high emphasis on customer satisfaction and with customers who were "consistently saying that network quality had to improve" and OFTEL "getting cute on customer service" the need to move beyond ISO9000 was more than apparent.

Delegates were, in any case, advised that forthcoming revisions to ISO9000 were now being structured along the lines of the EFQM Model with one standard replacing the present twenty, and that they could expect to see this standard published around February 2000.

The Business Excellence Model has forced Cellnet to align the efforts of statisticians, who once outnumbered managers, with business processes. Now, people satisfaction, when addressed by means of an employee survey, entailed a move away from a purely monetary focus:

"The Quality of Working Life survey showed that people did not want money all of the time, but proper training, access to universities and a clear career path".

The speaker also highlighted how Cellnet was "really learning" about the often neglected area of Impact on Society with the help of the Thames University resource centre in Slough. The company is currently implementing the environmental management standard ISO14001 as part of this, although the 'Impact on Society' criterion within the Business Excellence Model is clearly more wide reaching and as he pointed out elements were now in place to enable monitoring and measurement against the Model".

Further developments have included the complete retraining of all internal auditors so that their traditional image of "nit pickers" no longer applies, and the introduction of business scorecard measurements in the form of monthly technical management reports and key process reports which feed into a formal change control programme. He emphasised that the business scorecards employed were "one liners" rather than fourteen page efforts. Key elements of the business scorecard, which are interlinked, are:

- The customer perspective

- The financial perspective

- The internal business perspective

- The innovation and learning perspective

There are goals and measures for each which are underpinned by the key questions of How do customers see us?', 'how do we look to the shareholders?', and 'can we improve and create value?'

The key principles governing the business scorecard approach are:

- measures should be traceable throughout the organisation

- targets are achievable

- there should be a direct link to the business strategy

- there should be benefit to the customer and to the stakeholder society

- statistics should be appropriate, monitored and communicated, especially when there is good news.

Co-operation has also featured recently on the company agenda with a European initiative prompting a venture with Vodafone to provide coverage in the Highlands and Islands. This said the speaker "helped us to understand each other's business".

This popular presentation attracted a number of questions from the audience including "how do you engage employees in the planning process?" and "would you recommend others to implement ISO9000?" In answering the first of these questions Mr. Rogers explained how monthly team meetings "formed the most important part of the quality programme especially in customer care". He stressed that:

"Directors don't know best when it comes to understanding complaints. Staff drive most targets especially from the customer perspective".

In answering the second question he said that he would recommend ISO 9000 but "only as a foundation, a basis and a guide". He did point to the design control element as being particularly useful as it enabled a "fourfold improvement" to be achieved at Cellnet, whilst on the supply side the standard had helped to alleviate the "crazy" situation in which some 10,500 suppliers were managed by around 1,000 staff.

In conclusion Mr. Rogers said that he now believed that Cellnet was "turning the corner from being technology to being customer driven" and hinted that their customer operations arm would double within the next few years.

Developing Best Practice.

John Wydell, Senior Benchmarking Consultant for Eurodata, an integrated consultancy organisation formed in 1976 by 18 telecoms companies in Europe, described how a survey on businesses in the UK and Sweden (the most liberalised markets in the world for fixed network and mobile services) yielded the following results for SMEs and corporate customers:

* 29% of customers had dropped an existing supplier.

* Of these 27% had dropped that supplier for quality related reasons whilst 57% had dropped the supplier for reasons of price.

* 8% of all customers will drop a supplier for "poor service".

* The larger the company the more important quality of service is relative to price.

* 80% of customers place a high value on the fast repair of faults.

* 72% place a high value on staff knowing their products.

* 64% place a high value on staff understanding your business.

* 51% place a high value on a single point of contact.

A Spider Chart shows the difference between those attributes which customers say are important and those which the Telcos believe are important, both individually and in terms of the benchmark. A group of six to twelve Telcos will usually agree to participate in a particular study, agreeing on questions and definitions at a kick-off meeting and through correspondence. Studies may be undertaken annually to track progress. Only participants may buy the data, but any operator can join. Typical measures include:

* reliability of service e.g. reported faults per 100 lines

* waiting time e.g. faults repaired in 24 hours

* timeliness and completeness e.g. percentage of lines installed by time committed

* accuracy e.g. number of billing errors

* communications e.g. percentage of customers kept informed of fault repair progress

* politeness and responsiveness (percentage of customers very satisfied) .

Eurodata collects data through questionnaires and site visits and publishes customised reports with identifying best practice and recommendations. In identifying a best practice Eurodate splits a process into its main stages, such as fault repair into fault registration and initial diagnosis by the operator etc. It then determines the relative importance of quality metrics such as reliability and speed. This is correlated with customer satisfaction or retention e.g. percentage of faults repaired within 24 hours against percentage of customers very satisfied. The main cost drivers are identified e.g. direct staff costs per unit delivered, then normalise the data e.g. cost data using purchasing power parity. All of this is then transposed onto the Spider Chart to determine best practice.

Eurodata "provides a safe environment where competitor companies can agree benchmarking projects".

[Issue 116 (August 1998)]

BUSINESS EXCELLENCE THROUGH QUALITY CULTURE

Leadership, people management and customer satisfaction were key themes at the Third World Congress for Total Quality Management held at Sheffield Hallam University from 29th June to 1st July. With the title of 'Business Excellence Through Quality Culture the event attracted an international audience of around 185 delegates whilst a varied choice of subjects was provided by the 60 plus papers/presentations.

Measuring Customer and Client Satisfaction.

This subject accounted for seven papers/presentations. Four were specifically devoted to the subject of customer satisfaction indices and were entitled 'National Customer Satisfaction Indices' (Claes Fornell, University of Michigan), 'The Role of the Customer Satisfaction Index in Quality Management' (Anders Westlund and Jan Eklof, Stockholm School of Economics), 'Customer Satisfaction and Customer Loyalty' (Kai Kristensen, Aarhus Business School), and '100 per cent Customer Satisfaction for the next Millennium' (Howard Barrett, Arthur Andersen). The remaining three papers were 'Providing Customer Satisfaction' (Jonathan Gorst, Sheffield Hallam University), 'Managing the Quality of Management Training -the Role of the Client Satisfaction Index' (Agnes Zaludova, QOS Associates"

Czech Republic), and 'The Measure of Quality Culture in a Managed Care Setting' (Elizabeth Noble, University of Missouri).

Claes Fornell argued that economic measurement is effectively inadequate for the modern industrial world, emphasising the fact that productivity increases do not necessarily proceed in line with quality increases. The implications for business are that economic assets are not necessarily hard assets, and consequently a need has arisen to measure so-called; "intangibles", which include customer satisfaction and intellectual capital. An index of customer satisfaction, he said, attempts to capture one part of this, hence the importance of the new European Customer Satisfaction Index (CSI) which is being compiled this year, in line with that in the US, which was first produced in 1994.

This Index, he explained, would provide important information for investors about the relationships between the current condition of organisations and their ability to create wealth, a measure which traditional accounting is failing to address. It will also provide consumers with a voice in measures that reflect their economic living standards. He drew attention to the strong correlation which exists between market value added (the difference between what investors put in and what they take out) and customer asset value and suggested that in future "there will be strong empirical evidence of customer satisfaction as an economic asset". He described the national phenomenon whereby profitability does not derive from revenue growth but from cost cutting as "unsustainable".

Westlund and Eklof define the CSI as 'a sytem to model, measure, estimate and analyse the interaction between customer preferences, perceived quality and reactions on the one hand, and the performance of the company (or any economic agent) on the other':

'High quality CSI systems should fulfil the following characteristics: be based on theoretical (micro)-economic model of customer behaviour; give information about the level of satisfaction for the individual company/product; be able to aggregate into industry/sector and national indicators; be able to compare satisfaction with main competitors over time; and be able to indicate the relationship between efforts done within the company and their effects on customer satisfaction'.

The authors describe pioneering work undertaken in Sweden along these lines which has resulted in an Index which is based on a theoretical model linking quality, satisfaction and performance and the use of state-of-the-art econometric methodology. This provides, in addition to a numerical estimate calibrated on a scale of 0 to 100, a means by which to analyse inter-relationships between customer satisfaction, perceived quality, expectations, perceived value (quality given price), loyalty and complaints:

'The individual model parameters and CSIs are estimated using PLS (partial least squares techniques [Fornell, 1992]). A number of time series for the Swedish economy and individual sectors/industries linking customer satisfaction, loyalty, productivity, output and profitability are available. The data sets are extensively used for secondary analysis on their own as well as in combination with data for other countries'.

The authors then highlight the "strong positive relationship" which has been demonstrated between the year-by-year change in CSI and change in profitability (measured as return on assets) and evidence that suggests that a high CSI will tend to yield an increased shareholder value which will be reflected in the stock price:

'The relationship turned out to be very strong and clear. For the top quartile (in terms of CSI), an average 5% increase in adjusted return on portfolio was recorded, while for the bottom quartile a decrease by 2% was observed'.

Kai Kristensen identifies some of the gaps which still need to be addressed and describes a model which is designed to establish the conditions of optimum customer satisfaction and a control chart which monitors the satisfaction process:

'We need to create some kind of microeconomic model which will incorporate customer satisfaction as a natural element and which will relate the concept more closely to the bottom line. Furthermore, we need a statistical theory which will relate customer satisfaction to quality control where the basic idea is first to bring the process into statistical control, and afterwards continuously to monitor and control the process'.

'We have shown that if company resources have been allocated optimally, the degree to which you live up to customer expectations should be a linear function of the contribution to loyalty. This seems to be a very logical conclusion, which will improve interpretation of the results of customer satisfaction studies'.

Gorst, Kanji and Wallace describe a pilot study by South Yorkshire Police to apply the methodology of the American Customer Satisfaction Index (ACSI) in the British context in the public sector:

'Working closely with the police, a questionnaire was developed which addressed the requirements of a public sector index, while supplying the police with information that they are required to collect for the Home Office. These particular statistics are collated for the Association of Chief Police officers (ACPO) indicators. While some questions provided information solely for the ACPO indicators and were not used in the calculation of the index, they did act as a check in ensuring that people were dealing with the 10 point scales as compared to the way in which they would normally complete five-point scales. The index approach breaks down the measurement of customer satisfaction into a number of distinct dimensions. While the dimensions are separate, some overlap does exist between them.'

The paper summarises the dimensions and explains how some of the problems associated with them in the particular case of South Yorkshire Police, have been resolved.

Further Information

The Proceedings of the Third World Congress for TQM at Sheffield Hallam University are incorporated in Volume 9 Numbers 4 and 5 of Total Quality Management (ISSN 0954-4127). This contains a total of 51 papers.

[Issue 133 (Jan/Feb 2000)]

BREAKTHROUGH RESEARCH PROJECTS IN CUSTOMER SERVICE

The Institute of Customer Service, via its Breakthrough Committee, has commenced pioneering cutting edge research in the field of customer service. A total of 14 projects have been launched the first of which, entitled 'Understanding customer requirements in an Internet and e-commerce world', led by Professor Chris Voss of the London Business School, is nearing completion. The Breakthrough Committee comprises of senior representatives from Founder member organisations and senior academics and other Breakthrough research projects include:

* Identifying the customer service skills required in the future

* Understanding the implications of service displacement

* Predicting movements in customers' expectations

* Establishing a positive customer service reputation

* Rewarding and recognising front-line staff

The Institute of Customer Service has also commissioned the research and production of an Occupational Map for the customer service sector.

Further information may be obtained from: The Institute of Customer Service, 2 Castle Court, St. Peter's Street, Colchester, Essex, CO1 1 EW

[Issue 137 (June/July 2000)]

NEW INTERNATIONAL FOUNDATION FOR CUSTOMER FOCUS

A group of researchers from Sheffield Hallam University, The Aarhus Business School and the Stockholm School of Economics have banded together to form the non-profit making International Foundation for Customer Focus. Its aim is 'to enhance the comparative international measurement and analysis of customer orientation and focus'. Its objectives are:

* To facilitate global exchange of research/ know-how in the area of measuring and analysing customer focus.

* To facilitate set-up of global databases for national customer satisfaction indices.

* To represent the research community in regional programmes for developing comparable customer satisfaction index systems.

* To constitute an expert resource for auditing customer satisfaction measurement/analysis systems in industry and public organisations worldwide.

* To constitute a general international "think tank" in the area of customer focus research.

Further information may be obtained from Jan Eklof, The International Foundation for Customer Focus, The Stockholm School of Economics, Box 6501, 3E-113 83, Stockholm, Sweden.

[Issue 139 (Winter 2000)]

HOW TO MEASURE CUSTOMER SATISFACTION (BOOK REVIEW)

Authors: Nigel Hill, John Brierley and Rob MacDougall (ISBN 0-566-08193-8) 136 pages.

Publisher: Gower Publishing, Gower House, Croft Road, Aldershot, Hampshire GU11 3BR.

Details:

Three authors from The Leadership Factor present 14 chapters explaining simply and concisely how to undertake Customer Satisfaction Measurement (CSM) [now an ISO9000 requirement -Ed].

In their Introduction they point out that where CSM programme fails it is usually a consequence of the organisation's inability to translate the information gathered into effective action, rather than the information itself, and give an overview of the CSM process. They then discuss the setting of objectives and project planning, followed by how to conduct exploratory research:

'The best starting point for a CSM survey is to carry out exploratory research which allows the customers to set the agenda -to tell you what are the main things that make them satisfied or dissatisfied, so that you can get the survey design right. A survey is no different to a product. If it's not designed well it won't work, and it is the exploratory research that will ensure that the survey design is right -in other words that it asks the right questions of the right people'.

The reader is led through the processes of organising and conducting depth interviews, and recruiting and operating focus groups as part of this exploratory research:

'As a generalisation, a typical number of depth interviews that would be carried out in a business market is twelve. A very small customer base might need fewer. A large and complex customer base would need-more, but twelve is the average. In consumer or domestic markets a large number of depth interviews, perhaps thirty, would be normal, but focus groups would be more commonly used for exploratory research in that type of market'.

'For CSM exploratory research focus groups are similar to depth interviews, except that instead of talking to just one customer, a discussion is held with six to eight customers. It is normal to run four focus groups although more would be held for a complex customer base requiring segmentation. Where there are segments of customers who may hold very different views, it is normal to segment the groups. So, for example, the views of younger people and older people towards health care or pensions are likely to differ considerably. In this situation it is not productive to mix them in the same focus group, but better to run separate groups for younger and older customers'.

A brief chapter on sampling theory is followed by a yet briefer one on survey options before the reader is advised about how to tackle the issue of maximising response rates:

'Probably the most common question that we are asked when presenting our seminar on Customer Satisfaction Measurement is how to improve response rates on postal surveys. For anybody aiming to use this approach to measure customer satisfaction it is a vital question since the problem of non-response bias can invalidate the whole exercise if the response rate is low. Moreover, you should not forget the point of the exercise.

744

Measuring customer satisfaction is not just a matter of carrying out a customer survey, asking a few questions and getting some feedback. It is meant to be a measure, usually one that is monitored over time as a key indicator of organisational performance, so an inaccurate measure is worse than no measure at all'.

The authors point out that response rates of below 50% in general cannot be relied upon and describe four sets of techniques (essentials, advisables, marginals and avoidables) which may be used in order to raise response rates:

'The effectiveness of pre-notification has been shown by several academic studies. Their conclusion is that this measure almost always works, with telephone pre-notification the most costly but effective method (doubling response rates in some studies). Mail pre- notification has a small, but positive effect in consumer markets, but the research is inconclusive for business markets, although our own experience demonstrates a strong effect when pre-notification letters are sent to business customers for telephone surveys'.

'It is conventional wisdom that response rates and accuracy will be higher where respondents are confident of anonymity and confidentiality. Practitioner evidence strongly supports this view for employee satisfaction surveys and most types of satisfaction surveys in business markets where the respondent envisages an ongoing personal relationship with the supplier.

In mass markets, where personal relationships are normally absent, there is not conclusive evidence that anonymity increases response, although in potentially sensitive areas such as financial services anonymity is preferable. Of course, there is a trade-off here with follow-up strategies, which will be much more cost-effective if respondents are required to identify themselves.

In many consumer markets, it may therefore be better to ask respondents to identify themselves in order to improve the cost-effectiveness of follow-up strategies'.

'Many people mistakenly assume that an incentive is the best way to improve response rates. A large number of tests show that this is not the case. Most incentives have little or no effect and some tests have even shown a detrimental effect, typically by incentives such as prize draws or coupons which may be confused in respondents' minds with a selling approach. Even promises of charitable donations usually achieve little'.

Questionnaire design is next followed by a chapter on rating scales, then a short three page chapter on introducing the survey which explains whom to inform, how to inform them and what to tell. Some important messages are given such as the need to ensure that all customers know that the organisation is committed to customer satisfaction and is prepared to invest to achieve it, they need not to assume that all customers will correctly interpret the purpose of a CSM survey, and the strong evidence that promising feedback is 'the single most effective element in increasing response rates'.

The longest chapter (15 pages) is devoted to the analysis of results and explains what matters most, how to determine priorities for improvement (PFs), how to construct a business impact matrix, and how to produce a customer satisfaction index.

A somewhat shorter chapter follows explaining how to benchmark performance, which is accompanied by an appendix entitled 'satisfaction benchmark'. Readers are introduced to the concept of the market standing survey and a number of important issues are discussed:

'The satisfaction section of the questionnaire must be extended to generate scores for all the suppliers with whom that respondent is familiar. Not all respondents will be able to give scores for all competitors so you will end up with different sample sizes for each one. Consequently, for a market standing survey a large sample size is almost always necessary since you need a reliable sample for the smallest competitor against whom you want a reliable comparison'.

'The first and most important characteristic of organisations near the top of the satisfaction benchmark league table is a very high level of top management support and commitment. They do not just pay lip service to customer satisfaction but make it quite clear from their actions that satisfying customers really is the top priority of their organisation. This is most clearly demonstrated when difficult budgetary decisions have to be taken. Are additional resources made available to provide extra staff when the customer survey shows a problem with service levels, or does top management simply encourage customer contact staff to try harder?'

As well as actually benchmarking your results, The Leadership Factor also uses its wealth of experience in the field of Customer Satisfaction Measurement to evaluate the methodology that companies have used and suggests possible improvements that could be made to further the validity of their results.

Also provided is material that enable an organisation to feed back its results to all levels of staff throughout the company. This is crucial, as every member of staff who comes into contact with the customers, or whose job will ultimately affect customer satisfaction, must fully understand the survey results and their implications if they are to be motivated to improve customer satisfaction'.

The next chapter deals with the internal survey which may be used to enable employees to identify 'understanding gaps' i.e. where they do not fully understand what is important to customers or realise that the level of service they are providing is inadequate. The following chapter covers the subject of feedback, including how employees may be stimulated to address PFIs, and how to generate a satisfaction improvement loop to 'talk up' customer satisfaction. The final chapter then deals with 'Satisfaction, delight and loyalty':

'There is not only a close relationship between satisfaction and loyalty but also, in the critical "mid-table" area, there are substantial gains in loyalty to be made from quite small increases in satisfaction. We have very many organisations in our Satisfaction Benchmark database whose satisfaction index is hovering around or just below 80%. They can expect significant gains in loyalty not from inventing gimmicks to wow the customer but from addressing their basic PFIs and improving overall customer satisfaction by perhaps just two or three percentage points'.

Chapter Eleven

Human Resources Development and the Learning Organisation

Human Resources Development has an important link with quality which is reflected both in the Investors in People (IIP) standard and the People Management and People Satisfaction criteria of the Business Excellence Model, which have the next highest weighting after Customer Satisfaction and are intrinsically linked to it. Like ISO 9000 the IIP standard has been recently revised, whilst revisions to the Business Excellence Model have placed HRD within the compass of the criteria of Partnerships and Resources and People Results.

Key events of the 1990s have included the annual Human Resources Development Week organised by the Institute of Personnel and Development (reported in 1992 and 1993) and the establishment of the Learning Company Partnership in 1991, although People Management has also been addressed at various other conferences reported in Quality Matters, most notably those held by the Institute of Management (1992), the Conference Board Europe (1994), The Quality Methods Association (1995), and the Institute of Management Services (1998). The Learning Company Conference was reported in 1999 and 2000. Also included is an address from world expert Professor Emeritus of Kyoto University, Yoshi Kondo, who gave a Keynote Address on 'Quality and People' at the Sheffield Hallam conference of 1995.

Facilities Management: A Vital Aspect of ATQ.

The 'newly emerged' (premises) management discipline of Facilities Management provides a link between technology, managing change, the working environment and employment trends. Speaking on the subject Roger Henderson, Director of Anderlyn Consultancy, explained how attention once only paid to the production line is now applied in the same detail to the internal administrative processes by organisations which now recognize the meaning and importance of Total Quality.

Facilities Management has the objective of providing and sustaining an appropriate quality of the working environment to house the operations of its employing organisation. Traditionally this has been a reactive type of service whose past failures to anticipate unforeseen needs have resulted in widespread though somewhat unjustified criticism', and premises managers like others have been guilty of short-termism, reacting to the pressure point of the moment and taking short term decisions to the detriment of long term objectives.

The speaker quoted examples of buildings that were excellent works of art, but did not address the needs of people within them. He warned of the dangers of in-house managers assuming knowledge of what goes on and underlined the need for the facilities manager to have a direct link with the Board or other decision making forum. This is necessary so that the facilities manager can be made aware of policy decisions affecting premises in time for the implications to be assessed. Ideally the facilities management spokesman on the Board 'will be well enough briefed to challenge proposals in which the impact on premises has not been properly considered'.

User groups are described as being the best means for the facilities manager to impart and receive accurate and up to date information particularly in the case of major projects with a life span of several years. The user group, however, is not a decision making forum -rather a means of reflecting the views and reactions of users of accommodation and a channel of information which can identify pending problems and opportunities.

Finally, it is stressed that warnings of future developments which might cause problems do not come from a crystal ball but through the use of intelligent and well-informed anticipation. This can only be gained by the facilities manager being totally involved in all aspects of the business. There should be no no-go areas. The following concluding comment is considered important:

"Attention to quality at each and every stage from the analysis of individual requirements to the provision of a comfortable and controllable working

environment will be recognized as contributing considerably to success through people ".

Following this speech the chairman asked about the level and size of an organization which warrants a facilities manager and the answer was that a unit size of 100 probably warrants it whilst 300 to 500 becomes a 'sophisticated department'.

[Issue 37 (January 1992)]

WORLD QUALITY SYMPOSIUM

To commemorate World Quality Day on 14th November 1991 the British Quality Association hosted a one day conference at the Park Lane Hotel in London under the heading of 'World Class Achievement through People'. It was chaired by TV personality Brian Redhead and consisted of eight presentations covering both the manufacturing and service sectors.

The opening address was by Sir Denis Rooke who spoke of World Quality Day, now in its third year, as providing quality organisations around the world with an opportunity to communicate the quality message. He said that 1991 had been a 'remarkable year for quality', because 'though we don't get headline news there is ever-increasing public awareness'. The current recession was he said, 'an opportunity to take stock and take time to review company practices and procedures'.

Brian Redhead praised *The Times* newspaper for its four page 'Focus on Quality Assurance', saying that they had 'done us proud' at a time when quality was headline news throughout Europe, although, strangely, not in the UK. He also underlined Sir Denis' comments concerning the recession, urging delegates who were not already into Total Quality to think about the possibility of being out of recession in a situation where their competitors are.

Power to the People

The first paper was presented by Mr. Clive Jeanes representing Milliken Contract Carpets and focused on a five year study by the Massachusetts Institute of Technology into 'The Machine that Changed the World' (motor car).

This study exposed the huge gap in efficiency, quality and cost between the best volume producers (mainly, but not exclusively, Japanese) and the out-dated mass producers of Europe and the US. The study claimed that the findings were just as valid in the luxury car market in which European manufacturers particularly are now finding that the prices they demand can no longer continue to rise to cover the inefficiencies of their development and manufacturing processes:

'In 1989 the typical Japanese plant required one half of the effort of the typical American luxury car plants, half the effort of the best European plant, a quarter of the effort of the average European plant, and only one sixth of the effort of the worst European luxury car producer, to make a car'.

These findings were described as 'particularly alarming' for European producers, and to add to them it was noted that all of the Japanese plants greatly exceeded the quality level of all of the plants in Europe except one, which unfortunately was not the same one as the one with the best productivity. That plant required four times the effort of the average Japanese plant to assemble a vehicle.

The speaker's message was that the West does not make full use of its people and during his 17 day study tour to Japan gained 'some very significant insights' into the virtues of making full use of workforce talent by eliminating waste movements, standardising and simplifying work, and providing workers with greater responsibility and authority. Involvement in TQC activities was 'not an option, but an expected, integral part of everybody's activities'. All employees were expected to be involved in the twin company objectives of survival and total customer satisfaction.

Some Western companies are recognizing that 'not only does every operator and every clerk have a brain, they also have enormous experience of their jobs, of the problems they face, and in many cases, of what to do to solve those problems -if only management will ask them'.

Empowering people is seen as a key issue and the speaker advocates abolition of separate manager and worker canteens, privileged parking spaces for senior people 'and all the other irritating demarcation systems that create a 'them and us' atmosphere'.

As for education:

"We have operators, none of whom have an 'O' level or CSE grade 1,2 or 3 in maths, very competently keeping run charts, calculating standard deviations and setting up control charts".

The company clearly prides itself on the training which has enabled this and believes strongly in the role of managers as teachers, coaches and counsellors:

"People who did not do very well at school exams, when they realise they can learn new things put these into use and in fact use them to improve their working environment They start to believe in themselves, and in their capabilities and therefore in their ability to go on learning, and getting more knowledge and skills".

"Some of our best problem-solving breakthroughs have come from teams of people who, in terms of their formal academic achievements, would have been seen as failures ".

As a vehicle for group problem solving the company has formed Corrective Action Teams, which are said to have a participation rate of 65 per cent with some people participating in three or four a year. But the company also allows individuals to contribute through the 'Opportunity for Improvement scheme' which differs from a conventional suggestion scheme by asking for problems rather than solutions. In most cases a suggested solution follows. About 85 per cent of OFIs are able to be implemented and the contribution rate is around 25 per person per year. The participation rate here is around 97 per cent.

[Issue 38 (February 1992)]

QUALITY FOR HUMAN RESOURCES

The British Institute of Management presented their Second Annual European Human Resources Conference on 5th and 6th February at The Royal Garden Hotel, London, where a quality theme had been selected for this all important area of modern management.

In his opening address Malcolm R.H. Brooks, Managing Director of The Conference Board Europe, announced the formation of a new European Council on Human Resources. Like all Conference Board Councils it will pool the collective experience of its members and enable frank exchange of actual corporate experience in a confidential environment. Its first meeting is scheduled for 16th to 17th June in Brussels.

A principal message of the conference was the need for human resources management to be jointly developed and implemented with line management. It had to be focused on quality, productivity, teamwork and flexibility.

Managing Organizational Change.

Ms. Margaret Exley, Managing Director for consultants Kinsley Lord, who has extensive experience in managing change in the public sector, described how changing the corporate culture is one of the most demanding things one can attempt to do, and attempted to answer some of the key questions which are often posed by those seeking to transform the corporate cultures of their companies. The questions were namely:

* how do you get started?

* is top-down the only way?

* can you only achieve transformation if you have a charismatic leader?

* how do you deal with the sense of loss and demotivation which some people feel?

* what are the real pitfalls?

* once started, how can you keep up the momentum?

* how do you really change behaviour for good?

* how long does it take?

In attempting to answer these, Ms. Exley began by suggesting that to get started enough people have to have a fundamental desire for change, enough to outweigh the costs. As a practical example she explained how Rover had initiated change by putting poor quality work on display, and then referred to the Citizen's Charter, believing that that would only work if there is sufficient internal dissatisfaction with the old ways of working to stimulate an internal driving mechanism for change.

As for top down or bottom up, it was suggested that in practice some sort of balance was needed between both approaches and leadership, whilst being a vital component of any change programme, required the ability to be a coach rather than a sergeant major. The Chief Executive's role is central and tenacity and persistence are primary requirements.

Corporate communications were another vital component of change. Some people apparently believe that if you have told employees something they must have heard it and this is not necessarily the case.

Empowerment was noted to be 'at the heart of cultural change'. Higher authority invariably gives rise to less knowledge about what is needed to achieve change. Reference was then made to a 'work and society' study which indicated that some 71 per cent of workers felt uncomfortable not working to their full potential, 73 per cent felt that they could be more effective in their day to day work, whilst 17 per cent felt that they could be twice as effective.

The system within the company had to provide expression to the culture, and this was done through the company's 'underpinning processes' such as recruitment, compensation, promotion, performance, management, planning system, organizational structure and system of pay. Note the pay system is an underpinning process, not a starting point for change. The BBC was quoted as a practical case where a radical review of organizational structure led to an overhaul of the relations between internal service providers and programme producers, leading to the concept of 'producer choice'.

Now for the pitfalls, and these were basically identified as:

- trying to change the culture by working only on one dimension.

- relying on those with a vested interest in the status quo to bring about change (many companies do this even though it seems obvious, a major clearing bank being an example).

- uncoupling the change programme from the business (in one international chemical company the change programme became an end in itself and people saw it ultimately as dispensible and not linked to business success).

- seeing the change programme as being one department's concern (this is classic and fatal because in the end no other part of the organization takes it seriously) .

- not enough communication.

- misunderstanding resistance to change.

As for the benefits of cultural change, the speaker quoted the cases of British Steel who went from severe overmanning (double competitor's levels) to the best quality steel producer in Europe, productivity rising from 96 to 222 tonnes per worker; Jaguar cars' productivity rise from 1.3 to 3.9 cars per worker per year; and Pilkington who have enjoyed a productivity improvement of 300 per cent.

Questions included a challenge of the importance of the attribute of charisma and whether a non-charismatic person was capable of leading the change process. Ms. Exley replied by saying that it depends what one actually means by charisma, but otherwise broadly acknowledging that the attribute helps. It was, however, not a basic necessity and the attribute of persistence was felt to be more important. She pointed to the leadership success of John Parker of Harland and Wolf, whom she said 'has real persistence and vision'.

Enhancing Human Resources Effectiveness.

This session comprised of two presentations by John A. Lee International Personnel Manager, I.C.I., and Michael Haffenden, Director of Personnel for Hewlett Packard, which provided practical case studies to illustrate how and where improvements to human resources management have been achieved.

John Lee spoke of the culture being the 'glue' of ICI, who have had to adapt from essentially a UK/Commonwealth company to being a global one. Major acquisitions, the most recent of which was of Atlas Explosives in the USA last year, has meant that the company has had to integrate people from totally different managerial backgrounds. It has been largely successful, and has resulted in a move from being task focused to being contribution focused (a key move in enhancing human resources effectiveness).

Performance management 'must not be about measuring people so that you can assess reward but as a means to coach, train and remedy':

"In my experience the managers who have shown themselves to be most effective for managing and developing individual performance have had a reputation for being 'as hard as nails' but yet the most caring you can meet, and, moreover, are most caring when they part company. It's not very visible, but it quickly gets known".

The continuing determinant of continuous success is said to be that of raising the contributions of people at a rate that is continually ahead of competitors.

At Hewlett Packard it was noted that some 10 per cent of revenue was being spent on research and development, and it was therefore seen that they had to maintain a culture which encourages innovation, flexibility and commitment.

An emphasis is placed on 'doing the simple things well' and managers are expected to visit various parts of the organization to discuss matters with employees. Human resources are said to be 'far too important to be left to Personnel', and many organizations 'get it wrong' when it comes to giving a direction.

Under 'The H. P. Way' every department has a mission statement and in this respect the speaker said he thought Hewlett Packard went further than most companies. To give a direction the mission statement must be communicated. This will avoid much of the 'territorial squabbling' that holds many companies back, and form a basis for customer assessment.

The company practises 'Hoshin Planning', defining those 'breakthrough' issues which the company has to get right. They're new, different, drive a department forward, and are written and regularly reviewed by everyone to ensure ideas are not imposed. A complete involvement programme, typically of one to two days' duration, takes place annually.

Beneath these 'breakthrough issues' in the 'training pyramid' are 'improvement issues'. This year ensuring activity based costing is understood by management is a 'breakthrough issue'. Total Quality Control (TQC) has become an 'improvement issue' rather than a 'breakthrough issue'. [Juran's book *"Managerial Breakthrough"* discusses these topics in great detail -Ed].

The appraisal system at Hewlett Packard is 'not just the boss appraising subordinates'. Evidence is taken from subordinates of subordinates and extensive use is made of peer evaluation, and, in particular, internal customer feedback. The speaker stressed the importance of having this approach if it is really desired to have an effective performance appraisal scheme in your company -'you can't just take the views of two people and expect it to be effective'.

Formal structures in the form of bodies like Works' Councils are notably absent with more emphasis on informal discussion, such as the popular 'coffee talks', and being on first name terms so that no-one feels inhibited at talking to each other and, especially, at talking over matters with senior management. This system is said 'to work very well in enhancing communication'.

As regards the benefits which the company is obtaining from its strategy of developing an 'aspirational culture', delegates were urged to look at the company's stock price [and presumably reach their own conclusions –Ed]

[Issue 43 (July 1992)]

HUMAN RESOURCE DEVELOPMENT WEEK

The HRD 92 Conference and Exhibition took place at the Wembley Exhibition and Conference Centre from 31st March to 2nd April. The conference was attended by around 340 delegates and featured around 28 papers grouped under the headings of 'Corporate Human Resource Strategy' and 'The Management of Change' (Day one), 'Productivity through People' and 'Technology in Training' (Day two) and 'Addressing Standards and Quality' and 'Productivity through People' (Day three). The exhibition featured around 200 exhibitors and was supported with a series of visitor seminars.

Training as an Investment: measuring the Commercial Benefits.

Avery Duff, Personnel Director for B and Q describes how the impact of staff development can be measured through labour stability and labour turnover, and how staff productivity surveys have enabled improvements to be made in work scheduling and more flexibility to be afforded to managers to respond to peak trading periods:

'Many operators are now multi-skilled where previously specialists existed, for example: where three administration specialists previously were employed to do the jobs of cash control, invoice checking and checkout supervision, now any one of the administration staff will be able to do these jobs, giving the flexibility required as well as better job satisfaction.'

A programme has also been undertaken to train management in competence identification and validation, which is linked both to the individual's bonus system and that of the manager. Opinion and attitude surveys are used extensively to obtain an indication of morale.

Quality Matters identifies the following key quotation:

'Whenever possible we endeavour to quantify the benefits of training to our Operations management in their terms rather than the jargon of Personnel. For instance to encourage the use of a training package designed specifically to meet the company wide objective of attacking shrinkage, specific targets were set for each store and action points identified for each head office department. The actual benefit achieved for the organisation was to reduce shrinkage from £26 million to £19 million in less than one year'.

Japanese Human Resource Systems: how they can be used in the West.

Tony Barnes, Director of Human Resource Planning for the Europe-Japan Centre highlights 'hidden factors of Human Resources' which have assisted Japanese companies in achieving success. It is emphasized that the results of giving people greater value and obtaining greater respect and commitment are as essential to a company as smart technology, long-term planning and meeting customer expectations:

'To date many Japanese companies operating in the UK are achieving great success in expanding their business, production, quality, market share and in obtaining a commitment from people rarely seen before'.

The 'real secret' of Japan's success is identified as 'worker respect' based on the fact that leading Japanese companies are able to tap the collective brainpower of workers to generate a constant flow of innovations.

The 'Kaizen' or 'ongoing improvement' philosophy, involving everyone, is unfortunately 'a very weak concept in most Western Management' and its absence 'explains why many American and European companies have been able to remain exactly the same for a quarter of a century'. Its main essence is that 'our way of life, be it our working life, social or home life, deserves to be constantly improved'.

Quality Matters identifies the following as the key quotation:

'Looking at Human Resource systems and related subjects it has to be realized that some of these systems/methods, many of which originated in the west, can be returned to the west and in fact are already in place in many companies. Adaptation and specific applications have been and are being put in place -no one company has necessarily the right formula -it depends on the type of industry , workers, environment, geographic area etc. '

Developing competent Directors and effective Boards.

This subject is addressed by Dr. Colin Coulson-Thomas, Chairman of Adaptation Limited, who is also the author of two forthcoming McGraw Hill books 'Creating Excellence in the Boardroom' and 'Creating the Global

Company, Successful Internationalisation'. He explains that whilst most chairmen believe the effectiveness of their boards could be improved, survey evidence suggests that hardly any of them are equipped to bring about fundamental change.

An ongoing programme of Adaptation Limited surveys involving over 1000 directors of whom 70% were chairmen or chairmen and chief executives, led to the development of twelve distinct categories of services designed to improve the performance of individual directors and boards as a whole.

Given the many forms of board and the different types of director, standard approaches and training packages designed for managers are unlikely to meet the needs of a particular board and its individual directors. References to judgement, common sense, vision, wisdom, integrity and tact abound when chairmen are asked to describe the 'good director' and focus on the customer is regarded as-particularly important, but a different emphasis often emerges when chairmen are asked to consider actual performance in the boardroom:

'While chairmen are able to describe the qualities they look for in new directors, there is little consensus among them concerning the contribution expected from board members'.

There is a general consensus that an individual who is lacking in directorial qualities should not be put on a board just to 'fill a particular slot', and the two most commonly cited means of improving the effectiveness of aboard are training and changing the composition of the board. The highest training priority is seen as being to develop strategic awareness and business understanding.

It is noted that only one in eight companies operate a periodic, formal appraisal of personal effectiveness in the boardroom and that when and where boards are assessed this tends to be in terms of the overall performance of the business rather than the dynamics of the boardroom and the distinct 'value added' contribution of the board.

Quality Matters identifies the following as the key quotation:

'There is no such thing as a standard board. Each company is unique, and every board is made up of a particular combination of personalities.. Standard answers to the question of what constitutes effectiveness can be dangerous. A director who is competent in the context of one board may not be a suitable candidate for service in a different boardroom. The nature of the challenges faced, and the qualities and skills needed to overcome them will depend upon the situation and circumstances of the company. Each case needs to be considered on its own merits'.

[Issue 52 (April 1993)]

MANAGEMENT TRAINING: ARE WE GETTING ENOUGH?

The Institute of Management, with the assistance of Professor Peter Warr of Sheffield University undertook a major research project starting in 1991 to survey the training of managers in Britain, the findings of which have now been published in the form of a report entitled 'Training for Managers'.

Against a background of concern about the quantity and quality of management training in Britain the report examines the training undertaken by over 2,000 managers and shows that in 1991 some 88 per cent undertook training with the average time spent on training (both in works and non-works time) being of the order of eight days. A third, however, said that their company did not have a formal management training policy and half said that they felt that they had had 'too little' or 'far too little' training in that year.

Around 83 per cent of respondents said that they felt that organizations should require all of their managers to undertake some form of training every year whilst 89 per cent agreed that the business environment was changing so rapidly that they needed more training than in the past. Some 81 per cent of managers said that they felt that they would be more effective managers if they had more training.

The survey also revealed a need for better training, with 40 per cent saying that their most recent training activity had been of 'little', 'very little' or 'only some' help.

The report recommends that the suggestions made by the Constable/McCormick and Handy Reports of 1987, that leading corporations be encouraged to set a public standard of five days off- the- job training each year for managers 'should be at the heart of any policy for management training', and proposes that within the framework of the recently announced National Training Targets for Lifetime Learning, targets in days per year of manager training should be set to ensure that each manager undertakes some training each year (with allowances for the difficulties of resourcing management training in smaller companies).

The Director General of The Institute of Management, Mr. Roger Young, concludes:

"Managers receive more training than they' did five years ago, but it is not enough to meet business needs. Every organization should have a formal training policy covering the needs of all staff, not just managers. But managers also need to take greater ownership of their own training: they must not rely on their organization providing everything for them".

HUMAN RESOURCE DEVELOPMENT WEEK: PART 1

Human Resource Development Week, the annual exhibition and conference of the Institute of Training and Development, took place at Wembley between 30th March and 1st April with the theme of 'The Single European Market: Improving UK Awareness and Competitiveness'.

The conference featured around 40 speakers from around 36 different organisations representing government, industry, institutions, trade unions, the armed forces, television, commerce and consultancy, whilst the exhibition featured around 170 exhibitors. A considerable emphasis was placed on the identification and development of the 'competent manager' who has the appropriate skills and abilities to deal with the rapidly changing demands of the new business era, with panel sessions on 'The Citizen's Charter for Education and Training' and 'Training for National Standards'.

It would be impractical to seek to review all of the conference presentations (which numbered 26 over the three days, with some repeats), but a sample of those felt to be of particular relevance to quality practitioners has been selected.

Quality: the Culture at Marks and Spencer.

Ros Gardner (Customer Services Manager) and Bernie Hoar (Personnel Manager) for Marks and Spencer presented a paper outlining the quality philosophy as practised at Marks and Spencer. This began with a consideration of how quality is defined, notably by Israel Sieff who ran Marks and Spencer from 1916 to 1964 who describes quality as being 'doing what other people are doing but doing it better'. This definition, according to the authors, 'is still relevant', but is enhanced by more recent perceptions from amongst the company's food technologists, training and development advisors and others, focusing on ideas like 'getting it right first time' in terms of systems and services and 'offering better for less' in terms of product supply.

In tracing the history of Marks and Spencer the authors point to the role of specification buying and close working relationships with suppliers in making quality 'a vital ingredient in the expanding business', such that now quality influences every aspect of the business.

In the context of human resources the most significant recent developments are noted to be in the development of relationships between suppliers, customers and employees, with a distinct shift from paternalism to partnership which has 'supported the survival of the quality culture in today's tough economic climate'.

It is explained how buying teams, including technologists, now work with their opposite numbers in the supplier's company to study such matters as the development and application of new raw materials and manufacturing methods so that a joint search for ideas and improved quality and value can take place. Specifications are agreed between the company and the supplier 'to provide a benchmark of the company's quality standards'. Thus, whilst the values and principles of the company remain unchanged since the 1920s, the ways in which the company works towards them clearly has.

The company is amongst those which have opted for a flattening of the management structure. Employee involvement applies in all stages of any changes, so that employees might own the challenges that face the company and play their part in helping to overcome them. A number of mechanisms are described that have enabled staff 'to feel more valued and influential', such as Store Communication Groups, clear routes for career progression, performance related pay, a comprehensive benefits package, a comprehensive induction programme and retraining for change.

Initiatives to improve customer relationships include; coffee mornings with store management to gain feedback on a specific department or on perceptions of service in a store, in store customer surveys to evaluate the success or otherwise of action taken in response to customer feedback, and launch of a national Customer Care statement reported in The Daily Telegraph as "the Marks and Spencer version of the Citizen's Charter".

Four main stages to achieving 'Quality Service' are outlined followed with a description of how effective training has been applied to support the concept. Examples are; the introduction of levels 1 and 2 of the NVQ in retailing to the induction programme, monitoring the job training of new recruits, and the compilation of a one day programme of Managing Customer Care designed to encourage managers to look at service, strategy and systems in their stores. This latter initiative highlights the fact that good service can sometimes conflict with commercial reality and that management can frequently be a barrier to the provision of good customer care. Consequently it is shown that a balanced approach is needed.

It is concluded that:

'The lead must come from the top; the importance of quality must be understood right through the company from director to part-time sales assistant. Effective communication and training are essential and success can only be achieved by the commitment and, therefore, involvement of everyone'.

Outcome-based Qualifications in Europe and beyond

David Handley, Head of External Affairs for the National Council for Vocational Qualifications (NCVQ) presented a paper outlining the development of Britain's National Vocational Qualification system. This represented a radical departure from traditional practice both in the UK and Europe by incorporating the principles of defining standards of competence, placing an emphasis on work- based assessment and allowing for accreditation of prior achievements.

The paper traces the development of the NVQ system from 1986 and explains why it was decided not to follow the German system even though this was 'recognised as a thorough and successful way of training young people'. Many argued that a similar system would 'improve the standards of performance for a British workforce'.

It was accepted that traditional qualification systems based on learning inputs 'are out of date and incapable of meeting the needs of the labour market in the twenty first century'. What was needed was 'a vocational qualifications system which would enjoy more credibility with employers and ensure greater relevance to the needs of the labour market'. The traditional vocational qualifications based principally around the curriculum needs of young people following formal programmes of education and training, and still prevalent in Europe was, however, seen not to be the answer. This is because in Europe some 10 to 15 per cent of the national skill base needs to be renewed each year to meet changes in working practices, technology and retirement, but the number of young people entering the labour market amounts to just 2 per cent of the total workforce.

Vocational education systems have therefore to give access to the adult employed workforce. It is asserted that by having qualifications based entirely on the standards of performance required in industry it becomes possible to separate completely the qualifications from any prescribed forms of learning. The German system is criticised as 'not a system designed for adults'.

With reference to the European Commission's 'Memorandum on Vocational Training in the European Community in the 1990s' the author then outlines the case for national standards for vocational training rather than European ones. The EC's policy is to aim for 'gradual convergence of national arrangements while respecting the principle of subsidiarity'. This allows for diversity of education and training arrangements between member states and thus renders European standards 'hardly realistic'. The author clearly states his opinion that there is not a need for every country to have common standards so long as 'informal comparisons' can be made.

In December 1992 the EC adopted a resolution to enable individuals to present their vocational qualifications, education and work experience more

762

clearly and effectively to potential employers throughout the EC. Also to help employers to have easier access to clear descriptions of qualifications in order to establish the relevance of applicants attainments for job vacancies. Achieving agreement on occupation descriptions has not been easy. Work is organised in different ways in different countries. It is said to be 'probably easier to reach agreement on individual occupational functions, recognising that these might be combined into occupations in quite different ways by different member states in order to meet their national labour market needs'.

New directions in EC initiatives in this area are, according to the author, going to involve some element of experimentation and an evolutionary approach rather than a single solution imposed from above'. One possibility, however, is for an 'individual portfolio' that provides a summary of an individual's achievement set out in a common format agreed between member states for which Britain's National Database and National Record of Achievement are said to be well suited.

The author sees it as inevitable that there will be a European debate about standards and sees the question of comparing the outcomes of different qualification systems as being 'a vital part of any move towards transparency'. He concludes:

'We must aim to ensure that the outcomes approach to qualifications is understood internationally and respected as representing a truly significant advance which has firmly established the UK as being at the forefront of innovation in qualifications development'.

[Issue 61 (January 1994)]

QUEST FOR QUALITY

Wales investing in People

This conference, held at the Copthorne Hotel, Cardiff, on 18th November 1993, began with the presentation of IIP Awards to four South Glamorgan businesses: Bass Brewers, Bank of Wales, Robert Bosch of Cardiff and the South Glamorgan Training and Enterprise Council, by Michael Scholar, Permanent Secretary of The Welsh Office, who also gave a short introductory speech in which he described IIP as 'rightly a most sought after accolade' and 'an important stepping stone on the road to TQM'.

The first of these, Bass Brewers, received the Award for the Cardiff Brewery of Welsh Brewers. They identified a need to re-focus their needs with regard to quality standards, customer service and cost effectiveness. Their mission statement reads:

'We will attract, develop and motivate a team of people of outstanding quality who will share in the success they generate'.

They have also achieved registration to ISO9002 and to mark their success with IIP produced a special commemorative brew for the conference complete with IIP Award label.

The second winner, Bank of Wales, are an organisation with a comparatively short history in financial services, being founded only in 1980, yet its pattern of change and growth has provided an interesting example to others in the field. Now recognised as an important regional bank in the UK, they realised early on that quality training is fundamental to maintaining growth and remaining a successful organisation. Their Group Personnel Manager, Sandra Spray says:

'Investors in People has helped us to focus on demonstrating the Bank's commitment to developing each and every member of staff'.

She also points to further benefits in increasing staff commitment and encouraging staff to recognise their own responsibility towards self development.

Robert Bosch are a German multi-national operating in automotive components, electronics, telecommunications, consumer and capital goods, and their IIP award was presented to their first UK manufacturing operation established near Cardiff in 1991.

This 700 strong unit with round the clock operation was committed to TQM from the outset and their strategy was 'to design a total quality approach as a cornerstone of the corporate culture in Cardiff and ensure it was compatible with the customer's expectations'. This was done in recognition of the fact that it was essential for them to be able to meet the supplier quality assurance requirements of major automobile manufacturers if they were to survive and prosper.

Their continuous improvement strategy is based on the Japanese philosophy of 'Kaizen' (little steps forward every day) , -one form of TQM -whilst teamworking and synergy form an integral part of their operations.

South Glamorgan TEC are the first of seven Welsh TECs to receive IIP and BS5750 and the background to their achievements was described by their Chief Executive, Mr. Paul Sheldon, who was appointed in 1991 having previously managed a pioneering training and enterprise company in Liverpool. This company had a totally open door policy that ignored pre-qualification, entry requirements and trained people to their level of capability and need.

He believes that UK companies have the ability to become the best in the world once the need to make all of our people, and in particular senior management, the best trained in the world, is recognised. He sees the programme as being about improving individual performances by planning and taking action to improve the skills, knowledge and job satisfaction of all people and urges companies to 'plan to invest in people just as you plan to invest in property or equipment'.

With this award the TEC has demonstrated that it practises what it preaches and is well placed to provide expertise and funding to help other businesses to achieve the IIP standard. This includes provision of financial help to meet the cost of consultancy to assess one's current position against the standard and develop an action plan. Further IIP achievements and BS5750 achievements by Welsh enterprises were described in the supplementary booklet to the conference.

These include the first NHS unit in Wales to receive IIP, Orcare Business Services of Swansea, the Service Agency of the West Glamorgan Health Authority, who received their award in May 1993. Created in April 1991 following government reforms in the NHS, it became only the third NHS unit in the UK to gain the award and the largest public sector organisation in Wales to achieve it.

Orcare committed itself publicly to IIP in October 1991 and has instituted a personal Development Planning System for each employee, which ensures that everyone has the opportunity to formally discuss business objectives and training. Their General Manager Mr. Mike Kilgour, says IIP has been invaluable in enabling the company to greatly increase the commitment of their staff, achieve more efficient ways of working and double the operating surplus from income generation activities over the last two years. The company now returns back to the NHS around 10 per cent of their total running costs, which they point out is over £1000 for each member of staff.

Another IIP winner is Cardiff based casting producer John Williams Foundry, who claim to be the first foundry in the UK to gain the standard. Chief Executive Geoffrey Metcalf described it as 'a significant endorsement of the company's policy of the search for excellence in everything we do'. In the absence of any National Vocational Qualifications (NVQs) for foundries the company effectively created their own with assistance from the TEC, who are also helping the company to train their own trainers and assessors. The foundry, which was established over 100 years ago, has also achieved BS5750 Part 2 and the Ford Q1 Award.

[Issue 64 (April 1994)]

MANAGING HUMAN RELATIONSHIPS IN CONTINUOUS IMPROVEMENT

One of the real success stories in implementing quality through continuous improvement in an IT environment is surely at AT and T Istel. Their Director of Quality Leadership in the UK, Mr. Geoff Hutt described, at the

'TQM in IT' conference how the company has striven to recruit and retain individuals who are recognised as having most to offer in terms of creativity, innovation and motivation. In doing so Istel has recognised the need to be seen as a company that will add more to the lives of those individuals than any other potential employer [despite the current high levels of unemployment – Ed]. He said:

'The mainplank of our strategy to maintain continuous improvement is our Performance Management System which enables each member of our company to understand what is required of them, how they are doing and how they are rewarded. It also aligns each person's work objectives with those of the company and ensures each of us directs our efforts to satisfying our customers'.

The essence of this is the premise that the vast majority of staff come to work to do their best both for themselves and for the team, and that it is the role of management to render support, helping them to understand what their best really is and how they can develop themselves as individuals. [In accordance with Deming's notion that transformation of the whole begins with transformation of the individual -Ed].

It follows that the first and foremost requirement is to create for each individual a clear statement of what is required in terms of results and achievements, generated in such a way that the individual does not just agree to the requirements, but is actually and wholeheartedly committed to their attainment. The means for this takes the form of a document, known as a personal performance guide, which is created in an iterative process between each individual and his or her team leader.

These guides comprise of five sections: prime purpose (a concise statement of what the individual is paid to deliver), critical success factors (most people identify about six factors), key tasks (which use verbs rather than nouns to convey the message and typically number between 4 and 10 for each critical success factor), performance standards (usually one for each key task, easy generation of which provides an indicator as to how well the key task has been identified), and improvement objectives (usually few in number since more than three tends to result in a lack of focus and a failure to achieve any).

It is emphasised that the format presented for a guide should be used as a framework to develop and communicate what is required of an individual and not be a straightjacket into which those requirements have to be fitted.

The first guide, that of the CEO, provides a model in terms of content and format, which is then cascaded such that everyone gains a common understanding of the theory and process before discussing a relevant practical example i.e. that of their boss. This then provides the framework by which employees can create their own prime purpose and critical success factors and discuss them with their peers. In an open and supportive atmosphere a consensus is soon reached.

Each individual thus drafts his own key tasks and performance standards, and agrees the completed guide with his boss. A formal session later harmonises all of the completed guides, resolving any omissions or overlaps.

Monitoring and measurement then takes place not through direct observation but by deduction from behaviours demonstrated, which in turn are ascertained using a consultative focus group approach with people drawn on a random basis from different populations within the company.

A formal, documented review of performance takes place at least once a year and is 'in joint effort between the individual and the manager' with each completing a separate review and submitting it to the other for discussion and agreement.

He says: -

'The formal annual review for us is, in most cases, a formality. This is largely because of our emphasis on frequent, informal reviews, which build dialogues and relationships, and ensure that there are very few surprises at year end'.

This performance management system is described as 'the keystone' of the company's strategy towards realising continuous improvement by enabling each individual to take charge of his own working life and improve himself as an individual. His combined improvements, of course, have a clear value added effect on the solutions which the company provides to its customers.

[***Quality Matters comments***: This talk was very impressive. The 'open and supportive atmosphere' referred to in the presentation is without doubt a key driver for continuous improvement. This is possibly the single most important factor which has maintained the momentum of continuous improvement year upon year whilst many others have fallen by the wayside. Perhaps a good company to benchmark?].

[Issue 67 (July 1994)]

MANAGING FOR PERFORMANCE IMPROVEMENT

The Conference Board Europe held a one day quality conference in London, hosted by Royal Mail on 20th May. It addressed the subjects of self-assessment, leadership and benchmarking, people management, the management of value added activities and the measurement of customer satisfaction.

People Management

Two speakers addressed the people management issues: Kate Mailfert, Quality Director for Eastman Kodak, and Roger Emms, Pursuit of Excellence Director for 1993 European Quality Award winners Milliken.

Ms. Mailfert described how the Kodak Strategic Framework Model had been devised which focuses on five Key Result Measures which are published monthly (in the form of a scorecard) :

*Winning Team

*World Class Operations

*Marketing Excellence

*Management Effectiveness

*Product Leadership

These are linked to the assessment criteria of the European Quality Award.

Mr. Emms described how, in all of its 138 year history, it had been Milliken's policy not to have a quality department which was separate from the rest of the organisation and the company had gained from having no shareholders to satisfy for short term dividends. They had initially chosen to follow the methodology of universal measurement advocated by Philip Crosby, but quickly found that measuring everything in this way merely resulted in 'an awful lot of paperwork' so a different approach was needed. Measurements had to be made relevant to customer requirements, and had to be made visible. 'Don't let managers hide them away' was the advice. The need to drive out fear, as advocated by Dr. W. Edwards Deming, was then highlighted, as he warned that if people became frightened of telling the truth the company would not move forward. Mr. Emms suggested that people should be free to make their own measurements rather than having them set for them, and advocated the abolition of piecework pay, which apparently had not resulted in anyone in his company losing money. This move 'merely ironed out peaks and troughs'. Likewise, nobody lost through the abolition of sales commissions, and whilst everyone is being encouraged to 'work themselves out of a job' this is always on the understanding that they will have another afterwards.

Mr. Emms was asked what benefits he felt his company had achieved from the European Quality Award and in reply said that he felt that it had created a superb feedback document for potential customer perceptions of Milliken, rather than having a role as a marketing tool. 'It's a superb benchmark', he said.

[Issue 76 (April 1995)]

Quality and People

Amongst the many distinguished speakers from overseas Sheffield Hallam University was pleased to welcome Professor Emeritus of Kyoto University, Yoshi Kondo, whose paper 'Quality and People' highlights the length of time for which there has been a natural desire for quality (over a million years). It has a greater compatibility with human nature than either cost or productivity. He therefore argues that a request for quality improvement by senior management is far more likely to be accepted by the workforce than calls for cost reduction or productivity increases. This is 'thought to be the most appropriate and acceptable way for enhancing corporate performance'.

The perception, however, that cost increases and productivity decreases as quality is improved necessitates a balance to be struck between both quality and cost and quality and productivity. This identifies with 'an optimum point of quality of conformance with regard to the manufacturing cost', which is shown diagrammatically. This point clearly falls short of perfection and can be difficult to identify since quality improvement tends in many cases to be indefinable, though the quality improvement cost curve can be lowered through the application of a creative idea or concept. This has the effect of reducing total cost and thrusting the optimum towards zero defect. He says:

"The optimum is indefinable and movable, and we should not search for the indefinable optimum, but for the ways and means with which we can improve the quality with minimum cost. It may be said that an approach of this kind is 'breakthrough', which is quite different from the superficial optimisation".

He argues that a successful breakthrough will always be accompanied with a creative idea and a strong will on the part of those concerned and that this fact is in accord with Dr. Deming's observation that "Productivity goes up, as quality goes up. This fact is well known, but only to a select few".

The argument that "we must start with quality whenever we attempt to improve a company's performance" is supported by an argument that "there is something apart from money that strongly stimulates us to do good work". In identifying this 'something' he discusses the underlying motivational factors behind work and play, suggesting that "as work and money grow further apart, the distinction between work and play blurs, and the two begin to overlap".

It follows that "if we could identify the elements that make sport so enjoyable and take positive steps to incorporate them into our work, our work would definitely become more pleasurable than it is now", and an attempt is made to identify several such elements, such as the activity being

769

independent and voluntary, and the score having no direct relation with money. He argues:

"When manufacturing is conducted only by standardising and simplifying the work and by separating planning from actual execution and when the results of the work are indeed only in terms of money, how can we motivate workers by offering them meaningful jobs?".

It is suggested that all too often the importance of standardising work is emphasised from the standpoint of improving work efficiency and assuring quality, for example, through registration to BS EN ISO9000, which can be inconsistent with motivation since "it restricts the scope for creativity and ingenuity on the part of the people engaged in the work".

The characteristics of work standards are analysed and whilst it is accepted that "everyone must make conforming products and everyone must work safely", the belief "that standardised means and methods formulated after careful consideration of all the angles must be productive and efficient" is contested. He suggests:

"It is unlikely that any single standards could apply to everybody. This kind of standardisation of motion is absent from sport; if such optimally efficient standards for motion did exist in sports, everyone would be able to achieve a world record simply by sticking to the standard and there would be no need to hold the Olympic Games".

In order to continue to improve it is suggested that in practice there is no alternative but to "discover and develop the methods that suit us best" and to this end the author proposes four principles for making work more creative:

(i) When giving work instructions clarify the true aims of the work (rather than emphasising methods and means).

(ii) Ensure that people have a strong sense of responsibility toward their work (e.g. through stratification of data, correction of data by mean value or regression, and application of the orthogonal principle in the design of experiments).

(iii) Allow time for the creation of ideas (excellent ideas are most easily generated when problems have been pondered and one has arrived at a detached, meditative state of mind).

(iv) Nurture ideas and bring them to fruition (new ideas are fragile, if examined critically with the aim of picking them to pieces or squashing them they may easily be destroyed, before it is really known how good they are, or if they can be developed in superior ways. The main enemies of new product development are frequently within the company itself and managers need to become patrons of ideas and encourage their growth instead of throwing cold water on them).

[Issue 84 (December 1995)]

PEOPLE MANAGEMENT

"Bringing the People with you" was the title of this year's Quality Methods Association Annual Conference which for the second year was held in the elegant surroundings of the Glaziers' Hall in London.

The conference embraced the theme of 'The New Order' with key contributors including Chairman of the UK Atomic Energy Authority Sir Anthony Cleaver, Professor Shaun Tyson of the School of Management at Cranfield University, Senior Policy Officer for the TUC Chris Savage and eminent writer and broadcaster Professor Laurie Taylor. There was also, by popular request, a re-introduction of the after-lunch QMA Debate, which has been a popular feature of past QMA conferences.

Quality starts with People.

With people management as the theme it was fitting that the morning presentations should include a contribution related to the Investors In People (IIP) standard, and this task fell to IIP National Assessor Roger Rix. In his presentation Mr. Rix stressed the need for quality to start with people [rather than quality systems or control -Ed] and suggested that IIP provided the ideal means to achieve the initial impetus. Organisations which were not into IIP had, he said, a general lack of knowledge of the need to achieve coherence and embed quality thinking at all levels. It was "sad, but true" that many organisations had no guiding vision and even where a semblance of a vision existed there was all too often an absence of goals and targets:

"Some organisations view their business plan as a state secret, which does not help quality thinking".

Organisations that were serious about quality must, according to Mr. Rix, at least consider IIP, and to illustrate the reasons why he drew attention to new research that suggested a high level of satisfaction with the standard, in distinct contrast to certain other standards, though he did not mention any of these specifically. He did, however, draw delegates' attention to a substantial number of companies that were "belatedly pursuing IIP because other approaches had not helped them to harness their people resource in a holistic way".

He described how it "warmed his heart" to speak to shop floor operatives who all of a sudden began to enthuse about their jobs. As an example, he told how security guards had taken to monitoring neon tubes to ensure their timely replacement, an action which all too often would be unthinkable.

By way of figures he pointed out that as of August of this year some 2,422 organisations had achieved IIP with a further 17,515 committing themselves to attaining it. This indicates that some 20,000 organisations have become involved with IIP after just four years, with perhaps more importantly, some 23 per cent of the UK workforce participating in schemes associated with it. This record of achievement was said to demonstrate "impressive progress" that was "only a start".

It was the speaker's pleasure to describe how IIP had now been incorporated into national training and education targets for the Millennium agreed between the Government and the Confederation of British Industry .This incorporated a goal to have 70 per cent of organisations with 200 or more employees recognised as Investors In People.

The growth pattern over the last four years he said, "suggests that this target is realistically achievable". However there was a clear admission that more needed to be done if it was going to be achieved. An example given was improved networking opportunities provided for benchmarking IIP, and incorporation of IIP within sector schemes such as those which already exist in the legal profession, healthcare and financial services. In this respect he highlighted a recent initiative in the legal profession to combine IIP assessment with that already in place for other quite separate, standards.

Growing through learning.

The encouragement of learning is a most important aspect of people management which has been appreciated perhaps more than most by the Rover Group, last year's winner of the UK Quality Award. Barrie Oxtoby of the Rover Executive Management Team explained with the aid of the company brochure 'Rover: Success Through Learning' how a company might seek to grow through a combination of individual and team learning.

At the beginning of the presentation Mr. Oxtoby stressed that Rover had not set out to become a learning organisation but rather to align the learning process as a primary driver with the company's business objectives. Thus business drivers were used as the starting point, and learning was subsequently aligned with these.

Rover Yesterday, which was depicted by caption from *The Sun* bearing the headline 'Wreckers: Sun exclusive on the men who are on a sabotage mission', where management set standards that became ceilings, was contrasted with Rover Today where learning "is a natural instinct", and where leadership has shifted "from cops to coaches". Chief Executive John Towers is quoted as saying:

"Our major competitive edge is in the added contribution of people, stimulated by creative learning and development".

Seven fundamental beliefs drive empowerment at Rover:

(i) Learning is the most natural instinct

(ii) Creativity, involvement and contribution are fuelled by learning and development

(iii) Everyone has two jobs: the job and improving the job

(iv) People own what they create

(v) People need work and enjoy it if they are valued

(vi) Creativity and ingenuity are widely distributed and grossly under-used

(vii) Management do not have all the answers

In order to create a learning environment based on these beliefs Rover formed Rover Learning Business whose mission is to develop an environment of continuous learning for all. It has its own infrastructure to support group and individual performance in line with the findings of a survey of all employees on their own learning requirements.

Various elements of the learning strategy developed by Rover Learning Business were described by the speaker, such as Rover Employee Assisted Learning (REAL) whereby individuals are credited with one hundred pounds to invest in learning outside work; the Voluntary Personal Development Files designed to help individuals to create their own personal development plan which may be used as a basis for discussion with team leaders about personal development; provision of open learning facilities at all Rover sites, and the Group Learning Exchange Network (GLEN) a computer database used to record and store corporate learning and capture best practices from benchmarked activities around the world [The latter is very similar to Japanese practices -could this be a Honda import? -Ed].

The brochure highlighted the company's annual spend on learning and development (over £30 million), the company's ongoing partnership with the University of Warwick which has enabled some 1,000 employees to achieve post graduate qualifications over the last five years, and the current track record of the strategy (21,000 Personal Development Files, 12,000 employees participating in REAL and 7,000 investigating their dominant learning sense using a special book and tape provided for the purpose).

In conclusion Mr. Oxtoby commented:

"The most dangerous people in the organisation are those who feel that they have lost the capacity to learn. They will then resist change for fear that this will be exposed."

This presentation was popular with delegates as evidenced by the flood of questions which followed. The first of these questioned why, although 21,000 had volunteered to join the PDP scheme some 15,000 apparently had not. In reply Mr. Oxtoby said that this was like asking if a bottle was half full or half empty and said that even without the 15,000 he believed that the fact that 21,000 had opted into the scheme in four years was "pretty good". Though in the pockets the uptake was low, he accepted that there possibly were clues to be found about the leadership in these areas. Some people, he said, were naturally cautious about what they enter into, and the worst approach would be to make the scheme compulsory.

He was asked about the current state of union relations and emphasised that the unions at Rover were "part of the team". He described how every business unit currently had a training and development committee. This was represented in equal proportions by union and management, with little to distinguish between the two. He referred to Senior TUC officer Jack Adams' position as a board member of Rover Learning Business. "We've got good role models for the Learning process amongst our unions", he said.

A question on the extent of single status within Rover was answered with a confirmation that there was now no blue or white collar workers or hourly paid.

QMA Chairman Professor Tony Bendell had to halt the questioning and expressed his hope that some "osmosis" may be forthcoming between Rover Group and its German parent BMW.

Making a Reality of Employee Involvement.

Chris Savage of the TUC also supported his presentation with a brochure, namely the Report to the 1994 Trades Union Congress entitled 'Human Resource Management: A Trade Union Response'.

This states clearly that 'unions are not opposed to HRM strategies which respect their collective bargaining rights and are consistent with the development of high quality, well paid employment'. However, where HRM language is used 'as a smokescreen for anti-unionism', then 'trade unions can only resist such a strategy'. It highlights the Third Workplace Industrial Relations Survey (WIRS3) and its subsequent analysis by its co-author Dr. Neil Millward of the Policy Studies Institute which suggests that 'there is no correlation between anti-unionism and HRM' and that 'union derecognition is generally followed by a decline in communication with the workforce rather than a move towards the HRM model of industrial relations'.

With this background Mr. Savage compared and contrasted the British system of industrial relations with that of Japan where commitment to lifetime employment "is by and large still a feature of large companies" and there is "recognition by companies that they had a workforce for the long term":

"Toyota viewed their workforce as a fixed cost and because they had an expensive asset they knew that they had to invest in them and harness them effectively".

The speaker argued that by strengthening the status of employees and making them long term assets, a long term incentive to improve market share would be fostered within the company. Supporting this was reference to an OECD Job Study which confirmed a positive correlation between the length of employee tenure and the commitment of companies to invest.

He implied that the 'hire and fire' mentality, which is so prevalent in the UK, is in practice undermining our ability both to invest and to change with numerical flexibility (ability to increase or deplete the workforce) being favoured at the expense of functional flexibility (ability to change or shift between jobs). He suggested that it is this second form of flexibility that will deliver quality in the long run.

He expressed concern that the significant move toward union derecognition in this country, particularly in areas such as printing and mechanical engineering, has not led to the creation of alternative forms of employee involvement. He also described as "worrying" the fact that in companies where this derecognition has occurred, job evaluation surveys are rare and in a substantial number (about 25 per cent) health and safety and grievance procedures for employees were non existent.

Performance related pay was singled out as a "blind ideology" which unions "oppose in principle' on the grounds that it is "costly and doesn't work" as well as "pretty ineffective at motivating people". He quoted the Inland Revenue Staff Federation where apparently "a lot of mistrust was created and festered" as a result of implementing PRP.

Following the presentation Prof. Bendell questioned the extent to which union members actually experienced security of employment and suggested that unions, like other institutions were "having to change". The speaker maintained his stance that on the whole union members did have greater security of work and whilst unions have in some cases been an obstacle to change this was, for the most part, largely as a counter to aggressive management styles.

Tomorrow's Company.

In addition to being Chairman of the UK Atomic Energy Authority Sir Anthony Cleaver is also Chairman of the Royal Society for the encouragement of Arts, Manufactures and Commerce (RSA) Inquiry into 'Tomorrow's Company' which formed the basis for his presentation.

The Inquiry began in 1993 when a number of chairmen, chief executives and other senior executives from 25 top UK companies came together to develop, test and refine a shared vision of 'Tomorrow's Company'. An Interim Report followed which became the subject of face-to-face consultations with over 8,000 business leaders and opinion formers, with further valuable inputs being contributed by the RSA Inquiry Network of some 500 RSA Fellows.

The Inquiry has concluded that there are essentially four obstacles preventing more UK companies from joining the top performers:

(i) Adversarial supplier relationships (the Coopers and Lybrand 1994 Middle Market Survey suggests that just under three quarters of UK companies still have an adversarial approach to supplier relationships)

(ii) Complacency and ignorance of world standards (a recent IBM London Business School Survey entitled 'Made in Europe' revealed that whilst some 70 per cent of companies believed they were performing at world class levels, in practice only 2.3 per cent actually were)

(iii) Over reliance on financial measures (of the 11 companies that topped the Management Today profitability league between 1979 and 1989 four have collapsed and two have been acquired)

(iv) Misunderstanding on the part of directors about their duties (preventing them from making balanced judgments)

Tomorrow's Company is seen as being one which clearly defines its purpose and values, communicates them consistently to all those important to the company's success, develops its own success model as a basis for a meaningful framework for performance measurement, and values reciprocal relationships with customers, suppliers and other stakeholders. Four 'Agendas for Action' have been developed in an attempt to bring these attributes into British business and make more UK businesses perform to world class levels.

The QMA Debate.

In the Debate Professor Tony Bendell and leisure centre owner Brian Mee proposed the motion that 'we do not believe that the UK is capable of learning quickly enough to perform in the front rank of World Economics'.

Professor Bendell argued that at present values are seriously wrong in the UK and that we cannot learn quickly enough because the will to do so is sadly lacking. He said:

"We need to unfreeze and break the stranglehold of the city and the pension funds. For this to happen we would have to virtually demolish this infrastructure. At present we are fourteenth in Europe in terms of GDP per household, which is almost on a par with Iceland".

Mr. Mee likewise argued that "it is going to take a very long time for quality to permeate every level of British industry".

The motion was opposed by David Rhodes, Quality Director of Royal Mail HQ in London, and Barrie Oxtoby. Mr. Rhodes admitted that "it is late in the day, we have lots to do and it isn't easy but if people believe we can change and want to do it then we can". The only thing standing in our way, he said, was whether we as a society believe we need to change.

Mr. Oxtoby argued that the UK has shown itself to be capable of performing at the top and quickly, but accepted that it "needed to be roused". The man in the street if asked where the learning organisations are would most probably say the universities, yet they aren't. They could, however, mobilise the whole country, he suggested, if they were to end their inter-faculty rivalry and commit themselves to "igniting teamwork" in the spirit of the Scouts and Guides.

When it came to the vote the motion was heavily defeated, perhaps because delegates were afraid to confess their pessimism though there were comments from the floor both for and against. One delegate who opposed the motion said that we were more than capable of leading the world, but investment was most important. Another who supported it suggested that the UK was falling behind because it had no real visionaries to drive it forward. Even David Rhodes who opposed the motion agreed that the UK was sadly lacking in its understanding of the need to change. After the vote Professor Bendell challenged delegates by saying:

"You've told us we can do it, so how is this dramatic change going to be achieved?"

[Issue 85 (January 1996)]

I.I.P. STARTER'S HANDBOOK

An interpretation of the Investors in People standard has been consolidated into a Handbook by TQM International. This is very suitable for those who are starting to examine the standard and for those developing their approach to the requirements.

The Handbook begins with an explanation of the standard and its background, i.e. developing the potential of all employees.

The importance of IIP is examined and builds on the principle that most people would rather do a quality job than a poor one. This requires an organisation to be committed to developing its staff by recognising the value of continuous learning, training, and development. The benefits are described in terms of employees understanding their roles and responsibilities and as a training investment, quoting Peter Drucker "If you think training is expensive -try ignorance".

The Four parts of the IIP Standard are detailed:

1. *Commitment.* There is public commitment from the most senior level within the organisation to develop people, to achieve its objectives.

2. *Planning.* A written plan identifies the resources that will be used to meet training and development needs of all employees.

3. *Action.* Effective action to train employees and develop their potential throughout their employment with active support from managers.

4. *Evaluation.* The investment in training and development is assessed for its achievement and used to improve effectiveness.

The Handbook provides a view on how the standard works, how it affects both management and individuals, and how it fits in with a continuous improvement approach.

[Issue 102 (June 1997)]

E.U. PROPOSES STATUTE FOR EMPLOYEE INVOLVEMENT

The European Union has unveiled plans for resolving a 25 year deadlock over arrangements for employee involvement by proposing a new statute to govern the formation of companies.

The proposals, outlined in the final report of The Davionon Group, include provision for special priority to be given to the free negotiation between employers, employees and their representatives in each company and only if they fail to reach agreement should a set of reference rules apply.

The new solution is designed to meet the concerns of countries with advanced systems of participation who have feared that a European statute potentially could be used by companies to circumvent national rules, whilst at the same time avoiding the imposition of a foreign scheme on Member States where the direct appointment of employees' representatives to company boards is uncommon, The EC Commissioners Padraig

Flynn and Mario Conti have apparently welcomed the new proposals. More information is available (reference IP396) from The European Commission, 8 Storey's Gate, London SW1P 3AT.

[Issue 104 (August 1997)]

D.T.I. PEOPLE WINNERS RESEARCH: IMPLICATIONS FOR CONTINUOUS IMPROVEMENT

Provisional findings of the DTI's People Winners Research Programme have been presented to the Continuous Improvement Research for Competitive Advantage (CIRCA) Network based at the Centre for Research in Innovation Management (CENTRIM) at the University of Brighton.

David Francis of CENTRIM has led the project which has involved some 62 companies situated in the upper quartile of performers in their sector and is believed to be the most extensive in-depth study of its kind conducted in Europe during the 1990s.

With the aid of a 'People Winners Scorecard' he demonstrated how the most successful organisations had not followed a single path towards continuous improvement but rather had incorporated the finer elements of both European and Japanese management philosophies into their culture. Here top management relinquishes sole ownership of their company's future in favour of alignment of the whole organisation behind a shared strategy and plan. With middle management now perceived as enablers rather than 'bosses' the organisations typically focused on the management of co-operation with the development of multiple teams, problem solving by employees rather than 'experts' and work units which were based on teams rather than on individuals.

The structure of the winning organisation of 1997 was summarised as having alignment demonstrated by shared planning, energy demonstrated by a win-win culture, learning demonstrated by continuous people development, co-operation demonstrated by multiple teamworking, and responsiveness demonstrated by three way communication. Organisations were rated as being competent, intermediate or advanced in relation to these elements, according to the degree of involvement and commitment observed:

'The strength of this survey is that top management can assess how the company is performing through the eyes of the employees. The questionnaire helps to pin down where specific problems lie. Following the survey a series of top team (i.e. people who have authority to lead change) workshops might be undertaken in each of the five areas covered by the benchmarking questionnaire. The workshops would be followed by a review'.

The final report is due to be published later this year.

779

[Issue 112 (April 1998)]

FIRST NET -BASED LEARNING AND KNOWLEDGE MANAGEMENT SYSTEM LAUNCHED

British Telecom and Futuremedia have launched the first complete net-based learning and knowledge management system. Known as Solstra it offers an open solution for the convenient, cost effective and flexible delivery of learning to dispersed audiences via the Internet or an intranet along with an effective method of knowledge management.

The launch follows 18 months of joint development and a thorough Beta test pilot which involved projects at the Ford Motor Company at Dagenham who used it to trial their QS-9000/01 quality standard training course, and at The Civil Service College at Sunningdale.

Features include an' Administrator' function which provides human resources, and training managers and administrators with 'a higher level of management efficiency than previously available'. An open architecture can be quickly installed by organisations to operate across a range of heterogeneous IT platforms. It also protects and maximises investment in existing learning material by accommodating net-based products regardless of who produced them. Also it can be used by organisations to demonstrate enterprise-wide compliance to government regulations and standards such as Investors In People.

Commenting on the launch Mick Durham, Head of Solstra Services at BT said:

"Solstra is good news for organisations and employees alike. It enables employees to take control of their own career development like never before, whilst at the same time saving organisations money by reducing training costs and providing a gateway to valuable business information. Solstra acts as a powerful tool to help avoid isolated pockets of excellence lying 'untapped' and to ensure knowledge resources are properly shared".

[Issue 111 (March 1998)]

MANAGING INTELLECTUAL CAPITAL: A NEW REPORT FROM I.M.

The Institute of Management in conjunction with Informix Software have published a report on the management of intellectual capital which suggests that over three quarters of British executives believe that by managing intellectual capital more effectively their organisations will have a much better chance of both surviving and of gaining a competitive advantage.

Some 85% of executives report that by using the intellectual capital within their organisations they both avoid expensive mistakes and develop improved customer service whilst 83% believe that managing intellectual capital enables them to capitalise on unique skills and know-how. Only 13% of organisations, however, have a nominated person responsible for knowledge management and over half (51 %) do not measure it in any way. Business leaders believe that the most important sources of intellectual capital are individual employee know-how (69%), technical expertise (53%), and relationships with customers (47%). One in four managers also rate databases as an important source of intellectual capital.

The main barriers to managing intellectual capital are seen by executives to be failure to capture existing knowledge systematically (78%) , a culture of short-termism (66%) and lack of investment in staff training and development (50%). Roger Young, I.M. Director General comments:

"This is not just another management fad. The knowledge held within an organisation can be a company's most valuable asset, especially in today's global business environment where corporate knowledge can reside in many different business locations".

Alan Kerr, Vice-president of Informix Software for the UK, Middle East and Africa adds:

"Although IT plays a critical role in the way that information and knowledge is captured in any organisation it is not solely a function of the IT department. Those that implement a knowledge management system must be able to blend analytical IT skills with broader management skills. The art is to identify the culture of the organisation, capture the knowledge held within it and apply the technology to transform the knowledge into a usable form to bring competitive advantage".

Research was based on postal questionnaires to 3,000 IM members in September 1997 which yielded 630 responses.

[Issue 116 (August 1998), from IMS Summer School]

Gaining and sustaining Employee Involvement

Dr. Shapiro suggested that high and sustainable levels of employee involvement are dependent upon the creation of organisational environments that value, develop and motivate all employees and highlighted the need for management to develop improved skills and capabilities to manage employee diversity:

"We are now asking employees to think specifically about how they may improve their jobs. This is one of the least developed parts of organisational

development. It is fundamental to success but the one thing we are doing the least about".

The paper describes research by the Centre for Research in Innovation Management (CENTRIM) conducted with 14 organisations from eight European countries into the link between organisational approaches to employee involvement and the management of employee diversity:

'The research included interviews within each of the companies with employees from Director level through to shopfloor workers and administrative workers as well as with Trade Union representatives where they existed. We also collected relevant documentary evidence including employee statistics, policies and procedures'.

The research was undertaken in two stages, first purely in the telecommunications sector, then more generally including for example, Merloni Ellettrodomestici S.p.A (Italian white goods manufacturer), Siemens A.G. Power and Transmission Group, and Milliken Europe N.V. of Belgium:

'It was not felt that the diversity of the participating organisations raised particular problems in the analysis of data, since it was not the aim of the research to provide a comparative study. Instead, there was a greater interest in gathering examples across a breadth of different organisational experiences with equal opportunities and quality management'.

Findings showed that:

* Selection of team leaders and facilitators was often from the traditional hierarchy reinforcing previous inequalities.

* Little or no evidence existed of mechanisms to support flexi-working or TQM team meetings geared towards meeting the needs of people working at home or part-time.

* No attempt had been made to assess whether different groups of employees had different training needs to enable them to participate in the TQM process or whether different processes and approaches were required to enable and motivate different groups of staff to become involved.

* Little or no evidence existed of attempts to build equal opportunities into the fabric of TQM in the majority of organisations although there was some recognition that there was a possible link between the increased involvement this might achieve and TQM success.

* Insufficient attention had been paid by most organisations to the role of culture either in blocking or facilitating employee involvement.

* Little evidence existed of multi-communication channels being employed by the surveyed companies in order to spread company information to support employee involvement. For example, many of the organisations in the study were sharing information about strategy and financial performance only with more senior staff. In addition, many companies felt the communication channels they used placed too much emphasis on top-down communication at the expense of bottom-up, which limited involvement opportunities.

* The degree of involvement that an organisation seeks from its staff may be positively linked to an increasing exposure to employee diversity.

* A number of organisations that had made a strong commitment to equality and/or diversity had begun to make a connection between business goals and diversity.

* Managing diversity should not become a goal in itself but should represent a means of better achieving business goals.

The fundamental message was essentially that if people did not feel valued they would not be motivated to contribute. Recommendations included:

(i) An explicit statement of the role of diversity in gaining employee involvement so that it becomes an integral component of a human resource strategy designed to meet business objectives.

(ii) Introduction of a mechanism whereby employees are given the opportunity to help define the values which will guide the organisation, together with a means of assessing the extent to which the vision is being achieved.

(iii) Integration of employee diversity with management development programmes to enable managers to challenge existing stereotypes which define characteristics traditionally viewed as necessary for certain positions.

'A Danish savings bank has established a Code of Values to form the basis for guiding decision making within the organisation. However they recognised that values could not be formed and agreed solely by management -a participative approach was needed if they were to be truly shared values. Consequently, contributions were invited from all 1400 staff, a cross-section of customers, shareholders and representatives from the local community. An emphasis was also placed on achieving agreement on the values to ensure that they were widely accepted as norms. Having established the values the organisation then measures the extent to which the organisation has lived up to these values'.

Following the presentation Dr. Shapiro was asked first for some tips on how to manage employee diversity, then for some ideas on how to improve the involvement of a very diverse leadership which requires its members to show much more supportive behaviour with each other. In answer to the first question she advised first that one works out where diversity exists since it can enhance performance, then to consider the concept of developing competencies for managing diversity, which, she assured, has been done. In answer to the second question she urged that no attempt be made to try to lose the diversity in the leadership team described. Instead she said that it needed to be understood and valued as a strength by everyone so that a shared vision could be developed.

[*Quality Matters* thanks Mr. G. Briscoe particularly for his assistance at this event-Ed].

[Issue 121 (January 1999)]

KNOWLEDGE MANAGEMENT AND THE LEARNING ORGANISATION: A NEW REPORT

The European Foundation for Quality Management, in conjunction with The American Productivity and Quality Center (APQC) and The Knowledge Management Network, have published the results of a joint benchmarking study project on 'Knowledge Management and the Learning Organisation'.

It describes the eight month long benchmarking study into global best practice in knowledge management which was undertaken last year and involved a preliminary survey of 350 European organisations, and site visits to five European and two US organisations. Some key findings of the study were as follows:

*Knowledge management is a container term and can take the shape of various initiatives within the organisation.

*The added value of knowledge is its potential for action.

*Individual knowledge must be transformed into structural capital.

*Knowledge Management initiatives should be aligned with business objectives.

*Knowledge Management activities should be integrated into daily work.

*Communication comes first, archiving second.

*Restructuring reward schemes is a major part of Knowledge Management.

*Knowledge Management builds on Total Quality Management.

*Intellectual capital Indicators should be developed with employee participation.

*Leveraging future earnings is more important than cost savings, but tangible benefits have been reported.

[Issue 124 (April 1999)]

QUALITY AND THE LEARNING ORGANISATION

In 1991 The Learning Company Project was initiated as an ideas house for organisational learning, conducting sponsored and/or consortium based research and developing and evaluating the systems and processes associated with the emerging discipline of Knowledge Management. In the eight years since its formation interest in the ideas and practicalities of the Learning Company has grown enormously and is now beginning to impact significantly on the role of the quality practitioner with recent work focusing on the development of anew auditable standard for the Learning Organisation in agreement with the European Foundation for Quality Management (EFQM).

The first partial draft of this new document was revealed at this year's Learning Company Conference at Warwick University on 15th to 17th March, and is reviewed below along with the Keynote presentation.

The new Learning Organisation Standard.

Co-founder of the Learning Company Project Dr. Tom Boydell, now a principal of Inter-Logics and the Learning Company Project introduced the new standard and its aims with Paul Belshaw of the Derbyshire based consultancy Winning Paradigms Limited who also worked on the project.

They explained how essentially the new standard will augment the nine criteria of the revised Business Excellence Model which is due to be launched officially by the EFQM later this month and which has been designed with the objective of providing an increased focus on Innovation and Learning, the latter being represented as a reverse closed loop link between the Organisational Performance criterion and the Leadership criterion.

Paul and Tom described how the new standard will provide a measure of the learning organisation by introducing scoring criteria for learning on three levels under six general headings for each of the nine criteria. Organisations will thus be able to measure their progress using the principles of self-assessment and subsequently apply for an independent verification by trained assessors. Organisations that are at an advanced stage with respect to Innovation and Learning may therefore have this fact reflected and confirmed by means of a higher level assessment above and beyond that provided by the Business Excellence Model itself. The three learning levels are defined as follows:

(i) Level One (Implementing) -Doing things well, consistently, reliably, according to current best practice by applying simple, linear, cause and effect thinking.

(ii) Level Two (Improving) -Doing things better by consultation on what is done and how it is done, with continuous improvement built in through controlled systematic experimentation, "pull rather than push", lean thinking, self-managed teamwork, flow from supplier to customer and back, and long-term customer-supplier relationships.

(iii) Level Three (Integrating) -Doing better things by recognising, respecting and working with multiple stakeholders and their perspectives, working systematically across boundaries and timespans, and addressing complex issues not capable of being tackled by linear thinking.

It follows that at Level One the underlying management structure is likely to be one of command and control and whilst there may be good teaching and instruction in place, learning is liable to be confined to learning "to get the right answer" or "to do things the proper way" i.e. to conform, valuing, respecting and ultimately depending on authority. The classic Level One organisation may be expected, for example, to have achieved Investors In People, assessment to which is often viewed very much as a Level One process, although it was capable of being much more.

Level Two, by contrast, is characterised by adoption of the well known Plan-Do-Study-Act cycle familiar to Deming practitioners with reward systems encouraging rather than stifling experimentation and risk taking:

'At the operations level people get the information, materials, equipment, training, on a just-in-time basis. This is part of the true meaning of "lean thinking". In this way "push" –sending things out what the sender thinks people ought to want or need, when the sender wants to, is replaced by "pull" -delivering what, when and where the recipients consciously decide they want. There is thus a flow of product or service to customers from suppliers, and a flow of information to suppliers from customers. Customers and suppliers now start to choose each other and the choice is made not only on grounds of cost and reliability, but also on the way in which they can form a mutually supportive long-term relationship, learning from each other and helping each other to achieve their goals'.

At level Three the standard really comes into its own presenting a real stretch goal that challenges current frontiers of learning:

'Previous ideas of predictability and linearity -that is, of simple cause and effect thinking, leading to readily definable "best" solutions, no longer apply.

Rather, most problems have multiple causes, and can be analysed not in terms of neat certainties but only by the weighing up of multiple probabilities'.

'The boundaries between "the organisation" and its "environment" become much less distinct, and a far wider range of people become involved in shaping the mission, vision, and strategy as well as working on improving our operations. At the same time we have to learn to find solutions that recognise complex systematic interdependencies, and that can handle probability as well as predictability. All this calls for major changes in how we structure our organisations, how we define and handle power and other relationships, how we may see ourselves and others, how we make meaning from what we do and help others make meaning from what they do'.

Each of the above three learning levels may be assessed on six neuro-logical Levels which together determine at which point within a particular learning level an organisation lies. This is repeated for each Business Excellence Model criterion to give an overall score. The six neuro-logical levels are defined as follows:

- Connectedness

- Identity

- Beliefs

- Capability

- Behaviour

- Environment

Thus, under the Leadership criterion an organisation at Level Three could expect to be scored for connectedness according to the following requirements:

(a) There is a key leader (or small leadership group) who in the first instance initiates and champions the process of transforming the organisation so that it works in an integrated way.

(b) All other employees (including but by no means exclusively so the designated leader) and many other stakeholders understand and accept that they have a part to play in collectively defining, evaluating and when necessary redefining the organisation's mission (i.e. direction and common purpose).

(c) All other employees and many other stakeholders see themselves as having a leadership role to play within their own sphere of influence.

At level Two, which presents a lower degree of difficulty and therefore a lower scoring range, the above requirements are restated as follows:

(a) The key leader (or- small leadership group) is designated and known to everyone in the organisation.

(b) It is understood and accepted by everyone in the organisation (including the designated leader) that it is the designated leader's role to take into account ideas and feedback from employees and other stakeholders and thence define, evaluate and when necessary redefine the organisation's mission (i.e. direction and common purpose) and ensure that everybody in the organisation knows what these are.

(c) It is understood and expected by everyone in the organisation (including the designated leader) that it is part of the designated leader's role to take into account ideas and feedback from employees and other stakeholders and thence model and exercise leadership throughout the organisation.

The remaining five neurological levels associated with the three learning tiers of the Leadership criterion use a similar format to ascertain the extent to which

* People know what to do to achieve the Vision (Identity).

* People believe the Vision will be achieved (Beliefs).

* People and the organisation have the capability to achieve the Vision (Capability).

* People know how to behave to achieve the stated goals (Behaviour).

* The environment supports the above.

As can be appreciated the scoring system for such a standard is invariably complex with potentially 9 x 3 x 6 i.e. 162 individual scoring elements. The details and mechanism of scoring have therefore still to be finalised to make it more workable. The standard itself is as yet still incomplete in its totality. It is, however, in its early pilot stages and a working document is expected to be published late next year following the presentation of the first European Quality Awards under the criteria of the new Business Excellence Model. It will then present a real challenge to all organisations that really do claim to be excellent.

Tom Boydell commented:

"Lots of people don't understand what Level Three is about. It's about how we work with people who see the world differently and have different aspirations".

Organisational Unlearning.

In his Keynote Address with the above title Peter Hawkins, joint founder and Managing Director of the Bath Consultancy Group urged delegates to examine critically those factors which present a barrier to the transformation of organisations, and to take a closer look at the all important link between organisational learning and knowledge management. He was notably critical of Peter Senge's book 'The Fifth Discipline' [reviewed in Quality Matters Issue No 73 January 1995.-Ed], arguing that it views organisations too much as "discrete entities" and "does not show how individual learning becomes organisational learning", issues which he is hoping to address through his own work which is centred around the following:

* the connection between organisational learning, knowledge management and culture change.

* how to move beyond organisational learning as merely "another acquisitive, addictive, trophy hunting, bandwagoning development process that promises so much and delivers so little".

* how cultures evolve through unlearning and relearning.

He highlighted some of the flaws in current thinking associated with the discipline of knowledge management with reference to a Best Practice Club report which found that 80% of organisations reported that culture either actively or passively hindered knowledge management initiatives. In particular he pointed to the danger of making such initiatives solely a matter of creating, warehousing and accessing data which he said frequently resulted in "data overload" which "is blocking learning". He then made the following proposition:

"We do not need to learn more and more, or even learn more and more about how to learn. Rather we need to discover how to unlearn individually, organisationally, as societies, and as a total global species".

In describing some of his recent work he presented two case studies, the first from British Aerospace at Filton, near Bristol, and the second from 3i, Europe's largest financial investment trust investing in unlisted companies that are in the process of growing. In the first case the company was seeking to move out of infatuation with gold-plated technical innovation and become passionate about competing in a commercially different world, but fell straight into the pit by trying to create new learning in an old culture:

'The company produced a video spelling out the doomsday scenario for Filton if it did not compete on the new terms: cost reduction, reliability, process efficiency etc. A copy was sent at Christmas to every employee. When we walked the site and talked to staff at different levels early the next year there were three dominant reactions: Fatalism (they have secret plans to close the site and there is nothing we can do about it); Suspicion (they are painting a bleak picture in order to scare the unions off demanding too much); and Denial (Bristol would never let Filton close, it is too important for local employment, we have the best designers and engineers in the world and BAe would never want to lose that capability).'

The speaker described how this problem was tackled through the creation of 'direct unlearning experiences' which began with the breaking down of so called 'functional silos' by creating more learning and better relationships across departments and the transference of functional directors' time away from firefighting operational problems and towards the management of corporate development. This was coupled with a spearhead initiative from the Chief Executive:

'He went with the main union shop stewards on a learning visit to Boeing. They travelled, hotelled and ate together for several days. This in itself was a previously unheard of experience, but the most effective unlearning was when the boss, who was the one who always previously had the answers, said "I want your help in discovering how we can make Filton better than Seattle, for I do not know how to do it"'.

In the second case the company wanted to be "a most admired company" when it entered the Ftse 100 list of leading companies, and embarked on a massive series of surveys which the speaker jokingly suggested were there to keep Mori (one of its investee companies) in business:

'When I asked the senior executives what they had learnt from the last staff attitude survey their replies varied from "I am sure I have got it somewhere in my cupboard" to "Well, it had the usual complaints... I am sure you find the same things in all major companies"'.

There was, however, a cure for this "surveyitis":

'We designed customer focused teamwork development events for every team in the company. Instead of questionnaires we got every team to analyse who were their most significant stakeholders, inside and outside the company, and to go and interview them in mixed pairs from the team. On the first day of the event they often arrived with smart acetates and well analysed and groomed data. We then told them we did not want traditional feedback sessions, instead they were to role play the people they had interviewed and the rest of the team would role-play themselves, asking directly for feedback. At the end of role play, we asked them to stay in role and imagine they were now in the corridor away from each other, and to

speak out loud what they were saying about the meeting they had just had. "Did they feel listened to? Did they think their comments would make a difference? What did the team think and feel about the feedback they had just heard?" This was the moment of unlearning as the team displayed all its characteristic ways of defending, denying and discounting potential new learning from their stakeholders. Later in the workshop we would often ask them to come up with the ten best ways they had for ensuring that nothing would change. Both mechanisms were ways of eliciting the prison of the old culture, and to encountering what is standing in the doorway blocking the escape into new learning'.

The speaker then paid tribute to Nelson Mandela as he introduced his last unlearning concept, that of "paradoxical seizure":-

'One of his most well known creations of paradoxical seizure was at the Rugby World Cup Final, just after the first democratic elections, when the new flag of South Africa was still only a temporary experiment. Mandela was still seen as the devil incarnate by many Dutch Reform Afrikaners for whom rugby was also a key religion, and the Springboks or Bokas their idols. The "devil" entered the temple of Afrikaner Rugby "Ellis Park", wearing the Pope's (Francois Pienar's) clothing. He raised his fist in an ANC salute and said VIV A BOKA BOKA. I spoke to many who were there who describe seeing those with them (of course never themselves) go into paradoxical seizure..... their circuits were blown. Do you cheer or boo? What Mandela had done was to take something that the White South Africans cared passionately about: "The Springboks" being the best in the world and getting world recognition. Mandela, with his moment of magic, reframed the Springboks as being ALL South Africans. His brilliance had migrated the motivational roots of the old culture and dynamically reconnected it to the new culture. From that day on nobody could really oppose the new flag or the new president. He had got beneath the ingrained defensive mental models and stolen into the hearts of the old opposition'.

The same concept, suggested the speaker, could be applied to stimulate culture change in organisations and in his conclusion he offered delegates the following advice:

'When faced with the 3 "Ds" of Denial, Defensiveness and Discounting, do not rationally confront, as this will reinforce the resistance, but rather create paradoxical seizure to blow the old circuits so new connections can be made'.

NEW HUMAN RESOURCES BENCHMARKING SERVICE FOR THE FINANCIAL SECTOR

A new human resources benchmarking service for the financial services industry based on a comparison of specific quantitative measures and/or ratios is now being piloted by Beaufort Management Consultants.

The pilot scheme has resulted from a recognition of a need for an unbiased and independent supplier to provide a reliable, valid and confidential HR benchmarking service or tool based on the following observations:

* Comparative data is limited, of variable quality and difficult to obtain.

* Most reports are generic and do not accommodate specific industry/company requirements.

* By opting for 'easy benchmark options' companies gain limited comparative data often from a small sample.

* There is a current focus on qualitative issues i.e. best practice resulting in an imbalance between this and quantitative information.

* Many measures are simplistic with little effort made to find common definitions.

The approach being taken by Beaufort is distinguished by 'the careful identification of the actual ratios themselves which are derived in consultation with each participating company and through a generic list provided by Beaufort Consulting'.

Beaufort say:

'We believe the effort spent during this developmental phase is essential to providing the platform for an effective comparison of data and subsequent validation of competitive positioning. We also believe that, for completeness, the above measures should include some form of internal customer/service satisfaction index based on the collation and feedback of customer perceptions concerning HR service delivery'.

A workshop/network meeting (post report) will provide an open forum for the discussion of results and will form part of an iterative process to ensure future reports provide the information of most value to participants.

I.I.P. STANDARD UNDER REVIEW

Investors in People UK, the body responsible for the development and promotion of the Investors In People (IIP) Standard, have begun consultations with various employers, Tecs and professional organisations regarding possible changes to the IIP standard.

Current proposals include a strategic re-appraisal of the way in which the standard is managed and presented and a change to a modular approach with more elements offering a greater choice of targets for IIP registered employers.

These may include for example areas such as the management of diversity and management development which will be rated in a similar way to that already used to assess applicant organisations.

Other areas under discussion are; the introduction of a benchmarking scheme to allow IIP registered firms to benchmark themselves against other recognised organisations, a mentoring role for those prepared to help others achieve the standard, and the development of a shared marketing model for IIP which would highlight relationships between IIP and other standards such as ISO9000 and the Business Excellence Model. These provide signposts for organisations looking to pursue different progression routes.

INDUSTRIAL SOCIETY LAUNCHES 'MAKE LEARNING PAY' INITIATIVE

The Industrial Society has launched a new initiative called 'Make Learning Pay' consisting of the two joint themes of 'Learn to Develop Others' and 'Learn to Develop Yourself'.

Within the 'Learn to Develop Others' theme the Society is featuring:

* The Liberating Leadership Programme (developed from extensive research to find out what people wanted from their leaders and incorporating leadership training and Liberating Leadership Profiling a system for measuring leadership behaviours from which appropriate interventions can be designed to develop the organisation's leaders of the future).

* The School of Coaching (a three month programme developed in association with Myles and Downey).

* Fifty Ways towards a Learning Organisation (book by Andrew Forrest, Director of Learning and Development, covering subjects such as the board's

approach, policies and guidelines, barriers to learning, mistakes and blame, and learning methods).

Within the 'Learn to Develop Yourself' theme the Society is featuring:

* Fifty ways to Personal Development (sister publication to Andrew Forrest's book above outlining fifty different methods individuals can use to develop themselves).

* The Diploma in Employment Law and Personnel Practice (thirteen one day modules of which participants attend nine).

[Issue 135 (April 2000)]

LEARNING COMPANY CONFERENCE DEBATES BUSINESS EXCELLENCE

Two discussion groups debated Business Excellence at the Learning Company 2000 Conference held at Warwick University from 15th to 17th March. In the first Learning Company Project Co-founder and Professor of Management Learning at Lancaster University John Burgoyne, and Human Resources Development Consultant Trudi Wakeman discussed some of the pros and cons of the Business Excellence Model as a learning company tool with reference to a pilot application undertaken in the BBC.

She described the programme, undertaken in 1997, which she led following her attendance on a Business Excellence Award assessors course, in which three teams were established (a management group comprising of nine members and two staff groups consisting of twelve members each) and questionnaires supplied by TQMI for a series of workshops designed to evaluate various criteria of the Model.

Typical questions were as follows:

* Do managers act as role models in leading improvement processes?

* Do managers provide adequate resources to support all of the initiatives they launch?

* Do managers go out of their way to build effective relationships with customers, both internal and external?

* Does the department use regular two-way meetings to share information and gather employee questions?

* Has the department ensured that a list of all processes vital to the success of the business has been identified and communicated?

A scale of 0 to 5 was used for all participants where 0 was defined as "I have not seen or heard about any ideas, intentions or actions on this topic", 3 was defined as "I have seen widespread actions across the department, but they don't appear to be reviewed or improved", and 5 meant "The action and its review is a totally natural part of the way we all work".

Action points emerged from the questionnaire submissions and these were fed to the other groups.

As a result of the exercise, which streamlined some processes shortening them by up to a week, the following key benefits of using the EFQM Business Excellence Model were cited:

(i) It gives everyone a starting point.

(ii) It appears logical and generally receives a positive response.

(iii) It is comprehensive and provides a good framework upon which to build.

(iv) It assists people to become aware of various areas of the business and the values of the business.

(v) Scoring makes people think about their comments and perceptions.

Other learning points were:

* For scoring to work effectively everyone needs to approach it in the same way and the assessment needs to be repeated, say, a year later.

* Staff may not be really interested in all of the detail.

* One must guard against 'initiativitis' which can result in approaches becoming unpopular.

* Care is needed to ensure that discussions, especially on leadership related issues, focus on the practice of management rather than individual managers.

* Negative perceptions can arise if there is "seemingly endless measurement and control".

The second discussion group was led by Mike Pupius of Sheffield Hallam University, who has recently undertaken the task of developing a strategic framework within the university for deploying the principles and practices of the Business Excellence Model, and David Megginson, Chair of the European Mentoring Centre and Professor of Human Resources Development at the Sheffield Business School.

This discussion looked at the extent to which quality models such as the Business Excellence Model had the power to subvert hierarchy by virtue of their process orientation. Different approaches to self-assessment were examined, with rigour traded against cost to give a measure of the robustness of self-assessment, with further analysis examining methods of turning outcomes into action learning.

It was suggested that the thinking which is embodied in the Business Excellence Model could and should lead individuals and teams to a point where all could learn together and where more sophisticated learning concepts could be applied. There was, however, much core learning still to be learnt in order to enable more people to think in process terms.

Much of the current hostility towards quality was put down to quality assurance which merely "goes through the motions" as opposed to the EFQM approach which represents a different way of thinking about quality. This problem was then seen to be further aggravated by the fact that too many consultants were simply working with tools and nothing more, whilst others who were good at working with people and processes were not using the right tools.

Delegates were left to consider the following questions:

(i) If the Learning Company proceeds down the route of measurement are we in danger of doing so much violence to the original vision that we end up with something that is neither good quality nor good learning?

(ii) Is the EFQM sustaining the myth of governability of organisations?

(iii) With the assumptive world of quality as it is, focusing on measuring and re-measuring, are we now in a world of such discontinuity that this is 'old technology'?

[Issue 136 (May 2000)]

FACILITATING LEARNING ORGANISATIONS (Book Review)

Authors: Victoria J. Marsick and Karen E. Watkins (240 pages)

Publisher: Gower (ISBN 0-566-08039-7)

Distributor: Bookpoint (Telephone: 01235827730)

Details:

This book has twelve chapters sub-divided into five sections on the facilitation of change management initiatives. The first section discusses why companies embark on a learning journey and provides a model for a learning organisation and a case study from Sulzer Orthopedics Inc. to illustrate the application of the model.

The second section then describes how organisations can begin with the end of learning and knowledge creation in mind. It explains how companies can diagnose and plan for change towards desired goals as a learning and knowledge management system. The third section follows with a discussion on how to change reward systems in order to build systems-level learning capacity, whilst the fourth looks at learning as a lever to achieve business results. The last section examines future direction for the Learning Organisation:

'Change is seldom smooth, straightforward or pleasant. During the process, those at the forefront can seldom see the forest for the trees. They are lucky to figure out what is "the next right thing to do" among the mess and chaos of a changing human system. It takes considerable trust in a future vision and indeed considerable courage to continue to struggle forward. And this is what we think most makes Sulzer Orthopedics a learning organisation - considerable trust and faith in its future, even when experiencing trepidation, coupled with great courage'.

'While it supported empowerment in theory, ConsultPro was founded by a strong leader in a command and control era. The company was changing rapidly in response to anew environment, but remnants of these values had not disappeared. When compared to other organisations in our database, however, ConsultPro was actually doing better in empowerment and team learning. We identified these as areas of strategic advantage. Its scores on systems to capture and share learning were slightly lower than others in our database. Hence, we identified these as potential areas of strategic disadvantage'.

'There are many places to start designing a continuous learning system. Most organisations have some kind of a continuous learning infrastructure in place. A good starting point is to review the elements of the system that are in place against the company's values, vision and "doctrine". Assess the current system's reach and depth and decide on what might be missing or what might possibly impede efforts to create a learning organisation. Table 5.3 in the book provides a checklist of learning strategies that may need to be created or radically altered in order to create a continuous learning capacity at the organisational level'.

'To sustain learning as a way of life, Johnsonville Sausage emphasized changes in systems and processes of work. At Johnsonville Sausage, the systems of performance management, information sharing and rewards have been integrated to form a cohesive whole. To ensure this happened, the organisation was restructured to share ownership for business outcomes. Members were invited to participate in setting the vision and in

creating solutions to barriers that they perceived were standing in the way of success. They regularly create the contracts on which work is determined and rewards distributed. In countless ways, they take responsibility for decisions that affect the work that they do and the customers that they serve'.

'The Great Performance Share is a prime example of integrated systems supported by new ways of structuring work and learning. The GPS is a performance management system integrated with an information system and reinforced by a reward system. Each month, individual and work teams (which may be functional or project based) create contracts for performance which are targeted at one of the company's strategic initiatives. The contract is posted on the electronic bulletin board for everyone in the company to see. It is also sent via electronic mail to those in the organisation who will be affected by the activity. Using the electronic interface, or through personal contact, anyone in the company can comment on, or ask to join in, the proposed work. This discussion leads to a final contract for performance that may be up to six months in duration with action points in each month. On a weekly basis, progress towards the goal is posted on the electronic bulletin board and to the impacted individuals via e-mail. The monthly questionnaire sent to those impacted by the contract provides information on which to make financial distributions'.

'Given that everyone's work is governed by the GPS system, learning is motivated, supported and measured through the work that is done. Learning is still influenced by the capacity and interest of people in their learning - factors on which Johnsonville Sausage placed much emphasis in the earlier phase of its journey, again by changing systems and structures to support learning. In the current Johnsonville environment, the need for new learning is governed by the needs of the marketplace and environment. It is difficult, if not impossible, for members to see these needs because they are continually appraised in relationship to the GPS, which in turn governs their level of compensation and reward'.

As we look; across the transformational journeys of Sulzer Orthopedics Inc., the US Army, Johnsonville Sausage, and Public Service Electric and Gas, we are struck by a number of parallels. In each case, there has been one or more individuals at the top driving the vision, believing that learning can make a difference. A sidekick, a person with knowledge of the change process, has helped to bring the vision to life and to move people and systems without harming them. There has not always been a clear diagnosis of how things are or a map of where the organisation is headed. Sometimes, the map changed mid-stream. Leaders were able to admit that they were wrong and to redirect the change effort. They did this in conversation with their employees. They listened, they talked, they persisted. They saw a future that they could hardly describe but worked creatively and collaboratively to tease that future out of the stubborn marble of the organisation as it was. And most of all, they realised that becoming a learning organisation is in the details of daily life -how they interact with their people'.

LEARNING COMPANY TOOLKIT LAUNCHED

The Learning Company (Mike Pedler, John Burgoyne and Tom Boydell) have launched a toolkit consisting of activities, questionnaires and checklists to help organisations to become 'learning companies'. There are twenty activities in all, each designed to enable the 'energy flow' in the organisation to be measured, 'learning blockages' to be identified, 'critical learning events' to be pinpointed, 'less developed learning abilities' to be strengthened and the 'eleven characteristics of a learning company' to be approached.

Kits are available from Peter Honey Publications Limited, 10 Linden Avenue, Maidenhead, Berkshire SL6 6HB Telephone: 01628633946.

Chapter Twelve

Information Technology

Information Technology has been one of the world's boom industries of the 1980s and 90s and it followed that a definite market existed for a membership organisation devoted to the promotion of quality in this area. In 1986 The Quality Forum was established and led by former IBM Senior Lecturer Gordon Irvine, hosting regular 'Quality in IT' days as well as other specialist events. It supplied a buoyant market alongside Quality Matters for most of the 1990s until sadly the organisation disbanded in 1999 due to financial constraints brought about by a decline in the industry.

Key events of the decade included in the early years the development and subsequent uptake of the S.E.I. Capability Maturity Model, which was described by one of its architects, Michael Conrad of the Software Engineering Institute at Carnegie Mellon University, Pittsburgh, at the Quality Forum conference of December 1993, and the controversial tug of war notably between John Slater of Logica and David Ling of Hewlett Packard about the merits and demerits of third party certification in the UK and U.S. both of which preferred alternative approaches (TickIT and the Supplier Audit Confirmation Initiative respectively). The latter was reported early in 1994, a year which also saw the establishment of the Quality Forum TickIT Special Interest Group augmenting the already well established Software Metrics SIG.

As the decade progressed attention began to be focused on the looming 'Millennium Bug' which many feared would cause havoc throughout businesses and the world. In the event many fears proved to be unfounded although we shall probably never know whether any of the scaremongering and heavy last minute investment to try to put the problem right did actually pay dividends by averting catastrophe. True or not the Millennium Bug's place in history is at least documented here.

In addition to the Quality Forum's events the compilation below includes notably a review of the British Computer Society's Fifth International Conference on Software Quality Management in March 1997 which was reported in the 100th and 101st issues of Quality Matters and compares the ISO9000 based Tick IT with the emerging Software Process Improvement and Capability determination (SPICE) standard. Also included is a review of the 1998 Quality in Manufacturing Exhibition and Conference which in this year had an IT theme, whilst the compilation begins with an early submission gratefully received from Joe Goasdoue, then Quality Director for ICL, in 1989.

CHANGING THE CULTURE AT I.C.L.

The computer industry, like many others, has been criticised for its quality. Terry Ernest-Jones introduces his article 'Finding People with Time to Get It Right' with reference to computer staff who are 'too busy' to get it right when they produce software that is 'barely usable', and he refers to the need to break the 'downward spiral' in which the customer has 'become used to sub-standard programs' and the supplier has developed 'little incentive to improve standards'.

Certain manufacturers have, however, begun to take steps towards radically reforming their quality and responding to the challenge. One such company is ICL who have implemented an intensive programme of training, involving the company's entire staff of 20,000 in some 70 countries, designed to change completely the approach to quality and put the company on track for BS5750.

Central to the programme is ICL's Director of Quality Mr. Joe Goasdoue whose aim has been not to impose quality rigidly from a central point but rather to achieve a 'Quality Strategy Through Employees'. The essential features of the techniques used to achieve this are explained in Mr. Goasdoue's paper 'Changing the Culture', presented at the CBI/PE Inbucon Conference earlier this year. A resume of his paper as a contribution to *Quality Matters* provides a background to many important Quality topics and sets the scene for future issues.

Introduction

The report begins with a discussion of Total Quality Programmes in general, and it is noted that many fail because management does not understand the concept of total quality and associates it with a technique of staff motivation which they 'probably understand even less'. It stresses that many T.Q. programmes fail because management 'allow them to fail', and what is often perceived as a 'quality problem' is more often than not, in reality, a 'communications problem'.

The paper draws attention to the workforce noting that often they are not realising how important customers are and that they will often work 'day-in day-out doing a bad job not bothering about quality, happily making products and services that dissatisfied the customers'. But it stresses that

"Nobody wants to do a poor job...suffer abuse from dissatisfied customers or to spend most of his working day rectifying defective output".

It happens because 'it has been accepted for so long by their management that they regard it as acceptable', and is aggravated by managers who 'make it happen by decisions and procedures which get in the way of their staff producing defect-free work'.

Five essentials for a Total Quality programme are then stated:

* Top management commitment and determination expressed in deeds not just words.

* A common understanding and language of quality.

* A long-term plan against which progress can be measured.

* A set of core company values in which customer concern is paramount.

* A management style which emphasizes the priority given to people management and process management.

Background

The report describes some of the background to the ICL company and how market conditions have changed, necessitating the company to 'understand the business requirement in detail' for all of the markets in which they specialize. The former approach of 'only having to be experts in how to make computers work' and 'leaving the customer to figure out how to apply them' is no longer acceptable, and the company wasted valuable skills and resources. A need for an investment in quality improvement was identified.

Quality -The ICL Way

The company's Quality training programme 'Quality -The ICL Way' was commenced in 1987. It required seven basic commitments from each employee to :- change, customers, quality, teamwork, achievement, productivity and people development, and ten obligations of management: to be both a business manager and a people manager; to give strategic direction to his team; to be a strategic thinker; to ensure that every output is of the highest value; to have a responsibility for teamwork; to develop his people; to have a 'can do' attitude; to pursue innovation; to confront difficult issues; and to be able to undertake self-measurement.

It is accepted that the initiative involved in doing this is not easy and 'requires total commitment and hard work by all levels of management'. It is noted that

"when people have done work just about right or close enough and had it accepted all their lives it is hardly surprising that it takes a lot of effort to convince them that change is either necessary or possible" .

Also "We have our cynics, but we believe we are on the right track".

The Quality System

Implementation of the total quality system involved:

1. A clear statement of top management's determination to achieve a quality performance in everything and a demonstration of commitment through investment.

2. The training and education programme.

3. The re-orientation of managers at all levels to their real role as manager of people and processes responsible for creating an environment in which their staff can perform.

Around 80 quality improvement teams were set up around the world to find root causes of problems and provide feedback on major areas of non-conformance so that long-term solutions could be sought and scarce resources shifted 'from problem fixing and defect rectification into the higher added-value work of developing new products for our customers'.

It is emphasized that these teams are not Quality Circles (although Quality Circles exist), but 'totally action-oriented teams of line managers' who report to a steering committee composed of every member of the board.

The Company's Reaction

ICL received a National Training Award for its training programme, but it was hard won. To begin with management and staff 'mostly sat back and waited for somebody else to do something'. They needed to understand that if something obstructed them in the pursuit of meeting customer requirements regardless of rank, they were 'empowered to shift it or, if it is beyond their direct control, to kick and shout until it is shifted'. Managers had to 'be equipped and prepared to act on all issues raised by their staff' and it was recognized that 'while education and training are crucial they are not enough'.

Managers had to change from being 'administrators and technologists into being role models, advocates, leaders and helpers'. They had to 'think and work strategically', 'to commit emotionally to the importance of customers and how to satisfy them' and have the ability 'to manage people by providing leadership and assisting them to do their jobs better'.

Investing in People

These requirements gave rise to a second programme 'Investing in People' incorporating 'Managing For Performance Through the Year' involving use of a Performance Management Calendar stating when activities such as objective setting, appraisal, performance rating and pay review must be completed; and 'Developing Individual Capability' providing an established process for managers to assess training requirements, personal improvement plans and career development plans for his team. Also included are two further modules to improve management competence in recruitment and selection and manpower planning and development.

The Quality Philosophy

It is noted that the 'quality philosophy', its systems and procedures cannot stand alone and survive. It must be part of a total management culture supported by carefully integrated policies and strategies. 'Quality -The ICL Way' has made reward, performance and quality mutually independent and based on 'Pay for Performance' i.e. employees focus on improved performance which by definition must contain a requirement for improved quality. It is emphasized that

"Right first time, on time and every time' is only a slogan if employees cannot measure their own performance"

Some 230 bonus schemes around the world were reduced to two: Sales Bonus (standardised to focus their impact on the requirements of the business plan) and Management Bonus (a management incentive based on measured performance, unit profit and company profit).

The system is such that the performance of a business unit is entirely in the hands of the manager, able to exercise discretion (in the form of annual pay increases) to reward the performance of his staff whilst he in turn is rewarded on the basis of this performance.

Other forms of incentive are covered and it is emphasized that

"Simply telling somebody they have done a good job and thanking them is a much under-used form of positive recognition".

Excellence Award Scheme

An 'Excellence Awards Scheme' has been introduced run by each of ICL's autonomous operating divisions. The award criteria are commitment to quality (getting it right first time), commitment to customers and commitment to excellence (to become 'better than the best').

Process Management

The report then turns to process management, the need for every individual to be supported by 'business systems and processes that have been planned, designed and proven to meet defined requirements' so that their contribution can be maximised, and for processes to be carried out in the correct manner.

It is acknowledged that 'all work is a process and every process needs to be managed' and that 'every process needs planning, control and continuous improvement'. Three key roles in process management are identified:

* The process owner (the person you go to if you want to change the process)

* The process designer (person who produces the formed specification of the process)

* The process operator (person who does the work as per the specification)

The company has sought to clarify these roles with respect to all processes consistent with our programme to achieve company-wide accreditation to the ISO9000 standard'.

Five- Year Plan

'Quality -The ICL Way' is part of an overall five year plan (1986 to 1990) aimed to reduce the 'cost of non-quality' or 'price of non-conformance'. This was calculated to have been £160 million in 1986, and the company is aiming to enter the 1990s with it down to £80 million. They admit, however, that '1990 will be even harder' but the company is confident that it can achieve its goal as they have now identified where the problems and opportunities are.

Mr. Goasdoue concludes by advising management 'not to assume that educating your workforce or introducing statistical process control or anything like that 'will solve a quality problem' but to accept that 'quality must be part of the total business strategy rather than an optional extra'.

[Issue 31 (July 1991)]

THE APPLICATION OF TQM TO INFORMATION TECHNOLOGY

The subject of TQM in the Information Technology investment was discussed at the Bournemouth Conference of the Institute of Administration Management by Barry Stemdale-Bennett, Head of Corporate Systems for T.S.B. 'Trust Company Limited. His presentation drew attention to the growing realisation at Board Level that investment in I.T. frequently fails to provide real value for money whilst many companies have become very largely dependent on the use of computers. At the same time he pointed out that at present he could still find no book on TQM that was specifically orientated to IT.

A survey by Price Waterhouse showed that out of 252 UK IT directors interviewed 60 per cent experienced 'major runaway projects', whilst the D.T.I. estimate £850 million is being wasted each year through the purchase of inappropriate hardware and software. Quoting eminent computer consultant James Martin, it was suggested that there was 'a sense of anger' amongst much of top management because in spite of high IT costs, they were still not obtaining the information that they wanted from computers, and the systems were difficult to change.

Many projects are technically orientated with no beginning or end, and IT staff are often not present in the higher echelons of business because they tend to be misunderstood, with users regarding their systems as too technical, inflexible, and long-term, and with costs justified only on paper, not in reality.

A 'credibility gap' exists between expectations and performance of IT systems due to communication deficiencies between customers and IT people, and there is a major problem improving established systems essentially written in third generation languages, 'patched' over many years, that are batch orientated in multiple-hardware environments and supported with out of date documentation. Software and people are increasingly unable to keep up with hardware suppliers who are providing ever-more attractive price- performance ratios.

T.S.B. has 2,500 staff, around two thirds of which use pcs. The speaker expressed 'serious doubt' about whether they are used effectively and suggests this is the case in most organisations. Underutilisation can, he says, indicate lack of control over real needs and, if on line, can create an adverse impact on mainframe capacity.

All of this underlines the need for quality and a case is made for Board representation in IT It is the 'kiss of death' to make IT report to the Finance Director. There should be an IT Director with business experience, who has not merely come up through the programming route.

Management information should be controlled as a strategic asset to prevent multiple and incompatible data bases emerging, with duplicate data and high overhead costs:

'At the very least set up an overriding common technical environment for differing systems to communicate with each other, agree 'data ownership' and put in place a data administrator as an independent service for the benefit of the whole organisation'.

Customers should be encouraged to produce their own reports, to effective training and adherence to agreed standards, using a report writing generator, rather than relying on systems staff, and advice is given to 'be wary' of automating existing processes with no added value.

As regards the place of IT strategy the sequence must be a business strategy followed by an information strategy and then an IT strategy, all closely interlinked. A recent CBI survey showed that only 27 per cent of companies had any such link. But if the head of IT attempts to develop a strategy in isolation it will fail.

Fourth generation language based CASE tools are envisaged to improve development productivity in terms of analysis, prototyping, code generation iterations, as well as quality, but the advice is 'do not commit yet'. They are as yet only semi-integrated, lack standards and none can translate existing applications into a specification expressed in high level business terms for loading into a data dictionary. Now is just the time to plan for CASE and other advances such as the use of object orientated code. The IT quality assurance function should be mandatory, linked to a Policies and Standards Manual and closely allied to an internal audit.

The speaker was asked why IT should not report to the Finance Director and the answer given was that the Finance Director holds the purse strings and is remote from the operations of the business. He is 'judge and jury' and approves things which are financially orientated rather than business orientated. It was therefore recommended that IT should report to Operations. [The experiences described are very typical for all industries and the pitfall of IT reporting to the Finance Director has cascaded through companies since the very early applications –Ed].

[Issue 49 (January 1993)]

QUALITY IN IT : AN INTERNATIONAL PERSPECTIVE

The Q.A.Forum's conference of 8th and 9th December at the Gatwick Hilton Hotel, focused on the Information Technology industry, with particular reference to Europe, Japan and the USA. The event was very well attended with over 100 delegates from some 80 organisations (UK and overseas) indicating a high interest in the subject despite the recession. There were 16 sessions over the two days including many Case Studies.

World Trends in Quality in IT.

The conference theme was entitled 'World Trends in Quality in IT' and introduced by Paul Goodman, Technical Director of management consultants TOK Brameur who questioned the common belief that the West innovates whilst the Japanese copy. He pointed particularly to Japanese art as providing many examples of innovation and creativity.

He then asserted that what the Japanese had really succeeded in doing was to apply the concepts of quality to engineering environments, whilst in the West quality management has been 'patchy and often limited'.

He urged delegates to consider what could happen here if the Japanese approach of long term strategic planning (with quality as the critical success factor) were adopted to bring about a combination of the most desirable attributes of European and Japanese culture. The Nissan Newcastle plant was quoted as an example which 'surprised even their Japanese partners'.

Europe and Japan: Situations, Styles and Successes.

James Hemsley, Chairman of TOK Brameur and an experienced consultant specialising in the field of IT, highlighted some of the key differences and similarities between software development in Europe and Japan. With reference to a Spanish survey he described how around 40 per cent of Germans regarded quality as absolutely top priority whilst in the UK the figure was around 15 per cent, and roughly similar to the figures for France, Italy and Spain. It was, however, 'disturbing' that of the five countries the UK had the highest proportion of people (again around 15 per cent) that apparently considered quality as being 'of no importance'. This compared with a virtually zero figure for Germany.

He then described how the French software systems houses were now emerging as dominant in Europe, but with I.C.L. in Paris being 'regarded very much as a Japanese company'. He pointed to the generally high levels of attainment of Japanese workers in the fields of mathematics and statistics as giving them a 'major advantage' compared with the UK where such knowledge is confined to 'a very specialised minority'.

As regards languages it was noted that almost all Japanese professionals read English and/or another European language, whilst in Europe virtually no-one can read Japanese, although a few can speak a little.

The Japanese tendency to make considerable use of sub-contracting was contrasted sharply with Europe, where France was regarded as being closest in the computer services field. It was also noted that the Japanese were short of good software people in the field of package software where the USA enjoyed a distinct lead.

Japan was also observed to have a low number of lawyers, suggesting that litigation was 'not the way' there, with long term supplier relationships persisting unless a party becomes badly let down. In that event 'mutual shame' is customary as the customer and supplier are deemed to have had a shared responsibility for a quality failure.

[This point is highlighted particularly because lawyers are prolific in the - USA and in the West and blame is associated with 'non-compliance to contract' even if the instruction to the sub-contractor is wrong or inadequate - Ed].

The staggering success of the Japanese software company Nintendo was highlighted and used to illustrate the speaker's prediction that in the field of embedded systems Europe was in for 'a hard time'.

The speech highlighted six principal areas where Western industry was weak by comparison with Japan:

*outdated strategies

*short term horizons

*neglect of human resources

*failures of co-operation

*technological weaknesses in development and production

*government and industry working at cross purposes

Software Quality: Developments in Europe

Francois de Nazelle, President of the Software Committee of the French Quality Association and acting president of the Software Committee of the European Organization for Quality, gave an insight into recent developments of the E.O.Q. Software Committee.

He described quality as being a 'new challenge' in software engineering, but advocated the launching of a specific initiative dedicated to software quality rather than software engineering.

It was noted that at the E.O.Q. conference the Japanese delegation was twice the size of that of the UK, and the speaker pointed to a heavy emphasis on software metrics with practical, simpler approaches being increasingly advocated.

Delegates were introduced to the new international initiative SPICE (Software Process Improvement by Capability Evaluation), and to the launch of the Worldwide Software Quality Movement consisting of joint European, American, Japanese and Australian representation. This is to have a five yearly conference beginning in San Francisco in 1995 when the theme will be 'World Quality by International Teamwork'.

Dutch Social Security: a Case Study in Quality Improvement

A practical example of how quality has been applied in I.T. in Europe was described by Peter Dolle, who is currently Sector Head of a maintenance sector in G.A.K., the Dutch Social Security Office, and has been managing a quality initiative for the Maintenance Department of G.A.K. since 1989.

He described how G.A.K. was motivated to improve its methods in order to gain more control over its operations, and by a desire to even out large variations in procedures between applications.

At the start of the quality improvement programme there were few valuable metrics, the initial focus being on reliability and usability, but through a methodology nicknamed 'Quintessence' behavioural changes in maintenance programmers, analysts and managers were realised. This methodology combined strategic planning (with business driven quantifiable objectives), a quality culture and purposefully defined metrics designed to change behaviour.

This evolved into a TQM implementation methodology known as Applied Process Improvement (API) which consisted of five elements:

* management commitment

* management of change

* human resources (empowerment)

* business and automation processes

* measurement and control

A clear mission for the department was defined in customer service terms (not restricted by reference to the current implementation) and this was followed with the establishment of a Quality Metrics Council consisting of four managers and two members of a recently formed metrics support group. A Quality Metrics Charter identified key quality metrics which provided a foundation for process improvement.

The Quality Metrics Council developed quantifiable business objectives which were clearly measurable to avoid ambiguity, and a practical acceptance test was applied to each. Critical success factors were identified from the business objectives, which were subjected to a gap analysis to show where the organisation was performing well and where it was not.

A group was then formed to undertake cause and effect analysis for each metric, using a metrics template on A4 paper which contained the original objective and information relating to the gap between current performance and the target level. The Ishikawa Diagram was used in brainstorming sessions and a 'candidate solution form' was used to collect proposed changes.

A Bill of Rights, derived from 'The Principles of Software Engineering' by Tom Gilb, encouraged both top down and bottom up communication so that changes could evolve, and in particular a pact was introduced between management and non-management personnel that clarified that people would not be judged by the number of defects that were discovered during reviews or inspections, but would be judged on the number of errors passed on downstream.

An Impact Estimation Grid was used by the Quality Metrics Council to evaluate candidate solutions against key objectives, the objectives and metrics being categorised according to Functionality Usability, Reliability, Performance and Supportability, (using the mnemonic F.U.R.P.S.).

Inspection techniques were introduced with the results fed back into a prevention cycle consisting of data collection (e.g. from metrics database and defect lists), cause and effect analysis, candidate solutions, impact analysis and an action plan to prevent errors.

G.A.K. has its own training modules, typically of two days' duration, for each of several training topics and over a two year period some 180 employees have been trained.

The implementation of the 'V Model' for all new releases and software enhancements was described as an 'important vehicle for change', whilst requests for change are grouped into releases for each application system.

A special project was set up for the objective of achieving ISO9000 certification, under which all sectors are committed to a 10 per cent investment in quality (5 per cent for the ISO9000 project itself) and there are working groups to address each vital ISO9000 element (twelve in all covering areas like the maintenance process –procedural by V Model, service level agreements and management metrics).

The organisation responsible for the certification is the Institute for the Certification of Information Technology (ICIT).

The company says that it has achieved rapid results from the early use of selected metrics, and although a bottleneck was encountered in obtaining data for metrics this was resolved by arranging for metrics staff to collect data directly.

At the end of the first year a detailed Quality Perception Acceptance Questionnaire showed that results were related to the attitudes and perceptions of Sector Heads, and these results were used to shape quality education, training and facilitator programmes.

The company recognises that over the past decade too much attention was paid to technical training' relative to quality training and the training budget is now split into two thirds technical training and one third quality training.

The S.E.I. Capability Maturity Model

Michael Konrad of the Software Engineering Institute of Carnegie Mellon University, Pittsburgh, USA, gave a description of the Capability Maturity Model which he has been influential in developing.

This consists essentially of a five level 'roadmap' which shows how an organisation might mature and is described as 'a structural process improvement model for software development and maintenance -an organizational transformation model for the software process' and 'a guide for evolving toward a culture of engineering excellence'.

At the first (initial) level performance is driven by the competence and heroics of the people doing the work. Consistency and compliance to standards are driven by management priorities with the time schedule being essentially the top priority. High quality and exceptional performance are possible so long as the best people can be hired.

At the second level (repeatable) the major problems in software development become managerial rather than technical, and without management discipline good software engineering practices become typically 'abandoned in the crunch'. Key processes at this level include software configuration management, software project tracking and oversight, software project planning and requirements management.

At the third level (defined) companies move from a disciplined process to a standard consistent process. There is identification of inputs, how they will affect the process and their readiness criteria, and identification of outputs and their completion criteria, There is a shared understanding of how the process works and the role of each participant. Key process areas include peer reviews, intergroup co-ordination, software product engineering, integrated software management, a training programme, an organization process definition and an organization process focus, establishing and maintaining a standard software process for the organization. There is a common basis for measuring process performance across all projects and for long term improvement.

The fourth (managed) level moves from a standard, consistent process to a predictable process by applying the principles of 'statistical process control and addressing the special causes of process variation. The customer's needs are also addressed as part of a quality philosophy. The key process areas have now shifted to quality management (defining software quality goals; establishing plans to achieve them; monitoring software plans, activities and quality goals to improve customer and end user satisfaction; taking corrective action to bring forecasted process and product quality in line with goals); process measurement and analysis (measuring and analysing the performance of the project and adjusting to stabilize the process performance within acceptable limits).

The fifth (optimising maturity) level is characterised by continuous improvement of the software process, identification and elimination of chronic causes of poor performance and continued automation and use of new technologies. Key process areas here are process change management, technology innovation (including performing pilot efforts to assess new and unproven technologies before they are introduced across the organisation), and a philosophy of defect prevention. A predictable process evolves into a continuously improving one.

It was not claimed that the model provides all of the answers as it too is continually evolving and improving, and the optimising level five is not the destination of process management. The real destination is better products for abetter price to ensure economic survival and the optimising level is a foundation for building an ever improving capability.

Companies with ISO9000 were placed on an approximate par with level three of the model, although some delegates were clearly of the opinion that some companies could be attaining certification at a lower level.

The speaker was asked to compare the Model with ISO9000 and whilst he acknowledged that there was overlap, he explained that ISO9000 was written for a broader set of functions within the organisation.

Following the talk Chairman James Hemsley pointed to Bull's efforts in putting 10,000 people through an SEI type programme with SEI support as being 'a major initiative'.

Telecom Software Product Development Process Capability Assessment

The Quality Assurance of Bell Canada have developed a Capability Assessment Methodology for Telecom Software Systems called TRILLIUM which formed part of a Bell Canada partnership initiative with its major telecom suppliers to help telecom suppliers to improve the quality of their products and services. This initiative was described by one of its developers Jean Normand Dronin (who is currently leading the Canadian working group that will contribute to the ISO/IEC working group JTC1/SC7 WG10 effort on Process Assessment, otherwise known as the SPICE project -described by Francois de Nazelle previously). The Methodology used by Bell Canada is a specific development application of the SEI Capability Maturity Model (described by Micheal Konrad previously).

Work started on the model in April 1991 and a draft was produced in June 1991 with minor revision in September 1991, resulting in an assessment model focusing on ten key capability areas:

*process definition

*process scope

*personnel

*performance

*defect removal

*defect avoidance

*information management

*development environment

*process improvement

*customer support

Results in each area are scored on 1 to 5 and between April 1991 and July 1992 and a total of 11 assessments/evaluations have been made, with the most frequent observations being:

*ad hoc functional requirements

*ad hoc project management

*no quality assurance function

*poor or non-existent Configuration Management

*an absence of internal standards (for coding, design, documentation etc.)

The methodology has full ISO9000-3 coverage and mapping, references IEEE standards, uses IEC 300 for Reliability and Availability Management, and relates coverage and mapping to Bellcore standards. It is based on the SEI 'roadmap' concept i.e. a sequence of related activites that are mapped to capability levels.

[Issue 63 (March 1994)]

QUALITY IN I.T.

Information technology, and in particular third party certification of it, has become the centre of attention in recent months. The UK's TickIT scheme, for example, has been reported very negatively in the USA and a controversy has developed in which the scheme has had a cool reception, notably from

David Ling of Hewlett Packard. He claims that TickIT is 'an impediment to mutual recognition of ISO9000', and 'a non-value cost and source of confusion to suppliers and purchasers'.

This position has been countered strongly in the UK by John Slater, TickIT Project Leader, managing consultant for Logica and IT specialist advisor to the National Accreditation Council for Certification Bodies (NACCB). He clearly views the American perception of 'non value added bureaucracy' as being 'at odds with the UK experience' which suggests by contrast that the scheme has eased communication, enhanced auditor competence, and improved customer confidence.

At the conference 'TQM and IT' held at the London Metropole Hotel on 31st January and 1st February Mr. Slater presented a response to Mr. Ling. He gave a well received speech in which he traced the history of vendor appraisal schemes from the early vendor qualification programmes in early manufacturing to the present day universal quality management and certification process upon which the Tick IT sector scheme is based.

He argued in his presentation 'TickIT/ISO9000 certification: A Catalyst for Commitment' that whilst the ISO9000 series of standards may have the intention of being generic in practice this is not so and 'there is consequently a need for some re-interpretation if they are to be truly effective in achieving quality'. He described also the role of guides in pointing the way towards acceptable practice for building a quality system, but again warned of their weakness of assuming that the standards are generic.

His attention then turned to the Tick IT scheme to which to date some 350 companies have been certificated (16 per cent of which are from abroad) since its inception five years ago. He described how the continental approach to ISO9001 which regards the standard as a model rather than a specification, has been designed into Tick IT, and how recently Sweden has adopted the scheme with a series of direct translations. He explained also how representatives of various European countries were currently working to produce a Europe wide certification scheme for information technology.

At the end of his speech he was asked if he could seriously imagine a future in which a group of ISO certificates could replace, for example, the Civil Aviation Authority, and in reply he said that it was 'not beyond the imagination' as regulatory functions, for example in pharmaceuticals, were already moving rapidly into a third party domain. He warned of danger, however, if consultants, auditors and certification bodies begin to form alliances as this could result in quality systems being written merely on the basis of being easy to assess.

He also pointed in his summary to the need for a 'user counterweight' in order to prevent certification from becoming a 'commercial tax'.

Quality in IT: a Strategic Necessity

Brian Sellwood, Director of the ISL Software House, offered some explanation as to why the acceptance of the role of IT in contributing to company quality has been slow. However, with poor software quality now accounting for losses estimated at over £500 million a year it has become recognised as a key area for companies wishing to secure a competitive advantage.

With many computer systems designed originally to support a particular business function or organisation, data process duplication has flourished, resulting in enormous waste which has cost the country dearly. Consequently bringing quality assurance into the field of IT has become a strategic necessity.

The speaker pointed to outsourcing and Computer Assisted Software Engineering (CASE) tools as mechanisms which have enabled the adoption of processes and techniques which have made the IT solution delivery a more predictable event. Also the attributes of usability and availability at the place of work have grown in importance over the years in relation to IT service provision. Most important of all, however, is the need for the IT community to complete the culture change from IT technologists to business solution providers. It is suggested that it is the failure to achieve this transition which has led to so many TQM in IT programmes to experience difficulties.

Keys to successful Implementation

Further explanation for the failure of some 80 per cent of quality initiatives in IT were provided by Ian Gotts, Executive Consultant for KPMG Management Consulting. One reason is a failure to achieve the right balance between 'system' and 'passion'. This commonly results in narrow focused or 'hyped' TQM or poor and burueaucratic quality systems that are not linked to IT management, or in some cases simply not used at all.

Many of the staff who are engaged in information service provision are noted to be very high achievers for whom problem solving is already a habit. However, they often make poor team players and communicators, whilst many of the processes involved have long development cycle times, are difficult to quantify for process control purposes, and are subject to rapid technological change which makes them difficult to refine. Likewise software products are frequently not tangible models of their predecessors and the current lifecycle tends to consist of a once for all design rather than design for continual refinement.

Further to this the customer is seen as a new concept in many organisations. The traditional data processing shop had control of the information and hence the power whilst users were not even considered as customers, hence the failure.

A key message of the presentation was that the process of innovation needs to fit the culture. In this connection a 'checklist for success' was presented, beginning with the need for top level sponsorship (passion) followed by clear expectations of the expected benefits, rewards for risk taking, rewards for teamwork as well as individuals, and measurement of success (amongst others).

The final message was clear and simple: 20 per cent of Total Quality initiatives in IT succeed: make sure YOU are one of them.

Implementing TQM in Software Development.

The specific field of software development was considered by Graham Jordan, Quality Assurance and Standards Manager for Morgan Grenfell and Company Limited.

His presentation was interesting in that it gave delegates an objective opinion as to whether CASE tools actually succeed in reducing costs, using experience gained from working with the Quality Forum's CASE and Structured Methods Special Interest Group (SIG).

He says that in the short term these tools may make little difference and may actually increase costs, but in the long term can give 'enormous savings over the life of the system'. It is argued that they can speed up structured analysis and design if they replace manual methods and that they can reduce build times if they are integrated sufficiently with code and database generators. The so-called CAST tools (where T means Testing) can also 'revolutionise regression testing'.

In a special section entitled 'How to get the best from your CASE tools' he advised everyone concerned to ensure that staff are properly trained in both the technique and the tool that supports it, and to monitor the penetration of the tool i.e. what it is being used for and whether its functionality is being fully exploited. He then pointed to some of the long term gains which may potentially be achieved from the use of these tools i.e. enhancing one's ability to maintain and improve a system provided that the tools are used correctly. He also drew attention to the need for change control to be applied to the CASE environment during development if the benefits are to be realised.

He advised that all changes must be reflected in the tool as well as the application environment whilst the support team 'must be as well trained in the use of the tool as the developer'. Finally, he advised, 'don't change tools lightly'.

Driving Quality through Systems Development

There are currently a number of questionnaires and programs in existence which enable software developers and others to assess quantitatively the capability of a developer with regard to technical practices, managerial practices and the extent of the quality system. Much of this followed from work done at the Software Engineering Institute at the Carnegie Mellon University by Watts Humphrey who was asked by the American Department of Defense to devise a questionnaire by which contractors may be assessed.

Some of these developments were described by Dr. Darrell Ince, Professor of Software Engineering at The Open University who presented a series of about 25 questions based on this work, designed to provide a quick 'health check' for software development. Typical questions were:

*does the system documentation have built in traceability?

*what efforts are made to validate a design?

*what records exist that demonstrate that a programmer has carried out a test?

*does the quality manual cover the risk analysis that a project manager often has to carry out at the beginning of a project?

*are there standards and procedures in place for integration testing?

On this latter subject the speaker added that most of the errors which occur in integration testing are invariably in the system which has just been integrated.

The speaker then drew attention to a number of 'blind spots' that are often encountered in systems development, namely flexibility of the quality system, the human-computer interface and prototyping. He said:

'All too often I have found developers who have a quality system, or what they call a quality system -really the quality manual - which is applied to projects time and again without any modification..... At the beginning of a software project a project manager should decide which elements of the quality manual should be used to ensure the quality of the software that is delivered'.

It follows that it is the duty of the quality manager to examine a list of quality factors, identify those parts of the quality system which should be used to enforce the level of quality factor required, identify those parts of a quality system that should not be used, and possibly develop new quality controls which are not in the quality manual.[This is the Quality Planning function which is highlighted in the impending changes to BS5750\ISO9000 -Ed].

The need for flexibility is illustrated with reference to three examples concerning respectively the subjects of reusability, safety critical software and the case where a transaction based system is to be produced for a customer who employs keyboard operators in an area of the country where such staff are in short supply.

The human-computer interface (HCI) is also a much neglected area. Quality systems rarely consider them adequately. Consequently many computer systems are still being developed which do not take account of the capabilities of the user, the tasks which the user has to carry out or the environment in which the system works, even though it may meet the functionality requirements as laid down in the requirements specification.

Seven practical examples illustrate where typical problems occur with the interface. One was the chemical plant at which there was nearly a disaster because staff could not hear the auditory feedback designed to indicate errors and prevent users from conducting certain operations, at certain times. Another was the school where use of two commands by a teacher resulted in a whole database being lost. Others were the help system which even its developers could not understand, and the foreign exchange system which cost a bank of the order of £200,000 over two days as 'digital acrobatics' on the part of the users led to mishap after mishap.

In order to help prevent some of these problems the author recommends that the quality manual contains a user/environment questionnaire checklist; HCI design rationale procedure/standard and design review procedure/standard; Task specification standard, review standard, a procedure and review procedure; screen and window design guidelines and specification standard; interface evaluation guidelines and procedure; and an HCI evaluation report standard.

On the final subject of prototyping the author speaks of customers who have said during acceptance testing 'If only you had shown me the system earlier in the project I could have told you exactly what I wanted'. He points to prototyping as a means of both enabling the customer to preview the system before the commencement of major development work and as a means for developers to ascertain exactly what they are required to deliver rather than merely attempting to deliver something which reflects the requirements specification. It is therefore 'a valuable technique both for the customer and the developer'. Contrary to popular belief it does require considerable attention with regard to quality, particularly in relation to monitoring, controlling, planning and costing of the prototyping process, which needs to be incorporated into the quality assurance system. Quality assurance systems are themselves then noted for their frequent lack of guidance as to when prototyping is appropriate with staff often left 'with only a hazy view' about what prototyping is supposed to achieve. Production of a guidance document outlining the reasons why a decision to prototype may be taken is strongly advocated.

Also recommended is a section in the project plan that outlines prototype deficiencies since this can help to remedy the situation whereby customers become so impressed with a prototype they are tempted to request early delivery of a system which may be a good prototype but poor in production.

Prototype evaluation is then discussed. A common problem associated with prototyping is where an analyst and customer become engrossed in adding more and more functions to the point where the prototype becomes impossible to implement within the hardware and response time constraints originally detailed in the requirements specification. To help remedy this the author suggests that standards and procedures for prototype evaluation are incorporated into the quality system to aid the production of regular reports to the project manager that describe the functional growth of the prototype. [It may be that the requirements specification needs to be amended –Ed].

Other problems discussed include lack of adequate documentation for evolutionary prototyping, costing and resourcing of prototype-based projects and customer training (often rushed and inadequate).

Applying valid Software Metrics.

The somewhat specialised subject of software metrics was addressed by Kevin Pulford, Manager of Technology Projects for Marconi Systems, who presented an informative outline of the recently established Application of Metrics in Industry (AMI) method developed to assist the planning, identification and introduction of metrics programmes within organisations that produce or procure software.

The presentation began with a definition of software measurement as 'the objective assignment of numbers to attributes of a software process or product to help characterise it'. This was followed by a short explanation of the reasons why metrics are important. These were to realise improvement in product quality and the development process, helping in the pursuit and retention of BS5750 (auditors were noted to be keen at present to see evidence of a metrics programme not only existing but being used, and as a means of keeping abreast of the competition.

The speaker then explained where some of the advantages of using AMI, which has been sponsored by the EC under the ESPRIT initiative, lay. It was, for example, seen to be a 'well designed and proven set of management techniques' which has so far been tested on 19 projects Europe-wide. It also has a User Group established early last year to which companies can turn for help and information, there is a newsletter and a" handbook available, produced by the AMI Consortium. This consists of GEC Marconi (UK),

Corelis (France), RWTUV (Germany), GEC Alsthom (France), Alcatel (Austria), ATS (Italy), ITS (Spain), Bull (Germany), and the South Bank University (UK).

It was described how the method, which consists of four activities each subdivided into three steps has been heavily influenced in its inception by the Deming Plan -Do -Check –Act principle. Typically it has a duration of between one and four years and usually involves between 20 and 500 man months of effort. Costs are usually between 2 and 5 per cent of the project costs with recurring costs accounting for around 1 per cent of project costs.

The first stage (that of assessment) involves an appraisal of where the organisation currently stands, where it would like to be, and a comparison which should show whether the goals are realistic. For this comparison use of the SEI Capability Maturity Model is recommended, but companies were warned not to be too ambitious i.e. the objective is not to score as high as possible on the SEI model, but rather to highlight problem areas and identify where processes are missing.

The second stage (analysis) involves examination of the knowledge required to achieve the goals, and construction of a 'goal tree' to establish sub-goals. Only then are the actual metrics themselves considered for appropriateness. An example of a metrics derivation chart is presented in the conference literature.

The third stage (metrication) involves production of a metrics plan, for which the AMI Handbook provides an example, followed by implementation and verification. It is noted that the metrics plan should explain the objectives of the measurement programme, and define the metrics used so that they will be calculated in a consistent manner.

The fourth stage (validation) involves a presentation of the metrics to senior management using diagrams that are suitable for interpretation by data users, validation of results, (does the data show what is expected), and identification of areas whereby development methods may be modified with a view to improvement.

The presentation concluded with a list of factors which are likely to affect measurement programme costs. These include existing data collection, visible and controlled development processes, and the number of metrics used. This is followed by a list of recommendations for companies seeking to apply the method:

- keep it simple (lots of companies collect lots of metrics and are later unsure if they can all be used)

- think it through (a carbon copy of someone else's plan is not recommended)

- obtain commitment at all levels (suggested that data collection be done by engineers as they especially need to know why they are doing it)

- avoid over-ambitious goals

- write down and communicate where possible

Following the presentation the speaker was asked if he could provide further advice on the subject of data collection for AMI. He explained how the cost of data collection can often be reflected by the specific metric. Also he suggested that where a goal exists but is relatively unimportant and an expensive metric is only likely to support that one goal, there may be a case for choosing a lesser, cheaper metric.

Other Presentations

Mr. Pulford's emphasis on simplicity was echoed by Jon Hatton Snooker, European Director for Bureau Veritas Quality International Limited, who said that:

"Software metrics should be simple and easy to apply. With simplicity everyone can often see that it is the best way forward".

In explaining the viewpoint of the certification body he explained what certification bodies are looking for during audit and certification and after audit but before certification. A list of certification criteria was presented followed by an explanation of how third party certification with well documented quality systems had made companies successful. He described how up until 1989 only one of his clients had been lost whilst 10 per cent of the IT industry went under. Since then he had certificated around 150 companies only one of which had been lost, whilst 30 per cent of Britain's software industry 'had collapsed'. He also made reference to the 100 companies that had entered last year's Tick IT Awards (launched by Michael Heseltine in November 1992 and won for the first time by Intercom Data Systems, whose case study was presented at the conference). He contrasted this with the 89 entrants for the American Baldrige Award, which he believed attracted 'a trivial number' by comparison.

Andy Coster, Quality Manager for Oracle UK and Vice Chairman of the DISC Committee IST 15 for Software Engineering, contrasted ISO9001 and Tick IT with other approaches to quality, such as TQM, Baldrige, the European Quality Award, the SEI Model, Quality Circles and the interesting new international development: Software Process Improvement and Capability Evaluation (SPICE). This latter initiative is expected to enter an 18 month testing phase in September and has a prime focus on process improvement.

Independent consultant and author from the USA Tom Gilb also commented on SPICE saying that it has potential to identify quality objectives well, but these will still have to be quantified. He gave an interesting insight into the technique of Document Quality Improvement (DQI) claimed to reduce error rates by over 70% over three years, remove up to 85% of defects in paperwork through cumulative removal attempts, and rectify up to five sixths of identified defects at the first attempt. The optimum speed of checking each detail against a number of sources, rules and checklist, is of the order of 60 lines (of 10 words) per hour.

A buyer's perspective of TQM in IT was provided by Stuart Sim, Supplier Relations Manager from BT, who described how a project which suffered substantial delay in delivering the required performance and reliability was estimated to have cost his company many millions of pounds. The system became unstable from the viewpoint of computer operations and bug fixes led to further system failures. This led BT to radically rethink the way in which it procured IT and software. An explanation of some of the action taken is described. For example, the formation of a small Software Acquisition Team which is now responsible for working with suppliers in order to build better processes for risk management, project management and the use of metrics for capability assessment. They have also introduced a mandatory requirement for ISO9000 conformance for future entry on their qualified supplier list. Embodied in the presentation is also an undertaking to apply quality tools and to supplier assessment, which will incorporate a 'model of good practice' based on SPICE, which is noted to be already in widespread use in the USA.

Other presentations included case studies from British gas South Eastern, HM Customs and Excise, Land Rover and ODi Europe.

[Issue 64 (April 1994)]

TICKIT IN PERSPECTIVE?

The DTI has been active by launching a TickIT Award scheme, which is currently sponsored by IBM (UK) Limited, the first awards being presented in May 1993 to Real Time Engineering Limited (under 50 employees category); Intercom Data Systems Limited (under 150 employees category); and The Home Office Information Systems and Pay Services Division ED5 (in-house teams category).

The European Dimension

At European level, the EC Directorate General 111 (which has overall responsibility for Implementing European industrial policy) has welcomed TickIT as an important initiative as it uses international documentation to extend voluntary certification into new fields of technology. It is not, however, the only recognised scheme by which European companies can gain third party certification in the field of IT. The European Organisation for Testing and Certification (EOTC), for example, recognises only the Information Technology Quality Systems (ITQS) certification which is seen as a 'positive alternative' to TickIT and consists of a mutually recognised ISO9000 (EN29000) certification which includes software development. It remains to be seen whether it will ultimately be viewed as compatible with Tick IT, but all the evidence so far suggests that it will, with a common guidance document for the auditing of suppliers having already been published and submitted to CEN for standardisation. If this is the case, it is unlikely that it will remain dependent on the NACCB or indeed on any other assessment agency that is intent purely on following its own commercial interests.

Public Procurement

As regards public procurement the introduction of the Services Directive has meant that public procurers are no longer permitted to specify the use of particular methods, such as Merise or SSADM for the development of information systems which they seek to acquire. Now contractors who work with a recognised development method other than the one that the procurer prefers, may not be ruled out as a potential supplier on those grounds. To help public procurers to compare products (specifications and models etc) produced by different methods the EC Public Procurement Group (PPG) has initiated a comparison method called 'Euromethod' which aims to harmonise the methods used in information systems engineering in Europe. It is designed such that suppliers can reference appropriate Euromethod documents within their Quality Management Systems and have their practical usage of the Euromethod assessed as part of their Tick IT certification. The Tick IT scheme is thus being incorporated into the methodology for public procurement, and it is anticipated that a certification infrastructure incorporating the Euromethod will emerge within the next few years.

Sharing Experiences

To promote experience sharing a regular Tick IT Newsletter has been launched by the DISC Tick IT Office in London, whilst the Quality Forum has launched a Special Interest Group (SIG) dedicated to the sharing of experiences and information relating to Tick IT certification.

The first meeting of the Quality Forum SIG took place at the Sheraton Skyline Hotel, Heathrow, on March 2nd and featured presentations by Jim Elliott, Manager Software Product Services, BSI Quality Assurance, and Ken Johnson of Neville-Clarke Management Consultants, which were followed by four parallel syndicate sessions.

Positioning TickIT

Jim Elliott's presentation, entitled 'Positioning Tick IT' set the scene by explaining the scope of Tick IT and some of the reasons for having it, drawing attention to the recent Price Waterhouse and Logica reports which have highlighted the huge financial waste which has occurred in relation to IT systems procurement.

After pointing to the meaningless nature of certification without auditor competence, he highlighted the important role which Tick IT has had in establishing criteria for auditor competence in the IT field. He accepted, however, that it still lacked the international dimension that is clearly going to be critical for its development, and called upon the UK to appoint an international representative for the scheme as it is "difficult to see how the NACCB can represent the scheme because they have too many vested interests".

He clearly felt that other industry areas could benefit from schemes like TickIT and suggested that it ought to be extended perhaps beyond IT once the essential infrastructure was in place. For companies seeking certification he highlighted the pitfalls of internal auditing, pre-quality system products and projects, design verification, including (bought-in) product and grafted on quality systems as areas for attention. He advocated that where possible, companies should make use of guidance material rather than attempt to 're-invent the wheel', whilst implementation and registration should be managed as a project and not treated ad-hoc.

Mr. Elliott was asked whether he felt that the scheme could become 'a victim of its own success' if the present shortage of auditors and associated long lead times for assessment persist. He appeared to accept that it could, citing BSI's difficulties in obtaining trained auditors in the timescales required by organisations. He said that this situation provided another strong argument for establishing a more solid infrastructure for the scheme's administration.

He also agreed on the need to consider amending the present format of the Tick IT Logo, which one delegate described as 'ugly and cumbersome'. The logo presently has to be used in conjunction with both the certification body and the NACCB logo, which appears to be unpopular. [Emotive logo discussions are perennial – the parallel sector scheme LMRQAS committee is currently re-examining their logo- Ed].

He was questioned on BSI's stance regarding recertification, which currently has to take place every three years, and pointed out BSI's general opposition to it on the grounds that their six monthly continual assessment was "sufficient and a good process". He suggested therefore that the recertification process "may not be adding value", but accepted that for some organisations it had "paid dividends", and so could have benefits that were not immediately apparent. BSI has so far conducted 12 TickIT re-assessments.

[Issue 65 (May 1994)]

IMPROVING TICKIT

The first meeting of the QA Forum Tick IT SIG had four parallel syndicate sessions. One of particular interest was led by Stan Bennett who encouraged delegates to air their ideas on how Tick IT could be improved.

These possible measures to improve the Tick IT scheme were discussed in one of the afternoon syndicate sessions which was sponsored by the DTI. Here Stan Bennett used the popular 'pinboard technique' to identify problem areas and recommend possible solutions. Some of the issues that were highlighted included:

- the absence of IT in the logo

- lack of clarity as to how Tick IT might add value to the bottom line

- lack of alignment of Tick IT with the principles of TQM

- the need for more international recognition and commitment from BSI

- lack of maintenance of the standard

- lack of appreciation of the value of Tick IT auditors

- insufficient focus on prevention rather than definition and control

- the need for three logos which nobody appears to like

- a diminishing interest from government

The problems were categorised and a number of solutions put forward after account had been made of some of the strengths of the scheme, notably that of raising standards of professionalism within the IT industry, clarifying BS5750 for IT, increasing customer confidence and providing a useful catalyst by which to effect quality improvement.

Problems were tackled in a prioritised order, beginning with the costs of certification and lack of clarity on how the scheme impacted on bottom line results. Solutions proposed included:

- a recommendation for more publicity of case studies

- inclusion of a section in the Tick IT guide that describes how benefits might be measured

- production and circulation of a guide to the benefits of achieving Tick It by the Quality Forum

- the initiation of another Price Waterhouse report on the part of the DTI

Consideration to obtain user feedback brought a suggestion that the Quality Forum should join DISC so as to become an established user group, whilst DISC was recommended to listen more to user groups and refer user group representations to ISO.

Another problem, that of maintaining the standard, brought a call from delegates for the TickIT guide to be updated and soon if the scheme is to retain its credibility. Poor international representations promoted a call for the DTI to lobby the European Commission in order to enhance the scheme's recognition in Europe. A clear statement of ownership of Tick IT by the DTI was also called for. [A defacto responsibilty of ownership of the parallel scheme LMRQAS by the DTI's Radiocommunications Agency took place last year when registration was taken over from the Federation of Communication Services-Ed].

Interestingly the problem of auditor availability was not given a high priority and was not discussed at great length, but it was generally agreed that the interview panel to which Tick IT auditors are subjected every three years was currently creating a bottleneck, and the Registration Body of Assessors (RBA) was called to streamline the panel's activities to help alleviate the problem.

[Issue 66 (June 1994)]

OUTSOURCING MATTERS

Outsourcing (sub-contracting) is a major concern for management. It poses many problems both legal and technical and with new EC procurement rules management is currently having to review the implications of outsourcing contracts with some care. Some of the legal implications were considered at the recent conference on Outsourcing for future Competitive Advantage held in London on 19th and 20th April, which highlighted present day outsourcing trends and pitfalls, with particular reference to the outsourcing of IT products and services.

Pitfalls in IT Outsourcing

In addition to outlining the legal issues Mr. Rahman's paper also identifies a number of pitfalls relating specifically to the outsourcing of IT products and services which are worthy of mention:

(i) When lawyers are only consulted just prior to the conclusion of negotiations, who can at best only pinpoint the consequences of the contract, then just provides an option to abort. Solution: A contract which reflects the user-requirements is laid down at start of the transaction.

(ii) Provider agrees to User's form of contract prior to selection, but later 'discovers' problems once selected. Solution: User makes it clear that change of substantive points on the draft contract will not be accepted after selection.

(iii) Provider selected without the User clear about expected deliverables, and contract signed with an inadequate description of the Provider's contractual obligations. Solution: User ascertains what the IT department does and what the consumers of its services expect following outsourcing, ensuring that sufficient time is allowed to consult widely in the User organisation.

(iv) Legal difficulties associated with assignment of licensed software to a Provider, usually resulting in the User paying a large sum to the software house for retrospective consent to the use of the software by the provider, and compensation to the provider by way of indemnity for their breach of copyright. Solution: User assesses its software licences and identifies those which inhibit outsourcing before a provider is selected, and approaches software houses early for consents if required.

(v) Provider inadvertently or on purpose adds qualifications to its obligations in service descriptions which conflict with main clauses of a carefully negotiated contract. Solution: User takes care to distinguish between Service Descriptions and Service Level Agreement, and ensures that Service Descriptions are purely descriptive and form an integral part of the contract.

(vi) Termination of a long term contract results in the Provider acquiring assets of the former IT department of User, who is then unable to bring service provision back in-house. Solution: User considers consequences of termination at the outset and produces a 'prenuptial' agreement as part of the Services Agreement.

Maintaining the Quality of Service

Dr. Deming (ref. *The New Economics* p 52) has taught that management should view their organisations as systems i.e. a network of interdependent components that work together to accomplish an aim, and that anything less than optimisation of the whole system will ultimately bring loss to every component in the system. He further stressed that optimisation is a management responsibility. It follows that management's decision to outsource and subsequently select a provider is crucial to the optimisation process, and the need to maintain the quality of service is paramount.

Maintaining the quality of service with an outsourcing strategy based on short-term competitive tendering is difficult and fraught with problems. Consequently Deming's theory does not recommend it (ref. *Out of the Crisis* p 35):

'A long term relationship between purchaser and supplier is necessary for best economy. How can a supplier be innovative and develop economy in his production processes when he can only look forward to short-term business with a purchaser?'

The unhappiness experienced by General Motors when they introduced a bidding system on an annual basis for the supply of steel is used as a case in point, as are the hazards of poor service and irresponsibility inherent in shopping around for cheaper transportation.

In the IT field at least one major supplier (EDS, who supply to, amongst others the Driver Vehicle Licensing Centre and the Inland Revenue) has adopted this policy, with a ten year duration now being the norm for any outsourcing agreement.

Their Special Projects Director John MacNaughton likened outsourcing agreements to marriages, which resulted either in reconciliation or divorce, following a period where despair triumphs over expectation. He described how EDS and Midland had divorced when an expectation that maintaining a specified quality standard would automatically cut the company's losses failed to transpire.

He explained how a long-term relationship provided the opportunity for his company to understand a client's business more effectively than the clients themselves. This consequently enabled them to add value to the services the client provided and highlight waste in the form of useless data [so improving optimisation -Ed].

He accepted that EDS offered "a ridiculous price" for assets (including people) which they acquire through an outsourcing contract, even if they do not use them. He acknowledged that there could be benefits, such as acquiring personnel of an exceptional calibre. He also referred delegates to the requirements of the recently drafted Transfer of Undertakings (TUPE) Regulations which will govern the transfer of assets by outsourcing and incorporate the European Acquired Rights Directive into British Law. The Directive stipulates that where a ' relevant transfer of an undertaking occurs the contractual rights of employees also transfer. It is still not clear, however, how the regulations will work in practice, particularly with regard to such aspects as supplementary company and inter-company pension schemes. It is certain that in future acquired employees' conditions of employment will be an issue and where there is any attempt to change them, an equivalent package will have to be offered. In particular, any dismissal associated with the transfer is presumed to be unfair unless it can be shown to be the result of 'Economic, technical or organisational reasons'.

In the question session Mr. MacNaughton was asked for his views on the current 'rumblings and dissatisfaction' associated with long-term contracts in the USA, where they have been in existence for some time in contrast to the UK. In reply he pointed out that many such US contracts were placed in a competitive rather than a partnership environment, and were consequently seen as being price contracts. This problem, he said, "is endemic in IT outsourcing", [Perhaps Japan would have provided a better example -Ed].

TICKIT AND HARMONISING OF ACCREDITATION

At the first meeting of the QA Forum Tick IT SIG Ken Johnson of Neville-Clarke Management Consultants, provided an insight into the work being undertaken nationally and internationally to bring accreditation applied by different assessment bodies towards equivalence. Although given to an audience primarily interested in IT applications the information presented applies generally to all industries and nationally recognised Quality Schemes.

Harmonisation of Accreditation

The presentation by Ken Johnson began with an outline of the important distinction between accreditation i.e. 'the formal recognition (against published criteria) of the competence of impartiality of a Certification Body', and certification i.e. 'the act of certifying by means of a mark of conformity that a supplier's quality management system is in conformity with specific quality requirements'. In this description he was careful to distinguish this Category 1 definition of certification taken from BS4778 and ISO Guide 2, and the related category 2 type, 'Product Conformity Certification' i.e. 'the act of certifying by means of a certificate of conformity or a mark of conformity that a product is in conformity with specific standards or technical specifications', and category 3 'Product Approval' i.e. 'declaration by a body vested with the necessary authority by means of a certificate or mark of conformity that a product is in conformity with a set of published criteria'.

He then explained briefly the requirements for accreditation of a certification body i.e. no barriers against or favours for particular interests or groups; an administrative structure which ensures impartiality and independence from client interests; an identified governing board with responsibility for certification and competence in running sector schemes; organisational and financial independence; a published certification system, technical competence and integrity of auditors; documented procedures for assessment and surveillance; a method to ensure confidentiality; a means of protecting against the misuse of certificates.

This was followed with a description of the current position in Europe with regard to harmonisation of accreditation, and in particular the CEN-ECICT Project PTOO1 currently operating under EC Mandate BT -IT -226 which is in its second and final phase. It aims to establish a harmonised system of accreditation procedures in the Information Technology and Telecommunications sectors.

It is intended that under this scheme products need only be tested once at a participating laboratory in any member State i.e. the Test Report produced will be acceptable as equivalent to that produced by any other participating laboratory for the purposes of procurement or certification. Likewise a certificate produced by a participating Certification Body would be accepted as equivalent to that produced by any other participating Certification Body for the purposes of procurement.

It was explained how to achieve certification a developer would produce a sample of a (software) product which has been produced within a Quality System that has either been certificated or is capable of being so. This sample is then submitted to a Testing Laboratory which has achieved accreditation from the National Accreditation Council for Certification Bodies (NACCB) and uses standardised test processes and test proformas where they exist. The resulting Test Report then passes to an accredited Certification Body, who may then also assess the developer's quality system if it has not been certificated by a harmonised accredited Certification Body. The equivalence of Certification Body accreditation is assured through a common interpretation of the requirements for IT and telecomms and the mutual recognition agreement which exists between Certification Bodies.

The presentation concluded with an examination of the possible future role of the NACCB, which he said was "almost certain to become independent from BSI", and "could even become a government agency", but he said he thought this was unlikely. He hinted that the NACCB which became operational on 13th June 1985, could in practice become joined with the National Measurement Accreditation Service (NAMAS), with accreditation being overseen by the Government.

He was asked to give his views on the relative merits of certification bodies holding their own register as against maintaining a national register of certified companies. To this he said that whilst it was important for certification bodies to keep their own lists, a national list was 'invaluable'.

He was then asked whether he felt that the NACCB should perhaps become European rather than remaining national, and in his reply he said that a supranational position "would not be good", although the international peer review process to which it is subjected was described as "valuable".

He was also asked if and how an EC mandate to harmonise accreditation could in practice be applied to countries outwith the EC. The suggestion here was that the EFTA countries would not wish to be left out and so would comply, whilst other countries, notably Turkey, have apparently been quite adamant that they wish to participate in schemes like TickIT. He advocated the establishment of a TickIT Association and a Centre of Excellence in such countries which could liaise with universities and other competent bodies so that meaningful metrics programmes could be implemented.

Another delegate questioned the NACCB's role in ensuring consistency in the assessment of Tick IT applicants on the part of Certification Bodies, and on this somewhat contentious issue he said that uniform accreditation arrangements had to be applied, but at the same time was clearly of the opinion that the Certification Bodies should be free to apply their own interpretation to a degree. He commented:

"It would be bad if they were all clones because we need differentiators in the market. Companies value their partnerships with Certification Bodies these days".

The practice of selecting Certification Bodies on the basis of price was then raised, with a suggestion that some were doing "a less than adequate job" to keep prices down. In answer to this Mr. Johnson said that his feedback showed that the reverse was true, with "very few complaints" being registered about the conduct of TickIT auditors. The main complaint, he said, had been where auditors had raised non-conformance against the ISO9000-3 guidance document rather than the actual standard, -a practice which he defended on the grounds that companies "should be conforming to the guide anyway".

Finally, the speaker was asked if he felt that TickIT could potentially fall into disrepute by virtue of the fact that there are currently no plans to amend the scheme in line with the new ISO9000. He argued that this was a possibility and accepted the delegates' view that this was "a serious credibility issue", adding that there ought to be plans and that industry should now be applying pressure to DISC to take some action, given that industry is financing it with participating companies paying a minimum of £1000 a year to participate in it.

BENCHMARKING THE INFORMATION TECHNOLOGY FUNCTION

Conference Board Report 1052 'Benchmarking the Information Technology Function' presents the results of a survey of the benchmarking experiences and practices of 225 large and medium sized companies across a broad spectrum of industry with particular regard to the information technology function.

Author Charles B. Greene, Vice President of Pennsylvania based consultants The Executive Insights Group Inc. describes the stages of IT benchmarking from metric benchmarking of infrastructures to best practice benchmarking in applications and strategy. He explains how respondents provided information based on these three stages. A chart shows the frequency of metric and best practice benchmarking in each stage, using four frequency measures: regularly benchmarked, occasionally benchmarked, benchmarked once, and never benchmarked. It shows, for example, that 60 per cent of respondents never applied metric benchmarking to IT strategy, whereas 39 per cent regularly apply it to infrastructure. Whilst 48 per cent occasionally apply best practice benchmarking to their applications, only 11 per cent did it regularly.

The most common form of benchmarking is noted to be the regular or occasional metric benchmarking of infrastructures, which has been adopted by 75 per cent of respondents.

It is noted that companies that rate themselves as leaders in adopting new information technology are less likely to have benchmarked before, than those which describe themselves as 'mainstream'. This suggested that companies that do benchmark will be less likely to consider themselves as 'leading edge', as they have high performing companies as reference points.

Motivation for benchmarking is seen to come principally from cost assessment in the case of infrastructure benchmarking, but less so in the case of applications and strategy benchmarking, where the main drivers are seen to be competitive pressure and goal setting. Specific reasons are discussed for American Express, Lauder Information Services, Guinness, 3M and Pfizer Inc.

The main sources of information for benchmarking appear to be internal data and consultants. Partner selection appears to be determined by personal contact, especially in the case of strategy benchmarking. One company is noted for its unusual approach of selecting companies, which have been in difficulty and are in the process of instituting a turnaround, as it is perceived that it is these companies that are most likely to be realising improvements through creative solutions.

Some 27 companies that were surveyed were European and it is noted that for these total benchmarking expenditures tended to be higher than for the remaining companies, 178 of which were American and 20 Canadian.

Most of the companies apparently viewed their IT benchmarking as being overall a successful operation, with some 91 per cent reporting 'very successful' or 'somewhat successful' metric benchmarking of infrastructures, 80 per cent reporting 'very successful' or 'somewhat successful' best practice benchmarking of applications, and 83 per cent reporting 'very successful' or 'somewhat successful' best practice benchmarking of strategies. The only type of benchmarking that appeared not to work so well was metric benchmarking of strategies, which 29 per cent found either 'very unsuccessful' or 'somewhat unsuccessful'.

A discussion of the benefits of IT benchmarking highlights cost and productivity improvements as well as improvements in customer service and quality, with 59 per cent of respondents reporting reduced costs, 53 per cent reporting improved customer service and 50 per cent reporting an improvement in quality. Typical areas where improvements have materialised include the installation of common systems in administrative areas, consolidation of data centres, outsourcing of costing and/or the data centre, and the redesign of development and support processes.

A number of specific benefits are described for some of the major companies. Examples are Estee Lauder where benchmarking helped to shorten the development cycle, and Pfizer where it helped to solve reliability problems associated with the downloading of data from mainframes to personal computers.

The Report concludes with some Keys to Successful Benchmarking and a short discussion about the Future of Benchmarking, in which it is predicted that the priority and resources devoted to benchmarking will increase:

'Very few companies that have benchmarking experience expect to discontinue the practice. Most of the companies that do not have benchmarking experience intend to begin benchmarking. There is considerable interest in sharing experience in areas such as architectures, business and IT alignment and value of IT. The challenges will be to develop comparable data and appropriate partnerships '.

[Issue 69 (September 1994)]

TICKIT BENEFITS THE PUBLIC SECTOR

The continuing controversy concerning third party quality certification in the software sector has heightened recently with the release of a Position Paper by the Computing Services Association urging those who might be considering certification to national or international standards to 'learn from the British experience' as UK software quality 'is improving'. The paper, which, amongst other things, counters the attack on third party certification led by David Ling of Hewlett Packard, suggests that customers have gained much needed confidence in the quality of UK software products as a direct result of the UK implementing a system of third party certification. Also companies 'report huge reductions in maintenance costs without any increase in the cost of certification'.

To support the paper, KPMG Management Consultants, sponsors of the DISC 1994 programme of Tick IT seminars and workshops, have used figures to illustrate the sorts of benefits that can be expected from following a path toward TickIT certification, and provide an idea of their magnitude.

In a Benefits Summary, presented primarily to indicate benefits in the public sector, but not confined exclusively to it, members of the KPMG team illustrated first the internal benefits, and then the external benefits which have been realised. Internal benefits highlighted included reduced runaway projects, reduced waste and improved productivity, whilst the external benefits included an improvement in customers' ability to perform work more effectively, fewer PAC questions and more services able to be procured for the same cash limits.

An example illustrating internal benefits suggests that in a 25 strong development shop supporting a £10 million business where projects were typically 20 per cent over budget and 30 per cent late, it should be possible to cut waste by 25 per cent and realise savings of about £62,000.

In a similar example illustrating external benefits it is suggested that in a company where the reliability of printing and distributing 10,000 cheques a month is 95 per cent, a 1 per cent improvement could be realised with consequent savings of £7,200 per year.

These examples are not exhaustive; KPMG have more and are inviting companies to participate in syndicate work with them so that others can be realised. An example is a 25 per cent reduction in the number of cancelled projects. Similarly marketing gains which in some cases could amount to as much as 3 per cent of a turnover of £1 million i.e. £30,000.

Benefits at ED5

It is appreciated that these figures are based largely on assumptions and rules of thumb, although they are based on practical work undertaken by KPMG, which would suggest that they are realistic and do present a business case for third party certification in the software sector. The benefits at ED5, formerly The Home Office Establishment Division Five responsible for computing and pay services, are, by contrast, actual and include a 60 per cent reduction of rework on mainframe corrective maintenance and a 40 per cent reduction in the rerunning of jobs. These are aided largely by Quality Action Teams who, amongst other things, worked on the prediction of file size growth and improved it dramatically.

Certification to IS09001 was achieved in two stages, the first, which was largely concerned with repetitive processes being achieved in 1991, whilst the second, which included the more troublesome area of software development, was achieved in 1992. It is noted that this contrasts with the common practice in the private sector of certification in one part of the organisation.

During the three years taken to achieve certification, ED5 learned in particular how to define the purpose of their business so as to recognise where effort was being squandered on functions which did not add value. They realised savings by eliminating belated corrections highlighted by product reviews which had previously been considered to be a waste of time. Also they recognised the danger of over-procedurising functional descriptions as evidenced by a bid process procedure which extended to 30 pages in length. It has also equipped them for the emerging climate of Market Testing to which both they and their customers are to be subjected. Quality Manager Doug Carrick says:

"It has been admitted by everyone in ED5 that if we were what we had been five years ago and faced with market testing we would have been in a mess ".

[Issue 70 (October 1994)]

QUALITY DEVELOPMENTS IN I.T.

The Quality Forum has been very active recently with meetings being held for both the main Forum (Quality in IT and TQM groups) and the Special Interest Groups (Software Metrics and TickIT).

The first meeting, that of the Quality in IT Group on 13th September at the Heathrow Sheraton Skyline Hotel, focused on Software Quality in the late 1990s and introduced the 'Object Oriented' methodology for systems development, which is proving to be popular in the US where it has made for considerable time savings to be made in the delivery of systems benefits.

Considerable interest was shown in the technique, but whether it will turn out to be the 'panacea' that some imagine remains to be seen. It has been suggested that whilst the technique may offer some benefits in terms of speed of delivery, it could in practice make quality assurance very difficult, and hence the Quality Forum is keen to facilitate the development of a Working Paper that will assist companies to prepare QA functions that will work when "O-O" is introduced. The meeting also gave prominence to the issue of Open Enterprise Computing and the impacts that it might be expected to have on software quality.

The second meeting, that of the TQM Group on 14th September at the same location, consisted of four syndicates from which delegates were permitted to choose any two, under the general theme of 'Life After TQM', whilst the third, the Metrics SIG, held at the Heathrow Marriott Hotel on 4th October, focused on benchmarking and the use of Function Point Analysis to measure software complexity. The TickIT SIG, again at the Marriott on 5th October, focused on the automation of quality management systems and processes.

Automating Quality Management Systems

A number of companies have automated their quality management systems already. Others may be considering doing so, and for those companies the TickIT SIG provided a good insight as to what to expect, as well as an opportunity to sample both what is on offer and what is to come as regards automation software, of which there is at present no shortage.

Peter Short, Quality Consultant for IBM Hursley, described how his company has developed a mainframe based on-line quality management system using a VM/CMS application called Enhanced Quality Management Systems (EQMS) which provides a particularly useful electronic stapling facility which overcomes problems of file duplication, particularly, for example, of process descriptions. Ownership of processes is linked back to the individual responsible via an on-line telephone directory, whilst QMS files are linked to departments rather than individuals.

It was noted to have benefited the company by providing a common system for everyone that provided a single source of information i.e. only one copy that can potentially contain an error rather than several, and prevention of the quality manual from going 'on the shelf' i.e. the last version of a QMS can be readily archived and retrieved. More interesting, however, is perhaps the ability provided to BSI to tap into the company's QMS remotely and conduct surveys from their offices, so reducing the costs of surveillance visits. This matter, of course, prompted some debate, with at least one delegate pointing out the need for BSI to conduct interviews during their visits. The interviews were not, however, the main issue, as the key source of the saving came from the assurance that BSI were able to gain at their convenience, that the system itself was under control.

Kevin Hawgood and Jan Foster, representing Barclaycard Business Development (the IT wing of Barclaycard) described how they had been inspired to automate through the advent of Local Area Networking, which prompted a visit to Barclays Bank at Knutsford where a tool which had been developed in-house had been applied to automate the company's standards manual. This tool, an adaptation of the Windows Helpmate, used a development lifecycle methodology which was already proven and allowed monthly updates to be provided in place of the previous 6 monthly ones, and allowed a 20 page document to be converted into a helpfile in around two hours. The system, which became live in June, was said to have made staff 'very relieved' on account of the amount of paperwork which it saved. Audits later showed that the QMS was being utilised far more often and more readily than previously with people using it daily rather than merely tracking down paper copies periodically.

Automating Processes

Paul Saffer, Quality Director for EPG, explained how his company, which produces high value low volume software packages for the insurance sector, started working for TickIT in 1991 with the aim of improving their configuration management. They adopted 'Thenon', a comprehensive change management system for AS400 products used primarily for support, but also for development. It is self documenting with clear controls which enables authorisations to be readily seen, and eases the auditor's work as the company is clearly in control of support procedures. Packages are also reported to be secure from unauthorised changes, whilst maintenance costs have been reduced and customers have greater control of their live load and test load operations. An upgrade of Thenon is expected to be released later this year.

Derek Allen, of the CMC Partnership, introduced 'Assystant: A New Way of Managing Change' which CMC developed jointly with London-based Assyst International Limited. This is a 4GL software application which is powerful, easy to change and works on open platforms and is currently being prototyped by a leading jewellery stockist company. It is not at present commercially available, but has already enabled substantial reduction in stock levels to be achieved through the introduction of simplified business processes which integrate the office with the warehouse by VDU and barcoding. This has generated a flood of ideas for the further improvement of processes. Key features include the ability to create simulated organisational structures and sets of business process flows from those already in existence and from in-built case studies. A practical demonstration was given of the software.

Demonstrating Fitness for Use

The presentation by Mr. Warden and Ms. Evans was highly original in content and focused on assessing the integrity of systems. This presentation compared the modern practice of software testing and the position faced by engineers in the times of Queen Victoria, quoting from Willa Cathers 'Alexandra Bridge' which was written around 1900 i.e.:

"Whenever there is the greatest output of energy, wherever the blind human race is exerting itself most furiously, there is bound to be tumult and disaster".

Testing was, they suggested, a 'wicked problem' i.e. one with no simple or standard or perfect solution and where even the act of trying to implement a solution was liable to change the problems. This makes it costly, time consuming and difficult.

Some standards, such as the Test Documentation Standard ANS/I EEE 830-1984 may help, for example, in defining a test documentation set, but in no way will it solve all testing problems. Indeed some apparently obvious solutions may turn out in practice to be mere red herrings.

The speakers were confident, however, that some steps could be taken to at least reduce the testing dilemma i.e.:

*build in as high quality a software process as possible.

*determine the most complex yet essentially error free programs that can be constructed with this process.

*limit the complexity of programs which need to be highly reliable to what can be produced using the essentially defect free process.

*test programs as thoroughly as is economically possible.

*recognize that capability to build progressively larger defect free programs will improve as the software process is improved.

*acknowledge that testing starts at the beginning of any project and is an essential activity in improving both the product and the process.

Using these principles and the SEI Capability Maturity Model as a guide, the speakers developed a questionnaire, entitled the Testing Assessment Programme (TAP) questionnaire and an associated User Guide, which uses an original 'Pasta Model' to assign 'maturity levels' to types of code and methods of testing.

It defines a considerable number of characteristics and behaviours. Examples of a few of these are the levels for goals of testing; risk assessment; stop conditions and contractual sign off; scope of testing; costs and benefits of testing; selection, organisation and skills of testing staff; selection of tools, and involvement of users.

By examining the characteristics and behaviours for each level of each activity, as well as the various code levels, it becomes possible to gain an appreciation of what is needed to advance to a higher level for each of the aspects of testing described. It is emphasised that it is necessary to improve all aspects at a common pace, for example, there is no point in implementing tools until it is clear how they can support methods and the goals of testing, since weak areas will reduce the company's overall capability in testing.

It is suggested that companies may find the easiest way to start using the methodology is to apply it to a specific project in order to gain an appreciation of the testing capability for a particular system and then to build on the experience in order to assess the wider capabilities of the organisation, and identify common issues where improvements will produce the greatest benefits. [This is a building approach -not common amongst single project oriented software designers -Ed].

As regards completion of the questionnaire, a 50/50 mix is recommended between testing specialists and team leaders, and project managers with at least several in each category. Senior management participation is, however, also encouraged.

[Issue 71 (November 1994)]

LEARNING THE LESSONS OF FAILURE

The huge sums of money that are being lost through the failure of information systems and software development continues to be exemplified by the media with the October issue of *Communications of the Association of Computing Machinery* (ACM). This highlights the case of CONFIRM, a project hailed as 'a leading edge comprehensive travel industry reservation program combining airline, rental car and hotel information' which had to be cancelled due to malfunctions after an investment of three and a half years and $125 million. [The UK has also had its spectacular IT failure of this magnitude -Ed].

The article by Effy Oz, Assistant Professor of the MIS program at Wayne State University in the US, poses the question 'does a failure of this magnitude have to happen?' and provides a set of useful pointers to help in the avoidance of similar disasters in the future.

The article makes the important point that failures in software development today are not uncommon, yet there is little reported research on the subject, with journalistic accounts of cases 'tending to be simplistic and to highlight the sensational' whilst lawsuits 'tend to emphasize the other party's failures to comply with the contract: rather than to outline the subtleties of interaction between the parties'.

It suggests that questions like 'How severe should the difficulties be to warrant alerting the client?' and 'If management does not share information with the client, are the individual members of the project team expected to blow the whistle?' should be addressed by means of professional codes of ethics and standards of conduct. To this end the author directs the reader to two of her recent works: 'Professional Standards for Information Systems

Professionals: A Case for a Unified Code of Ethics' (*MIS Quarterly*, 4, December 1992) and *'Ethics for the Information Age'* (Wm.C.Brown Dubuque, Iowa, 1994).

Many existing codes, such as that of the Institute Certified Computer Professionals (ICCP) are seen as creating a dilemma for the employed professional whose interests may become divided between employer and client. Also the need to notify supervisors early when persistent problems are identified is clearly apparent, and a fear driven culture may be a great inhibitor. In the case of CONFIRM:

"Some employees did complain about the technical problems – several of them paid for this with their jobs ".

In its 'Principles for Managers of the Service Provider' the article condemns the practice of trying to entice clients with unrealistic short schedules as 'not just unethical, but also potentially very damaging to the company's own effort'. Project plans are advised to be treated as part of the client's contract even if formally they aren't. Adoption of a Code of Professional Standards is urged at specifies the course of action to be followed by employees in the event of experiencing persistent problems with systems that are under development.

In its 'Principles for Clients' it recommends that the status of projects be checked periodically (by an independent consultant if necessary) and to watch for 'alerting signals' in the developer's camp:

'When executives and other employees of the developer are massively dismissed or voluntarily look for new positions ; ask questions. When the rats abandon the ship it is probably sinking'.

[Issue 72 (December 1994)]

I.T. QUALITY: COMPUTERISED SYSTEMS VALIDATION

From the Quality Forum I.T. meeting *Quality Matters* reports on the syndicate presentation: 'Computerised Systems Validation: A lot more than Quality Assurance' by Mike Hewson, of Praxis, the software engineering arm of Touche Ross Management Consultants.

Mr. Hewson's presentation focussed on recent pioneering work by the pharmaceutical industry to provide a means of demonstrating that computer systems are productive, secure and do not corrupt data. This is important in this industry as recent regulations are demanding that all data be stored and traceable back to source. In the United States, the license granting Drugs Administration (FDA), have begun to lay down guidelines which reflect a trend away from quality control of data and towards more general requirements for systems validation. A spokesperson for the FDA has recently announced:

"The pharmaceutical manufacturer cannot adequately validate the reliability and performance of a computer system unless the manufacturer knows the specifications of the hardware and software and has access to the programs and other data that demonstrates that the system complies with the specifications".

In Europe, the EC Guidance on Good Clinical Practice lays down several guidelines which refer to computer systems; for example Section 3.3:

'If trial data are entered directly into a computer there must be adequate safeguard to ensure validation, including a signed and dated print-out and back-up records. Computerised systems should be validated and a detailed description for their use should be produced and kept up to date'.

What is not clear from the regulations, however, is just what actually constitutes a system of validation and how such a system is intended to operate. According to Good Manufacturing Practice (GMP) validation is defined as:

'The action of proving, in accordance with the principles of QMP, that any procedure, process, equipment, material, activity or system actually leads to the expected results'.

By contrast, a leading manufacturer's QA policy defines validation as:

'A systematic review of a computer system and its operating environment (including documentation, controls and security) to assure management that the system is operating as intended and will continue to do so'.

Clearly there is some variation here, and the consistency needs to be improved. In order to do this it was suggested that in forming a validation protocol, it needed to be understood that users need to be able to demonstrate that systems have been properly developed, perform properly, are used properly and are maintained properly. This demonstration is to be achieved through orderly documentation recording conformance with Standard Operating Procedures (SOPs).

As a first step, a retrospective validation could be used consisting of an evaluation of the computer system, that establishes what documentary evidence already exists, followed by rework using change control to bring the system up to a pre-defined status i.e. with any missing documentary evidence being put in place. A set of Praxis Guides has been produced to help companies do this in conjunction with the ISO10000 series and SPICE.

Common results from retrospective evaluations are:

* lack of clarity of roles and responsibilities (for example no-one responsible for ensuring that the correct number of licences are issued for the use of the system, or that updates from suppliers are installed).

* documentation numbering and organisation is flawed, in particular with a lack of ownership of documents.

* frequently a total absence of configuration management [a serious problem in IT- Ed].

* there is a high level of variation in vendor assessment which has resulted in systems entering routine use, with wholly inadequate capabilities.

This may then be used as a foundation for prospective validation, which is based on a principle of right first time. It involves the application of a validation protocol for development, installation, commissioning and production. Again Praxis has produced a set of guides for this, for use in conjunction with Good Management Practice, SPICE, and ISO9000-3 (applied to software development). Key criteria include:

*framework products from the supplier which are preferably represented as a quality management system certificated to ISO9001.

*system specifications of hardware and software to defined and proven methods.

*implementation specifications in defined and proven languages which use defined and proven tools.

*test specifications at module, sub-assembly and system levels.

*defined development and maintenance lifecycles.

*documented verification that the hardware and software meets user requirements, with system testing successfully completed and a configuration baseline established.

*user acceptance test specifications for product functionality and performance; data handling, calibration and security; user documentation; and the operational environment.

*documented verification that the hardware and software conform to the 'system specification'.

*defined installation, acceptance and calibration processes.

*specification of operating ranges, fully loaded performance and operator efficiency and documented verification to show that the system performs according to the system specification throughout all anticipated operating ranges.

*verification that the system consistently produces a product or performs a function meeting predetermined quality attributes, and that a maintenance process is in place.

The speaker emphasized that as the FDA and other bodies potentially have the power to prevent products from being sold on these grounds, despite huge investments in them, the seriousness of the situation should not be underestimated, and suggested that in time, other industries may also follow the example currently being set in pharmaceuticals.

[Issue 74 (February 1995)]

IT QUALITY INITIATIVES AT RISK

Quality Initiatives in the information technology sector are at risk, according to the latest report by The Quality Forum. The conclusion follows from a motivational survey of IT quality practitioners which showed that there tended to be no apparent match between the motivational needs of quality practitioners and the motivational content of their work. Findings suggest that quality roles tended to be based on the implementation requirements of quality management systems and fail to provide the feedback needed by staff to appraise the effectiveness of their work. Consequently staff remain in the dark about the value of their work and experience difficulty in demonstrating their case to senior management. Concern about security is said to be 'widespread' and the implications for the IT industry 'significant', raising questions as to how the quality message is to be sold to the IT workforce if the quality practitioners themselves are de- motivated.

According to the Forum:

'If senior managers do not perceive the value of quality management they will be reluctant to invest further in quality initiatives. As staff become more dissatisfied they may leave'.

The survey, which was undertaken by Software Futures Limited under sponsorship from the Quality Forum, used 21 measures and comparison data from the US where available. Appropriate frequency distributions were produced for the 21 measures as they related to the quality practitioners and a set of 18 'Notched Box and Whisker plots' illustrate the improvement differences for example between quality practitioners and system developers. The report was produced by Dr. Isobel Nicholson, Principal Lecturer at the University of Central Lancashire and Richard Warden, Founder Director of Software Futures Limited.

QUALITY IN IT: MANAGING THE TRANSITION TO CUSTOMER SERVICE

The latest Quality Forum 'Quality in IT' day took place on March 2nd at the Heathrow Marriott Hotel, and featured presentations from Marilyn Bush, who is currently based in Abingdon and assisted in the development of the SEI Capability Maturity Model at Carnegie University. She gave a well received description of the SEI Model, and Garrey Melville of Bull Information Systems outlined an interesting framework to improve the customer focus of the IT Department.

The presentation by Garrey Melville was unusual with a wide application throughout industry. Entitled 'Transition to Customer Service: the IT Department Challenge' the paper highlights the need for IT departments generally to change their approach and become more customer focused. It suggests that the IT Department has the potential to become one of the most powerful divisions within a company, but a detailed analysis of current trends has shown that IT directors need to run their IT departments more in the style of an IT services company if these benefits are to be realised. Thus, a complete change of emphasis is required.

Often it is the IT directors themselves who recognise the need for change and start the process, though sometimes it may be forced by the main board of the organisation. It does not, however, always work:

'It was found that many IT departments began their transition process only to find things grinding to a halt after several weeks or months. This was good news for management consultants who found themselves on very long term contracts, but as far as the department was concerned, their problems seemed to get bigger and bigger, and the projects longer and longer'.

This was not either the end of the story. Many IT departments were in the dark about the many interdependencies that exist in a service business, and in consequence major projects began and either stopped or became ever larger as key interdependencies emerged from the woodwork. This has had serious financial implications:

'The transition costs increased, staff morale together with the confidence in management reduced, change issues magnified, in some cases well out of proportion '.

The paper suggests, however, that this need not happen. These 'costly stalling steps' can be avoided, and not with any great expense or difficulty, just a little 'preliminary ground work conducted up-front'.

The paper highlights seven 'critical success factors for service excellence' and six important transition steps which need to be addressed:

'From an operational standpoint the seven factors identified appear rather basic and in many respects they are'.

The seven factors or interdependencies were used as focal points for a 'drill down analysis' and an audit of each is used to provide a 'clear and candid picture' of where a particular department is placed on the customer transition curve. This avoids the common management mistake of underestimating the health and fitness of the organisation at the outset, which has led and continues to lead to some appalling financial disasters on a grand scale:

'Short sighted managers set unrealistic business goals for the future, with little or no comprehension of where the department sits today. Each time a project fails they have another attempt at establishing their departmental strengths and weaknesses. It is an expensive exercise'.

The comparatively simple audit system proposed by contrast 'will not only dictate the starting point for the IT department, but will provide the foundation for the planning and organisation that will follow'. It operates on three levels and although it is rigorous, its principles are straightforward and are delightfully clear in the paper:

'Clear recommendations on how comprehensive the department's planning processes are, whether they are in line with the department's transition programme and industry standards, emerge with a degree of clarity that can frighten many people as their approach towards business is questioned'.

The output from this approach is a series of actions based on risk analysis methods which are prioritised and scored. Impact analysis then also takes place on both the organisation and the department on the actions that arise to provide a clear structure showing how to move forward and when. Emphasis is placed on enabling the organisation and the department to move forward as one, using the most appropriate method [team workshops, pre and post audit, Key Individual Project Involvement (KIPI) etc.].

The adoption of the principles outlined are said to 'position an IT department in a better light to provide its customers with improved service and support' which in turn 'should lead to a fitter IT operation and a healthier attitude towards change and improvement'. The follow through usually results in operational and structural change tailored to where the IT department in question lies on the transition curve.

Further Information.

Garrey Melville is the UK Marketing Manager of the Systems Integration and Services Group of Bull UK. He has been actively involved in marketing many different types of professional IT and non IT services over the last decade. The output of his work has been the development of a number of business methodologies for services. These include the identification of the key service interdependencies that an IT department requires to consider to make a successful transition to becoming a customer oriented unit.

[Issue 78 (June 1995)]

QUALITY MANAGEMENT: RECENT DEVELOPMENTS

It is now a little over two years since The Institute of Quality Assurance (IQA) presented its conference on Quality Management Strategy: The Future, which addressed the issues of standards, testing and certification. With a two year gap which has seen the publication of the amended ISO9000 (BS EN ISO9000) standard and growing controversy over its suitability for example in the software industry and to small businesses, The IQA (Britain's leading professional institute in this field) has considered it timely to present a similar event to further address these issues, which was held at The City Conference Centre on 17th May.

Norman Burgess, Chairman of the IQA Business Development Board, chaired the event, which consisted of seven presentations. Initially a review is given of a controversial presentation, on The Supplier Audit Confirmation (SAC) Initiative, (Hewlett Packard's 'alternative route' to third party certification) by their American representative David Ling.

The Supplier Audit Confirmation Initiative

The Supplier Audit Confirmation (SAC) Initiative stipulates five eligibility criteria, namely

* recognition amongst the leaders for customer satisfaction within its industry of operation, by virtue of evidence supplied from customer surveys conducted by independent industry recognized sources.

* a formal documented quality system which encompasses, but is not limited to, all of the elements of the appropriate BS EN ISO9000 standard.

* ability to demonstrate a culture of senior and middle management participation involvement and support of the quality system.

* evidence of an effective independent audit system that has been in continuous operation for at least three years, whereby competent auditors assess the quality system against all of the elements of BS EN ISO9000 but are not limited to them.

* ability to demonstrate the existence of an environment of continuous improvement that is verified in managerial policies and procedures.

In addition the SAC Draft lays down a number of specific criteria for initial audits, certification and on-going assessments to be followed by certification bodies. These include, for example, requirements for sampling, witnessing and participation in internal audits as described within the SAC certification sampling guideline; conducting of third party audits of the internal audit, corrective action and management review processes at a system level every three years; and verify annually that the supplier still meets all of the eligibility criteria. This means, for example, that the company has at least maintained its status as a leader for customer satisfaction as indicated by the aforementioned surveys, that the culture of senior and middle management involvement, participation and support is still there, and that the environment of continuous improvement is still present.

Certification bodies, for their part, are required to define a certification sampling table for third party participation in internal audits based on the size and multiple sites of the supplier's operation.

In his presentation Mr. Ling described BS EN ISO9000 as "a useful quality tool with their quality improvement programme", but emphasized that the value of it had come from their doing the work rather than from third party auditing. The conference literature indicates clearly the increased emphasis on system level external audits and detailed internal audits. This distinguishes it from conventional third party certification in which the emphasis is more firmly placed on detailed external audits and conformance to requirements.

He described the four phases that are underway to establish the SAC initiative as a recognised route to third party certification. These require industry consensus and communication, physical development, refinement to enhance credibility and establishing its presence by incorporation within the ISO CASCO Guides. He pointed out that at present 46 companies have endorsed the Draft document, a list of which is provided in the conference literature.

Not surprisingly the presentation attracted a number of questions from the floor most notably from John Slater, Managing Consultant for Logica, who is a well known opponent of SAC and advocate of the UK's TickIT scheme, the development of which he has been closely associated with. He was particularly critical of the SAC's eligibility criteria, arguing that they were, for the most part "very subjective" and offered potential for certain companies to "buy their way in ". Mr. Ling accepted the subjectivity argument, defending it on the grounds that an element of subjectivity was required if the right level of feedback and constructive improvement was to be achieved. He said:

"We are not getting rid of third party certification if people find that it is of best value, but we feel that this gives more choice".

David Murray of the IQA then drew attention to the first of the five eligibility criteria and suggested that there was a danger that this could become "an easy way through for the international elite" which could lead to "enormous dissatisfaction", particularly in the UK where few companies have formal codes of conduct as is the case in the USA. When asked who was going to judge these eligibility criteria, Mr. Ling replied "we are hoping to get feedback to tie it down".

As regards the position of the SAC in Europe Mr. Ling said that he had "kept close communication" with the European Commission and highlighted the target area of telecomms where he said he especially wanted to see the SAC route put into effect.

He was asked to comment on the added value of SAC and in this respect he pointed to:

*better integration of management's quality objective with the ISO effort.

*an increase in managerial engagement with the business value of ISO9000.

*potential for improvement of the competency of ISO9000 internal assessors.

*reduction of preparation costs by continuing internal and external assessments.

*establishment of a precedent for future standards such as ISO14000.

[Issue 97 (January 1997)]

NEW GUIDE TO ADDRESS MILLENNIUM PROBLEM IN IT

In a little under three years from now people all over the world will be celebrating the one in a thousand year event of a changing millennium. After the party, however, what will happen when people turn on their computer systems? A new guide from The British Computer Society attempts to explain:

'Symptoms will include incorrect accounting, erroneous reports, operational mistakes, (e.g. releasing newer stock before old), system access failures, and application failures. The failures and errors occur whenever a system uses a date after 1st January 2000'.

It follows that some users may not even have to wait until 'after the party'. They may experience problems before:

'In 1993 a large supermarket chain discovered that they had problems with the shelf life date of their tins of corned beef: their bar code system could not cope with dates into the next century, i.e. for products with a shelf life, at that point in time, of more than seven years. As the date was held in the format of DD/MM/YY the system reported that the tins were "past expiry date" as they showed as being 93 years old'.

The Guide points out that there is no way of accurately predicting what errors will actually arise. The results of such a prediction would depend on knowing the exact data and logic applied by hundreds of thousands of programmers in millions of programs written over the last 30 to 40 years. It does, however, offer some ideas for coping with the problem:

'A key recommendation is for each business unit to appoint a Year 2000 Programme Manager, with authority and accountability to oversee the work. The programme needs to be completed well before 1st January 2000 - although some advanced companies regard the deadline for replacement, or technical completion of remedial work, as lying between July and November 1998, or even earlier, where a full year-end test is prudent'.

'The projects, or programme of projects, should be all embracing and phased. It should include the production of a complete and accurate inventory, the completion of impact analysis, problem resolution, testing and implementation. The inventory (of all IT applications, databases and infrastructure) is necessary to begin the assessment of risk and to plan action - be it in-house remedial and replacement work, or establishing the compliance status of components from third parties'.

The Guide gives some idea of some of the costs which could be involved:

'A major bank has calculated that it has 280 million lines of code to examine, of which 80 per cent have date functions in them. They estimate that the project will cost them US $100 million to fix'.

It is suggested that even for a small business unit to ignore the problem would be can 'action of professional and business management folly', as the problem occurs in an estimated 80 per cent of computer applications worldwide. Cases are presented for replacing rather than fixing and for adopting the so-called "processing window' and date field expansion techniques as cost effective solutions. Some 'tools' such as code analysers and modifiers, database converters and system date simulators are also advocated. [Manual back-up systems may also be considered -Ed].

SOFTWARE QUALITY IN IRELAND

This month a review is presented of The Fifth European Conference on Software Quality, which was held in Dublin, with particular reference to the four Irish papers by Tony Moynihan, (Dublin City University), Reinhard Schaler (University College Dublin), Bill Kearney (Lotus IBM) and Eamonn McGuinness (AIMware Limited, Galway.)

Automation Strategies and Quality of Global Software

The paper by Bill Kearney, with the above title, is concerned particularly with the design and management of a Global Automation Testing Strategy and after outlining a potential Global Automation testing process, describes some of the tools issues associated with the design of a Global automation testing system and various testing areas (Smoke Testing, Functional Testing, Regression Testing and Layout Testing).

A set of steps is suggested for the creation of a Software Quality automation process for functional libraries followed by some guidelines for the design of test automation. The latter aims particularly to address the issues of readability, consistency, portability and maintainability of global automated scripts. The author is keen to point out one of the key problems which often affects the development of test automation i.e. it is frequently done with little or no regard for future maintainability or portability of code:

'Many people dislike attempts to encourage style guidelines; however, the use of a consistent style can greatly improve the overall readability of a collection of scripts produced by multiple contributors. Use of a style convention does not mean you like the style; it means you are willing to sacrifice some of your own aesthetic preferences for the overall consistency of the code in a project'.

A list of key features which an automation tool must support in order to work in a global environment is given, along with advice about the working which will be used for creating the automation:

'For a higher or mixed model, designing the automation testing system becomes very similar to the model used for a development environment. Language dependent parts of the code should be resourced out for ease of translation and the remainder should be written with cross-language support in mind. Any test tool will impose restrictions on how best to design the system but fundamentally the model will use a functional library i.e. re-usable functions are written to do generic tasks e.g. File Open, File Savers and the scripts use these functions rather than manipulating the product VI directly. The key advantage is that the automation scripts basically remain static but the underlying libraries can be changed or rebuilt to run on a different language'.

The paper concludes with some examples of where Lotus Notes, noted to be 'a powerful tool in the management of a Global Automation testing strategy' can be applied, along with an explanation of the lessons learned over the last two years:

'In Lotus we focus on producing multiple baselines to redress our results against. We store previously good and bad results. Therefore if the same bug occurs in subsequent builds of a product we can automatically identify a test failure. It is possible to extend this context in a global environment and store multiple baselines for 'English' and localised builds of a product. The advantage of this model is that scripts can be regressed against a wider range of baselines to indicate pass or fail'.

Achieving Increases in Software Process Maturity: Some Irish Case Studies

Eamonn McGuinness describes the experiences of five Irish companies which committed to and executed process improvement projects: Motorola Manufacturing (Dublin), Quay Financial Software (Dublin) Voluntary Health Insurance (Dublin), Tellabs (Shannon, Co. Clare), and Telecom Eirann (Dublin).

With regard to these companies the author focuses on ten fundamental aspects of process improvement, namely the sponsor's role, assessment variations, the improvement lifecycle, resourcing and managing the project, the role of training and coaching, process automation, results obtained, how improvement is sustained, experience with clusters and networking and aspects critical for success.

The scope and size of each of the companies varies as does the approach taken. The computer integrated manufacturing department at Motorola for example employs 50 software engineers and is responsible for software ranging from personnel and finance to factory support and product test. They use SEI Software Engineering Institute assessments and are noted for their 'good use of customised workshops where engineers were facilitated in exploring the SEI Capability Maturity Model, best practices in a particular software engineering area (e.g. software testing, software project management etc.) and their own processes'.

They were assessed at SEI Level Two in October 1994 and at Level Three in November 1995 :

'They have internal product process, resource and productivity metrics that report on items such as customer satisfaction, cycle time, productivity, in-process faults, released defects etc. These are monitored to gauge the

success or otherwise of the process improvement efforts. For example, one of the Q4 1995 charts showed a marked increase in the number of in-process faults, which was offset by a decrease in the number of post-release defects. These results were the fruits of introducing an updated Review Process'.

They are also noted for their 'aggressive policy with respect to software process improvement'.

'Some of the engineering staff wondered at times if the stretch goals were too ambitious but when the going got tough the sponsor got going. He set the goal with the group, continuously monitored the project and cleared all roadblocks for the process improvement efforts. Sometimes this involved difficult negotiations with business managers on deliverables and timescales. When these negotiations were getting difficult, he had his own senior manager publicly support the improvement efforts of the software group. He participated actively in the process improvement steering team but was careful not to lead it. He even participated in one SEI assessment of his own group'.

Quay Financial Software (a CSK Company) develops, markets and sells software for the international financial markets and employs around 100 software engineering staff. They have achieved ISO9000/TickIT certification and are examining the SEI CMM and SPICE. They are noted for their 'heavy use of automation for their process' but whilst they had a strong sponsor initially 'the arrival of a new senior manager with an interest in process improvement probably saved the project from mediocre results'.

The in-house IT department of Voluntary Health Insurance has around 20 employed in software development. They are noted for their production of guide books (Guide to Reviews and Guide to Metrics Collection) and for their approach to testing improvement:

They choose to assess their testing practices by looking at process, product and resource metrics. They found for example that on average 44 per cent of project effort was devoted to testing. They used this and the other benchmarks taken at the end of the improvement project to assess the progress made with the new testing practices '.

Tellabs are one of the R and D arms of a multinational telecomms provider that also has a large manufacturing base in Ireland. They employ around 30 software engineering staff, have achieved ISO9001, and invested in the very latest form of SEI assessment (the CMM Based Assessment/Appraisal for Internal Process Improvement). They used directed workshops on the SEI CMM to educate teams and identify practices that are missing or need improvement, whilst the R and D Director sponsored the process improvement efforts:

also accommodate the software process definitions embodied within ISO 12207:1995 which defines the software life-cycle process, and the existence of non-UK accreditation routes such as that of SWEDAC, the Swedish accreditation body, which has been authorised to accredit certification bodies wishing to provide TickIT certification since October 1996.

Efforts to go beyond this, however, by developing some form of 'Tick IT Plans' certification have received little support with concerns that a target could be set which is perhaps too tightly defined. One delegate suggested that business metrics could be incorporated into 'Tick IT Plans'. Unless it had the necessary infrastructure support even Roy Farmer expressed doubt as to whether such certification could ever be realistic.

[Quality Matters comments: Whether TickIT will eventually become superseded by SPICE or whether the two schemes will co-exist as separate standards remains to be seen. Certainly whatever transpires it would appear that greater alignment to business goals will be needed coupled with a realistic and acceptable method for setting and appraising any target-based profile. An element of cross-fertilisation ultimately between the two standards would appear to be inevitable.]

Insourcing, Outsourcing and Facility Management

Frequently, when management discuss a possible change of technology or the introduction of new tools, only purely technical consequences are evaluated. Rarely is an assessment also made of the total financial and organisational consequences to evaluate whether the application of the technology or tool is actually good business.

The paper entitled 'Insourcing, Outsourcing or Facility Management -Quality in the Decision Process' by Kim Trans of Kommunedata I-S of Denmark describes how the financial consequences of a change in computer based technology might be assessed and a financially optimal choice made. It is noted that in some cases a mixed solution of insourcing, outsourcing, and facility management may be appropriate:

'Choosing the best production technologies and identifying their corresponding costs has become a difficult task for modern companies. This is partly due to new ways of organising company production, as insourcing, outsourcing and facility management are emerging as methods for company management. In order to choose among them, an evaluation procedure is needed, which shows the differences in cost structure of the technological possibilities available. Such a tool has with great benefit been used in the. author's company, where it is used to evaluate computer services, ranging from insourcing of pc support to the evaluation of entire facility management contracts. The method used can be transferred to other domains with proper modification of the used assessment rules'.

A criterion of 'isolated functionality' is introduced which confirms that it is possible to evaluate corresponding economic scenarios without uncontrolled interference from other technologies. This to a degree constrains the method in that it implies a hierarchically based organisation of company production, but to compensate a 'needed isolation level' can be reached if one uses a set of interface descriptions which connect the technology in question with its environment. The existence of alternatives confirms that the evaluation is sufficiently broad in scope for application to proceed.

Surveys of the ways in which decisions relating to insourcing, outsourcing, and facility management in the author's company yielded a set of five data sources and categories:

* hardware (excluding hardware maintenance but including hardware removal and incorporating the costs of hardware procurement, installation and configuration/reconfiguration, and removal).

* software (excluding maintenance, servicing and upgrading but including removal and incorporating costs of procurement, installation, removal, data conversion such as conversions of databases, and indirect costs such as that of support software which is distributed to all software that depends on it).

* knowledge (all costs related to employee knowledge and experience, both existing within the company and needed to use, service and maintain the technology in question).

* production (all variable costs which can be related directly to the technology and products in question including CV usage, secondary storage, materials, and hardware and software maintenance).

* organisational consequences (including performance change, efficiency change, indirect gain, depreciation period, technology domain, mainstream conformance, and estimated total lifetime).

The criteria of the last category are used to evaluate the total gain in relation to the costs highlighted by the other four categories. In this connection it is noted that the cost due to the removal of the old technology, at least as far as software is concerned, can be estimated using the COCOMO model, which is based on the number of programming lines:

'The COCOMO model is highly usable when applied to the removal of old software, as the model can be used to estimate the cost of a possible reprogramming of the original functionality in another programming language. Effective use of the COCOMO model demands experience in software cost estimation using the model and knowledge concerning the new technology as both are necessary to specify the 15 corrective factors which specify the differences between the involved technologies'.

The results obtained for each of the five categories enable three key 'decision values' to be defined :

(i) total initial cost (defined by hardware, software and knowledge categories)

(ii) maintenance cost (defined by the production category)

(iii) profit potential (defined by the organisational consequences category)

In this connection it is noted that profit potential 'may have a dynamic structure due to the domain of technology application, the amount produced and the overall state of the corresponding market segment' whilst total initial cost 'may have a dynamic structure due to a dependence on removal costs which relate dynamically to the created technology bindings in existing software'. Consequently real time information is needed to assess these values.

The three 'key decision values' are related to insourcing, outsourcing and facility management by a comparison for each alternative, with the corresponding market prices. If the value is less than the market price, then the suggestion is to insource whilst if it is higher then the suggestion is to outsource. Facility management (a specific form of outsourcing) applies where the total maintenance and management of special purpose equipment, including operators, is involved, as with the maintenance and management of an IBM MVS mainframe computer, including system software and applications.

Practical examples illustrate how the model may be applied in practice- and a break even point used to ascertain when it would be most economic to change from one technology to another.

The Usefulness of CAME Tools in Software Quality Assurance.

Heiko Grigoleit of the Faculty of Computer Science at the University of Magdeburg, Germany, described the paper with the above title which he co-wrote with Keiner R. Dumke of the same university. It concerns the effectiveness of software metrics tools which are collectively grouped under the title of Computer Assisted Software Measurement and Evaluation (CAME) tools. These tools are usable for process, product and resources evaluation in all phases of the software life cycle, including the problem definition, and their 'usefulness' is assessed using a framework incorporating metrics definition, selection of the evaluation criteria, the tool-based modelling and measurement, the value presentation, and the statistical analysis. This framework 'represents an incremental technique for the application of quantification of quality aspects in a required quality assurance'.

The authors distinguish between two types of software measurement framework, the informal which consists of general components of textual descriptions (questions, rules and "laws", experience notices and standards [such as TickIT and SPICE] and the formal, consisting of algebraic approaches, axiomatic approaches, functional approaches and rule-based approaches. The COCOMO model provides an example of a formal functional framework. Other examples are also given, and a table of benefits and weaknesses of the four formal measurement approaches is given.

The reader may note, for example, that the functional variety has the benefit of 'a compact definition of experience' and the weakness of being 'hard to use for new development paradigms'. Other more general problems relating to measurement and evaluation frameworks include: -

* too little experience of the use of modern or new paradigms.

* a lack of supports for the adjustments of the evaluation criteria.

* a lack of characteristics of the given or used (acquisition) software.

* no exact knowledge about the most applied metrics.

The authors contend that the efficiency of CAME tools depends on the definiteness' of the software development process and that with the goal being a measurement based control system the implementation of a measurement data base is required. This, however, presents a problem as regards obtaining usable measurement values from the used metric tools. This is reflected in their General Object-Oriented Software Measurement Approach which involves:

*measurement choice (choosing software metrics and measures from a general metrics class hierarchy).

*measurement adjustment (two tools provide measures to be used as initial empirical evaluation criteria for an 'accepted quality') .

*measurement migration (refinement of the metrics 'mutations' in the development phases for the given development paradigm).

*measurement efficiency (analysis of the algorithmic character of the software measurement and the integration of tool-based 'control cycles' in the software development process).

Some 20 CAME tools are studied in relation to this framework and it is concluded that 'the present CAME tools are not a suitable means of complex software evaluation' as they are 'mostly based on existing assessment methodologies such as the Function Point method'. The paper then gives some guidance as to how software metric tools should be selected:

'The tool should be designed specifically for the respective software/hardware platform. The philosophy of the CAME tool should be applied consequently. The tool-specific conception of modelling presentation and merit as evaluation should not be violated. Both hardware and software platforms are subject to a highly dynamic development process. Specific parameters of the software development environment should be known to ensure correct and complete input information for the CAME tool. A profound analysis of the empirical aspects such as effort and costs is an imperative precondition for a proper use of a selected CAME tool (for the right use of the right metric tool)'.

Further studies are seeking to define standards for essential components for a higher flexibility for integrated tool-based software measurement.

[Issue 101 (May 1997)]

SOFTWARE QUALITY MANAGEMENT '97 (PART 2)

Software Process Improvement in Small Enterprises

There has been relatively little attention paid to the issue of software process improvement in small enterprises, but this is set to change in the near future with the development of a new software product from Prodacta Computer Service and Systems of Germany. This promises to be an exciting development, and an outline of the presentation by Ms. Gabriele Seidel of Prodacta describes how the product was developed.

The main focus of the presentation was Q-PRIME, an ESSI PIE Project (Process Improvement Experiment project undertaken as part of the European Systems and Software Initiative). This allows an organisation to try out new procedures, new technologies and organisational changes before deciding whether to replicate it throughout the software developing unit. It has sought to introduce the concept of software process improvement to small enterprises which have an initial software process maturity level. The project began in January 1996 and is expected to continue until June 1997.

Building on findings from the Fraunhofer Institute the strengths of small enterprises are seen to lie in fact that they are team based, produce innovative ideas and products, and frequently possess a wealth of know-how and competence. They tend to be weak, however, on processes and procedures, and project management. Prodacta, as a company with 75 employees, with 16 currently employed in software development, sought to develop an enabling tool that would build on strengths and help to overcome the weaknesses.

The speaker accepted that the initial process analysis had not been easy, as the job of defining sub-processes such as configuration management was far from simple. It was found, however, that once a specific application was chosen, definition became easier. Various templates and tools were developed, although the reluctance of certain individuals to part with their code for the sake of the common database did present some difficulty [not an uncommon problem -Ed].

Implementation of the configuration management process was followed by document management. Here, with the need to reduce paperwork to a minimum being considered paramount for a small enterprise, it was decided that no document should be written unless somebody demanded it. Document management began with a definition of a document for sub-processes, and since then there has been systematic refining of the 'bottom up' concept and use of tools to generate documentation. Technical process management followed using electronic mail, groupware and workflow tools, and 'public folders' based on a shared information base.

The resulting commercial product (the Prodacta ProNet) now serves as 'a toolbox for automating client server network administration tasks and processes' which 'integrates and enhances the concepts supported and recommended by manufacturers'. It is described as 'a perfect tool for migration to Windows '95 and Windows NT 4.0 and corresponding applications'. Features include:

*centrally managed installation of workstations including partitioning, formatting and initial operating system and application installation by BootControl.

*flexible documentation of current software and hardware components within a network with Scanwatch and Report Manager.

*automated configuration maintenance of discrete workstations with ClientEdit.

*initial installation of complete workstation in under 30 months.

Business benefits envisaged include: ~

*more activities in parallel (improved planning).

*reduced development time (improved documentation, automated documentation, improved design).

*less time required for debugging (improved configuration management).

Distribution by Hewlett Packard is viewed as proof of a defined development process.

Software Process Improvement at ABB

A total of ten of the 42 papers were devoted to the subject of software process improvement, but the paper by C. Welsch and H.Lichter provided the only case study. It was regrettable that neither speaker gave the presentation, as it would most likely have attracted substantial interest given the plethora of theory but scarcity of practical application information that accompanies this vital subject. The paper is, however, reviewed below and it is hoped that it may stimulate the interest of readers.

The paper is unusual in that it describes software process improvement initiatives which are not part of a company-wide, globally controlled programme, but which have evolved locally in various locations, with ABB Corporate Research of Heidelberg providing the necessary coaching and co-ordination. The initiatives have been 'strongly influenced' by the SEI Capability Maturity Model which ABB Corporate Research adopted both to make management aware of the need to improve software processes and to guide and control the implementation of the improvements. Most of the initiatives have thus started with a CMM assessment and some have had follow-up assessments to measure the success of the improvements.

Three case studies are described, from ABB Kraftwerksleittechnik (KWI), ABB Netzleittechnik (NET), and ABB Calor Schaltanlagen and ABB Daimler-Benz Transportation (Adtranz) which are considered together. These are followed by ten 'theses' which describe the lessons learned.

The first company employs 850 with 90 in the Rand D department which is where the initiative was focused. Their business is the development of control systems for power plants and the products range from controllers to operator stations and engineering systems. With software forming a major component in these systems it follows that there is merit in seeking to improve software process maturity:

'A team of people from KWL and the information technology department of ABB Corporate Research was in charge of defining and guiding software process improvement measures. They worked closely together with the operational units who eventually were to apply these measures'.

'At the beginning the improvements aimed at introducing new software technologies, such as CASE tools or object-oriented programming, according to recommendations from a business analysis by external consultants. During implementation of the recommendations, however, it turned out that the software process at hand was not structured and documented well enough to allow efficient use of these technologies'.

The paper explains how the focus was moved away from technologies to the software process itself:

'Preparing templates and guidelines for documents defined by the process model was considerable work. Whenever possible we adapted published standards for this purpose such as the various IEEE Software Engineering Standards. This not only saved work, but also enhanced the acceptance by software engineers and management'.

The second company supplies a network control system called SPIDER which integrates functions such as energy management, low and medium voltage distribution, supervisory control and data acquisition. The development of SPIDER spans three sites in three countries:

'In order to manage its software projects NET has developed a software process model which takes into account all major aspects of software projects: organisation, planning, implementation, and control. Quality assurance is integrated in this process model as well. The process model is based on the traditional phased V-like model. It is applied in every development project. A software process group consistently maintains and improves the process model'.

The paper explains how, following a CMM assessment, this model was found to be weak both in the early detection of errors and in the efficiency of testing. It then describes how the Systematic Module and User Interface Test (SMUIT) project (funded by the European Community as the Process Improvement Experiment 21612 of the European Systems and Software Initiative (ESSI)) has been applied to SPIDER yielding the following results:

- identification of those modules that are poor with respect to quality attributes such as complexity, readability and maintainability.

- identification of those modules that contain dead, never used code.

- identification of those modules that are not testable due to their complexity with regard to the number of linear independent paths.

- identification of those modules that should be re-engineered.

The last two companies are treated together as they both faced similar problems with their control systems engineering. In particular the share of engineering costs relative to overall production cost was steadily increasing, with poor tool support of engineering activities being identified as the main reason. They therefore commenced a joint project to develop a common integrated tool platform for control system configuration and maintenance which uses the so-called object-oriented approach (CH bought-in class framework with object-oriented data base system). Prototype development began in 1992 with a team of five to seven members and has since expanded to a team of 30 working in Germany, Sweden and Switzerland.

The paper explains how the software process 'evolved in a fairly uncontrolled manner' and became 'less and less adequate'. It was characterised by ambitious project goals, a complex project structure, a lack of systematic analysis and design (no published object-oriented analysis and design methods used nor any CASE tools), and poor documentation of existing implementation (rapid changes to software led to rapid obsolescence of documents):

'When starting the improvement activities the software process maturity at Adtranz as well as ABB Calor Emag Schaltanlagen was rather low. A CMM assessment which was conducted at Adtranz late 1995 and which also included the development project mentioned above, rated the maturity roughly at 2 on the CMM scale'.

The senior management of the companies involved accepted that this state of affairs was not satisfactory and so embarked immediately on a software process improvement initiative which would

(a) standardise forward engineering of object-oriented analysis and design.

(b) enhance and automate documentation of work results.

(c) reverse engineer existing (insufficiently documented) object-oriented software.

'Support for reverse engineering was not only needed for re-documenting the legacy software, but -even more importantly -for keeping the upcoming implementation (source code) and its documentation consistent. It is typical for most software projects that the source code evolves quite rapidly, while the documentation remains unchanged and is soon out of date'.

A Process Improvement Experiment (PIE), funded by the European Community, has since been implemented consisting of CASE tool evaluation and definition of a process model. Subsequent process improvements have followed a spiral-like path of implementation which is illustrated diagramatically.

The ten 'theses' of lessons learned are as follows:

(i) Focus on people and processes rather than technology (only people can bring an improved process to life).

(ii) Basic improvements are management oriented (the promised benefits of CASE tools can only be achieved if their use is part of a well-designed -and actually employed –software process).

(iii) No software process improvements without clear responsibility, (significant results can only be achieved by continuously improving the

867

development process, therefore it is extremely helpful to have a group responsible for pushing software process improvement activities).

(iv) No change of well-worn processes without new people (software process improvements aim at re-engineering existing processes and the involvement of external software engineering experts facilitates the acceptance of new measures).

(v) Process maturity assessments guide, control and sell the improvement process (they build up awareness of software process improvement at managerial level and help to identify the state of practice concerning the software process, the main deficiencies in the development process and the quantification of improvement measures).

(vi) Adoption of standards accelerates implementation of improvements (they save work by avoiding 're-invention of the wheel' and they tend to receive better acceptance by management and developers than individually designed solutions).

(vii) Pilot projects must be open minded towards innovations:

'In the SPI initiative at KWL we felt at times a somewhat "defensive" attitude towards innovations in pilot projects. Although not exactly rejecting the new practices, the pilot project members seemed to be not very interested in the success of these practices. In such cases the application of the new practices was more and more evaporating, and eventually substituted again by the former behaviours. In the SPI at Adtranz and ASS Calor Emag Schaltanlagen the situation was very different. Here, the success of the process improvement initiative was to the most part due to the enthusiasm and openness of the project members'.

(viii) The main obstacles to improvements come from organisational and human factors (the lack of software engineering knowledge in management and software development makes the management uncertain when it comes to assessing the value of new software engineering measures, and where software developers view SPI programmes as a threat to jobs they resist them).

(ix) Software process improvements need long-term management support (programmes typically last two to three years and when daily business needs delay improvement activities or result in them not being conducted seriously management has to avoid the "valley of tears").

(x) The investment in SPI is high, the return of investment is medium and long-term (in this case investments were between 1 and 2 person years annually per initiative).

[Although the excellent ABB case study was on the technical application of software the 'lessons learned' have general managerial application to most improvement projects -e.g. Juran engineering projects in the 1960s gave similar management results -Ed].

Process Improvement Experiments for Rapid Return on Investment

Daryl Chandler-Griffiths, Quality Manager for Fame Computers Limited of Birmingham presented the experience and results from ESSI experiment 21265 DATM-RV 'Determination of appropriate tools and methodology for a combined RAD-'V' life cycle' which consisted of case studies designed to experiment with efficiency and effectiveness improvements in Rapid Application Development (RAD), Object Oriented Analysis (OOA) using CASE, Unit Testing, System Testing and Automated Quality Management Systems.

The case studies in question had an average budget of £37,000, took on average 80 days to complete, and had an average return on investment of 176 per cent. A set of objectives and results are presented for each case study along with benefits gained. Whilst it is accepted that these case studies are somewhat specialised, the following observations may be of interest:

'One of the strengths of the RAD process is that it captures business requirements directly from the business analyst or expert users to the developer. Requirements were captured by extracting system behaviours using behaviour analysis. This entails tabulating function, condition, response data for each requirement based on create, read, update and delete transactions with an associated risk assessment. This minimalist approach to test specifications ensures that testing can be more readily factored in-process during the RAD development and has proven to be an excellent method of capturing and documenting user requirements for RAD'.

'Over 20 per cent of the system was tested through the experiment revealing 4 major and 20 minor errors that had passed through sign-off by the analysts. It was calculated using a conservative estimate that each error costs £3,000 to correct in the field, therefore on the basis of field correction of major errors only, a cost of £12,000 was saved. Against a cost of £2,100 to perform the planning and execution of tests this represents a 600 per cent saving. By extrapolation across the remainder of the system a total return on investment of 151 per cent was forecast. As the baseline project is expected to grow beyond the estimated size of 750 FP the return will be proportionally increased'.

'Static analysis and coverage analysis tools for the Windows 95 environment with full UK support are very thin on the ground. Those available middle out at around £6,000 before taking into account the considerable labour required to understand the tools, and to integrate the tool with the development environment.

For these tools to be accepted as part of the development process they should require very little effort and provide valuable summary analyses. In practice with the tools reviewed, none integrates seamlessly with the build environment and information has to be filtered out using macros. In addition the tools appear to have largely inherited their procedural roots providing few object-oriented metrics such as inheritance levels etc.

The existing use of code standards and the fact that coverage analysis only verifies that there is intrinsic high coverage of O-O systems at unit level, meant that the added value of the case study was insufficient to be adopted in-house, also attributable to the fact that there was no real business objective for improving the in-house unit testing process. However, a business objective for the Quality Assurance of third party outsourced software did arise; in this case, the case study processes represented a valuable process to assure the standards of the software and the quality of outsourced unit tests and show potential for adoption. This is testimony to the essential requirement for a case study to be underpinned by a business objective in order to reduce the risk of failure'.

Other results include a 429 per cent return over three months for the OOI case study derived from the use of Function Point Analysis, and "markedly improved access and awareness of the documentation process and instant management information from on-line audits and non-conformances" from the Automated QMS study.

The author offers the following advice with regard to the use of case studies of this type, which are in effect small controlled experiments that reveal the effect of a process or technology:

*When planning the case study there should be a clear linkage between the experimental objective and the hypothetical impact of the proposed improvement process so as to reduce the risk of experimental failure.

*A baseline project is essential in order to track the effects of experimentation and clearly indicate the value added by the experimental technique.

*The outputs from the case study must be defined and as part of the experiment plan and fulfilment of the experimental objectives continually kept in mind.

PROCESSUS - a Methodology for Quality System Improvement

Ms. Romana Horvat delightfully presented the final paper selected for review, a welcome contribution from the University of Maribor, Slovenia. This introduced the original PROCESSUS methodology designed to assist software organisations to establish and improve their quality systems. It resulted from a project undertaken in Slovenia in 1994, involving co-operation between the research group of the Laboratory for Information Systems and local industry .Finance came from the Slovenian Ministry of Science and Technology and is loosely based on a combination of ISO 9000 and the CMM.

The paper outlines in tabular form the three types of organisations which participated in the PROCESSUS project (large information organisations, internal information centres, and small software organisations) and their essential characteristics. It then describes how the model was evolved first from a CMM-ISO directed comparison, and then an ISO-CMM directed comparison:

'By adding new KPAs to CMM structure we obtain such a form of the integrated model which is shown in a Figure. Also in the figure new KPAs are placed on transition between respective CMM levels. At the same time we defined the succession of establishing KPAs on transition between respective areas, where the direction is bottom-up similarly as with CMM'.

The six new KPAs in question are quality system management, organisational structure management, contract management, product delivery management, document control, and included product management:

'When compared to the original form of CMM the integrated model seemingly becomes very extensive. However, we should not forget that some new areas can be easily included in the quality system (e.g. contract management, product delivery management, included product management). Setting up of these areas does not essentially increase the amount of time needed for transition on a higher level but, on the other hand, brings several advantages, -mainly as regards the work with the customers'.

Three types of assessment are envisaged, preliminary, intermediate and global, which are expected to take 8 to 16 hours, 3 to 6 hours, and 15 to 25 hours respectively, depending on the complexity of the assessed area. It is noted that the last assessment, which assesses the whole quality system, may be performed as a self-assessment, second party assessment or third party assessment. A questionnaire is featured to assist the assessor.

Experience with the model so far has shown that only companies which have recognized the quality system as a strategic issue with the support of top management have been successful with its implementation. Without this support there 'was no success' in the quality system introduction even if specific persons responsible for quality performed their work very well.

The PROCESSUS methodology is being refined, with most notably SOKCE being used as a 'source for accurate guidelines'. On-line courseware is also being introduced in response to the 'great interest' which has emerged from the work, as well as groupware workshops using the Internet.

[Issue 108 (December 1997)]

ORACLE GUARANTEES MILLENNIUM COMPLIANCE

Leading Japanese electronics manufacturer Sony have announced that they are to switch from IBM mainframe to Unix platforms in 1998 following a re-engineering of its manufacturing and supply chain systems across Europe and adopt Oracle Applications version 10.7.

The move follows a recognition by Sony that they could not assure that all of their IBM mainframe systems would be millennium compliant by the Year 2000 and a guarantee by Oracle that their applications could be so compliant.

Licence fees alone are said to have a value of some £1.5 million.

[Issue 111 (March 1998)]

NEW ORGANISATION TO ADDRESS SOFTWARE COMPLIANCE

Anew organisation known as the Initiative for Software Compliance (iSC) has been formed to assist company directors and others to ensure that their IT systems comply with the law. It is a not-for-profit company, limited by guarantee, which has been formed following the recent targeting of specific company directors for prosecution by software industry reinforcement agencies such as the Business Software Alliance (BSA). The BSA have recently been criticised for offering inducements to employees to telephone a hotline to inform on the illegal copying of software programs in their organisations.

Amongst other things the iSC will address the absence of standards available for individual, directors and organisations to measure their methods and procedures against the requirements of the law, and offer 'health checks' to assess a company's liability risk. This can be followed through with various services which will lead to a formal certification of compliance.

Director of the iSC Michael Ludlam comments:

"The iSC is already attracting large companies which, with our help, are beginning a Continuous Compliance Programme (CCP). Once they have it in place, the CCP will not only be a robust defence against legal actions from software developers and the software industry's enforcement agencies, but will also put the managers back in control of this increasingly crucial area".

CYBERQUALITY

The strong IT focus at this year's Quality in Manufacturing (QM '98) exhibition at the National Motorcycle Museum, Solihull, on 8th and 9th September, was reflected in the staging of 'Cyberquality', a new feature of the event, which consisted of eight seminars. Sponsored by quality management software specialists Deans Hill Systems Limited, 'Cyberquality' included case study presentations from British Telecom and Waterford Crystal, both of which highlighted impressive bottom-line benefits directly attributable to IT solutions.

These were supported by presentations by SPC consultant Richard Monkhouse in which further impressive bottom-line benefits were highlighted, deriving specifically from software application, whilst from US based Micrografx Inc. Ivan Dunn described how their process mapping software saved one company $8 million. Brian Pollit, New Process Manager for Marconi Communications, explained how a pilot system which combines Deming's Theory of Profound Knowledge with a real time quality information system, is enabling thousands of control charts to be monitored in real-time in background mode. The scene was set, however, by David Best, Director of Deans Hill Systems, who described how IT has been applied to create "The Complete Solution" for integrated management systems using quality assurance as starting point.

QA plus IT equals Profit

David Best's paper affirms:

'It is our belief that with an integrated and complete computerised management system companies can operate more consistently and more efficiently. System operators become increasingly familiar with the system style. This encourages use. If the users of the system are active, your data collection tasks can become easier -especially if your computer systems are fully networked'.

The case is presented for investment in networks in organisations with more than five employees on the grounds that there will be less data duplication, improved system security and better communications. In his speech he highlighted the main problem with isolated pcs, namely that they tend to rely on duplicated information which arrives late. He also made reference to the need to involve the accounts department in the integration process, describing the fact that these people frequently are reluctant to accept such involvement as "unfortunate", whilst the paper advocates a focus on high cost problems or causes as 'the best way to high cost savings'.

It is argued that the data collection system should aim to gather cost details as this can make the information considerably more useful in guiding actions', whilst a high volume of low unit cost problems may have a detrimental effect on customer perceptions:

'The experience of a customer of ours is a clear example of this use of information to identify real problems. This company is a major, tier-one supplier to the motor industry, whose customers include Rover, VW, Ford and Mercedes amongst others. They are using our software package - PROQUIS -to record their customer complaints and then to analyse them by cause, with costs. Two reasons were identified as the causes of about 80% of their customers' problems. This has allowed them to focus management attention. They have now reduced their parts-per-million failure rates significantly and saved a great deal of money along the way. They also have much happier customers, resulting in a number of large new contracts'.

The paper explains how the software (the PROfessional Quality Information System) is being extended into the areas of QS9000, Health and Safety, Preventive Maintenance and ISO14001 whilst others, namely Pegasus Opera (the accounting and manufacturing software system) are approaching 'The Complete Solution' from another direction by incorporating QA components.

The PROQUIS software as advertised currently covers every section of ISO 9001 and extends into areas of QS9000 without the need to purchase expensive 'add-on' modules. It installs itself simply from a disk or CD-ROM, contains standard and flexible import facilities with which to bring in existing data, will produce over 100 standard reports with user-definable range selection criteria, and runs on IBM compatible pcs and pc networks. It is described as 'the price performance leader by a significant margin'.

Automating a trans-continental Customer Care and Complaints System

Kieran Mulhall, Business Analyst for Waterford Crystal, described how his company selected Q-Set, a Lotus Premium Business Partner specialising in Notes/Domino development of generic packaged software products, in its efforts to move from a paper-based to an automated quality management system:

'Waterford achieved ISO9001 for its three plants in the early nineties using a paper-based manual system. The achievement of ISO14001 Environmental Management System was set as a target to be achieved during 1998. The company was determined to employ different methods of document control in its application for ISO14001 registration'.

'As the result of a business visit to the US market, by the General Manager of Quality Assurance and the Quality Manager of Brand Extensions, it was discovered that there was a need for standard methods for processing

874

customer care issues and giving feedback to sales and marketing teams throughout the organisation. This visit led to the launch of the Quality Systems Project. The project increased focus on supplier development, customer care and establishing the organisation structure required to support the needs of a changing portfolio of products'.

With the project scope clearly defined as "Create a Global Customer Care Solution through the implementation of a Quality Management System that was capable of supporting both ISO9001 and ISO14001" a cross-functional project team was established to source and implement a suitable solution. The paper describes how the team undertook a requirements analysis which yielded a set of requirements in two categories (Customer Care Requirements and ISO Requirements).

The team sought to avoid the high maintenance costs experienced with ISO 9001, provide consistent reporting, and then produced a list of six potential vendors for whom a set of evaluation criteria had been devised and categorised. A short-list of three vendors was then drawn up using these criteria which, for example, examined Security at User Level, Year 2000 compliance, modular implementation, implementation support, and the frequency and type of application updates. The Q-Sys system from Q-Set was then selected following site visits and demonstrations. It was selected because:

* it harnessed the global infrastructure that Lotus Notes offered (Waterford Crystal already had a Lotus Notes based solution managing projects between the Waterford and US sites).

* the user interface was considered friendly so training was not a major concern.

* Q-Sys was a complete quality package that encompassed sixteen databases.

* the customer care module was comprehensive and included a facility for product code capture.

* Q-Set offered innovative suggestions and placed high emphasis on not modifying the system.

* the Q-Sys presentations were of a very high standard and the pedigree of Q-Set 'was very impressive considering its relatively short four year life'.

* there was a prestigious customer portfolio which included Sita, United Distillers, Pepsi and informix.

The Q-Sys Customer Module was put live in Waterford in October 1997 and the documentation required for ISO14001 has been entered into Q-Sys and has received a preliminary audit by inspectors:

'Time was taken to ensure that a standard set of fault codes were agreed for use among all the defect reporting systems in Waterford. This ensured that the same coding structure applied to customer complaints covering all product from all sources both Crystal and non-crystal'.

Benefits from the project to date are quantified at around IR£40,000 to IR£50,000 per year, deriving principally from the avoidance of long-term overheads to support the control of ISO14001 documentation and the development of the Customer Care Department to support the growth of the business.

With capital investment being around IR£45,000 this suggests a payback period of about one year. This could be considered to be much shorter, and the savings significantly greater, if intangible benefits are considered. These could be; the clearer picture of customer complaints, the applicability of other Q-Sys modules such as calibration to areas like plant maintenance, and the fact that Q-Sys has become a store for non-quality related documents such as IT procedures, if taken into consideration.

Future plans include the roll-out of Q-Sys Customer Care to the rest of world markets, transfer of all remaining ISO9001 documentation by the end of 1998, implementation at sister company Stuart Crystal, and possible integration of Q-Sys with the new Products Development System (Phoenix).

Q-Set has recently been nominated for the 1998 Lotus Beacon Award "Excellence in Customer Satisfaction". Their groupware products are specifically designed to support global or multi-site enterprises with business integration of process improvement and multiple-standard registration. They are currently used in around twenty countries.

Applying IT to Process Management

The presentation by Micrografx described how their 'ultimate tool for process improvement' called Optima! ™ has been applied by Eli Lilly and Company. This global research-based pharmaceutical corporation is perhaps best known for its manufacture of the anti-depressant drug Prozac, but also supplies the insulin substitute Humulin, which was the subject of the presentation.

Humulin has a complex manufacturing supply chain which involves the manufacture of three bulk chemicals prepared in two different plants, the creation of 66 different formulations in nine different plants, and the production of 25,000 packages in 19 plants around the world. The opportunity for waste to arise in a supply chain of this nature is clearly considerable. Consequently as part of their drive for continuous improvement it became the subject of a re-engineering project:

'Lilly asked its Applied Computational Modelling (ACM) Group to build a computer model of its biosynthetic human insulin supply chain. This would allow Lilly to determine whether its inventory was correctly positioned to accommodate the variability in the manufacturing cycle times and whether the inventory levels could safely be reduced lowering the company's high cost of capital'.

The speaker explained how the organisation had specifically sought to identify constraints, bottlenecks and value-added aspects of the supply chain which typically had high stock levels, low profit margins, a high cost of product sold and involved the deployment of expensive machinery. He explained how the Micrografx Optima! ™ had been found to be "the easiest to use and cheapest process mapping tool" which has the advantage of allowing for some contingency planning without the need to retain too much inventory:

'The supply chain was mapped across fifteen different departments using Swimlanes ™ to show the functional roles within the organisation. Each activity symbol was assigned data, such as duration, cost, capacities- and resources. After the data was entered, ACM ran multiple simulations from daily to annual "snapshots". The results, available in both- graphical and tabular format, validated overall cycle times, inventory, shipping and resource utilisation levels'.

The $8 million saving was later realised when ACM changed the formula of the transaction generators, schedules and cycle times and re-ran the simulation under the scenario of an unplanned shutdown of a bulk plant for 60 to 90 days. The result was as follows:

'If Lilly would switch to accelerated processing during emergencies, the customer service levels at the end of the chain would not be affected by any downtime at the front of the chain. What's more this analysis allowed Lilly to reduce its bulk inventories without any shortage impact on shipments'.

The author of the paper, Mark Stanford of Micrografx, argues the following case for investment in IT for process mapping:

'Process management tools have become a reality today because there has been a change in belief by those who manage these systems. This change is driven by the realisation that many of these processes can now be mapped and analysed. Before these electronic processes became the norm, it was exceedingly difficult to collect data about processes from so many different facets of the organisation in a way that was practical and that could effect change in a reasonable time frame. Now that this is possible, the acceptance and adoption of process management tools is taking flight'.

The Optima!™ software is specifically designed for process analysis and improvement and allows for each step in a process to be quantitatively and qualitatively described. It allows answers to questions like 'What would the addition of another piece of equipment do?' or 'What happens if you change the flow-pattern of a process or have certain tasks take place simultaneously?' to be answered without needing to purchase or move equipment or hire employees. As the simulation is running the software graphically depicts the various steps via changing colours. Reports may be viewed in tabular or graphical formats from statistics automatically collected during simulation or customised to suit specific needs.

Management Systems in the Cyber Age

Stuart Jones of BT Quality and Business Services, Stockport, described how the BT Intranet has been used to realise financial benefits of the order of £230 million over four years:

'Early on we took the decision not to wait until everyone had access but to provide electronic information in parallel with paper information. We also quickly reduced wholesale distribution of documents by providing people with concise summaries and references to either Intranet documents or to fax on demand (where people phone a number, dial in the number of the document they want and then have it sent to a fax machine of their choice). Without exception everyone liked this approach -it reduced filing and made it easier to find information only required infrequently. In the first year, in one small part of BT we saved £100,000 in paper distribution costs alone'.

A formal information management structure was introduced to ensure that it was clear who had responsibility for specific information areas, with 'franchise holders' being responsible for the publication of information in their assigned areas.

A balanced scorecard approach is used to evaluate the benefits, some of which are not easy to manage in purely financial terms, others being more obvious:

'The sales and marketing team for business customers have an information resource called "Factfinder". This provides details about all of the products and services we provide and is in regular use by people when talking to customers. The document used to be published in a 5cm-thick paper file that cost £410,000 a year to publish with two people managing the information resource.

The lead time for new information to be published was at least three weeks. 'Factfinder' was convened to the Intranet -still with two people managing the information. However, the publishing costs are now nominal (50Mb of hard disk space) so delivering a real cost saving of £410K a year. In addition information is now published and available in less than two days and is always up to date. An added advantage is that everyone in BT has access to the resource and this has been used to help all BT people act as sales agents for our business'.

Following the presentation the speaker was asked how documents might be retrieved should the system go down and he answered by saying that in most cases it did not matter if the information could not be obtained over a short period of say an hour. Business critical information on the other hand had local back-ups. Intranet networks "were inherently resilient", he said.

[Issue 126 (June 1999)]

SOFTWARE TESTING AND PROJECT MANAGEMENT

These were two of the subjects covered at the latest Quality Forum meeting at The Roundhouse Hotel, Bournemouth on 1st June. Paul Gerrard, Business Development Manager for software testing consultants Systeme Evolutif, introduced the Test Organisation Maturity (TOM™) Model as a means of assessing and improving the test process whilst Mike Watson of Stubhampton Technologies Ltd. described a simple but effective technique for managing small projects in large organisations.

The Test Organisation Maturity Model

Paul Gerrard explained some of the problems associated with current testing practice and identified some of the potential areas for improvement with the aid of the TOM™ Model which his organisation developed some two years ago and subsequently piloted. Some of the problems which he identified were that

- too many errors are commonly found in production or being reported by customers.

- testing frequently takes too long and delays delivery.

- testing is too expensive.

- there can be difficulty in finding volunteers to undertake testing.

- testers frequently see no career path associated with their activity.

He exposed several myths associated with testing such as the belief that it doesn't add value, that software is becoming easier to test, that software quality is improving and that testing by its very nature is random and cannot be systematised. He highlighted weaknesses associated with the Capability Maturity Model (CMM):

'The CMM (and related models) have been found lacking when it comes to testing practices. The detail presented in these models is sparse, to say the least. We have found that these models did not match the way we conducted testing improvement projects. The models are based on assessments that identify whether certain good practices are used or not, and present a staged sequence of process improvements. The recommended process improvements consist of the good practices not currently being adopted. The assumption is that these practices will increase testing effectiveness and improve software quality'.

'Several problems with such approaches (particularly the CMM) have been documented but we would emphasise one in particular. We believe that these models are all solution or "remedy based" and miss the point. We fear that many organisations use remedy-oriented approaches blindly. Assuming that any organisation's problems can be solved by adopting the "next level" practices may be dangerous'.

The TOM™ Model is advocated as it addresses the primary concern that the outcome of the assessment should address the problems being experienced. It consists of a simple questionnaire comprising of twenty questions each of which has a scoring level of one to five. These concentrate on symptoms of poor test process maturity and the results are used to calculate a TOM™ maturity level:

'For each numbered question there are three examples of maturity. If one of the three columns headed Low, Medium or High resembles your situation, score a 1,3 or 5 respectively. If you are "in between" score 2 or 4. You must score each question between 1 and 5. If you score less than 5 for a symptom you should assign a priority to that symptom. The priority indicates how much it "hurts". A priority 1 symptom can be ignored. A priority 5 is extremely painful and must be addressed'.

The Model generates up to seventy prioritised improvement suggestions based on the assessment data entered. These can then be used to identify the improvements that are likely to yield the most benefits to the organisation. Typical symptoms are:

- testing has no deliverables of value?

- of the faults that are found there is a perception (based on evidence) that many should have been found in earlier test stages?

- users perceive that they are responsible for testing?

- significant requirements and design defects are found by system and acceptance testers?

- there are gaps in the testing -features of the system may be released untested?

- test budgets are unreliable because there is no rational method of estimating test activities?

- decisions to release into production are based on 'gut feel' and not an objective assessment of the quality and readiness of the software?

Examples of potential process improvements include:

* define distinct test objectives for sub-system, system and acceptance tests.

* document objective measures of test coverage for each test stage in Master Test Plans.

* undertake an early assessment of software risks to provide direction for the testing.

* define project planning templates including standard test activities in a test strategy.

* document a policy for the use of test case design techniques.

* train senior testers and qualify them at Information Systems Examinations Board (ISEB) level.

The assessment data is currently being used by Systeme Evolutif to survey testing practices across industry.

Managing Small Projects

Mike Watson argued that commonly small projects are reduced to the one liner "can you do this item of work", and this approach, he suggested, was fraught with danger:

'From the moment you make the decision to jump straight in, the project is out of control. You will be pulled around by outside influences and you will have no means of managing changes, measuring progress and checking quality. You do an excellent technical job but it may well be the wrong one'.

Very often people in this position have no-one to turn to for help, only a collection of so called "well meaning people" keen to offer advice, especially if they are not going to be involved with the project, and there can be considerable difficulty in differentiating the "vital few" tasks from the "trivial many". The speaker suggested that from an organisation's point of view a small project's methodology must be:

*safe (not expose the organisation to more risk than that which currently exists).

*successful (able to bring in small projects faster, cheaper or better than at present).

* streamlined (must not slow down the project manager to the extent that effectiveness is lost).

Likewise from the project manager's viewpoint the methodology must be:

- simple (to learn and to use).

- Selectable (capable of being timed to fit differing project characteristics).

- scaleable (able to complement other, possibly larger, methodologies).

Such a methodology, which has recently been piloted in the broadcasting and life assurance sectors, was then outlined. It consists essentially of one mandatory and four optional sample forms covering the following areas:

*Project Definition (mandatory).

*Project Risk Assessment (if risk identified).

*Change Management (should outcomes be unclear).

*Project Quality Plan (if certain quality elements need to be specified).

* Budget Plan for project (if a separate budget is needed).

The speaker emphasised that this is not "rocket science". In deciding which of the optional forms to use the project manager would normally propose to the project sponsor who would then take the decision.

Following the presentation the speaker was asked to justify his comment that large projects "were easy" in the light of the fact that many large project methodologies recommend that such projects be broken down or reduced to several smaller ones. In reply he commented that such advice was usually a consequence of the financial risks associated with large projects rather than their management i.e. lots of organisations want to see nine months of development coupled with twelve months' payback.

QUALITY FORUM DISCONTINUES

It is with regret in this issue of *Quality Matters* to report the discontinuance of one of the UK's leading quality organisations, The Quality Forum. Founded in 1986 The Quality Forum was at the forefront of the quality movement in software and information technology with thriving Special Interest Groups covering specialist areas such as Software Metrics, Business Excellence and Tick IT.

Regular updates from the BSI DISC committee were regularly featured together with specialist subjects such as Attractive Quality Creation and the SEI Capability Maturity Model, which were often not covered at the more generalised events hosted by other organisations.

The principal reason behind the demise is put down to a nationally receding trend on the focus on quality. [This is sad but true, but it is hoped that the expertise gained over the years will not be lost-Ed].

Over the past 11 years *Quality Matters* has had a close association with the Quality Forum, reporting on their activities and where many of their members have been subscribers to *Quality Matters*, via the Forum. We would particularly like to thank The Quality Forum and its staff {particularly Gordon Irvine) for the help and assistance given to *Quality Matters* over the past eleven years.

NEW CONTINUOUS COMPLIANCE PROGRAMME FOR IT

In its first venture outside public sector publishing The Stationery Office has become the first organisation to market and deliver the new IT Continuous Compliance Programme, the corporate benchmark for managing I.T. related risk.

The programme is based on the independent Standard developed by the Initiative for Software Compliance (iSC) which enables organisations to establish and maintain a legally compliant IT environment. Compliance can be demonstrated through a certification programme to the Standard which covers all IT related legislation including the Data Protection Act 1998 which came into force on March 1st.

Chapter Thirteen

Quality in the Financial Sector

A leading role in this industry sector has been played throughout the 1990s by the Financial Sector Special Interest Group (FINSEC) of the Institute of Management Services. Co-ordinated by Graham Briscoe, Operations Support Consultant for Royal and Sun Alliance, the annual FINSEC conference has been held in London most years and reported in Quality Matters each year since 1991.

A popular tool in this industry has been Business Process Re-engineering (BPR) and in 1994 the first quantified research in the UK to assess the success of application in the financial sector was presented at FINSEC. This was followed in 1996 with a FINSEC sponsored study by Portsmouth University into the effectiveness of software being used for BPR, whilst in 1997 and 1999 there are case studies covering the application of another popular tool, the Balanced Business Scorecard. In 1998 the conference was held in Scotland for the first and only time when Customer Service was the theme.

Further overlap with other quality topics is reflected in the financial sector Business Excellence Award presentations, benchmarking case studies in the financial sector, and case studies in disaster recovery (Manchester bomb, 1996), change management and managing knowledge.

QUALITY FOR FINANCIAL SERVICES

Quality Matters was pleased to be represented at The Institute of Management Services Financial Sector Specialist Group Conference at the Marlborough Hotel, Bloomsbury Street, London on 23rd April, at which the subject of 'Productivity Through Total Quality Management in the Financial Sector' was addressed.

The conference was chaired by John Waller, Associate Director, Operations Development, General Portfolio, who, in his introductory speech, pointed to the recent inundation of legislation in the financial sector during the past five to six years. He gave as examples the Building Societies Act and the Financial Services Act, which coupled with the fact that markets fluctuate more frequently than they used to, gives rise to an extremely competitive situation. Expectations, he said, would therefore have not only to be met but beaten to remain in business, and customer satisfaction and Total Quality could not be treated in isolation as they were mutually dependent.

The Need for Quality

Paul Hollingworth, Senior Manager for Training and Quality Management at General Portfolio, followed with a presentation on 'Why the Financial Sector Needs TQM'. The reason became self-evident from the analogy of the boiled frog, taken from Charles Handy's *'The Age of Unreason'* to which he referred in his opening lines:

'A frog, placed in cold water, will sit there as the water is very gradually heated. Having become comfortable with the continuous change it will eventually let itself be boiled alive.'

'Like the frog, to avoid our fate we must recognise that continuous change at some point has to be discontinued and demands a change in behaviour. Survival of the UK companies in the Financial Sector requires transformation of the way we manage '.

He added that behavioural change must be preceded by attitudinal change and asserted that revising our understanding of and attitude to the relationship between cost, quality and productivity was fundamental to this.

He pointed to statistics which showed that in 1980 the world's nine largest banks were French, German, British or American with the top Japanese bank, the Dai Ichi, in tenth place. Now the top nine are Japanese with the Banque Nationale de Paris tenth and the largest American bank Citibank down from third spot to seventeenth.

The success of the Japanese banks is attributed to the fact that they never forget that wealth is created not by the service sector but by manufacturing industry. Only those organisations involved with adding value to the Earth's natural resources are in fact creating wealth. The financial sector merely redistributes it. Japanese banks have therefore invested long term in the establishment of trusting, mutually beneficial customer-supplier relationships, along the entire chain to the customer with the manufacturing companies. These now dominate most world markets, and there exists a deep understanding of the need to invest in the prevention of failure, for long term success. The British Financial Sector, by contrast, is 'nearing the edge of a precipice'.

"Many manufacturers in the UK will tell you that they regard their bank and insurance companies as necessary evils. They will tell you that the relationship is essentially parasitic. Each party regards the other with distrust and, even though the relationship may turn out to be long term, the view they have of the relationship is too often short term".

In addition the operation of many financial organisations is driven by a desire to survive in the market place competing on premium or interest rates or emulating products and services devised by competitors. A 'spiral of reactive management' exists, from which executive management is struggling to break free.

The reaction to increased legislation and customer expectation has been generally traditional in the form of investment in new products, new systems and new organisations financed through cost-cutting and repackaging, chasing productivity and short term profitability. In some cases customer care programmes have trained front office staff 'to smile as they apologise' but the causes of problems remain. Most clerical staff work 'with a conflict of interest within a system which forces them to sub-optimise their roles as order takers and customer satisfiers'.

To transform the situation, continuous improvement 'should underpin the corporate change strategy with a state of mind which permeates every aspect of the operation. Calling in O and M to sort out the filing system once every 18 months is not the answer'.

By harnessing the commitment of everyone it is possible to recognize that every process in every system in every sphere of operations can and must be continually improved. Hope and exhortation on its own will achieve little. However, with a structural approach using employee training and development it is an essential component. It was suggested also that companies may even in some cases have to consider co-operation with their competitors.

Application of BS5750 to a Financial Services Company

The next presentation was from Gordon Henderson, Head of Corporate Quality for Girobank plc., the first bank to have been awarded BS5750 Part 2, and considered the approach taken by Girobank to achieve the standard.

This approach was essentially that of a triple focus on quality improvement, customer care and quality assurance. It was project orientated and started in November 1988, with registration achieved in January 1990.

Much of the speech concerned aspects of the standard which have already been discussed in *Quality Matters* for example the need for a regular review of contract performance with customers, a system of vendor appraisal, supplier relationships which lead to reduced inventory, systematic analysis of customer complaints and internal errors, methodical application of appropriate corrective action, staff having current and relevant job procedures, and records of training. Some elements initially incorporated into the standard for manufacturing, such as inspection, measuring and test equipment had comparatively few applications, but was still applicable. Similarly handling, storage package and delivery assumed less importance but were still there to be addressed.

The problems encountered were of interest and primarily included:

*translation of manufacturing jargon into the financial services context (although this problem is apparently not as difficult as it appears).

use of discretionary statements such as 'as requested', 'appropriate' and 'timely consideration' (checking with BSI for clarification of these is recommended).

*auditors' judgments (two BSI auditors may have differing views, hence there is a need for dialogue).

*perceived bureaucracy (which can be minimised with the use of flowcharting techniques and use of distribution lists which only provide staff with those aspects of the standard that they need to know).

The main weakness in the standard appeared to be the fact that it 'can drive compliance rather than improvement, and Mr. Henderson suggested that you need more than just a quality system to stimulate continuous improvement in financial services. He emphasized that the primary focus was not to create a marketing tool quite so much as a means of driving good business practice. As in other industries the standard has to be seen as a means to an end rather than an end in itself.

As regards benefits, a number of internal measures were highlighted which showed that errors by keyboard operators had fallen by 52 per cent to 0.8 per 10,000 transactions, Post Office errors were down by 65 per cent to 9 per 10,000 transactions, customer complaints on transaction data processing were down 61 per cent to 3.3 per 10,000 transactions, customer telephone calls answered within 20 seconds improved by 160 per cent, inventory was reduced by 38 per cent. The number of staff suggestions also rose from under 1000 in 1988 to around 5,000 with 35 per cent adoption and savings of £771,280 in 1990, and there was a net financial benefit of £4.33 million.

The next step for Girobank was said to be registration to BS5750 Part 1. A question session followed in which Mr. Henderson was asked if he had had value for money from BSI. In his response he acknowledged that Girobank had 'found them to be a good supplier although fees are quite expensive'. He said that the financial services market represented a good market for BSI, and whilst the financial services sector was proceeding up a learning curve in relation to the standard, BSI were likewise going up a learning curve with financial services. The conclusion was that they 'probably were value for money in relation to the benefits'.

Mr. Henderson was then asked how much Girobank had spent and told delegates that consultants had been used for 12 months and that there had been no other incremental costs besides this. For implementation overall a figure of £4.4 million was quoted.

Mr. Henderson also pointed out that line managers were responsible for documentation and advised that as regards job descriptions:

"You can be as innovative and experimental as you like, but once you have decided what you want to do, fix it in place ".

Girobank has recently received the Institute of Administrative Management's Total Quality Award.

Other Presentations

Several other presentations were given at the conference, relating to specific aspects of quality. These included 'Building Quality into Software Development' by Jacqueline Holdsworth, Quality Manager, Lloyds Bank plc.; 'Statistical Process Control' by Stan Bennett, Principal Consultant (Quality) E.G. Consulting Limited; 'Quality Circles' by John Kemp, Quality Service Manager, Abbey National plc.; and 'Management Services in the Quality Culture' by Bob Spencer of Tillers Management Services.

Jacqueline Holdsworth highlighted sizing and estimation as a 'hot potato' for systems development:

"Subsequent performance against the estimates is, whether we agree or not, an indicator of our productivity in our customers' eyes. When we slip budgets and targets it is evident to our customers that we are losing productivity. For this reason our first estimates are made within cost bands we have previously established with our customers. This removes the degree of accuracy which otherwise would lend an appearance of scientific precision to the estimate, and would make it appear immutable".

She went on to describe reviews and inspection as an opportunity for learning and feedback, with the use of mandatory Independent Phase End Reviews to provide an independent objective assessment of project status at well-defined stages of the project life cycle.

In the afternoon Stan Bennett discussed the implementation of Deming-style SPC to financial services, including for example the application of process control charts to improve loan processing times. He said that he was 'amazed' at how few processes in service industries actually have a tolerance standard, and emphasized the need to distinguish between special causes of problems for which corrective action can often be taken locally without management involvement, and common causes which are natural variations associated with the way processes are set up and require management attention. Many managers, he said, were engaged in fire-fighting special causes, contrary to Deming's philosophy which says that managers should only work on common causes of control chart variation as no one else can and this is where the bulk of process improvement comes from.

John Kemp described how during 1988 and 1989 some 12,000 employees of Abbey National attended a two day customer care programme entitled 'You are the Difference' at an expense of £5 million. This introduced participants to a range of interpersonal and stress related skills and found that staff had both enthusiasm and commitment, but certain procedures, work practices, rules and regulations impeded them. The quality circle approach seemed an attractive way forward, but there appeared to be a high failure rate and limited experience in service industries, so it was decided to talk to members of organisations who had some experience, notably the Friends Provident Life Office with whom Abbey Life already had a close business relationship. This was positive but it was decided that rather than following the mass briefing style that had been applied by the banks, they began by convincing managers with a three day residential course and introducing the process gradually.

The term 'Quality Improvement Teams' was preferred to 'Quality Circles' to avoid the 'not invented here' syndrome and previous negative opinions about Quality circles in general. Facilitators, recruited on a voluntary basis, have also been trained to support and boost the confidence of the team leader, help with resources beyond the team's control and provide an important communicative role between teams. Some 200 to 300 people within the company are currently involved with the QI Teams which have a budget of around £20,000 a year which is spent chiefly on training. The view was that by getting managers to partly finance training, better commitment was being obtained.

The final speech, by Bob Spencer, asserted that in management services the response to TQM is essentially mixed. In a minority of institutions, management services is taking the lead. In others there exists apprehension. In the majority, management services is uncertain about its role and the stance it should take. He highlighted product costing as an area that few organisations are into and one with which more will soon need to be involved.

Open Forum

The conference was concluded with an open forum in which, amongst other things, the panel was asked how highly it rated the quality management standard BS5750. Jacqueline Holdsworth said that it was a 'first step and a very positive step', whilst John Kemp noted that some companies may have to get BS5750 in order to meet customers' requirements.

They were also asked whether the Q.A. initiative had to come from the top, (this meant the Chief Executive) or had it to be 'sold'? Paul Hollingworth referred delegates to Jan Carlzon's book *'Moments of Truth'* (reviewed in *Quality Matters* Issue 14), whilst Jacqueline Holdsworth advised that delegation be 'avoided at all costs'.

[Issue 42 (June 1992)]

QUALITY IN FINANCE: FURTHER PRACTICAL DEVELOPMENTS

This year the same group followed through with another one day conference entitled 'Productivity Through Total Quality Management in the Financial Sector –Further Practical Developments'. The event was held at the Marlborough Hotel, London, on 28th April. It showed that Total Quality Management is flourishing in the financial services sector as more companies are applying for and gaining, certification to BS5750, with more areas of the industry achieving success.

Quality as a Way of Life

In January 1992 Prudential became the first insurance company to have part of its organisation registered by BSI to BS5750. Prudential have also been awarded the Institute of Administrative Management's 'Administering Total Quality for Success' Award for 1991 and the 1991 Northern Ireland Quality Award for Service. To enlighten delegates as to how the Prudential achieved these successes Dr. Steve Tanner, Quality Initiative Manager for Prudential

Life Administration, presented a paper under the title of 'Quality -A Way of Life at Prudential'.

Dr. Tanner explained how Prudential had studied the advancements made at Girobank and how they had come to see them as leaders in the financial sector, and so had become a role model. In the presentation he explained their actions, with a team of managers acting as facilitators, to plan and support the quality initiative. A four-point quality strategy was adopted:

- control of processes (service excellence could only be delivered through capable processes).

- customer focused culture (listening to customers and reacting quickly to their changing requirements).

- continuous improvement (a strategic imperative which addressed leadership, improvement activity, education, measurement and benchmarking, reward, recognition and continuance).

- communication (upward, downward and horizontal to ensure everyone is kept in touch with TQM both in Life Administration and Prudential in general).

The award winning training programme was written specifically to achieve the stage objectives and was 'Life Administration' branded i.e. it was not an off-the-shelf training package. All training was conducted by Prudential staff and its effectiveness was evaluated by external consultants.

In the first stage staff -from board member to supervisor -were trained over a six week period which equipped these personnel with knowledge. This was followed with training in training skills and team leadership. Teams then worked together to improve quality. Supervisors trained clerical staff and natural supervisor-led work-groups were formed with the objective of tackling quality improvement. It was emphasised that:

'The strategy adopted has successfully delivered a high level of employee involvement. We believe that we would not have achieved such a high level of participating if we had used normal Quality Circle techniques'.

The company was careful to allow for different learning speeds and styles of delivery. The 'Way of Life' programme has now been extended to include 'Serving Customers –Our Way of Life' which began with half-day Business Awareness Sessions in which the head of Life Administration discussed the 1991 business results and presented a vision for 1992 and beyond. There then followed a presentation by Dr. Westwood of the Manchester Business School in which he gave his own personal view of the outlook for the financial services industry.

A two day module under the heading of 'Barriers to Customer Service' is to be presented to all staff this year, and following this a third module has been designed to provide a forum for staff to share experiences and ideas and resolve difficulties associated with quality improvement activities.

Turning to the matter of BS5750 Dr. Tanner pointed out that the Prudential was not one of those organisations which had been under intense commercial pressure to achieve the standard. It was, however, recognised that the administration of an assurance business is an area that is highly regulated by legislation and the standard, with its focus on process control, contained requirements that would improve the degree of control, for example in the areas of internal quality auditing, control of non-conforming material and management review. In addition the standard's focus on procedures was seen to provide a way of reviewing all of the existing procedures and documentation which controlled processes.

A team-based approach was adopted which ensured total ownership of the quality system and procedures and it was explained how it was not unusual to find teams working late at night and at weekends with members taking their procedures home to work on them.

It was recognised that some of the jargon used in the standard had to be simplified and to do this several methods were used, but one notable example was the development of a 'user friendly' questionnaire by a group consisting of a designer, copywriter, quality engineer and a clerical worker. This translated the quality manual into 'everyday language' and was used in training sessions for an exercise in which groups conducted a self-assessment.

Registration has, amongst other things, improved consistency between the various departments within the Industrial Branch of Prudential Life Administration, e.g. changes to similar processes in Reading were not being implemented in Belfast.

Inculcating Quality into the Culture

The second presentation described the approach taken by the financial services arm of American Express, IDS Financial Services in the US and its affiliate ACUMA Limited in the UK. The presenter was Martha Reeves, Manager, Employee Relations, Communications and Development, ACUMA.

In her paper it is emphasized that 'we cannot build long term client relationships without first building long term employee relationships' and to help achieve this employee loyalty IDS which employs around 3,600 head office staff and 7,000 financial planners around the US, has instituted a 'Best Place to Work' programme which has:

* accommodated individuals by providing more flexible work arrangements and more flexible benefits for employees.

* developed employee involvement in decision making by introducing an expectation that everyone will understand how the business works and an assumption that everyone will share key information.

* a 'Bright Ideas' programme which encouraged teams of employees at all levels to work on ideas that could potentially improve the work environment, improve service to clients or improve the efficiency of operations, going beyond a simple 'suggestion box' by requiring employees to thoroughly research ideas, conduct cost/benefit analyses, work together as a team, and think about processes across functional business units.

* asked individuals to constantly learn and improve their own performance, for example through a tuition reimbursement programme for courses taken at universities and colleges.

* recognised the value of having a variety of disciplines in the organisation by sponsoring disciplines like education and humanities as well as the traditional MBA student.

* instituted leadership training that focuses primarily on treating individuals as individuals, to provide them with the right style of leadership for their level of ability and motivation.

* implemented upward feedback (allowing 'subordinates' to evaluate 'bosses'), which managers have come to trust.

* established teams supporting regions of the country which make their own decisions and organise their own work with managers acting as facilitators to provide resources and assistance rather than directing through hierarchical control.

* produced a 'work-and-family' series with the help of psychologists to address domestic issues.

ACUMA, by contrast, has around 350 head office staff and around 400 financial planners in 16 offices across England. It is just over two years old and is therefore young in relation to the century old IDS, and is said to 'react quickly and steer more easily'.

'In a matter of months we have launched a quality awareness programme and put in place cross-functional teams based on the Malcolm Baldrige Quality Award'.

The following quotation is felt to be particularly important:

893

'In both companies the Chief Executive Officer shares information frequently with employees. There is little information that needs to be withheld from individuals. The free flow of information helps individuals understand how their contribution fits into the whole '.

In the questions which followed Ms. Reeves was asked about the company's policy regarding laying off of employees and she explained that whilst there has not been a formal 'job for life' scheme adopted, the problem had been very much eased through the institution of 'career' breaks, such as five year career sabbaticals.

[Issue 56 (August 1993)]

QUALITY AND CHANGE: BACK TO BASICS OR QUANTUM LEAPS?

This year the IMS Financial Services Specialist Group met at the Grosvenor Thistle Hotel in London to consider which approach might be most suitable to their field and to propose some methodologies that might be used.

Business Process Restructuring: the Quantum Leap

The first presenter, John Houlihan, Vice-President of European Operations Management Practice for consultants Booz, Allen and Hamilton clearly advocated the quantum effect as he challenged delegates to 'make a leap' and opt for the methodology of Business Process Restructuring (BPR).

He suggested strongly that management should change their thinking away from the idea that their company serves a market, and towards the concept that capabilities can drive a market, citing the example of American Airlines as a case in point.

Performance, he said, should be measured in relation to how well the company can access a market, since one cannot serve a market if the customers cannot be reached. The concept of the 'Extended Enterprise' was proposed as a means of improving in this area. This, however, implies the existence of relationships which are markedly different from those of traditional purchasing, with partnership sourcing that qualifies the vendor according to his capabilities. The benefits, he said, could amount to up to 12 per cent added directly to the customer, which was 'a huge effect':

"The fact that a credit card company and a supermarket and a marketing chain may combine to form an extended enterprise makes sense. You just need processes to combine them that are not purely transactional".

The organisation that delivers capability was noted to be typically multi-skilled with a lean management structure, tightly integrated work processes

894

and a high level of interdependence within the business system. It is essentially a restructured organisation but the restructuring has been slow, often because BPR is not on the Chief Executive's agenda. Functional barriers do persist even though radical organisational change is imminently needed, the team based accountability is hard to accept, and quality programmes are not aimed at full organisational integration. The result is that the benefits, whilst there to be gained, are simply not realised.

In addition, many companies which do actually attempt BPR, experience problems, for example, by redesigning when they should eliminate, using the analogy that they were 'fixing the leaky taps while the house is burning down', use empowerment as an excuse to abdicate leadership, unleash some kind of re-engineering army, try to manage change "at 50,000 feet" and end up "on a flight to nowhere".

The benefits, however, are there without trading of cost and service. Cost reductions of up to 70 per cent may be achieved, whilst new product development times are halved and customer lead times reduced by up to 60 per cent.

It was suggested that to realise these benefits, just a few simple principles needed to be followed, namely

- "build bridges between functional towers"

- "rally the troops before charging the hill"

- "capture the elephants before chasing the mice" [Pareto –Ed]

- "secure the foundation before painting the rooms"

- make it easy.

The approach recommended was one of identifying capabilities; developing a baseline of performance, cost, speed and quality; putting a 'stake in the ground' to drive major (50 per cent plus) improvements in cost, time and value; selecting high potential processes; profile those processes to be able to understand flows and performance levels; restate targets to drive improvements to each key process; establish priorities on what to implement first; develop the plan; and implement and monitor.

The Productivity Opportunity

The scene was set by Roger Stenson, Assistant General Manager, Group IT, for Norwich Union Insurance, who spoke of the opportunities currently presented by the successful application of information technology used in conjunction with the currently popular technique of business process re-engineering (BPR), which he says 'represents the beginning of the adaptation of business to the effects of the information explosion'.

Echoing the words of Dr. Deming he said that:

"We should expect a period of continuous change and instability in which the aim is to optimise the productivity of the process, not the people".

Business Process Re-engineering was seen as the means to this end, with a careful balance being struck between radical BPR which entails a radical exploitation of IT and adaptation of products to facilitate processes, and incremental BPR which entails the removal of process inhibitors within present constraints of the organisation and the IT system. The potential savings from incremental BPR was emphasised with reference to the 50 per cent reduction in computing costs over the last seven years, which was attributed almost entirely to the application of successive incremental changes.

A major productivity opportunity is, he said, being presented by the fact that computing and communications are 'halving in price every year', with mass use shrink wrap software being high in demand and critical to the success of the business.

In foreseeing the end of the office and its associated paperwork he suggested that in future the path toward more effective use of the person would be indirect, involving 'more productive use of premises, communications, technology and knowledge itself'.

TQM, BPR, and Workflow Management

Elizabeth Gooch, Managing Director of EG Consulting and Geoff Wilmer, Total Quality Co-ordinator for Clerical Medical delivered a joint presentation which highlighted Dr. Deming's eleventh point i.e. the need to eliminate work standards and numerical goals for people in management.

Ms. Gooch explained how last year she had visited Dr. Deming and asked how one could manage without measures, given that the financial sector is regulated by money, which is only 'the most basic of measures'. His reply was "I do not disagree with measurement. I disagree with arbitrary measurement".

In short he was saying that where standards are set they need to be meaningful to workers, management and the customer, and in two out of the three cases these meaningful measures were not difficult to ascertain, according to Ms. Gooch. Meaningful measures to the customer were speed and accuracy of service, whilst for management they were measures such as work throughput, productivity, service levels and costs. Meaningful measures for staff, however, presented a greater problem or at least they appeared to.

Clerical Medical Investment Group, a mutual society, embarked on a programme of training for culture change, building customer awareness and developing a process understanding in every member of staff, in 1991. Design teams were established to examine the various elements of a TQ programme (structure required, training material needed, overall objectives, communication channels etc.). A TQ steering group was set up, to which various TQ co-ordinators within functional business units had a direct line. Consultants assisted with background work to ensure an agreed approach.

Three years later, in accordance with the company's vision, the company has achieved sufficient savings by way of improvements, to cover the initial costs, and survey feedback has confirmed that the company has 'a much improved view of who the customer is'. Problem solving tools and techniques have been used regularly with 'real success' and 'some real success' has been gained from experimental teamwork. Something, however, was still missing. Initial enthusiasm had 'raised staff expectations beyond belief' and whilst there had clearly been some success, improvement activity suffered from inconsistency:

'The amount of activity is patchy, efforts are sporadic and focus is often lacking mirroring this are people's expectations and behaviour from highly involved to peripheral input, to none at all'.

With the help of EG Consultants, the company then set out to identify the 'missing ingredient', examining first TQM, which focuses on the relation between the customer and the people, then BPR which focuses on the inter-relationships between processes and the customer, and finally Process Management which applies the techniques of production or workflow control to a clerical environment.

The methodology of Process Management is seen as important as it allows managers to understand, measure, control and improve the work which they are responsible for, continuously and with the help of their staff. Staff are organised around the work rather than the other way around and an element of process control is introduced. Unfortunately, the single purpose of improvement frequently cascades into many measurement systems creating 'a myriad of information requirements' each of which acquires its own data collection exercise. Many of these become a mere analysis and fail to provide meaningful information:

'I've seen Supervisors produce work reports for their Managers who never even ask themselves what the information means – it's just another job for the boss. When it's done they can get back to the real work '.

Herein lies the root of the problem. During the company's TQ training all staff had commented on the waste incurred through compiling statistics and measures used within the operating areas:

'Staff found it hard to know what to measure to ensure real value from their efforts. Supervisors just did it because they had to. We had a cottage industry but for what purpose ?'

Clerical Medical responded to its challenge by launching a 'Performance Measurement' system last spring, with the aim of establishing 'measurement with a purpose'. This began in two business units, complementing the TQ programme. Staff were trained to develop their own measures, unravel the processes, introduce controls and finally implement workflow management themselves.

The pilot was successful, as evidenced by a 50 per cent improvement in productivity within just six weeks, service levels which 'improved beyond compare', evidence of improved morale, and a notable reduction in processing turnaround times. The fear of rejection and cynicism by the staff, on the part of management, 'just did not materialise'.

The company is now looking to build on this success by applying the added concept of process workflow management, which will involve using the devised measures as planning tools to assess how many staff are likely to be required and with what skills, to clear the work in hand.

Productivity -so what's new?

Companies have been seeking to improve productivity for a long time, but as previously mentioned the methods adopted in pursuit of this improvement have been traditionally flawed. Action has focused on the people, not the system, but this has not been the only problem, as David McKee, Head of Productivity Services for TSB Bank explained.

In his presentation entitled 'Productivity –so what's new?' he provided a historical outline of the subject of work measurement at the corporate, macro and micro levels since the 1960s. This highlighted two further aspects of productivity which has hampered, and perhaps still is hampering efforts to improve it:

(i) There has been little or no common understanding of what productivity is.

(ii) Few systems for measuring productivity are alike.

These observations were then placed in the context of the speaker's own company:

'At the grass-roots level, some areas had charts everywhere measuring productivity. -"Yes", they said, "productivity is increasing. Everyone is working harder". Working harder maybe, but was productivity increasing?'

Individual definitions of productivity varied and no-one really knew the answer to the question. This needed to be resolved, before the whole aspect of improvement could be tackled, so there was 'much discussion and debate' which eventually led to 'some innovative concepts'.

Research and discussions gave rise to the view that productivity was 'a composite measure'. The traditional view of productivity as merely the ratio of output to input makes no reference to cost, and the speaker made clear his support for IMS chairman John Heap's view that to make practical use of the term it is necessary to consider which resources are being used, how these are measured, whether the timescale of measurement is important, and perhaps most importantly, how value is determined. Suddenly, he says, a simple ratio becomes more complex.

Value, according to the speaker, 'is a factor of productivity which is an expression of both effective use of resources and the capacity for innovation and self-renewal'. A recent definition of productivity in terms of 'value added per hour worked' is supported, although it is accepted that it is "a concept we are not used to in this country".

The presentation introduces the concept of 'innovative ability' i.e. a measure of a company's ability to improve its output in such a way that is assigned a higher value by the market. He observed how TSB considered this quality related concept in the compilation of their own original corporate level productivity index.

This measure uses the concept of Customer Required Outputs, questioning what the customer values and is prepared to pay for, but does not count outputs which are only used internally. Inputs, however, take the form only of paid hours, which takes no account of the cost of labour and is not responsive to outsourcing or contract staff.

A second measure, the Network Productivity Index, helps to overcome the cost problem by being itself a cost based measure which provides an indication of the relative effectiveness of each branch, cluster, area or region in converting input costs to outputs. This measure also uses Customer Required Outputs and therefore retains the all important consideration of customer values, although its application to the production of league tables, as suggested in the paper, has to be questioned.

Results driven Benchmarking

David McKee highlighted the fact that few systems for measuring productivity were alike, which would tend to suggest that productivity measurement generally is still grossly sub-optimised. There has been little attempt to establish and share best practice and as previously mentioned definitions have been many and varied. A major move has, however, been launched which could greatly improve productivity benchmarking in the financial sector.

Irene Unwin, Controller -Quality and Performance Improvement for the Britannia Building Society, described how the company embarked on a major re-think as to how mortgages were delivered to existing and potential customers in the light of the housing recession in 1992. This culminated in an operational benchmarking programme for the lending process which began in March 1993.

The Britannia was not alone at this time in wanting to benchmark mortgage and related processes and in 1993 the Britannia, along with five other banks and building societies agreed to form a consortium which, for the first time, would concentrate on the improvement of business processes rather than on just financial measures. It was agreed that benchmarking within the consortium would be facilitated by an independent consultancy.

Within Britannia a four phase approach of plan, collect, analyse, and adapt and improve [similar to the Deming Plan, Do, Study, Act cycle-Ed], was adopted. Presentations were given first to the Executive Board, and then by cascade to those directly involved in the study. It was agreed that the Quality function would facilitate the benchmarking process, whilst the Executive for Lending would be responsible for taking action on the results and areas of identified opportunity.

Quantitative and qualitative measures were agreed by the consortium and data collection was achieved through direct observation, use of tracking sheets, and management information reports, process mapping and site visits. Information and learning was discussed with all relevant parties:

'It is good to bring back new ideas but equally important is having the confidence to introduce them having witnessed other successful approaches'.

Importance is attached to the integration of benchmarking data with market and customer research information to produce a more complete picture of customer perceptions, and benefits are cited in terms of *delivering a core business service to new customers.

*improved quality of service to existing customers in maintaining their mortgage accounts.

*identifying and turning opportunities into sales.

*improved customer retention.

*comparative process costs.

*operation of the lending process to maximise resource utilisation and efficiency.

The speaker accepted that it took some time for the financial services organisations to accept that the sharing of information was going to work to their mutual benefit. However, with this resistance overcome it has helped the organisations to learn and become far more outward looking than before, bringing facts to the decision making process and to focus on and specify what needs to be changed and why. She made reference to a number of 'critical measures' which benchmarking had highlighted which the company realised it should have been applying but had not been.

Benchmarking has now been adopted as a fundamental management tool for business planning with the results being used to drive incremental improvements and to fuel a re-engineering programme for the lending process.

[Issue 67 (July 1994)]

BPR RESEARCH IN THE FINANCIAL SECTOR

At the Institute of Management Services Financial Group Annual Conference the results of the first quantified research co-ordinated in the UK into the success of Business Process Re-engineering (BPR) in the financial sector was presented. This was by Chris Skinner, Managing Consultant for the Highams Systems Service Group, who joined forces with Bristol University during 1992 and 1993 to survey over 75 financial services and related companies such as General and Life Insurance Companies, Building Societies, Brokers and IT vendors.

The survey specifically examined why companies had chosen to re-engineer, what they hoped to achieve by doing so, how they defined the terminology, and what the principal differences were between it, TQM and Organisation and Methods (O and M).

901

The paper was first published in *'Business Change and Re-engineering'* , Volume 1 No 2 (Autumn 1993) and has three authors: Chris Skinner, Jeff Watkins, Technology Director of MBA Programmes, Bristol University and John Pearson, Director of Pearson Profiles. Its full title is 'Business Process Re-engineering: Hype, Hazard or Heaven?

The report describes how hype in the 1990s has created 'a new management cult' which is clearly popular although far from clear to define. When asked how many were currently involved in BPR around a quarter of delegates raised their hands. Three years ago, said the speaker, 'hardly any hands would have been raised'. Its benefits, however, are questioned:

'Does this cult mean real results, or is it just a hazard that will leave egg-on-face for the Board?'

In November 1992 Bristol University seized an opportunity to find out by handing out questionnaires to some 200 conference delegates who were either engaged in a BPR project, or were about to implement one. This was followed by a second survey involving the mailing of questionnaires to around 100 further organisations. The two exercises yielded 75 responses in all by July1993 out of a total of 350 potential participants.

The report lists the proportion of respondents in each sector (banks 29%, life assurers 18%, composite insurers 15%, consultancies 11 %, IT companies 10%, general insurers 7%, building societies 5%, and insurance brokers 5%) .By title or position 29% of respondents were classed as Business Managers, 28% IT Managers, 26% Directors, 13% Internal BPR Consulting Staff and 4% Chief Executives.

Findings showed that there was much inconsistency in the way in which BPR was defined (over sixty different definitions). These were, however, consolidated to provide one standard definition i.e. 'a conscious reshaping of an organisation behind a new corporate vision, the market place and the customer', whilst its objective was summarised as 'to yield sustainable improvements in profitability, productivity, service and quality, whilst maximising the potential of the individual and the team'.

When asked why their companies were investing in BPR most (96%) cited the need for continuous improvement as either 'important' or 'of absolute importance', with implementing cultural change also scoring highly (86%) and increased customer expectations close behind with 85%. The belief that world recession was a principal reason was somewhat confounded as it scored a comparatively low 58%.

In assessing the benefits of BPR all respondents (100%), cited increased customer focus and improved profitability as 'important' or 'of absolute importance', whilst improved quality was cited by 95%. Improved corporate flexibility and speed of service delivery were both cited by 86%.

Most of the companies apparently saw BPR as complementary both to TQM and continuous improvement, although some (around 10%) felt that it was simply O and M re-packaged. Interestingly, however, around 25% of respondents apparently viewed BPR as conflicting with existing IT strategies and it is concluded that 'few companies totally accept BPR's underlying principle of having no sacred cows: especially IT'.

It is implied that often companies are entering into BPR with a view that they are constrained by their existing systems, and yet are determined to retain them:

'It may be that a company determines it cannot face the upheaval of throwing out existing IT systems, but this can only be determined further to a completely fresh view of the company's approach to technology'.

The report highlights BPR case studies such as those at National Vulcan Engineering Insurance and TSB which suggest that to achieve success it is often necessary to 'break through the established approaches to IT'. Actually benefits achieved by one such company which took this action, include notably a 100% increase in productivity, a 40% reduction in administration costs and a reduction in claims handling time from 28 days to 4 during a two year period in which a decline in their chosen markets was completely turned around. This is contrasted with the survey results in which around 63% of respondents said that any technological implementation would 'need to integrate with existing databases'.

It is concluded that whilst BPR 'is being hyped aggressively' and is delivering 'radical results and massive benefits', it 'can still be hazardous' even with the necessary top level commitment. Strong communications internally and externally are viewed as essential as is a clear vision prior to commencement, and a specific employee focus, which was notably absent from 80% of respondents' schemes. Likewise, making IT a 'sacred cow' could jeopardise the entire programme.

[Issue 78 (June 1995) – 1995 IMS FINSEC Conference]

Birmingham Midshires: enacting Change

The Keynote Address was given by Michael Jackson, Chief Executive of the Birmingham Midshires Building Society, which is currently the country's thirteenth largest building society with 1,500 employees, assets totalling £4.3 billion, 120 branches and 22 property services shops.

The company enjoyed a period of explosive growth in the early 1980s, but it was short lived, and by the early 1990s seriously lost momentum. A series of mergers gave rise to "management indigestion' as each time it was perceived that the next merger would somehow create the right culture and import the right people. This view, of course, was nonsense and the company eventually realised that it was in danger of becoming a 'boiled frog'.

The Main Board sensed the heat in 1990 and decided to take a leap by appointing a new Chairman and Chief Executive and in the second half of that year foundations were laid for enacting change, which included, amongst other things, Executive Team Workshops which defined a vision and values:

'Those present were asked to cut out words and pictures which best described our current strengths and desired ones in the eyes of our customers. A montage was built up by those present. The words which seemed to appear most were the words FIRST and CHOICE. From this exercise and detailed research into customer required values the vision statement was formed'.

The resulting vision statement read as follows:

'By being FIRST CHOICE for our customers, our people and our business partners we will grow, profitably'.

An acronym of FIRST was devised to reflect the values which customers had identified as attributes which would cause them to make Birmingham Midshires their first choice i.e. Friendly, Informed, Responsive, Service orientated and Trustworthy. The term 'business partners' reflects the nature of the relationship the company is seeking to establish with its suppliers.

The Executive Team also formulated a values statement called 'Pillars of Excellence'. This contained 'echoes of Deming' notably a belief that people in the organisation should be innovators and should take calculated and communicated risks without feeling that they will be punished if they fail. Also a belief in the importance of having fun through one's work was emphasised.

Further booklets were produced and cross-functional teams formed to plan and implement quality projects.

The paper explains how the Executive Team has introduced communication processes 'to overcome unhealthy feelings of fear, uncertainty and doubt', including the 'listening to you first' programme (annual staff attitude survey which results in actionable items put forward by the staff), and the 'face to face' programme (requirement of Executive Team to visit branches in the field and departments in the centre where those being visited set the agenda - said to result in around 200 actionable items a year).

It is then explained how each executive has a budget for the reward of staff 'who deserve extra recognition' which supports a performance related pay system which the staff are said to have proposed and designed themselves'. Then, under 'Objectives Setting and Appraisal' it is explained how all staff 'identify, set and agree their objectives with their manager in line with the published corporate goals and objectives' using Personal Development plans which 'document the new training and learning experiences to be gained in the next year'. It is noted that extensive use is made of self-appraisal and personal feedback.

New corporate governance procedures incorporate a Board Operational Policies Guide that 'is considered by outside experts to be one of the most advanced in the UK'. A summary of results achieved indicates a notable increase in profit per staff member from under £4,000 in 1990 to over £20,000 in 1993, an increase in return on capital from under 5 per cent in 1990 to over 15 per cent in 1993, and an increase in operating profit by 150 per cent from £15.9 million in 1990 to £39.7 million in 1993.

In 1993 the company was voted the UK's top company for customer service in the inaugural Customer First award scheme sponsored by *The Daily Telegraph* and First Direct and last year attained the Investors in People award.

In his conclusion the CEO accepted that whilst his company had achieved much in a relatively short time he would perhaps have done a few things differently a second time around, notably that he would have concentrated much earlier on the human resource elements of the change. He pointed to the next stage of BPR being linked closely to 'new supporting HR policies and best practice'.

The presentation was professionally delivered and warmly received and prompted several questions, for example, on how performance was measured across the cross-functional teams and to this he answered "by constantly listening". He explained the existence of some 200 measures which were currently summarised on ten sheets of paper, and stressed the importance of addressing customer issues promptly.

Homeloan Management: Utilising Outsourcing for Administration

Homeloan Management Limited is the UK's largest provider of outsourced mortgage administration and system bureau facilities handling over £3 billion of mortgage assets. Their Managing Director Barry Meeks explained how outsourcing might be applied to the administration function in order to improve the competitive position of mortgage lenders.

He began by addressing the current supply and demand mismatch in the mortgage lending market and suggested that rather than fighting a price war on the basis of 'cashbacks galore' more attention should be given to the issue of customer retention to which he believes many lenders have 'paid lip service'.

Customer retention will, he says, become more a factor of service and less a factor of convenience, corporate loyalty or price. He asserts that in future lenders 'will need to win and retain existing customer loyalty in much the same way as they are now viewing customer acquisition'. Consequently 'the efficiency of service delivery will be key'. He says:

'Over the last few months Homeloan Management have spoken to Top 10 lenders in the UK who cannot launch new products within 3 to 4 weeks. They have inadequate systems to cater for database marketing, and would like to re-enter the market for commercial mortgages but cannot because their systems are three years out of date. Or they are lenders who cannot easily improve systems delivery to make their administration demonstrably better than the rest'.

'There are literally hundreds of thousands of existing or previous homeowners who today find themselves disenfranchised from the mortgage market because of problems they incurred during the height of the recession. They may or may not feel that their current lender played fair with them during that time and only future redemption rates will really tell'.

In this climate he suggests that viewing administration as a reactive element 'kicked in' in the wake of the salesman or marketeer is 'a recipe for disaster':

'Too often superb marketing campaigns have been destroyed by poor or flawed administrative back up'.

It follows that administration 'will become an integral part of the marketing process' which will 'differentiate the good from the mediocre'. As such 'must be pro-active and exceed the customer's expectations'. Hence 'it must be evident and obvious to the customer that administration is viewed as a key differentiator by your business'.

Questions to be asked include:

- are employees well trained and informed?

- are back up systems in place and functional e.g. quotation systems?

- is any follow-up written material well presented and concise and free of jargon?

It is argued that administration needs to be targeted and selective as it 'goes to the core of how the customer views the efficiency of the business'. Needs, for example, for technical assistance, which differ between customers. Systems should reflect this, and a case for less automation rather than more is presented on the grounds that many people do not always want to deal with machinery.

A third party solution is not, according to the speaker 'a cheap option' and there are no 'secret formulas', but there can be 'very distinct and measurable advantages over other solutions open to a lender'. Some of the benefits summarised include:

*a totally variable cost solution

*availability of low cost infrastructures with tried and tested systems

*availability of flexible options to meet the business demand supplemented by advanced support services

*contractual agreement to minimum service standards

It is argued that fears of loss of control and of customer contact are unfounded 'and can be addressed in the design of any appropriate solution'. He proposed that in future many lenders may 'share a common administration platform,' an event which at least one senior director of a major UK Building Society sees as 'a logical step forward'. [For many but not all. Internal politics will be a barrier, and those that overcome it may reap a reward -Ed].

An extension of the market for purchased servicing rights similar to that which already exists in the USA i.e. the right to service a portfolio for an up front sum, is envisaged, and HML is currently scrutinising such developments.

Sun Alliance: A new Culture

Bob Hellen, Systems Manager for Sun Alliance Management Services, described how his company, which supplies IT services, business consultancy and facilities management to the Sun Alliance group, has initiated and implemented a culture change.

Initial research from facilitated sessions in 1992 confirmed that staff not only were able to contribute more to the running of the organisation, but wanted to do so to such an extent that management became convinced that they were wasting their assets with the current working mode. [Not unusual in the financial sector e.g. as when NatWest Bank introduced TQM –Ed].

This led to the formation of six 'Breakthrough' groups whose role was to examine the key areas of management development, communications, marketing, customer relationships, business transformation and short term improvements, with the objective of removing waste and improving

907

efficiency. Group members came from many grades, locations and departments.

A staff survey in early 1993 helped to establish measures and distinguish between views that were common across the whole organisation and effects that were localised. Targeted areas for improvements resulted again with several 'Deming echoes', such as the removal of grade consciousness, elimination of fear generated by some managers, involvement of staff in decision making where they have the knowledge and experience. [There is no substitute for knowledge -Ed], and creating more consistency in the appraisal process [understanding variation -Ed].

A 'Breakthrough Office' headed by a full-time senior manager co-ordinated activities effected the survey recommendations. Following workshops, attendees of supervisors and managers produced their own 'contracts for change' which incorporated personal action plans. A customer survey then highlighted the need for improvement in key areas such as responsiveness, promotion of services and overall value for money. In 1994 the Breakthrough Office was expanded to include a Communications Unit. Two day customer focus workshops were then held for all 1400 staff.

A third survey, in April 1994, conducted by independent consultants, 'confirmed significant improvements right across the board', and this year a theme of 'continuous improvement' has been introduced so that 'Breakthrough will not be perceived as 'a special project' or 'something with a separate existence'. [This part of the programme has 'echoes of Juran' -Ed].

The 'great success' of 'Breakthrough' has led to its adoption by other parts of Sun Alliance, which all have culture change and first class customer service as major components of their business plans.

Some interesting 'key findings' are noted:

(i) Three years is not an unreasonable time for a well managed, well sustained change programme, and people need to know this, otherwise the dawning reality that change will take time may be painful and reduce enthusiasm.

(ii) Believing that launching a culture change programme will lead automatically to new behaviour is a mistake, since words and workshops mean nothing until people actually do things differently.

(iii) People need to be encouraged to accept and seek change and be empowered to make and suggest changes, and simply throwing money at it, or telling people what to do, will not achieve results.

(iv) Only when there are clear signals that managers are totally behind the changes will others feel comfortable enough to take risks, hence managers must lead by example.

(v) Transformation is the responsibility of everyone and the contribution of individuals should be both welcomed and expected.

Mr. Hellen was asked whether there was executive pressure to produce financial gains. He explained that other than the normal budget there were no financial targets and all measures were soft.

He was later asked about the steps that his company had taken to remove the grading structure and commented that "grade does not confer particular abilities", but whilst information is supplied on a need to know basis rather than by grade internally, there remains a problem externally in that outside people frequently, by nature, want to speak to someone with rank. He explained how he was seeking to persuade outsiders to change this view and accept "that traditional hierarchical structures are outmoded".

CALLING THE WITNESS: SIMULATION SOFTWARE AIDS BPR

Business Process Re-engineering (BPR) is the latest facility to be incorporated into AT and T ISTEL's process simulation software tool called WITNESS. The extension follows the successful application of the software last year to process mapping using the IDEF methodology (a process diagramming standard which currently finds favour with the American Department of Defence).

The software can now be used for all phases of a BPR project from capture through development, refinement and testing to implementation. It will characterise the existing process, highlighting bottlenecks and under-utilised resources. WITNESS can evaluate a large number of alternative redesigns in a short time without risk to existing business, predict and cure teething troubles so that they do not become a reality, prove the robustness of a design by running under extreme conditions, and show potential benefits arising from redesigned processes so that an informed cost-benefit analysis can be performed. The company says:

'The biggest barrier to the adoption of BPR is the risk inherent in radical redesign of processes. WITNESS reduces this risk by allowing animated computer models of redesigned processes to be constructed in a very short time, so that errors or omissions can be eliminated before implementation. This reduces the number and duration of pilot studies required and increases the probability of getting it right first time'.

Companies which are reported to have realised benefits so far include the Birmingham Midshires Building Society, Britannia Building Society and United Friendly Insurance. Benefits at United Friendly include improving the effectiveness of branch administration, and identifying the impact of new Lautro regulations and realising the most efficient way of complying with them. They have increased sales using existing staff by freeing time spent on excess administration and ensuring that processes used in the launch of new products have the capability to meet more demanding customer service levels.

[Issue 90 (June 1996)]

QUALITY IN THE FINANCIAL SECTOR

The Institute of Management Services (IMS) continues to lead the way for quality practitioners in the financial sector. The last three issues (March to May) of their journal *Management Services* provides an informative overview of research conducted by Portsmouth University, and sponsored by FINSEC, the IMS Financial Sector Special Interest Group, into currently available Business Process Re-engineering (BPR) software for the financial services industry. They also have complementing articles on benchmarking at Abbey National and process benchmarking in retail financial services.

FINSEC held their annual conference entitled 'Staying One Jump Ahead: New Insights for the New Millenium' at the CBI Conference Suite in London on 17th April.

Mortgage Express: back from the Brink

Mortgage Express was one of four companies shortlisted for the 1995 UK Quality Award and the story of its success, presented by Managing Director Keith Greenough at this year's Annual FINSEC Conference, makes interesting reading.

The company was formed in 1986 as a wholly owned subsidiary of TSB Bank plc, who are now part of Lloyds TSB. It prospered well in its early years during the artificial boom of the mid to late 1980s but when the housing market collapsed in the early 1990s hard times loomed:

'The recession was deepest in the south of the country where most of our customers live and we were facing losses running into hundreds of millions. There was no alternative other than to withdraw from the market and focus all efforts on overcoming the massive problems of mortgage arrears and bad debts. The shock waves this sent through the organisation were enormous. From rising star to black sheep in a matter of months. The business was to be closed. Everyone was facing redundancy and morale and trust in top management were at rock bottom'.

The paper describes how to resolve this crisis. TSB appointed a new team and rather than opting for the traditional approach of liquidating all bad debts as quickly as possible and cutting costs to the bone they decided to embark on a course of Total Quality Management. This began not with ISO9000 but with an appraisal of the then new EFQM model for business excellence. This is noted for its ability to provide a measured assessment of performance, introduce a baseline for benchmarking either internally over time or externally in relation to other companies (e.g. the Award winners -Ed), involve people at all levels in the assessment process, and effectively amalgamate Quality Management with Business Management.

Over the next four years some 300 communication events were led by top management. Planning and objective setting processes were totally redesigned so that corporate goals were effectively deployed down to individual performance objectives. This was much needed as in 1993 only 26 per cent of employees reportedly considered that their director was accessible. This has now improved to 70 per cent, following a major change programme in 1994 in which 100 'leaders' from all levels of the organisation became involved in defining role model behaviours and formulating a 360 degree (full circle) performance appraisal system.

The results which have stemmed from this programme have been most encouraging. Some 87 per cent of staff now reportedly agree that the organisation was committed to its mission. Also 80 per cent agree that their boss had commitment, whilst 81 per cent believe that there is now good co-operation between departments. This reflects a strong focus on human resource management which has been reinforced with attainment of the Investors In People (IIP) standard:

'Our people goal is to enable all our employees to achieve their best. We stress the mutuality of interest in this goal. Best means best for the individual and best for the company. The cornerstones of our people management strategy have been communications, teamwork, involvement, personal development and making work fun '.

'We believe that capturing people's hearts and minds and engaging them in the challenges of the organisation are vital for success. A prerequisite is that everyone understands where the company is going and how well it is performing. This is why we have invested heavily in internal communication since 1991. Our approach stresses face to face contact and regularity, so as to promote participation and trust. We have scheduled communication events on monthly, quarterly and annual cycles. Our annual staff opinion research, which is conducted each year by a team of staff volunteers, is an invaluable annual healthcheck and has been the source of many new Human Resource initiatives'.

The strong people focus has been supported by substantial streamlining of mortgage processing systems and procedures which have been reduced from eight to two for each of the 27 portfolios which the company manages. A much enhanced system of measurement covers all key processes and assesses them in terms of process effectiveness, customer perceptions and impact on business results. This contrasts with the pre-1991 approach which focused almost exclusively on the measurement of sales figures:

'Measurement of customer perceptions is perhaps the most difficult. To tackle this we introduced new ways of "listening to our customers". These include traditional methods such as customer research and event-based surveys but also some more original approaches. For example, we hold weekly meetings that anyone can attend when we listen to recordings of telephone conversations with customers'.

The financial achievements of the organisation cannot be ignored: a £38.4 million profit in 1995 which represents a £110 million turnaround since 1992.

Essential Business Physics

The one paper in the conference to live up to the sub-title 'to the new millennium' is the interesting concept of Bob Spencer of the Tillers Group in the application of non-linear 'natural' processes to management. [Although non-mathematical it probably is too theoretical in language to appeal to many managers-Ed].

The approach considers two processes; Engineered and Natural, and compares and contrasts them in combination. Engineered processes are defined as:

* Linear by design i.e. predictable

* Optional and subject to obsolescence

* Familiar and managed

Bob Spencer makes the computer analogy that these are the equivalent of 'application software'.

He defines Natural processes as:

* Non-linear i.e. unpredictable

* Unchangeable

* Unfamiliar and unmanaged

These are analogous in computer terminology as 'operating systems'.

The author considers the non-linear dynamics of the physics of natural processes. When applied to business processes he shows that they are much more complex than their linear counterparts. However, even the linear managed framework still can have an incorrect long term prediction.

The analysis considers 'Chaos and Change' and examines the states of processes [which include organisations -Ed] in equilibrium or instability. The author concludes that for Change there are two options:

(a) Continue to use conventional methods on engineered processes, but with an awareness of the influence of natural processes especially about the state of equilibrium.

(b) Encourage self-generated change through the natural processes.

The prediction is that there will be a significant movement in the role of management and change agents. These are beginning already with 'Empowerment' and the 'Learning Organisation'.

[Issue 91 (July 1996)]

SOFTWARE FOR BPR

Recent issues of the Institute of Management Services Journal *'Management Services'* provides an informative overview of research conducted by Portsmouth University, and sponsored by FINSEC,(the IMS Financial Sector Special Interest Group), into currently available Business Process Re-engineering (BPR) software for the financial services industry.

Three articles are presented on this subject which focus on nine software packages that were considered to be representative of those that are typically available and currently being used. They are divided into three categories i.e. making the present process, analysing possible improvements and facilitating new ways of working.

The first article, on BPR Enabling Software by Richard Lakin, Nick Capon and Neil Botten, explains some of the reasoning behind mapping the existing process. For example, to make duplicity of effort, non value adding work, and delays, clearly visible. Consideration is given to the reasons for using a computer tool such as the improvement of consistency, and the four modelling methods that are commonly used for BPR (Flow charts, Role Activity, Diagrams, Action workflow and IDEF). Various criteria for software evaluation are then listed and reduced to two (effectiveness and usability) before the three chosen software products: ABC Flowcharter 4.0, RADitor 1.6 and Design/DEF are reviewed in support of the modelling methods of Flowcharting, RADs and the Integrated DEFinition Method (IDEF) relative to these two key criteria:

'We read the outline specification of 13 tools which supported flow diagram modelling. Some are very simple to use such as ABC Flowcharter and Visio.

Others offer more extensive features such as Benchmarker Plus and Workdraw. ABC Flowcharter is reviewed as typical of these packages, since many companies we interviewed used it'.

Various strengths and weaknesses are identified for each product and some users' comments are reported, notably from Portman Building Society where, in relation to Design/DEF 3.5 one user particularly stresses that it is not necessary to model existing processes "to the nth degree", but merely "to have sufficient knowledge for them to be redesigned".

In conclusion the authors say:

'Tools that are primarily designed to model existing processes are not particularly good at simulation or supporting the new process, yet it is in the latter that most companies are concerned. This is shown in the evidence provided by two companies interviewed who used ABC Flowcharter to do the mapping but had to use other software to simulate proposed new processes'.

In the second article on BPR Modelling Software Gary Love and Nick Capon compare the top-down and bottom-up approaches to BPR. They give examples of companies which have adopted each before reviewing three mid range tools which were considered to be particularly appropriate for the re-engineering of Financial Services administrative processes. These were CASEwise, Business Design Facility (BDF) and Processwise Workbench. Of these BDF from Texas Instruments is the most expensive at around £6,000 per user, whilst CASEwise from the CASEwise Company is the least expensive at around £3,495 per user. With ICL's Processwide Workbench retailing at around £4,995 per user it is quickly seen that all of these packages cost considerably more than some enabling packages. This clearly reflects the greater difficulty that is encountered when one seeks actually to redesign the processes to achieve significant improvements.

Again strengths and weaknesses are identified for each, for example CASEwise has the 'distinctive strength' of a comprehensive data repository .This can be used to construct a record of all aspects of the current and new processes and is said to be an 'adequate' tool to meet the needs of incremental BPR programmes. However, simulation of the new process is described as 'unspectacular' and there is according to the authors, a lack of provision for importing and exporting process information from or to other packages.

In conclusion the authors say:

'At the redesign stage of BPR, carefully constructed models of the as-is process can highlight where there are opportunities for improvement. IT tools can also assist by calculating the total time, resources and costs of alternative new proposed processes compared with each other and the

present as-is process. Many IT modelling tools support this, either in themselves or by allowing export of key figures to a spreadsheet package for analysis. However, such methods are not good at predicting the ability of a new process to cope with peak demands'.

The third article, on IT applications which support the BPR solution, by Peter Francis and Nick Capon, examines workflow (automating the passing of information) as the application which 'presents the greatest opportunity for radical improvement in financial services applications where large volumes of paper of a fairly structured nature were being processed, although acknowledging its weakness of being prone to user resistance.

The authors reviewed outline specifications for 23 tools with the emphasis on the less expensive end of the market, and selected two, Staffware, priced at £500 and Lotus, priced at £345 per user for a 50 user application.

Staffware is highlighted as 'the best selling structured workflow system, offering sophisticated routing facilities combined with intuitive graphical process mapping, and potential benefits are identified notably in the areas of cycle time and efficiency, and empowerment and control:

'In mortgage application processing the actual work involved may only take minutes but turnaround time is often measured in weeks. This discrepancy is due to delays in forms being passed on, rekeyed, filed etc. Using Staffware the recipient of a form will receive it within 60 seconds of its electronic posting and be notified of its arrival. Thus Staffware can eliminate much of the non-value added work and increase the amount of "real work" accomplished'.

Lotus Notes, by contrast, is 'essentially an integrated document management and messaging system' which 'owes its success to its flexibility, ease of use and potential for dramatic organisational changes'. It is noted to be 'ideal for the creation of process wide applications, allowing users and systems to be linked and share information electronically, independent of their functional or physical location or computer platforms'. Benefits are described in the areas of customer service and product development:

'Customer service is the front line of customer contact and is increasingly becoming a key differentiator. A "Notes" call logging system enables any rep. to access the service history of a particular client and to be aware of that client's system and particular needs/problems. Also for sales support, access to a "Notes" database of the latest products and prices allows every enquiry to be handled immediately, thus increasing the chance of sale'.

'"Notes" can assist with the setting up of project databases, covering project meetings, testing details, technical plans etc. This allows access to all information by each project member, fostering collaboration between

departments, a lack of which is one of the chief factors in slowing down product development'.

As regards workflow in general the authors say:

'While workflow offers considerable benefits on its own merit, it is when combined with BPR that it may enable radical change and offer dramatic increases to productivity. Traditional systems are often designed for functional departments as opposed to cross-functional processes and therefore workflow can be used to create a "unified process infrastructure" linking different systems and users together seamlessly. The utilisation of such a workflow solution allows the elimination of much non-value added work'.

[Issue 102 (June 1997)]

QUALITY: THE BUSINESS OF ADDING VALUE

The IMS Financial Sector Specialist Group (FINSEC) chose 'The Business of Adding Value' as the theme for its 18th Annual Conference. Seven presentations by those at the sharpest end of the sharpest industry explained how modern management techniques are being applied to add value to their organisations.

The techniques include Business Excellence Self-assessment, benchmarking and process improvement, the so-called 'Balanced Scorecard' approach, and the home grown 'Continuing Professional Development' scheme developed by the IMS to assist its members. Add to this the practical aspects of business recovery planning, which may not on the surface appear to add much value until havoc strikes, as in the case of last year's notorious 'Manchester bomb' or the yet to come 'Millennium IT "bomb"', the ingredients were there for a significant teaming event, from which *Quality Matters* has selected the following four papers for review:

'What NatWest has learnt from Business Excellence Self-assessment' by David Watts, head of Corporate Development for NatWest Life;

'Transformation through Benchmarking and Process Improvement by Derrick Sheppard of the Financial Processes Redesign Team of Allied Domecq plc;

'Building a Balanced Scorecard' by John Geanuracos of Renaissance Solutions Limited;

'Business Recovery Planning in Action: Lessons from last year's Manchester Incident' by Angus Jordan, Group Risk Controller for Royal & Sun Alliance Insurance.

Adding Value through Self-assessment

NatWest Life is a relatively new addition to the NatWest group, launched in 1993 as a brand new life assurance company which was designed and built in 15 months. Already its record is impressive, however, rising to become the twelfth largest company in its industry, as ranked by new business income, within a year of its formation, and, as has been previously reported, becoming a finalist in both the European and UK Quality Awards in 1996. How did they do it? The paper explains how, by continuously adding value, they have been able to capitalise on the fact that they are a relatively new entrant:

'Starting out from scratch meant that we were able to benefit from detailed research into customer attitudes. Extensive pre-launch research revealed that of the 200 or so products we sold to our customers in our previous position as independent financial advisers just twelve would meet 95 per cent of all customers' needs. That allowed us to put together a focused portfolio of products which today includes term assurance, bonds, mortgage related products and personal pension plans'.

The paper explains how the EFQM Business Excellence Model has further helped the company to 'be action oriented and focus on delivering results in order to meet or exceed promises':

'The Vision drives our strategy and annual Business Plan which is structured jointly around the Balanced Business Scorecard approach and the Business Excellence Model. From the Corporate Plan each Division of the company develops its own objectives which form the basis of departmental and individual action plans. But these are not imposed on people. Through a comprehensive Performance Management System objectives for the year are agreed through open discussion between each member of staff and their manager. Everyone has a Role Profile which defines their job and their key accountabilities and core competencies required to achieve them'.

The Performance Management System is supported with Personal Learning and Development Plans for all employees which record training needs both for current jobs and potential future needs. In addition an annual staff satisfaction survey supports People Management, with each Division developing action plans through working groups using the results obtained, and there is annual rather than three yearly assessment to the Investor in People (IIP) standard. Particular attention is paid to the salesforce:

'In order to provide the right level of service, it is vital that we know how they view us. So we carry out regular surveys of salesforce satisfaction. Our first survey in October 1992 (just before our launch) showed that 46 per cent of NatWest's sales force rated the service they were then receiving as excellent. By April 1993 that figure had risen to 76 per cent -and during the first quarter of 1995 it had reached 93 per cent.'

The Business Excellence Model demands a stringent approach to customer satisfaction and readers will note that there is far more to this at NatWest Life than the mere processing of complaints and indeed there are no targets for a so-called 'acceptable level' of complaints:

'We aim to measure every area of our business and every conceivable point of contact between NatWest Life and its customers. After all if you do not measure satisfaction how do you know whether or not it's improving? We also publish a Customer Satisfaction Index, which is effectively a monthly index tracking the different measures we take. This enables us to monitor overall trends and to assess the impact of our actions on customer satisfaction'.

A description of the 1996 European Quality Award submission, which generated 176 areas for improvement, is followed by an outline of the 1997 application which was submitted in March:

'Rather than sit back and wait for the assessors' feedback report, this year we have immediately conducted our own assessment of the full document and this has immediately prompted a number of areas for improvement which we can do something about straight away'.

The author explains how each of the nine Business Excellence criteria has a sponsor, usually at Executive level, who then own action plans relating to their field:

'Collectively the nine sponsors form the Business Excellence Council whose responsibility is to set up a challenge process between its members, to prioritise action, to ensure that positive progress is being made and to really drive Business Excellence throughout the company. This works well because it also enables members to provide mutual support for each other in difficult areas'.

The author chairs the Business Excellence Council which he says gives him 'the rare privilege of being the boss over the Executive team'.

The presentation prompted a number of questions including how the organisation measured the performance of administrative services and the relative cost of quality. In response the speaker explained how a series of internal service standards have been developed as part of an ongoing internal measurement of customer satisfaction, and how quality had no budget, no manager and no director, just a strategy of 'mid market pricing'.

Transformation through Benchmarking and Process Improvement

Derrick Sheppard enlightened delegates about how the value added through benchmarking and business process improvement can be used as a foundation for total transformation. He explained how in 1993 and 1994 he had chaired the Pensions Administration Large Scale network (PALS) administration expenses surveys. He concluded that the administration and development of the PALS system from 1996 would be best outsourced to Arthur Anderson (consultants).

The PALS system surveys were limited in that there were no costs analyses over major activities, concerns over data integrity, little correlation with business practices, and only broad indicators available on account of organisational complexity, different quality and levels of service, and the varying scope of pensions services.

Benchmarking of pensions industry best practice was undertaken with a search for people inside and outside the industry of around the same size as Allied Domecq. A Benchmarking Partnership was established in 1995 consisting of Allied Domecq, Grand Metropolitan, Guinness, Lloyds Bank, and Unilever, the objectives of which were to assess business practices in all areas of the pensions business. Activity based costs analyses were used to cover all major in-house activities and enable valid comparisons to be made, and a high degree of integrity and consistency in data was achieved.

Two major reports resulted, covering business practices and costs analysis respectively, and in June 1996 a Business Process Review (BPR) was introduced. This had a two year timescale involving flowcharting of key processes and the establishment of performance measures. The speaker believed 'this worked well giving sound results, thorough and significant efficiency improvements, and allowed benchmarking to be undertaken at process level. It also helped to develop multi-skilling and to be an agent for continuous improvement'.

Attendance at the 1996 European Benchmarking Forum provided several important lessons. These included the need to communicate a (forward looking) Corporate Vision as was the case with Shorts plc's Focus 2000, and how to incorporate simple benchmarking questions to selected Annual Benchmarking Reviews. The event also highlighted the Business Excellence Model as a form of benchmarking.

A revised approach to (their termed) BPR has followed in 1997 with, in particular, more selective use being made of process mapping and use of oCTAVE software flowcharting metrics. Delegates were cautioned about the potential for obsessive process mapping to generate "huge wallcharts of things to map" which do not add value and serve merely to confuse.

In the questions which followed, the speaker was asked about how confidentiality issues were approached, and he referred in his answer to the now established rules of benchmarking protocol. He was then asked about whether with regard to pensions industry best practice, as the best he could hope for was the best in the group. He agreed in principle, but pointed out that benchmarking was continual, and that his organisation was already "looking out".

Building a Balanced Scorecard.

John Geanuracos outlined the concept of the Balanced Scorecard approach which has been used to transform Cigna Insurance, a troubled US full service underwriter.

The technique was noted particularly for its ability to successfully target knowledge management investments in key processes in what has been one of the first major applications of knowledge management concepts to the American financial services sector.

The author argues that corporations which are using the Balanced Scorecard are breaking through implementation barriers. These are defeating other organisations and that the clear articulation in a Balanced Scorecard of business unit strategic objectives, with links to associated performance drivers, has enabled many individuals to see often for the first time, the links between what they do and the organisation's long term objectives:

'The Balanced Scorecard is like a prism, taking the thousand points of light being generated around the organisation and focusing them on the critical few targets with the intensity of a laser. The' results achieved by such strategically aligned organisations can be dramatic'.

[Not physics but the idea is understood-Ed].

Use of the Balanced Scorecard is supported by means of a Balanced Management System. This is defined as 'a governance system which uses the Balanced Scorecard as the centrepiece in order to communicate an organisation's strategy, create strategic linkage throughout the organisation, develop business planning, and provide feedback and learning against the company's strategy'.

Their case study of National Insurance shows how by adding value the approach may be used to completely turn around a company by shifting its focus from 'generalised' to 'specialist' business. It is explained how Balanced Scorecards were established at Corporate, three Divisions and 20 SBUs. These led to a $441 million reduction in annual operating losses in 1994 and a uniformly positive Net Operating Income (NOI) in 1995 with most recent data available (November 1995) showing a 232 per cent increase in NOI. The paper points out that such turnarounds are extremely rare in the property and casualty world.

If there is a catch it could only be that a good Balanced Scorecard has to be tailored to the situation, there is no 'best answer' that will work for all companies. However, once in place it clarifies the vision throughout the organisation, gains consensus and ownership by the executive team, provides a framework to align the organisation, integrates the strategic planning and implementation process, focuses human resources strategy and drives the capital and resource allocation process. Most of the companies which have adopted the approach have used it to determine incentive compensation:

'A recent poll of 60 large corporations that had introduced the Balanced Scorecard in recent years discovered that forty of these companies used the Balanced Scorecard to determine incentive compensation and that another ten companies planned to do so shortly'.

It can be noted that the approach usually demands a complete reappraisal of a company's rewards structure:

'Organisations that use a Balanced Scorecard to successfully align the board room with the back room will find themselves dissatisfied with traditional incentive compensation models. Such structures are typically linked to short term financial results, not the long term strategic performance of a Balanced Scorecard. The question is not whether a corporation must change its reward structure, but when and how'.

Adding Value through Disaster Recovery Planning

Manchester city centre on the morning of Saturday June 15th 1996 was the scene of one of the largest peace time explosions the UK has ever experienced as a 1.5 tonne bomb concealed in a parked van exploded causing massive devastation and millions of pounds worth of damage. Royal & Sun Alliance's Manchester offices experienced the full force of the blast yet were able to recover a £300 million turnover business thanks to added value through disaster recovery planning.

The paper by Angus Jordan and Julia Graham, Group Risk Manager for the Royal & Sun Alliance, explains the immediate reaction to this catastrophe which left 34 staff injured. It explains how a Crisis Team was assembled and business subsequently resumed:

'Our recovery plans began within an hour of the blast with initial contact being made between the company's local and head office managers and our disaster recovery consultants Comdisco. Experts from our Group Risk Management, Information Technology and Facilities Management departments arranged to meet local managers and Comdisco representatives early on Sunday morning within 24 hours of the explosion at a hotel in Manchester'.

The role of the Control Group which met daily at 8.30 am in the immediate aftermath is outlined:

'The number of different business requirements meant that no fewer than four separate but parallel recovery plans were put into action, but with a number of common issues. These included switchboard messages for customers and staff, communication with Manchester-based staff at home, electronic main messages across the company's systems and transportation for essential employees to reach emergency locations'.

The paper concludes with a list of lessons learned from an event which is described as 'as educational as it was challenging'. These include:

*ensure plans are in place

*ensure key data is accessible

*only bring staff in when they can work or help

*operate a clear desk policy

*ensure key staff take time off after the initial process

*don't assume staff will be as willing to relocate as you might think

*don't assume you will automatically have staff support for more than two weeks
*don't ignore sites that are not directly impacted

*don't expect sympathy from customers for more than a few days

The Millennium 'IT Bomb'.

In change to the advertised schedule Graham Briscoe of Royal & Sun Alliance outlined some of the potential pitfalls which could await from a disaster yet to come, namely the 'Millennium Bomb'. He explained his role in The British Computer Society Working Party on the Year 2000 Problem and presented a far from attractive picture in terms of the losses which certain organisations might expect to incur as a result of date changes in computer software and so-called 'legacy systems'.

Amongst the practical examples cited were a major oil company who currently have 85 seabed installations which rely on embedded chips which the manufacturer cannot guarantee will be Year 2000 compliant. The result is that they now expect to have to spend £125,000 in modification costs for each installation. Another possible problem concerned automated traffic lights [remember the chaos in the film 'The Italian Job'? -Ed].

The speaker advised delegates to seek contract guarantees for Year 2000 compliance, and to check particularly for new ranges of machines which have the ability to process old program codes, installed systems in which only the latest version software has been provided by suppliers, and any embedded chips which are over five years old.

In a supporting paper, reproduced from *The British Journal of Administrative Management*, a simple 'Timebomb Test' is presented to examine whether one's own pc is Year 2000 compliant:

'Reset your computer clock to 23.58 pm, 31 December 1999. Then -and this is vital -power off the machine and take a break for a few minutes. Reboot, and see what time and day the machine thinks it is. If you are lucky or have a reasonable new pc you should see the time indicated as a few minutes past midnight on New Year's Day 2000. If you are unlucky you will see any one of a range of Weird dates -and some of your software might have started acting peculiarly'.

The same paper describes how bad things could get, as well as how to 'defuse' the so-called 'bomb':

'Average sized companies in Britain may have to spend as much as 25 to 30 per cent of their IT budget to resolve the problem. And many large companies will find they just don't have the time to update all their systems before the year 2000.'

[Issue 114 (June 1998)]

DELIVERING EFFECTIVE CUSTOMER SERVICE

Recent examples of changes in approach to customer service are highlighted in the Spring 1998 issue of *Customer Focus*, the journal of The Customer Service Network, which explains how health insurance specialists BUPA changed their approach to customer satisfaction measurement, and the May 1998 issue of Customer Service Management which explains how the UK retailing sector, once notorious for poor customer service, is beginning to mend its ways:

'In the old days, BUPA used to survey customer satisfaction by postal self-completion forms. This was cumbersome, had a poor response rate and took three months to get the results. Not surprisingly, a "so what?" attitude was inhibiting action. If there was no root cause analysis, why do the research in the first place?'.

'First, BUPA re-vamped the way in which customer satisfaction was monitored. This included researching the expectation as well as the actual service delivery. Focus groups were established to better understand why customers contacted BUPA and to obtain a reaction about the way they were treated.

For every type of contact experience, the focus groups established the preferred approach from the member and from BUPA. From this, changes to the contact management process were initiated with written follow-ups and telephone acknowledgments'.

'Until recently, at least in the UK, very few grocery food retailers, for example, made any attempt to identify their customers by name, let alone manage a relationship with them. Of course, in particular stores (up-market fashion retailers for instance), some members of staff know their customers by name, and can relate to them as individuals, giving them advice on what to buy, and helping them with problems. But this was not a central plank of these retailers' marketing platform'.

'The reason for this situation in grocery retailing is that, until recently, it was simply not cost-effective to use excellent customer service as a competitive weapon. Retail margins were tight, and marketing spend was better allocated elsewhere. Nor were the technologies available to enable the customer to be treated as an individual cost-effectively. This has changed with maturing of many retail markets, including consolidation amongst suppliers and ending of many opening hours restrictions. Customer service and loyalty marketing have become two of the key themes in retail competition'.

W. Edwards Deming in *'The New Economics'* advised the following:

'An educated customer may have a firm idea about his needs, what he would wish to purchase. He may be able to specify these needs so that a supplier may understand them. A wise customer will nevertheless listen and learn from suggestions from a supplier. They should work together as a system, not as one trying to outdo the other'.

Is this happening? Below *Quality Matters* reviews the Institute of Management Services Financial Sector Specialist Group (FINSEC) one day conference of 19th May, which this year was held' north of the border at Napier University in Edinburgh. Two of the eight presentations focused on the use of IT and simulation to improve customer service, whilst two further presentations examined call centre recruitment and related continuing professional development of call centre staff and management.

There was also a welcome appearance from Lesley Munro-Faure, Executive Director of The National Society for Quality through Teamwork (NSQT) who enlightened delegates as to the potential benefits of improvement through teamwork, which are as applicable to financial services organisations as they are to any other. However, she stressed "it requires changes in culture and changes in behaviour at all levels in the organisation to succeed".

Two papers were selected for review on topics of general interest. These were by The RT. Hon. Viscount Younger of Leckie, Kt. KCVO TD DL, Chairman of The Royal Bank of Scotland and Chancellor of Napier University, and Nigel Hill, Director of Service Leadership.

Customer Service is a Board Issue

Viscount Younger's paper with the above title emphasised the need for customer service to be treated as a boardroom issue with Board members acting as 'very visible ambassadors and models for customer service values'. Their commitment, he said, 'has to be seen as unwavering' and they 'need to demonstrate and live these values through all that they do'. He pointed to the strong parallels which exist between customer satisfaction and people satisfaction:

'Some boards still fail to recognise the paradox of demanding that employees deliverexcellent service to customers, while treating staff badly and refusing to invest in the conditions, support and systems that they need to deliver that service'.

The 'ideal board', he says 'needs dual vision, building long term relationships with customers while still meeting short term targets' arguing that the more satisfied customers are the more likely they will be to remain. He argues the case for customers to be made 'to feel they're in charge' and in particular for measures to be taken 'to let them see behind the scenes' and 'meet the people who help them':

'Just as it's reassuring to see the kitchen in a restaurant, or meet the person doing your operation, breaking down the barriers that separate you from your customers can have a real impact. And that goes for the board too'.

The speaker acknowledged that board time is an expensive commodity, but surely not so expensive as losing touch with market realities. In order for a board to make the most of its opportunities he offered the following suggestion:

'The board has to meet, so why not somewhere where there are customers? Why not combine it with a store or branch visit, or sit in on a focus group? Whatever it takes to expose the board to real customer experience. The board would ensure that it encourages the type of environment where staff feel empowered. You can't order empowerment to happen, you have to foster it'.

He emphasised the fact that great customer service 'is only possible when you'd be comfortable and even proud to let your customers see how you treat your staff' and stresses that it is the board's responsibility to ensure that this happens.

In turning to the role of information technology he explained how the Royal Bank of Scotland had spent around £100 million on a new "front of house" computer system which helps to ensure accuracy at the "point of sale" whilst at the same time saving valuable customer time previously spent completing forms. He argued that the board should, wherever possible, consider just exactly how technology, systems and procedures, will first of all, help customers and secondly add value:

'Above all, you need aboard that won't let processes get in the way of serving the customer. Far too many organisations seek to employ the "Sir Humphreys" or "jobsworths" of this world, where needless bureaucracy generates work for itself, slowing down the service we give'.

The need for the board to constantly test and revise its customer research programmes was stressed, along with the need to discuss customer satisfaction figures frequently and analyse the type of complaints received, not just the quantity:

'The ideal board would recognise and welcome customer complaints as a key source of information. They would monitor and track complaints, and set up systems to investigate the silent majority who leave without warning. They would talk to customers about what they value and what they would most like you to improve. Board members themselves would take an active role in helping to retain the customer'.

Innovation is seen as an expectation whilst inertia anywhere in the organisation is something to be challenged. Board members are encouraged to demand 'why, why, why?' and in particular to talk to customers to ascertain their vision of the future. Coupled with this is the ability to recognise when a market is dying and having the resolve to make a timely exit:

'If you're lucky, and have built a strong relationship with your customers, they will tell you when you're out of touch. Turn round and tell them "we don't do that" and your business will join the ranks of the other dinosaurs. Flexibility of mind is as important as being fleet of foot. Twenty years ago, who could envisage the success of a company like Direct Line, that gas companies would be selling electricity and vice versa, or that your bank account would get you cheaper phone calls?'

In conclusion Viscount Younger spoke of the conference as 'an ideal opportunity to start raising the service standards' whilst the board 'acts as a catalyst for releasing and focusing energy'.

Measuring Customer Satisfaction.

Nigel Hill's presentation, entitled 'Using Customer Surveys to gain an accurate measure of Customer Satisfaction' enlightened delegates about a few home truths regarding customer satisfaction, namely that whilst on average companies lose between 10 and 30 % of their customers every year, and five out of six companies claim that improving customer service is a top priority, 37% do not monitor it at all and a further 40% only do so by reviewing customer complaints. This, he suggested, was totally unsatisfactory, and consequently most organisations needed as a matter of urgency to review the ways in which customer satisfaction was monitored and assessed. Some basic principles were then described for doing this, namely:

(i) Measure importance as well as satisfaction (satisfaction is a relative not an absolute concept so it is necessary to ascertain, relative to what was expected, what was important in the first place i.e. to generate both 'importance ratings' and 'performance ratings' and then compare them).

(ii) Customers define the criteria for measurement (Many organisations determine the criteria for measurement internally, yet all of the evidence suggests that suppliers rarely have an accurate understanding of customer priorities, so detailed discussions are needed to establish what matters most to customers -focus groups in consumer markets or with internal customers or 10 to 20 one to one in-depth interviews in business markets).

(iii) Use random sampling to eliminate bias (a systematic random sample is recommended).

(iv) Use stratified random sampling to reflect customer value (in most business to business markets a representative sample requires customers to be included in proportion to their value, so the customer list needs to be sorted in order of account value and divided into strata with a different sampling fraction applied in each case i.e. if top 20 customers account for 40 % of sales then they represent 40% of the sample).

(v) Sample individuals not just companies (Merely using a 'main contact' at each company will result in a sample based on individuals with whom someone simply has the most contact. A list has to be compiled of all of the individuals affected by the product or service which is representative of the people with whom the organisation deals and those influential in determining the level of customer satisfaction -i.e. if Purchasing Managers are most influential and account for 40% of the decision process across customers generally then they should comprise 40% of the sample).

(vi) Choose appropriate sample size (It is not a larger customer base that creates a requirement for a larger sample size to improve accuracy but the number of segments into which the results have to be broken down -i.e. if a retailer has 90 outlets and wants to compare the relative importance of those outlets in satisfying customers, it will need a minimum sample of 18,000 – assume 200 is the minimum reliable sample size).

(vii) Compensate for phenomenon of 'non response bias' (The lower the response rate, the more the sample is likely to be biased towards the most and the least satisfied customers, but sending out more questionnaires to get more back is no solution as it is the low response rate that causes the problem, so follow-up strategies are often needed to improve response rates - assume at least 50% response rate is needed).

(viii) Do not assume customer will correctly interpret survey purpose (Many customers confuse surveys with selling approaches whilst others correctly distinguish research from selling but still see all research as a brain picking exercise which benefits the supplier rather than the customer, hence it is essential to successfully communicate the fact that the main beneficiary of the survey process is actually the customer).

(ix) Indices must accurately reflect customer perceptions of the organisation (It is essential to end up with an overall index of customer satisfaction which can be monitored from one year to the next so that organisational improvement can be effectively monitored. As customers' satisfaction judgments are heavily influenced by the things that are most important to them, indices must be weighted in favour of their most important requirements -a method is described for doing this).

In describing how to keep customers informed the speaker offered the following advice:

'If you have a very small number of customers in a business market it is most productive to explain the process personally to each one through well briefed customer contact staff However, with even a medium sized customer base and a more selective programme of customer visits this could become very costly but a personal letter to each one would be quite feasible.'

'With a very large customer base a special mailing would be costly, although you should take into account its long term effectiveness in building customer loyalty, compared with a similar spend on advertising. If cost does rule out a special mailing you should at the very least use existing communication channels to inform customers of your CSM programme. This may include printing a special leaflet to be enclosed with an existing mailing or creating space in an existing customer publication such as a newsletter'.

In his speech he spoke of customer delight as a "red-herring" stressing that it was "an absolute fact" that people do not derive delight from normal products and services such as a water supply or mortgage and urged delegates to focus on "doing best what matters most".

He explained how there was "a direct link" between customer loyalty and profitability and highlighted the existence of trend data in the US which confirmed this link. "Only the most satisfied customers will remain loyal", he said, and in his conclusion he suggested that the link between customer loyalty and customer satisfaction was potentially "a powerful predictive tool". For those starting out he recommended examination first at the relation between customer satisfaction and customer loyalty.

[Issue 116 (August 1998)]

IMS SUMMER SCHOOL 1998

The Institute of Management Services celebrated 25 years of its annual Summer School this year at Christ's College, Cambridge from 12th to 14th July. The theme was 'Predicting Tomorrow's Trends Today from Yesterday's Lessons' and as in previous years the presentations were divided into four groups of four papers classified under the headings of 'Quality', 'Technology', 'Productivity' and 'People'.

Workflow and Imaging: a Pioneering Approach

Friends Provident was established just over 165 years ago and specialises in life assurance, savings plans, pension schemes and permanent health insurance. They have around 3600 employees of which some 1100 work in the Customer Services Division which operates from Dorking, Salisbury and Manchester. The paper describes how a pioneeeing workflow system was piloted at the Manchester site and resulted in substantial improvements in both productivity and quality:

'Friends Provident embarked on a study to identify how our time was being spent. This identified that over 40% of time was being taken up by tasks that were designated as non-productive. For example, finding files, matching correspondence, photocopying, collecting and collating printer output -all seen as part of the job but pointing to the need for a radical fresh look at our document management procedures. A study group then went on to define a Target Environment for Customer Services Division to be aiming for. This highlighted new technology as a major component, including slicker data capture tools, improved printing capabilities, and a workflow and document management system at the core driving the processes and providing a solution to automation of many of the non-productive tasks'.

'The incoming work was separated by either distribution channel or region, but because of the effects of peaks and troughs this would often lead to uneven workloads. The practical logistical problems of transferring work across sites to compensate, and then keeping track of what had gone where, made this a last resort option. This in turn led to inconsistent turnaround times. The same logistical problem meant that we were experiencing problems at certain peak times of the year, such as nearing financial year-end when a high proportion of business is received. We were also facing difficulties in coping with growing business because of accommodation, and recruitment constraints, particularly at Dorking. '

With the help of a consultant detailed Statement of Requirements and Invitation to Tender documents were prepared and mailed to the leading providers of workflow and document management technology. These set out the functional requirements needed, details of the projected volumes of the ultimate system, and the technical architecture that Friends Provident wanted to use. From a shortlist of three, DST Systems Inc. of Kansas was finally selected, the US already having some experience of the use of these systems, although their use had been mainly confined to funds administration rather than life assurance which was viewed as being a more difficult application area owing to the number of steps involved e.g. in processing an application:

'The pilot phase was to last up to six months and be very much a learning period. The system was to be implemented without any significant process re-engineering; we had to remember that this was a live implementation with real customers being serviced and so risk was to be minimised. If there were problems and we had re-engineered the process it may not have been clear whether the problems were caused by the re-engineering or the new system itself. For these reasons the measurements for success of the pilot were not set high. If broadly we were using the same number of staff to handle the same amount of business and if we had learnt about the potential of the system for a complete implementation and if it was technically robust, then this would constitute a successful pilot'.

At the end of the pilot period productivity turned out to be just 93% of the previous norm, which on the surface appeared to be poor, except that some important lessons had been learnt in the process. First, it was recognised that staff had been trained too quickly, then it was recognised that the network infrastructure and IT support ability needed to be much stronger:

'Staff had been used to dumb terminals and for pcs they needed to learn about Windows, use mouse etc., as well as navigating this particular system. In hindsight they had been shown the system, but training had not included them being asked to prove they could apply what they had been shown'.

'Mainframe applications at Friends Provident had a very high stability, but this was the first large client server application and showed the comparative fragility of such systems. Also, because the users were totally dependent on the system being available to deliver work to them, there was nothing they could do when it was down, However, the majority of the time, response time from the system, including retrieval of images from optical storage was up to specification'.

They also learned that the system should not be regarded as a solution in its own right but combined with an intensive rethink of certain key processes, and that user roles needed to be redefined:

'Every time a work item is passed from person to person for subsequent action there is a time delay and the inevitable refreshing of what has gone on before. So, paradoxically, despite installing a workflow system it is better for the work not to flow through many users, but to be dealt with by the first recipient. This led us to the conclusion that user roles should be redefined so as to be able to process as much of the work as possible with just one stop. If we could also increase the range of work that each user could perform then we would also have a faster workflow because the work would not be awaiting the availability of a few key staff but had a much wider spread of users to be delivered to'.

With these key learning points, plus the knowledge that this was a work push rather than work pull system, it was decided to set up a Model Office run by a separate group of people on a different site, and restore Manchester to its original system and then use it as a benchmark. This had a working group of 23 staff and took five months to assemble. It ran for six weeks at the end of which time a group of ten people were clearing the work which previously required 23 people.

'We introduced what we termed central scanning which entailed all incoming work to be processed on this system being delivered to a central site for scanning. This would be a pointer to the future, whereby work could be scanned at one location but delivered through the workflow system to any other site where the appropriate skill was available. We could therefore give customers and agents one address, but have the flexibility to use our resources to best advantage'.

Roll out followed using an implementation team of 20 business and systems analysts extracted from the user community and there are currently around 550 production uses of the system in Salisbury, Dorking and Manchester. The benefits gained to date are described as 'very impressive':

'We have seen large increases in new business and have been able to absorb this through far less recruitment than would otherwise have been necessary It has not been necessary to make any redundancies because productivity gains have been matched by growth in business. Productivity has been virtually doubled. Quality has improved by 10%. Consistency across the Offices is assured by the system, and our call centres have immediate access to the case records making dealing with customer enquiries far simpler. Staff are better aware, more customer focused, and are achieving greater job satisfaction through performing broader roles. They are also enjoying enhanced job grades to recognise their improved skills'.

BENCHMARKING AND BALANCED SCORECARDS IN THE FINANCIAL SECTOR

This year's Institute of Management Services (IMS) Financial Sector (FINSEC) conference at The Royal Institute of British Architects in London on March 23rd was devoted specifically to the tools of benchmarking and balanced scorecards.

Chaired by Mike Jackson, Chairman of Results Plus limited and former Chief Executive of Birmingham Midshires Building Society the event featured Janice Kite, Customer Service Manager for 1998 European Best Practice Benchmarking Award Winners Johnson and Johnson Medical as special guest presenter. She was joined by three presenters from the financial sector, Tom Guinane (Head of Policy Servicing for NatWest Life Assurance), Dave Rusk (Senior Business Excellence Consultant for Royal Sun Alliance Life), and Liz Quinn (Corporate Improvement Manager for Halifax plc) and these three presentations are reviewed below.

Benchmarking at NatWest Life

NatWest life was launched on 4th January 1993 and their benchmarking journey described by Tom Guinane dates back to 1995 when the first new business benchmarking exercise was undertaken. This was followed by projects to benchmark underwriting and premium collection in 1996, and claims, mortgage endowment reviews and pensions five year eligibility in 1998. This year a combined underwriting and new business benchmarking exercise has been planned along with a project to benchmark surrenders and maturities.

The process adopted follows a six step procedure of Prepare, Collect, Publish, Analyse, Act and Review and operates in accordance with the protocol developed by the Bancassurers Benchmarking Forum which has the following basic around rules:

(i) Complete honesty even, if it is uncomfortable.

(ii) The data is not to be used or shared outside the group.

(iii) Information behind the hard data is to be shared in order to aid understanding.

(iv) Feedback on actions taken and their impact is to be provided.

The first two of these principles were described by the speaker as "absolutely essential" along with the condition that one could not practically have the

932

second rule without the first. To these he then added the following 'Golden Rule':

"Make sure that the definitions of the data to be collected are agreed, accepted and understood".

This, he said, was very important as the definitions which are used in benchmarking are frequently slightly different from those normally used in the organisation and if they are misunderstood it can be "very difficult to conduct any kind of meaningful analysis". He also emphasised the need for effective communication:

'In order to ensure success there is an overriding need to communicate with your people throughout the whole exercise. It is important they know what is going on, why it is going on and what role they are playing. The people at the sharp end of processes should also be involved in analysing the data and helping to reach conclusions on actions'.

The changes made as a result of benchmarking exercises are, according to the speaker, frequently "not startling", but cumulatively there can be a great deal of benefit. Some examples from NatWest Life include:

* Redesigned direct debit instruction.

* Moved medical underwriting to processing teams.

* Provided advisers with electronic progress update.

* Automatic lodgment of direct debit instructions.

* Automatic receipt and processing of amended or cancelled direct debit instructions.

* Changes to pattern of policy review dates.

* Confirm address details at policy issue stage.

Care was needed, however, when analysing data and deciding what to change, the speaker suggesting that it was all too easy simply to ape other organisations rather than adapt ideas to one's own organisation. In this respect NatWest Life have found process mapping to be an extremely useful tool:

'This identifies any differences to each company's version of the process. There is no right or wrong, but it is important that these differences are recognised so that the data gathering and analysis can take them into account. Also, the differences in processes are often a prompt for companies to change their processes'.

The speaker's concluding message was therefore "adapt not adopt".

The presentation prompted a number of questions from delegates, beginning with an enquiry as to the extent to which NatWest Life had bench marked other industries for best practice. In reply the speaker confirmed that NatWest had approached the public utilities informally and that plans were underway to benchmark their collection processes for payments and arrears.

This was followed by a request for some hints on benchmarking team selection to which the speaker advised "the people engaged in the process must be involved not project managers imported from outside".

Another delegate observed that many of the changes concerned direct debits and asked if there was some kind of message to be inferred from this. The speaker said that there was no particular inference intended, but did highlight the high level of customer sensitivity associated with direct debit processes and used this reasoning to justify the quite considerable emphasis that NatWest had placed on this area.

There was then a request for advice on the selection of companies to benchmark against and suggested that this was essentially process driven. He was then asked how benchmarking stood out from other techniques and replied:

"It is based on hard factual evidence rather than applying theory from a book. It is also a window into other organisations even though it can be unsettling and bring you home with a jolt".

Balanced Scorecards and the Business Excellence Model

Dave Rusk, who is an assessor for both the UK Quality Awards and the North West Quality Award, explained how when used well and in tandem the Balanced Scorecard and the Business Excellence Model were complementary frameworks which together formed a very powerful lever for improvement. They were not, as some appeared to believe, competing frameworks or mutually exclusive alternatives:

'Both have the advantage of being wide ranging systems, helping companies see the world through the eyes of all stakeholders. Both help companies understand the need to look at "upstream" activities as well as "downstream" results'.

He described the origins of both approaches, drawing attention first to the change in the way the Business Excellence Model has been applied by organisations since its inception i.e. from a little used instrument for the purposes of gaining an award to a diagnostic tool and now, more recently, as a driver for the planning process and a guide for capital expenditure decisions. Then, he explained how the Balanced Scorecard likewise serves as more than just a measurement system:

'The power of the Scorecard lies in its range and balance: perceptions and indirect internal measures; "leading" indicators to do with things happening now and "lagging" indicator/results which show the outcomes of past actions. It is a means of defining business strategy -indeed the Scorecard should tell the story of what the strategy is. Having a strategy is a prerequisite to successful use of a Scorecard'.

The relationship between the two approaches was described in terms of the analogy between a watch and a calendar i.e. both are instruments to measure time but they are viewed in different ways and at different intervals:

'The Business Excellence Model is comprehensive and companies compare themselves to its stretching vision of organisational excellence. The Balanced Scorecard adds discipline to the results section of the Business Excellence Model and companies who use it compare their performance to their own plan expectations. Assessment against the Business Excellence Model is usually done annually whilst the Balanced Scorecard is usually updated monthly'.

'Balanced Scorecards are typically used monthly to analyse performance against plans and to help identify where corrective action is required or perhaps where the strategy itself needs to be changed. The Scorecard can also be used to link individual reward and incentivisation to objectives and as the basis for capital expenditure decisions'.

Within Royal Sun Alliance Life the two approaches are used both at company and at business unit level. All plans are tested against the Business Excellence Model and the organisation has some 200 trained assessors, 25 of which are dedicated to external awards. All twenty business units are now self-assessed annually. The Scorecard on the other hand is the only piece of briefing information which is despatched prior to monthly review meetings and at business unit level it is used both to monitor performance and as a framework to cascade objectives.

Following the presentation the speaker was asked why the Balanced Scorecard was necessarily linked to the Results side of the Business Excellence Model rather than the Enablers. This, he said, was due to the leading and lagging concept which was unique to the Results section of the Model.

The Halifax Balanced Scorecard

Liz Quinn's presentation described how the concept of the Balanced Scorecard was introduced at the Halifax in 1993 with line implementation following in 1996. Application has since been extended through the development of corporate performance measurement into a 'scorecard framework' and by building the concept into individual planning, appraisal and reward across Head Office.

She explained how prior to 1993 the organisation was weak in terms of its measurement strategy and this was important in an age when non-financial performance was beginning to be viewed more and more as a key to profits, as against the purely historical measures of profits, assets and cost/income ratio. The Balanced Scorecard was seen to be an ideal instrument to create the right balance between retention of aspects of financial and procedural performance and the need to bring customer satisfaction and people satisfaction measures into being at branch level.

Introduction of the Balanced Scorecard at retail network level brought with it a need for a different form of management approach and style. In particular it required the performance of a person, a team or the Halifax as a whole to be questioned in four ways:

(i) Financial and business: Is progress towards the Mission maintained in terms of key results that need to be achieved?

(ii) Customer: Is there a clear and acted upon understanding of what it takes to delight the customer?

(iii) Process: Does the way things are done internally help in achieving excellent service and enable it to be done superbly?

(iv) People: Are we adequately geared to support each other with the expertise, understanding and teamwork needed for a good job to be done now and in the future?

The speaker suggested that these questions affected everyone and needed to form the basis for how every job is tackled. This led to the Balanced Scorecard being used as a foundation for performance planning which has three principal elements i.e. departmental planning (around the current operating plan), individual planning (derived from the departmental plan), and ongoing review (of plans throughout the year). The Balanced Scorecard is thus used as a template to ensure that departmental and individual objectives cover everything that needs to be covered.

Interviews with senior managers led to agreement and approval for critical success factors after some persistence, although what is important will vary by department. Each department thus develops its own scorecard on the basis of what is important to it. There are now 1000 business units using the Network Balanced Scorecard following piloting in parallel with the existing system. The present system is pc based with laptops for area managers and benefits claimed for the Scorecard approach are as follows:

* Greater focus on customers and staff.

* Raised awareness and understanding of the new agenda.

* A common platform and language for performance.

* Clear linkages to performance management.

* Improved feedback and action planning.

These benefits have since inspired Head Office to reappraise its role in the organisation and acknowledge that it needed to view itself as the foundation of a customer focused business rather than simply the top of a command and control structure. In this area implementation has followed a similar approach to that used by the retail networks i.e. with individuals' scorecards being written by the individuals themselves rather than the managers, and beginning with the planning process.

In looking to the future Ms. Quinn described the Balanced Scorecard as "as much a change management initiative as a performance measurement initiative in its own right" and explained how financial objectives were expanding with the development of the Corporate Balanced Scorecard, which would also incorporate environmental performance management.

This latter topic clearly stimulated some interest amongst delegates which led ultimately to the question 'How does a bank measure environmental performance?' In her reply Ms. Quinn gave two examples of initiatives which the Halifax was in the process of evaluating namely the placing of recycling bins in offices and energy efficient valuations on houses.

[Issue 136 (May 2000)]

RIDING THE MOMENTUM OF CHANGE

Change management was the theme of the Institute of Management Services' 21st FINSEC conference held at The Royal Institute of British Architects on May 9th.

Five papers are reviewed, with two papers on Knowledge Management by Tim Connolly (one of two co-founders of the consultancy, Partners for Change) and Victoria Murgatroyd (Practice Group Leader for Know, the Knowledge Management Consultancy of The Post Office Consultancy), and papers by Dr. Phillippa Collins of Heriot-Watt University on 'The Role of the Manager in an Automated Workplace', and Gary Wigglesworth, Change and Programme Director of Egg on 'Changing the Change Community: the Ultimate Challenge in the New E-world'.

937

First, however, the paper by Maggie Gill of the Client Services Division of Zurich Financial Services, describing the application of Production Management in the financial sector, is reviewed as an example of fast-tracking into tangible benefits.

Production Management in Action

Production Management (PM) is a relatively recent concept in the financial sector with Zurich Financial Services being one of its pioneers. It is defined as 'a set of common processes, tools and techniques, and behaviours which provide a consistent framework for managing work and resources' and has been adapted for use in the financial sector by EG Consultancy with whom Zurich have a close partnership.

The technique essentially involves the adaptation of manufacturing workflow principles to office and service environments. Its seven key components may be listed as follows:

* Measure workloads and staff skills available

* Plan to proactively match workloads to skills and drive continuous improvement

* Appoint a Team Manager to map out a daily work plan

* Allocate work in bite-sized chunks according to business priorities and available skills and resources

* Monitor by frequently communicating progress against the daily plan to drive performance and encourage achievement of the plan

* Analyse to encourage a culture of continuous improvement

* Monitor sustained continuous improvement

Application of these elements means that Team Managers devote 75% of their time to 'walking the job' and getting to know their teams to coach and encourage consistent pace and quality of performance:

'The measurement phase identifies potentially uncomfortable issues about where people are spending their time, for example, where £20 an hour people are performing £5 an hour tasks. It provides no hiding place and challenges the extent to which people are working or training on activities which really do meet customer and business needs'.

'PM enabled Client Services to confront issues like over-promising at recruitment, where the reality of the role requirements often don't match the expectations raised. New style contracts, like term-time or twilight shifts,

with stripped out levels of employee benefits could be used to maximise our productivity and use of systems and buildings as well as saving on costs. PM also rationalises expectations of training and development making sure we train for business needs not for personal preference'.

Application is not without its problems as the paper illustrates, and considerable skill is needed to convince people that their jobs are not being devalued but rather that there is a shift away from being multi-task skilled towards concentrating on single or fewer tasks. Equally some managers may perceive their roles as being reduced in both scope and size and so an effort is needed here to reposition understanding of the Team Manager's role so that the focus is geared towards being with the team as against continually being in meetings.

The technique was tested in June in Client Services' Life and Pensions Servicing and one of its technical teams. Benefits have included:

* Next day processing with backlogs reduced from thousands to nil

* A significant quality improvement stemming from reduced queries and rework which has helped to sustain increased pace and consistency

* 30% improvements in efficiency with average response times to clients improving by over 100%

Ten sections across Swindon are now working with PM, the first phase of implementation having been completed on 30th November.

Ms. Gill was asked how morale was maintained during the implementation and she explained how positive redeployment had been favoured with no redundancies. Staff were consulted all through the process and there was active support throughout from the human resources function. The complete process was facilitated by a strategic decision at the outset to stop recruiting administrators.

Managing Knowledge

Tim Connolly's presentation focused particularly on the area of knowledge transfer, 'and contained the underlying message of 'beware them there consultants'. He explained how after talking with managers, particularly those who had worked with large consultancies, there was widespread frustration about the fact that consultants frequently seek to apply standardised techniques of knowledge transfer even though all organisations are unique. He described this practice as "a good way of damaging the relationship with the client", damage which was then compounded by the common tendency "to load projects with as many consultants as possible'.

Consultant luring, he explained, frequently incurs a massive premium (a make-up of some 300 to 400%), which he argued "had to be justified by value":

"The organisation must be left with sustaining mechanisms without the organisation becoming dependent on consultants".

He described how it was perfectly possible to manage a seven figure project with just one 'consultant' providing a framework and support and facilitating team working without recourse to the huge sums which are sometimes charged. The key is moving from a so called 'expert advice' approach to one of leverage:

"The traditional view is to provide a deliverable, such as a report or a specification, along with assistance in implementation. Often you can see what you are getting with this, but in practice it is a closed box solution with lots of risks".

He suggested that rather than consultants taking prime responsibility for delivery their role is often better placed as a "shadow workstream leader". There was no reason why this "shadow" concept should not contain an element of deliverability, but the primary focus would be on enabling the client team to perform their task rather than the deliverable itself.

In looking to the future he spoke of the need for flexible resourcing and for consultancy to be viewed as "an outsourced competence". Life, he said, was not about a string of change projects, as much of what is learned from change projects can be applied to day to day management. What was important, however, was the recognition of the skills sets associated with change management and it was with this that the basis for future outsourcing arrangements with consultancies should be structured.

The presentation by Victoria Murgatroyd was supported by a 'Residential School Student Handbook' paper entitled 'Managing Knowledge', published by The Open University Business School, which describes the Post Office Consulting case study in some detail. This highlights the recognition on the part of the senior management of Post Office Consulting that 'a focus on knowledge is critical to its performance and that the ability to innovate quickly in response to changing market demands requires knowledge to be mobilised'.

Post Office Consulting (formerly Royal Mail Consulting) views itself as a "hub" of knowledge in the Post Office that 'will lead in facilitating development of knowledge management in Post Office and knowledge management products for the world Post Office market'. With around 1300 full time and associate consultants and a turnover of around £60 million a year they are unquestionably the largest 'internal consultancy' in the UK and their 'new management approaches' have encapsulated the knowledge theme.

This has involved an abandonment of the notion that decisions could only be made by passing them up the line i.e. checking everything up with the boss, and the introduction of 'location dependent working' whereby consultants are no longer required to have a physical base in London, Swindon or Chesterfield, but are able to work remotely in 'virtual teams':

'As project teams are less constrained by the physical requirements of location, they can be formed from a more appropriate mix of consultants representing a broader range of skills, disciplines and parts of the business. The use of new information and communication technologies (ICTs) is therefore fundamental in underpinning the way Post Office Consulting has transformed itself into a more fluid, networked organisation enabling consultants and their knowledge to come together for client projects in ways that would not have been possible under the former structure'.

Under their 'Knowledge Programme', which was instigated in 1997, consultants have the status of 'knowledge workers' whose value to the organisation lies in their ability to apply knowledge and expertise to client projects. Thus, the ICTs do not serve so much as 'knowledge depositories' quite so much as mechanisms which link people together and facilitate communication i.e. they link people to people and people to information.

An important component of this is TeamWeb, a Lotus Notes based tool which has been developed to facilitate discussions and decision making in a 'virtual' working environment, and which the speaker estimated would have saved the organisation £100,000 had it been deployed on a major project two years ago.

The catalyst for managing the knowledge core process at the practitioner level is the 'professional head' who is responsible for co-ordinating the knowledge activities which form part of the group's Balanced Scorecard and for guiding the professional development of the group as a whole:

'The professional head of each practitioner group (or their designated representative) is a member of the Knowledge Process Forum which meets bi-monthly and is the forum for managing the knowledge core process across the groups. A significant part of this work is to ensure that the elements of the Knowledge Programme are supporting the aims of Post Office Consulting to work as a knowledge organisation. To this end a knowledge process model has been formulated to guide the various elements of the Knowledge Programme. It is a cyclical model consisting of four stages -capture, deploy, use, review'.

Ms. Murgatroyd elaborated further on the use tools, referring specifically to the 'After Action Reviews' which Post Office Consulting 'had borrowed' from the US Army and which they had been using now for around 18 months which were "very popular", and Knowledge Interviews which had proved to be "an extremely powerful tool for looking at the ways people think". She also explained the role of Knowledge Mentors, which had now been introduced in 20 out of the 23 practitioner groups, following requests by users for a single point of contact responsible for the Knowledge Excellence Framework.

She was asked about how successful Post Office Consulting had been at deploying information and guarded against information overload. In her answer she said that the key to information management was timeliness and resisting the temptation to simply release information "willy nilly". She also explained how the organisation's knowledge database now had individual capabilities inbuilt enabling an effective input to be applied to training and development activities on an annual basis.

The Role of the Manager in an Automated Workplace

Dr. Phillippa Collins, who is currently one of the UK's leading researchers in call centre management, modified the title of her presentation to 'The Role of the HUMAN Manager in an Automated Workplace', in order to reflect the importance of the human dimension, which in her view is all too often ignored in the constant pursuit of automation. "Do we really want a 24 hour society?" she asked, questioning whether the round the clock availability of services is desirable, or simply the result of the work driving the people:

'Radio took 38 years to reach 50 million users. TV took only 13 years to attain the same volume. The Internet has taken just 4 years. According to experts in this field, by 2003 E-Business will account for 40% of global GDP. If this use of Internet technology results in companies achieving more consistency, reliability and quality, and in providing a level of customer service -the product or service arriving in the right place at the right time at the right cost –then we will all benefit. There are certainly benefits in adopting the model of the virtual organisation. The question we must ask is: if that model is good for business, is it necessarily good for us as a society?'

She was notably critical of the financial sector for its role in forcing people to behave in the way which suits big business:

'Some banks and building societies are discouraging the use of coins and notes by charging for over-the-counter transactions. They are charging us for withdrawing our money from cash points. They give discounts for the use of direct debits. They are slowly pressurising us to operate in a way that minimises their costs but increases our inconvenience'.

She foresees the development of interactive television as 'a popular sales channel' but questions whether the resulting 'self service' mode really will be in everyone's best interests:

'Dot.Com companies are all very well, but lack of attention to basic processes such as delivery led to many disappointments last Christmas. Is this progress? By the time we are all networked and linked to the Internet by whatever channel-digital TV, computer, or whatever new technology is on offer, the number of "traditional" outlets for accessing goods and services will have withered. This then opens the opportunity for big business to impose monopolistic practices against which we have no weapons as we have already destroyed the alternatives'.

The 'fantastically clever' information systems which are now being deployed to run our businesses have, in her opinion, 'resulted in antiseptic environments where people are treated as a nuisance, and someone has to be responsible:

'Next time you order something from the Web or use e-mail instead of telephoning a friend, ask yourself whether the convenience outweighs the loss of social contact and camaraderie. What is the long-term price of our self-service community? Business professionals could have an important influence in this debate concerning the future of our society. Are you prepared to join in?'

Dr. Collins has just completed a study of work allocation in BT where she questions the role of the manager vis a vis the engineer, once all the engineers have laptops, as will be the case at the end of this year. "The engineer will represent the company, not the manager", she suggested. She is currently running workshops on behalf of BT throughout the UK, has visited six Life and Pensions companies, and is working with Shell Expro on the application of Smart Working concepts in the oil industry. Her latest report 'The Evolving Call Centre' is due to be published in the June issue of the journal *'People Management'*.

Changing the Change Community

The paper by Gary Wigglesworth provides an interesting contrast to that by Dr. Collins, describing the virtual change management community as 'the key to enabling continuing excellence' and highlights the five 'competency communities' into which it is divided as follows:

* Navigation (enabling excellence in management and leadership processes, transformation, strategic analysis, strategic planning and delivery, and journey navigation and management)

* Organisational effectiveness (enabling excellence in enablement, leadership, ownership, organisational design, and cultural development)

* Technology (enabling excellence in requirements definition, technology awareness, and systems and functional architecture)

* Process (enabling excellence in methods, measurement, implementation, dress rehearsal, and process development)

* Project Analytics (enabling excellence in project management, methodologies, communications, generic soft and hard skills, and scheduling and planning)

The paper describes how each member of Egg's internal consultancy fits into one of these 'competency communities', each of which has a coach who identifies the skills contained in a particular community and manages the transference of these skills. It is explained how, with this structure and people in place, an average project which may normally take up to a year to deliver can be delivered in a quarter of the time:

'Anyone can have an idea for change, however the idea must be owned by a sponsor. The sponsor will be responsible for the overall implementation of the change, including budget and helping to remove issues and risks, which impact the overall delivery of the project. The idea will often have been originally generated by the research undertaken within the internal consultancy. The idea will be discussed with their Journey Manager from the internal consultancy. As the Journey Manager has the holistic view of the full programme, a decision can be made whether to complete a feasibility study'.

'When requesting funding for feasibility, the idea will initially be approved from an IT architecture perspective and then from a strategic perspective. Resource with the requisite skill sets and knowledge are then assigned to the feasibility study. The scope of the project is identified, the impact of its implementation identified and cost benefit analysis is completed to identify the viability of the idea'.

'The resource allocated to the feasibility study will normally continue through to full implementation. They will identify the requirements in more detail, produce functional specification, technical specifications and testing documentation. The project manager allocated will report on budget, milestones, risks and issues, and dependencies to the sponsor and Journey Manager. The Journey Manager will then be able to view the full programme of milestones, dependencies, risks and issues, and dependencies and manage these at a programme level. The sponsor will help remove obstacles within the project and ensure the idea is delivered to timescales, cost and quality. As the project moves through its lifecycle, resource will roll on and off as required and assigned to other projects when not fully utilised'.

Chapter Fourteen

Improving Quality in Education

It could be argued that education should be the starting point for both the appreciation and application of quality. Yet experience appears to suggest that this area has been one of the most neglected both before and after the 1990s. Leading lights in this area have included most notably American consultant Myron Tribus who, as a regular speaker at BDA events has spoken at length about the need for reform. Other commentary may be noted from UK consultant Jon Choppin, whose contribution on education was gratefully received for publication in Quality Matters in 1993 and Edward de Bono, whose article is featured in Chapter 16.

In British education the 1990s may be remembered as an era of command and control for schools with an emphasis on mass inspection driven by the regulatory body Ofsted whose intervention was notably despised by Deming practitioners. On a more positive note, however, there has been a drive for improvement inspired at least in part by the Business Excellence Model (ref. Foxdenton School case study in Chapter 3, and the St. Mary's College case study from Northern Ireland reported in October 1996 and May 2000).

In addition to the various Deming related articles the compilation below includes notably the IQA's education conference of 1993 entitled 'The Teacher as Manager' which considered the application of ISO9000 (at that time BS5750) and the piloting of IIP in the education sector, and various articles on quality in higher education featured at the Sheffield Hallam conferences of 1995 and 1996 and the 11th World Productivity Conference in Edinburgh in 1999.

BRITISH DEMING FORUM: A NEW EDUCATIONAL PHILOSOPHY

Simple as A B C

Considerable emphasis was placed throughout the British Deming Association Annual Forum on the importance of bringing the quality philosophy into the field of education, To show how this has been done in practice quality counsellor Myron Tribus known for his innovative interpretation of Deming's work in the US, described the application of quality management in the education system with the assistance of two high school pupils Lisa Marie Polk and Omen Wild, representing the Mount Edgecumbe School in Alaska, where a process of transformation has been taking place.

Myron Tribus has made it clear that he has 'very little patience with those who persist in talking about the "education industry" because 'the metaphor is misleading and the attempt to bring market forces to bear in education runs counter to our understanding of what education is all about'. The school is not a factory and the student is not the product, rather the education of the student.

Experience to date, he says, has shown that when properly adapted quality management can make as great a difference in education as it has in industry, but it is necessary to make some important redefinitions both of quality and of management.

In industry quality 'is what makes it possible for your customer to have a love affair with your product or service. It is possible to produce a temporary infatuation by telling lies about the product or service, by lowering the price or by adding clever little features, but these will not last. It takes quality experiences to sustain devotion'.

In education, quality 'is what makes learning a pleasure and a joy. Some measures of student performance may be increased by threats, by competitions for grades or by prizes, but the attachment to learning will be unhealthy. It takes a quality experience to create an independent learner'.

In industry, the people work in a system and the job of the manager is to work on the system to improve it continuously with their help. In education the teachers work in a system and the job of the Principal (Superintendent or Department Head) is to work on the system to improve it, continuously with their help. Also the students study and learn in a system and the job of the teacher is to work on the system to improve it continuously with their help.

Joy, however, is ever changing and what is thrilling at one stage becomes infantile at another. Hence the teacher needs to be ever alert to engage the students in a discussion of what constitutes a quality experience. David Langford, a teacher at Mount Edgecumbe School in Sitka, Alaska, has reported that he has often devoted as much as two weeks to a discussion with his class concerning what it takes for them to have a quality experience.

'Teachers with conventional experience may consider this to be "a terrible waste of time", but the evidence is there to show that once students understand and accept what it means to do quality work, they learn with such speed and effectiveness that they more than make up for the time spent in defining a quality experience'.

Dr. Deming has made it plain that he is against the practice of giving an annual evaluation to all employees and Myron Tribus has added that 'if the evaluation process is so damaging to adults, think what it does to children'. It classes half of each generation as 'inferior' and what is worse they believe it for life (as witnessed by the number of people who believe they are no good at maths or cannot draw):

" The only legitimate excuse for examinations is to enable teacher and student to get together and decide what to do next. Examinations for the purpose of ranking are very destructive both for quality and for people".

This was later qualified, however, with an admission that there could be a case for random examination testing for the purpose of evaluating the effectiveness of the education system, so long as this was not designed to grade students. The use of outcomes 'as a basis to judge, reward and chastise portions of the system of education', which has formed 'a cornerstone of President Bush's approach to the improvement of education' in his America 2000 programme, was firmly condemned.

These ideas were further reinforced in a presentation by Theresa Hicks, a teacher from Wilmington City Schools, Wilmington, Ohio, which explained how Deming's 'methods of Profound Knowledge' had been applied to the teaching of young children in the seven to eight year old age range.

She explained how, rather than giving stickers or rewards to only one or two students she establishes how nice it would be if they didn't have to try to out do each other to compete for some prize from her which would be 'very subjective' and make their subsequent own feelings of personal value clearly dependent on whether they were lucky enough to win her 'lottery of judgment':

'As a class we decide that if I must choose one student to be recognized for a special prize like student of the month they will put their names in a jar and we'll treat it for what it is: a lottery'.

947

Recognizing that children love stickers she tells them that if they feel they want a sticker or want to give someone a sticker as a way of showing they like them or what they have done they are free to get them:

'The problem is not with having stickers, but in who gives them and why. As teachers we must stop ranking students and dishing out rewards and punishments. Once we have adopted the Deming philosophy, and understand that ranking results in sub-optimisation of the system then never again will this be done'.

Competition is seen to have a role but only in so far as it is 'part of the fun', as for example in games:

'Winners and losers alike must maintain the competition is present in a non-threatening manner just because the act of competing is what makes it fun'.

[Reference the 'Olympic ideal' -Ed].

It is noted that students appreciate 'a feeling of self-control not evidenced in other classes'.

Questions and Answers

As previously reported a feature of the Forum was a substantial allocation of time to afford delegates the opportunity to question the speakers, in particular Myron Tribus.

Lisa and Omen were asked if they still took state exams and they said yes but only because the state rules require it. The school does not specifically teach what is on the test schedule and test results often show this, but the evidence is clear that this is more than compensated for in other areas.

They were asked when they can start learning these techniques and it was pointed out that at Mt. Edgecumbe pupils start at 13 or 14, but Omen said he would like to have learned earlier. One delegate suggested that as the Mt. Edgecumbe system was unusual outside, perhaps this could have a detrimental effect on their careers and they accepted that it was likely that some could suffer from this. [This happens with the Rudolf Steiner system - Ed].

The subject of resistance to change at the school was raised and Omen accepted that he, along with some others, 'had almost rejected TQM because they thought it 'was being rammed at them by administrators', but when this approach stopped it caught on quickly'.

On the subject of discipline Myron Tribus suggested that by comparison with a standard group of 200 teenagers where about 15 to 20 would usually need discipline, disciplinary problems were 'very low'.

Another delegate questioned how, without ranking, it could be decided who should go to university, and the reply here was that whilst test scores are often lower than normal, students compile a portfolio to illustrate the type of work at which they are strong and this 'blows away the administrator's barrier'. Myron Tribus quietly announced that Lisa had in fact turned down a place at Harvard as she wished to study quality management and added that 'admission tests applied by universities are designed to test if you can survive at the university'. They have 'nothing to do with life and work'.

Myron Tribus was then asked what he felt about the UK Government's intention to 'introduce more testing and grading than ever before' in four stages of the education system, and he said that he 'could not think of anything more damaging' for the nation's children. These tests were, he said, 'expensive, destructive and not even validated for the purposes they are trying to achieve'. Anonymous statistical sampling was, he thought, a much better solution. The Government's system was 'terrible'.

When asked to comment on the Japanese system, however, he pointed out that the Japanese are not exactly pleased with their education system. Many Japanese feel that it is too rigid and highly competitive. Dr. Deming, though, made the important point that although there was pressure, great pains are taken to ensure that no Japanese child is ever humiliated, in stark contrast to the West.

Finally the question was asked 'how do you break the stupidity of inspection in education?' Myron Tribus replied by saying

"You know better so you've got to speak out. The teachers don't want it so you have got allies".

He recommended that people 'get politically active' on this issue.

[Issue 50 (February 1993)]

TOTAL QUALITY EDUCATION

Quality Matters is pleased to feature an article kindly submitted by Total Quality Consultant Jon Choppin who, following 20 innovative years in comprehensive education, moved via the Ford Motor Company to become a leading exponent of TQM in industry. He briefly considers the lessons that education might learn from modern industrial practice.

The Ways of Industry

British industry, as with so much of our present society, is busy finding its way to a more sensible, profitable and successful operating culture.

Education, in undergoing more fundamental change than in previous decades, looks for inspiration to industry. What would be disastrous, would be the adoption of the many out-of-date practices, that parts of British Industry still foster. There is, of course, much that is good, and many appropriate lessons to be learnt from the manufacturing environment, but such lessons must be taken whole, that is with a full understanding of how and why particular methods achieve success, and how they become part of an overall culture. There is a need for an academic approach. All practice must be founded in theory. All theory must be woven into a cohesive and collective understanding of a complete learning and caring operation, that we call 'school'.

Total Quality Approach

In industry, this approach is often described as Total Quality, and it now has many founding fathers, each of whom have contributed to a reservoir of ideas and concepts; Deming and Crosby from the USA, Ishikawa and Taguchi from Japan, John Oakland and Frank Price from the UK.

The successful company, considers this reservoir, and dips into the theory to develop a strategy for their own development. The emphasis on 'Quality' is not what it appears, at first glance. The theory actually moves away from the out-dated concept of 'inspection'. Industry is no longer obsessed with the checking of finished results, adding the 'tick' of Quality. Rather, Quality is seen as a concept only possible in the finished result, if it is tightly managed in the processes leading to that result.

The Japanese gurus have taken this further, and Taguchi, perhaps the most influential, perceives Quality stemming as much from planning and preparation, as from the performance of the processes. Quality, therefore, is dynamic, rather than static. The concept has been unhooked from the single dimension of product quality, results-based. In educational terms, we become obsessed with testing and tabulating results. This is a one-dimensional approach.

Three Dimensional Quality

The second dimension can be achieved by placing emphasis, and indeed effort and resource, on the processes that operate to produce the results. We have scope to organise these processes how we will, and by first appreciating exactly which processes are operating, devising tight control mechanisms, if we ensure that we are always improving, we can obtain what appears to be the best. Results will improve, even though we now place less emphasis on them.

However, we rarely establish anything from scratch. We enter institutions that are busy operating. They already have a culture, a set of values, a way of doing things. The processes, therefore, appear set, and the mind is restrained within what is perceived to be acceptable. It is only by unhooking the mind from this set way, by seeing that we could be moving in different directions, using different processes, dwelling on different priorities, that we can enter the third dimension.

Here we are not restricted to the 'normal' way of doing things. We can use other processes. We can adopt other practices, other structures, other organisational patterns. It is truly dynamic, we don't have to do things, to find how they work. We are able to conduct analyses of different functions, to predict the outcomes, and discard those that are unsatisfactory, before we have actually put anything in motion. Thinking comes before planning, planning before preparation, evaluation before doing.

Unnatural Practices

This will never occur naturally. All change has the inbuilt difficulty of being less well-understood than the status-quo. Only the very confident are prepared to sacrifice the known, for the unknown. Fearing change is integral with man's instinct for survival. Such different ways of thought are unnatural, and cannot be achieved successfully without a cultural change.

Three ingredients are essential:

*The dreamer

*The direction

*The manager

The Total Quality environment is one in which there is a consensus of values and views of the purpose of the organisation. In industry, this is easy. We are here to generate wealth. It is the lack of a consensus, with regard to the meaning of 'education', let alone its practice, that creates alienation, frustration and high internal energy costs.

(Internal energy is the energy a company expends to business with itself. With different people pursuing different goals, having different values and being judged by different criteria, much work done by one, is partially undone by another).

In the Total Quality company, the consensus of objective is achieved by lifting 'customer service' to be the ultimate concern of the company, and therefore everyone within it. With a common purpose, the internal customer relationships are identified, and actively pursued, in the belief that the external customer can only be well served if the internal customer's requirements and expectations are met.

One of the major tasks of education is to define its customer base, and perceive from the array of students, parents, governors, local authorities, potential employers, government ministers, exactly what is required and expected, by whom. Many in industry are finding that there can be no real quality, without a negotiation. Every quality relationship is a meeting of minds; two experts coming together to thrash out a relationship for their mutual good. Hence, this has become a generally accepted definition of Quality:

"Quality -meeting the negotiated requirements and expectations of the customer".

So without customer relationships, quality is impossible to achieve. Negotiation has to be achieved before the actual process delivers the Quality results. (Retrospective negotiation still occurs in industry; it's called apologising!). Negotiation is the interchange of thoughts and ideas two parties come to the negotiation with different requirements, and different knowledge and experience, this neutral stance is imperative, if both are to feel that the outcome is for the mutual good. Developing systems for effective communication is essential. Equally, though, we need the appropriate tools. Careful use of jargon and defining words and concepts, so that there is a common understanding, is as important as providing the time and the place for such communications. Is this a dream?

The Dreamer.

Ancient societies had dreamers, as indeed do those primitive tribes still able to survive on this planet, despite the uneven trade of 'your forest' for 'our civilisation and diseases'. The dreamer has an important function to perform, to perceive a different, better world. Such a person is worth feeding and clothing. He/she could prove to be the salvation of the tribe.

Today's dreamer needs to be educated. By understanding the present, as well as the potential future, the dreamer can perceive the direction in which the organisation must move. However, the dreamer will always partially inhabit this new world, and will always see everything from a different perspective to his/her colleagues. The dreamer must therefore be tolerant and tolerated, but above all, he/she must be enthusiastic. Such enthusiasm is born out of the certainty, that eventually others will understand the dreams.

Pragmatism is not traditionally an aspect of the dreamer's approach. Today's dreamer needs to be managed, so that our complex society can be helped to achieve the dream.

The Direction.

Following several decades of goal setting, the message is now clear. What is required is cultural change', rather than just add-ons, to our present way of doing things. The move to Total Quality is a move towards perfection, and whilst we never arrive at perfection, it will always be a sensible direction in which to travel.

Never-ending improvement now becomes the driving force. Change will cease to be a one-off, but will become the ever-present way of life. Developing a community that understands this and can come to appreciate and feel secure within such an environment, is an essential prerequisite.

A clear appreciation of the present culture, its values and the actual practice it encourages and supports, is another prerequisite. Only by knowing where we are today, can we adequately move in a controlled direction. This may be particularly difficult to achieve in some of our bigger schools that have diffuse organisation. Some have departments, functions, even buildings, that have made them a melee of conflicting cultures. These apply different pressures on those that work within them. Of course, the students bring their own cultural values to the party, as well, creating an array of diverse motivations and priorities. What a challenge! What an opportunity! What gain there will be for everyone as we move to a more unified culture, where the good of others and the beliefs and values of others become as important as our own.

The Manager.

Total Quality has to be managed, and managed with great care and understanding. Management is yet another concept that is not MISunderstood, rather it is just NOT understood. Few take the trouble to define what is meant by a manager, and those that do conflict in their definitions. Mostly, each individual is left to 'manage' according to his/her own working definition. Most believe themselves to be good managers, whilst shaking their heads in despair at their colleagues.

Defining exactly what should be managed by whom, is the future challenge for schools. Industry is busy coming to terms with such questions. Many of the more successful companies are collapsing tall edifices of multi-layered management structures, to replace them with flat organisations, having a clearly defined senior management function (to be planning for the longer term), management function (to be responsible for the short term) and everybody (to be managing now, effectively, within prescribed definitions and values). Some wear more than one hat, but have to be clear which hat is being worn at any one time. Thus when a student and the headmaster both walk near a piece of litter, it behoves both of them (equally) to pick it up.

The Messages.

Much emphasis will be placed on the function of managing education. In this discussion, three thoughts are recommended. Management is a pro-active concept, always most successful when conducted forwards, that is in advance, planning, initiating and getting it right first time. Old-fashioned management techniques relied upon checking after the event, dealing with failure, and regulating processes already in action. The modern manager is a facilitator or enabler. The manager establishes a process that has all the ingredients to be self-regulating and with a high probability of success. This is the basis of Total Quality Management.

A large consensus of understanding and belief is necessary for successful TQM. Indeed, TQM has been referred to as Management by Common Sense. If the outcomes of such management are not perceived as common sense to those involved, they will impose a veto. They just won't perform, or if they do it will be at an unacceptably high cost.

There are no real differences between industry and education. Much can be learnt from each other. By looking 'academically' at the modern ideas and concepts that are now being introduced into industry, rather than slavishly following those that have been in use during the last forty years, we can quickly move towards Total Quality Education.

[This issue is currently topical with the very recent pronouncements by Secretary of State John Patten to introduce more testing into schools, which has vigorous opposition from both teachers and parents on the grounds of 'no consultation' i.e. there is no agreement on what are the 'negotiated requirements'! -Ed.]

[Issue 57 (September 1993)]

QUALITY FOR SCHOOLS

The Institute of Quality Assurance conference at the City Conference Centre, London, entitled 'The Teacher as Manager' provided an informative insight into some of the issues facing the nation's schools.

A snapshot of the current situation was provided by Duncan Graham, education consultant and school governor who also has the role of Education Adviser to the IQA. Quality, he said, 'was on everyone's lips' but was in danger of being devalued through over-use and misuse. It was, he said, the easiest thing in the world to claim quality but the hardest is to justify it, and England's education system was a case in point with 'more assertion about quality and standards than proof'.

954

He highlighted the lack of consensus which appears to exist as to the purpose of education and its expected outcomes, and the confusion which exists between standards and basics. International comparisons have shown no evidence that standards here are too high or that they are declining, but teachers must address 'the low expectations which bedevil our system' and the need for consistent information from schools. The Government had, he said, to learn to distinguish between inefficiency and cheapness, as the school with large classes can be cheap but not efficient, and it was emphasized that within the EC only Portugal spends less per head on education than the UK.

The limitations of league tables and of Ofsted inspections were described as 'only too patent', whilst there was a 'glaring omission' of a coherent system whereby schools can validate themselves. He said:

"We've got league tables which can be both misleading and destructive. Improvement by humiliation is not the way to do it".

[The recent Dearing Report recommendations to abandon league tables is a step in this direction -Ed].

The accreditation of schools to test the National Curriculum in a manner akin to that adopted in California and by BTEC was advocated, with schools encouraged to develop their own systems in preference to being forced to accept systems that are set up by the Government. Real quality, he said, begins in schools, and consequently should not be imposed. He emphasized:

"The greatest privilege we have is to share in the education of the next generation and we need quality systems to help us to do this, replacing assertion about quality with proof of it".

In the question session which followed Mr. Graham was asked whether in the context of setting standards for the delivery of the National Curriculum more could be made of the Curriculum Awards Scheme. In his reply he said that he saw the scheme as 'a good model that celebrates success', but emphasized that it was only a model. What was really needed, he said, was 'a recognisable standard that was common currency'.

Investing In People.

Rob Wye, head of the Department of Employment's Schools and Partnerships Policy Branch which is responsible for management of the Teacher Placement Service and the piloting of the Investors in People standard in Britain's schools, explained why he felt that Investors in People was especially appropriate for schools as they are in the business of investing in the workforce of the future through investment in their own staff.

He said that the standard was 'just as relevant for the smallest primary school as the largest university' and was envisaged to be 'an extremely effective tool' for the management of change, which has become a highly relevant issue for schools with the National Curriculum, increased autonomy, introduction of National Vocational Qualification (NVQs), changes to initial teacher training and teacher appraisal. These changes and the ways in which schools are inspected are set to have a profound influence on the ways in which schools are managed.

In the pilot programme some 50 schools are working in partnership with local TECs and in Education Business Partnerships to develop a strategy for implementing IIP in schools, with the aim of extending it to all TEC areas.

To date some 200 organisations have the status of 'Investors in People', which includes two schools, whilst a further 2000 are said to have action plans that demonstrate formal commitment. Training and Enterprise Councils (TECs) and Scottish Local Enterprise Companies (LECs) are said to be at an advanced discussion stage with a further 3000. Around a quarter of companies with Investors in People have under 50 employees.

Mr. Wye was asked to explain the variation in costs for IIP assessment across the country. He said this was mainly due to the fact that local TECs had been left to determine their own price scales. Some had evidently found funds from their own sources and charged nothing whilst others hadn't and had charged hundreds of pounds. This, he said, 'was being looked at'.

A further delegate expressed concern at the prospect of identifying a consultant with expertise in implementing IIP in education, and was reassured by Mr. Wye that it was the intention to assist every TEC to have at least one consultant available. [A gap in the consultancy market clearly exists here -Ed].

Kates Hill School: A BS5750 Case Study

One of the two schools currently registered to BS5750 is Kates Hill Primary School, Dudley, West Midlands, who achieved certification in February 1993. Their case study was presented by the school's Quality Manager Ms. Janeen Slack and headteacher Ms. Pearl White.

The school, which received a Schools Curricuulum Award for Community Involvement in 1990, started along the road to BS5750 largely as a result of external pressures, notably the Education Reform Act 1988 which demanded a thorough rethink of management structure and job specifications.

The Local Education Authority encouraged investigation of the relationship between quality assurance and education and four staff were invited to participate in four days of BS5750 awareness training with advisers from the LEA and Wolverhampton University.

956

A consultant helped to give common understanding to the words used in the top level manual and the Procedures Manual, and in generating an action plan and a direction for the school.

Staff worked in groups to document the working of the school on a daily, termly and yearly basis. The top level manual was completed in four months with handling, storage, packaging and delivery equating to the learning environment, process control relating to the process of delivering the curriculum and corrective action being control of the total system subject to a monthly senior management meeting.

It was found that by writing the procedures down, gaps were soon revealed, although many of the standard's requirements were already being complied with, merely lacking documentation or being seen as part of a whole system [i.e. the standard helped staff to appreciate the concept of a whole system - Ed].

The final Procedures Manual consisted of some 35 procedures relating to the management of the quality system, with 13 of these relating specifically to the running of the classroom.

The speakers were asked about their cost of registration which Ms. White said roughly equated with the cost of employing a new teacher. She explained how when she considered whether or not that teacher would have made the same impact as BS5750 her conclusion was 'probably not' and whilst registration seemed expensive her view was clearly that the school would save in the long run.

[Issue 68 (August 1994)]

DEMING EDUCATION INITIATIVE

This year's British Deming Association Annual Conference included the first report of the BDA Education Initiative Group, formed last year with the aim of creating greater awareness of Dr. Deming's teaching and its application in the field of school administration and the management of learning.

Jane Seddon, Principal Director of the Regional Staff College in the West Midlands, Jack Bovill, a schools chairman in Central London, and Brian Read, the BDA's Director of Advisory Services described the progress of the Group to date, which has involved the establishment of a pilot project in which ten selected schools have begun a programme of three two day seminars and instituted ongoing deployment.

Mentors worked with the schools from Autumn 1993 and eight of them are now reported to be through the first stage of identifying the components of their learning organisation and barriers to its optimum operation. The second stage, which is set to begin in September, will focus on the key concept of understanding variation in all processes through the simplicity of the control chart. Deployment Flow Charting is to be used as a means to understand processes and unnecessary complexities, and serve as a tool to trigger the journey of continuous improvement.

During the presentation the present education policy in Britain was severely criticised, particularly with regard to bid related funding, the promotion and piloting of performance related pay, and the arbitrary setting of standards which was said to be 'futile'. It pointed to substantial gaps between the aims of schools and what was actually going on in classrooms, created largely as a result of the expectation of teachers to implement policies which they have had no say in creating. Also contributing is the tendency of middle managers to view school policies only in terms of their particular areas of responsibility rather than within the broader school perspective. Weaknesses in the present system of Ofsted inspections were also highlighted, not just in terms of cost (estimated by one delegate to be in the region of £100,000 per school) but also in its failure to provide systematic improvement feedback.

The report concludes:

'Without the distraction of chasing for league position, schools have a better chance of nurturing a whole community of continuous learning. When our schools are uniformly focused to that end, then we really shall be raising standards'.

[Issue 75 (March 1995)]

CONFERENCE BOARD EUROPE LATEST REPORTS

This month *Quality Matters* is pleased review Conference Board Report No.1078-94-CH, entitled 'Partnerships for a Prepared Workforce' which features highlights from the conference 'Challenge to America's Employers' held in Atlanta, Georgia.

This conference co-sponsored by Bell South, The Conference Board and the Southern Regional Education Board, called on employers, educators and government leaders to rethink their roles in preparing youth for the global workplace and in facilitating the transition from school to work. Eight papers were presented covering 'Perceptions of Work Force Preparedness', 'Co-operating to Compete', 'New Strategies for Abiding Problems', 'Building School-to-Work-legislation, A New Learning Product', 'Breaking Down Conventional Barriers', 'Making School-to-Work Connections', and 'North Carolina's New Educational Standards'.

In the first paper Executive Vice-President of Corporate Relations for the Bell South Corporation Buddy Henry reveals that in present day America 40 per cent of high school graduates graduate with a general track diploma that 'neither prepares them for college nor a vocational technical career', and urges readers to 'think of the adverse impact this huge group of underemployed young adults is having on national competitiveness'. He then points out that the same proportion (40 per cent) of business executives say that they cannot modernise their equipment because their workers do not have the appropriate skills, which he says 'really gets at the issue of international competitiveness'. He emphasises the principle that 'we cannot have a first place economy with a second-rate education system'.

The second paper on 'Co-operating to Compete' has four authors: journalist and moderator Hedrick Smith; John Hall of Ashland Oil; Bill Johnson of Instrument Transformers Inc; and Jane Raulerson of General Box. Mr. Smith asks the three others to describe their experiences in hiring high school graduates. Comments included:

'We are finding that a high school graduate is simply unable to deal with the complexities of a modern oil refinery. Some other type of training is necessary. We are also finding that many of the kids are not prepared for basic tasks'.

'Where I live 40 per cent of the graduating class drop out of school. I am lucky to find a high school graduate that is not on drugs'.

'The problems I have with workers is not that they cannot read and write, it is that they simply do not care'.

Mr. Smith comments:

'If you travel to Germany and Denmark you will notice the respect accorded to work and the range of career opportunities made available through apprenticeship training systems. In many large German companies I met middle managers who were graduates of an apprenticeship system who had moved all the way up; it had not been a limitation in their career'.

He contrasts the lowly 10 per cent of American high school students who were studying calculus with the figure in Japan, which was nearer 80 per cent and calls for a change in public attitudes which currently leaves around three quarters of the country's children not finishing college. He concludes with a call for reinforcement of the 'real need for people to forge partnerships that have not been formed before'.

It was not all negative, however, as he pointed to more and more people in the US recognising that they are part of the solution and an increasing willingness on the part of Americans to effect change once they finally face up to the problems and understand that they are part of the solutions.

In the next paper John L. Clendenin, Chairman and CEO of Bell South, highlights two key problem areas, namely lack of means for employers to keep educators up to date on the new skills that they require, and the high number of students who do not just lack the higher skills that most jobs require, but perhaps more importantly the foundation they need in order to learn those skills. He suggests that employers are the key to solving these difficulties, through assuming a higher level of involvement in education:

'It is not enough to donate equipment to schools now and then. It is not enough to donate executives' time to deal with administrative matters. Nor is it enough to send out employees to tutor youngsters now and then. We need to work with educators to spell out in detail what skills we need from youngsters and work with them to develop the curricula to produce those skills'.

The next paper, by Augusta S. Kappyer, Assistant Secretary for Adult and Vocational Education for the US Department of Education highlights two recent pieces of legislation to tackle America's chronic education problem, namely the Goals 2000 Educate America Act and the School-Work Opportunities Act. The first of these provides for national voluntary standards which states and communities can use as benchmarks for the improvement of the calibre of academics in schools, and for development of a system of occupational skills standards which will help to bond academic and vocational education. The second aims to provide a framework for partnerships among business, labour, schools, parents and teachers in a non-prescriptive way by defining what the parameters of a good system might be and allowing communities and states to devise their own methods of bridging the gaps between school-based and work-based learning:

'There are excellent career academics, excellent tech-prep programs, and some excellent co-operative education programs, but they are highly localised, highly fragmented, and have nothing to do with each other as a system, We are hoping that this piece of legislation will provide the framework for knitting together some of these good initiatives and creating at a state and local level the kind of system that will work on a permanent basis for all young people'.

The final paper, by North Carolina's Governor James Hunt outlines the work of the North Carolina Education Standards and Accountability Commission, which is leading the National Alliance of Business' State of the Year's attempts to link educational standards with the demands of the workplace. It explains the state's interesting forthcoming 'unconditional guarantee':

'If you find that our students cannot perform the jobs for which you hire them, send them back and we will retrain them at our cost'

It then describes how the state's Commission on Work Force Preparedness is designing a comprehensive state work force development system as part of a $600 million a year project to improve workforce preparedness, This includes, a school-to-work transition program called Job Ready which draws businesses into partnerships with schools to help create youth apprenticeship programmes, improve technical education and enrich career development programmes that begin in primary grades. He then explains his role within the National Governors' Association's School-to-Work Roundtable in which twelve state governors are currently working with top CEOs and educational institutions to further develop and apply the techniques pioneered by North Carolina. A practical example explaining the take-up of the scheme by one major employer (Siemens Energy and Automation) is described.

[Issue 76 (April 1995) – 1st Sheffield World Quality Congress]

Applying TQ Principles to School Improvements in Sheffield.

Throughout the conference Sheffield was promoted as a 'Quality City' with the organisers keen to emphasise local achievements, which include a commitment on the part of around two thirds of the city's largest companies (130 in all) to achieve the Investors in People (IIP) standard, which is believed to be the highest participation rate of any UK city. This is quite apart from the city's well established reputation for excellence in steelmaking, medicine, cutlery, sports facilities and higher education.

The paper entitled 'The Application of Quality Management Principles to School Improvements in Sheffield' by Charles Sisum, Head Teacher of Wisewood School describes how a co-educational secondary school with 650 pupils in the Hillsborough district has embraced TQM and, with the support of local industry, realised real improvement albeit from rather hesitant beginnings.

The story begins in 1991 when the school was inspected by HM Inspector of Schools and knew it could do better. Jolted into action, a third of the school's staff accepted the offer to attend a TQM teaching weekend instigated by Mike Pupius, Director of Quality for Royal Mail North East, as part of a collaborative effort by the education and business communities of the city to increase school effectiveness. This weekend 'marked the beginning of the never ending journey down the road of continuous improvement' and was 'a great success'.

The author explains how, prior to attending the event he had been 'led unthinkingly to accept that the relationship of school to pupil and parent should be one in which the former decided what was required by the latter and that the latter should be jolly grateful'. After, however, he appreciated that 'within our schools we were all, in various ways, customers of each other':

' I began to see that the perspective offered by TQM would fundamentally change the relationships within our school community and, through the application of such principles the opportunities for growth and personal development of staff and pupils alike were most exciting'.

961

Following circulation of a brief report of the training weekend at a staff meeting shortly afterwards a full staff training day was arranged for later in the term. It was accepted however that they had faltered by attempting to cram too much detail into this, rather than keeping to broad principles and then allowing time to practice the tools and techniques introduced. This was seen in hindsight to be the right course. 'Some considerable frustration' resulted, although fortunately there was an opportunity to clarify some of the misunderstandings at the next staff meeting. Creation of a Steering Group followed, membership of which was open to all staff and Governors:

'Steering Group membership settled down to a regular number largely composed of those who attended the initial training weekend but with a few very encouraging additions'.

The twelve members committed themselves to reading widely about TQM in an educational setting and to work at translating various TQM ideas and practices into terminology that would have universal acceptance, whilst positive modelling of behaviour was given 'paramount importance'. The strategy adopted was one of applying TQ principles at every opportunity and supporting colleagues who showed signs of working in a quality way.

A Statement of Purpose of the Aims and objectives of the school has subsequently been formulated with the involvement of pupils, parents, Governors and staff , which has carefully avoided using the terminology of visions and missions, and this now appears in all form rooms, handbooks and information packs.

With the help of the Parent Teachers Association political Governor appointees have been persuaded that 'the days of paternalistic decision making on behalf of the electorate are over and gone forever'. Research amongst pupils has led to the formulation of an effective anti-bullying policy and a daily channel of communication between school and home has been constructed with the help of Pupil Planners. Other benefits include a more focused approach to the positioning and conduct of business meetings.

In his speech the author described how his experiences of school improvements in Maryland convinced him of the need for more emphasis on teaching and learning in British schools and praised neighbouring Newlands School for its achievements in applying TQM. He also outlined the role of the Strategic Education Forum within the City Liaison Group, notably to disseminate information on TQM practices to the education sector and align the Sheffield School Improvement Project with TQM principles. The paper however highlights some of the difficulties currently facing the education sector:

'The principles of TQ measurement underlines the flawed thinking of current Government policies in relation to the education world where we are almost

overwhelmed by examination out-turn figures but have no baselines against which to judge them The political context of our schools continues to be very problematic. It is interesting to reflect that the current Government has forced through a vast panoply of education legislation in the name of the customer i.e. the parent. I am not sure that the customers believe that the Government has a true understanding of their views. An opportunity for the application of some gap analysis would seem to present itself'.

Following his speech Mr. Sisum was asked whether there were plans in Sheffield to involve other sectors of education such as universities in the quality improvement project. He confirmed that many already had a role as stakeholders with Sheffield University (as distinct from Sheffield Hallam University) being particularly instrumental in offering TQM awareness to schools. He added that it was intended in the near future to commence a project of continuous improvement in which both universities would be involved by providing trainers. He explains how whilst in the United States he had observed the very important role played by higher education in evaluating school improvement projects and expressed a hope that Sheffield might build upon this example.

[Issue 77 (May 1995)]

Quality in Universities.

Sheffield Hallam University was pleased to welcome from Sweden Professor of Terotechnology at the Lund University of Technology, David Sherwin, who, although British by birth, has chosen to work in Sweden on account of its 'academic freedom' which he believes has been stifled in the UK.

In his paper he points to parallels between industrial TQM and best university practices, but suggests that much of what industry has learnt in this area has either been not applied or mis-applied by universities.

He turns most notably to the question of research, asserting that lecturers "should teach what they research and research what they teach". Without research the quality of teaching he believes will decline irrespective of how well the lecturer teaches, and in consequence a university which concentrates on teaching at the expense of research will decline:

'As its teaching gets out of date and increasing emphasis is placed upon teaching technique, the entry quality of students and degree standards will deteriorate. This is arguably occurring in Britain, the USA and Australia in former polytechnics and technical colleges and in state universities'.

He argues that the notion of having teaching universities and research universities should be resisted by the profession, but it is not.

On the quality of university management he clearly opposes the Management by Objectives approach, and pointed to the lack of economic success of countries in which it is popular. He is notably critical of 'inadequate leaders' which have acquired power in new universities which have remained hierarchical since their days as colleges.

On the quality of university administration he argues strongly that administrators are failing if academics feel ruled by them. They are, he says, in the best position to ascertain which rules need to be changed in order to make the lives of those they serve easier, but without being charged with that duty the improvements do not materialise. He presents a strong case for administrators to be made more conscious of who their customers are and of their duty to serve them, warning that if left unchecked administration can easily become self-serving.

The application of quality principles can, however, lead to effective administration and he points to numerous examples in banking and insurance, suggesting perhaps that universities should look to this sector for some new initiatives. Recent UK government action introducing the concept of 'accountability' to universities has not helped:

'In practice this involves collecting and collating a lot of statistics, some of which must come from academics. The administrators have been guilty of passing such requests on without checking whether the data are already available. They have been too slow to set up systems to capture the data on its way into the university. Faculties and schools have had to hire their own administrators to keep accounts and data which should be done by the expensive central offices'.

On motivation he argues that universities have the most diverse and intelligent workforce, which dislikes being driven and must be led. This leadership he says 'must involve no deception or illogicality' and there must be freedom from fear of dismissal and harassment 'so that they can pursue their studies unfettered by feelings of injustice or undue pressure to produce results before they are ready or not to take an unpopular viewpoint'. They must, he says, 'have the freedom not to conform to norms and not to be judged harshly if their line of research proves unpopular or unfruitful for a period'.

He points to serious 'negative feelings' induced by insensitive management arising from an unhealthy level of power being vested in a 'Management Cabinet' (including administrators) or a Council that does not work full-time with the university, and suggests that 'unsubtle motivation methods more suited to salespeople' must be abolished.

Finally, on the role of government he is notably scathing of the politicians who made examples of certain 'unproductive lecturers and students in subjects unpopular with the government' and used them 'to judge the whole university system'. This he clearly views as 'anti-quality' since it is a basic premise of quality 'that samples be fair or random and do not mix products of separate similar processes'. The methods currently advocated for assessing academic staff are, he alleges, 'inherently unfair and spurious':

'To judge research output by numbers of papers published is like judging a carpet by its size alone. To assess on the basis of total amount of grants from research councils is even worse; some research requires more expensive equipment, and researchers who lack it, having not broken into the "magic circle" are bound to progress more slowly. Some do not really need money at all, but have been driven into inventing projects which do in order to get some "brownie points"'.

He argues that if universities are to be centrally controlled then the government had better get it right, because if their way turns out to be poor, all universities will end up poor and the country will suffer. He condemns 'casual moving of the goal posts at the whim of each new minister' and the research centres that 'started cynically to attract money, then closed down less than three years later' when' even an elementary analysis of work in progress and parallel experience could show that it takes about seven years for the money and result flows to settle down'. He advocates a return to the old tenure system, albeit subject to reform, on the grounds that quality was better served by it. He concludes:

'Draconian pursuit of value for money has exactly contrary effects to those desired. The equivalence of vocational and academic entry qualifications and the fitness of colleges to become universities has not been objectively assessed. To abolish the CNAA with no substitute in sight seems very foolish. Academic freedom is not just threatened but nearly dead.'

The author can say all this from Sweden, but is there a British academic who dares to support him?

Applying Baldrige to Education.

In the United States a Baldrige Education Pilot Program has been launched this year in which schools have been invited for the first time to complete the Baldrige application, although no formal Award will be presented until 1996. The applications are to be reviewed by a team of Baldrige Evaluators who will use eleven core values:

*learning centred education

*leadership

*continuous improvement and organisational learning

*faculty and staff participation and development

965

*partnership development

*design quality and prevention

*management by fact

*long range view of the future

*public responsibility and citizenship

*fast response

*results orientation.

Sheffield Hallam University was pleased therefore to welcome from the USA Ms. Linda James to explain how these core values are likely to be interpreted and outline the preliminary results of a study designed to determine the dimensions of change based on Baldrige self-assessments in six institutions: two public doctorate granting institutions, three universities (two public, one private), and a community college.

The paper begins with an assertion that record declines in public confidence in higher education institutions in the US over the last ten years have paralleled record decreases in budget appropriations. Since higher education is being seen as increasingly important to national welfare, many colleges are being seen not to deliver. A loss of public trust and confidence has resulted which has generated strong external pressure for change in campuses right across America.

Change in education, she argues, 'has most often taken the guise of reform': -

'By the time a campus launches one reform effort, competing efforts are on the horizon sparking a new change cycle. Before one effort is institutionalised, a new and often competing effort is launched. The result has been fractional change efforts'.

Accelerating change is argued to require models of effective efforts and examples of institutions that have effectively instituted change as a result of these strategies. The Malcolm Baldrige Award Criteria are seen as providing such a model with the three major streams of thought (Systems Theory, Organisational Learning and TQM) enhanced by the addition of the concepts of the Assessment Movement.

In describing the eleven core values the author points to:

* A need for institutions to show evidence that they are aware of what is necessary for students to be successful not just in graduation but also afterwards. (Learner-Centred Education)

* Teachers must be actively involved in quality activities such as training and communication so that the institute's true status is understood and the use of data in setting strategic directions is enhanced. (Leadership)

* Continuous improvement is based on learning cycles that utilize data and information to simplify and improve work-processes to facilitate both incremental and breakthrough improvements. (Continuous Improvement and Organisational Learning)

* Training is integrated and aligned with key institutional directions. (Faculty and Staff Participation and Development)

* Work processes and flow are simplified so new programmes cannot be seen as obsolete prior to introduction. (Fast Response)

* The efforts of various different functions are to be co-ordinated and interventions with suppliers (such as feeder schools) placed 'upstream' to reduce the need for corrective action. (Design Quality and Prevention)

* Planning anticipates changing customer requirements and technological changes with plans and strategies supported with resource allocation, employee development and supplier relationships. (Long Range View of the Future)

*All decisions and strategies are data based with measures and indicators used which most influence the achievement of institutional aims i.e. student outcomes. (Management by Fact)

*There is a willingness to form partnerships both externally e.g. with community groups, businesses and sister institutions and internally e.g. with unions and through cross-training and networking. (Partnership Development)

*The Institute serves as a model regarding environmental, ethical and health concerns in planning, setting policy and conducting business. (Public Responsibility and Citizenship)

*Results are guided and balanced by the interests of all stakeholders using a balanced synthesis of performance indicators that is communicated to all stakeholders. (Results Orientation)

The evaluation and scoring is described followed by the preliminary results of the study which suggest that scores in the education sector are 'well below the points typically scored by Baldrige Award winners' although it is still early days. The low scorers are noted to often 'have the right ideas', but implementation is 'spotty', few gains or positive trends are evident, and 'functional areas probably do not work well together'. Middle scorers, by contrast, tend to score high in two or three categories but frequently exhibit signs of weakness in information and analysis and results, with absence of clearly defined outcomes hindering programme alignment and feedback loops poor. The higher scorers may have 'outstanding scores in four or five areas' and the involvement of academic units in faculty initiated assessment tends to be good with strategic direction well understood and information flows relatively smooth and uninterrupted.

[Issue 93 (September 1996) - 2nd Sheffield World Quality Congress]

Quality Management in Higher Education: an Empirical Study.

The paper by K. Narasimhan of the Bolton Business School entitled 'Quality Management Systems in HEIs in the UK: an Empirical Study' describes a survey undertaken in 1994 into the progress achieved by the higher education sector' as a result of following TQM and related practices. It describes the methodology of the survey (146 postal questionnaires sent to higher education institutes predominantly funded by HEFCs) and the interim findings generated by the 60 'positive usable responses'. The paper describes

(i) The status of quality systems in UK higher education institutes

(ii) The extent of commitment to quality systems at institutional level

(iii) The use of feedback systems by higher education institutes to achieve representative stakeholder views

(iv) The extent of training received by various groups of staff

(v) Methods of obtaining the views of stakeholders

In the first case there is seen to be a considerable contrast between the pre-1990 universities and the post 1990 universities and non-university Higher Education Institutes (NUHEIs) as regards the uptake of research and consultation activities in the field of quality.

Fewer than half of the pre-1990 universities which responded are engaged in such activities and in just under a third there is no involvement at all. This contrasts with an over 70 per cent involvement for the post 1990 universities and the NUHEIs. A disappointing 15 per cent of pre-1990 universities are either using or even considering using external consultants to facilitate in the introduction of quality systems. Although 38 per cent of them have a 'quality champion' (i.e. a person who is committed to the concept of 'Quality Service' and has the task of implementing a quality system), nearly three quarters of post 1990 universities and two thirds of the NUHEIs have such a person.

The contrast continues in the figures relating to the extent of commitment to quality systems where again under half of the pre-1990 have a statement of quality policy for their administrative and support services, as against 74 per cent of the post-1990 universities and 86 per cent of the NUHEIs.

Less than 40 per cent of pre-1990 universities apparently have a quality policy which identifies customers, or a quality improvement process subsystem that extends beyond academic matters. Again this contrasts with the post 1990 universities of which 84 per cent have such a subsystem and the NUHEIs for which the figure is 71 per cent.

Most of the HEIs (over half in each category) make extensive use of student opinion in order to modify their curricula and make some use of the views of academic staff in order to modify curricula and the quality policy [where it exists –Ed], and improve services and staff appraisal.

A disappointing proportion of HEIs extensively utilise research funding bodies' views for modifying quality policy, though interestingly here it is the pre-1990 universities which have a quality policy which lead with 31 per cent as against a miserable 11 per cent for both post-1990 universities and the NUHEIs. They also lead in the use of input from the Higher Education Quality Council (HEQC) in order to improve services, again with a steady 31 per cent whilst the post-1990 universities and the NUHEIs trail at 11 and 18 per cent respectively.

The extent of quality training in HEIs would appear to provide the most disappointing finding of all with no HEI in any category having provided either customer awareness training or training in the application of quality improvement tools for all of their staff. In other areas of training, such as the training of senior managers in the general principles of quality management and the training of support staff the post-1990 universities are perhaps most encouraging (47 and 48 per cent having provided these two types of training respectively). No top managers of pre-1990 universities have been trained in the application of quality improvement tools, which contrasts markedly with the post-1990 universities of which 21 per cent have trained all of their senior managers in these tools.

Under 'methods of obtaining views of stakeholders' the author contrasts the 8 per cent of pre-1990 universities which use 'satisfaction' surveys to solicit stakeholders' expectations with the 95 per cent of post-1990 universities which do so, though the balance is somewhat restored by the benchmarking statistics which would appear to favour the pre-1990 universities, less than a third of which do not practise it. More than half of the post-1990 universities apparently do not benchmark.

Improving Quality in Irish Education.

The Creggan area of Londonderry (Derry) has experienced some of the worst civil disturbances in the Western world during the last twenty five years incurring an enormous social, economic and human cost. Within this socially disadvantaged region children have suffered greatly with problems which few in the UK may comprehend or appreciate the existence of within their own country. This undoubtedly produces a challenge to all those concerned with the improvement of quality in education.

St. Marys College is located in the Creggan area and caters for the educational needs of around 950 girls in the 11 to 18 age range and in the lower 65 per cent of the ability range. Its story was told by its headmistress Miss Geraldine Keegan who last year received an OBE for services to education.

In her presentation Miss Keegan described how, in the early stages of her challenge following secondment to Northern Ireland Electricity in 1991, the school (as it then was) set about the task of identifying its customers (pupils, parents, suppliers, staff and the community), and its core business (that of providing quality learning). Then, with the help of local clothing manufacturers for Marks and Spencer, Desmond and Sons, they raised awareness of the quality philosophy by inviting a quality manager from industry to educate the Board of Governors and staff about the benefits which Total Quality can bring if implemented correctly.

At first union representatives were not convinced, but two hours and twenty questions later the quality manager won the day, helped by the fact that everyone connected with the school and its activities had a strong desire to make it successful, not just in terms of Northern Ireland or UK standards, but on a World Class basis:

"Total Quality has a natural place in the education system. It was not necessary for us to import a ready made TQ package. We can embrace the principles via the present school system without too much jargon or too many slogans. It is inseparable from standards and is based on continuous improvement which is fundamental to the development of all organisations including schools".

A teacher survey revealed that the teachers had faith in Desmond and Sons and as a result they consented to be interviewed by five managers from the company for between one and half and two hours for the purposes of generating diagnostic feedback. The resulting document highlighted the speaker's management style as the top priority for improvement, followed by staff training and development. The results were fed back to the staff in small groups. They included comments such as the following:

"If a cleaner dropped dead on the floor the teachers would possibly trip over her".

Follow through action included the establishment of School Improvement Groups (quality circles) which have generated "some wonderful ideas", most notably in the area of communication which "no longer seems to be a problem". In addition each term a member of staff volunteers to sit on the senior management team that tasks, such as the administration of the school budget, and compilation of the school timetable, (which had previously been the province of senior management only) , now became a focus for the involvement of staff.

Other initiatives have included the formation of a Pupils' Council, which has also generated "some great ideas" such as the establishment of a school breakfast scheme designed to cater for pupils who for one reason or another did not have one at home, and the name change from 'St. Mary's School' to 'St. Mary's College'. This helped to overcome the negative psychology associated with Northern Ireland's rigid and perhaps politically punitive division which exists between grammar and secondary school education.

The school has also pioneered a Higher Education Liaison Programme (HELP) into which pupils and parents contract, for example, into a Homework Club supervised by parents, which is shortly to be introduced to other schools in the UK.

Introduction of the School Improvement Programme has not been painless and there have been some difficulties, such as the lack of awareness of 'crisis points' especially around the end of term and the inevitable cynicism, which has resulted in a 'splinter group' which now has its own School Improvement Group. Nonetheless there have also been some notable positive achievements such as the achievement of a National Schools Curriculum Award in 1992, a Charter Mark for excellence in the delivery of public services in 1992 and 1995, shortlisting for the European Alcuin Award for Excellence in Educational Innovation in 1994, and achievement of the Investors In People (IIP) standard last year.

Following her presentation Miss Keegan was asked to elaborate on the activities of the 'cynics' who had formed their own group and whether they contributed to the overall school development plan. In her reply she said that she had not yet found any organisation which had 100 per cent involvement in Total Quality and emphasised the need rather to attain a 'critical mass' of involvement. The establishment of the 'cynics' group in this case created a form of semi-involvement which minimised the damage which they could cause and could ultimately lead to a positive contribution.

Applying Deming in Education.

Many of Myron Tribus' presentations have had an educational theme and reported on Deming initiatives in the USA. It is pleasing therefore to see that in the UK there are also some such initiatives under way, as evidenced by the paper by C. T. Fitz-Gibbon of the University of Durham, which is entitled: 'Will Joy in Work be helped or hindered by Value-added Indicators - Applying Deming to education'.

The paper describes how the Curriculum Evaluation and Management Centre of the University has been involved with the development of a national "value-added system" for the School Curriculum and Assessment Authority and an A level Information System (ALIS):

'This started because a governor of a school asked the author to comment on the results of some A level mathematics which were causing concern. A typical response to such a request might involve interpretation of raw data in a rather generalised off-the-cuff fashion without good statistical evidence and would include numerous inaccuracies, untested assumptions and a total lack of adequate quantification i.e. not science but opinion. The author's answer was not to confess ignorance but to suggest a way to find out by inviting other schools to share data'.

A dozen schools agreed to share their data and to meet each year to receive reports. This yearly meeting and the provision of reports back to each school became absolutely central to the project. It gradually became clear that, valuable as the database was for research purposes, the dramatic value and usefulness was to provide schools with evidence of the progress made by their pupils in comparison with that of similar pupils in other schools'.

'In the second year of the ALIS project measurements of students' attitudes and satisfaction with school were introduced. Thus, concern was focused on client satisfaction measures as well as client success measures'.

'What was of concern was quality of life, perhaps what Deming would have called "joy in work", and the hope that effective schools would be concerned that students enjoyed their time and got on well with the teachers as well as achieving well in their examinations'.

Considerable emphasis was placed on the need to drive out fear and a set of strategies was devised to remove the possibility of fear being introduced by virtue of creating a measure of "teacher effectiveness". Seven strategies are listed:

'All schools saw the data but they had each chosen a code name and this code name was known only to the school and the CEM Centre. All the data

was published under these code names and if a school felt that its code name had become known, it could be changed. This enabled the data to be openly shared without any school being worried about its reputation'.

'Local education authorities supported the project but most agreed that they would not have access to the data unless the schools agreed that they should. Thus, there was feedback to the level of management that ran the school but not to a higher level of management that was in a sense responsible for schools and of monitoring schools'.

The paper is notably scathing towards the Office for Standards in Education (OFSTED) which is described as 'a peculiarly English phenomenon'. Since OFSTED clearly did not have proper standards in inspection, it was necessary to create the Office for Standards in Inspection (OFSTIN) to draw attention to the quite alarming fear introduced into the system by inspection and to the unscientific and unprofessional nature of OFSTED's activities. It must also be noted that OFSTED consumed a budget of approximately three times as great as the entire budget of the Economic and Social Research Council.

The paper highlights the fact that there have as yet been no published studies of the reliability of the inspectors' ratings of teachers, lessons or schools, nor any published studies on the validity of inspectors' judgments.

[Issue 132 (December 1999)]

11th WORLD PRODUCTIVITY CONGRESS (PART 2)

Breakthrough in Quality Circle Education: a Tertiary Experience.

Ngee Ann Polytechnic is the only tertiary institution in Singapore which has both incorporated the teaching of quality circle concepts into its curriculum and encouraged its students to form quality circles. It is also the only institution of higher learning to receive the National Outstanding QC Award, the Public Sector's Outstanding Statutory Board Award, the National 3Ps award, the Excellent Progress Award and Distinguished Effort Awards.

The paper by Lim Siew Choon, Senior Lecturer in the Department of Business Studies and Manager (Industry Training and Development) of the Polytechnic's Centre for Business and Management Development describes the educational breakthrough that has been achieved through the formation of student quality circles and Academic Excellence teams and outlines the ongoing Joint NP Industry Quality Circle Scheme through which students work jointly with industry to realise productivity improvements.

The history of quality circles is traced back to 1981 when the Polytechnic decided to embark on the formation of Work Improvement Teams following publication of the Report of the National Committee on Productivity earlier that year. A Functional Organisation Chart was drawn up in December 1981 and a Productivity Steering Committee officially appointed in February 1992.

This Committee was chaired by the Chief Executive Officer (the Principal) and comprised all Heads of Department. The first series of promotional activities was then launched in November 1982 concurrently with the first national Productivity Month Campaign.

The first staff circle known as "The Link" was formed in August 1982 which is still active and has to its credit three Ten Star Awards, two Outstanding QC of the Year Awards and seven consecutive PS21 Public Sector Distinguished Effort (WIT) Awards. The paper points out that since 1983 the Polytechnic's quality circles have won a total of 20 three star, 19 two star, 6 one star, 52 gold, 44 silver and 30 bronze awards, and that staff participation as of 30th April 1999 was 98%.

The first non-engineering student Work Improvement Team was inaugurated in August 1985 and the paper explains how it consisted of a group of final year students which came together to address a common student problem, namely the distribution of notes during lectures. The paper then moves forward to 1988 when the Business Studies Department organised its first Work Improvement Team Convention. Since then there have been 13 such Conventions at which 80 student projects have been presented. Some 24 of these projects were also presented at 12 National QC Conventions winning a total of four gold, twelve silver and eight bronze awards:

'Two teams from the Polytechnic participated in the First International Student Quality Circle Convention at Lucknow, India, in December 1997. We won three top awards during the convention, namely the Deming Award of Excellence, Ishikawa Award of Excellence, and Best Team "Turn Out Award"'.

The joint NP-Industry QC Scheme began in 1992 and since then around 250 students from both engineering and non-engineering departments have participated in the scheme. More than 80 projects have been completed and 38 of them have been presented at the National QC Conventions winning a number of prestigious awards. Perhaps more importantly, however, the financial savings to participating companies from these projects has amounted to over 5 million Singapore dollars:

'The scheme which started with only two companies in 1992 i.e. Motorola Electronics Private Limited and Excel Machine Tools Private Limited has now extended to 18 companies with student participation from 8 academic departments. Some service organisations which participated in this scheme were Citibank and Singapore Island Country Club.

The first NP-Industry QC Convention was held on 12th February 1998. It marked another milestone in the productivity movement at Ngee Ann Polytechnic. Students who had successfully completed NP-Industry joint QC projects shared their experiences with their juniors. The primary objective was to motivate the juniors to take part in in-house QC projects and NP-Industry QC projects'.

The latter part of the paper deals with the more recently established Academic Excellence Teams (AETs) which are comprised of groups of academic staff of any grade from the same or different departments examining work related issues, and the Polytechnic's suggestion scheme:

'The first AET Best Practices Seminar was held in January 1999 with the focus on Student Administration. Thirteen projects from the academic departments were presented. The AET seminar has provided a platform for staff members to share their proven ideas and best practices which can be adopted across the Polytechnic. This should greatly enhance learning in the Polytechnic and help to build the foundation for implementing benchmarking and continual improvement processes. Though it is a small beginning it is an important step forward in cultivating a quality culture'.

'With the implementation of the Electronic Staff Suggestions System on Lotus notes the names of suggestors and evaluators are now indicated. This allows for open communication and sharing of ideas. Suggestors can also channel their suggestions directly to key evaluators, thus improving turnaround and processing time. In addition, good suggestions are identified and highlighted in Staff Stuff, the Human Resource Web Page'.

The paper concludes as follows:

'As the Polytechnic enters the new millennium our thrust will be on two fronts -encouraging our staff members to adopt QC as a way of life, and educating our students with a QC mindset so that they will become ready models for the workforce of the next millennium.

Making studies in quality concepts a compulsory subject in our curriculum also ensures that our current 14,000 strong enrolment are imbued with a mindset for a quality conscious culture. Our efforts are currently being reinforced with the latest Public Sector's PS21 (Public Service for the 21st Century). The QC movement has been identified as one of the four cornerstones of the campaign .

We shall integrate QC with the Staff and Student Suggestions Schemes in our continuous strive to provide abetter service to all our customers' .

Improving Quality in Education.

Two of the three papers from the education sector came from Ireland. The first, by Geraldine Keegan OBE, Headmistress of St. Mary's College, Derry, provides some useful benchmarking data for education establishments seeking to apply the Business Excellence Model since the school was last featured in Quality Matters in October 1996.

The school has achieved three Charter Marks and is the only public sector organisation in Northern Ireland to have been awarded the Northern Ireland Public Sector Prize twice. They are currently engaged in a programme which aims to develop the best measures of customer satisfaction within the education sector:

'We believe that pupil satisfaction is not about giving pupils more of what they want and less of what they don't want, but rather about involving them in decision making processes about the best service we can provide for them and about communicating clearly to them the reasons for making decisions that affect them. This is achieved mainly through the School Council who meet every two weeks but also through timetabled form and year team meetings, assemblies and surveys'.

Recent developments include modification of the school's people survey to include questions relating to health and safety and equal opportunities and a question relating to the school's recently installed computerised wireless network system.

The second Irish contribution was from the Department of Education and Science and concerns 'the most fundamental change ever to the Irish examination system:

'The examination system traditionally has been a closed one with limited feedback to students on their performance. In some cases this caused unnecessary confusion and worry in relation to grades. Given the national importance and high public profile of the examination it was seen as essential to administer it in as open a manner as possible and that every opportunity should be taken to allay concerns and secure public confidence particularly among the major stakeholders, students, teachers and parents. The objective was to reduce the number of appeal applications and to build confidence in the system through demonstrated transparency'.

A decision was taken to allow students access to their marked scripts in advance of the deadline for appeal applications so that they could make an informed decision on whether or not to appeal. As a guide during access each student could also inspect the detailed marking scheme for each subject.

The Education Minister announced the change, which followed from benchmarking with the New Zealand Qualifications Authority, in May 1998.

As a result of the scheme the number of appeal applications fell from 11,500 in 1997 to 6,200 in 1998 (a 47% reduction). In 1999 some modifications were made to the original scheme, for example to reduce the bulk of material needing to be stored in schools. The UK Examining Authorities are now benchmarking the scheme.

The remaining paper is from the Lahti region of Finland where an Educational Consortium consisting of ten institutes from various educational sectors and the Lahti Polytechnic has been formed. A Total Quality Management (TQM) philosophy underpins the activity of the Consortium with benchmarking playing a major role.

Every unit of the Consortium, which was formed in 1996, has a Quality Co-ordinator responsible for the development of benchmarking. These Quality Co-ordinators belong jointly to a company-wide Quality Co-ordinator Team which has participated in a project for the Board of Education with the aim of developing recommendations for the application of quality management to the management of vocational education at national level:

'Internal benchmarking has been possible for units during the whole history of the Consortium. The Quality Co-ordinator Team analyses all assessment results. It has been also possible to read and analyse application documents of other units. The Quality Co-ordinator Team will start benchmarking with other educational organisations and enterprises as well. The Consortium will arrange a seminar for this purpose this autumn'.

Further Information.

Copies of the conference papers, which also include a list of addresses for papers featured, and a description of various Member State national quality policies, may be obtained from Ms. Adilia Crespo, Consultora, Secretariado para a Modernizacao Administrativa, Rua Almeida Brandao No.7, 1200-602 Lisbon, Portugal. Telephone: (+)351213921500.

[Issue 137 (July 2000) – Deming Transformation Forum, Brighouse, Yorkshire]

Introducing Deming to High School Students.

Education has featured highly at past Deming conferences and this year a case study from Canada described how three consultants were invited to design a 10 to 20 hour programme to introduce the System of Profound Knowledge at high school level by the North Simcoe Business Development Centre following consultation with local teachers. This move stemmed from a mandate by the North Simcoe Development Centre to improve employment opportunities in the area.

Two of the three consultants (Kathy Elsdon and Emily Harris) gave the 45 minute presentation which had the intriguing title 'Snowblowers, Chocolate and Kurt Russel', Kurt Russel being the star of a film entitled 'Executive Decision', which forms part of the Deming route towards quality improvement:

'We begin the "systems" discussion with a definition of systems and examples that they relate to i.e. a stereo system, the educational system, respiratory system etc. We take a moment in the class to discuss common characteristics that include purpose, suppliers, inputs, process, outputs, customers and support systems. We also discuss the fact that systems are interrelated and interconnected. This is where the movie helps demonstrate the points discussed'.

'Near the end of the movie Kurt has to land a large jet plane filled with passengers. He has some experience as a pilot in small planes. He knows something about speed, flaps, landing gear etc. He also knows that there are manuals on board and he happens to have the assistance of a flight attendant (played by actress Holy Berry). As he makes a change in one system (e.g. lowering the landing gear) other systems are affected. Will he be able to safely land the plane? We'll never tell. We do ask the students to identify all the subsystems in the landing system and how they interact. From this scene they can also identify inputs, support systems, and build a rudimentary flow chart of how to land a plane'.

The 'snowblowers' concept derives from a particularly Canadian situation whereby snow-blowers replace shovels for the clearance of winter snow. The scenario is pictured of a man who purchases a snowblower which proves to be unfit for its purpose and poses the following questions for the students:

(i) Is the customer right to be upset?

(ii) What was the difference between the customer's "wants or expectations" and his "need"?

(iii) What could the sales clerk have done to improve the level of service to the customer?

(iv) As the business owner who wants satisfied customers what would you be prepared to do, if anything, for this customer?

'This is an interesting activity as the students begin to explore the application of the premise that we must look at quality through the eyes of the customer. They also have an opportunity to examine this situation from a systems perspective as they identify the inputs to the snowblower selling

system: 'Knowledge of the sales clerk about the product is essential' product knowledge from the customer is not. And there is a distinct relationship between Systems and Psychology as they identify communication skills need by the clerk'.

'Chocolate' relates to a game which mimics Deming's Red Beads Experiment using M and Ms in place of the beads. A customer tells the students he will buy all of the green M and Ms that they can produce, but all of the other colours are considered to be defective product:

'Students work in groups of 4 or 5, assigning roles of Worker, Supervisor(s), Chief Supervisor, and Recorder within each group. Each Worker is given a bag of M and Ms (the individual size - about $1 Canadian). All are trained in detail on how to correctly open the bag and hold it to dispense only green M and Ms. A production run is 10 M and Ms. Following each production run the Recorder reports on the number of green M and Ms. A chart is built on the blackboard. After each production run there is a reaction from "management" -the person running the game: more training is required, slogans are developed to motivate employees, rewards are given to those who have improved (we use a specially designed copper engraving of the Queen –a Canadian penny, and, finally, there are threats of firing'.

'Students readily see that the defects (non-green M and Ms) already exist in the system. Additional training, rewards and threats have no impact on the number of green M and Ms that each team can produce. Natural variation exists within the system -both in the number of green M and Ms and in the total number of M and Ms in a bag'.

In order to review the material covered in the programme a further game known as "Quality Quest" has been devised based on a television game show called "Jeopardy". This has quiz categories such as 'Teams and Communication', 'Customers', 'Quality Facts and Figures', and 'Systems Thinking'. Students, in teams, select their questions from the categories and have a set time limit in which to answer. Benefits from the programme are reported as follows:

* More students and teachers learned the basics of Total Quality, numbers rising from 100 students in four years to 250 in the first year of teaching this 'Co-operative education' class.

* Strengthening of the relationship between the North Simcoe Development Centre and the schools of North Simcoe.

* An evolution at community level stemming from the initiative of strengthening relationships between education (principals, teachers, students and parents) and employers (local businesses and community organisations).

* A positive impact on student transition from school to work.

Chapter Fifteen

Quality and the Small Business

With small businesses forming the bedrock of the economies of most nations considerable emphasis has justifiably been placed on encouraging the uptake of quality concepts in this section of industry in recent years. A notable landmark was the launch of the European Quality Awards for small businesses in 1996, which was subsequently rolled out at national level.

An issue that has been contentious throughout the decade has been the appropriateness or otherwise of ISO9000 for small businesses. This was discussed at the IQA's specialist small business conference in 1992 which begins this short compilation, which introduced two of the country's key activists of the decade in the field of small business quality, namely consultant Lionel Stebbing and the current Chairman of the Federation of Small Businesses (FSB) Ian Handford, who also gave the IQA's Millennium John Loxham Lecture. An overview of the latter is also given.

Further articles cover early application of the EFQM Business Excellence Model in SMEs in the UK in 1996, research into the level of health and safety competence in SMEs in 1998, benchmarking tools for SMEs, and the launch of two alternative quality standards for SMEs (the Irish Foundation Mark and the AQMCI Foundation Standard), the former being launched by Excellence Ireland, the latter by the IQA, in 2000.

[Issue 47 (November 1992)]

QUALITY SYSTEMS AND THE SMALL BUSINESS

This year has been particularly difficult for small businesses in Britain as many industry sectors, perhaps most notably construction, have suffered the effects of recession more strongly than ever before. For many the problems are not quality related but are purely a question of cash flow and customer depletion, but for others the issue of quality systems certification, and particularly supplier pressure to achieve BS5750/ISO9000 registration in a competitive environment, is a major source of strain.

With over 90 per cent of British businesses having fewer than 10 employees and some 78 per cent having a turnover of under £100,000 per annum it is clear that small businesses form a vital component in Britain's economic structure and one which urgently needs assistance in understanding and implementing the tools and techniques of quality management, for which certification to ISO9000 forms an identifiable base line.

In order to address this imperative the Institute of Quality Assurance, with the support of The Federation of Small Businesses who represent the principal voice of the small business community in Britain, held a one day conference at the Forte Crest Hotel, Regent's Park, London, on 6th October entitled 'Quality Systems Certification and the Small Business'.

The conference chairman was management consultant Lionel Stebbing of Stebbing and Partners International, who is currently the author of two books: Quality *Management in the Service Industry* (ISBN 0-13-747148-3), and *Quality Assurance: the Route to Efficiency and Competitiveness* (ISBN 0-13-747221-8).

BS5750 : is it helping?

In his introduction Mr. Stebbing questioned whether, with the amount of money and effort available at the present time, the quality management standard BS5750 really was going to help the small business sector in Britain. There were many, he said, that feel that BS5750 is 'being rammed down the throat' of small businesses in the UK and who are questioning the applicability of it to their activities.

In order to illustrate his point he cited the example of design control, stating that in a small business it was hard to imagine design being controlled in the same way as with a large organisation. He questioned whether, for example, in a field like fashion design, design really could be controlled in the way imagined by the assessment bodies and suggested that in practice design was 80 per cent training and 20 per cent inspiration. The notion that design should be controlled was, he said, nothing more than a 'fixation', and for the most part the imposition of requirements by regulatory authorities and purchasers to achieve BS5750 Part 1 certification was of the nature of a 'sledgehammer to crack a nut'.

He also criticised the use of the word 'product' in the standard, as it applies to services. Quite a number of people, most notably those involved with the provision of health care and related services, resented the use of this terminology and it could be inferred that this created a negative attitude towards the concept of quality systems certification as it applied to them.

Clear concern was voiced about the documentary requirements of purchasers and regulatory bodies, and it was suggested that the manner in which quality manuals were reviewed left much to be desired. It was emphasised that the standard makes reference to a requirement for a quality manual only 'where appropriate' and it was open to question whether this is in fact the case with small businesses.

BS5750 : the Small Company Perspective.

The opening address was given by Ian Handford speaking on behalf of the Federation of Small Businesses (FSB) which he described as 'a very democratic institution which has been a very successful growing organisation' using its main strength, its members, to carry its message through to government. He drew delegates' attention to the fact that some 60 to 80 thousand businesses were going under each year, and suggested that this did not engender confidence amongst the small business community.

The FSB, he said, was not against standards, but one should always consider whether or not a standard is appropriate, and pointed out that many small business owners still view registration to any standard with a considerable degree of scepticism. It follows that the cost and time have to be within the means of the business concerned if that business is to have confidence in the registration system.

Many large organisations are now demanding certification which has had the effect of applying pressure, but this could in the end be 'the final straw' for many companies, and the view of the FSB was that in many cases this imposition was both 'unfair' and 'impractical', quite apart from being far from the intention so far as Total Quality Management was concerned.

It was suggested that the present costs of achieving registration often could not be justified for the small i.e. 'micro' business, with compliance costs for such businesses out of proportion by comparison with large and medium sized organisations.

The DTI's definition of what constitutes a small business i.e. the '200 figure' was heavily criticised and delegates were asked whether we really are to believe that all 5 million small businesses are going to be able to be brought within some kind of typical scheme. It was emphasized that a good in-house system may in many cases exist in a non-written form in a small business, and suggested that one positive practical step forward could be the development of some form of miniature version of the standard which would have greater suitability to the small business.

Quality systems auditing was felt to be 'a very different animal' in the case of the small business and the necessity for two annual visits was questioned with the implication that in many cases one visit per year would be adequate.

Following the presentation a delegate from the Rural Development Commission asked whether the FSB had been involved in the creation of BS5750, as he clearly believed that the formulating committee should have had some small business representation. Mr. Handford accepted that the FSB had not had such involvement, but probably had not heard of the standard or been consulted at that time.

[Issue 70 (October 1994)]

I.Q.A. LAUNCH CERTIFICATION GUIDE FOR SMALL BUSINESSES

The Institute of Quality Assurance (IQA) has launched a guide to quality systems certification that has been written specifically for the small and medium sized enterprise. Written by Alan Griffin, a Fellow of the IQA with some 35 years of experience in quality management in SMEs, the Guide aims to circumvent perceived bureaucracy and provide an easy to read outline of the standard's requirements, quality manuals and procedures, implementing a documented quality system, control of measuring and test equipment, maintaining effective quality control records, conducting internal audits and management reviews. Also the quality system post registration, as well as how to prepare for the assessment itself.

Some useful addresses are included along with a glossary of terms relating to quality concepts.

Pam MacAlester, Chairman of the Wessex Region Federation of Small Businesses comments:

"It is a great satisfaction for us to know that the calm professional guidance which Alan Griffin has given so many of us in Wessex will now, through this book, be available to a much wider audience, and we are confident that they will benefit as we have done from his sound knowledge of the subject, his years of experience, and his good sense ".

BS5750 TOO RIGID FOR SMALL FIRMS?

A new report entitled 'Small Businesses and BS5750', based on survey responses from some 4,000 small companies, has concluded that the quality management standard BS5750 is overly rigid and formal for smaller companies which often rely on the 'hands-on' approach of owner managers. It is suggested that informal quality systems based on the personal involvement of business owners and employers with detailed knowledge of their customers' requirements are not necessarily inferior to the more formal BS5750 certification. The survey was sponsored by the Department of Trade and Industry, BSI and the National Westminster Bank. The report was compiled by Francis Chittenden of the Manchester Business School.

QUALITY AND THE SME.

Quality improvement programmes are viewed by many if not most Small and Medium sized Enterprises (SMEs) being largely the province of the larger organisation. Yet as larger organisations continually strive to obtain ever higher standards of business excellence, which they must if they are to keep pace with international competition, their supply chains are without doubt highly dependent on the 186,000 or so small businesses (fewer than 200 employees) which exist in the UK. It follows that if the larger organisations are to continue to realise the higher levels of business excellence which they desire so the small companies which supply them also have to improve. It is likely that this will require a fundamental change in attitude on the part of many small businesses.

[*Quality Matters comments:* many dispute that companies with 200 employees are in this category, the companies at highest risk are much smaller. In the present economic climate many small companies would give a lot to be in the same position as their Japanese counterparts –to have stable relationships and prompt payment.]

The Case for ISO9000

It has been argued that the former standard BS5750 or ISO9000 (now BS EN ISO9000) is inappropriate for many SMEs on account of the fact that it results in more paperwork than is necessary and that it is bureaucratic and biased to the manufacturing sector. Yet for many SMEs the process of working for certification can be both rewarding and revealing. It need not be bureaucratic and it could be just the start which some SMEs need so that they can work in partnership with the larger organisations which in turn will be striving to become world class.

In order to assist the smaller company in assessing how BS EN ISO9000 can benefit them the Department of Trade and Industry (DTI) has recently published 'Implementing BS EN ISO9000: A Guide for Small Firms' which describes, amongst other things why traditional inspection routines are no longer appropriate business practices for small businesses. It advises which of the three BS EN ISO9000 (ISO9001/2/3) standards is most suitable for a given company, why there is not and need not be a special version of the standard for small businesses, why many larger organisations are encouraging smaller suppliers to seek registration, and how to use third party certification as part of an ongoing joint quality initiative and basis for partnership sourcing:

'Research has shown that an inspector's powers of concentration can drop by 50 per cent within 20 minutes of starting the job, and that 15 per cent of inspectors' decisions will be wrong. Therefore, you cannot rely entirely on post-production inspection. Inspection can only spot mistakes. A public system focused on your procedures will help you get things right in the first place'.

'Many small business deliver simple products or services, where customers can check quality by final inspection. This type of 'what you see is what you get' service such as window cleaning or unbound photocopying, cannot contain any hidden defects, so BS EN ISO9003 may be appropriate '.

The comments of several small business employees are featured to provide an indication of some of the benefits that might be expected from undertaking the certification process. For example, Pat Martin, founder of PVC based adhesive and sealant manufacturer Stelmax, which currently has twelve employees, says:

"I used to think BS EN ISO9000 was just for the big fish in the sea. But I increasingly recognised that quality is important to all firms -large, medium and small. Although I understood BS EN ISO9000 would not change the quality of the products, I did not know that it could guarantee their consistency, a factor that was likely to become more and more important in and increasingly competitive market at home and abroad".

Similarly Martyn Hogg of Acorns Nurseries of Cardiff, which provides full day care for children aged between six weeks and five years and has around 60 employees says:

"The advantages of a documented system within the organisation are apparent in many ways. Our sites are remote from Head Office and it has helped us ensure standards are the same throughout. We have traceability for the service we provide and records are kept correctly, stock control ensures adequate consumables are available, customers are responded to quickly and parents' concerns are easily transferred between nurseries as all paperwork is uniform. Most of all an efficient management system allows the *nursery nurses to get on with what they are best at -looking after the children".*

The Acorns Nurseries case is also interesting in its approach to the use of consultants:

"The local Enterprise Agency, Cardiff and Vale Enterprise, were running a self-help course for small businesses seeking BS EN ISO9002 and for approximately £350 we learnt a consultant's role for ourselves. This also meant that nobody could hold us to ransom from outside the organisation as all the skills for BS EN ISO9002 are in-house".

The Guide provides some advice about how to set up a BS EN ISO9000 system which includes a section explaining the amount of paperwork which is required and why it is needed i.e. a quality system requires paperwork just as a financial system requires book-keeping. The emphasis throughout is on simplicity:

'It is useful if you can stick to just one copy of your quality manual, which everyone has easy access to '.

For companies which are interested in employing a consultant a guide to the costs is given, along with details of the Diagnostic and Consultancy Service which provides subsidised management consultancy for firms with under 250 employees with up to £10,000 being available for the purchase of consultancy services and a further £2,000 for diagnosis.

The costs of attaining certification are broken down into initial costs and ongoing costs and practical examples described so the actual costs borne by four small businesses, Delyn Commercial Contractors Amenity Cleansing Service, The Buckland Leadership Centre, Colibri (gift distributors), and the Focus Housing Group Maintenance Department. For the latter, which has around 40 employees, the costs of achieving certification are totalled to £16, 187 of which the largest expense is 20 days' consultancy (£9,400). These are weighed against the benefits which are totalled to £33, 166 for the first year of which the principal saving was in unoccupied property turnaround (£27,120).

The Guide advises that the installation of a quality system be regarded in much the same way as any other medium term investment and stresses that it need not be complicated to be effective. It concludes with a clause by clause dissection of BS EN ISO9000 and a list of sources of help and advice.

The Case for Self-assessment.

It has been argued, though it may be questioned, that there are better ways for a small business to seek to improve the quality of its business than to follow the BS EN ISO9000 route. Certainly it is not the only option that is open to the smaller business and many may prefer the European Foundation for Quality Management (EFQM) Model for Self- assessment, which the EFQM is currently piloting for SMEs with a view to presenting a new European SME Award in 1997. A pilot exercise is currently underway in 21 countries with two SMEs in each country applying the Model to their business and completing a 30 page Self Assessment Document. The EFQM meanwhile is training 41 pilot assessors to assess the new Award in various countries.

The EFQM is particularly keen to assist the smaller company to apply Self-assessment and realise benefits from it, as evidenced by the Secretary General Geert de Raad's appeal in the February 1996 Issue of their newsletter Quality Link to various regional Quality Organisations to promote the Self Assessment approach as the way forward, and the inclusion of presentations from SMEs at their Winners' Conferences which are taking place throughout Europe during the spring.

In the UK one such Winners' Conference, sponsored and hosted by the British Quality Foundation took place at the Royal Lancaster Hotel on 5th March affording delegates from large and small businesses alike the opportunity to hear from last year's European Quality Award Winner TI Europe and two previous winners of the UK Quality Award, TNT Express UK and ICI High Performance Technology, as well as from four SMEs: Griffin Factors (cash flow management company with 400 employees based at Worthing and 9 regional offices), Dutton Engineering (Woodside) Limited (Subcontract sheet metal company with 28 employees based at Sandy, Bedfordshire), Lawson Mardon Plastics (packaging subsidiary of Swiss based Lawson Mardon Packaging employing 160 at Sutton in Ashfield, Nottinghamshire), and Heath Springs (spring manufacturer employing 120 at Redditch, near Birmingham).

Sue Jex, Director -Quality and Processes for Griffin Factors, described how her company, which had a turnover of around £5 billion in 1995, adopted self assessment initially as a tool for holistic measurement which led to the company becoming strong throughout i.e. to remove or strengthen weak links so that they are no longer weak any more:

'Colleague's behaviour and your own behaviour will not become perfect overnight -but if you buy into the ideals you can discuss, learn and move forward'.

She described how the model challenges the company to make continuous improvements and how her company rose to this challenge by involving more people in the planning process, introducing lunchtime seminars so that managers could share knowledge and any member of staff could learn, improving communication within the business, embracing the principles of the Investor in People (IIP) standard, and taking positive action to change previously established behavioural norms that were hindering progress.

Looking to the future, she explained how the Model had become 'a welcome toolbox whose principles and ideals are widely understood and valued' which has not only provided 'a recognised, structure for the company that helps them to prioritise improvements activities, but also has provided a means for the company to further help its clients and aspire to achieve world class performance'.

The paper by Dutton Engineering (Woodside) which is perhaps the most informative of the four, was presented by Business Manager Tina Mason and describes how the company has built on its BS5750 certification in 1984 by launching a Total Quality initiative in 1989 and progressing naturally into Partnership Sourcing in 1991. It is explained how the self-assessment model provided a framework for continuous improvement with a holistic view of the organisation replacing the former project driven approach. Also explained was how the speaker used a two day assessor course run by a recognised consultancy as a basis for her role of 'project champion':

"The more I learnt, the more I became convinced that this was a real, usable tool that we could use to lift our performance to world class levels".

Corporate commitment was gained through membership of the British Quality Foundation (BQF) and in the future the company intends to use the new BQF software for self-assessment, ASSESS. For SMEs that believe self-assessment is either expensive or unnecessary, the speaker had this to say:

" Many smaller companies are guilty of introspection, and whilst they may have some good business practices any small advantages they currently enjoy can easily be eroded by market forces or by the competition. Using the Business Excellence Model made us realise that it does not matter how good we believe we are, what is important is how good our customers think we are, and we needed to do some formal external measurements of that".

The company is interesting in that it operates a system of annual hours (employees contracted to work a given number of hours over a twelve month period rather than per week) which, they argue, builds in increased flexibility as well as dispensing with the need to incur premium payments for overtime or unsocial hours. Employees are thus encouraged to become committed to their work rather than being driven by a routine, whilst job descriptions which were viewed as 'too restrictive for free thinking people' have been eliminated along with the entire principle of mass inspection. Multi-functional teamworking has also been enhanced.

Lawson Mardon Plastics were represented by Operations Director Steve Isherwood. As with Dutton Engineering the company began with ISO9000 and subsequently enhanced this with IIP and the paper describes how the Business Excellence Model was seen to reflect the culture and practice which the company desired to adopt. It is explained how a BQF Award entry was submitted in 1994 which scored around 250 points but, perhaps more importantly, provided a feedback report which enabled them to identify shortcomings. They then developed a more complete strategy which earned them a score of around 400 points when they re-submitted for the UK Quality Award in 1995.

For the benefit of the sceptics and those who see Business Excellence from the bottom line viewpoint, the speaker pointed out that over the last four years the company has doubled its turnover to around £15 million and sees itself as becoming a large business "in the not too distant future".

Heath Springs were represented by its Chief Executive Edward Roberts CBE who is the former West Midlands Regional CB Chairman and the founder Chairman of the Central England Training and Enterprise Council and of the IECs National Council. He has also appeared on television, notably on the Today Programme, Question Time and Newsnight.

His paper describes how the company, which has a turnover of around £4.5 million, became the first spring manufacturer to gain the Ford Q1 Award and how he had viewed his company as a comparatively good performer until, as an invited member of the BQF Award jury, he began to see award entries that were "in another world". Consultations with his Quality Manager led him to understand "that this was a significant business tool that was going to take some special management time and expertise to sell to all the team and in particular to make sure that the senior management team really believed it and owned the process". He explained how at first sales people had been sceptical but how, following an open and frank discussion, they soon saw the relevance of improving the quality of the organisation, not just the product.

The question session soon showed that he was not alone in experiencing this kind of initial reaction from sales and marketing personnel. When asked to comment on the need for companies to change from traditional commission based reward systems he was decidedly adamant that a team had to work as a team and that linking any part to monetary rewards could have disastrous consequences. The self-assessment route clearly helped his company to overcome this difficulty as evidenced by his answer to the question "What aspects of the model delivered the fastest results?" His answer was "Bringing the team together under one goal".

Software for Self-assessment.

For organisations wishing to follow the BS EN ISO9000 route to continuous quality improvement there have been software products on the market for some time to facilitate automation of the process. The self-assessment concept is decidedly more recent and organisations wishing to follow this route have had little from which to choose. The BQF has, however, sought to rectify this by launching a new software product called ASSESS which provides the SME in particular with 'an inexpensive and credible method of measuring competitive performance and identifying areas for improvement'.

The product is available in two forms: 'Rapid Score', which is relatively quick and designed to provide a credible and thorough picture of the organisation's strengths and weaknesses without requiring a major commitment of time or other resources, and 'Valid Score' which is more intensive and rigorous, and is designed to be used with assistance from BQF experts and in conjunction with a full-blooded assessment programme.

The product has been designed by, amongst others, the EFQM, ICL, Rank Xerox, Nissan, The Bristol Quality Centre and Texas Instruments, who conducted a global benchmarking operation. Users of Valid Score who attain a score of over 350 points will be entitled to use a 350 plus Logo and Certificate showing the date of validation whilst those attaining 500 points may display a similar 500 plus Logo and Certificate.

[Issue 92 (August 1996) – 2nd Sheffield World Quality Congress]

Achieving Excellence in SMEs.

Since last year's conference there has been significant progress in the Sheffield Excellence Initiative, a not-for-profit partnership of Sheffield based organisations committed to assisting small and medium sized enterprises (SMEs) in the region to adopt the principles of the EFQM Business Excellence Model.

The paper by Tony Dodd and Mike Pupius of the Sheffield Excellence Forum traces the history of the Initiative from its roots in 1992 when, following adoption of the EFQM Model, Royal Mail Sheffield helped to establish the Sheffield and South Yorkshire Total Quality Forum. This subsequently led to the development of the Sheffield Centre for School Improvement and the Sheffield Excellence project which stemmed from a partnership between steel makers Avesta Sheffield and Sheffield University. The paper highlights lack of awareness of the principles and techniques of business excellence coupled with the high cost of learning and application as being the main reasons why smaller organisations have tended not to advance from the state of registration to ISO9000 to the concept of a permanent continuous improvement culture. Indeed many of them had only been cajoled into seeking certification by the demands of large business customers:

'Whilst the Quality Forum members were attempting to address the awareness issue by their very existence, lack of resources made this an impossible task. In early 1995 an opportunity was identified to access European Regional Development Funds (ERDF) to allow both of the above issues to be addressed. This would allow activity in SMEs. If Business Excellence could be introduced into the community via SMEs, community

organisations and schools then Sheffield would have taken the first key steps towards becoming a 'quality' city'.

With these funds a recipient organisation need typically pay only around 25 per cent of the cost of the support provided to greatly enhance its 'circles of excellence' which are shown diagrammatically in the conference book. Sheffield Excellence Forum members thus enjoy the following at a greatly subsidised rate:

*six days of training spread over two to three months beginning with an introduction to the EFQM Model and self-assessment to identify strengths and improvement opportunities, and ending with an action plan to address the improvement opportunities.

*two one day workshops sharing implementation experiences with other organisations.

*three days of one to one support designed to prevent any feelings of isolation once training is complete and ensure successful implementation.

*access to a central repository for Quality related items, including the quality libraries of many of the contributing partners, much of which would otherwise be beyond the reach and pocket of smaller organisations.

In addition to the above there is also the Sheffield Excellence Development Programme which provides a series of half day workshops in which groups of five or six SMEs develop their own self-assessment, create a continuous improvement implementation plan based on it, and implement it with the support of a mentor.

A further new initiative is the Sheffield Management Extension Programme operated by FDM Human Resources in association with the training managers Action for Employment. This harnesses the skills of umemployed managers under the government's Training for Work initiative to undertake projects such as the preparation and construction of manuals for the Investors In People initiative. Managers are matched to specific company assignments and are available for up to six months.

[Issue 98 (February 1997)]

TRAINING SURVEY HIGHLIGHTS SKILLS CRISIS IN SMALL COMPANIES

The success of Britain's small business sector is being threatened by a lack of strategic business skills according to a recent survey report by The Institute of Management and Cambridge University.

The report entitled 'Developing Managers for Smaller Businesses' finds in particular that whilst many managers accept that they lack important skills, they remain in the dark about where to turn to gain the training that they need.

A majority of managers (56 per cent) for example accept that they lack skills in strategy and planning, with 54 per cent lacking skills in training and development, 54 per cent in marketing and sales and 50 per cent in leadership.

The survey, which was based on discussions with opinion formers at national and local level, semi-structured interviews with managers of 20 small firms, and the responses of 503 IM Members to postal questionnaires, found that whilst managers average 2 to 3.5 days of training per year, about one in five undertakes no training at all and in firms with less than 200 employees this rises to one in four. The survey also found that many available training courses are considered to be inappropriate for small firms because they are seen as being aimed at the circumstances of large companies which are very different:

'The "big company" model of managing and career development does not apply to smaller businesses. Providers need to start from the standpoint of the small business customer; understanding their perspectives and respecting their differences '.

The IM's Director General Roger Young has called for government action to improve access to information and advice to meet this pressing need.

[Issue 105 (September 1997)]

ENVIRONMENT LOANS FOR SMEs

The European Commission and the European Investment Fund (EIF) have announced that they are to make a fund of 1.8 billion ECUs available to enable Small and Medium sized Enterprises to make environmental investments.

Funded by 26.5 million ECUs from the EU budget the project will make loans to SMEs with less than 100 employees prioritising those with less than 50, contributing up to 50 per cent of the costs of projects which generate significant environmental benefits (for example through pollution prevention or reduction, energy savings or improvements in the quality of products and services). The EIF has delegated responsibility for the approval and administration of individual loans to intermediary financial institutions in the Member States and interested companies in the UK have been advised to approach Barclays Bank. More details [ref: IP553] from The European Commission, 8 Storey's Gate, London SW1P 3AT. Telephone 01719731992.

E.C. ASSISTANCE FOR SME INNOVATION

The European Commission has announced a new 7.5 million ECU scheme to facilitate technological innovation on the part of Small and Medium sized Enterprises. Known as the I-TEC scheme it is designed to help SMEs overcome the traditional problems which they face in accessing funds by contributing to the project appraisal costs of venture capital operators. High growth technologically innovative companies are seen as being a key source of new jobs but can experience difficulty in raising venture capital as the expense of assisting new technologies deters potential investors.

The new scheme aims to build within venture fund companies a lasting capability to appraise and manage early stage investments. To this end it will contribute up to 50 per cent of initial appraisal and management costs via participating venture capital operators who will be selected by the European Investment Fund on the basis of a solid track record and an agreement to dedicate at least 25 per cent of their newly raised capital to early stage investments in technologically innovative SMEs. More information [ref: IP589] from the E.C. address as above.

[Issue 114 (June 1998)]

Health and Safety Competence in SMEs.

The results of Safety Solutions' investigation into standards of competence in health and safety in SMEs, undertaken on behalf of the European Commission late last year, were presented at the Eurosafety '98 Conference, at the Queen Elizabeth II Conference Centre, Westminster, on 27th and 28th April. The Executive Summary of the research report states the following:

'This study confirms that health and safety competence within SMEs in the UK does not uniformly meet the required standards. The cause of this shortfall has been found to be due to a number of elements; principally a lack of knowledge and understanding of health and safety procedures, which has regrettably, in some cases, resulted in complacency regarding the requirements'.

'It is suggested that the disparities between small and medium-sized companies, with regard to the existence of health and safety and competence levels, be explored in more depth in a secondary study. One conception is that small companies are adversely affected due to the fact that they do not have comparable provisions to spend on health and safety management like many medium companies. Nevertheless, the amount of time spent on health and safety is not necessarily directly proportional to the level of risk in a company'.

The research involved interviews with 300 SMEs of which 225 (75 %) were small companies (1 to 50 employees) and the remaining 75 (25 %) were medium (51 to 400 employees). Findings of the research are included in the Safety Solutions report and details the lack of awareness and application of safety training.

At the conference Ms. Jacqueline James, Health and Safety Policy Chairman of the Federation of Small Businesses (FSB) commented:

'The FSB does not accept that "qualifications" in a specific topic is necessarily the only indicator of ability or competence, as many valuable training opportunities arise that do not specifically lead to a qualification. We are, however, very supportive of approaches being made by some local authorities to provide short training Seminars of specific H and S Management issues to small firms in their locality. A good example is that of Test Valley District Council where the EHO is proposing to provide such sector-specific seminars to small firms in Hampshire, with brief supporting Information Sheets for delegates'.

Ms. James called for the Health and Safety Executive (HSE) to exercise greater control over Local Authority enforcement officers who are responsible for interpreting and applying the same H and S legislation at local level, yet are outside the direct control of the HSE except through the issue of Enforcement Guidelines.

[Issue 120 (December 1998)]

BENCHMARKING TOOLS FOR SMEs

In addition to the high prominence afforded to SMEs at this year's European Quality Forum in Paris (a whole day of pre-conference activity was devoted to it) several people with an SME focus were presented at this year's Benchmarking Forum in Cardiff.

These included papers by The Welsh Development Agency on 'Integrating Networks to generate Competitiveness among Regional Small Firms', by The Manchester Business School on 'Benchmarking the Finance Function: A practical Approach for SMEs', and by Cranfield University on 'Benchmarking Tools for SMEs'. This latter paper, by Alexandros Standalakis and G. Nelder is reviewed below.

The tools in question are the ADAPT –CORE tools which have been devised by Cranfield University in association with the ADAPT Co-operation Of Regions in Europe (CORE) project commissioned by the European Social Fund to improve the competitiveness of SMEs in five European regions (Nordrhein Westfalia and Hessia in Germany, Aragon in Spain, and Bedfordshire and Tyneside in the UK).

Unlike conventional benchmarking methodologies these tools allow companies to take small steps towards business excellence and learn from those which have better practices rather than simply seeking to compare themselves with the rest. The benchmarking process is applied at the top business level to provide information on the company profile and subsequently identify means by which the benchmarked company can improveits performance. In this, emphasis is not placed on criticism of the company's current performance but rather on recommendations to managers about actions which the company can take to improve its performance.

There are four component sub-processes as follows: -

(i) Data collection and performance measurement (data is collected in qualitative and quantitative formats horizontally and vertically in the company so as to profile it, identify communication problems, understand strengths and weaknesses, and analyse their correspondence with critical success factors that affect the business):

'To overcome the problem of objectivity over a single dataset, the EFQM based questionnaire is distributed both horizontally and vertically within the organisation. Top and middle management datasets are essential for the analysis process, as managers emphasise and actualise the basis for decision making through crucial internal information. The process also recognises that shopfloor workers are of high importance as they provide the foundations for the business operation. Ideally, returns from shopfloor workers will account for as much as 40% of the received datasets form any given company.'

'The completed questionnaires are subsequently analysed to provide a consensus set of data, which is employed to provide information about the company profile'.

(ii) Mapping of company profile (on a performance reference grid so as to position the company against external practices and its peers):

'To position the performance and competitiveness 'of an SME, the Enablers versus Results graph is employed, which has been developed employing the proven practice performance grid used by the CBI, IBM and the London Business School for the Probe Benchmarking Initiative. Through the Enablers/Results grid, sources of superior performance expertise are identified, regardless of company sector'.

(iii) Knowledge transfer from better practices (direct comparison of the performance of the company with that of better performing enterprises):

'The grid provides the opportunity for a higher degree of control over the choice of benchmarking partner. For example, an SME classified as lagging might select to improve its practices (enablers) to become identified as a

"pursuing success" company before attempting to become a World-Class manufacturer'.

(iv) Provision of recommendations about better practices (prioritising the areas for improvement through the use of an lease versus effect grid'):

'A company which is classified as "exposed" can develop a benchmarking partnership with a company which is "pursuing success". Consequently both companies will be of complementary performance and will learn from each other's practices, towards achieving World-Class status'.

The process is being supported through a web-based tool which was designed and developed to support trans-regional and trans-national co-operation aiming to enhance the accessibility of best practice across regional and national boundaries. Both the process and the tool have been designed to comply with the needs of SMEs for a benchmarking approach that is accessible, incremental, gives benefit at each stage, builds confidence alongside progress, and enhances the competitiveness of the micro-level companies.

[Issue 134 (March 2000)]

NEW QUALITY STANDARD FOR SMEs

A new quality standard designed to introduce small and medium sized enterprises to basic quality management has been launched by The Association of Quality Management Consultants International (AQMCI) in conjunction with the Institute of Quality Assurance.

The AQMCI Foundation Standard for SMEs requires a regularly reviewed annual plan related to objectives, targets, training and resources but does not require an ISO 9000 style documented system. It is therefore envisaged that it will be less imposing to SMEs, free from the perceived cost burdens and bureaucracy often associated with ISO 9000, whilst at the same time encouraging improved performance. Training to the standard is available through AQMCI. Details are available from David Hewings, The Association of Quality Management Consultants International, P.O.Box 152, Newton Abbot, Devon. TQ13 7YU.

[Issue 135 (April 2000)]

QUALITY FIRST FOR TIPPERARY

Three small businesses based in South Tipperary -Diesel Injection Services, Montip Engineering and My Own Food Products have become the first three organisations to receive the Foundation Mark for Quality in Tipperary. The pilot for this project was completed in July 1999 by the South Tipperary County Enterprise Board.

The new Foundation Mark is modelled on existing quality recognition schemes such as ISQ 9000 and Excellence Ireland's a Mark, but is geared specifically to the needs of smaller owner-managed businesses.

There are five key elements (Leadership and Planning, People Management, Management of Resources, Operations and Process Management, and Results). The first four of these are grouped collectively under the heading of Management Practices'. For each of the elements managers are required to ask themselves a number of questions, positive answers to which indicate that the organisation is operating 'in a quality way', whilst negative answers indicate areas for improvement. In support of the new Mark, Excellence Ireland state:

'Micro-enterprises in their first years of business need a framework to help structure a formal way of managing their business, and to define the key processes required to do so. The Foundation Mark, as part of Excellence Ireland's overall Business Excellence programme, enables them to lay the foundations for their future direction, and to take advantage of all opportunities to enhance their competitiveness both at home and the international arena'.

The Foundation Mark was funded through the EU Adapt Programme. More details may be obtained from Excellence Ireland, Merrion Hall, Strand Road, Sandymount, Dublin 4.

[Issue 139 (Winter 2000)]

QUALITY ISSUES AFFECTING THE SMALL BUSINESS

The annual John Loxham Lecture hosted by the Institute of Quality Assurance, was held this year at the Manchester Airport Hilton Hotel on World Quality Day, 9th November, and was given by the National Chairman of the Federation of Small Businesses Mr. Ian Handford.

In his talk, which proved popular attracting an audience of around 160, he spoke at length about the burden of over-regulation currently being borne by small businesses in the UK, and called upon the Government to declare an 'amnesty' on new legislation for two to three years to help ease the present administrative chaos.

He described it as a "nightmare" for entrepreneurs to be continually faced with pressure to conform to the requirements of a multitude of inspectorates each with their own little inadequacies and made reference to a recent FSB survey which showed that whilst 70% of small businesses were keen to expand their commercial activities they were in practice largely deterred from doing so as a result of the bureaucratic barriers which they faced.

As for quality related issues he spoke of ISO9000 as a contributor to the "disillusionment" of small businesses and was notably critical of the way in which the standard was sold. Standards must be affordable, relevant and practicable in use rather than threatening the viability of the businesses they seek to help, he said.

Not all of the message was negative, however, as he pointed to future partnership development with the IQA and proposals for a self-certification scheme for small businesses that would aim to cut through a lot of red tape.

Questions from the audience included one about the perception of quality by small businesses and in particular whether most viewed quality purely in relation to over-regulation as against a mechanism for improvement. In his answer Mr. Handford emphasised the need for quality to be affordable. It may be an ideal, but frequently for a small business it is not a priority. Regulations on the other hand are mandatory with everyone hoping that they will not become " a shifting playing field".

Ian Handford has been self employed since 1970 following an earlier career in office administration. He continued to work in his office service business until last year. He was a founder member of the then Federation of Self-employed and Small Businesses in 1975 and became FSB National Chairman in 1998. He has wide experience of lobbying at the national level and has met most leading ministers and politicians of successive governments as well as policy makers in Whitehall. As a proliferate writer on business matters he has achieved considerable profile in the media.

A full report of Mr. Handford's lecture will be published in *Quality World* early in the New Year .

Chapter Sixteen

Miscellaneous Articles

A number of articles featured in Quality Matters do not fit easily under any of the previous chapter headings. Nevertheless they are certainly worthy of inclusion either because they cover more specialised quality subjects, such as waste elimination, quality costing, Kaizen, and Minimalist Manufacturing, or because they are based on more general themes as in the case of the presentations by, for example Dixie Dean and Edward de Bono, who is well known for his pioneering work in the field of Lateral Thinking and who was a Keynote Speaker at the 1999 EFQM Learning Edge Conference, which has now become an established spring event complementing the main EFQM Business Excellence Forum in the autumn.

A number of the articles in this section relate to the assessment of the relative success or otherwise of the application of TQM, which has to some fallen into disrepute during the 1990s largely as a result of misapplication. Special mention is also made of the work of Joseph Juran, who alongside Deming has been recognised as one of the outstanding contributors to the quality movement for many decades.

A significant proportion of the articles relate to the twin subjects of certification and accreditation without being directly concerned with ISO9000, and cover, for example the merger of NAMAS and the NACCB to form UKAS in 1995, which was a key institutional change of the 1990s. This was followed by the first UKAS accreditation withdrawal in 1997, which was to have important legal implications. Other articles such as the book review 'Living Tomorrow's Company' featured in January 1999, and the Keynote address by Martin Brenig-

Jones, Head of Corporate Quality for British Telecom at the 1999 Sheffield Hallam conference, look toward future trends in management. Last but not least there is the First Quality Conference for Public Administrations in the EU held in May 2000 and representing another milestone in the never ending quest for quality which at last is at least making some impact in the otherwise slow moving public sector.

WORLD QUALITY CERTIFICATION

One of the most prominent, and at times controversial issues facing modern day quality management is that of certification of products, services, systems and processes. Standards form the basis of certification, but their evolution has varied as different conventions have given rise to variations in priorities for assessment criteria and methods; the issue of whose convention to apply has not always been straightforward.

On 8th and 9th October an international conference was organised by the Institute of Quality Assurance and the European Organization for Quality at the Heathrow Penta Hotel, London, which sought to explain the progress that has been made thus far in the field of certification and provide a forum in which interested parties could voice their opinions and question distinguished speakers on aspects which may be giving them concern. Around half of the delegates were from overseas with strong representation from Eastern Europe and Brazil in particular.

The opening address was made by Sir Denis Rooke, FRS, President of the IQA, who described the event as 'a confirmation of solidarity within Europe' with quality certification now a worldwide issue. The search for ultimate quality, however, remains 'a search for a never ending goal'.

The Qualification of Assessors

One important and sometimes contentious issue associated with certification is the qualification of assessors, and this was addressed by Philip Corner, Chairman of the Assessor Registration Board of the Institute of Quality Assurance.

He said that the standard ISO10011 Part 2: 1991 defining qualification criteria for auditors was 'a great help' in laying down minimum qualification criteria for quality system auditors, and then listed several qualities which he believed were important for auditors to possess:

* ability to evaluate perceptions (overcome hostility, gain co-operation, and have no more time to waste than the person being questioned).

* open mindedness (willing to accept new ways of getting things done).

* a sense of fairness.

* an ability to perceive the truth.

* ability to resist distraction (aversion for red herrings).

1001

* courage to make conclusions known (even if this means dashing hopes).

* integrity (not abusing power and trust).

* ability to think logically (to evaluate whether parts of a quality system are logically consistent with each other and with the standard).

* ability to detect ambiguity, recognizing whether the question being answered is that being asked, and identifying 'politicians answers'.

* a sense of proportion (understanding what is likely to work and what isn't).

He said he felt that the standard fell short by insisting only on a secondary education, and it had too little to say on the all-important subject of product knowledge. He also felt that its stipulation of four years' experience in the workplace should be 'an absolute minimum'.

He recommended that at least one member of an auditing team had technical knowledge sufficient to enable the team to know where to look for failure, and emphasized the need for auditors to be able to recognize the type of organisation with which they are dealing.

Finally he suggested that to maintain an adequate supply of good assessors in the future there will need to be more women recruited, particularly in the 'caring professions' where they predominate and where they frequently possess the right qualities for the job.

Delegates were advised that the scheme originally set up for the benefit of assessors in the UK is currently being applied in 36 countries.

[Issue 35 (November 1991)]

QUALITY COUNTS

In recognition of the need to control quality at all stages of the production and distribution chain the Institute of Packaging selected a quality theme for its biennial conference held this year at the Hilton National Hotel, Warwick on 17th and 18th October.

Conflicts in Quality

Management consultant Dixie Dean, who has some fifty years of experience in industry, expressed his concern that many conflicts in the quality chain are being overlooked rather than investigated or resolved.

He identified eight potentially conflicting areas, and whilst reference is made to specific examples in the packaging industry, the principles are equally valid in other industries:

(i) Sampling vs improved cleanliness

Random sampling of incoming materials is still practised by many
companies as part of the quality system, but many companies are unaware
that such sampling can cause contamination and in that in this neglected area
the training of personnel can be critical. Also question -are the statistics as
valid as you think?

(ii) Innovation vs inspection

An audit Inspection may identify serious deficiencies in an innovative
company's quality control procedures (sometimes they have virtually none)
and the recommendation is made that the company is unsuitable. However,
their innovation potential is being ignored, for the sake of control
procedures.

(iii) Development vs specifications

Writing a specification particularly at an early stage on a new idea,
innovation or invention, can be thwarted with difficulties due to limitations
of knowledge and detail available at that stage.

(iv) Assembly of multiple components vs on-line operations

Assembly can be a real weakness and observation of technical factors which
may influence assembly and performance, need on-going improved
assessment if quality is to be assured. [The Japanese are superb in this area –
Ed]

(v) Conflicts of discipline

Politics can dictate that departments compete for recognition to such an
extent that the Purchasing Dept. says only the quality man is allowed in the
purchasing department of a supplier, which can be a disaster. The need for a
packaging co-ordination function to sort out priorities between disciplines is
stressed.

(vi) Conflicts in training

A large number of companies still believe that learning by example and
experience, is not only the best way, but call it training. The result is
attitudes that resist change. To motivate you must create interest: the attitude
of 'don't tell them anything because they will be more dangerous if they have
a little knowledge' is a disaster.

(vii) The 'fail when in doubt syndrome'.

When faced with a situation where a certain feature is 'out of specification' this may or may not lead to a clear-cut decision. However, if the person who has to make this decision reflects the wrong decision may give rise to criticism, the safety tactic is to 'fail', especially if a superior can subsequently over-ride it and take over the responsibility for the use of an apparently sub-standard material. Consequently many companies have poor quality built into their specifications. Many have 'grown like Topsy' with irrelevancies still there ten years later. [This conflict is at the heart of the Juran philosophy for 'Fitness for Purpose' judgement – Ed]

(viii) Environmental issues

Today's environmental issues are in constant debate and anything 'bad' about packaging is seen as 'good news' by the media. Consequently the general public's reaction to packaging is growing in an alarmingly biased manner. Minimising the depletion use of both non-renewable and renewable resources; minimising total energy involved in materials and the total packaging operation (including recovery processes); and minimising pollution, are all translatable into improved quality of life (incorporating the land, atmosphere and all water sources).

In conclusion:

'Too frequently certain facets of a (Quality) situation i.e. statistical control, TQM, BS5750, are glibly accepted by the fact that they all represent a step in the right direction. Although no-one is likely to deny this, we are all occasionally slow to recognize the weaknesses which remain and are slow to move onto the next thinking challenge '.

[Issue 57 (September 1993)]

QUALITY MANAGEMENT FAILS TO DELIVER?

Quality management is failing to deliver all of its promised results according to a major new report from the Institute of Management.

The report, entitled 'Quality and the Manager', based on written self-completion questionnaires sent to 4000 members of the former British Institute of Management, showed that of the 880 respondents (22 per cent) only around 8 per cent saw their organisation's drive for quality as very successful. The majority either claimed only a moderate success or were neutral.

Some 71 per cent of managers reported that their organisations had implemented a formal campaign, whilst a further 11 per cent said that they intended to do so, with 21 per cent of organisations having introduced a campaign within the past year, 40 per cent within the past five years and 10 per cent dating back beyond five years.

Some 80 per cent expected their quality campaigns to run indefinitely whilst just 3 per cent foresaw their campaigns ending within a year. Less than half of the respondents claimed an improvement in sales or profitability although the majority reported improvements in less tangible benefits such as teamwork and morale.

Four out of ten believe that all employees should have ownership, whilst a third believe responsibility lies with senior managers. Nine per cent feel it lies with quality control specialists.

Quality of management was seen as a bigger barrier than quality of employees with over half seeing management quality as at least a minor difficulty. Less than four per cent judged commitment from trades unions as a major difficulty, although one in ten highlighted lack of commitment from middle managers, supervisors and employees as a major difficulty.

Most respondents apparently believed that quality management did not significantly increase their level of discretion or improve their career prospects, and only 13 per cent judged their training in quality management as 'very good'.

Over half believed that they needed more training in quality management tools and techniques whilst a third said that they wanted more training in project management skills and quality management philosophy.

Some correlation is reported between the organisations that take the quality performance line and those whose quality programmes are judged a success. Difficulty in assessing the impact of quality of bottom line performance is recognised, however, as impeding the maintenance of the momentum of some quality initiatives.

Less than half of the organisations have achieved a formal quality standard such as BS5750, although approximately another quarter are said to be aiming for one.

The Director General of the Institute of Management, Mr. Roger Young, says:

"The survey provides mixed news. It is encouraging that so many organisations have made a formal long term commitment to quality management but it is disappointing that some lack of commitment by top management together with inadequate resources is a barrier to achievement. Implemented properly it can improve profits, employee motivation and customer loyalty. It affects every aspect of an organisation's performance and should be seen as a prerequisite not an optional extra ".

Eliminating Waste at Thorn Lighting

In the present climate of recession many if not most or all organisations are eagerly seeking to reduce costs. Some would argue, however, that the key to building a successful enterprise or country lies not so much in cutting costs as in eliminating waste, and the excellent presentation with the title of 'The Understanding, Investigation, and Elimination of Waste within a Medium Sized Company' by T.S.F. Gerloch and J.L. Packer of Thorn Lighting, Spennymoor, County Durham, explains how one northern company has challenged the traditional perception of waste and made waste elimination central to their drive for Total Quality.

The paper argues that waste, rather than being 'items that physically go out with the rubbish' is 'any activity that increases costs but does not add value to the company' and its elimination requires resources and opportunities to be maximised to their full potential without incurring a detrimental effect to the customer.

A cost of quality trend, showed graphically how the company follows a typical trend of prevention, appraisal and failure costs and illustrated how these costs accounted for around 3 per cent of turnover early this year. As a clear improvement shown on similar costs in 1989, it could be concluded that as the way in which the company operates is improved, the level of waste in various activities is reduced. Also some unnecessary or redundant functions can be removed, enabling a saving to be made. Elimination of waste could thus be said to be the output of continuous improvement, but this assumes that there are no further costs, and the paper suggests that this assumption could in practice be incorrect, since a considerable amount of waste is invisible. So rather than assuming that the elimination of waste is the output of continuous improvement, perhaps a better approach may be to consider continuous improvement as an output of the elimination of waste. i.e. focus on waste elimination as the means to identify problems and opportunities.

Three stages of development are outlined for tackling waste elimination:

(i) a basic education for all in what constitutes waste so that no one remains a 'willing waster' by virtue of being in ignorance.

(ii) an awareness programme whereby everyone is trained to become a 'waste watcher'.

(iii) provision of tools and power that will enable everyone to actively investigate, reduce and in time eliminate the sources of waste, so that 'waste watchers' are enabled to evolve into 'waste busters'.

In their outline the authors point out that whilst it is possible to become an expert on the general nature of waste no-one can become an expert on all of the wasteful practices in the company, and advocate that the person who can best contribute the ideas that will lead to waste savings will invariably be the person who has at some time caused or been affected by the problem. Hence the involvement of every one in the company [or country -Ed] is required.

It was then explained how resources might typically be wasted i.e. by expending them aimlessly, using them uneconomically, failing to take full advantage of them or indeed by destroying them. A division of resources into categories is recommended to help manage the 'vast array of wastes' that contribute to loss.

A typical company resource profile was presented, divided into the groups of people, time, materials, space, energy, information, reputation, equipment and money. Of these the key resource identified is people, since this resource influences all of the others. Various types of waste are then described:

* staff losses (high labour turnover is bad because it represents an investment that is leaving for good, and the real costs of turnover equate to an average of six months' salary and up to two years in some jobs before effective replacement is achieved).

* absenteeism (there are lots of hidden costs here, such as permanent over-staffing to cover the expected level of absenteeism, temporary workers and/or overtime to cover additional unexpected losses, and the impact on morale if it stays unchecked).

* waste in training (giving the wrong training to many people, using people just to fill in spaces on courses, lack of a structure that allows training to be implemented in the workplace, giving irrelevant training with too many 'flavours of the month', management wanting training but being unaware of what is appropriate, and using training as a 'quick fix' rather than for long-term development).

* fire-fighting waste (a major UK service organisation with a multi-billion pound turnover was found to spend 2 hours 35 minutes per 7 hour day on this, whilst in another so called 'successful' company one whole day of each employee's time was likewise spent every week).

* waste in meetings (many people spend over 40 per cent of their working time at meetings, some senior managers over 60 per cent, yet many of them lack purpose, have poor or no agendas, are not prepared and result in unclear actions).

* design changes (notably costs incurred through excessive paperwork in operating the procedure, use of obsolete parts, re-handling of products, replacement jigs and fixtures).

Further examples mentioned include failure to meet customer demands and expectations the first time, estimated to cost most companies 15 to 30 per cent of their sales revenue, and the cost of replacing materials when a substitute cannot be obtained on the same terms:

'It can be alarming to draw a flowchart all the side effects of material shortages from the time spent sourcing more supplies to the delays in production '.

Much of the waste, unfortunately, is embedded within a total system, being part of the way people work since they have always done things in the same old way, and it appears small and insignificant, as a consequence of being thinly spread, until it is finally examined as a whole [i.e. within the context of a total system -Ed]. Hence there is a need for everyone 'to become a detective and ask questions', and perhaps not just ask whether the activity is being done with minimum waste, but also whether a particular activity should be done at all.

It is suggested that companies should beware even of costing some individual types of waste as reactions such as 'is that all?' or 'It's not worth my effort' may not be uncommon. Videoing of everyday examples of waste on the other hand may be 'a valuable way to make the subject tangible and increase people's awareness of the extent of the problem'.

It is explained how Thorn has learned from past experience, for example, when a suggestion scheme resulted in 'waste busting' being perceived to be the responsibility of a specific group of people, and one man 'waste audits', whilst producing good savings were found to be unsustainable.

It was illustrated practically how success may be achieved at individual and team level, with an example of how an individual's study of company car usage resulted in savings of over £15,000 per year. Also described was the case of a team which achieved a 70 per cent reduction in scrap costs and work in progress, and a reduction in changeover time from 30 minutes down to 2 with bottom line savings of £130,000. This was a project 'to eliminate non-value added operations in the manufacturing process and promote customer-supplier relationships.

WINNING THROUGH VISION

The 24th David Hutchins International Total Quality Users Convention, entitled 'Winning Through Vision' was held at the Royal Lancaster Hotel in London on 12th and 13th October, featuring 22 presentations.

First Steps in Process Re-engineering

Process re-engineering is a popular concept at the moment and to help explain it simply, P. Coldwell, Head of Process Management for British Telecom gave a presentation entitled 'Process Re-engineering -First Steps'.

Beginning with the age old quotation from Machiavelli's 'The Prince' (1513), that 'There is nothing more difficult to plan, more doubtful of success, nor more dangerous to manage than the creation a new system', the speaker explained how the subject of change management has always been fraught with danger, no matter how desperate the need for change is:

'The initiator has the enmity of all who would profit by the preservation of the old system and merely lukewarm defenders in those who would gain by the new one'.

It is suggested that process re-engineering 'will shake the very cultural foundations' of the organisation, as it will almost certainly lead to changes in the way people work. If it is a planned move (rather than being spontaneous) the company may well be half way there, but it goes without saying that the commitment of the Chairman is critical. If he doesn't want to do it, do not attempt, is the advice.

Process re-engineering is seen as 'the way towards radical improvement' rather than a means towards incremental gains of the type that would be achievable through localised improvement or the more disciplined approach of continuous improvement through process management. It is implicit that radical improvement is more likely following radical change, but the business risk likewise increases by at least the same ratio and could be tenfold.

Process re-engineering is defined as:

'Taking a fundamental look at what you do, determining if that is a reasonable activity to continue doing, then without regard to present methods, technology or people, deciding how most efficiently it should be done'.

The radical change resulting from it was equated to either a whole number of small changes which, when gathered together is radical, or a total zero-based review of the organisation, completely ignoring politics. Given this radicalness senior management is advised not to talk in terms of process re-engineering when considering it. A better approach is to use terms and concepts that are familiar, then seek to create an environment that is conducive to it once the ideas have been favourably received.

It was explained how the 'triple headed monster' of recession, competition and regulation drove BT to re-engineer 'probably the most open telecommunications market in the world'. Whilst regulators have set targets that have remained fixed in appearance for the last four years, in practice things have far from stayed the same. Three years ago there may have been some credibility in the argument that overmanning existed. This is now much more difficult to justify, the speaker claimed, pointing out that some 70,000 people have left BT during the last two years.

In his paper Mr. Coldwell refers to 'enjoying the transformation and the benefits that successful implementation can bring', but equally 'opening up new concepts to your engineers, managers and other people can be disastrous'. It is suggested that once the rationale for change has been established a simple plan for business transformation needs to be made that includes 'a broad spectrum of the necessary change levers' incorporating cultural, organisational and technological involvement. The Board, he says, must be convinced of the need to do this.

In this, one should aim to 'capture the totality of operations' and 'debar escapees', remembering that existing organisational boundaries may have little relevance to the operational effectiveness of processes, and so should be ignored. Outside help may be used 'to get the best dispassionate view of existing prospects'.

To ensure the totality of operations classical value add methods are advocated with five logical elements:

*understand current activity

*develop a vision

*improve processes using Continuou Improvement

*identify processes for radical change

*re-engineer and automate the 'chosen few'

Value chain analysis helps to define those processes which are of the real add value type and to identify those support processes that add that value is advocated. However, one is urged not to become discouraged if some support processes appear to perform in a negative way. Convincing Finance and Personnel Directors that their role is merely supporting can be fun, he says.

Where organisations are by tradition vertically focused one may need to create a more lateral focus and to enable this it is suggested that process owners be made responsible for the delivery of lateral processes. Readers, however, are urged to beware of organisational theorists that advocate organising business along the horizontal axis, since as many if not more problems can occur.

A model implementation plan for process re-engineering is presented along with examples of successes from the now 50 process improvement teams which have become 'the key to maintaining enthusiasm'. These include:

* reduction in stock holding of 50 per cent.

* improvements in delivery performance from 10 to 3 days.

* financial improvements of over 100 per cent in Chargecard (one of BT's products) operations.

* a 50 per cent on time improvement for Megastream.

By building on benefits like these, BT is now looking to make process re-engineering a core part of the company's future plans and has launched a revitalised programme aimed to drive more vertical change with each aspect being championed at Divisional Managing Director level.

[Issue 69 (September 1994)]

DOES QUALITY WORK?

To help managers to gain a clearer picture of what can be expected from TQM, The Conference Board has compiled a 'survey of surveys' to show what companies have experienced in the US and suggest a possible model for success. A total of 20 surveys is featured along with a conclusion which attempts to answer the question 'Does Quality Work ?' with sound reasoning.

It begins with an Executive Summary which highlights the continuing spread of quality improvement initiatives throughout American industry and the increasing use of Baldrige Award criteria as a means to self-improvement. It suggests that a long-term link between use of the Baldrige criteria and improved business performance exists.

The method by which survey data was selected is then described along with details of the screening process which consisted of four criteria:

*a focus on TQM practices of organisations

*results based on a sample of multiple organisations

*information provided concerning the nature of the TQM practices studied

*no obvious major flaws in methodology

It is noted that these screening criteria disqualified around a dozen studies, including one on employee suggestion schemes which failed to show how many suggestion systems were actually part of a TQM process.

In the Introduction which follows some of the reasons for producing the report are described, notably the comments and concerns expressed by members of The Conference Board's Total Quality Management Center Steering Committee and Quality Councils, about media reporting of the effectiveness of TQM during 1992 and 1993. Also this responded to the desires of Conference Board members to have a broader assessment based on a larger sample of companies than had hitherto been available.

The 'Review of TQM Research' then describes the surveys and some of the important points stemming from them, pointing out the fact that findings may differ and in some cases may consist merely of the opinions of the executives who completed them. Case histories of individual companies and programmes are excluded from the report, which has purposefully taken the approach of presenting only conclusions that have been drawn from the data obtained i.e. not the opinions of respondents.

Examples of surveys presented include the Alophastat Research Corporation Survey of US Manufacturers which observes that 'Quality is a way of life in a quarter of all firms with TQM processes'; the AMA Survey on Quality and Customer Satisfaction Programs which is 'helpful in defining TQM -style approaches'; the ASOC/Gallup Survey of Executives and Directors which suggests general satisfaction with the impact of TQM on performance among individuals at the top of large US companies'; the Automotive Supplier Survey which 'indicates that managers perceive improvement-focused TQM practices to be effective tools for change'; the Conference Board Overview of Successful TQM Cases, a qualitative study of advanced TQM processes which concludes that 'while the financial performance of participating companies varies, each would probably have performed considerably worse had it not made the changes associated with TQM'; the Ernst and Young and American Quality Foundation International Quality Study which 'found that the value of many TQM practices varied with the initial level of the organisation on the three performance measures used (profits, productivity and quality)'; and the IBM Internal Study of Market Driven Quality which is said to be 'the first to provide detailed comparative data on the performance of TQM practices'.

An analysis of the surveys reveals that more than half of the US companies which have adopted TQM rely on the Baldrige criteria as an integral standard by which to define TQM and measure quality progress. Also the large number of internal and market measures used suggests that TQM drives bottom line performance indirectly, first by improving internal performance which then improves market performance and ultimately profits. A table illustrates 'a plausible explanation' of how TQM practices may be linked to bottom line performance.

In the final section of the analysis and in the Conclusion a core set of TQM elements is identified from the survey information, which provides a platform upon which to build a successful model of TQM using a 'shopping list' approach. It is suggested that:

'A shopping list does not ensure a successful dinner party, but it certainly reduces the likelihood of a disaster'.

[Issue 70 (October 1994)]

POLITICAL PRESSURE: THE ENEMY OF QUALITY?

The ability of public sector managers to resist political interference in their operational decisions has declined markedly over the last three years according to the results of a recent survey by the Institute of Management (IM) and the Centre for Public Services Management at the South Bank University.

The survey involved the despatch of some 3,000 questionnaires to IM members working in the public sector, and 800 to senior managers in local government and the Health Service. This produced 1,160 responses which suggests that some 40 per cent of public sector managers feel inadequately supported for dealing with political influences. It is said to be 'particularly disturbing given the respondents' experience of increased political interference'.

The managers were apparently least enthusiastic about performance related pay which the report suggests 'needs to be more carefully designed to meet specific circumstances rather than be subject to blanket introduction'.

A majority of managers (73 %) were, however, reported as willing to accept and implement change and the introduction of quality programmes is said to have received positive acceptance. Although there has been an increase in the use of quality management techniques it is noted that public sector managers in general have not been empowered to change the more direct means of control, e.g. hiring, firing and grading of staff. The report queries:

"We are willing to change but a period of stability is needed in between each initiative rather than trying to rush everything through at once".

A third of public sector managers apparently lack the training and development to cope with change, with some lacking the crucial tools that they need in order to manage effectively, particularly with regard to decisions on personnel policy. There is also noted to be a strong trend towards the use of organisational mission statements, but a much lower trend towards relying on a sense of mission as against the use of rule books to regulate staff activity.

In response to the findings the IM's Director General Mr. Roger Young commented:

"Reforms in the public sector mean that many more managers are coming into direct contact with their political masters. If politicians want public organisations to be empowered to take decisions and run their own affairs then these same politicians must give organisations the freedom to do so".

[Issue 74 (February 1995)]

BOOK REVIEW: Keiretsu: inside the Hidden Japanese Conglomerates.

Authors: Kenichi Miyashita and David Russell (225 pages).

Publisher: McGraw Hill (ISBN-0-07-042583-3)

Details:

Kenichi Miyashita, former senior editor of PHP (highly respected Japanese publishing house) and David Russell, an American journalist with over a decade of experience in Japan, who is currently managing editor of Tokyo Business Today, together present what is described as 'the first unbiased examination of the Keiretsu' and its 'inner system of corporate co-operation'.

After introducing the Keiretsu as 'the most basic "geography" of Japanese business' the authors present nine chapters, which describe the evolution and operation of the three basic types of Keiretsu: horizontal, vertical and distribution and attempt to provide an indication of their present and future trends.

The first chapter sets the scene with the observation that everyone is in practice surrounded by the Keiretsu at the present time:

'Quietly, secretly, without warning, keiretsu have infiltrated our daily lives and engulfed almost every thing we know'.

The term itself does not readily translate into English, but has a broad meaning of 'affiliate with' or 'connect to' and the authors have sought to simplify this by defining a keiretsu, in its simplest form, as a group of individual units viewed together, usually as a hierarchical organisation'. They are typically united by a flow of, for example, money or personnel or in some cases personal loyalty [almost feudal -Ed]. They are by no means confined to Japan, and indeed on the first page several non-Japanese examples are cited. What distinguishes the Japanese keiretsu, however, is their sheer size:

'Certain Japanese keiretsu are not merely loose connections between a company and a few of its related firms, but groups of thousands of companies all working for a single large firm. Other keiretsu are made up of dozens of these huge firms (together with their thousands of small companies) bound together as gigantic industrial combines. Even this would not in and of itself merit much attention, but against the background of US-Japan trade friction, the term keiretsu, replacing the more colourful, but less accurate expression Japan Inc., has become a label for fraternal collusion to keep foreign goods and services eternally knocking at the door'.

The number of keiretsu is also significant, estimated to be 'in the thousands and much higher'.

In the second chapter the evolution of the keiretsu is traced to the Meiji Restoration of 1868 in which hereditary shoguns were effectively replaced by elite civil servants, whilst in the third a description is given of what essentially forms the heart of the horizontal keiretsu i.e. banks and trading companies. The role of the main banks as central clearing houses for information about group companies and providers of management assistance is noted:

'In the worst case, if one of the group firms is in serious trouble, the main bank is expected to step in with both financial assistance and a whole new management team selected from among the bank's executives'.

The critical role of the general trading companies or 'Sogo Shosha', of which there are nine key players, as providers of credit to small and medium sized enterprises is also introduced:

'Whereas the main banks in a sense "insure" the business of the top level of their group companies, the shosha "insure" the thousands of fringe firms, both inside and outside their own group, via trade credit'.

It is noted that the average amount of trade credit outstanding for the manufacturing sector is more than double the corresponding level in the US, largely as a result of the 'Sogo Shushas', the influence of which 'has enormous impact on the ability of small Japanese companies to do business smoothly':

'The banks, which would normally have to perform innumerable credit checks on thousands of small companies, can relax and expand their guaranteed loan base because the shosha has done all the credit checking in advance and so assumes the risk itself'.

[the number of accountants employed in Japan is of orders of magnitude less than in Western countries -Ed].

In contrast to the US government's view that shoshas 'control imports and distribution to such an extent that they limit the entry of American goods to the Japanese market' the authors contest that 'the import of cheaper US goods and their sale inside Japan at comparatively high prices would provide a guaranteed high margin business' which 'no shosha would be likely to turn down'.

The fourth chapter introduces 'other common structural features of the big horizontal keiretsu', such as presidential councils, cross-shareholding, interlocking directorates and intragroup trade patterns whilst the fifth describes The Big Six horizontal keiretsu, which are essentially bank centred, and how they work.

The sixth chapter contrasts the horizontal keiretsu where the members all belong to the same 'club' and the relations are basically 'horizontal' with the vertical type each of which is pyramidal and headed by a single powerful company. Examples of the vertical type include Toyota, Hitachi and Matsushita Electric. The third type, the distribution keiretsu, is then introduced as a subgroup of the vertical type, which controls much of Japan's retailing, deciding which products will appear in stores and showrooms and at what price. Most major manufacturers are noted to possess both of these vertical forms, which together are viewed as an 'hourglass' model. This brings implications for sub-contracting:

'In Japan the big firms have never liked dealing with independent subcontractors, precisely because they are independent. If a manufacturer effectively controls its sub-contractors the whole structure of manufacturing changes. First, a large part of design work can be farmed out, freeing up staff at the parent company for other projects. Second, the quality as well as the efficiency of production can be assured because the parent and the subcontractor exist in a long-term relationship '.

Cost implications are significant since it is invariably cheaper to undertake work in a sub-contracting plant than in the main parent plant.

The seventh chapter elaborates on the functioning of the large vertical keiretsu in automobiles and electronics, again emphasising the pyramidal nature of the structure which in practice renders the big companies no more than traders, with the main work of design, testing, production, assembly and delivery being undertaken almost entirely by sub-contractors. The special case of Toyota, the largest industrial combine in Japan, makes particularly interesting reading, developing as it is into something of a hybrid between a vertical keiretsu and a horizontal one.

The eighth chapter, entitled 'Voices from inside the Pyramid' by contrast reads like 'Tales from the Crypt'. It features actual comments from sub-contractors working within the pyramid, which the authors describe as 'revealing'. They contrast markedly with the common view that the large manufacturers 'treat their sub-contractors rather well' and 'nurture the little companies in their groups and help them to grow'. The president of one small machine shop, for example, says:

'The whole song and dance stops as soon as you look below the big companies' first tier factories. At the first tier sub-contractors things may not be too bad, but as you go down to the second and third and fourth tiers, people are being fired left and right'.

A different complexion therefore emerges. The executive managing director of a leading sub-contractor for a major car maker is later quoted on the subject of quality:

'At fixed intervals the parent conducts inspections of all the important firms in its keiretsu. People from the Quality Control section come around and inspect your factory from top to bottom. Our people are terrified of these visits because they can use any excuse to shut you down '.

Most revealing, however, are perhaps the comments of a vice-president of an electronics related firm working within the pyramid of one of the smaller auto manufacturers:

'What is the purpose of a keiretsu anyway? If all it makes us do is hate the people we work for and pushes us towards bankruptcy, retirement or an early grave, what's the point? All the big Japanese companies are competing with each other to save Y10 on a Y4,000,000 product. It just can't go on: We're dying'.

The last chapter concludes that whilst 'Keiretsification' has been unquestionably successful in 'raising the national standard of living from poverty levels to among the highest in the world' and that membership in the horizontal keiretsu offers 'very real' benefits, interestingly the major benefit is not in the form of profit, the vertical keiretsu is essentially inflexible and some of the distribution keiretsu 'are in trouble'. Some changes are therefore envisaged, notably more companies crossing keiretsu lines to stay in business:

'By the end of this decade only a small fraction of today's number of keiretsu stores will remain and the retail market for most goods will become much more open '.

As for American industry, three areas are identified where it is likely to benefit from adaptation of keiretsu strategies, namely supplier relations, spinning off noncore businesses into affiliated subsidiaries and learning to co-operate in R and D ventures:

'Grounds for trust and real co-operation must be established, both because the costs of R and D are skyrocketing, and because the markets are growing more competitive every day'.

[Issue 73 (January 1995)]

JURAN: LESSONS OF A LIFETIME

Dr. Joseph Juran, one of the founder 'gurus' of the world Quality movement has given his last lecture. This was entitled 'The Lessons of a Lifetime in Managing for Quality' and was given in Florida USA in conjunction with the Juran Institute's conference IMPRO 94.

Over the years Dr. Juran has been lecturing to large audiences, but the last one of around 600 delegates from all over the world and representing all different disciplines and industries was probably one the strongest.

The contributions to the Quality movement of Joseph Juran has been immense. According to most observers only W. Edwards Deming has a comparable record. Both built on Walter Shewhart's work in the late '20s,' early '30s.

To distil his contribution into one day, he was aided by modern technology with a group of 'One Minute Videos' which illustrated basic Quality thinking in many situations.

The coverage of Quality was wide-ranging and besides some of the specific major contributions (given below) the presentation covered Statistical Quality Processing, Measuring Customer Satisfaction, and Total Quality Management.

Throughout his career Dr. Juran has coined phrases which have focused on a concept he wished to promote e.g. 'Pareto Analysis: The Vital Few and Trivial Many', 'Management Breakthrough', 'Chronic Waste', as specific contributions in a Quality Management context. In this last lecture, many of these phrases were to the fore.

Three key areas were emphasised to achieve world class quality:

- A Quality Strategy should be defined for company objectives.

- The leadership roles of managers to reach the objectives.

- The Quality tools and methodology to be used.

Whilst these were well understood by many practitioners they were often neglected in the everyday management activities according to Dr. Juran.

The greatest challenge and effort in his lifetime in Quality has been devoted to stimulating an understanding amongst senior executives of the significance of Quality management. [Hence the coined phrases -Ed]. About ten years ago at an IQA meeting in London Dr. Juran initiated the analogy between financial concepts and quality to arrest the understanding of senior executives for Quality Management. He developed this thinking into the now named 'Juran Trilogy' which transforms financial planning, financial control and financial improvement, into quality planning, quality control and quality improvement. The Trilogy was the key to capturing their understanding and acceptance.

The main obstacles that remain are the acceptance of the economic arguments for Quality (which get confused) and the need to motivate for Quality. Recognition of the Need for Quality by senior management has been a recurrent theme in many of Dr. Juran's lectures and he believes national and international award schemes help to motivate by public acclaim.

The interaction of Quality and company economics can be clarified if two different aspects of the Quality function are separated and put into (again) their financial contexts:

*Income Oriented Quality: these embrace product features which produce customer satisfaction, are competitive and create income.

*Cost Oriented Quality: these are activities which give freedom from dissatisfaction, defects, failures and reworking.

Typically in a Juran lecture an amazing statistic was revealed; on this occasion he said:

"We spend a third of our time redoing what we did before, although there may be very good reasons for doing so".

This was an example of 'Chronic Waste'.

Also characteristically Dr. Juran concluded with his predictions for the future:

- That ISO9000 would eventually sweep across the world

- There will be increasing demands put upon suppliers

- Quality Awards will be an intense stimulus and there will be a growth in awards worldwide

- Quality competition will intensify with the growth of multinational companies and common markets

[Issue 94 (October 1996) –7th ICM Conference on TQM, Dublin, 25th – 26th September]

Designing a Cost of Quality Programme

A key paper at the conference was presented by Dr. Rodney McAdam of the Ulster Business School which focused on the ongoing research being conducted into the cost of quality and present day trends associated with it.

The presentation, which had the above title, highlighted the cost of quality programme adopted by Short Brothers in 1992. This is based on strategic objectives, and the model of Prevention, Appraisal and Failure costing (PAF) which is commonly applied.

The model, says the speaker, is "one of the best" for traditional functional businesses but does suffer from some quite serious limitations, namely:

* classification, (sometimes it is difficult to identify which class to use for a given cost).

* reporting levels (can be inappropriate).

* accountability (it can be difficult to trace exactly where a particular cost has been incurred).

* standardisation (it can be difficult to identify a trend line).

In order to compensate for some of these weaknesses anew process-based methodology has therefore been launched which offers better defined accountability, cost collection at source, improved accuracy, better definition of trend lines and the potential for automation. These factors were noted to be particularly relevant with regard to Section Five of the EFQM Business Excellence Model which seeks evidence of targets for business processes.

The trend towards this new approach was supported by evidence from an Ulster Business School benchmarking exercise of some 100 UK and Irish companies. This study, which examined in particular; marketing strategy, branding, customer development, quality strategy and product innovation, showed that virtually without exception companies which scored highly in their quality strategy had a quality cost system which was integrated with a Total Quality programme.

Speaking as an assessor for the Northern Ireland Quality Award Dr.McAdam advised delegates that EFQM assessors will be seeking evidence from companies about how they measure quality costs and recommended that cost of quality reports, examples of which were shown to delegates, be used to demonstrate the integration of a cost of quality programme with other initiatives. He stressed the need in particular for accountants to be involved in the design of the system and for the focus to be broader than merely production costs i.e. sales and design need to be incorporated as well, especially in larger companies. Finally he emphasised:

"Quality cost collection only adds value when action is taken to reduce the cost. It can be a dead system if the management team is not on board".

[Issue 95 (November 1996)- EFQM Edinburgh Forum]

BPR at Nortel

Nortel is a $10 billion international corporation operating in the vibrant, fast moving telecommunications industry and, as mentioned last month, they have a 51.85% share in NETAS, one of this year's three European Quality Prize Winners.

Their director of Business Process Support Services (Nortel's internal Business Process Engineering Consultancy) Peter Knowles, described how they are beginning to re-engineer the re-engineering process.

The paper highlights several readily identifiable and recurrent problems associated with Business Process Re-engineering (BPR) and explains how they have been tackled by Nortel. The problems are essentially:

* Re-engineering projects typically take 18-24 months to complete.

* Long duration projects suffer dilution, resource draining, constant questioning, loss of momentum and often fail to fulfil early ambition (if they ever finish at all).

* The business requires that problem and opportunity situations are addressed in two to three months rather than two or three years.

* Business planning cycles are no longer five year or even one year 'windows'.

With only one in three BPR projects typically successful and a success which is seldom sustained, not to mention the costs in terms of time and money, it is tempting to adopt the 'defeatist attitude' and conclude that BPR is nothing more than a 'passing fad' and that it is better to avoid it and move instead to the next doctrinal approach to business management. This, however, was Nortel's answer:

'Nortel's belief is that it cannot afford to turn its back on the powerful holistic change messages which are philosophically "given" in BPR'.

Two alternative approaches to BPR are then considered, the 'Decide Change Approach' and the 'Do Re-engineering Approach', and the constraints on each examined. With the 'Decide Change Approach' the constraints identified were as follows:

- No common view on what BPR is (how do you recognise it?).

- Cannot/will not release people.

- It wasn't provided for in the budget.

- Must make something of effort already expended.

- Don't/can't turn down business (process change).

These constraints were used to focus on and address positively the classical problems which beset re-engineering projects at start-up, yet are frequently ignored or suppressed until it is too late.

With the 'Do Re-engineering Approach' the constraints identified were as follows:

It takes months to:

- Assemble a cross-functional team.

- Teach a cross-functional team what BPR is about.

- Design a new detailed process.

- Pilot and rollout new process detail.

- Provide "chart turn" to get approval for the "next stage".

- To get a sponsor to give approval to implement (if they ever do).

Also:

- Some BPR projects start with a 'Case for Action' which does not warrant BPR.

- It takes a lot more than three months to deliver Enabling Technology for a process.

Nortel concentrated on the constraint removal and concluded that 'substantial energy' can be released as a result. The paper explains how an 'accelerated change capability' consisting of two processes (a 'get ready' and a 'do it' process) has been developed and applied successfully:-

'Nortel used its "Alpha" re-engineering process on a key project (Q1 '96) and the resulting new (Competitive Intelligence) subject process was successfully implemented within the three months. This experience brought further earnings which are now being used to refine the re-engineering process and to develop a companion "Implementation Repeatability" (Beta) process'.

[Issue 101 (May 1997)]

QUALITY IN INTEGRATED MANAGEMENT-EOQ FORUM

This event staged in London by the IQA, was the 4th in the EOQ series. It took place at the Park Lane Hotel, Piccadilly and was co-sponsored by Sharp Electronics and NQA.

Because of the European flavour it was supported well from Europe with speakers and attendees, but the UK interest was low. Speakers were from Italy, Sweden, Netherlands, France, USA, the EFQM and the EU but the texts did not live up to the theme of the Forum with too few of the speakers addressing the vexed question of integrating quality into management.

The IQA, as the European organisation's full member organisation, was supported well by its EOQ colleagues. Otto Neumayer, President of EOQ, made it clear that the Forum was an EOQ event not just a British one. Tito Conti, Past President of EOQ gave the most convincing presentation on day one, reminding that 'fashions' or 'fads' rather than substance have dictated management trends in recent years. He cited quality circles, SPC, Business Process Re-engineering and Benchmarking as having been 'oversold' and been responsible for giving somewhat false hopes. Together with the obsession with compliance and standards, these tended to miss the real opportunity offered by the 'total quality' concept.

He felt that a critical review was needed and pointed out that, contrary to what most speakers say, 'quality' was not a strategic issue i.e. not discussed in Boardrooms. Quality should 'metabolise' into the body of management and Conti saw the growing use of self-assessment as a diagnostic tool -TQM based. He felt, however, that self-assessment could be easily abused by focusing on 'scores' rather than on improvement opportunities.

He also mentioned the other aspect of integration, that of integrating management itself toward goals and customer preference. In his view integration presented a cultural challenge.

Quality in Construction Projects

The next speaker hardly addressed integration, but his talk was perhaps the most significant as it dealt with the difficult (in quality terms) Construction Sector.

Norman Haste is now Project Director for the controversial building of Terminal 5 at Heathrow Airport, having switched recently from the completed second Severn Crossing where he was Project Director of the contracting parties –a switch from poacher to gamekeeper so to speak.

As such, he gave a sterling account of how, despite the restrictions imposed by the "Government agent", the project was completed on time and within budget. However, when the contracting partners are not able or willing to accept the conventional strictures of quality assurance (because of time/cost) and yet the nature of the project demands good quality -then 'assurance' was obtained via a specially organised independent QC authority. They have the power of 'veto' and the logic worked.

Turning to the important Heathrow project, Mr. Haste explained how a different and unconventional (for the construction sector) approach has been chosen. British Airports Authority (the client) wishes to embrace the 'whole of supply' chain and has set up partnership arrangements with its contractors and suppliers, much on the lines now favoured by the petrochemical industry, and indeed as promoted by the DTI in its recent promotions. They emphasise the common objective in which all parties 'Strive for Five' (a new fad?) in which each function within the project targets 5 out of 5 in the key areas of Quality, Safety, Cost, Time and Environment (five in all).

We shall know in year 2000 how successful BAA have been in their quest.

International Accreditation

Harry Gundlack, of the Dutch Accreditation Body -RVA -is the new Chairman of the International Accreditation Forum, and spoke extensively about the proposed QSAR scheme (Quality System Assessment Recognition). This is working in parallel with the IQF, but is a creation of the ISO/IEC and as such there is concern about its potential value to the world. An extensive survey is being carried out by the interested parties.

Meanwhile the European Accreditation of Certification (EAC) has developed several mutual recognition agreements, so within Europe we can foresee the 'one stop certification' goal reaching fruition, especially now that environmental management and auditing' are embraced by the various certification and accreditation bodies.

It was stated that there are (end 1996) some 180,000 certificates for ISO 9000 in issue worldwide, and that there are some 450 certification bodies involved, with some 45 countries carrying out the additional business of accreditation. The IAF is to become a legal entity at its meeting in Japan in July, when the Regional accreditation bodies PAC (Pacific) and SARAC (Sth. Africa) will join with the European EAC.

Unfortunately the paper planned by Ian Day on behalf of the IIOC (International Independent Organisation in Certification) was replaced by one from Mr. Henderson of SGS. This did not carry the political flavour that might have been expected from Mr. Day but did give an insight into the possibilities for integration as seen by the certification bodies.

However, Mr. Henderson felt that "there was not much benefit in integrated audits at present". He is after all a business development manager, and as such might have been disappointed at the slow take up in this- area. He did highlight the benefits of certification as reported in the recent (SGS) MORI poll and listed an unusual break-down of the 20 requirements in ISO9001. This grouped; clauses 1 to 8 relating to Management, Clause 9 relating to Process, 9-13 relating to verification and 14-20 relating to improvement.

The benefits were thoroughly endorsed by the speaker from Sweden, a small business in Gothenburg involved in designing, installing and servicing alarm systems for industry and commerce. This was an endorsement of everything that ISO9000 stands for but it said nothing about integration by the many UK companies benefiting from quality management systems.

Management Systems Standards

David Wooliscraft is Divisional Director responsible for Standards Development at BSI, and as such he is concerned with the whole panorama of British Standards. He outlined the work of the Management Systems Sector Board which is one of the 8 sector boards, and brought up to date the current activities which includes the revision of the ISO9000 series, the completion of work on the ISO14000 series of environmental standards, and the work on occupational health and safety.

He reported on the consultations carried out by BSI in 1996 concerning the UK attitude to the integration of the management system standards. It appears that whilst industry does not want any more individual standards in this area, there were problems in total integration, and therefore a more likely outcome is that in future, standards will be 'aligned'. That is to say that the common 'core' elements like policy, planning, measurement and corrective action, could well be the same in all system standards, leaving flexibility with the other elements of management to cater for the different uses.

The above may lead to easier auditing, and better communication but there was no clear enthusiasm from the audience. It may be that industry will be content with the stability that is now offered by the 1994 issue of ISO9000. Also it could be held that 'significant' changes to that standard, made in the name of improvement or user friendliness, could militate against yet another change to the management systems of the many companies who have struggled to get their certification and are only now reaping the benefits. They might resist change on the basis that what they have done is perfectly adequate as it stands.

Whether the BSI delegation can hold its own against the 'improvers' within ISO will sharpen attitudes when new drafts are presented for UK debate. Meanwhile ISO Technical Committees have undertaken to 'liaise' to ensure closer alignment in systems documentation.

Question Session

Day one of this conference closed with a question session to the remaining speakers on the panel. There was some debate and disagreement as to whether ISO 9000 represents the basic level of management system, perhaps the lowest common denominator, or whether it is better seen as a worthwhile achievement, associated as it so often is with a fair degree of 'flag waving'. In terms of international competition Conti felt it only expressed the entry level and that other factors made for real competition.

In post conference debate with speakers particularly Stanley Marrash of the USA it was clear that many countries are still on a 'high' with regard to ISO 9000 and are along way from the integration aspect that was the theme for the Forum.

The sponsors of the event took display space to offer their services and it was good to see the efforts made by the EOQ at the European Quality Week last year and to be repeated on Nov. 10-16 1997.

European Perspectives

The second day was brought to life by Geert de Raad, Secretary General of the European Foundation for Quality Management (EFQM) who called for the whole subject of quality to be made more exciting if people and organisations are going to be inspired by it. Accompanied with this was an unmistakable need for a greater willingness to learn from others and for a determined effort to be made by everyone to remove the anxiety which accompanies change.

He argued that it is not difficult to instigate change provided that everyone is aware of the reasoning behind it and has a united vision as to where the organisation wants to go. He enlightened delegates about recent work which he has undertaken with auto manufacturer BMW, describing the different perceptions of its Board Members about their involvement with Total Quality as "a real eye opener".

In his paper he describes the evolution of the EFQM Business Excellence Model and contrasts it with ISO9000 certification which, he argued, was essentially a short term process which lacks the necessary incentive of encouraging an organisation to strive for continuous improvement:

'An organisation that is dedicated to getting an ISO certificate can generally do so within one year. But that is not the intent of the certification process. A certificate allows an organisation to start working on improving the now well defined jobs and activities. That is where the largest gains are made'.

Antonio Silva Mendes of the European Commission Directorate General III, and former Vice President of the Portuguese Association for Quality, enlightened delegates as to the progress of the European Quality Promotion Policy, which has now been running for three and a half years and is "now achieving a level of maturity". He explained how, rather than intervening in a legislative way it was the intention that the Policy would "act as a facilitator and get synergies through a unified strategy". He outlined two specific projects upon which DGIII hoped to build, the first entitled 'Benchmarking for Success' which is Irish led and envisaged to form the basis for a European company benchmarking network.

The second entitled 'A Quality Project for SMEs' is led by various European Chambers of Commerce or 'Eurochambers' and has essentially three objectives:

(i) to create awareness in the quality field.

(ii) to support dissemination of information of best practice management.

(iii) to create a favourable environment for SMEs to participate in an European benchmarking network.

He also described how a new European customer satisfaction index known as EVRIX is being created through collaboration between the EOQ and the EFQM, utilising the expertise of university networks chaired by the Stockholm Business School. He explained how it was the intention that national customer satisfaction indices would be developed with the objective of achieving integration at sectional and European level, whilst a companion project involving the Directorate Generals for Industry would bring the initiative truly onto the world stage.

1027

Bertrand de Joulsin de Noray, Technical Director of Mouvement Francais pour la Qualite and Vice President of the EOQ, spoke on the subject of 'breakthrough management', arguing that conformity, improvement and breakthrough needed to be simultaneous management activities. Also that traditional marketing studies were "unsuited for innovating and anticipating customer expectations". He called for a re-examination of traditional responsibilities:

"New product identification and development is no longer just a job for the marketing department. Each person in the company becomes an entrepreneur and has to participate in this quest to uncover latent needs. And in order to ensure that this dynamism doesn't end in chaos these efforts and energies have to be supported by a vision, a common objective, a shared feeling which ensures that the company is based on solid foundations".

Global Quality

The final speaker, Dr. Stanley A. Marrash, Chairman and CEO of Stat-A-Matrix in the USA, described how the World Quality Council had been formed last year to bring companies around the world together to integrate quality and management. He gave his opinions on how ISO9000 "is moving to the next plateau" through the development and application of the QS9000 initiative for the auto industry .This adds sector specific requirements and incorporates the need for continuous improvement.

He argued that with regard to ISO9000 there were now "enough people doing it wrong that there is a danger that it will lose credibility". He called for a redevelopment of consistency of purpose as advocated by the late Dr. W. Edwards Deming.

Amongst Dr. Marrash's many achievements is the creation of a unique programme leading to a Master of Quality Management degree (current enrolment over 100 students) sponsored by Stat-A-matrix and Loyola University, New Orleans.

Other presenters included notably Sir Denys Rooke, former Chairman of British Gas and a Past President of the IQA who argued that there was "no justification" for the privatisation of British Gas; Professor Sir Frederick Warner, also "a Past President of the IQA, who gave an insight into some of the damaging effects of environmental pollution; and John Owen, Associate Director of Sharp Electronics (UK) Limited, who described Sharp Electronic's Integrated Management Standard [see Chapter 2 – Ed]

GEMBA KAIZEN

This year's Engineering Quality Forum annual lecture was given by Masaaki Imai -'the man who brought Kaizen to the West'. The lecture took place at the Institute of Electrical Engineers on 11th November. This was a change by the organisers because of the overwhelming response which exceeded the capacity of the Institute of Civil Engineers venue.

The title of Mr. Imai's lecture 'GEMBA Kaizen', when roughly translated means Shop Floor (Gemba) Continuous Improvement (Kaizen) with the emphasis on this occasion on shop floor activities. A more strict translation of Gemba is 'real place' i.e. where the action takes place, and Kaizen is 'good increments'.

The concepts behind these words were developed. Mr. Imai believes that western management has neglected shop floor activities, preferring to concentrate on financial management and sales, and that the Japanese inherent approach for small improvements, when cumulative, brings dramatic results. His view is that attention to the shopfloor activities has made a major contribution to Japan's competitive success.

It was pointed out that 'shop floor' does not just mean the production site (although most examples were taken from manufacturing) but in many functional areas in all industries 'where the action is' e.g. customer interfaces in services.

Management approaches are contrasted. In the West, innovation and technology changes command attention. Management is attracted to the dramatic. Kaizen is undramatic, often subtle, but is ongoing, not a one-off change.

Mr. Imai demonstrated a simple assembly process which illustrated what was 'value added' and what was 'muda' (waste). The skill in Gemba Kaizen is to identify which part of each process is giving added value and gradually improve to reduce waste -which may not necessarily be tangible e.g. wasted time.

The Kaizen strategy is based on 3 principles: Concepts, Systems and Tools. The contribution of senior management, middle management and shop floor was compared for these principles, e.g. Senior management makes the greatest contribution to Concepts, whilst shop floor contributes mostly to the 'process' (tools).

The belief is that common sense should prevail, where a simple approach should solve 90% of problems, with most solutions as low cost improvements, and the organisation giving support where required.

This approach was given emphasis in a problem solving sequence of 5 Steps. When an anomaly is found:

*Go to 'Gemba' first. (Most managers work from their office, and are not too familiar with the 'shop floor' activities).

*Check 'Gembatsu' (equipment/process) status, performance etc.

*Take temporary counter-measures 'on the spot'.

*Remove Root Cause.

*'Standardise' to prevent recurrence.

Commitment by the workforce was described in 'The Morning Market' -a shopfloor Tool Box meeting -where all rejects are displayed on a table- with the accompanying question "why produce rejects?" This is followed by practical line solutions.

A Question from the audience on this topic was "How long is the meeting?" -Answer '10 minutes' -"if not solved by Gemba, the Root Cause is identified". The principle of the meeting is 'Never take over into Today from Yesterday'.

Gemba Management (the organisation of Gemba principles on the shop floor) e.g. Housekeeping, Standardisation, Discipline, was described, where 'Muda' (waste) has high priority. 'Muda' is defined as: 'Everything the Customer does not pay for'. Some examples of the sources of waste on the shopfloor (in manufacturing) were given. These were: transportation of parts, Inventory -parts on floor, Machine downtime, Rejects, Plant layout - length of line, Lead Time. Mr Imai quoted The more people -the more rejects. The longer the line -the more space -the longer the Lead Time".

Key Tools to Manage Improvement are: Design of Experiments, Failure Mode Effect Analysis, Statistical Tools, combined with Gemba Tools- where the principle is "No rejects from previous process' with the inspection of one's own work.

The motto for reject work: 'Don't give it -Don't make it -Don't send it'.

Training for "Gemba' is an intense indoctrination on "the process' where a knowledge of detailed activities is regarded as imperative. An example of Process Improvement (Dip Soldering) was illustrated as an intense concentration on reject reduction. From a reject rate of 0.4% (4000 ppm) in 1977, by a series of actions was reduced to 40 ppm in 1980, and then down to 3ppm in 1982.

Each time when significant improvement has been made it is the shopfloor's responsibility to maintain it, but with management taking the initiative to 'standardise' the improved procedure i.e. do not just let supervisors 'run the show'. All need to see that improvements are a 'Team Effort'.

There were several questions from the audience. A popular one was the relationship between Gemba Kaizen and ISO9000. Mr. Imai's response was that 'Conformance to Standards, unless Kaizen is Applied First DOES NOT WORK'. In reply to a question of what happens to workers displaced by improvements the response was -in Gemba Kaizen the end result is Redeployment NOT Redundancy.

Another questioner referred to the techniques given in the lecture and applied on the shopfloor which he considered were 'standard practice' for work study engineers in the UK e.g. changing/improving set-up times, reducing 'machine downtime', improving lay-out, reducing handling etc. Mr. Imai agreed, but pointed out that this was done by the (trained) 'Gemba' themselves not by additional engineering, except on new plant i.e. different responsibilities were involved.

The lecture was based on extracts from Mr. Imai's new book on Kaizen which is due to be published early in 1997.

[*Quality Matters comments:* The questioners in the audience put the key issues, with the last questioner on work study techniques making a clear point i.e. that none of the techniques are new, only the diligence of application. The principal difference appears to be the total commitment of Japanese management to apply the principles, and the discipline of the workforce to carry them out. UK management often has a different agenda and the workforce can be suspicious of that agenda, e.g. redeployment or redundancy for workforce led improvements?]

FUTURE UKAS ACCREDITATION PRACTICE

The United Kingdom Accreditation Service came into being in August 1995, merging the former NAMAS and NACCB, largely as a result of pressure for improvement from industry. It has taken 12 months to establish the membership and structure of the new body which now has some 100 employees, and the first public seminar, organised by the National Forum for Conformity Assessment and Quality Policy, was held on 3 December. National Forum member Norman Burgess reports the event.

The seminar attracted almost 200 participants from across the laboratory, testing and certification business, and allowed UKAS to obtain first hand reaction to their ideas for change.

Their proposals arise from criticism and observation made over many years concerning both the laboratory accreditation activity and the certification body activity and comprise 6 actions aimed at UKAS generally, 2 actions directed towards improving laboratory accreditation, 5 at the Certification Body side, with 14 aimed at customer satisfaction alone. (The full proposals make up a 4pp document available from UKAS).

Proposal 1 redefines the role of UKAS so that accreditation is highly regarded but flexible enough to meet genuine needs. Actions 2,3,4,5 and 6 concern the mechanics of the operation, expiry dates on certificates, obtaining customer feedback, firm pricing based on work done rather than levies, and teams capable of accrediting to more than one standard.

For laboratories, scopes of accreditation will be broadened whilst proficiency, testing will involve greater participation with the labs.

Certification bodies will be asked 'to assist in identifying 'soft' organisations, that is, those that issue certificates too easily compared to their tougher compatriots. The scope of accreditation has long been a 'thorny' topic and there is group working towards use of the minimum '39' recommended by the European Accreditation of Certification Committee. Likewise there is to be UKAS action on the incorrect use of the 'crown and tick' logo and the issue of certificates against the 'wrong' ISO9000 standard. Generally UKAS would prefer to exercise a 'light touch' but the extensive debate that followed the UKAS presentation suggested that this may not be enough.

After the detailed explanation of the above plans by Dr. Munro, Chief Executive of UKAS, speakers from the floor outlined their concerns:

"What was being done to make certification more meaningful by greater emphasis on products rather than systems and sectorisation activity?"

"What about joint audits with other state bodies?"

"Will there be a reduction in the number of certification bodies to make the task of control more manageable?"

Dr. Munro said the objective of the changes was to improve the impact of accreditation on business and public well being, but, wisely, would not be drawn into too many specific situations.

Roger Brockway for UKAS felt that ISO9000 topped up by 'industry sector schemes' (like AS9000) gave added value, but they must be 'market driven' i.e. UKAS cannot be pro-active (perhaps a pity!)

It was revealed during debate that UKAS is now looking more widely than Europe for harmonisation and particularly to ISO/IEG Guide 61, Guide 62 for certification bodies and 65 for product certification. It was expected that the EN45000 series would then be made identical to the ISO Guides.

There was some debate concerning the point at which standardisation (of practices) gives way to 'guidelines'. The IAF (International Accreditation Forum) Guideline is only two and a half pages!

In response to questions about the performance of UKAS itself, it was announced that UKAS will develop a 'charter' rather like other public bodies and there will be an active programme of getting feedback from the actual 'clients' of certification bodies. The audience included a high proportion (probably 50%) of laboratory operators many of whom were concerned at the long delays involved in that side of UKAS (formerly NAMAS). Improvement was promised.

The 'hoary' topic of mixing advisory services with certification activity brought the response that 'prescriptive' advice as opposed to 'helpful' advice is not tolerable in the work of certification.

The afternoon session was given over to 4 presentations, 3 from the organisation most affected by the activities of UKAS:

'The Laboratories' Perspective' (Geoff Matthews of BMTA)

'The ABCB View on Accreditation' (new Chief Executive)

'The Inspection Bodies' Perspective' (Safety Assessment Federation)

A prime concern of the laboratories is that whilst 70% of revenue for UKAS comes from the laboratory activity, it does not have adequate representation on the Board of the company, with no non-executive director. They are also concerned about the possible loss of the 'crown' in any new UKAS logo.

Tim Inman of ABCB (representing half of the UK certification bodies) expressed their concerns:

*extensions to scope -consistency in UKAS operations

*interpretation of external Guidelines, etc., many of which are to be addressed in the' 'new' approach by UKAS

Their sentiments were clear -'unless we add value -we can kiss certification goodbye'.

The accreditation of Inspection bodies is very new, stemming from the issue of EN 45004 and UKAS have taken this on. Their representative wants a 'level playing field' to allow Mutual Recognition Agreement (MRAs) and sees accreditation as a route to regulation in a field of increasing competition. However, the long established insurance body inspectorates do not want to change merely to conform to the role of the voluntary schemes (like certification). They work to ISO/IEC 65.

In summing up the seminar, the Chairman of UKAS Dr. Bryan Smith (formerly ICI) focused on the importance of the possible Customer's Charter: the Sectoral Focus; the international MRAs and the 'soft' certification bodies. The theme of 'adding value' would seem to be an additional requirement if we accept that business improvement is the key to greater efficiency. It remains to be seen how the conformity assessment industry, with UKAS at its heart, will survive that challenge.

BOOK REVIEW - TQM: An Integrated Approach

Author: Samuel K. Ho (292 pages).

Publishers: Kogan Page (ISBN 07494 1561 4).

Details:

Principal Lecturer in TQM at Leicester De Montfort University Professor Samuel K. Ho describes and elaborates on the TQMEX Model of Total Quality which aims to incorporate the best aspects of Western and Eastern quality management.

The Model is described in the third chapter following two introductory chapters on basic TQM principles and the philosophy of six of the leading so-called 'gurus' (W. Edwards Deming, Joseph Juran, Philip Crosby, Kaoru Ishikawa, Shigeo Shingo, and Yoshido Kondo). It is based on a combination of five concepts (The Japanese 5S System, Business Process Re-engineering, Quality Control Circles, ISO 9000, Total Productive Maintenance and certain identified TQM 'Kitemarks'). Each of these concepts is analysed in turn in the chapters which follow, but first the author offers the following advice:

'Companies starting to implement TQM should follow TQMEX step by step. Companies which have already gone through some degree of improvement using some of the steps should review what has not been done and do it as their next step of improvement'.

As a prelude to TQMEX the author recommends consideration of the so-called 'Ten TQM Commandments':

- Approach: management led

- Method: prevention not detection

- Objective: total customer satisfaction

- Measure: the costs of quality

- Standard: right first time

- Scope: ownership and commitment

- Theme: continuous improvement

- Ability: training and education

- Communication: co-operation & teamwork

- Reward: recognition and pride

Also recommended are consideration of 'The Four Pillars of TQM' (satisfying customers, system/process, improvement tools, and people) and 'The 4Cs of TQM' (Commitment, Competence, Communication, and Continuous Improvement).

Chapter Four on 'The Japanese 5S Practice' makes interesting reading if for no other reason than the fact that so few Western organisations are actually applying it. The 'One is Best' principle for example is a far from common ideal, yet would appear to be an entirely logical concept:

'It is worthwhile to emphasise the importance of a principle of organisation called "one is best". Examples of application include: one set of tools/stationery, one page form/memo, one day processing, one stop service for customer and one location file (including local area network server for file sharing). In particular for 'one day processing' there is an ancient Chinese saying "let today's work belong to today"'.

Likewise the phrase 'Everyone is a Janitor' is unlikely to roll off the tongue of most Western managers, nor are they likely to see 'Visual Management' as an aid to Seiketsu or 'Standardisation' or to use 'trouble maps' as an indicator of those workplaces and processes that are trouble free.

There is an informative guide to the application of 5S in an office environment which few readers will perhaps have considered, whilst enthusiasts for pictures and photographs will find no shortage of illustrations of good and bad practice.

Chapter Five on BPR is perhaps a little less enlightening, though the reader may note that 'if BPR is being carefully incorporated into the company wide TQM process, as the TQMEX Model suggests, organisations will ensure the effectiveness of one of the most potent weapons available in the corporate armoury to meet the challenges of the future'.

The author presents the 'Velocity Ratio' (Value Added Time as a proportion of Total Elapsed Time) as a measure of the dynamics of change and provides a useful guide to the application of Total Quality Purchasing, notably in relation to Just-in-Time (JIT) operations where there is little room for unreliable supplier performance.

Chapter Six (Quality Control Circles and Problem Solving) with 40 pages is the longest of the ten chapters, and with much of it devoted to a description of the Seven Quality Control Tools is arguably the least interesting, until of course one reaches reference to the 1990 World Cup Semi Final where the notorious penalty shoot-out serves as an illustration of the so-called 5S Problem Solving Method:

'The shooter usually makes guesses on what has been done before him, and what would be the goal-keeper's next guess. This disturbance could affect the decision of the shooter. It is usually at this critical moment that he makes a mistake -by doing something which is not part of his plan or simply forgetting his original plan completely. Then in most cases the results are: either giving chance for the goal keeper to catch the ball (because of the fear of making incorrect guesses) or shooting the ball outside the goal (because of the worry that the goal-keeper might reach the ball)'.

The author uses the 5S Method to deduce that the real cause of the missed penalties was in fact lack of proper training [Mental/Confidence training? - Ed].

Chapter Seven (ISO9000 and Quality Audit) is again a lengthy affair (38 pages) which many readers may prefer to skip if they have achieved ISO 9000 and are maintaining it effectively, although even these readers and the ISO9000 cynics should find the six 'Mini Cases' in this chapter both informative and useful -it's not as boring as it sounds.

Chapter Eight (on TPM) is somewhat different, returning to what is probably the book's best strength, that of encouraging Western uptake of Eastern practices without compromising Western ideals. In this short chapter the reader gains an insight into the Japanese Productive Maintenance Excellence Award a 10 –point Checksheet. With the help of two Japanese 'Mini Cases' the author demonstrates that 'TPM dramatically improves productivity and quality and reduces costs':

'Fujikoshu had the employees make actual improvements on the equipment and get their hands dirty. Their TPM programme resulted in cutting the number of stoppages to 1/150 of their former level, raising equipment efficiency by more than 30 per cent, and reducing non-conformance to 1/3 of what it had been. Along with this value-added productivity improved by 30 per cent'.

With the TQM Kitemarks of ISO9004-4:1993, the Deming Prize, the Baldrige Award, and the European Quality Award concluding the theory, the final chapter is devoted to 'TQMEX in the Real World' and describes where each element of the Model has been made into a video seminar, how a firm might 'acquire' the TQMEX Model, and how the Model accords with (modified) Dr. Deming's words "Quality (TQM) will last forever".

[Issue 103 (July 1997)]

FIRST UKAS ACCREDITATION WITHDRAWAL

In what could be a significant case in the High Court on 20th May, the withdrawal of accreditation from the certification body Professional, Environmental and Caring Services QA Ltd. (PECS) by UKAS was upheld.

Quality Matters has obtained published documents showing two sides of a story which could be entitled "Who Audits the Auditors?" PECS is the first UKAS accredited certification body to have its accreditation withdrawn. The circumstances were claimed by PECS to be controversial and with high-handed unilateral actions from UKAS.

The dispute originated and seemingly was only involved, in the timing of access. PECS claimed that after a rescheduled "perfunctory visit", which raised no major problems, follow-through activities of a corrective action plan fell into oscillations for future visits.

UKAS say they withdrew accreditation because of refusal of PECS to comply with accreditation requirements with respect to "the provision of access for the performance of surveillance and follow up of non-conformities". Since withdrawal of accreditation would lead inevitably to the liquidation of PECS, and the appeals mechanism did not work, PECS felt that they had to appeal to the High Court for a judicial review.

The significance of the case, although unfortunate for PECS, may be in what was legally revealed. In the course of the case the legal position of UKAS was examined. It appears that it was on this issue that the PECS case failed. PECS say that because UKAS "have no procedures or documents that legally describe the powers that they choose to exercise. As a result they can act in any manner they wish" i.e. a decision from UKAS is the only one required. Since there is no legal position, a judicial review was not granted, so the judgment went in favour of UKAS.

Commenting on the case the Chief Executive of the Association of British Certification Bodies (ABCB) Tim Inman says:

"The withdrawal of accreditation from a certification body must be a matter of regret. However, the High Court rejection of the PECS appeal sends the powerful message to all accredited certification bodies that UKAS will adopt

an uncompromising stance with those who do not maintain the required standards".

Detailed background information around the case suggests that there is "a story behind the story" with communications ignored and personality difficulties.

One area where all parties seem to agree is concern for the fate of PECS certificated clients, many of whom are small businesses. PECS were concerned about a logical painless transfer of certification for their clients. After the PECS liquidation, UKAS advised that PECS certificates were only valid until 23 August 1997.

[Issue 105 (September 1997) – 24th IMS Summer School, Queen's College, Cambridge, 20th – 24th July]

The Future of the Organisation

The paper from the 'People' section, with the above title was presented by Professor Colin J. Coulson-Thomas, Willmott Dixon Professor of Corporate Transformation at the University of Luton.

Through his own consultancy Adaptation Limited, and various collaborative arrangements he offers a range of executive, director and board development and corporate learning and transformation services. He has helped some fifty boards to improve board and corporate performance.

His paper addresses the subject of Business Process Re-engineering (BPR) and some of the misconceptions surrounding it, and presents the findings of a European research project called COBRA (Constraints and Opportunities in Business Restructuring: an Analysis) which examined around 100 European re-engineering projects. Findings were as follows:

(i) Overall, most applications of BPR are concerned with the improvement of existing processes and relatively short term savings of cost and time. They tend to involve layoffs a 'headcount reductions', and many organisations are avoiding use of the term BPR in view of its negative connotations.

(ii) In the main BPR is 'done' to people and they are not sufficiently involved in the process. BPR projects tend to be 'top down' and driven by organisational imperatives.

(iii) Relatively few BPR products involve 'green-field' exercises, new ways of working and learning, or result in the development of new strategic capabilities or the creation of new markets or services. Most initiatives concern business and support processes rather than direction setting, management or learning processes. Goals such as improving the quality of working life, taking the heat off people, or creating more creative cultures are few and far between.

The author argues that it need not be this way:

'The COBRA team found that substantially greater involvement and participation can significantly improve the acceptability of BPR outcomes without necessarily increasing the implementation time. There are also many options for radically improving how we can access, develop, harness and apply the commitment and talents of people '.

'There are new models of organisation such as "virtual corporations" or " network organisations" which could be adopted and which are more flexible and responsive than the relatively bureaucratic forms we have inherited from the past. While they present new management challenges, they may be "more fun" for those who work within them, and hence more conducive of innovation and learning. They can also enable smaller organisations to successfully compete against those which are much larger'.

'Rather than stop -as most BPR exercises do-at the boundary of an organisation they could embrace the whole supply chain. "Network re-engineering" focused upon the supply chain. Also putting an emphasis upon changing how organisations interact in the marketplace has enabled radically new services to be introduced without necessarily turning the worlds of existing employees upside down. It can also create new opportunities for small and medium-sized enterprises to co-operate and collaborate'.

'With an appropriate "front end" in place, the virtual or network organisation can appear to have a more appropriate, welcoming and accessible capability than competitors many times as large. The customer or user does not know, and may not care, to where a call is diverted -across an office or between continents and network members -so long as relevant expertise is accessed and a satisfactory response is obtained'.

Various publications are introduced for the interested reader, including:

* 'The Responsive Organisation: Re-engineering new patterns of work' which presents a holistic methodology and tools framework that synthesises the experience and lessons for re-engineering practice and new ways of working, along with 21 detailed case studies and various briefings, including notes on 101 specific tools and techniques.

* 'The Competitive Network' which contains a methodology for re-engineering supply chains using the enabling technologies of electronic commerce.

* 'The Future of the Organisation: Achieving Excellence through Business Transformation' which presents a range of approaches which can be used to implement more holistic and people-centred approaches to management.

[Issue 109 (January 1998)]

UKAS REDEFINES SCOPE OF ACCREDITATION

The United Kingdom Accreditation Service (UKAS) has adopted a new means of defining the scope of accredited certification bodies based on the system developed by the European Accreditation Council (EAC). The new system is based on 39 broad scopes of accreditation and replaces the system which uses four digit Standard Industrial Classification codes of which there are hundreds. This means that certification bodies will have the flexibility to move into new certification areas without needing to seek and extension of scope from UKAS.

JURAN: A LIFETIME OF INFLUENCE (Book Review).

Author: John Butman (260 Pages)

Publisher: John Wiley (ISBN 0-471-17210-3.)

Details:

A powerful biography of, arguably, one of the two leading management 'gurus' of the twentieth century, the other of course being William Edwards Deming.

The author takes the reader on a voyage through time which begins in 1904 in 'a World without Quality' and ends seven chapters later in 1990 at the end of 'The Desperate Decade'. The final chapter, entitled 'Guru at the Dikes' then describes Dr. Joseph Juran's assessment of the present day as "living behind the quality dikes". The analogy is drawn as follows:

Although we receive wonderful benefits from technology we also face substantial risks –from catastrophe to annoyance. "We are like the Dutch", he says. "They have taken advantage of technology to push the sea back and gain a lot of land, and all the advantages that presents. But it's a dangerous way to live because the sea isn't content to stay back. It wants to push back in. To hold back the sea, the Dutch rely on technology in the form of dikes. Once built the dikes must be maintained forever. "We're in the same situation when we adopt technology",says Juran. "We rely on quality - quality is our dike -to protect us from these annoyances and these terrible dangers".

Chapter One describes, in the main, Juran's schooldays and concludes with Juran's graduation in 1924, whilst Chapter Two covers the American inter-war years from 1920 to 1941. The latter describes how Juran and Deming had worked together at the same Western Electric Hawthorne plant (manufacturer of equipment for AT and T and working laboratory for inquiry into the emerging issues of the large industrial organisation) in 1925 and 1926:

'Juran came to Western Electric at a time of great excitement and change in the way business was conducted in America. The postwar recession had ended, a period of economic prosperity (under newly elected President Calvin Coolidge) had begun and AT and T had assumed the basic shape it would hold for the next sixty years or so'.

It was at this time that Juran first began to question management's reliance on a system of mass inspection. The author describes an early assignment of Juran to investigate the production of a small circuit breaker which ultimately led to improved quality of the circuit breaker as well as a lower cost of production:

'The experience for Juran was a seminal one. He had faced and solved a chronic problem through a process of investigation and improvement that he could repeat, and he had realized cost reductions and quality improvements that were measurable and significant, and that required no capital investment. But he had been unable to apply his learnings more broadly, stymied by a rigid structure and the not-invented-here mentality it engendered'.

Chapter Three, with the intriguing title of 'The $42 Billion Garden Hose' covers the war years making no secret of the fact that Juran, a Jew, had a "seething hatred" of the Nazis. It explains Juran's role in the so-called Lend-Lease Administration following his 'escape route' from Western Electric where a transfer of power above him had left him vulnerable to 'a man whom Juran had offended in the past'. It describes how he became assigned to 'his favourite role -as a roving project-based problem solver' and realised improvements for example in document control having recognised "a problem that lent itself to analysis by tools", albeit, with a style that was naturally 'abrasive', He had, however, succeeded in proving 'that his skills were transferable from industry to government' and, in so doing had become 'motivated to write'.

His first book, *'Bureaucracy, A Challenge to Better Management -A Constructive Analysis of Management Effectiveness in the Federal Government'* was published in 1944 and is described in the latter pages of the chapter, whilst Chapter Four, 'Launching the Cause of Consultancy', describes his second and perhaps better known, *'Management of Inspection and Quality Control'* which was published in 1945, and third, even more well known *'Quality-Control Handbook'* which was published in 1951. It also describes Juran's introduction to the world of consultancy and to his post of

Chairman of the Department of Engineering at New York University where he was joined a year later in 1946 by W. Edwards Deming.

Chapter Five, the longest chapter at 38 pages, focuses specifically on the year 1954, when Juran first visited Japan, seven years after Dr. W. Edwards Deming's first visit. A lengthy description of American activities in post-war Japan is followed by a somewhat shorter explanation of Juran's message to the Japanese, that 'quality was as much about management as it was about statistics':

'Juran acknowledged, if obliquely, the need for Japan to improve through methods other than the capital-intensive, technology-based solutions so beloved by manufacturers in the United States'.

Juran's 'cycle of improvements' explained in terms of the concept of 'the quality atom' (a strategy for creating improvements little by little, one by one, that gradually accrete into big changes and huge improvements) is outlined along with the germs of his ideas for 'breakthrough' improvements with which his name later became notably associated. The chapter concludes by explaining how Juran's most important and lasting message to the Japanese was delivered in a special lecture to senior executives:

'Juran sums up his message to the Japanese by saying that he talked "about the organizational barriers to quality management and suggested that they try to find ways to institutionalise programs within their companies that would yield continuous quality improvement. That is exactly what they did. And around those programs the Japanese built a quality revolution".

Chapter Six, with the delightful title of 'Breakthrough and Bliss' describes the period from 1954 to 1975 when Juran entered 'The Freelance Life' which was characterised by 'the virtually continuous revision and regular republication' of his now famous *'Quality Control Handbook'* along with a crystallization of some of his earlier ideas which culminated in the publication of perhaps his greatest work, the book *'Managerial Breakthrough'* in 1964. This highlights the fact that both breakthrough and control are necessary for the survival and health of a company, since breakthrough brings good changes whilst control prevents bad ones. The various elements which comprise the breakthrough sequence are described.

Chapter Seven focuses heavily on the so-called 'Japanese miracle' and reproduces Juran's well-known graph of quality against time which shows how Japan outstripped the West during the period from 1950 to 1990 which resulted in crisis for the USA in particular during the 1980s:

'The key measuring instruments were not designed to register issues related to quality; the money measurements -market share, sales growth, unit growth, profits, ROI, and so on -indicated that things were fine. Not until

their financial instrument panels began to register problems did American managers truly hear the case for quality'.

Despite the boom in the advice business, however, there persisted a strange kind of apathy in the form of 'a yawning gap between the idea of quality and the achievement of quality' which was perhaps only 'thrown into more visible relief' by the well publicised intervention of Philip Crosby, whilst Deming 'was strong on philosophy and exhortation, but less able to provide wisdom about how to organise and what to do when, with whom, and about what':

'In Juran's opinion, although Deming calls for the "elimination of slogans and exhortations", his Fourteen Points fall into the category of slogans. "If anybody else had come up with those, they would have been ignored", says Juran'.

With Juran's influence over the same period far from obvious the chapter of negative observations finally gives way to one of enlightenment about the facts that 'quality remains a central issue for our business organisations and our society' and that 'those who most deserve the appellation of "guru" tend to like it least':

'Juran did not seek to become a guru. He did, however, successfully play out his chosen role as self-described "renaissance man of quality", and, in the process, helped to define and broaden the role played by independent advisers to business'.

The author concludes:

'He has been so unprotective of his ideas, so willing to offer his energies and services, so unwilling to make a public fuss over credit, so ubiquitous and longevous, that his ideas have been thoroughly assimilated into good business practice '.

It follows that 'Juran's ideas are more evident in our business organisations today than is his name'.

[Issue 110 (February 1998) - Inaugural CEOs' Best Practices Summit, White City, 21st January]

Leading with Alliances.

Nature rewards co-operation and penalises competition. It follows that where alliances can be struck which serve to enhance co-operation and diminish competition a stronger body will result with superior leadership, a higher capacity for innovation, and a vastly improved market share. It sounds obvious, but can managers and politicians be convinced?

Findings suggest that more than 20% of the annual revenues of the Fortune 500 will come from alliances by the year 2000 as 'alliance competency' evolves into a distinct discipline of both art and science. Further evidence, notably from The Lared Group, suggests that partner compatibility is inversely proportional to business justification in the success rate of alliances over time i.e. research into 235 companies revealed that the issue of partner compatibility was considered to be far more important to executives as alliances evolved than it was at the initial inception of the relationship.

Executive awareness and attention at the inception phase thus tended to focus more on the strategic and business reasons for the alliance than on the compatibility of the partners. Unfortunately this does not tend to produce a strong and lasting alliance (over 73% of companies surveyed cited differences in corporate culture and issues of compatibility related to culture as causes of alliance failure).

Jurgen Weber, Chairman of the Executive Board of Lufthansa German Airlines believes that the success of many corporations today is directly related not just to their relationships with customers but also to the number and quality of business relationships with other companies. He argues that most companies can no longer operate by themselves in order to fulfil their need. This philosophy has led Lufthansa, along with five other airlines (United Airlines, Thai Airways, SAS, Varig and Air Canada) to join forces under the banner of 'The Star Alliance' in order to integrate frequent flyer programmes and offer seamless booking and travel capabilities across all six airlines.

This is viewed as a way in which all six can secure their place in the deregulated and otherwise highly competitive global air transport industry, although it does not compromise the variation in culture between the carriers which is clearly a form of service differentiation which customers appreciate. The benefits for each carrier, as well as customers, promise to be considerable. This can be, for example, by enabling common utilisation of facilities and joint purchasing as well as simplified ticketing, more convenient flight connections, and improved baggage and ground services.

In North America a different kind of alliance has emerged between Nortel and recruitment specialists Manpower Inc. who have located an office opposite Nortel's Toronto headquarters as well as five other Nortel locations in Canada and the US. This enables a demand for up to 200 temporary employees per day to be recruited swiftly and with the required skills. The same philosophy has been adopted with other large organisations with similar requirements with the result that they have been able to tailor make staffing alliances to specific requirements, upgrading them as appropriate. With this approach Manpower Inc. has established itself as the world's largest staffing organisation providing over one and a half million people with employment every year and an annual sales revenue of the order of $8 billion.

In the debate David Ball commented:

"Some 35% of income at Nortel comes from alliances. Alliance management, however, is one of the most difficult areas of management. You have got to want as much success for your partner as you want for yourself. All alliances fail in the end and you need to plan for that. Success should mean did it succeed in its objectives? The EFQM Model provides a framework to articulate goals and how to achieve them and reduce the risk of proposed alliances failing".

Profesor Dr. Hans Dieter Seghezzi said:

"There have been numerous acquisitions in Silicon Valley where small companies have exhibited breakthrough innovation that large companies don't have. Small companies though can fear their loss of independence and with this attitude they have not made the most of their opportunities. Forming virtual organisations can be good training for small companies".

In the US Jeremy Coote dismissed suggestions that a merger was a failed alliance on the grounds that "if you have to acquire your partner, you've failed". He pointed to "full information sharing" as being the key to success and explained how SAP America had a clear department with responsibility for dealing with partners which "sometimes could be out of step with the main organisation".

Other discussions highlighted the need to discuss gain sharing early in the formation of alliances, and to review them regularly, whilst successful alliances were seen to be those which

*are clear on costs and payoffs

*offer new opportunities and capability

*have the ability to mediate problems and handle the unexpected

*understand philosophy and culture over structure

*possess the ability to capture learning

Leading through Stakeholder Symbiosis.

In addition to rewarding co-operation and punishing competition nature also strives to achieve balance. Symbiosis in the ecosystem enables that to happen. In business the analogy comes in the form of stakeholder symbiosis. A small number of leading organisations, including the last two winners of the European Quality Award (SGS Thomson and Brisa), have grasped this concept. Others are catching on.

Nortel provides a particularly excellent case study for stakeholder symbiosis not least because its business results have been spectacular. Sales have increased from under $300 million in 1991 to around $3 billion today as both customer and employee satisfaction have risen meteorically, whilst their impact on society has gained much needed public recognition, particularly in education which is viewed as partnership, not patronage. The underlying philosophy is that "stakeholder symbiosis does not mean having to rob Peter to pay Paul", but rather that "unselfish behaviour in symbiotic partnerships is enlightened self-interest".

In an attempt to demonstrate the existence of direct correlation between financial results, customer satisfaction and employee satisfaction the organisation conducted statistical analyses of 1995 employee and customer survey data at both corporate and business unit level. Focus group research involving Nortel customers and employees in eight countries was undertaken in order to gain a deeper understanding of the issues that surfaced from the quantitative work as key drivers. Further questions were then added to the demographic section of the 1996 Employee Opinion Survey. Here the employees primarily served to enable improved comparisons to be made between the customer and employee data. Further statistical analysis was then commissioned using the 1996 survey data.

Findings showed that there was strong correlation between how customers rate their relationship with Nortel personnel and their overall satisfaction with Nortel. Comparison of the Employee Satisfaction Index scores of a group of Nortel employees with the satisfaction scores of the customers they serve revealed that when employee satisfaction was high, customer satisfaction tended to be high also, even though research and benchmarking studies suggested that employee satisfaction scores generally will typically lag behind customer satisfaction scores by about 15 to 20%.

From this work the organisation has ascertained those employee behaviours which will tend to give rise to loyal customers and determine business success and how the work environment tends to constrain or enable these behaviours. This information is now being used to focus investments in Nortel people and guide ongoing work to improve processes.

In the debate David Ball commented:

"We need to hand over the drive to people to innovate, self organise and bring customer value, but to do that they have to be partners. Empowerment is essential but without alignment it can result in chaos. It is worrying talk about having to concentrate on shareholder rather than stakeholder value. Shareholder value is one result, customer satisfaction another, as is employee satisfaction. They are all outputs so we have got to measure all. Successful companies may not call it stakeholder symbiosis but the direct correlation is there. Anyone involved in corporate turnover sees a pattern".

In the US Mitchell Fromstein said:

"What you do for one stakeholder can impact on the interest of others, but we don't know the timing of when one stakeholder will benefit from what you do for another. For example it takes a while for employee satisfaction to impact on the customer. Therefore you have got to have a long term view".

In summarising Carla O'Dell said:

"The companies that are thriving by serving all have leaders with a mindset that is looking for 'out of the box' solutions to seemingly conflicting priorities".

Further Information

The Inaugural CEO Best Practices Summit and Global Satellite Broadcast was sponsored by 3M, Nortel, The American Productivity and Quality Center, The European Foundation for Quality Management, and Fortune Custom Projects. A follow-up report of the event is published in the March 30th issue of *Fortune Magazine*. The Arthur Andesen Global Insights '98 Discovery Tool may be obtained from The International Institute for Learning Inc., 110 East 59th Street, Sixth Floor, New York, NY10022 –1380 USA.

[Issue 114 (June 1998)]

CREATING THE VALUE-ADDING FINANCE FUNCTION

Finance functions will have to redefine and realign their roles, competencies and performance evaluation to meet the business needs of the new millennium, according to a recent report from Business Intelligence. Survey evidence collected by Business Intelligence reveals that 98 % of finance directors believe that finance professionals need to develop a broader set of business skills such as a knowledge of strategic performance measurement skills, strategic financial analysis, negotiating and better communication skills. Some 57% say that they are now being required to measure their contribution to the business in non-financial terms as well as by traditional finance reports.

Case studies from organisations such as Burger King, Hertfordshire County Council, BT, Electrolux, DHL, Electronic Data Systems and British Nuclear Fuels explain

*how finance professionals can develop their traditional skills-bank to shape the strategic direction of the company and achieve a competitive advantage.

*the role of the finance professional in managing and implementing balanced performance measurement systems.

1047

*the technologies which can support the creation of a value-adding finance function i.e. what is available and how to make the correct choices.

*tools and techniques for driving change throughout the finance function.

'At EDS finance has become an added-value service as a result of a major re-engineering exercise. This has led to the creation of standardised customer-facing processes and cost savings that run into hundreds of millions of dollars. "Since 1990 revenue has increased by about 103% whereas our controller group costs have reduced by 11% of the total finance and accounting cost: revenue has reduced from 3.2% to 1.2%", says Heather Stuchell, Process Review Manager'.

Surveys in 1997 showed that on average less than 20% of a finance department's time is spent on value-adding activities such as budgeting and planning with over 80% spent on day to day accounting operations. The report explains how best-practice finance functions are able to turn this around so they apply more than 50% of their time on key decision-support activities.

Copies of the report, entitled 'Creating the Value-adding Finance Function' by James Creelman, former Editor of the *TQM Magazine* and *Managing Service Quality* are currently available from Business Intelligence Limited, Third Floor, 22-24 Worple Road, Wimbledon, London SW19 400.

[Issue 120 (December 1998)]

EQF LECTURE - QUALITY MANAGEMENT AT BRITISH AEROSPACE: RENAISSANCE AT WORK

Occasionally there is a presentation or subject which stands well above the rest, but it is rarer that both subject and presentation reach this level. However, this was the case for the Annual Engineering Quality Forum (EQF) Lecture given by John Weston, Chief Executive of BAe on 9 November at the IEE.

The Lecture with the above title describes how BAe with its numerous acquisitions of companies after nationalisation of the aircraft industry in 1977, became a conglomerate of enormous size (120,000 employees) and complexity, embracing many diverse companies and cultures.

Around 1990 the turnover rose from £5.6 billion to £10.6 billion yet at the same time the main product lines hit recession. Cash levels fell sharply and a rights issue failed to make a difference. Airlines in recession returned surplus aircraft leaving BAe with the leasing costs. In 1992 the company hit financial crisis point with only £100m above the banks lending limit –any lower and the company would have been in the hands of the banks.

Whilst this was daunting enough, a survey of staff views revealed some disappointing revelations (including that a large majority did not believe what management told them!). Management had to accept that their style was too aggressive and confrontational. The terms of reference for the Personnel function were seen as too narrow.

A complete reappraisal of the business was vital and key decisions were made to rationalise the products and company portfolio. Inherited businesses within the group were viable in their own right, but did not fit in to BAe e.g. a construction company in Holland, and a property development company in the UK. Others, like Rover, were cash hungry for new development, competing for this scarce resource with other main products. These companies were sold as 'going concerns'. Further rationalisation of the products particularly in the Defence business meant that the company had to radically reduce staff -a painful process.

The revue, however, also revealed the good news, some excellent products, high skills in advanced technology, trustworthy partnerships and a wide appreciative customer base.

Fortunately the Board had initiated a change programme in 1990, with total senior management commitment, but found that communication of this needed a much higher priority. The 1992 crisis brought this into stark focus. The Board found that the European Quality Model 'was a very useful tool' and that communicating the company's Mission and Values was an important practical step and not as some think 'a guru fad'.

Determination was necessary to express the key words for the culture change e.g. "Quality in All that we do", give 'Exceptional Service', provide 'Superior Products' using Engineering in critical technology, 'Working together in collaborative action', "Embrace Change" with process improvement.

Company priorities were changed, and listed. First: the Customer -appreciate his needs. Second: People -as the company strength -using 'Investors in People' as a tool. The list then includes Performance, Partnerships, Profit, and Innovation and Technology -to keep a competitive edge.

These principles took time to move through the staff layers in the company, and an investment in training at all levels was necessary. To put through these changes whilst the company was going through rapid downsizing (>50%) was particularly difficult. However, the company retained the confidence of the workforce by treating people as well as possible during severance. Several schemes were introduced, early retirement, generous severance packages, retraining, and interest free loans to start up new businesses with consultancy counselling.

High priority was put on early communication to those affected by changes or closures, to reduce uncertainty and quickly answer the individual's question "does that mean my job?" The workforce has been reduced to 46,000. Management now adheres to the principle "we do what we say and say what we mean".

Adoption of the (EFQM) Business Excellence Model has shown where the greatest potential for improvement lies. John Weston commented "this would justify a paper on its own!". Other tools which have contributed are "Investors in People", 'Team Working', statistical process control and Pareto Analysis. Shortening the lines of communication has been achieved by the company reducing the levels of Management from 11 to 4.

Significant reduction in cycle times and development processes are now around 30 to 50% in military aircraft manufacture, compared with previous projects. John Weston gave several examples of workforce redeployment and flexibility which would not have been believed at the beginning of the decade.

Summarizing the recovery and the lessons learned John Weston observed:

* BAe now only sell aircraft to 'blue chip' companies (Lower prices, less risk and lower long term costs).

* Advanced Business Planning is seen to be the key corporate process, which now cascades down to all parts of the business process, involving as many of the workforce as possible.

* Reserves have been rebuilt from £0 to £600M and banking agreements renegotiated.

* Disposal of companies removed £5 billion of sales which only realised £7M profit, raised £1,200M cash and off-loaded £2,000M off the balance sheet debt.

* Cash performance from £1500M debt to £511 M in Bank, with share price from 88 pence to £20 (before share split) and company value from £300M to £8,000M, giving 'best performance stock' in FTSE 100 for two out of the last three years.

* EFQM assessments: some companies in the BAe group have some good scores in some categories, but "we have a way to go to get any company in the group into the 700 points World Class category, although we have the determination to get there".

* With People -"The workforce now believes the company has a future, and that they can do well in it. Opportunities are there now for Personal Development Plans, Open learning and contribution to the company planning process.

* BAe believe the Corporate approach is now on the right track and that the investment in training is in place for the future.

After the lecture questions were asked on the selection process of which elements of the portfolio to reduce or promote. Mr Weston responded by saying "there was no time to ask accountants to do Cost Benefit Analysis, we had to assess each situation 'on Management Instinct'. In hindsight we can see which were the critical decisions but it would be wishful thinking to believe we knew the specific significance of them at the time".

Another question was "why did BAe keep their emphasis in the military market place when they had commercial companies they could develop e.g. Rover?". Mr. Weston replied that BAe had good knowledge of the Defence Industry and despite the downturn many potential orders were for the Middle and Far East, not affected by the end of the Cold War. Rover on the other hand required a large investment with a relatively low market share, only Rolls Royce and Mercedes could survive with such low level numbers. Subsequent recent events with purchaser BMW has proved this to be the case.

The last query concerned the perennial question of the possibilities of future relationship with GEC. On this Mr. Weston said:

"This is a typical City speculation. When BAe were at their lowest ebb and only valued at £300M there was the danger that some company like GEC, who had that sort of money to spare might step in. Now the position is quite different".

[*Quality Matters comments:* the audience, including the very experienced members of the EQF, were impressed by the frank and open presentation, to many the best given by a C.E.O. The clear commitment to the Quality approach to management and its link to success for the future of the company was refreshing. When in 'survival mode' accelerated change becomes a requirement but it is the way it is done that matters. If the approach is seen to be fair and constructive, the remaining workforce will embrace change more readily. Here is an example of the saying "The most enduring business advantage is the Quality of Management".]

LIVING TOMORROWS COMPANY (BOOK REVIEW)

Author: Mark Goyder (192 Pages).

Publisher: Gower Publishing, Gower House, Croft Road, Aldershot, Hampshire GU11 3BR. (ISBN 0-566-08020-6)

Details:

In 1992 a debate had emerged in the UK about the role of business and its effect on British culture. It stemmed largely from the series of spectacular apparent successes and failures that had arisen in the wake of privatisation in the 1980s which led to a feeling by many that values in British society had become 'uncomfortably out of balance'. Questions were asked such as 'who should be the real beneficiaries of success?', 'were the spoils being distributed in an equitable way?' and 'were sources of capital, and their hired help, top management, being disproportionately rewarded?'

The Royal Society for the encouragement of Arts, Manufactures and Commerce (RSA), whose role crosses the frontiers of constituencies, disciplines and ideas, subsequently conducted an Inquiry known as 'the Inquiry into Tomorrow's Company' which was chaired by Sir Anthony Cleaver. This initially challenged over 70 business leaders to provide their vision of the company of the future. Twenty five of them agreed to participate in the Inquiry and support it with the sponsorship of their companies. The author led the staff team on the inquiry which published its final report in 1995 and was a best seller, selling over 150 copies a month two years after publication.

The momentum from this report inspired various members of the investment community to develop a new and better range of investment criteria for companies and in 1996 a dedicated Centre for Tomorrow's Company was established in London, under the Directorship of the author.

In this book he describes the battle between the two contrasting views of business which have emerged, namely that which reduces it to a narrow concept of contracts and transactions, and that which focuses on the inspiration of people to produce extraordinary results. Ten chapters serve not as a 'how to' manual or guide to business perfection but rather a practical and thought-provoking discussion of the major issues facing UK business which proposes agendas for action by managers, educators and investors alike.

The book begins by taking the reader forward in time to the year 2059, the 200th anniversary of the publication of John Stuart Mills' book entitled *'On Liberty'* which concentrated on the abolition of so called 'unaccountable power'. The concept is extended to modern day accountability and presented as descendent James Mills' *'View from the Future'*. It predicts that in 2020 shareholders will expect businesses to take steps to invest in the health of the communities in which they operate 'as a simple matter of risk management', arguing that to trade shareholder accountability for so called 'stakeholding' is 'to sacrifice clarity for blancmange':

'In Tomorrow's Company far-sighted business leaders will stop thinking about accountability as a restriction of their freedom. They will start to see it as an enhancer of their freedom. They will acknowledge that no business can survive unless it continually passes the market test of identifying and meeting some human need. They will realise from the force of the evidence quoted (described in Chapter Three) that the businesses which survive and prosper longest will be those that meet such needs most competitively, while at the same time behaving in away that wins the widest trust in their activities. Accountability in a wider sense will be seen as the necessary accompaniment to efficiency'.

The second chapter, entitled' A Romance and an Adventure' questions the notion that businesses are in existence solely to make a profit for their owners and whilst it argues that there is 'nothing wrong with investors judging their investment exclusively in financial terms' it draws the line, 'when half truths are claimed as whole truths' and 'exclusive statements of purpose replace inclusive ones'. Thus 'we are here to create value for our shareholders' becomes corrupted into 'we are only to create value for our shareholders'. This exclusive preoccupation with the shareholder is, says the author, 'anything but entrepreneurial'. It is then suggested that the leaders of tomorrow will need to be 'less assertive, less dominant, and less surrounded with the trappings of power' i.e. viewing leadership 'as service rather than controlling':

'Leaders point out to people what they have in common, appealing to that part of their make-up that wants to belong and contribute, and help a group to realise together a potential that they would never achieve as competing individuals'.

In Chapter Three, entitled 'Value and Values', the author expresses concern at the 'cynicism' which exists in the UK and which is tending 'to drive away from business the very people that business needs'. He suggests that in the long run those 'who think they are running firms' will be beaten by those 'who are building companies' and dispels a series of myths such as 'visionary companies require great and charismatic visionary leaders' and 'visionary companies share a common subset of core values'.

Chapter Four is entitled 'The Rules of the Game are changing' and explores such concepts as learning in teams, the shift in intelligence away from corporate headquarters, and the demise of so called policy manuals and nine to five working. It is predicted that companies which rely solely on checks and controls will, in the end, be left behind by competitors who have learned how to compete without compromising trustworthy behaviour:

'Tomorrow's Company will have clearly stated the values that it stands for. It will make such values apart of its appraisal processes. Its bonus payments will reflect not only how much profit a leader contributed, but how faithful he or she had been to the code of behaviour. It will promote adventurous and entrepreneurial people –but only if they share those values. And it will create an atmosphere in which the majority of honest employees quickly challenge behaviour that is inconsistent with those values'.

Chapter Five, entitled 'The Two Surfaces of Success' and Chapter Six, entitled 'The Inclusive Approach', are the two longest chapters (both 21 pages). The former deals with the so called 'hard' and 'soft' aspects which characterise success i.e. the gritty texture of competition and cost reduction' which is contrasted with 'the pliant texture of collaboration and value creation'. It is argued that in order to be successful a business 'must be able to recognise the importance of each surface', it being 'the toughness of the competition that makes it important that your business is sensitive and has its own personality'.

In the latter chapter the importance of measurement is highlighted along with the 'continuing gap between what managers believe to be important for the success of their companies (their success model) and the measures actually used. Mention is made notably of the European Business Excellence Model and its role 'in helping businesses to measure what really counts, instead of measuring what they have always been in the habit of counting'. Examples to illustrate the points raised are presented from IBM, Grand Metropolitan, Birmingham Midshires Building Society, Blue Circle, Unipart, Hewlett Packard, Toyota, and Federal Express:

'Supertracker is a barcode based system that enables the company to identify exactly where any package is in its system. It also makes possible a daily measure of customer service called SQI (Service Quality Indicator). Every late delivery', every damaged item, every invoice adjustment, every lost item is recorded and scored. At the end of the working day the total is calculated and made known to every employee. In 1994,the typical total score was 130,000. Within the next five years the company's aim is to cut the score to one tenth of that total, without allowing for increases in volume'.

Chapter Seven, entitled 'Corporate Governance' considers the relationship with investors is considered in more depth arguing that it does not take long to detect sloth (defined as the decline of enterprise or loss of entrepreneurial flair) in the way corporate governance works in the UK:

'Several senior people admitted to the Inquiry that when acting as pension trustees they had set crude performance targets which contributed to precisely the kind of short term investor behaviour which they found so

1054

unhelpful to their own companies. The fund managers in their turn have limited time and limited information on which to exercise judgment across their widely diversified portfolios. They also tend to be measured by the pension funds whom they serve on the basis of periods as short as one or two years. This is where the traditional textbook theory of corporate governance as accountability to owners starts to break down'.

Chapter Eight on 'Investors' further analyses the relationship between fund managers and companies arguing that the key to risk management in an extended, expert-dependent business is the assessment of people and their values rather than 'the traditional stable-door controls on behaviour'. It calls for an improvement in the quality of the dialogue between companies and investors along lines already being taken, in the USA (ref: 'Communicating Corporate performance: A Delicate Balance for Managements, Shareholders and Boards of Directors', The Conference Board, New York 1997).

Chapter Nine, on 'Work, Wealth and Worth' looks at measuring and reporting social impact as the basis for dialogue whilst the short tenth chapter entitled 'Divine Discontent' features a short case study from Honda which is used to illustrate the fact that 'it doesn't take long to identify a company which is on the inclusive journey'.

[Issue 129 (September 1999) – 5th Sheffield World Quality Congress]

The Future of Quality

The presentation by Martin Brenig-Jones, Head of Corporate Quality for British Telecom, was likewise thought provoking, considering amongst other things the future role of quality managers and the need to build on the EFQM Excellence Model. He described the Model as "really, really superb", but indicated that by itself it was "not enough" since businesses must be able to do more than assess the way they are today or were yesterday:

"We must formulate a new understanding of what we do with quality. We must look at 'New Quality' as how we transform businesses. There's a new role for quality that is interesting and challenging".

He explained how, looking to the future, BT was measuring the health of the business against the EFQM Excellence Model using a diagnostic tool that would "see if it was fit for transformation" and was launching a programme called 'e3' which stood for 'Enterprise, Efficiency and Excellence'. This, in parallel with the concept of a "Director of Revolution" was, he believed, going to make BT "more entrepreneurial, innovative and creative" to the extent that they would "evolve into something different":

"We want to develop a culture so people feel they are running their own bit of the business. We can't set up lots of little businesses but we can focus on

value creation with everyone doing something to create value for the business. We now have value centres with teams clear about the value they are creating, and value centred leaders helping to develop an entrepreneurial climate."

"We want managers involved more with looking at how small businesses operate and there is talk of managers acting as mentors for small companies. We also have an organisation called BT UK Enterprises which is people running their own businesses such as Yellow Pages. These are good breeding grounds for leaders of the future".

In the questioning which followed Hans Bajaria 'asked Mr. Brenig-Jones about the future role of ISO9000, given that it was written in an era of stable rather than unstable technological development. He asked in particular whether, with such large amounts of time being required to write and document all of the necessary procedures there was a possibility that ISO 9000 might be "killed off".

The speaker gave the following answer:

"ISO9000 forms a very basic level of sustainability but we need a balance between control and freedom. We have no problem with ISO9000 as it is a basic foundation that reminds people of the need for good management controls. It functions across all operations and the intranet based management system has eliminated a lot of paperwork.

"We did review our approach last year and weighed up the positive with the negative and decided for now to stick with it. The new 'healthcheck' will incorporate some of the audit activities of ISO9000."

[Issue 134 (March 2000)]

Managing an Award winning Call Centre

At Qualitex Ms. Paula Davis, Training and Competence Manager for CIS Limited, Britain's only co-operative insurer, described the approach taken by her organisation which enabled them to win The British Insurance Award for training last July. This was essentially ' a tale of two call centres' which explained how two inefficient call centres, dealing respectively with non-life service and deposit accounts, were rationalised into one single streamlined unit which now gives customers a single point of contact with the organisation.

The motivation for the change stemmed essentially from a combination of three pressures namely competition (increasing proliferation of providers of financial services in general), increased regulation, and customer demand. In considering these, senior management asked themselves what kind of experience they wanted customers to have, bearing in mind their mission "to put the customer at the very heart of the business". Their conclusion was that they needed an approach that would provide choice, consistency, and quality. This approach was affectionately nicknamed 'The Martini Approach' (Anytime, Anyplace, Anyhow.)

In order to achieve the change a management team comprising of field staff was formed which resulted in "a wonderful fresh outlook". There was prioritisation of products with the highest priority being afforded to the most flexible accessible products which had high volumes of transactions. A dedicated outbound call team was established and there was a strong emphasis on building internal relationships to put an end to channel conflict such as the sales channel's perceived threats deriving from developments in administration. Recruitment methods were also reviewed, the speaker pointing out how psychometric tests were not always useful for revealing the best candidates, especially in call centre roles where staff in service roles often need a very different skills mix to those involved in sales. A dedicated service centre training team was formed to tackle this issue.

Performance management is addressed monthly by means of a 'desk review' organised by team leaders. This review is based on the core quality indicators of efficiency, quality of call handling, and general conduct. Each member of staff has a 'learning log' in which the core quality indicators are set out along with examples to illustrate 'positive behaviour' and demonstrate clearly just exactly what 'good quality' really is. A Merit Award scheme supports this with points being available for schedule adherence, outbound performance, and good use of wrap up codes.

Continuous Voice Recording (CVR) is used to feed into the desk reviews and this is used to monitor call quality and identify trends. A teleconnect scripting tool (TCS) enables standardisation of calls and the benefits of having a single user interface was emphasised:

"Advisers are often good at systems navigation but it adds a lot of time to processes. Also an adviser can become more concerned with systems navigation than with the quality of advice."

Since rationalisation, the organisation's rate of appointments arising from calls has risen to 2,500 per week which equates to a rate of 60%, in an industry where rates are often as low as 1 in 20. Call volumes have risen from 9,300 per week in January 1999 to 60,000 per week in January 2000. The service level currently stands at 90% of calls handled within 30 seconds whilst a staff retention rate of 90% places CIS in the top 20% of their industry for this measure. The number of staff employed, however, has risen from 100 to 240 with 86% of staff now 'multi-skilled'.

The speaker concluded:

"We can enable a quality culture. The key is for people to embrace it."

1057

Minimalist Manufacturing in Action

One group of 'Quality Culture' seminars commenced with Peter Durant of Arthur d. Little who used case studies from Bass Brewing and British American Tobacco (Argentina) to illustrate the benefits of applying Arthur D. Little's pioneering Minimalist Manufacturing approach which consists basically of the following four step methodology:

(i)   Characterise variability of the current process.

(ii)   Quantify improvement opportunity

(iii)   Develop the link between process variables and process outcome

(iv)   Achieve improvement through deployment of well-understood techniques

Each of these stages was described in detail beginning with an investigation of the different ways in which variation propagates within a system, and then following through with an understanding of the temporal effects of adjustments and the application of 'robust control' in order to distinguish between different forms of variation. Graphical charts were used to illustrate:

*Drift (consistent movement in more or less one direction)

*Transient (a movement which, if left unattended will tend to reverse itself)

*Set up/adjust (a variation that affects all elements of a production batch)

*Accidental (a variation attributable to a breakdown)

Various events and patterns are examined in order to identify systematic causes of variation. Once the process variability has been established the improvement potential can be quantified e.g. 30% between a good day yield and a difficult day yield. The link between process variables and process outcome is developed and sustainable improvements realised over, typically, a six to nine month time span. The following principles were highlighted:

- Improvements on many fronts will deliver compound benefits; 'golden nugget' solutions rarely exist.

- Systematic problem solving approaches give long lasting results.

- The plant must be used as a learning environment.

- Use minimum resources of information, interventions and control.

- Focus on 'lost opportunities' and learn from 'things gone wrong.'

- Isolate disruptions and thereby control processes.

- React only to statistically significant events.

'Bass had invested £60 million in three state-of-the-art packaging lines at Cape Hill – two for bottling and one for canning. To respond to changing consumer demands, it commissioned a new facility for small batch runs. From the outset, however, the facility failed to meet the required production targets. In a four week assessment, we pinpointed the many factors that were contributing to the inefficiencies: operators using different methods of working, poor changeovers, inadequate maintenance, unclear organisational responsibility and substandard information management. With Arthur D. Little's guidance, the company set a target improvement in efficiency of 22.5% based on a statistical analysis of hourly performance. Putting the line under a microscope we monitored the manufacturing process 24 hours a day for three and a half weeks, recording minute-to-minute data on disruptions and output'.

'As one example: changeover performance was poor, having a big impact on efficiencies and quality levels. Many hours were lost each week as the lines were switched between different products, and after every changeover the efficiencies dipped for a number of shifts while the line 2settled down2 and the set up was fine tuned. As in many manufacturing companies, Bass' range of stock keeping units has been increasing in number and variety, and the proliferation of multipacks, bottle shapes, label types and positions demanded far more line changeovers. Introducing changeover checksheets,, clear documentation and structured storage for changeover parts contributed significantly to the dramatic improvement in performance. Other improvement activities ensured that worn and failed parts were maintained or replaced after changeover, in contrast to the "remove and forget" approach that had prevailed in the past. Operators now examine all such parts off line to identify the causes and patterns of failure'.

'The results have been dramatic with sustainable improvements in output of 30% achieved in 8 months. With the learning, systems and methods we transferred to the workforce Bass is continuously increasing output. Morale is high, as people take more responsibility and see direct results for their efforts'.

At BAT Argentina similarly impressive results were achieved. They had installed two new technology lines which deteriorated rapidly with efficiencies falling and reject rates rising. Minimalist Manufacturing was subsequently introduced leading to new maintenance and cleaning procedures and improved scheduling and training. Productivity improved by around 40% and reject levels were reduced by 80% as systematic causes were eliminated.

The speaker left delegates with four questions to consider as follows:

- Is excellence in manufacturing performance either critical or a Key Success Factor for the business?

- Do you have periods of good performance that can be replicated?

- If not, then can you explain why you cannot replicate?

- If you did achieve it, would it deliver significant value?

He suggested that if the answers to these questions were 'yes' then Minimalist Manufacturing will bring benefits to one's business.

In the questioning that followed the speaker was asked about how he achieved 'buy-in' to the approach and to explain the direct link between the changes made at Bass and the bottom line benefits. In the first case he stressed the importance of demonstrating to people how variation in practice makes their jobs more difficult and how "hit and miss" approaches to work serve as a contributory cause. In answering the second question he explained how Bass were being forced to outsource some of their packaging operations as a direct consequence of the poor performance of the £60 million lines and that as a direct result of applying Minimalist Manufacturing they were able to avoid having to choose between continuing to outsource or investing £20 million in another line. The case implemented paid back for Bass in one year, he said.

[Issue 135 (April 2000) – EFQM Learning Edge Conference, Belfast]

New thinking for the New Millennium

Dr. Edward de Bono's presentation was entitled 'New thinking for the New Millennium' and in terms of style bore some resemblance to that of the late Dr. W. Edwards Deming. Just as Dr. Deming was renowned for his 'Fourteen Points' Dr. de Bono is known for his 'Six Hats' which represent different thinking modes and have brought huge bottom line benefits to many large organisations, including Siemens, British Telecom, Prudential, ABB, Statoil, IBM and Boeing. The 'Six Hats' were introduced as follows:

* White (information seeking with everyone looking for information in parallel and assessing what is available and what is needed)

* Red (denoting feelings, intuition and emotion and acts as signal to the effect that it is acceptable to provide emotion so that one is not obliged to insert it at every point of a meeting, particularly as intuition is not always right)

* Black (signifying caution, risk and danger, not to be over-used)

* Yellow (representing logic and the process of making benefits and values a reality; necessitates development of value sensitivity and assessment of value in one's own ideas)

* Green (the 'creativity' hat demanding that everyone be creative whenever it is in force so that possibilities, rather than merely data analysis and logic, makes progress happen)

* Blue (symbolising process control and the thinking process itself, necessitating that situations be defined before action is taken)

In accordance with de Bono's philosophy control must pass to each of the 'Hats' in turn to create six different modes of thinking which, when applied correctly, result in a very powerful tool as everyone's talents are utilised in parallel rather than against one another. The whole dynamics of meetings therefore changes and the effects have been so profound that the US judiciary is currently considering the introduction of a mandatory requirement for all juries to be trained in the Six Hats Technique.

"Thinking can be changed and can be taught, and is the mechanism by which we deliver and enjoy our values", the speaker asserted.

Elsewhere in his speech Dr. de Bono exposed the flaws in a number of long-standing beliefs, such as the belief that if one simply analyses information one will be able to generate ideas, and the belief that progress can be made by merely providing standard answers to standard situations. These beliefs were, he said, "inadequate" and the audience was challenged to make change by considering the 'what can be' element of constructive thinking, as well as the traditional 'what is'.

He was particularly scathing toward the 'argumentative' mode of thinking which he said was "extremely ineffective" and "not a constructive way of moving forward". He stated that with argument one is not exploring a subject but merely making a case.

Strong emphasis was placed throughout on the need to design value concepts for the future and in particular how to design value from information input and to understand creativity from the standpoint of self-organising systems. "More technology will not create value", he said.

There was no supporting paper for this presentation, but Dr. de Bono has recently published a book (ISBN 0-140-28776-0) entitled *'New thinking for the New Millennium'* in which he elaborates on a number of other important quality related concepts. For example, competition:

*'Some years ago I wrote a book called "*Surpetition*". This was meant to contrast with traditional "competition". Competition comes from the Latin and means "seeking together". So organisations spend most of their strategic energy looking over their shoulders at the competition. If the competition are cutting prices so should they, etc., etc. I suggested that "value creation" was more important, and even the creation of "value monopolies".*

Six years after I wrote this book research I showed what I predicted: those organisations that focused on competition did badly, those that focused on value creation did well. Cutting costs, downsizing and efficient housekeeping are often necessary but they are not sufficient long-term strategies. Value creation is essential'.

Another example is improving quality in education:

'The "academic game" is a very special game. You are required to take in and remember quite a lot of information. You have to store this. Then, on demand, as in examinations, you are required to sort through the stored information and give it back. Youngsters who are poor on the input or storage side have no chance at all in the academic game. In my experience, however, these youngsters may be very good thinkers. If they are asked to think about something which does not depend on stored knowledge, they perform very well. Indeed, in the "thinking lessons", such youngsters surprise their teachers and their classmates. A boy who was regarded as "dumb" is suddenly seen to be a very good thinker'.

'Is it possible that one day dominance by aggression will be replaced by "dominance by wisdom"? Is it possible in any system that ultimately depends on popular choice, that this popular choice would be sufficiently wise to make the right choice (for all parties, and long-term as well as short-term)? I believe it is possible, but only if we teach thinking in all schools and from an early age. There is no existing school subject that is more important. There is no subject that is more neglected'.

Dealing in Difference.

Gerard Kok and Anne Murphy of KPMG Alliances in the Netherlands presented a report and workshop on the subject of alliances and why they so often don't succeed. They described the huge sums of money currently being invested in flawed relationships as a "depressing picture", but suggested that the future need not be as gloomy as the immediate past, particularly if a sound methodology is used for choosing and selecting a partner, such as that which KPMG are currently in the process of promoting. The speakers highlighted the following three facts:

(i) Around 70% of alliance failure is due to relationship issues or things connected with them.

(ii) The criteria for partner selection and partnership in action are often highly disconnected and this can be a cause of failure.

(iii) It is rarely the differences, but the attempts to remove differences that usually cause the greatest problems.

A key question in dealing with these points is whether to focus on opportunity or on risk when an alliance is being considered:

"When we focus on opportunity the output is 'hearts and minds' with people working towards the same objectives and values. This is attractive and feels good. A focus on risk, however, leads to rules and regulations and command and control. People cannot share their information and there is an 'arms length feel' to very narrow agreements. What tends to happen is that accountants typically focus on risk whilst human resources are seen to be 'hearts and minds' but often are not in practice. Lawyers, who are defensive, then drive the deal whilst the engineers, who frequently have the answers, are largely ignored".

They stressed also that what works in one company may not in another and cited the mismatch between Wal Mart in America and Wal Mart in Germany as an example. "You cannot just pick up one culture and impose it on another", they said, and recommended that people should first of all try to work with their differences rather than argue who is right, and then to work on a task encouraging others to do likewise.

[There are some striking examples in the UK, where Japanese companies have recognised culture differences from the outset and have been very good at promoting change -Ed].

In their report they elaborate further:

'The greater the differences, the greater the potential for creativity, learning and outstanding results. What goes with that, however, are a number of fundamental challenges to the way most organisations are understood and managed. Many organisations currently manage these challenges by trying to minimise differences between partners mistakenly believing that integration is synonymous with uniformity.

To make partnering at multiple levels a success organisations need to recognise that it is the attempt to minimise differences, not the differences themselves which are the root cause of conflict. It is one thing to espouse

*values of trust and flexibility, and quite another to act in such a way as to
replace command and control with radically new ways of working together'.*

Four tools are prescribed to help deal with this:

- The Partnership Profiler (to clarify business assumptions)

- The Partnering Grid (providing views of ambition and difference)

- The Prioritiser (to clarify implicit assumptions)

- The Negotiator (to create a win-win partnership)

*'While one partner may naively believe they are happily working towards a
"Hearts and Minds" relationship where everyone shares the same basic
values and assumptions, the other, trapped into escalating risks and
narrowing opportunities, is convinced that the relationship is drifting
towards an "Arms Length" position. The signals each party unwittingly
sends the other carry messages of separation and distrust. Caught in a
vortex of misinterpretation and misunderstanding the relationship will
undoubtedly slide deeper and deeper into "Grid Lock". In partnering,
prevention is better than cure.*

*Commitment, confidence and trust are built on ongoing relationships which
accommodate changes in conditions, objectives 'and personnel. Since all
partnerships are compromises, partners should spend less time trying to
harmonise and align, and more time trying to understand each other. To this
end we use "The Partnering Grid" as a framework for mapping expectations,
perceptions and movement. Resulting agreements and actions accelerate
joint activity for mutual benefit and give a confidence and energy boost to
both motivation and results. The ground is then laid for a new language for
partnering which enables ongoing health checks, diagnosis, prevention and
cure to be carried out by the partners themselves'.*

[Issue 136 (May 2000)]

QUALITY IN PUBLIC ADMINISTRATION

Public administration has been a neglected area for many years when it
comes to quality management, and the fact that no public sector organisation
has yet attained the standard required to win the European Quality Award for
the Public Sector, despite its existence for almost four years, reflects this.
The need for quality, however, has been recognised, most notably by the
Directors General (DGs) of the European Commission who established a
Steering Group involving all fifteen Member States and a smaller Working
Group in the second half of 1998. In 1999 the Finnish Presidency laid the
foundations for a series of major international conferences to address this

theme. In parallel with this a Common Assessment Framework (CAF) was developed based on the principles of the EFQM Business Excellence Model), the Speyer Academy in Germany, and the European Institute of Public Administration (EIPA) in Maastricht in the Netherlands for adoption by public administrations throughout Europe. The purposes of the CAF are as follows:

(i) To serve as an introductory tool for public administrators who want to improve their managerial skills and may be interested in applying quality management in their organisations, and would like to apply a simple self-assessment to the organisation in order to gain a feel for the use of these types of tools.

(ii) To act as a 'bridge' across the various models and methodologies in use in quality management in public administration in the- various EU countries by introducing a measure of comparability between the results which are produced by the different systems.

(iii) To allow the introduction of benchmarking studies between public sector organisations.

The CAF has been pilot tested in seven public sector organisations in three member states including organisations at central, regional and local levels of public administration with varying degrees of exposure to quality management. This testing has not, as yet, provided a reliable base for measurement or comparison of performance between public sector organisations, but it is expected that this base could be established with wider usage. It is also envisaged that the results provided by using the CAF will be 'calibrated' against those derived from the more established models such as the EFQM Business Excellence Model and the Speyer Model, which would enhance the opportunities for comparison and benchmarking across EU public administration.

Decisions relating to the future development and application of the CAF are now to be taken by national administrations and other interested parties, following the First Quality Conference for Public Administrations in the EU which was held at the prestigious Lisbon Congress Centre from 9th to 12th May and attracted just over 1000 delegates.

The conference was opened by His Excellency Antonio Guterres, Prime Minister of Portugal, who called for a digitalisation of public administration procedures across Europe, the making of all public information available on the Internet, and lifelong training for all people in public service so that they can keep pace with technological development.

In the plenary sessions that followed Spiros Pappas, Adviser 'Hors Classe' to the European Commission, spoke of the need for subsidiarity "to blossom as a guiding principle for politicians to deal as closely as possible with local problems", but warned of danger if networking becomes perceived as "the rebirth of bureaucratic monsters", whilst Johani Turunen, Finnish Permanent Under Secretary of State, stressed the need to share experiences rather than standardise. "Our administration structures and cultures differ, therefore it is hard to find standardised solutions", he said.

Geert Bouckaert of the Catholic University of Leuven in Belgium, who also represented the Speyer University in Germany, spoke of the biggest challenge for the future as being that of making effective governance visible and to convince society that it is happening.

Ms. Isobel Corte-Real, until recently Director General of EIPA, explained how the state had a "decisive role providing essential services that the market could not provide" and called for a reduction in the distance between the public and private sectors so that both could advance at the same rate. She described the conference as "a meeting point and a starting point for more ambitious goals".

Ireland's Assistant Secretary at the Department of Finance, Eric Embleton, emphasised the need to invest in leadership skills training in the public sector, as leadership was an area which has always tended to be "overmanaged and overcontrolled", and stressed the urgency of moving from structure to processes, which although difficult had to be done.

Finally, Portugal's Secretary of State for Public Administration and Administrative Modernisation, Alexandre Rosa, underlined the importance of including public administration in society's quest for quality, for if it were to be excluded society would eventually dispense with it. This inevitably meant that there had to be state reform which was the result of a balanced process. This was "an important strategic need" along with reformation of the "inner workings" of the state machine and a tailoring of institutions to the needs of society.

The remainder of the conference consisted of 39 case studies which comprise the conference literature, which were divided into four parallel streams, namely 'New Millennium, New Management: Emerging Best Practices in Public Management', 'The Search for Excellence in Public Administration: Quality Management in Action', 'Public Administration in the Age of the Internet: Innovative Uses of New Technology', and 'The Citizen is King: The New Emphasis on Citizen Service'. Of these papers ten covered the general subject areas of customs and taxation, and education, and an overview of these is given.

Customs and Tax Initiatives.

Papers were presented detailing the best practice initiatives underway at The Office of Revenue Commissioners (Ireland), The Swedish Board of Customs, The Keski-Uusimaa Tax Office (Finland), The Inland Revenue

Department at the Ministry of Finance, The Dutch Tax and Customs Administration, and The Aarhus Customs and Tax Region in Denmark.

The Irish presentation describes a tax consolidation project which began in 1995 and involved the consolidation of income tax, corporation tax and capital gains tax codes. The need came about as a result of the fact that in 1994 Ireland had 40 separate Acts containing over 2,000 sections and 50 schedules of income tax, corporation tax and capital gains tax law. The subsequent consolidation was then effected by means of a partnership between the Revenue Commissioners, the Office of the Parliamentary Draftsman and the private sector. The partnership was structured as follows:

(i) A small core team of two full-time Revenue officials with the necessary expertise and experience in drafting tax legislation and two people from the private sector with the requisite skills and technological resources together with clerical support.

(ii) A part-time panel of six referees (for private sector tax experts and two serving tax officials to examine and refine draft consolidated legislation as it was prepared by the core team).

The actual consolidation of the law was implemented using a system of parallel processing:

'The primary function of the referees was to ensure that the draft legislation prepared by the core team was an accurate consolidation of the precursor legislation and to identify any omissions or departures of substance from the precursor legislation'.

The Taxes Consolidation Bill 1997 was published in October 1997 and enacted into law on 30th November 1997, exactly two years after the core team commenced work on the project and well ahead of the 3 to 4 year time frame initially envisaged. Stated benefits are:

* a 50% reduction in the volume of tax law in Ireland.

* involvement of the private sector in preparing draft legislation.

* more user friendly and accessible law.

* facilitation of future amendments into law.

* simplification and rationalisation of content.

* rational and coherent structure to tax law.

The Swedish Customs have recently developed new working methods to improve the efficiency of trade and are currently extending these, through co-operation with trade and industry organisations and other national authorities, so as to be able to offer a 'Stairway of Service' for companies. The system is based on the concept of risk analysis and has five steps. All operators in foreign trade (importers, exporters and agents) will have a rating in the system and all internal and external Customs processes will be re-engineered. As a company improves the documented quality of its Customs routines, Swedish Customs will be able to offer it more opportunities to use simplified procedures and better services. Each level contains opportunities as well as requirements. On the upper three steps a rising number of measures are carried out by the operator in accordance with officially approved quality assurance programmes such as pre-audit controls at traders' premises. Fewer interruptions in the flow of goods will be achieved when the company assures the quality of its internal procedures and introduces checks minimising the risks of irregularities. "Great interest at international level" has been reported about this scheme, which began in January, with regard to benchmarking:

'Today we co-operate most extensively with the Netherlands where a benchmarking project is being run. Its objective is to arrive at a method by which two or more countries can assess an individual company in such away that their joint assessment will be acceptable to the customs administrations of all the countries involved'.

The Uusimaa Regional Tax Office in Finland is one of nine regional offices of the National Board of Taxes, and the Keski-Uusimaa Tax Office is one of the eight offices of the Uusimaa Regional Tax Office. They use 'atmospheric surveys' and development discussions to assess the effectiveness of management strategies and future challenges to management. A Management Team analyses these and presents findings to the entire personnel, and the effectiveness of the operation is assessed at weekly meetings and quarterly follow-up meetings of the Management Team. Personnel are divided into teams of 10 to 15 members with members of the Management Team acting as support persons:

'A prioritisation of the 'team's new tasks is carried out during the warm-up phase by reducing other tasks of the team members. The teams design their own tasks and monitor the progress of their work. In this way the independent initiative and creativity of the teams have been increased'.

An education work group surveys training needs and expectations annually for the next year's curriculum and a work capacity team consisting of employees is responsible for design operations related to work capacity maintenance and meetings. The work capacity team produces an annual work capacity plan for the development of the physical and mental work capacity of the office. Process description and development was launched following training by an external consultant and last year detailed process descriptions were introduced into the teamworking ethic. This has resulted in 'a more detailed and more coherent insight' into the Tax Office's operation.

The achievements of The Inland Revenue Accounts Office Cumbernauld were recognised most notably in 1998 when they became the first public sector organisation to be awarded the European Quality Prize, along with AVE (a business unit of RENEE, the public sector Spanish rail operator). They have bench marked their payment processing system against British Telecom, Access, Readers Digest and Marks and Spencer, and use benchmark data from Rank Xerox, D2D and TNT (UK) Limited as an input to their Strategic Planning Process. A recent benchmarking exercise with Teleconomy (an independent consultancy) has enabled significant improvements to be made to their telephone answering standard. They are currently involved in a research project with the University of Strathclyde testing a jointly developed Integrated Performance Measurement Model. Recently, with the introduction of new computers and software, they are now developing a best practice database which all employees will be able to access via the organisation's Intranet and which the public may also be able to access.

The Italian contribution concerned the electronic filing of data on tax returns and payments by Fisco Telematico (a network that connects the Italian tax administration with around 100,000 operators, such as banks and post offices and plays a key role in enhancing and simplifying the relationship between the tax administration and the taxpayer). Through this network the Italian tax administration receives on-line information about tax returns and payments enabling difficulties associated with collecting data through traditional channels to be largely eliminated.

Essentially, all information transmitted electronically is protected and can only be read by the administration and by those who forward the tax return. This technological innovation, built around the objectives of the tax reform, is said to have "started a real revolution in the Italian tax system" with the percentage of mistakes being made by taxpayers falling from 28% to just 3% and a reduction in the time taken to collect tax return and payments data from two years to only three months. The system also affords the opportunity for intermediaries to offer their customers an improved service and to become more competitive in the area of tax consultancy.

It is envisaged that shortly, through the deployment of this system, all taxpayers will have the opportunity to fill in and send their tax returns directly via the Internet, whilst the system itself will be extended to other areas including the Mortgages Office and Customs. Benchmarking partners for this project have included the Inland Revenue in the UK. (Electronic Lodgement System), the Internal Revenue Service (USA), the German Bundesministerum der Finanzen, the Dutch Tax and Customs Administration, and the Spanish Agencia Estatal de Administracion Tributaria.

In the Dutch case the execution of legislation and regulation is embedded in a system of quality assurance and a Fiscal Monitor (measurement instrument based on personal standardised interviews among the different defined client groups) has been developed. The focus on taxpayers is based on the idea that a better quality of levying can be achieved by structuring data by taxpayer or by groups of taxpayers and there has been a change from 'document oriented' to 'client oriented' action. The importance of good registration, for example, led to file management becoming a separate main process:

'Finding links in data that is already available leads to new information, e.g. characteristics that might be a strong indication of fraud. For this purpose the new techniques of data-warehousing (a facility for consulting data by subject) and the application of data-mining (searching for coherent new information) will be applied. The strong focus on data (character-orientation) in automation is expanded increasingly to form an integrated, multimedia orientation on data, text, speech, (moving) images and sound. This development is gradually becoming visible in the Dutch Tax and Customs Administration's image to the outside world, and the possibilities offered by this integration can also be used for internal purposes'.

Job descriptions are currently based on carrying out tasks in specific working fields or areas for attention, but these are soon to be replaced by descriptions which focus on roles and areas of result with the knowledge and expertise aspects related to this.

In Denmark the Aarhus Region was established on 1st April 1990 when the Customs Service and the National Tax Service merged. It is now the largest of 29 Customs and Tax regions outside Copenhagen and employs 330. They have conducted a total of fifteen user surveys in five years which have demonstrated that user satisfaction can be achieved more than one might expect in such an organisation provided that the organisation conducts itself well and engages in open dialogue. Improvement groups are formed following each survey and every 40 days meetings are held with business people facilitated by local television.

Index